COMBUSTION

FOSSIL POWER SYSTEMS

A Reference Book on Fuel Burning And Steam Generation

JOSEPH G. SINGER
Editor

Third Edition

Published by

COMBUSTION ENGINEERING, INC.

1000 Prospect Hill Rd.
Windsor, CT 06095
1981

Line illustrations by
J. P. Amenta

Design and Layout
C. Mays
W. Van Saun

RAND McNALLY
Printed in U.S.A.

Table of Contents

APPENDICES

DEDICATION

This edition of Combustion is dedicated to the many people
who contributed their time and talent.

TECHNICAL CONTENT

J. B. Anderson
A. A. Arstikaitis
G. F. Barcikowski
W. G. Benz
B. C. Bley
R. N. Bruce
K. A. Bueters
H. E. Burbach
B. W. Carle
J. R. Comparato
A. J. Cozza
K. E. Crooke
W. B. Ferguson
D. J. Frey
D. Frabotta
C. Futterman

F. Gabrielli
H. A. Grabowski
J. E. Gwiazdowski
T. B. Hamilton
J. M. Harmon
R. P. Hensel
S. T. Hinckley
J. L. Hutchings
R. C. Kunkle
C. W. Lawton
R. E. Lorenz
G. R. Lovejoy
J. A. Makuch
O. Martinez
M. S. McCartney
T. J. McGowan

N. C. Mohn
W. H. Pollock
G. Prohazka
P. C. Rader
J. A. Ray
J. W. Regan
D. M. Rode
R. W. Santalla
W. F. Siddall, Jr.
R. S. Skowyra
W. R. Sylvester
D. Tawse
G. W. Thimot
W. H. Tuppeny, Jr.
J. W. Quinn
R. N. Wiechard

RESEARCH

Power Systems Library

PRODUCTION

J. C. Gorski
T. F. Gawlicki
K. R. Owens

PATIENCE

Alice Singer, wife

Preface

This third edition of *Combustion* should be useful to power-plant design and consulting engineers, utility and industrial plant personnel, as well as mechanical and chemical engineering students oriented toward fossil-fueled steam generation. Because of the world's interest in the greater use of coal, this book emphasizes the technology of large pulverized coal-fired steam generators and their ancillaries. Also stressed are coal characteristics and their impact on steam-generating system design.

The text updates and considers in greater detail the methods and equipment used for burning fuel, generating steam and recovering heat that were included by Otto DeLorenzi in the 1946 edition. The scope of the text also goes considerably beyond the material included in the 1966 edition.

Except for Appendix A, this book does not use the Système Internationale (SI) units of measure. A principal reason is that, in the United States and many other countries, the design of steam generating systems is based on the Codes of the American Society of Mechanical Engineers (ASME). At this printing ASME has not designated a date for issuing either converted or preferred SI-unit standards. It is unlikely that U.S. utility and industrial power plant engineers will issue design specifications in SI units until the ASME has revised its standards to SI metric.

In addition, there is no question that a gradual transition from customary U.S. units and meter-kilogram-second metric to the SI metric will continue to the turn of the century. As a consequence, the results of various tests and investigations in this text are reported in the units in which the data was generated (either customary U.S. or metric measurements).

Please note that throughout this book many illustrations and figures are used to explain physical and chemical phenomena. The values in these figures are approximate and are for illustration only. None of the values should be used for design standards or other purposes where exact values are required. Combustion Engineering, Inc. cannot take responsibility for any unauthorized use.

Realize also that it is not possible to design an operating fossil power plant with the technical information given in the book. Although extensive, the text is limited to only introductory material on many of the subjects and is only the "tip of a large iceberg" that represents the accumulated experience of the technical personnel of a major steam-generator supplier such as C-E.

INTRODUCTION

Combustion Engineering—An Introduction

The world today faces a critical challenge as nations strive to satisfy the basic human needs of food, shelter, and clothing which are so dependent on adequate supplies of energy. The great increase in the use of energy has come at the expense of our fossil fuels—coal, oil and gas—and people are more aware that natural resources have finite limits.

As we search for the ultimate solutions to the energy crisis, we must at the same time continue to look for interim ways of meeting the immediate growth in demand for energy. Technological improvements in mining, moving, processing and using fossil fuels can, of course, stretch energy-resource reserves, as can a determined effort at conservation. Similarly, application of technologies such as coal gasification or fluidized-bed combustion can widen the use of the world's vast coal resources. And finding new ways to make the best use of our energy supplies is what Combustion Engineering's tradition is all about.

A NEW NAME
AND RAPID GROWTH

To tell the story of Combustion Engineering is to trace the development of fossil power technology in the United States. The year 1912

marks a milestone for C-E. The organization bearing the Combustion Engineering name was formed in that year, although its roots had been firmly planted in the 1880's.

The merger of the Grieve Grate Company and the American Stoker Company brought together two well-known manufacturers of fuel-burning equipment to become Combustion Engineering Corp. The Grieve grate was a specialized grate capable of burning anthracite-coal screenings; the American Stoker Company manufactured a screw-type stoker to burn bituminous coal. Soon, the new organization acquired a license to build a single-retort underfeed stoker of English design. Known as the Type E stoker, it remained popular for small boilers for many years.

During the twenties, other stoker technology was acquired as were manufacturing plants along the Monongahela River south of Pittsburgh, Pennsylvania. C-E fabricated all its stokers in this plant which was built about the turn of the century. In addition to the Coxe traveling grate and the Green chain grate, C-E offered several types of underfeed stokers including the Type E, the Low Ram Stoker, the Skelly Stoker, and the C-E Multiple-Retort Stoker.

As the Company grew, new stoker designs were developed such as the Lloyd Traveling

Grate and the C-E Continuous Ash Discharge Spreader Stoker. But as grate surfaces grew to 24-ft wide by 28-ft long in size, the traveling grate stoker reached a practical limit—and a unit this size burning anthracite could generate only about 200,000 pounds of steam per hour. Despite its limitations, however, the continuous ash discharge spreader stoker remains in use today on boilers burning coal, wood, and bark.

A QUANTUM JUMP IN COMBUSTION TECHNOLOGY

In 1918, C-E launched into the developing technology of pulverized-coal firing. Overcoming the limitation placed on boiler capacity by the size restrictions of stokers, pulverized-coal firing opened the door to a large expansion in capacity of coal-fired boilers.

Capitalizing on a pulverized-coal firing system for steam locomotives, Combustion Engineering successfully adapted this technology to stationary utility boilers at the Oneida Street and Lakeside Stations of the Milwaukee Electric Railway and Light Co. This pioneering work, done jointly with Milwaukee Electric's engineers and the Bureau of Mines, marks the most important single development in the art of solid-fuel combustion in this century. As a result, in 1980, the Oneida Street Station, where pulverized coal was first put to use by a utility, was named an Historic Engineering Landmark by the American Society of Mechanical Engineers.

MANUFACTURING CAPABILITY EXPANDS

It was not until 1925 that C-E entered the steam boiler business, beginning with a bent-tube boiler design installed in the early twenties at the Ford Motor Company's River Rouge plant. For this same installation, Combustion had supplied the pulverizers and fuel-burning equipment. The Ford Company's 200,000 lb/hr boilers were among the first large units specifi-

cally designed for pulverized-coal firing.

Acquisition of two boiler companies augmented C-E's manufacturing capabilities. At the former Heine Boiler plant site in St. Louis is located one of C-E's manufacturing plants today, while the present major manufacturing facility in Chattanooga is on the former Hedges-Walsh and Weidner Boiler Co. site.

Until this time, steam-generating units were an assembly of separate components bought from different manufacturers. With the addition of these two boiler companies, C-E was able to combine all components (boiler, superheater, water-cooled furnace, fuel-burning equipment and heat-recovery equipment) into one coordinated design.

THE MOVE TOWARD MERGER

Paralleling the growth of Combustion Engineering in this period was the Locomotive Superheater Company, founded in 1910 to further the use of superheated steam in the boilers of American locomotives. This company had established a manufacturing facility in East Chicago, Indiana, where today Combustion Engineering assembles coal pulverizing equipment. With the development in 1914 of a patented forged return bend for joining two tubes, the Locomotive Superheater Co. produced heat exchangers that very quickly were accepted as a standard in the railroad industry. Virtually all of the steam locomotives subsequently built in the U.S. were equipped with these superheaters. In 1917, The Superheater Company, as it became known, began designing and building superheaters for use in stationary boilers and the superheater design achieved prominence in the stationary boiler field. It was here that the paths of Combustion Engineering and the Superheater Company crossed.

During the Great Depression, Combustion Engineering was reorganized as a subsidiary of The Superheater Company. Close ties developed between these two organizations, leading to the eventual merger of the two in 1948 under the name of Combustion Engineering-Superheater, Inc. In 1953 the name Superheater was eliminated and the Company took the name by which it's known throughout the world today—Combustion Engineering Inc.

C-E: PIONEER IN BOILER DESIGN

After its entry in 1925 into the steam-generating equipment business, Combustion made many significant contributions to furnace design and firing techniques.

Traditionally, boilers had refractory-lined furnaces. But with the advent of pulverized-coal firing, refractory-lined furnaces could not tolerate the high heat-release rates without severe ash-fouling and erosion problems. Consequently, it became necessary to cool the furnace, at the same time protecting the refractory, by lining its inside surfaces with tubing through which water flowed as part of the boiler circulating system. Combustion was in the forefront of this development.

Initially, bottom water screens shielded only the furnace floor as in the Oneida and Lakeside Stations of Milwaukee Electric in 1920. In 1923 at the Springdale Station of West Penn Power Co., water-tube use was extended to the rear furnace walls. The first installation of water tubes on furnace side walls was also in 1923 at Consolidated Edison's Hell Gate Station. In 1925 the Cahokia Station of Union Electric became the first boiler with bottom, rear and side-wall water tubing.

Water-cooling technology matured from bare tubes on wide spacing to close-spaced tubes with welded fins, then to tangent tubes presenting a completely water-cooled metal surface to the flame. Today's modern boilers have fusion-welded furnace walls, a C-E development in 1950 at the Kearny Station of Public Service Electric and Gas of New Jersey. During this era steam generator sizes expanded rapidly, until in 1929 Combustion put into service at the East River Station of New York Edison Co., (now Consolidated Edison) the first unit to develop steam at 1,000,000 lb/hr.

As the search for higher efficiency of utility plants continued, operating pressures and temperatures also rose. In the mid-1920's most utility boilers supplied steam to turbines at 400 psig, with a few as high as 600 psig. By the late 20's, some boilers were sold for throttle pressures of 1200 pounds per square inch, including C-E boilers supplied to Milwaukee Electric and Kansas City Power and Light. In this same period, steam temperatures increased gradually from between 500°F and 600°F to the 700°F to 750°F range, a substantial advancement considering the materials available at the time.

PULVERIZED FIRING DEVELOPS

The pioneering work on pulverized-coal firing at Milwaukee was followed in 1927 by the introduction of tangential firing in which fuel and air are introduced into a furnace from its four corners instead of through front or rear walls. First installed commercially at the U.S. Rubber Co. plant in Detroit, Michigan, this firing system provides the optimum in rapid and intimate mixing of fuel and oxygen to promote efficient combustion. Later, in 1940, a major modification to the basic tangential firing idea was applied to a boiler at Duke Power Co's., Buck Station—the fuel and air nozzles in the corners were made vertically tiltable. The new design permitted the flame envelope created by the tangential action to be moved up and down within the furnace, thereby changing the heat-absorption pattern of the furnace wall. The resulting variation in temperature of the hot gases entering the superheater surfaces provided a means of controlling steam temperature. C-E has had such tangential firing as its preferred method of suspension firing of most fuels for over 50 years.

Another equipment design to become a standard in the industry is the C-E Bowl Mill, introduced commercially in 1933. Originally based on the Raymond technology, this pulverizer design has been modified and increased in size over the years from a coal capacity of 3500 lb/hr coal to more than 100 tons/hr to keep pace with the requirement for supplying fuel to larger and larger steam generators.

WELDED DRUMS LEAD TO HIGHER PRESSURES, TEMPERATURES

A major contribution to the development of modern steam generators was the welded boiler drum. Until the late twenties, heavy pressure vessels were made of formed plates riveted together with the joints caulked to prevent leakage. This construction physically limited operating steam pressure.

At its Chattanooga plant, Combustion developed and perfected processes, techniques, and machines for fusion welding of heavy plate to form cylindrical shells for drums. The first such welded drum was dedicated as a National Historic Landmark by ASME on May 2, 1980—50 years after the drum was successfully tested. Welded construction permitted steam pressures to increase and, in 1931, Combustion installed the first boiler to operate at 1800 psig at the Phillip Carey Co. in Lockland, Ohio. By 1953, C-E had designed the first 2650 psig unit for the Kearny Station of Public Service Electric and Gas of New Jersey.

With improved endurance of materials that could tolerate higher operating temperatures and pressures, outlet steam temperatures began to climb from the 750°F level. By 1939, steam temperatures reached 925°F when C-E installed another pioneering unit at the River Rouge plant of Ford Motor Co.

The first unit to exceed 1000°F total steam temperature was sold to the Public Service Electric and Gas of New Jersey for its Sewaren Station in 1949. This boiler was designed to operate at 1050°F at the superheater outlet. Steam temperatures continued to inch upward; the Kearny unit of the same utility, purchased in 1953, was designed to operate at 1100°F and 2376 psig at the superheater outlet and 1050°F at the reheater outlet. In 1954, the C-E supercritical pressure unit for Philadelphia Electric Co's. Eddystone Station was designed for outlet conditions of 1210°F at 5300 psig.

In the search for higher efficiencies, the utility industry adopted the reheat cycle. This concept involved reheating steam in a section of the boiler after some of its energy had been extracted through expansion in the initial section of the turbine. The reheated steam, now at or near the initial steam temperature, was then returned to the final section of the turbine.

Although a few reheat units had been built in the 1920's, it was not until after World War II that the surge toward reheat in the utility industry began in earnest. Combustion sold the first post-war reheat unit to Boston Edison Co. for its Edgar Station in 1947. In the following years, reheat designs became the norm, with C-E supplying more than 630 reheat units to utility users around the world.

CIRCULATING SYSTEM ADVANCES

Combustion Engineering designed and installed its first Controlled Circulation® steam generator at Montaup Electric Co. in Somerset, Massachusetts in 1942. In this design, controlled circulation of water is assured by using pumps to provide a positive flow through the heat-absorbing tubes in the furnace walls; the available pump head permits the use of distribution orifices in the tube circuits. The Controlled Circulation steam generator overcomes the problem of decreasing thermal-circulation effect as the operating pressure approaches the 3208 psia critical point. This positive-circulation design has been well accepted in the utility industry around the world.

A license agreement was signed in 1953 with Sulzer Brothers of Switzerland for the rights to build and sell their Monotube steam-generator design in the United States. (The Monotube design is a once-through type steam generator in which the water that is introduced at the inlet of the unit passes continuously through the tubing, where it is heated to the desired outlet temperature with no internal recirculation.) In 1954, The Philadelphia Electric Company purchased the first unit of this design for its Eddystone Plant. This unit was designed to operate at 5300 psig and 1210°F at the superheater outlet, the highest pressure and temperature for a unit of commercial size ever. The unit went into operation in 1959, followed by several other supercritical and subcritical pressure installations of the Monotube type.

Combustion's next advancement in high-pressure technology area was the Combined Circulation® design which uses the principle of Controlled Circulation in the furnace walls (recirculation of the fluid by pumps) superimposed on the once-through flow of the Monotube design. This design eliminated the Monotube-boiler requirement for a high through-flow in the furnace walls during start-up and the necessity for a correspondingly large turbine bypass system. The first unit of this design was installed at the Tennessee Valley Authority's Bull Run Station and placed in operation in 1966. It was designed for 3650 psig superheater outlet pressure at 1003°F superheater and 1003°F reheater outlet temperatures. The steam capacity of 6,400,000 lb/hr served a turbine capable of generating 900 megawatts. Many similar units of this type followed.

BROADENED CAPABILITIES

Combustion Engineering developed and produced air preheaters of the plate type in the early 1920's to provide heat recovery from the hot gases leaving boilers, thereby improving boiler efficiency. During the same time, the Ljungstrom continuous regenerative-type air preheater was developed, in connection with the first turbine locomotive. In the U.S., the first Ljungstrom installations for industrial power plant boilers were made in 1923.

In 1925, the Air Preheater Corporation was founded, jointly owned by the Ljungstrom Turbine Manufacturing Co. of Sweden and the James Howden Co., Ltd. The Superheater Company acquired this company after the Depression, along with the exclusive license to manufacture the Ljungstrom® Air Preheater in the United States and Canada. The Ljungstrom Air Preheater utilizes a rotating heating element made up of closely spaced metal plates packed in baskets through which alternately pass the hot gases leaving the boiler and the cold combustion air going to the furnace.

This air preheater design, manufactured in C-E's Wellsville, New York facility, has been universally accepted in the industry and has been applied to steam generators of all manufacturers.

Combustion Engineering pioneered flue-gas scrubbers for sulfur-dioxide removal with research and development work begun in 1963. A pilot facility was constructed in its Windsor, Connecticut, development laboratory, followed in 1966 and 1967 by experimental field work on a Detroit Edison Co. unit at the St. Clair Station. C-E made the first commercial scrubber installations in the United States in 1968 at Union Electric Co's Meramec Station and Kansas Power and Light Co's. Lawrence Station.

In 1977, C-E Walther, Inc., a subsidiary of C-E acquired Pollution Control-Walther, an American company producing the Walther (Cologne, Germany) design of rigid-frame electrostatic precipitators. With this acquisition, Combustion broadened its scope of supply in environmental control systems, which now includes fabric filters, dry sulfur-dioxide removal systems, wet electrostatic precipitators, rod scrubbers and wet scrubbers.

It was also in 1977 that C-E re-entered the ash-handling field, a move aimed toward providing full-scope ash systems for pulverized coal-fired boilers and associated precipitators, fabric filters, or dry scrubbers. Beginning with the Combusco water-sealed ash drag conveyor designed in 1919 by the Underfeed Stoker Company, Ltd., Combustion furnished many bottom-ash hoppers and removal systems, and pyrite hoppers for C-E pulverizers. Today, it is a prime supplier of large submerged scraper conveyors, under license from its associated company EVT of Stuttgart, Germany.

Meanwhile in 1955, C-E's nuclear power activity had begun with the design and construction of a prototype marine nuclear propulsion system. Going into operation in 1959, the S1C prototype operated for more than 10 years, both as an R&D and as a Naval training facility. In 1967, another C-E reactor, the BONUS plant, achieved full operation as the first nuclear power plant in the United States with an integral superheating core. Also in 1967, the Company sold its first nuclear steam supply system to the utility industry with Consumers Power's purchase of its Palisades nuclear station.

During the years, C-E continued to diversify into new markets while strengthening its position in traditional ones. A case in point is the Company's activities at the international level which began in 1923. Since that time, Combustion—through direct sales, associated companies, and licensees—has gained world-wide reputation as a leading supplier of steam-generating equipment with installations in more than 70 countries. About 40 percent of the free world's electric power currently is generated by equipment of C-E design.

THE MODERN C-E: GROWTH AND DIVERSIFICATION

Industrial expansion and general business growth characterized the U.S. national economy during the 1950's and 60's. Reflecting confidence in the strength of its position in the utility and industrial power fields, C-E took steps to expand its range of products and services for a changing and growing marketplace.

During these eventful years, C-E transformed from a manufacturer of steam supply systems into a multifaceted organization deeply involved in building products, oil and gas exploration, production, refining, and petrochemical plants. Starting with The Lummus Company acquisition in 1957, Combustion Engineering has operated with the policy that successful diversification is built upon technology or markets familiar to C-E.

Today, C-E is helping to meet the energy challenge head-on by offering to energy-related industries, nationally and internationally, equipment and services in a blend of technologies including:

- utility and industrial power generation
- oil and gas exploration and production
- petroleum and petrochemical processing
- environmental control and energy conservation
- steel production; pulp and paper manufacturing; and mineral production

THE YEARS AHEAD

We have reviewed the history of C-E as the company came of age and matured in the utility and industrial markets, and have examined its many significant contributions. Advances made over the last 66 years in the development of energy conversion processes from fossil fuels have been great. Those individuals who have worked in the industry during some part of that time have witnessed not only tremendous growth in the art and science of fuel burning and steam generation, but also remarkable changes in the lifestyles of people throughout the world brought about in part by that growth. There are underway today new developments which will open new vistas for fossil fuels. That is what much of this book is all about.

For Combustion Engineering, the future holds great promise. A dedication to service and the courage to lead—attributes which have been major influences throughout its history—guide the company's operations today. As it faces the technical challenges of our energy future, C-E will continue to build on its tradition as a leading supplier of steam-generating and other energy equipment.

CHAPTER 1

Steam Power-Plant Design

The design of equipment for a fossil-fueled steam supply system starts with the application of certain basic fundamentals governing the relationship between properties of matter that define the conversion of energy from one form to another. Known as the first and second laws of thermodynamics, these cornerstones of power-plant design provide a quantitative method of looking at the sequential processes of working fluids as a function of temperature, pressure, enthalpy, and entropy. The design of a modern-day power plant represents, however, more than the application of thermodynamic data. It is a synthesis of economic considerations with thermal performance criteria that govern the selection of steam-generating equipment, whether the installation is for producing steam at an industrial site or utility power plant.

In this first chapter, which presents an overview of power-plant design, the opening section explores basic thermodynamic cycles: Carnot, Rankine regenerative reheat and other cycles are covered. A second section describes certain general design approaches relating to industrial installations. The third section deals with the principal factors involved in the selection of steam-generating equipment for electric utilities. Finally, the concluding section examines power-plant economics.

THERMODYNAMIC CYCLES FOR POWER PLANTS

Historically, the roots of thermodynamics go back to attempts to quantify instinctive concepts of systems designed to produce work from various energy sources. For continuously converting heat into work, the first practical power systems used steam as a working fluid.

By definition, a thermodynamic cycle is a series of processes combined in such a way that the thermodynamic states at which the working fluid exists are repeated periodically. Customarily, in an electric generating station, the fluid is cycled through a sequence of processes in a closed loop designed to maximize generation of electric power from the fuel consumed consistent with plant economics.

The design of a specific power plant represents an optimization of thermodynamic and economic considerations, the latter including inital, production, and distribution costs. In this first chapter, basic thermodynamics and economics applicable to large utility and industrial power plants will be presented. These form the basis for the selection of plant cycles and equipment. In this connection, it may be mentioned that an outstanding treatment of the subject is given in the Zerban and Nye book

Power Plants, 1960 edition, particularly with reference to Chapter 2.

LAWS OF THERMODYNAMICS

The first and second laws of thermodynamics govern the thermodynamic analysis of fluid cycles. These laws are stated in equation form as follows:

FIRST LAW

$$\Delta E = Q - W + \sum_i (\pm h_i \pm e_{xi})\, m_i$$

(1)

where ΔE is change in energy content of system, Q is heat transferred *to* system, W is work transferred *from* system and $(h_i + e_{xi})m_i$ is energy convected into or out of system by mass, m_i, with enthalphy, h_i, and extrinsic energy, e_{xi}.

Extrinsic energy, e_{xi}, is dependent on the frame of reference. For a fluid system, e_{xi} = kinetic energy + potential energy = $V_i^2/2_{gj} + z_i$, in which V_i is velocity and z is elevation above datum.

This equation applies equally to processes and cycles, steady- and transient-flow situations. For example, in a closed system where fluid streams do not cross the boundary, $m_i = 0$, and if the process is cyclic, then $\Delta E = 0$ and Eq. 1 becomes

$$\sum_{cycle} Q = \sum_{cycle} W$$

(2)

This implies 100 percent efficiency.

As another example, if the steady-state adiabatic expansion in a turbine is being analyzed, then $\Delta E = 0$, $Q = 0$, and Eq. 1 reduces to:

$$W = - \sum_i (h_i + e_{xi})m_i$$
$$= m[(h + e_x)in - (h + e_x)out]$$
$$W = m\left[\left(h + \frac{V^2}{2_{gj}} + z\right)_{in} - \left(h + \frac{V^2}{2_{gj}} + z\right)_{out}\right]$$

(3)

When changes in kinetic energy and elevation of the fluid stream may be neglected, Eq. 3 reduces to the familiar $W \simeq m(h_{in} - h_{out})$.

SECOND LAW

$$\Delta S = \left(\frac{Q}{T}\right) + I + \sum_i S_i$$

(4)

where ΔS is change in entropy of system; $(Q/T) = \Sigma_i (Q_i/T_i)$ i.e. the sum over the system boundaries of the heat transferred, Q_i, at a position on the boundary where the local temperature is T_i, and I is irreversibility. (For consistency with other second-law statements, $I \geqq 0$. For reversible processes or cycles, $I = 0$; for irreversible processes or cycles, $I > 0$.) $\Sigma_i S_i$ is the entropy flow into and out of system associated with mass flow, m_i, into and out of system. For a reversible cyclic process involving a closed system, $I = 0$, $\Delta S = 0$, $\Sigma_i S_i = 0$ and Eq. 4 reduces to

$$\left(\frac{Q}{T}\right) = 0$$

(5)

The steady-flow, adiabatic expansion of a fluid through a turbine is governed by the following equation.

$$I = - \sum_i m_i s_i = -m(s_{in} - s_{out})$$
$$= m(s_{out} - s_{in})$$

(6)

For reversible, adiabatic expansion, $I = 0$ and the process is characterized by the familiar isentropic property, $s_{out} = s_{in}$. Turbine expansion is not wholly isentropic. This nonisentropy is taken into account by defining the turbine efficiency. The primary advantage of writing the second law in an equation (Eq. 4) rather than the usual inequality is its usefulness in analyzing processes and cycles in a direct, quantitative, manner, similar to the first law analysis.[1]

Eqs. 1 and 4 thus provide quantitative means of examining all processes encountered in power-plant analysis regardless of the fluids used or the specific cycle employed.

CARNOT CYCLE

In 1824, Sadi Carnot, a French engineer, published a small, moderately technical book, *Reflections on the Motive Power of Fire.*[2] Carnot made here three important contributions: the concept of reversibility, the concept of a cycle, and the specification of a heat engine producing maximum work when operating cyclically between two reservoirs each at a fixed temperature.

The Carnot cycle consists of several reversible isothermal and isentropic processes, which may be viewed as occurring in either the nonflow or flow device shown in Figs. 1A and 1B. In the first instance, the heat source and sink are placed in contact with the device to accomplish the required isothermal heat addition (a-b) and rejection (c-d) respectively. The insulation shown replaces the heat reservoirs for executing the reversible adiabatic processes involving expansion (b-c) and compression (d-a). The process characteristics for good heat transfer and work transfer are not the same and are partially in conflict; Fig. 1B, therefore, shows a flow system for executing the Carnot cycle with the work and heat-transfer processes assigned to separate devices. For both nonflow

and flow systems, the state changes experienced by the working fluid are shown in the temperature-entropy diagram of Fig. 1C.

The classic Carnot cycle is such, then, that no other can have a better efficiency between the specified temperature limits than the Carnot value. Other cycles may equal it, but none can exceed it.

$$\text{Carnot} = \frac{T_h - T_1}{T_h} = 1 - \frac{T_1}{T_h.} \tag{7}$$

where T_h is the temperature of the heat source and T_1 is the temperature of the heat sink, all in terms of absolute temperature.

Practical attempts to attain the Carnot cycle encounter irreversibilities in the form of finite temperature differences during the heat-transfer processes and fluid friction during work-transfer processes. The compression process d-a, moreover, is difficult to perform on a two-phase mixture and requires an input of work ranging from a fifth to a third of the turbine output. When realistic irreversibilities are introduced, the Carnot cycle net work is reduced; the size and cost of equipment increase. Consequently, other cycles appear more attractive as practical models.[3]

In relation to the Carnot efficiency, the high-

(A) Non-Flow Device   (B) Flow Device   (C) Temperature-Entropy Diagram

Fig. 1 **Carnot cycle**

temperature heat source cannot be defined in terms of maximum temperature. Instead, the weighted average of the temperature of the working fluid must be calculated, involving the heating of the feedwater as it leaves the last heater, and the evaporation, superheating, and reheating processes.

RANKINE CYCLE

The cornerstone of the modern steam power plant is a modification of the Carnot cycle proposed by W. J. M. Rankine[4], a distinguished Scottish engineering professor of thermodynamics and applied mechanics. The elements comprising the Rankine cycle are the same as those appearing in Fig. 1B with one exception: because the condensation process accompanying the heat-rejection process continues until the saturated liquid state is reached, a simple liquid pump replaces the two-phase compressor. The temperature-entropy and enthalpy-entropy diagrams of Fig. 2 illustrate the state changes for the Rankine cycle. With the exception that compression terminates (state a) at boiling pressure rather than the boiling temperature (state a'), the cycle resembles a Carnot cycle. The triangle bounded by a-a' and the line connecting to the temperature-entropy curve in Fig. 2A signify the loss of cycle work because of the irreversible heating of the liquid from state a to saturated liquid. The lower pressure at state a, compared to a', makes possible a much smaller work of compression between d-a. For operating plants it amounts to 1 percent or less of the turbine output.

This modification eliminates the two-phase vapor compression process, reduces compression work to a negligible amount, and makes the Rankine cycle less sensitive than the Carnot cycle to the irreversibilities bound to occur in an actual plant. As a result, when compared with a Carnot cycle operating between the same temperature limits and with realistic component efficiencies, the Rankine cycle has a larger net work output per unit mass of fluid circulated, smaller size and lower cost of equipment. In addition, due to its relative insensitivity to irreversibilities, its operating plant thermal efficiencies will exceed those of the Carnot cycle.

REGENERATIVE RANKINE CYCLE

Refinements in component design soon brought power plants based on the Rankine cycle to their peak thermal efficiencies, with further increases realized by modifying the basic cycle. This occurred through increasing the temperature of saturated steam supplied to the turbine, by increasing the turbine inlet temperature through constant-pressure superheat, by reducing the sink temperature, and by reheating the working vapor after partial expansion followed by continued expansion to the final sink temperature. In practice, all of these are employed with yet another important modification. In the previous section, the irreversibility associated with the heating of the compressed liquid to saturation by a finite temperature difference was cited as the primary thermodynamic cause of lower thermal efficiency for the Rankine cycle. The regenera-

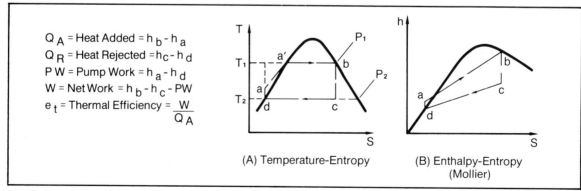

Q_A = Heat Added = $h_b - h_a$
Q_R = Heat Rejected = $h_c - h_d$
PW = Pump Work = $h_a - h_d$
W = Net Work = $h_b - h_c - PW$
e_t = Thermal Efficiency = $\dfrac{W}{Q_A}$

(A) Temperature-Entropy

(B) Enthalpy-Entropy
(Mollier)

Fig. 2 **Simple Rankine cycle (without superheat)**

Fig. 3 Regenerative Rankine cycle

tive cycle attempts to eliminate this irreversibility by using as heat sources other parts of the cycle with temperatures slightly above that of the compressed liquid being heated. Fig. 3 is an idealized form of such a procedure.

The condensed liquid at f is pumped to the pressure P_1, passes through coils around the turbine, and receives heat from the fluid expanding in the turbine. The liquid and vapor flow counter to one another and, by reversible heat transfer over the infinitesimal temperature difference d_T, the liquid is brought to the saturated state at T_1 (process b-c) and then rejects heat at the constant temperature T_2 (process e-f). Such a system, by the second law, will have a thermal efficiency equal to a Carnot cycle operating between the same temperatures.

This procedure of transferring heat from one part of a cycle to another in order to eliminate or reduce external irreversibilities is called "regenerative heating" which is basic to all regenerative cycles. Though thermodynamically desirable, the idealized regenerative cycle just described has several features which preclude its use in practice. Locating the heat exchanger around the turbine increases design difficulties and cost. Even if these problems were solved, heat transfer could not be accomplished reversibly in the time available; further, cooling as described causes the vapor to reach excessive moisture content.

The scheme shown in Fig. 4 permits a practical approach to regeneration without encountering these problems. Extraction or "bleeding" of steam at state c for use in the "open" heater avoids excessive cooling of the vapor during turbine expansion; in the heater, liquid from the condenser increases in temperature by ΔT. (Regenerative cycle heaters are called "open" or "closed" depending on

Fig. 4 Single extraction regenerative cycle

whether hot and cold fluids are mixed directly to share energy or kept separate with energy exchange occurring by the use of metal coils.)

The extraction and heating substitute the finite temperature difference ΔT for the infinitesimal dT used in the theoretical regeneration process. This substitution, while failing to realize the full potential of regeneration, halves the temperature difference through which the condensate must be heated in the basic Rankine cycle. Additional extractions and heaters permit a closer approximation to the maximum efficiency of the idealized regenerative cycle[5], with further improvement over the simple Rankine cycle shown in Fig. 2

Reducing the temperature difference between the liquid entering the boiler and that of the saturated fluid increases the cycle thermal efficiency. The price paid is a decrease in net work produced per pound of vapor entering the turbine and an increase in the size, complexity and initial cost of the plant. Additional improvements in cycle performance may be realized by continuing to accept the consequences of increasing the number of feedwater heating stages. Balancing cycle thermal efficiency against plant size, complexity, and cost for production of power at minimum cost determines the optimum number of heaters.[6]

REHEAT CYCLE

The use of *superheat* offers a simple way to improve the thermal efficiency of the basic Rankine cycle and reduce vapor moisture content to acceptable levels in the low-pressure stages of the turbine. But with continued increase of higher temperatures and pressures to achieve better cycle efficiency, in some situations available superheat temperatures are insufficient to prevent excessive moisture from forming in the low-pressure turbine stages.

The solution to this problem is to interrupt the expansion process, remove the vapor for *reheat* at constant pressure, and return it to the turbine for continued expansion to condenser pressure. The thermodynamic cycle using this modification of the Rankine cycle is called the "reheat cycle." Reheating may be carried out in a section of the boiler supplying primary steam, in a separately fired heat exchanger, or in a steam-to-steam heat exchanger. Most present-day utility units combine superheater and reheater in the same boiler.

Usual central-station practice combines both regenerative and reheat modifications to the basic Rankine cycle. Fig. 5 is a temperature-entropy diagram of a single-reheat regenerative cycle with two stages of feedwater heating. For large installations, reheat makes possible an

$$Q_A = (h_c - h_a) - 1 - m_1(h_e - h_d)$$

$$Q_R - 1 - m_1 - m_2 (h_g - h_h)$$

$$W = (h_c - h_d) + 1 - m_1 (h_e - h_f) + 1 - m_1 - m_2 \\ (h_f - h_g) - PW$$

$$e_t = \frac{W}{Q_A}$$

$$PW = (h_a - h_l) + 1 - m_1 (h_k - h_j) \\ + 1 - m_1 - m_2 (h_i - h_h)$$

Q_A = Heat Added
Q_R = Heat Rejected
W = Work
PW = Pump Work
e_t = Thermal Efficiency

Fig. 5 **Regenerative cycle with single reheat and two feedwater heaters**

Fig. 6 **Reheat regenerative cycle, 600-MW subcritical-pressure fossil power plant**

improvement of approximately 5 percent in thermal efficiency and substantially reduces the heat rejected to the condenser cooling water.[7] The operating characteristics and economics of modern plants justify the installation of only one stage of reheat except for units operating at supercritical pressure.

Fig. 6 shows a flow diagram for a 600-MW fossil-fueled reheat cycle designed for initial turbine conditions of 2520 psig and 1000°F steam. Six feedwater heaters are supplied by exhaust steam from the high-pressure turbine and extraction steam from the intermediate and low-pressure turbines. Except for the deaerating heater (third), all heaters shown are closed heaters. Three pumps are shown: (1) the condensate pump which pumps the condensate through oil and hydrogen gas coolers, vent condenser, air ejector, first and second heaters, and deaerating heater; (2) the condensate booster pump which pumps the condensate through fourth and fifth heaters; and (3) the boiler feed pump which pumps the condensate through the sixth heater to the economizer and boiler. The mass flows noted on the diagram are in pounds per hour at the prescribed conditions for full-load operation.

SUPERCRITICAL-PRESSURE CYCLE

A definite relationship exists between operating temperature and optimum pressure of a cycle. The supercritical-pressure cycle is in use worldwide to obtain the highest possible thermodynamic efficiencies with fossil-fuel steam-generation equipment.

A regenerative-reheat cycle is used with 6 to 8 stages of feedwater heating and, because of the high inlet temperature and pressure, two stages of reheat can be justified and have been used in several installations. Fig. 7 shows a typical supercritical-pressure steam turbine heat balance. Seven feedwater heaters are shown with steam extractions from the various turbines supplying energy for the regenerative heating processes. For such supercritical pressure plants, cycle efficiencies exceeding 40 percent have been reached.

Philadelphia Electric Company's Eddystone 1, a double-reheat supercritical unit with original outlet steam conditions of 5300 psig, 1210°F, was the high-water mark of cycle efficiency for conventional steam plants. It was capable of producing electrical output with an input of less than 8200 Btu per kilowatt hour.

PROCESS-STEAM CYCLES

In many instances, power and heating needs may be combined in a single power plant which will operate at a high annual load factor and thermal efficiency. For heating service, the steam may be generated at a pressure and temperature sufficiently high that exhaust from the turbine is at steam conditions suitable for delivery to the steam mains and distribution to users. The needs of industrial plants for process steam may be met by similar arrangements using either turbine exhaust steam or extracted steam from an appropriate turbine stage. The selection of optimum exhaust or extraction conditions will depend on the proportions of power and process heat required of the particular plant. Process steam requirements are usually in the low pressure range with modest superheat required if at all; consequently, initial steam pressure and temperature will generally be below the limits of current technology with a commensurate easing of boiler and turbine design requirements.

The great variety of power/process-steam requirements offers a continuing challenge to designers. Cycles have been developed and applied over a wide range of capacities extending from the small industrial power plants to large central stations serving the heating needs of a metropolitan center or the power/process needs of a major petro-chemical installation. The steel, chemical, and paper industries are three examples from among the many important industrial users of process steam cycles.

Fig. 8 shows a schematic diagram of a power/process cycle using a back-pressure turbine. After steam is generated at a suitable working pressure, it is admitted to the turbine and emerges usually in the superheated state, c. After desuperheating, saturated steam, d, enters the heater and is entirely condensed. Be-

Fig. 7 Reheat regenerative cycle, 800-MW supercritical-pressure fossil power plant

Fig. 8 Power process cycle using a back-pressure turbine

cause the steam required for power generation will not equal at all times that required for process work, some means of controlling the exhaust steam pressure must be employed to avoid variations in the pressure and, therefore, the steam saturation temperature. The control method depends on the circumstances. An ordinary centrifugal governor fitted to the back-pressure turbine will cause the quantity of available exhaust steam to be controlled by the load on the turbine. Should the available exhaust be too small, live steam may be passed through a reducing valve into the desuperheater. If the quantity of exhaust steam exceeds requirements, then the excess steam may be blown to atmosphere, into an accumulator, or into a feed tank through the spill valve.

Another version of the process cycle uses

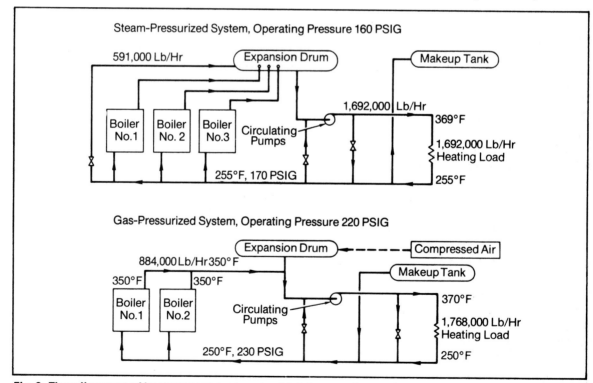

Fig. 9 Flow diagrams of heat process cycle using high-temperature water

high-temperature water circulated by pumps to supply energy for process and heating. The thermal head is provided by a water "boiler," the entire system being pressurized by use of steam or gas (compressed air or nitrogen) contained in an expansion drum as in Fig. 9.[8]

GAS-TURBINE/STEAM-GENERATOR COMBINED CYCLES

A combined cycle is any one of a number of combinations of gas turbines, steam generators (or other heat-recovery equipment), and steam turbines assembled for the reduction in plant cost or improvement of cycle efficiency in the power-generation process. This definition omits the wide variety of combined-cycle possibilities for industrial applications, which are limited in their variety only by the particular process requirement. Nevertheless, the underlying principle of all these arrangements is similar, in that they all depend on the energy contained in the gas-turbine exhaust and take advantage of the fact that the gas turbine is otherwise subject to the losses associated with elevated stack-gas temperatures and the combustion of fuel hydrogen.

Analogous to mercury-steam or steam-ammonia cycles, the combined gas-steam cycle is a binary cycle although not normally thought of as such. The principle is to improve efficiency by increasing the working fluid temperature through use of the high-temperature capabilities of the internal-combustion turbine while utilizing the external-combustion (steam) turbine to reduce the sink temperature. The penalty involved is the required compressor work performed by the gas turbine.

Gas turbines fire natural gas, jet fuel, light distillate oil or, with proper prefiring treatment, a wide range of residual and crude oils. Open-cycle gas turbines are used to satisfy both the peaking and reserve requirements of the utility industry because of their quick-starting capability and low capital cost. Their poor thermal efficiency and use of prime fuels, however, place them at an economic disadvantage when operated for long periods of time. Depending on the particular manufacturer and

fuel utilized, heat rates ranging from 12,000 to 16,000 Btu/kWhr (HHV) may be obtained.

A number of major design modifications may improve this heat rate, such as increased compressor pressure ratios and higher gas-turbine inlet-gas temperatures. In addition, the station heat rate associated with present gas-turbine designs may further be improved by utilizing the energy contained in the turbine exhaust gases. For example, a 50-MW gas turbine might discharge approximately 2,200,000 lb/hr of exhaust gases at about 900°F, with an equivalent value of 450×10^6 Btu/hr of energy or approximately 75 percent of the initial fuel input. But only a limited amount of this energy can be recovered in simple waste-heat equipment.

TYPES OF COMBINED CYCLES

Combined-cycle installations may be categorized into four broad classifications, each primarily dependent on how the steam generator is used in conjunction with the gas turbine.

1. Gas turbine plus unfired steam generator.
2. Gas turbine plus supplementary-fired steam generator.
3. Gas turbine plus furnace-fired steam generator.
4. Supercharged furnace-fired steam generator plus gas turbine.

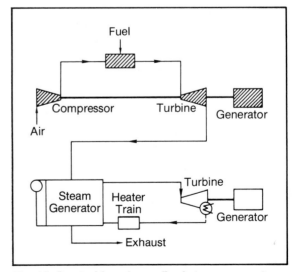

Fig. 10 **Gas turbine plus unfired steam generator**

Gas Turbine Plus Unfired Steam Generator

In this concept, a steam generator is installed at the discharge of a gas turbine to recover the energy in the gas-turbine exhaust and supply steam to a steam turbine (Fig. 10). All the fuel is fired in the gas turbine, and the steam generator depends entirely on the gas turbine for its heat. The steam generator is designed for low steam pressures and temperatures, with available gas-turbine exhaust temperature limiting maximum values to approximately 850 psi and 825°F.

In most applications, the steam turbine will produce approximately 30 to 35 percent of the total plant output, with the remaining 65 to 70 percent being supplied by the gas turbine(s). Because the power from the steam turbine will be produced without any additional fuel input and there is only a small decrease in gas-turbine efficiency because of the back pressure of the steam generator, the overall plant thermal efficiency will be improved over that of the open-cycle gas turbines. Depending on the particular steam cycle and fuel, net plant heat rates on the order of 10,000 to 11,000 Btu/kWhr (HHV) may be obtained.

Gas Turbine Plus Supplementary-Fired Steam Generator

Gas-turbine exhaust contains from 16 to 18 percent oxygen and may be used as an oxygen source to support further combustion. Therefore, a modification of the simple waste-heat application is the use of a supplementary firing system located in the connecting duct between the gas turbine and the steam generator (Fig. 11). The firing system will utilize a portion of the oxygen contained in the gas-turbine exhaust and be selected to limit the maximum gas temperature entering the steam generator to approximately 1300°F.

With a given gas-turbine size and this gas-temperature limit, the steam generation will double that of a simple waste-heat application, and the steam turbine will supply a greater proportion of the plant load—approximately 50 percent of the total electrical output. The higher steam-generator inlet gas temperature will allow steam conditions to be increased to levels of 1500 psig and 950°F. The steam turbine designs are nonreheat and may be either condensing or noncondensing. For most arrangements the final steam conditions are primarily based on the steam-turbine economics. Net plant heat rates of 9,000 to 10,000 Btu/kWhr (HHV) are possible with this combination of equipment.

Gas Turbine Plus Furnace-Fired Steam Generator

The previous cycle used only a small portion of the available oxygen in the gas-turbine

Fig. 11 **Gas turbine plus supplementary-fired steam generator**

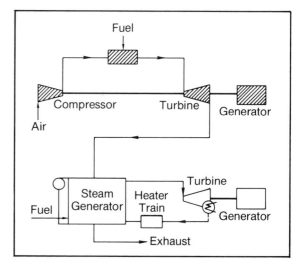

Fig. 12 **Gas turbine plus furnace-fired steam generator**

exhaust. Another adaptation is the design of a plant which utilizes essentially all of the oxygen in the turbine exhaust to support further combustion. Typical gas turbines operate with 300 to 400 percent excess air and thus can support the combustion of approximately three to four times as much fuel in a downstream boiler as was burned in the gas turbine. The majority of fuel can now be fired in the boiler and 70 to 85 percent of the total plant power generation will be supplied by the steam turbine, with the remaining portion by the gas turbine (Fig. 12). The gas turbine may be considered as both an independent power supplier and a forced-draft fan for the boiler. Any of the high-pressure, high-temperature steam conditions utilized by modern steam turbines can be incorporated into this combined cycle.

And although the gas-turbine fuel in the previous arrangement is presently limited to gas and oil, this cycle allows the use of any fossil fuel in the steam-generator.

Plant heat rates of 9,530 Btu/kWhr (HHV) have been obtained[9].

Supercharged Furnace-Fired Steam Generator Plus Gas Turbine

Another configuration for a combined cycle includes the installation of a steam generator between the air compressor and the gas turbine (Fig. 13). The air compressor serves as a

Fig. 13 Supercharged furnace-fired steam generator plus gas turbine

forced-draft fan and pressurizes the boiler, where all the fuel is fired; the products of combustion, having been partially cooled within the boiler complex, are then discharged through a gas turbine. Additional heat is recovered by heat exchangers installed at the exhaust of the gas turbine. They are used as economizers or feedwater heaters.

Although gas turbines require relatively high excess-air quantities, the firing system for the supercharged furnace is designed to operate with excess-air levels commensurate with conventional units and the air compressor is selected for this small air capacity. The steam turbine supplies the majority of the plant electrical generation, with the gas turbine either selected to provide sufficient power to drive the air compressor (Velox cycle) or sized to supply additional power generation. Heat rates range from 9,000 to 10,000 Btu/kWhr (HHV) with these cycles.

Numerous technical papers have been published on the various gas-turbine cycles and the particular economics of their application.[10] These should be consulted for specific information related to current developments.

INDUSTRIAL POWER-PLANT DESIGN

This section focuses attention on the overall design elements of the industrial or institutional power plant, exclusive of the marine propulsion plant. Many of these elements are involved also in the design of more complex utility power plants, which is the subject of the next section. In addition, other chapters of the book will cover specifics of the design of boilers together with their various components and supporting systems.

The most elementary type of industrial power plant incorporates a boiler as a heat source and a heating system as a load to dissipate the thermal energy released by fuel fired to the boiler. The thermal transport medium may be steam or hot water, but in either case it will be returned to the boiler at a lower temperature level. Figs. 14 and 15 show these elementary plants.

Fig. 14 Basic elements of a steam-heating plant

From this point onward, the industrial or institutional power plant may encompass various degrees of complexity. Power may be generated in a condensing plant, thus making the equivalent of a small central station. Steam may be supplied to process directly and not returned as condensed feedwater. On the other hand, it may be passed through a turbine acting as a reducing valve, followed by use for heating and process as shown in Fig. 16. Cycles may range from the simplicity and low level of thermal efficiency exemplified by the noncondensing steam locomotive to the most complex and efficient thermodynamic arrangements proposed for central stations, including combinations of steam and gas turbines. Boiler size may extend from the generation of a few thousand pounds

of steam per hour to several million in large installations, and the same capacity spread is true of turbines for power generation. In short, the industrial power plant can be used to illustrate virtually every aspect of the thermal engineering involved with a fossil-fueled plant.

TRENDS IN POWER-PLANT DESIGN

Up to this point the term *industrial power plant* has been used without definition. In engineering terms, there is no physical difference between industrial and utility types. At one time, power generation was a part of virtually every industrial power plant, but this is no longer the case. There are several reasons for this change, which accelerated during and after World War II:

1. The public-utility systems are more securely and effectively interconnected electrically, and service is very reliable.

2. The cost of *purchased* electric power has resisted the effects of inflation better than almost any other commodity.

3. The demands for additional electrical power have generally grown faster than the demands for heating, thereby exceeding the capabilities of back-pressure generation.

4. It has been found that the same dollar investment brings a greater return when applied to production equipment or facilities expansion than when spent in the power plant.

The end result has been that the majority of

Fig. 15 Basic elements of a high-temperature water-heating plant

Fig. 16 Basic elements of a plant for back-pressure power generation

industrial power plants built since WW II have been for space heating and process steam. The exceptions have been based upon situations such as the following:

1. Coordinated demands for steam and power, accompanied by the availability of waste fuels suitable for combustion in boilers. Examples are found in such industries as pulp and paper, chemicals, petroleum and steel, plus certain types of raw-materials processing, such as bagasse and grain refuse.

2. A balanced growth of electrical and steam-heating requirements. This is found in many institutional settings, such as universities, hospitals of various types, penal institutions, and some district heating schemes in metropolitan areas. Here, back-pressure power generation has marked economic advantages.

POWER-PLANT STUDIES

The starting point of an industrial power plant is an engineering study. Power and steam loads must be ascertained and costs estimated before construction can be considered. In some instances, the organization for whom the power plant is being built may have an engineering staff of sufficient size and experience to make preliminary studies, develop the detailed design, evaluate bids, award contracts and supervise construction. But most often, a consulting engineer is called upon to perform one or more of these functions.

In any case, a preliminary report must be written to obtain authorization of capital funds. Not only does this report consider the total investment, but it also evaluates outlays for such items as operation, maintenance, depreciation, insurance, interest, and taxes. With its primary emphasis on economic factors, the preliminary report must be written so as to be intelligible to those whose background may be in finance or law rather than engineering. And whether the report deals with a new power plant or an extension to an existing one, it always includes a tabulation of steam and power requirements.

A salient part of the preliminary report is the charting of anticipated loads for different conditions, such as daily load curves for winter and summer, weekdays, Saturdays, Sundays and holidays. Special consideration must be given to any unusual operating conditions and to the time of peak loads. If a manufacturing operation is involved and if it incorporates some process equipment with marked swings in demand, a detailed study should be made of the nature and frequency of the operation and its steam and power demands. As a part of load studies of existing plants, the peaks and valleys should be investigated with the objective of determining whether corrective measures might be taken to level out the load to increase effective output.

Typical load curves, as shown in Figs. 17, 18, and 19, help to determine the size of such equipment as boilers, turbines and auxiliaries. Studies must then be made of the capability of the equipment to meet not only the conditions plotted on the basis of past experience but also those forecast for a limited time in the future. Load curves should be made for both power and steam requirements, and due consideration should be given to the relative growth of power and steam in the future.

The engineer with the assignment to study the power and steam requirements must become thoroughly acquainted with the operating characteristics of the proposed installation or the extension to existing facilities. In the case of a hospital supplied by an isolated power plant, dependability of service is of paramount importance. The same may be true of an industrial process of a continuous nature, where an emergency may be very costly and possibly hazardous as well. On the other hand, some installations may have firm electrical connections to outside sources. Here, the design emphasis might be on continuity of service despite outage of generating plant equipment. In other situations, power and heating interruptions may be inconvenient, but may not cause severe problems or losses.

Based on the definition of the problem and the detailed technical analysis, the preliminary report should offer conclusions and recommendations. These should include estimates of the required capital investment along with

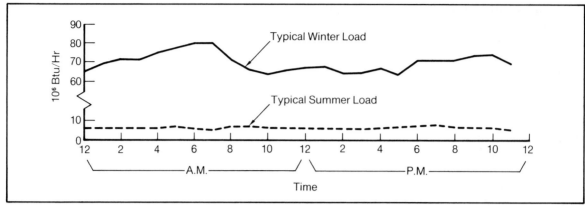

Fig. 17 **Summer and winter heating loads in a high-temperature water installation**

operating costs and fixed charges. In most reports of this nature there will be a number of analyses of economic alternatives, to aid management in making decisions prior to authorization of construction.

DESIGN INVESTIGATIONS

Detailed design follows acceptance of the preliminary engineering study and authorization to proceed. Some topics of the preliminary report are investigated more thoroughly as part of the design process. The studies are coordinated with the purchase of materials and equipment and the making of detailed construction drawings.

The number and scope of design investigations will vary from plant to plant. As a very minimum, decisions must be made as to choice of cycle, selection of fuel, number and types of

auxiliaries, extent of instrumentation and automatic control, and plans for isolated or interconnected operation.

CHOICE OF CYCLE

In the design of a new plant, careful consideration must be given to the choice of thermal cycle. If an existing plant is to be enlarged, consideration might be given to "topping" the plant with a steam cycle operating at a higher pressure. Alternatively, the same cycle may be retained and expanded.

If electrical-power generation is a factor, the choice will be that of a superheated-steam cycle. Although an almost infinite variety of steam conditions could be studied, the designers usually limits themselves to choosing among a few widely used cycles for which standard equipment is available.

Fig. 18 **Widely fluctuating process load curve**

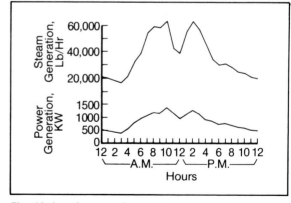

Fig. 19 **Load curves for back-pressure steam and power generation**

If space-heating and process use constitute the entire load, then it is possible to make a choice between a steam and a high-temperature water cycle.

After World War II, high-temperature water installations became quite common. On the other hand, the use of steam has been widespread since the early development of central heating. Much equipment is on the market to use steam as a source of heat, although some of this can be adapted to high-temperature water by the addition of a heat exchanger.[11]

Because of its relatively large heat storage capacity, a high-temperature-water system provides a means of close temperature control. The heat-storage capacity also forms a reserve so that large-use demands may be met without affecting the temperature of individual heat-consuming units. The distribution lines for a high-temperature water system are much smaller than for a steam system of the same heating capacity, and no steam traps or condensate pumps are required. Each of these factors must be evaluated in terms of the requirements of the proposed installation.

Power plants serving institutional complexes may have to distribute steam or high-temperature water over a large area with terrain varying sharply in elevation. In addition to space heating, there may be limited requirements for low-pressure steam for use in kitchens and laundries. Distribution and return lines must be designed, and heat exchangers may be required for local sources of steam or to reduce thermal losses. The choice of steam versus high-temperature water cycle must take all of these factors into consideration, as well as recognize that institutional power plants such as prisons may have to function with somewhat less than the highest quality of operating and maintenance personnel. See Chapter 8, Industrial Boilers, for a further description of high-temperature hot-water equipment.

Large industrial power plants with substantial process and electric loads are likely to make use of more advanced cycles. Some of these plants may be owned by an electric utility company and operate under a sales contract in which the industry purchases both steam and electrical output. In certain instances, the industry may supply byproduct fuels and retain ownership of portions of the power plant.

CHOICE OF FUEL

Selection of fuel is based on a combined investigation of availability, cost, and operating requirements. Most industrial power plants use solid, liquid or gaseous fuels, either singly or in combination. Although generally these are commercially available fuels, sometimes they are byproducts of manufacturing and processing.

When comparing fuel costs, the following factors should be tabulated:

- base price of fuel
- cost of fuel delivery
- cost of handling and reclaiming
- cost of labor, including firing and disposition of refuse
- cost of plant services, including power
- fixed charges on fuel-handling and burning equipment

Careful study of these outlays, adjusted to an annual basis, will provide a foundation for fuel choice. Other less tangible factors should also be evaluated, such as reliability of supply, future availability, individual fuel cost trends, ease of conversion from one fuel to another, and extent of future plant expansion.

Charges for byproduct fuels depend upon the method of accounting for process and power-plant costs. In some industries, such as steel and petroleum refining, byproduct fuels must be either burned in power-plant boilers as fast as they are produced or consumed as atmospheric flares. Other byproduct fuels, such as some types of wood and plant refuse, may be stored for limited periods. The economics of such byproduct fuels can become very complex or be as simple as the necessity of disposing of them immediately by some form of combustion. In many instances conventional solid, liquid, or gaseous fuels must be fired to supplement by-product fuels.

CHOICE OF AUXILIARIES

No steam power plant is complete with merely a boiler and a turbine. Auxiliary equipment is required in the form of fans, pumps, heaters, tanks and piping. In some instances, heat-recovery equipment is added to boilers, and generally some form of water-conditioning equipment will be required. Both fuel and ash handling systems are necessary if solid fuel is fired. If all electrical requirements cannot be satisfied through back-pressure operation, a condenser is a necessity.

The designer of an industrial power plant must investigate to some degree each of these auxiliaries. In the case of tanks and piping, the investigation may be to determine optimum sizes and selection from among alternative piping and equipment arrangements. In other cases, the designer may decide only whether to use the auxiliary equipment.

Motor or Turbine Drives

In most industrial power plants, the designer has a choice of steam-turbine or electric-motor drive for rotating auxiliaries. Electric drives are used commonly for such items as forced- and induced-draft fans and pumps for boiler feed, condensate and fuel oil. Yet the possibilities and advantages of turbine drives should not be overlooked. These may contribute to improvement of plant heat balance and assure continuity of boiler plant operation in the event of power failure. Where more than one fan and pump are installed for each plant auxiliary service, the combination of motor and turbine drives becomes attractive, with provision for the automatic starting of the steam-driven auxiliary in the event of power failure.

Because continuity of service is absolutely essential for the boiler feed pump, it is common practice to provide a steam-driven pump for use in the event of electric power failure. In addition, provision may be made to start this pump automatically if there is a marked drop of pressure in the boiler feed line.

Unlike the case of the boiler feed pump, the question of turbine drives for forced- and induced-draft fans does not have a clear-cut an-

swer. Consideration should be given to the probability of electric-power outage and the necessity for maintaining full-load output in the event of such outage. The economics of operation must be weighed against the requirements for service continuity.

INSTRUMENTATION AND AUTOMATIC CONTROL

Industrial power plants vary widely in their use of instrumentation and automatic control. Instrumentation may be installed as an aid to operation, as a means of keeping records of use of fuel, steam and electricity, or for both purposes. Automatic controls may be specified to reduce operating personnel to a minimum and to assist in maintaining operation at a high level of efficiency.

Instruments assist in the operation of a power plant as well as in the collection of information on the cost of steam and power consumption. The designer must keep in mind the type of data which must be available at all times to the operator and must select the correct instruments to provide this information. Some of these instruments will be of the indicating type, while others will record data over prolonged periods. Both types are essential; some overlapping and duplication of readings can be justified because of the differing uses for operating and recorded information.

Every industrial power plant will incorporate instrumentation to indicate boiler and turbine loading. It is also common practice to provide instruments to show various steam and flue-gas temperatures, air and steam flow, feedwater and steam pressures, and electrical outputs. The extent of this instrumentation will depend upon the type of power plant and the amount of information required for accounting purposes. Where there are large heating or process loads serving many separate buildings or departments, flowmeters are essential for determining consumption and allocating costs.

DRAWINGS AND SPECIFICATIONS

To build a power plant, drawings and specifications must be prepared to obtain bids and exercise proper supervision over purchasing and construction. The objective of such drawings and specifications is to describe the work to be done, primarily from the point of view of the results to be achieved. The engineer must use extreme care to see that they are clear, concise, and capable of but one interpretation. The drawings describe the work graphically and dimensionally while the specifications represent verbal descriptions.

It is well to consider the specifications as the rule book which governs the entire project. The drawings should indicate the location of equipment, including interconnecting piping and wiring. Between the two, the work to be done should be clearly set forth, with nothing essential omitted and with a determined effort to avoid inconsistencies and unnecessary overlap. The specifications should set forth the functions and limits of each item shown on the drawings. By their very nature, specifications are intended to be very detailed about what is to be done, even though they may include some general stipulation or conditions which relate to the work as a whole.

As an example, consider a piping system for an industrial power plant. The drawings will show a piping layout, including detailed dimensions, and will indicate the pressure characteristics of the system. The specifications should list all design requirements: design pressure and temperature; operating pressure and temperature; the grade designation, sometimes called the schedule, of piping, fittings and valves; the type and pressure characteristics of joints, including any special requirements. These piping specifications should also contain provisions covering quality of materials and workmanship, including inspection and acceptance requirements.

PERFORMANCE SPECIFICATIONS

In the specifying of power-plant equipment, it is sometimes expedient to write a performance specification, with only such descriptions or physical limitations as are necessary to provide for the desired quality of materials and workmanship. Within this framework, the manufacturer is given as much freedom as possible to provide equipment which will best fulfill the functional requirements of the installation. By reason of specialized experience, a manufacturer frequently can best determine the detailed design of the particular equipment it supplies, given all the factors for performing economic analyses of available alternates.

ELECTRIC UTILITY POWER-PLANT DESIGN

The objective of this section is to show the steps that must be taken and the decisions that must be made in the preliminary design of a central station for the generation of electric power. These must precede the detailed final design which involves the efforts of large teams of engineers, designers and drafters.

Electric utilities are continuously thinking about generating facilities that must be in operation as much as ten or more years in the future. The *final* design and construction of new capacity will typically require not less than four years. For these reasons, all basic decisions must be made at least that long before the capacity is needed.

Management must find the best practicable answers to four fundamental questions about the provision of additional capacity: When? How big? Where? What kind? In more formal language, the following steps must be undertaken.

1. Forecast of loads to determine timing and size of additions.
2. Selection of plant location.
3. Selection of types of equipment.

Each step is the subject of a subsequent discussion and involves the careful weighing of both economic and technical alternatives.

FORECAST OF LOADS

The answers to When? and How big? are approached by making a forecast of future electric demands. Such activity is a continuous function in a major utility and is, necessarily, a matter of judgment in interpreting company records, economic trends, population shifts, technological changes and regulatory factors.

There are two significant characteristics of electric demand (usually called "load") in this connection: the peak load, which is the maximum demand on the generating plant for a relatively short period, as 15 minutes or one hour; and the average demand over a longer period, usually a month or a year. The ratio of the two is called the *load factor* and is typically in the range 40 to 60 percent.[12] A system with a relatively high load factor is fortunate in that it uses, on the average, more of its installed capacity profitably; it spreads its investment costs over a greater production than would be true of another system of the same size, having the same peak load, but with a lower load factor. The high-load-factor system can therefore afford to spend more money for more efficient equipment that will reduce operating costs. The chief of these is the cost of fuel, expenditures for which vary directly with station output. Improvements in station thermal efficiency are one way to reduce the outlay for fuel.

The records of electric demands are usually kept in three major classifications: residential, commercial, and industrial. Special records applying to unusually large users of power are also available.

The forecaster studies the history of each type of load but chiefly gathers all available data on the growth of the area which is being studied. The forecaster watches population shifts, growth of suburban shopping centers, trends toward air conditioning and electric heating, changing processes in industry, development programs to attract new employers, statistics on per capita use of electricity; in short, every factor that bears on the future use of electrical energy in the area under investigation.

The result of this process is a graph showing the expected peak loads and load factors for a period of years into the future. An example of a peak-load forecast is the line X—X in Fig. 20.

To be reasonably sure of carrying the peak load of any given year, the total generating capacity of the system must exceed the expected peak load by a margin for reserve. The necessary reserve is of two kinds.

■ Spinning reserve is the excess generating capacity that is in operation and on the line at the time of peak load. It must be at least equal to the capacity of the largest single generating unit in use at that time on the system or its interconnections. It is necessary to provide spinning reserve to guard against the possibility of a mishap to the largest unit causing loss of its generating capacity, even if only for a few minutes.

■ Reserve for scheduled outages is generating capacity that is installed on the system but is not necessarily in operation at the time of peak load. Such reserve is needed because equipment must be inspected and overhauled at regular intervals. The amount of this reserve must be not less than the size of the largest unit that will be overhauled during the peak load season.

DETERMINING SYSTEM RESERVE REQUIREMENTS

A simplified example will illustrate the point. Assume a system composed of twelve identical generating units, each capable of generating a continuous output designated as M kW, where M is any number. The total installed capacity is 12 M kW. The spinning reserve is one unit, and the reserve for scheduled outages is another unit because an overhaul typically takes about

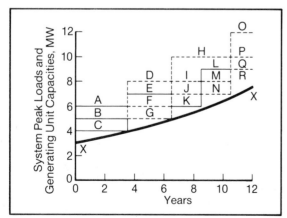

Fig. 20 **Relationship between peak loads and installed capacity**

a month. This system can be expected to carry a peak load of 10 M kW, its firm capacity.

If the system consists of six units each of 2 M kW capacity, the installed capacity is the same as before, but deduction of the spinning reserve will bring its capacity down to 10 M kW, and the further deduction of reserve for scheduled outages will leave a firm capacity of only 8 M kW. However, it may be possible to schedule the overhauls of six units wholly outside the peak-load season, depending on the character of the system load variations through the year; this would make the firm capacity of the system 10 M kW as before.

Another example is indicated in Fig. 20. The system is assumed to consist of six identical units each of M kW capacity. Line A indicates present installed capacity. Deduction of spinning reserve gives line B, and further deduction of reserve for scheduled outages leaves the firm capacity, line C. Another unit must be in operation before the peak-load season of the fourth year. If this unit is of M kW capacity, the new situation is indicated by lines E, F and G. Similarly, other M kW units must be added, one before the seventh year, one before the ninth year, and so on.

If the seventh unit is twice the size of the earlier ones, the installed capacity in the fourth year is shown by line D. Spinning reserve must now be 2M kW, the size of the largest unit. Reserve for scheduled outages will, however, be M kW, making the firm capacity line G, the same as if unit seven were of the smaller size. It follows that installing a large unit increases the firm capacity of a system only by an amount equal to the capacity of some smaller unit.

When the second larger unit is installed, as is indicated for years seven to ten, the firm capacity will increase by 2M kW if it is possible to schedule outages of the two larger units out of the peak-load season (lines H, I and J). Otherwise line K will give the firm capacity.

Further additions of capacity are also indicated on Fig. 20. Solid lines apply to M kW units and dash lines to the larger 2M kW size.

The foregoing is known as the block system of generating capacity addition. The objective

is to install the equivalent of two blocks more than the peak load, one to provide spinning reserve and the other to permit scheduled outages. This method of capacity addition has the virtue of simplicity and has been commonly used since the early days of the utility industry.

EVALUATING SYSTEM CAPACITY ADDITIONS

Several factors have led to modifications and deviations from this method of capacity addition. Not only has load grown but so has available unit generating size. At the same time, knowledge of system operation has become more complete, and reliability of components is better understood. This means that entire systems may be simulated by mathematical models and that unit outages may be predicted by probability methods.[13]

Using this approach the necessary system reserve requirements may be less than under the block system, but the largest single unit should not exceed 5–10 percent of the total system capacity. As a matter of policy, many systems refrain from increasing unit size until predicted load growth requires successive units of the larger size.

In practice, these considerations for system capacity additions are far from clear-cut for a number of different reasons.

■ The units will be of different types, sizes, ages and vulnerability to accidental shutdown.

■ The actual capacity of a plant varies with condensing water temperature, and at times is subject to variations caused by changes in the fuel.

■A system usually includes transmission lines which are subject to interruption of service from weather and other such causes quite different from those that affect generating units. Outages from such interruptions may be greater than the loss of a single unit.

■There is the possibility that not only one unit, but two or more, may suffer unexpected interruptions simultaneously or following closely upon one another.

The graph of Fig. 20 plots predicted annual peak loads for certain future years. Another informative graph is constructed by getting from system records the numbers of hours per year in

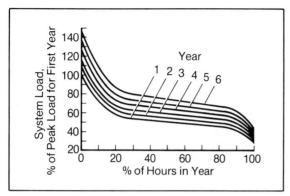

Fig. 21 Load-duration curves

which the load equalled or exceeded a given amount. The system minimum load will correspond to 8760 hours per year, and the maximum load will appear, in all probability, for only one hour. Such a graph is called a load-duration curve. Fig. 21 represents an idealized example. The areas are energy units expressed as kWhr, and the total area under the curve, divided by the area of the rectangle enclosing it is the annual load factor.

The chief value of this curve is to emphasize the brief period during which peak loads must be generated in the typical system. Even though the curve is drawn for a past year, its shape will not change markedly in the future unless the character of the load changes materially. Load-duration curves can, therefore, be drawn for future years, subject to the uncertainty of the predicted peak loads and load factors discussed earlier in this chapter.

It is apparent from the series of curves on a single set of axes in Fig. 21 that the system already has enough equipment to generate all but a relatively small part of the predicted loads. These peaks last a short time and involve only a small amount of generation above a horizontal line representing the system firm capacity. Assume for the moment that all equipment in the system is in good condition and can be expected to operate successfully throughout the period under study. On this assumption, the problem of meeting the future growth in peak load can be solved simply by providing the cheapest possible generating capacity large

enough to take care of the growth in load; its fuel economy is not of prime importance because it will be used only a few hours per year, whereas investment costs go on continuously and must be kept to a minimum.[14]

CHOICE OF POWER-PLANT ADDITIONS

Generally, load-distribution requirements for most utility systems follow the pattern of Fig. 21. A typical utility may have three distinct load requirements—base, intermediate and peak. Prior to the mid-1970's, the traditional methods of meeting these load requirements were to have large nuclear and high-efficiency fossil-fuel steam plants designed for 6000 to 8000 hours of operation per year supplying base load. Specially designed fossil-fuel steam plants and former base-loaded fossil plants would supply intermediate load. Low-efficiency installations required to operate for 500 to 2000 hours per year would supply the peak-load and reserve requirements of the system. Gas turbines, old steam plants, and hydro-pumped storage plants would supply this latter capacity. (It should be noted that there is no clean-cut line of demarcation between load categories. Plants designed for one mode of operation may, in practice, be required to operate in other modes which were not originally contemplated.)

Traditionally, utilities purchased new additions of the largest and most efficient steam cycle available. If availability factor was judged to be decreased somewhat with such an optimal selection, then some compromise may have been made. These new units were assigned to base-load service and expected to operate at a capacity factor equal to their availability for approximately the first 10 years of commercial operation. This relegated previously base-loaded plants within the system to cyclic or lower load-factor operation.

Currently, several factors are operating to change this pattern. Improvements in heat rate have diminished. Utilities with a mix of nuclear and new fossil may require the fossil plants to enter cycling service directly. Finally, although the new fossil units may be designed for an efficient thermodynamic cycle, tail-end emission control systems may have high parasitic power requirements. Similarly, the new plant may be fueled with low-sulfur coal transported great distances at considerable expense. Such factors may result in the new fossil unit having higher generation costs than some of the older plants, with a corresponding influence on the selection and loading of equipment for the most economic dispatch.

Final decisions as to size and timing may well be tied in with decisions as to location and type of equipment, as well as licensing and regulatory requirements that can result in exceedingly long construction lead times. However, the analysis and study described to this point will disclose a relatively small number of practical possibilities, each of which must be studied in some detail to set up comparative investment and operating costs over a period of years. At the same time it is important not to neglect the effect of each alternate possibility on the cost of operating the existing system.

SELECTION OF PLANT LOCATION

The location of an electric-generating station is determined by analysis of many factors that influence the selection in diverse ways. During the study and forecasting of future loads, it will usually become apparent that only a few attractive sites are available. Each of these must be studied to determine the effect of individual factors on its desirability. The object is to make an engineering economic analysis that will disclose the best choice, which in general is the location that will result in the lowest total cost to the owner in the long run.

CONDENSING WATER SUPPLY

As is well known, a steam turbine requires a relatively great quantity of condensing water for its economical operation. Under average conditions it is estimated that about 800 tons of water are required for each ton of coal burned. The supply of water should not vary through the year, its temperature should be as low as possible, the water should not be corrosive to the usual materials, and it should not contain suspended material that will interfere with the

flow through pumps and tubes. These considerations suggest a river, a lake or an ocean, and central stations are located whenever possible on the bank of some such body of water.

The alternate to such a location is to provide cooling towers in which forced or natural-draft circulation of air cools the condensing water nearly to the prevailing wet-bulb temperature. Although the investment in cooling towers is high compared to once-through cooling, this higher cost is somewhat offset by the smaller waterfront construction and tunnels.

The extent to which condensing water is available sets a limit on the amount of power that can be generated at the site. Advanced steam conditions not only achieve greater cycle efficiency but also result in less rejection of heat to the condenser. For example, for the same initial steam conditions and a limited amount of condensing water, selection of a reheat regenerative cycle permits greater power output than a nonreheat cycle, everything else being equal. This can be of considerable importance to central stations which are being redeveloped on sites having limited amounts of cooling water. Fig. 22 shows the reduction of heat rejection to condenser cooling water as cycles of increased thermal efficiency and decreased net plant heat rate are incorporated in power plants.[15]

Fig. 22 Heat rejected versus net plant heat rate based on 1.5″ Hg back pressure

PUBLIC OPINION

The effect of public opinion on the choice of a site can be profound. If the public thinks of a power plant as an ugly, noisy, dirty place, spreading dust and ash around the neighborhood, it instantly objects to admitting one to genteel surroundings. The remedy is to design and build central stations that have good architectural treatment, that are clean and as quiet as possible. Many public utilities have done this quite successfully.

OTHER CONSIDERATIONS

Additional concerns include availability of municipal services and suitable labor, appropriate zoning, convenient access, climate, tax situation and the like. Room for growth and freedom from undue risk of flood and earthquake are ordinarily essential.

The nature of surrounding installations may play a part in the selection. For example, the height of stacks will be subject to Federal Aeronautics Administration regulations and would be restricted near an airport.

In many site selection problems, one possibility is that of adding to an existing station. To do so has obvious economies in making use of existing facilities, no matter how much new construction may have to be provided. If the existing station site is large enough and has enough condensing water, and especially if it was designed for expansion, it is unlikely that a new site can compete successfully. Each case must be studied on its merits; the danger is in assuming that the "obvious" answer is the best.

Finally, in all studies and analyses, it is essential to remember that future conditions determine the best solution. All available data apply to past years, or at best to the present, and must be reviewed critically to ensure that the most likely future conditions have been derived or projected from them. This statement applies to every engineering economic study.

SELECTION OF TYPES OF EQUIPMENT

Having determined the size, timing, and location of the installation by the steps previously described, we must tackle the question, *What kind?* In practice, the steps are not taken separately and in succession; they overlap considerably but may follow the sequence described in the following text.

The primary choice is among the several plant fuel cycles; that is, conventional fuel, nuclear energy, and internal combustion (diesel or gas turbine). The possible consideration of hydro or purchased power would take place before site selection, and is outside the scope of this book. Strictly on the basis of total economy, steam with coal fuel frequently will be preferred in the larger sizes, with internal combustion having an advantage for smaller units.

The size range within which each type of plant fits best is reasonably well defined by experience and will not be the subject of intensive study in the typical instance. Capacity installed for peaking purposes may be subject to very different economic evaluation than is the case for base-load generating equipment. Heat rate economies dominate the latter, while availability of peak shaving capacity for short periods is of most importance in the former.

Assuming that a conventional steam cycle has been selected, studies will be made to find the best conditions as to steam and reheat pressures and temperatures, number and location of extraction stages, condenser pressure, and a host of similar cycle characteristics.[16] Only with experience and judgment as a guide is it possible to keep the combinations of variables within practical bounds. Even with the help of advanced methods of analysis, the basic method of solution is to assume a reasonable set of conditions and calculate the required investment in the central station and the resulting cost of operation under future load conditions. In some instances, the influence of a variable can be isolated and analyzed by itself, but all too often a change in assumed design conditions will be reflected throughout the cycle, resulting in an unexpected and perhaps undesired change at another point.[17]

The sizes of the units will have been fairly well determined by the studies of load growth and estimated capital cost. The unit system, under which a single boiler serves a single turbine, each with its own auxiliaries, is rather generally accepted, but there may well be exceptions, especially when a station has a process steam load in addition to an electric load.

At this point, a number of subsidiary economic studies will be required: for example, heater and condenser surface, turbine versus motor-driven auxiliaries, voltage of electric auxiliary drives and extent of building enclosure. The object is always to reduce the initial investment without increasing maintenance and operating costs unduly.

Investment costs are initially determined by making a preliminary design of the feature in question and estimating from quotations and past experience the cost of its purchase and installation, keeping in mind the fact that such matters as building volume, foundations, steel work, steam and water piping, electrical wiring, and controls cannot be ignored.

Operating costs are estimated by calculating plant performance over the necessary range of loads under the assumed conditions and applying load duration data to find annual costs. It is generally necessary to include maintenance costs for a complete comparison.

The several assumed combinations are compared by standard methods of engineering economy to find the one that promises the lowest overall cost over the life of the station, giving due regard to the time value of money.

See reference 16 for a typical engineering economy study peformed for application to a large utility system.

The result of this engineering process will be to produce a set of preliminary arrangement drawings showing the station as it has been conceived; a set of abbreviated specifications covering the important equipment, structures and systems; a reasonably reliable construction cost estimate; and a report covering the alternates considered, advantages and disadvantages of each, comparative investment and operating costs, and other data individual to each case. Management will be able to base its decision on this material if it is complete and well presented. Then and only then does the detailed procurement and design process be-

gin. The steam-turbine/generator and the boiler are purchased first, followed by other major components as dictated by their respective design and fabrication lead times.

As the equipment is purchased, hundreds of studies of comparative economics of the vendor offerings are made, based on capital costs, energy costs, and probable costs of operation and maintenance. The following section describes how such conventional power-plant economic studies are made.

SOME UTILITY TERMS

CAPACITY FACTOR: a measure of the output of the plant over some time period. Capacity factor is the ratio of the energy generated by the unit during the time period to the energy that could have been generated had the unit run at its full rating over the entire period.

NET PLANT HEAT RATE (NPHR): the fuel-heat input required to generate a kWhr and deliver the generated power to the transmission line leaving the plant. The term "net" implies that energy needed to supply auxiliary equipment must be deducted prior to calculating NPHR. Plant efficiency can be calculated by dividing 3413 Btu/kWhr by NPHR.

REPLACEMENT POWER COSTS: the cost of supplying replacement energy in the event of a forced or scheduled outage. Replacement power may be available within the utility's system by operating units with high operating costs or may have to be purchased from other utilities.

AUXILIARY-POWER CHARGES: charges assessed to account for the effect of auxiliary-power requirements on the net output from the plant to the utility's grid. A *demand* charge, proportional to the cost of new generating capacity, applies regardless of the duration such auxiliaries are expected to run. An *energy* charge is applied against the time the auxiliaries will be in operation. The magnitude of the energy charge depends on fuel costs and other operating costs in the utility system.

POWER-PLANT ECONOMICS

Costs associated with owning and operating power-plant equipment are a basic concern of both the design engineer and the user. Often, the initial cost of the equipment must balance against the operating cost over the plant lifetime. Before discussing how such comparisons are made, it is necessary to consider the two general categories of power-plant costs.

Much of the money spent by a power-plant owner is for goods and services consumed within a relatively short time after acquisition. This category includes outlays for wages and salaries, operating and maintenance supplies, and fuel. Called *expenses,* such payments are normally made from revenue.

In contrast, other owner expenditures are for items whose usefulness continues for an extended period and which produce revenue in the future; money spent to construct a power plant is a typical example. Termed *capital investments,* expenditures of this nature are not ordinarily paid directly from revenue; this is because current revenue most often would be insufficient to cover large capital expenditures, and because the equipment is expected to provide service well into the future.

POWER-GENERATING COSTS

Total power-generating costs, or bus-bar costs, are the sum of fixed charges, fuel costs, and operation and maintenance (O&M) costs. The fixed charges are associated with the capital investment, whereas the fuel and O&M costs are generally treated as expenses.

FIXED CHARGES

Capital costs are translated into annual costs by calculating the fixed charges on the plant or equipment.

Fixed charges are those costs incurred during each year of a plant's lifetime independent of how much energy production takes place in each year. Included in the fixed charges are usually all of the costs that are proportional to the capital investment in the plant, e.g. depreciation, required return on investment, prop-

erty insurance, federal income taxes, and state and local taxes.

Some components of the fixed-charge rate, such as depreciation, are bookkeeping expenses which do not represent cash outflow during the operation period. Other fixed-charge components, such as property insurance and *ad valorem* taxes, represent annual outlays which are in direct proportion to part or all of the initial investment. The required return on the investment and the income taxes associated with this return are a major part of the annual fixed charges. Also included is an interim replacement allowance, which provides for any intermittent replacement of equipment required before the end of the scheduled plant life. *Not included* in annual fixed charges are relatively constant fixed costs, such as liability insurance or plant staffing expenses, which bear no direct relation to the plant investment and are somewhat independent of the extent to which power is generated. (Such expenses are included in the plant operation and maintenance category.)

The proportionality constant that converts the initial capital cost of the plant to annual fixed charges is the fixed-charge rate. Therefore, the fixed charges on the plant are

$$C = IC \times FCR/100$$

where C = fixed charges, \$/yr.
  IC = initial capital cost, \$, and
  FCR = annual fixed-charge rate, %

(8)

or, on a per-unit-of-energy-generated basis:

$$c = \frac{IC \times 10^3 \times FCR/100}{G} = \frac{10 \times IC \times FCR}{G}$$

(9)

where c = fixed charges, mills/kWhr, and
  G = energy generation, kWhr/yr.

In utility accounting, fixed-charge percentages are applied annually to the depreciated (book) value of the investment, and consequently, the amount charged to a specific plant decreases from year to year. When this procedure is followed for evaluations, it is necessary to calculate fixed charges and all other costs year-by-year over the life of the plant, to discount each future year's total costs to obtain the corresponding present worth, and to sum all these present worths to obtain the grand-total "present-worthed" cost of the plant being evaluated. This gives a single figure by which the relative economics of proposed plants may be judged.

A simpler procedure giving the same result is to use levelized annual fixed charges; that is, to apply a *constant* fixed-charge rate each year to the initial investment in such a manner that the present-worthed grand total of the constant charges equals the corresponding total of variable charges. The use of levelized fixed charges does not yield the year-by-year forecast of costs given by the more detailed approach, but such annual breakdowns are not usually required for evaluations. A conceptual approach to developing a fixed-charge rate is shown in Table I.

FUEL COSTS

For most economic evaluations, converting fuel costs on an as-received basis at the plant to fuel costs per kilowatt-hour of power produced is sufficient. The relationships to do this are

$$F = \frac{FC \times NPHR}{10^5}$$

(10)

where F = fuel cost, mills/kWhr
FC = fuel cost, ¢/10⁶ (million)/Btu
$NPHR$ = net plant heat rate, Btu/kWhr

or

$$F = \frac{FC \times NTHR}{10^3 \times BE (1-APR)}$$

(11)

where $NTHR$ = net turbine heat rate, Btu/kWhr
BE = boiler efficiency, %
APR = auxiliary power requirements (as a fraction of gross plant output)

Thus, if fuel costs for a coal-fired unit are projected at 200¢ per million Btu, and the net plant heat rate is 9300 Btu/kWhr, the fuel cost, F, is 18.6 mills/kWhr.

Table I. Typical Fixed-Charge Rate for Depreciable Portion of Plant

Component	Percent
Interest or return on investment	8.6 *
Depreciation * *	3.3
Interim replacements	0.4
Property insurance	0.5
Federal income taxes	3.0 * * *
State and local taxes	2.4 * * *
	Total 18.2

*Levelized value: (50% debt @ 10% + 50% equity @ 14%) × .72 levelized average investment
* *Straight-line for 30 years
* * *For investor-owned companies

TIME-DEPENDENT COSTS

The time it takes to complete a project affects present-day direct costs (such as material and labor) and indirect costs (such as construction facilities and services) in two ways. Escalation takes place between project initiation and actual delivery of equipment and services. The utility also incurs interest charges on payments that must be made before the plant is placed into service. The magnitude of these escalation and interest-during-construction (IDC) costs on the steam-generating equipment depends, of course, on the vendor's escalation provisions and terms of payment. These charges can typically add 50 percent to the original cost of long, lead-time equipment, such as boilers and turbine-generators. Therefore, changes in the present-day price of new equipment, either upwards or downwards, are highly leveraged in their impact on the evaluated cost of the equipment installed in the plant.

Although each equipment payment is subject to different escalation and IDC charges as a result of the timing of the payment, the net effect of these charges can be represented by single factors. Each factor is a weighted-average of the charges on individual payments. The final, fully escalated cost of the equipment is greater than the present day cost of equipment by the factor F, where:

$$F = E_d \times E_c \times I_c$$

(12)

and where;

F = total factor to be applied to present-day costs to account for escalation and interest during construction

E_d = escalation factor during design period to start of construction

E_c = escalation factor during construction period (See Fig. 23)

I_c = interest factor during construction period (See Fig. 24)

Figs. 23 and 24 depict graphically the values of interest and escalation multipliers during the construction period based on typical cash-flow patterns for power plants.

Consider a unit with a present-day cost of $500 million. With construction beginning two years from now and commercial operation six years from now, escalation is expected to be 7 percent per year, and interest during construction, 8 percent per year:

$E_d = (1.07)^2 = 1.145$
$E_c = 1.135$ (See Fig. 23 for 48 months and 7%/yr.)
$I_c = 1.16$ (See Fig. 24 for 48 months and 8%/yr.)
$F = 1.145 \times 1.135 \times 1.16 = 1.51$

This plant then would have a capital cost at the commercial operation date of:
$1.51 \times \$500 \times 10^6 = \$755$ million

ECONOMIES OF SCALE

Many of the cost components that make up total power-plant costs are fixed; that is, they are independent of plant size, or else they increase slowly as plant size increases. If total plant costs increase at a slower rate, percentage-wise, than the rate at which design plant output increases, economies of scale are present. Recent power-plant construction experience indicates

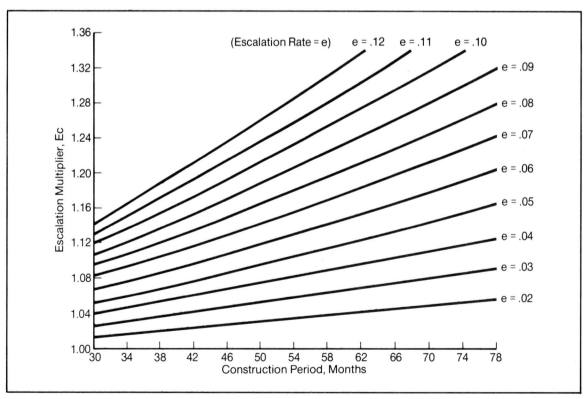

Fig. 23 **Escalation multiplier**

that economies of scale appear to exist in the steam-generating plant, the turbine-generator, the condenser, and switchgear, and consequently, in total plant costs.

This type of cost behavior is often represented by some form of power relationship, less than unity, and usually between 0.7 and 0.85. With a power relationship "k," this would be expressed as follows:

$$\frac{IC_1}{IC_2} = \left(\frac{PO_1}{PO_2}\right)^k$$

where: IC_1 = capital cost of plant 1
IC_2 = capital cost of plant 2
PO_1 = output of plant 1
PO_2 = output of plant 2 **(13)**

Thus, if the cost of a 600-MW generating unit is expected to be \$1200/kW, the total cost for a 900-MW unit will be, with k = 0.8

$$\left(\frac{900}{600}\right)^{.8} \times \$1200/kW \times 600,000\ kW$$

$$= \$995,000,000$$

Economies of scale are only one factor involved in the choice of unit size. Consideration must also be made of such factors as reliability, mode of operation, financing requirements, availability of sites, and regulations.

PRESENT-WORTH AND LEVELIZED COSTS

Present-worth and *levelized costs* are terms often used in discussing utility planning, evaluations, and engineering economics in general. The concept of present-worth costs is frequently explained by the statement that "a dollar today is worth more than a dollar tomorrow." While this sounds reasonable, it is important to understand the basis for the statement. It has nothing to do with inflation or escalation of costs. It simply means that a dollar received today can be invested and, by "tomorrow," will be equal to a dollar plus interest.

The concept of present worth or present value is a corollary. The present worth of some future expense (or revenue) is the amount that would have to equal that future expense (or

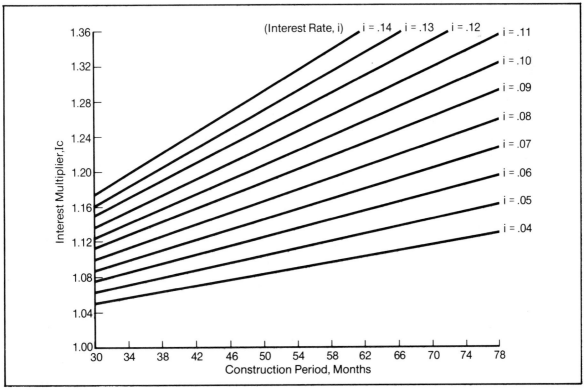

Fig. 24 **Interest multiplier**

revenue) eventually. Total present-worth costs are simply a way of combining payments made at different times to account for the value of interest. All utility expenditures are in this category.

Present-worth costs are calculated by simply reversing the process of calculating compound interest. Therefore, C_o is the present worth of some cost, C_1 occurring at time t in the future

$$C_o = \frac{C_1}{(1 + r)^t}$$

(14)

where r is the interest rate or discount rate.

The expression $\frac{1}{(1 + r)^t}$ is called the discount factor or present-worth factor.

Thus, the present worth of a payment of $100,000 to be made three years later, assuming a discount rate of 9 percent per year, is

$$\$100,000 \times \frac{1}{(1.09)^3} = \$77,200.$$

In other words, a payment of $77,200 now is equivalent to a payment of $100,000 three years later, assuming the money can be invested to generate a rate of return of 9%/yr.

The total present-worth costs (PWC) are the sum of all costs associated with a project properly discounted or present-worthed to a common point in time.

$$PWC = \sum_i \frac{C_i}{(1 + r)^t}$$

(15)

Total present-worth costs can be used to compare two alternatives that involve different cost expenditures over the life of a project.

A closely related concept is levelized costs. Levelizing is an averaging process which gives more weight to costs occurring early in the life of the project. To obtain levelized costs, it is only necessary to divide the total present worth of the payments involved by the sum of the present-worth factors. For instance, levelized total costs (LC) are given by:

$$LC = \frac{\sum \dfrac{C_i}{(1 + r)^t}}{\sum \dfrac{1}{(1 + r)^t}}$$

(16)

The resulting levelized cost is one, constant, annual value which is equivalent (i.e. has the same total present worth) as the non-uniform series of actual annual costs.

Thus, for non-uniform annual expenses of $157 million; $165 million; $167, $163, and $170 million over the first five years of operation of a new generating unit, the present-worth costs and levelized costs, using a 9%/yr discount rate, are shown in Table II.

ECONOMIC ANALYSES

Most evaluations involve comparisons between different plant designs, alternative components or various modes of operation. To perform a consistent evaluation, everything that affects a utility's cost of providing service should be taken into account. Usually this results in a study to determine which alternative has the lowest combination of capital cost (or fixed charges), fuel cost, and O&M cost.

DEFINITION OF DISCOUNT RATE

The discount rate is usually defined as the desired after-tax return on investment. Generally, it is the minimum return that any project must provide in order for the project to be accepted.

The following formula takes into account that the interest payments on debt are tax-deductible expenses:

$$r = f_s r_s + (1 - t) f_b r_b$$

where: r = discount rate

 f_s = fraction of investment in the form of stock

 f_b = fraction of investment in the form of bonds

 r_s = the annual return to stockholders, %

 r_b = the interest rate on bonds, %

 t = fraction of net income to be paid out as income tax

***Table II.* Levelized Costs and Present-Worth Costs of a New Generating Unit**

Year	Present-Worth Factor	Expenses 10⁶$	Present-Worth Expenses, 10⁶$
1	0.917	157	143.9
2	0.842	165	138.9
3	0.772	167	128.9
4	0.708	163	115.4
5	0.650	170	110.5
Totals	3.889		637.6

$$\text{Levelized Expenses} = \frac{\$637.6 \times 10^6}{3.889}$$
$$= \$164 \times 10^6/\text{yr}$$

This discussion will be referring to the evaluation between two different total power plants and could apply equally well to the choice between steam-supply systems, alternative pump designs, or operating cycles. Most evaluations can be classified into one of two approaches. The first of these is what is often referred to as the "revenue requirements method." This method leads to a comparison of generating costs (or revenue requirements) on a mills/kWhr basis, between alternatives. An equivalent-revenue-requirements comparison can also be made by contrasting the total present worth of all costs, i.e. present worth of fixed charges on the capital investment plus the present worth of fuel and O&M costs. A comparison of present-worth totals, instead of mills/kWhr is only valid in the case where each alternative produces the same energy.

The revenue-requirements method, therefore, necessitates that all capital costs first be converted to annual fixed charges and then combined with annual revenue requirements for fuel and O&M. It is then possible to calculate total present-worth revenue requirements for each alternative or levelized annual revenue requirements. The alternative with the lowest revenue requirements is the preferred choice in the evaluation.

The second method of performing an economic evaluation is what is often known as the "capitalized-cost" method. With the revenue-requirements approach, capital costs were converted to annual costs by use of the fixed-charge rate. The fixed charges could then be combined with fuel and O&M costs which were already on an annual basis. Conversely, with the capitalized-cost method, just the opposite is done. Annual costs such as fuel and O&M are divided by the fixed-charge rate (i.e. capitalized) so that the result can be combined with capital costs. This gives a very quick way of comparing the difference in operating costs with the difference in capital costs between various alternatives.

The system planner is still faced with the traditional problem of balancing plant capital cost, expected capacity factor and fuel cost in determining which steam cycle to choose. A curve system (Fig. 25), using the capitalized-cost method described previously, is useful in performing such comparisons.

OTHER ASPECTS OF THE SELECTION OF POWER-PLANT EQUIPMENT

Intensive economic and cost analyses of the type described in the preceding section are

---

PRESENT WORTH

Present worth of a fixed annual cost, FC, for n years at r %/yr. (If FC is equal to 1, this expression is equal to the sum of the present-worth factors for n years.)

1. $PW = \frac{FC}{r}\left[1 - \left(\frac{1}{1+r}\right)^n\right]$

Present worth of an annual cost, AC, which is escalating at e %/yr:

2. $PW = AC\left(\frac{1}{r-e}\right)\left[1 - \left(\frac{1+e}{1+r}\right)^n\right]$

where r is again the discount rate.

3. To obtain levelized annual costs (when escalation is taking place), divide the results obtained in expression 2 by the sum of the PW factors from expression 1.

very important in choosing the size, type, and equipment manufacturer for power and steam generation. But there are other surprisingly potent variables influencing the eventual generation economics of a given installation that the evaluating engineer has to take into account. Among these variables are:

a. the reliability of the many critical compo-

nents associated directly with the generating process;

b. the reliability of fuel supply of a specific type and heating value during the lifetime of the plant;

c. regulatory obligations, present or future, that a plant is bound to observe during operation or, in the event of failure of equipment having an actual or alleged effect on public health or safety, shut down the generating operation;

d. compatibility with *future* regulatory requirements, which have to be anticipated during the siting and equipment-selection process; and

e. compatibility with future *social* and *political* requirements.

So, in addition to the effects of inflation (escalation and changes in interest rates) presented above, there is no question but that we must anticipate large but uncertain capital-cost increases in the construction of utility and industrial power plants because of federal and state regulatory impact. Laws yet to be enacted in the areas of clean air, clean water, conservation, resource recovery, public-safety, public health, aesthetics (plant visual impact), and product liability can be expected to affect decision making even more than purely economic and equipment-availability considerations.

The degree of uncertainty in establishing the estimated future cost of fossil plants is very high. Thus, decisions about equipment and services made on presently perceived uncertainty and conventional economics ignores the probable course of any particular plant vis-a-vis regulations yet to be imposed.

Fig. 25 Breakeven capital cost changes versus improvements in heat rate. EXAMPLE: Going from an 1800 psig, 1000°/1000° cycle to a 2400 psig, 1000°/1000° cycle results in an improvement in cycle efficiency of 160 Btu/kWhr. What is the breakeven increase in capital cost? Given: 70 percent capacity factor, $2/10⁶ Btu fuel cost, and 16 percent/yr fixed charge rate. Solution: Enter at point A; read the result at point B, about $15/kW.

REFERENCES

[1] Edward Arthur Bruges, *Available Energy and the Second Law Analysis.* New York: Academic Press, 1959.

J. H. Keenan, "A Steam Chart for Second Law Analysis." *Mechanical Engineering*, 54:195–204, 1932.

M. W. Thring, "The Virtue of Energy, Its Meaning and Practical Significance." *Institute of Fuel. Journal*, 17:116–123, 1944.

C. Birnie and E. F. Obert, "Evaluation and Location of

the Losses in a 60,000 KW Power Station," *Proceedings of the Midwest Power Conference*, 11:187–193, 1949. Chicago: Illinois Institute of Technology, 1949.

Allen Keller, "Evaluation of Steam-Power-Plant Losses by Means of the Entropy-Balance Diagram." *Transactions of the ASME*, 72:949–953, October 1950.

C. A. Meyer, et al., "Availability Balance of Steam Power Plants." *Transactions of the ASME. Journal of Engineering for Power*, 81, Series A: 35–42, January 1959.

[2] E. Clapeyron and R. Clausius, "Memoir on the Motive Power of Heat" in Sadi Nicolas Leonard Carnot, E. Clapeyron and R. Clausius, *Reflections on the Motive Power of Fire; and other papers on the 2nd law of Thermodynamics*. Gloucester, Ma.: Peter Smith, 1962. Also published as a Dover paperback.

[3] Edward F. Obert and Richard A. Gaggioli, *Thermodynamics*, 2nd Edition. New York: McGraw-Hill, 1963, pp. 384–416.

Newman A. Hall and W. E. Ibele, *Engineering Thermodynamics*. Englewood Cliffs, N.J.: Prentice-Hall, 1960, pp. 447–520.

[4] William J. M. Rankine, *A Manual of the Steam Engine and Other Prime Movers*, revised by W. J. Millar with a section entitled "Gas, Oil, and Air Engines" by Brian Duncan. London: Griffin and Co., 1908.

James B. Jones and G. A. Hawkins, *Engineering Thermodynamics: An Introductory Textbook*. New York: Wiley, 1960.

[5] C. D. Weir, "Optimization of Heater Enthalpy Rises in Feed-Heating Trains." *Institution of Mechanical Engineers. Proceedings*, 174:769–796, 1960. Discussion by R. W. Haywood, pp. 784–787.

G. Chiantore, et al., "Optimizing A Regenerative Steam-Turbine Cycle." *Transactions of the ASME. Journal of Engineering for Power*, 83, Series A: 433–443, October 1961.

J. Kenneth Salisbury, *Steam Turbines and Their Cycles*. Huntington, N.Y.: Robert E. Krieger, 1974, Part 3: Cycle Analysis.

[7] Anon., "The Reheat Cycle—A Re-Evaluation." *Combustion*, 21(12): 38–40, June 1950. Papers given at the Symposium on the Reheat Cycle sponsored by the ASME and held in New York, November 29–December 3, 1948. *Transactions of the ASME*, 71:673–749, 1949.

J. K. Salisbury, "Analysis of the Steam-Turbine Reheat Cycle." *Transactions of the ASME* 80: 1629–1642, November 1958.

J. K. Salisbury, "Power-Plant Performance Monitoring." *Transactions of the ASME Journal of Engineering for Power*, 83, Series A: 409–422, October 1961.

[8] Paul L. Geiringer and Floyd Hasselriis, "High Temperature Water for Process Heating Combined with Power Production." *Proceedings of the American Power Conference*, 26:580–590, 1954. Chicago: Illinois Institute of Technology, 1954.

J. A. Eibling and B. A. Landry, "The Steam Generating Station as a Source and Sink for the Heat Pump." *Mechanical Engineering*, 73(7): 554–558, 564, July 1951.

[9] J. B. Stout, et al., "A Large Combined Gas Turbine-Steam Turbine Generating Unit." *Proceedings of the American Power Conference*, 24:404–411, 1962. Chicago: Illinois Institute of Technology, 1962.

[10] F. L. Robson et al, *Technological and Economic Feasibility of Advanced Power Cycles and Methods of Producing Nonpolluting Fuels for Utility Power Stations*. Final Report. July 1, 1969–December 31, 1970. Report No. PB 198 392. (Contract CPA 22-69-114). Springfield, VA: National Technical Information Service, 1971.

Henry J. Blaskowski and Joseph G. Singer, "Gas Turbine Boiler Applications." *Combustion*, 28(11): 38–44, May 1957.

W. H. Clayton and Joseph G. Singer, *Steam Generator Designs for Combined Cycle Applications*. Combustion Engineering Publication TIS-3322. Windsor, CT.: Combustion Engineering, Inc., 1973. Also in: *Combustion*, 44(10): 26–32, April 1973.

[11] Owen S. Lieberg, *High Temperature Water Systems*. New York: The Industrial Press, 1958.

[12] Edison Electric Institute. Statistical Committee, *Glossary of Electric Utility Terms*. New York: Edison Electric Institute, 1970.

[13] AIEE Probability Applications Working Group, *Application of Probability Methods to Generating Capacity Problems*. AIEE Paper CP 60–37. New York: American Institute of Electrical Engineers, 1960. (Unpublished).

C. J. Baldwin, "Modern Scientific Tools Used in the Power Industry for Tomorrow's Problems." *Proceedings of the American Power Conference*, 24: 94–105, 1962. Chicago: Illinois Institute of Technology, 1962.

[14] R. D. Brown and D. A. Harris, *Large Coal-Fired Cycling Units*. Paper given at the ASME-IEEE-ASCE Joint Power Generation Conference, Portland, Oregon, Sept. 28–Oct. 2, 1975. Combustion Engineering Publication TIS-4558. Windsor, CT.: Combustion Engineering, Inc. 1975.

Peter H. Benziger and Joseph G. Singer, "Design for Cycling at Chalk Point." *Proceedings of the American Power Conference*, 34:415–423, 1972. Chicago: Illinois Institute of Technology, 1972.

[15] Stanley Moyer, "Industry's Water Problems." *ASME Paper No. 6 WA-141*. New York: American Society of Mechanical Engineers, 1961. Also in condensed form in *Mechanical Engineering*, 84(3): 46–49, March 1962.

[16] James W. Lyons, "Optimizing Designs of Fossil-Fired Generating Units." *Power Engineering*, 83(2):50–56, February 1979.

[17] W. A. Wilson, "An Analytic Procedure for Optimizing the Selection of Power-Plant Components." *Transactions of the ASME*, 79:1120–1128, July 1957.

CHAPTER 2

Fossil Fuels

Fossil fuels used for steam generation in utility and industrial power plants may be classified into solid, liquid, and gaseous fuels as in Table I. Each fuel may be further classified as a natural, manufactured, or byproduct fuel. Not mutually exclusive, these classifications necessarily overlap in some areas.

Obvious examples of natural fuels are coal, crude oil and natural gas. Residual oils which are fired in boilers might be considered as a byproduct of the refining of crude oil. Wood, although a natural fuel, is rarely burned in boilers except in the form of sawdust, shavings, slabs and bark which remain as a byproduct after lumbering and pulping operations. Coal is the natural fuel from which coke, coke-oven gas, char, tars, chemicals and industrial gases may be converted by carbonization. Coal may also be gasified to obtain industrial gases for heating, chemical reduction, and hydrogenation and synthesis reactions.[1]

Of all the fossil fuels used for steam generation in electric-utility and industrial power plants today, coal is the most important. It is widely available throughout much of the world, and the quantity and quality of coal reserves are better known than those of other fuels. Many studies have been made of coal availability and utilization and should be consulted for more detailed information.[2]

FORMATION OF COAL

Coal forms as the result of a natural chemical process in which plants absorb carbon dioxide from the atmosphere. Sunlight, moisture and other factors convert carbon dioxide into compounds containing carbon, hydrogen and oxygen, such as sugars, starch, cellulose, lignin and other complex substances that make up the plant structure. Under favorable conditions, vegetation is converted into some of the many forms of coal now known to mankind.

When organic matter begins to change to coal, peat is the first product. In a block of peat one can often see, with the naked eye, woody fragments of stems, roots, and bark. As peat is buried, it is cut off from the oxygen in air, and rapid decay of its organic matter is prevented by slowing bacterial action. The weight of more vegetation falling on the peat helps to compress and solidify it, as does the weight of water when the deposit sinks below a lake or sea, as has often happened. Sometimes, mineral sediments have settled from muddy flood waters while vegetable matter was accumulating and formed "partings" or layers of shale in the coal vein. At the end of coal-forming periods, swamps remain flooded for a long time, and earthy sediments are deposited in thick beds over the peat, further compressing it and starting "coalification," the coal-making process.

Many kinds of coal are found in a natural deposit. In some, transitions from the extremes of lignite to anthracite exist in a single bed. It is generally assumed that differences in rank of coal are not caused by different source materials but by the agencies of coal formation.

THE FORMATION CYCLE

Geologists usually name time, pressure and temperature as the agents that change peat into different types of coal. Chemists include microorganisms as an additional important factor.

Time, it must be remembered, is in itself no agent; it is merely the duration or period during which an agent has an opportunity to act. It becomes crucial, however, because many organic chemical reactions are slow. In fact, it is believed that reactions are going on slowly in most complex organic substances. In a short period the results of such reactions would be negligible, but over millions of years the total results must be large. Although the greatest single factor in the process of formation was probably time, other factors must also be sought, because coals of the same age and, in fact, in the same bed, are of different rank.

Generally, pressure is considered to be the factor of next importance, because coal of higher rank is generally found in regions that have been under high pressure. Anthracite, for example, is associated with earth-folding or mountain formation, which processes bring about great internal pressure. Experimentally, it has not been determined that pressure alone can change organic substances chemically.

Likewise, heat has played an important part in this great natural chemical industry. The temperature need not be high, for time brings about a relatively great change even at the low temperatures prevailing in the earth's crust.

Man completes the cycle by burning the various products of the natural process to carbon dioxide, and then nature starts all over again.

There is no satisfactory definition of coal. It is a mixture of organic chemical and mineral materials produced by a natural process of growth and decay, accumulation of debris both vegetal and mineral, with some sorting and stratification, and accomplished by chemical, biological, bacteriological and metamorphic action. The organic chemical materials produce heat when burned; the mineral matter remains as the residue called ash.

CLASSIFICATION OF COAL

Coals are grouped according to rank, the degree of progressive alteration in the transformation from lignite to anthracite.

Table I. Classification of Fuels

Natural Fuels	Manufactured or Byproduct Fuels
Solid	
Coal	Coke and coke breeze
	Coal tar
Lignite	Lignite char
Peat	
Wood	Charcoal
	Bark, saw dust and wood waste
	Petroleum coke
	Bagasse
	Refuse
Liquid	
Petroleum	Gasoline
	Kerosene
	Fuel oil
	Gas oil
	Shale oil
	Petroleum fractions and residues
Gaseous	
Natural gas	Refinery gas
Liquefied petroleum gases (LPG)	
	Coke-oven gas
	Blast-furnace gas
	Producer gas
	Water gas
	Carburetted water gas
	Coal gas
	Regenerator waste gas

For the purposes of the power-plant operator, there are several suitable ranks of coal:

- anthracite
- bituminous
- subbituminous
- lignite

Table II. Classification of Coals by Rank[a]

Class and Group	Fixed Carbon Limits, % (Dry, Mineral-Matter-Free Basis)		Volatile Matter Limits, % (Dry, Mineral-Matter-Free Basis)		Calorific Value Limits, Btu/lb (Moist,[b] Mineral-Matter-Free Basis)		Agglomerating Character
	Equal or Greater Than	Less Than	Equal or Greater Than	Less Than	Equal or Greater Than	Less Than	
I. Anthracitic							
1. Meta-anthracite	98	. . .	. . .	2	. . .	. . .	nonagglom-
2. Anthracite	92	98	2	8	. . .	. . .	erating
3. Semianthracite[c]	86	92	8	14	. . .	. . .	
II. Bituminous							
1. Low-volatile bituminous coal	78	86	14	22	. . .	. . .	
2. Medium volatile bituminous coal	69	78	22	31	. . .	. . .	
3. High-volatile A bituminous coal	. . .	69	31	. . .	14,000[d]	. . .	commonly agglomerating[e]
4. High-volatile B bituminous coal	. . .	. . .	. . .	. . .	13,000[d]	14,000	
5. High-volatile C bituminous coal	. . .	. . .	. . .	. . .	11,500	13,000	
					10,500	11,500	agglomerating
III. Subbituminous							
1. Subbituminous A coal	. . .	. . .	. . .	. . .	10,500	11,500	
2. Subbituminous B coal	. . .	. . .	. . .	. . .	9,500	10,500	nonagglom-
3. Subbituminous C coal	. . .	. . .	. . .	. . .	8,300	9,500	erating
IV. Lignitic							
1. Lignite A	. . .	. . .	. . .	. . .	6,300	8,300	
2. Lignite B	. . .	. . .	. . .	. . .	. . .	6,300	

[a] This classification does not include a few coals, principally nonbanded varieties, which have unusual physical and chemical properties and which come within the limits of fixed carbon or calorific value of the high-volatile bituminous and subbituminous ranks. All of these coals either contain less than 48% dry, mineral-matter-free fixed carbon or have more than 15,500 moist, mineral-matter-free Btu per pound.

[b] Moist refers to coal containing its natural inherent moisture but not including visible water on the surface of the coal.

[c] If agglomerating, classify in low-volatile group of the bituminous class.

[d] Coals having 69% or more fixed carbon on the dry, mineral-matter-free basis shall be classified by fixed carbon, regardless of calorific value.

[e] It is recognized that there may be nonagglomerating varieties in these groups of the bituminous class, and there are notable exceptions in high-volatile C bituminous group.

Reprinted from *ASTM Standards* D 388, Classification of Coals by Rank.

Being extremely broad, these terms fail to define rank completely. Many investigators have attempted to set up some scientific system of classification to accurately define the boundary lines of variation. Some better known bases for classification are those of Persifor Frazer, Jr., who made the earliest published classification of American coals in 1877; M. R. Campbell and S. W. Parr, who both published papers on the subject in 1906; David White, with publications in 1909 and 1913; and O. C. Ralston, whose graphic studies of some 3000 coal analyses were made in 1915. Each of these will serve to type a coal within narrow limits, but the suitability of a given coal for a specific purpose is best established by actual trial in the equipment for which it is selected.[3]

The American Society for Testing and Materials (ASTM) has established perhaps the most universally applicable basis for classifying coal according to fixed carbon and heating value (calorific value) calculated to a mineral-matter-free basis. As shown in Table II, this scheme represents a further development of the proposals of S. W. Parr. The high-rank coals are classified according to fixed carbon on the dry basis, and the low-rank coals according to Btu on the moist basis. Agglomerating indices differentiate between certain adjacent groups.

In commercial practice, it frequently suffices to calculate to a dry, ash-free basis. The ash, however, does not correspond to the mineral matter in coal. Thus, if the ash-free basis is used when classifying coal according to rank, significant errors may be introduced. Remarkably uniform results, however, are obtained from heating values of coals of a given rank and source when calculated to a dry mineral-matter-free basis.

In ASTM classification by rank, the agglomerating index, or caking quality of a coal, indicates the dividing line between noncaking coals and those having weakly caking properties. The noncaking designation applies only to coals that produce a noncoherent residue which can be poured out of the crucible as a powder or flakes that will pulverize easily with thumb and finger pressure.

The transformation of vegetal matter through wood and peat to lignite and finally to anthracite results in a reduction of volatile matter and oxygen content, with a simultaneous increase in carbon content. This is illustrated graphically in Fig. 1 in which moisture-and-ash-free volatile matter, fixed carbon, oxygen content, and high heating value are given for various ranks of coals as well as wood and peat.

RANKS OF COAL

The method of "proximate analysis" identifies the degree of coalification of the higher

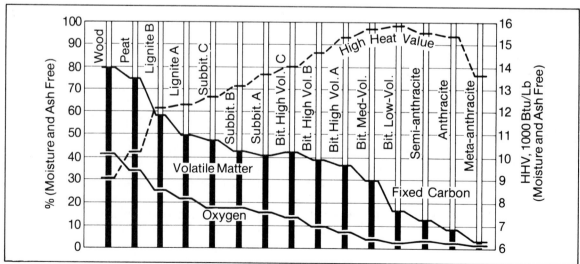

Fig. 1 Progressive stages of transformation of vegetal matter into coal

rank coals. In this method, a chemical analysis determines four constituents in coal: (1) water, called moisture; (2) mineral impurity, called ash, left when the coal is completely burned; (3) volatile matter, consisting of gases driven out when coal is heated to certain temperatures; and (4) fixed carbon, the coke-like residue that burns at higher temperatures after volatile matter has been driven off. For the lower rank coals, heating value and caking and weathering properties determine rank. The coal rank increases as the amount of fixed carbon increases and the amounts of moisture and volatile matter decrease. (Moisture and volatile matter were squeezed and distilled from coal during its formation by pressure and heat, raising the proportion of fixed carbon.) On an ash-free basis, the difference in constituents between a typical lignite, the lowest rank of coal, and an anthracite, the highest rank, is clearly shown in the following analysis:

	Lignite	Anthracite
Fixed Carbon (FC)	30%	92%
Volatile Matter (VM)	33%	5%
Moisture (H_2O)	37%	3%

The following description of coals by rank gives some of their physical characteristics.

ANTHRACITE

Hard and very brittle, anthracite is dense, shiny black, and homogeneous with no marks of layers. Unlike the lower rank coals, it has a high percentage of fixed carbon and a low percentage of volatile matter. Anthracites include a variety of slow-burning fuels merging into graphite at one end and into bituminous coal at the other. They are the hardest coals on the market, consisting almost entirely of fixed carbon, with the little volatile matter present in them chiefly as methane, CH_4. Anthracite is usually graded into small sizes before being burned on stokers: the "meta-anthracites" burn so slowly as to require mixing with other coals, while the "semianthracites," which have more volatile matter, are burned with relative ease if properly fired. Most anthracites have a lower heating value than the highest grade bituminous coals. Anthracite is used principally for heating homes and in gas production.

Some semianthracites are dense, but softer than anthracite, shiny gray, and somewhat granular in structure. The grains have a tendency to break off in handling the lump, and produce a coarse, sandlike slack.

Other semianthracites are dark gray and distinctly granular. The grains break off easily in handling and produce a coarse slack. The granular structure has been produced by small vertical cracks in horizontal layers of comparatively pure coal separated by very thin partings. The cracks are the result of heavy downward pressure, and probably shrinkage of the pure coal because of a drop in temperature.

BITUMINOUS

By far the largest group, bituminous coals derive their name from the fact that on being heated they are often reduced to a cohesive, binding, sticky mass. Their carbon content is less than that of anthracites, but they have more volatile matter. The character of their volatile matter is more complex than that of anthracites and they are higher in calorific value. They burn easily, especially in pulverized form, and their high volatile content makes them good for producing gas. Their binding nature enables them to be used in the manufacture of coke, while the nitrogen in them is utilized in processing ammonia.

The low-volatile bituminous coals are grayish black and distinctly granular in structure. The grain breaks off very easily, and handling reduces the coal to slack. Any lumps that remain are held together by thin partings. Because the grains consist of comparatively pure coal, the slack is usually lower in ash content than are the lumps.

Medium-volatile bituminous coals are the transition from high-volatile to low-volatile coal and, as such, have the characteristics of both. Many have a granular structure, are soft, and crumble easily. Some are homogeneous with very faint indications of grains or layers. Others are of more distinct laminar structure, are hard, and stand handling well.

High-volatile A bituminous coals are mostly homogeneous with no indication of grains, but some show distinct layers. They are hard and stand handling with little breakage. The moisture, ash and sulfur contents are low, and the heating value high.

High-volatile B bituminous coals are of distinct laminar structure; thin layers of black, shiny coal alternate with dull, charcoal-like layers. They are hard and stand handling well. Breakage occurs generally at right angles and parallel to the layers, so that the lumps generally have a cubical shape.

High-volatile C bituminous coals are of distinct laminar structure, are hard and stand handling well. They generally have high moisture, ash, and sulfur content and they are considered to be free-burning coals.

SUBBITUMINOUS

These coals are brownish black or black. Most are homogeneous with smooth surfaces, and with no indication of layers. They have high moisture content, as much as 15 to 30 percent, although appearing dry. When exposed to air they lose part of the moisture and crack with an audible noise. On long exposure to air, they disintegrate. They are free-burning, entirely noncoking, coals.

LIGNITE

Lignites are brown and of a laminar structure in which the remnants of woody fibers may be quite apparent. The word *lignite* comes from the Latin word *lignum* meaning wood. Their origin is mostly from plants rich in resin, so they are high in volatile matter. Freshly mined lignite is tough, although not hard, and it requires a heavy blow with a hammer to break the large lumps. But on exposure to air it loses moisture rapidly and disintegrates. Even when it appears quite dry, the moisture content may be as high as 30 percent. Owing to the high moisture and low heating value, it is not economical to transport it long distances.

Unconsolidated lignite (B in Table II) is also known as "brown coal." (Further differentiation between the various lignites and brown coals is given in Appendix A.) Brown coals are generally found close to the surface, contain more than 45 percent moisture, and are readily won by strip mining.

PEAT

Peat is not yet a commercial fuel in many countries where it is found, because of its very high moisture content and low heating value. It is a heterogeneous material of partially decomposed organic matter (plant material) and inorganic minerals that have accumulated in a water-saturated environment over a period of time. Its color can vary from yellow to brownish black, depending upon the degree of biological decay, mechanical disintegration of the plant fibers, and the presence of sediment. A water-saturated environment inhibits active biological decomposition of the plant material and promotes the retention of carbon and oxygen that would normally be released as gaseous products of the biological activity.

The universal problem in utilizing peat is its high moisture content. Even after draining a peat bog and solidifying the peat, it can still contain 70 to 95 percent water.

The sulfur content of peat is normally quite low, varying from negligible to less than 1 percent in dried peat. On the other hand, the ash content of peat can vary from 2 to 70 percent in assays of dry peat from a variety of sources.

COAL MINING

The two general methods of mining are stripping (open pit) and underground. In underground mining the coal is undercut, topcut, or sheared and then blasted. Loading may be by hand or machine. If hand-loaded, the miners remove most of the larger visible impurities while shoveling the coal into mine cars or onto conveyors. With machine loading no such removal of impurities in the mine is possible. In strip mining the overburden is removed by large power shovels, and the coal by smaller shovels. If the coal is hard it is blasted prior to loading.

Most coal seams contain interstratified bands of impurities which must be removed in a coal-cleaning plant. Few coal seams are clean enough to be mined by mechanical means and the coal shipped directly to market without mechanical cleaning.

Small strip mines frequently load coal of inferior quality. Outcrop coal from such mines is weathered, frequently mixed with impurities, and of low calorific value.

On the other hand, the better strip mines do not mine coal near the outcrop. Coal seams firm up and become equal to deep-mined coal when the overburden reaches a depth of 10 to 30 ft, depending on rank of coal and character of overburden. In general, coal resists weathering with increase of rank. Some anthracites can be mined to the outcrop, while low-rank bituminous coals usually are not acceptable if the overburden is less than 20 ft.

Practically all large, mechanized mines (underground and strip) have preparation plants in which the coal is sized, mechanically cleaned, and otherwise prepared to give a high-quality fuel conforming to size specifications.

COAL CLEANING

The oldest methods of cleaning coal use picking tables. These tables consist of a horizontal conveyor over which the coal moves slowly in comparatively thin layers. Workers are stationed on both sides of the conveyor to pick the impurities from the coal. This is probably the best way to clean lump coal.

Most mechanical cleaning processes depend on differences in specific gravity of coal and associated impurities to effect a separation. Other physical properties of coal and refuse utilized to a minor extent are shape, resiliency, coefficient of sliding friction, electrical conductivity, and froth-flotation differences. Magnetic separators are used widely to remove tramp iron and thus prevent such material from eventually getting into pulverizer mechanisms, with the resultant possibility of equipment damage.

Coal-cleaning processes may be wet or dry, depending on whether water or air is used as the medium. In general, wet processes are more efficient than dry. With coal for which dry processes are suitable, the product is dry and highly desirable. Coal from wet-process cleaners must be dried by drainage, centrifuges, filters, or heat dryers to avoid excessive water in the final product.

COAL SAMPLING

A sample must represent the bulk of the coal from which it is taken. The items that should be most representative are ash and moisture content. The weight of the gross sample and the method of collecting and handling it depend on the size of the coal, the moisture and ash content, and the purpose for which the sample is collected. The collection method should insure representative ash and moisture content. After collection, the sample must be handled so that the moisture content does not change. If the coal is very wet, considerable moisture may be lost during the handling. It may be necessary to stabilize the moisture in the gross sample by air drying before crushing and quartering. In such cases, the air-drying moisture loss must be determined.

The standard methods for sampling coals and preparing them for analysis are ANSI/ASTM *Standards* D 2234, Collection of a Gross Sample of Coal, and D 2013, Preparing Coal Samples for Analysis.

COAL ANALYSIS

Two types of coal analyses are in general use: the proximate and the ultimate analysis, both expressed in percent by weight.

The proximate analysis gives information on the behavior of coal when it is heated; that is, how much of the coal goes off as gas and tar vapors, called the volatile matter, and how much remains as fixed carbon. The proximate analysis is easy and supplies useful information to assist in the selection of coal for steam generation. Along with the determination of volatile matter and fixed carbon also given are the moisture and ash contents and the heating value in Btu per pound. Sulfur is given as a separate determination. ANSI/ASTM *Standards* D 3172 is the basic method for proximate analysis of coal and coke.

The ultimate analysis gives the elements of which the coal substance is composed. These elements include carbon, hydrogen, nitrogen, oxygen and sulfur. Ash content is determined as a whole, and, when desirable, separate analysis is made on the ash. *ASTM Standards D 3176* is the standard method for ultimate analysis of coal and coke.

Coal analysis may be given on several bases, and it is customary to select the basis to suit the application. Thus, for the purposes of classification, the dry or moist and mineral-matter-free bases are generally used. In combustion calculations the as-received basis is applicable.

AS-RECEIVED BASIS

The as-received analysis of a fuel represents the actual proportions of the constituents in the fuel sample as received at the laboratory. The sample may be fuel as fired, as mined, or in any other given condition.

MOISTURE-FREE (DRY) BASIS

Moisture content is variable, even in the same coal, under different conditions of handling and exposure. For example, coal as received at a plant may contain an amount of moisture different from that received at the laboratory for analysis, and both may vary with weather conditions. Also, in a plant burning pulverized fuel, the coal may carry one percentage of moisture as delivered to the raw-coal bunker, another as delivered to the pulverizer, another as delivered to the pulverized-fuel bunker (in a storage system), and still another as fired. Furthermore, when a laboratory determines an ultimate analysis as wet, as-received, or as-fired, the moisture can be reported as hydrogen and oxygen and added to the hydrogen and oxygen of the coal itself.

DRY MINERAL-MATTER-FREE BASIS

As mentioned previously, because the ash does not correspond in percentage to the mineral matter in the coal, errors are introduced which become significant in problems of classifying coals according to rank. Two formulas available for making such calculations from the

PARR FORMULAS:

$$\text{Dry, Mm-free FC} = \frac{FC - 0.15S}{100 - (M + 1.08A + 0.55S)} \times 100$$

$$\text{Dry, Mm-free VM} = 100 - \text{Dry, Mm-free FC}$$

$$\text{Moist, Mm-free Btu} = \frac{Btu - 50S}{100 - (1.08A + 0.55S)} \times 100$$

Note: The above formula for fixed carbon is derived from the Parr formula for volatile matter.[4]

APPROXIMATION FORMULAS:

$$\text{Dry, Mm-free FC} = \frac{FC}{100 - (M + 1.1A + 0.1S)} \times 100$$

$$\text{Dry, Mm-free VM} = 100 - \text{Dry, Mm-free FC}$$

$$\text{Moist, Mm-free Btu} = \frac{Btu}{100 - (1.1A + 0.1S)} \times 100$$

where
Mm = mineral matter
Btu = British thermal units per pound (calorific value)
FC = percent of fixed carbon
VM = percent of volatile matter
M = percent of moisture
A = percent of ash
S = percent of sulfur

The formulas can be used to check analyses and frequently to identify the source and rank of the fuel. For example, the heating value of coals of a given rank and source are remarkably uniform when calculated on a dry, Mm-free basis.

In commercial practice it frequently suffices to calculate to a dry, ash-free basis as follows:

$$\text{Dry, ash-free FC} = \frac{FC}{100 - (M + A)} \times 100$$

$$\text{Dry, ash-free VM} = 100 - \text{Dry, ash-free FC}$$

as-received basis, are the Parr and approximation formulas. (See adjoining box.)

ITEMS OF PROXIMATE ANALYSIS

Coal as mined and shipped contains varying amounts of water. Accurate determination of this water is not as simple as one would expect, since the sample frequently can lose moisture on exposure to the atmosphere. This is particularly true during the reduction of the sample for analysis. To prevent this loss, it is customary to air-dry the entire sample under specified conditions before fine grinding for analysis. The moisture is then determined by a standard procedure of drying in an oven, and the loss in weight is corrected for the air-drying loss. The moisture in coal does not represent all of the water present, since water of decomposition (combined water) and water of hydration are not given off under the conditions of test. The moisture content of coals varies widely. In the high-rank low-volatile bituminous coals it is frequently under 5 percent. High-volatile bituminous coals may have as much as 12 percent and lignite, as high as 45 percent as mined. The finer sizes will often retain more moisture than the coarse sizes of the same coal subjected to rainfall or wet-washing.

ASTM defines total moisture in coal as that moisture determined as the loss in weight in an air atmosphere under rigidly controlled conditions of temperature, time and airflow as established in *ASTM Standards D 3302.*

INHERENT MOISTURE

Inherent moisture in coal is that moisture existing as a quality of the coal seam in its natural state of deposition and includes only that water considered to be a part of the deposit, and not that moisture which exists as a surface addition. There are a number of other terms relating to moisture in coal, including: bed moisture, equilibrium moisture, air-dry moisture loss, free moisture, water of hydration and others of lesser consequence.

CONDITION OF WATER IN COAL

Like many other substances of vegetable origin, coal contains water in the ordinary condition, which may give the coal a moist appearance. Coal also contains water that is frequently but erroneously called "water of combination," this water being concealed, as in hydrated salts, by the dry appearance of the material. The condition in which the so-called "water of combination" in coal exists is problematical; in the true chemical sense the water is probably not "combined," that is, united with another substance in definite proportions, as determined by its relative molecular weight and the number of molecules.

There is no sharp line of demarcation; the "free" water cannot be separated with exactness from the "combined" water by chemical analysis. Under all ordinary drying conditions, there is a tendency for more than the "free" water to leave the coal. But the "combined" or, "inherent" water, is distinctly different from the "free" water in its properties, as it has a subnormal vapor pressure and an energy change is involved in its combination with, or separation from, the coal substance. In other words, the inherent water is held more tenaciously and cannot be entirely removed by drying the coal in ordinary air which contains relatively large quantities of moisture.

PRACTICAL EFFECTS OF WATER

As ordinarily found in the market, coal, when superficially dry, contains water; an anthracitic or low-volatile coal in this condition contains possibly 2 percent water; a high-volatile bituminous coal, 6 to 10 percent; and a subbituminous coal, 14 to 18 percent. Even finely crushed or powdered coal does not become dry in ordinary air and requires an artificially and thoroughly dried atmosphere to remove all of its water content.

Humidity conditions may appreciably alter the weight of exposed coal, independently of the actual fall of rain or snow. In other words, coal is frequently hygroscopic. After being transferred from storage in an atmosphere of 40 percent humidity to one of 75 percent humidity, a bituminous coal, for example, may gain 3 percent and a subbituminous 7 percent in weight by absorption of moisture.

FREE SUPERFICIAL WATER

In wet coal, the water in excess of a certain percentage (which depends on the kind of coal) is mechanically held in the free state, its vapor pressure and other properties being, for all practical purposes, normal. This excess moisture may be termed superficial or accidental moisture. All water in the coal above approximately 3 percent in the anthracite coals, 12 percent in bituminous, and 22 percent in the subbituminous coals may be so classed, although this line of demarcation is more or less variable even among coals of the same kind.

The percentage of superficial water retained by coal that has been wetted and the water drained off is greatly affected by the size of the coal. In screenings or slack, which contains pieces of many different sizes, the particles pack closely together and form small interstices which retain water by capillarity. Screened lump, on the other hand, or run-of-mine with a large proportion of lump, has much larger interstices and relatively less surface to be wet, and therefore retains less water. See Table III.

There is no ready means of separating sharply the superficial and the inherent water of coal. Unless the air is saturated, the superficial water can all be removed by air drying, the rate of evaporation depending on the temperature, the humidity of the air, and the fineness of the coal. But at the same time, part of the inherent water leaves the coal and continues to do so as long as its vapor pressure is higher than that of the air.

By the expression "inherent water" in coal or in any material, therefore, is meant the water which exists as such but which has a vapor pressure less than the normal.

VOLATILE MATTER

The volatile matter is that portion which, exclusive of water vapor, is driven off in gas or vapor form when the coal is subjected to a standardized temperature test. It consists of hydrocarbons and other gases resulting from distillation and decomposition.

Table III. Water Retention After Draining[1]

Kind of Coal	* %	** %	*** %
Bituminous, New River, WV.:			
Screenings *a*	22.27	2.52	1.03
Sized "buckwheat" *b*	3.17	2.35	1.00
Bituminous, Pittsburgh bed, PA.:			
Screenings *a*	18.73	2.68	1.15
Sized "buckwheat" *b*	2.62	2.73	1.25
Bituminous, Macoupin County, IL.:			
Screenings *a*	28.60	6.84	.32
Sized "buckwheat" *b*	16.71	6.63	3.40
Subbituminous, Big Horn County, WY.:			
Screenings *a*	32.58	14.24	6.38
Sized "buckwheat" *b*	18.70	13.79	6.65

[1] From H. C. Porter and O. C. Ralston, "Some Properties of the Water in Coal," U.S. Bureau of Mines, Technical Paper 113. Washington; U.S. Bureau of Mines, 1916.
 *Total water content of coal after soaking and draining.
 **Normal water content in commercially "dry" coal.
 ***Water retained in coal after "air-drying" in laboratory at 35°C.
  a Through ½ inch mesh screen.
  b From ¼ inch to 1 inch in diameter.

Volatile matter is determined by prescribed methods which may vary according to the nature of the material, but in the case of coal and coke Method D 3175 is used.

Temperature and time are a vital concern in this test, since they actually determine the definition of volatile matter. Temperature must be 950°C ± 20°C, and heating time must be exactly 7 minutes.

The main constituents of volatile matter in all ranks of coal are hydrogen, oxygen, carbon monoxide, methane and other hydrocarbons, and that portion of moisture that is formed by chemical combination during thermal decomposition of the coal substance. The composition of volatile matter varies greatly for different ranks of coal.

Volatile matter is used to establish the rank of coals, to indicate coke yield on carbonization processes, to provide the basis for purchasing and selling, and to establish burning characteristics.

Because of the arbitrary nature of this test, caution must be used in comparing the results of volatile analyses with those obtained from tests run in other countries. Details of the various national standards vary greatly.

FIXED CARBON

The fixed carbon is the combustible residue left after driving off the volatile matter. It is not all carbon, and its form and hardness are an indication of the coking properties of a coal, and therefore, a guide in the choice of fuel-firing equipment. In general, the fixed carbon represents that portion of the fuel that must be burned in solid state, either in the fuel bed on a stoker, or as solid particles in the pulverized-fuel furnace.

The fixed carbon in a proximate analysis is a calculated figure obtained by subtracting from 100 the sum of the percentages of moisture, volatile matter and ash.

ASH

Ash is the noncombustible residue after complete combustion of the coal. The weight of ash is usually slightly less than that of the mineral matter originally present before burning.

For high-calcium-content coals, however, the ash can be higher than the mineral matter due to retention of the oxides of sulfur.[5]

The ASTM definition for coal ash is the inorganic residue remaining after ignition of combustible substances, determined by definite prescribed methods. This definition is followed by two notes, one of which states that ash may not be identical—in composition or quantity—to inorganic substances present in the coal before ignition. The second note specifies that, in the case of coal and coke, the methods shall be those prescribed by *ASTM Standards D 3174*. This method determines the ash content by weighing the residue remaining after the coal is burned under rigidly controlled conditions of sample weight, temperature, time and atmosphere, oxidizing or reducing.

Although the definition of ash content used in other countries is similar to the American definition, the ashing conditions may be different. Therefore, it is desirable to spell out the conditions used, particularly when the results from laboratories in different countries are to be compared.

During the burning process, various chemical and physical changes take place. The conditions of oxidation determine the number and extent of such changes; thus, a great degree of variability can be expected in separate determinations of ash content even on portions of the same coal sample unless standardized procedures are closely followed. In particular, this is true of coals with relatively large amounts of carbonates or pyrite.

Ash is usually considered the product of complete oxidation of coal. It is composed of the oxides formed from the mineral constituents of coal. However, these minerals may be present in two forms in coal: as visible impurities, or as minute impurities so finely divided and so intimately mixed that they may be considered a part of the coal structure.

The term *inherent* or *fixed ash content* is used to designate that portion of the ash content that is structurally part of the coal and cannot be separated from it by mechanical means. This is a relative term, however, and will have different values, since mechanical separation is accomplished at varying levels according to the size of the coal.

In general, when the term *inherent ash* is used, it is assumed it refers to the residue that remains after coal has been broken to the size at which it is to be used, cleaned by a mechanical process, and incinerated. Probably the first test developed for coal, the determination of ash content continues to be one of the most important of the tests performed.

SULFUR

Sulfur is separately determined, and its amount is useful in judging the corrosiveness of the products of combustion of a fuel. Combustion of sulfur forms oxides, which combine with water to form acids that may be deposited when the combustion gas is cooled below its dew-point temperature.

Sulfur in coal occurs mainly in three forms. It can be present in organic combination as part of the coal substance; it can be present as the sulfide ion in pyrites and marcasite; or it can be present as the sulfate ion. Rarely, sulfur may occur as elemental sulfur, but in insufficient quantities to be appreciable. ANSI/ASTM *Standards* D 2492 gives a standard test method for the determination of the forms of sulfur in coal; sulfate sulfur and pyritic sulfur are first determined, and organic sulfur is found by determining the difference from the total sulfur.

Two methods are generally accepted for total sulfur determination. Eschka's method converts all the sulfur present in the coal to the sulfate ion, which is then precipitated as $BaSO_4$.

DULONG-TYPE FORMULA

$$HHV = 14,600\,C + 62,000\,(H - \frac{O}{8}) + 4050\,S$$

where: C, H, O and S are carbon, hydrogen, oxygen, and sulfur in the coal, respectively, expressed in fraction of a pound usually as fired. The results are approximate because the formula does not take into account the heats of dissociation and similar phenomena occurring during the combustion reactions. For low-rank coals, the heating values obtained by this formula are generally too low.

The Eschka method requires a time period—including sample preparation—of up to 24 hours, so a more rapid method of high-temperature combustion has been adopted. Details and analytical procedures for both of these methods, as well as the bomb-washing method, an alternate third method, may be found in *ASTM Standards* D 3177.

HEATING VALUE

In the U.S., the calorific or heating value of a solid fuel is expressed in Btu per lb of fuel on as-received, dry, or moisture- and ash-free basis. It is the amount of heat recovered when the products of complete combustion of a unit quantity of a fuel are cooled to the initial temperature of the air and fuel.

Heating values as determined in calorimeters are termed high or gross heating values, and include the latent heat of the water vapor in the products of combustion. The most common type of calorimeter in use today is the adiabatic bomb calorimeter, and *ASTM Standards* D 2015 covers this test. In actual operation of boilers, the water vapor in the combustion gas leaving is not cooled below its dew point, and this latent heat is not available for making steam. The latent heat can be substracted from the high, or gross, heating value to give the low, or net, heating value.

This deduction in Btu per lb of fuel is equal to the total pounds of water vapor per lb of fuel (moisture in the fuel, plus vapor formed by combustion of hydrogen of the coal substance) multiplied by the latent heat of evaporation at the partial pressure of the vapor in the exit gas. The value used varies from 1030 to 1080 Btu per lb of water vapor. Lower heating values are standard in European practice, and higher heating values are standard in American practice.[6]

For anthracite and bituminous coal, gross heating value in Btu per pound of coal can be calculated approximately by a formula of the Dulong type. (See adjoining box.)

ASH-FUSION TEMPERATURE

When coal ash is heated, it becomes soft and sticky and, as the temperature continues to rise, it becomes fluid. *ASTM Standards* D 1857 is the method for measuring fusibility of coal ash. This test is an observation of the temperatures at which triangular pyramids or cones prepared from coal ash and coke ash attain and pass through certain defined stages of fusing and flow when heated at a specific rate in controlled, mildly reducing, and where desired, oxidizing atmosphere.

This method is empirical, and strict observance of the requirements and conditions is necessary to obtain reproducible temperatures and to enable different laboratories to obtain concordant results.

Four stages of fusion temperature are usually reported in American practice:

1. Initial, or the first rounding of the cone

2. Softening, when the height has diminished until it is equal to the width at the base

3. Hemispherical, when the height of the lump equals one-half the width of the base

4. Fluid, when the mass is no higher than one-sixteenth inch

The test for fusion temperatures may be run in either a reducing or an oxidizing atmosphere. The ash-fusion temperature given in most existing tables is the softening temperature (H = W) in a reducing atmosphere. This subject is expanded in Chapter 3.

REACTIVITY OF COAL

Coal reactivity may be defined as the rate that it combines with oxygen at temperatures above the ignition point. Within the confines of this definition, reactivity and rate of combustion are deemed to be synonymous.

Since coal-rank classifications are based on varying combinations of volatile-matter content, heating value, and agglomerating characteristics, it is obvious that a correlation would exist between rank and reactivity. It should be equally obvious that the rate of combustion is influenced by the particle size and its influence on surface area to mass. A change in the surface area of agglomerating coals results from the plastic or semiliquid states that the particles undergo when heated. For additional information see Chapter 12.

Differences in reactivity from one coal rank to another also can be explained by the changing levels in organically bound oxygen with rank. Organically bound oxygen is considered to be that which is an inherent part of the coal structure exclusive of water and mineral matter. As rank decreases from low-volatile bituminous to lignite, organic oxygen increases by a factor of 5 to 6. When the fuel is heated, a portion of this oxygen becomes available for the oxidation process. To this extent, the fuel has its own built-in oxygen supply. As the oxygen level increases, the fuel reactivity increases. Lower-rank subbituminous coals and lignites, therefore, are more reactive than are bituminous coals and do not require the same degree of fineness to insure complete combustion. See Chapter 12 for additional information on the influences of the oxygen content on pulverizing requirements.

FREE-SWELLING INDEX

Free-swelling index (FSI) or coke-button test is a small-scale test to obtain information on the free-swelling properties of a coal.

The test, covered by *ASTM Standards* D 720, consists of burning a one-gram sample of coal in a covered crucible under specified conditions of temperature and time. The button formed is compared to a series of standard profiles. The larger the index, the greater is the swelling property of the coal. The test is often used as a quick, rough check of whether a coal is oxidized.

GRINDABILITY

This test determines the relative ease of pulverization of coal in comparison with coals chosen as standards. The Hardgrove method has been accepted as the standard, and *ASTM Standards* D 409 is the Grindability of Coal by the Hardgrove-Machine Method.

Each Hardgrove machine is calibrated by use of standard reference samples of coal, having grindability indexes of approximately 40, 60, 80 and 100. Standard coals may be obtained from the U.S. Bureau of Mines in Pittsburgh for the purpose of calibration.

The Hardgrove-index number reported by

the laboratory is based on an original soft coal chosen as a standard coal whose grindability index was set at 100. Therefore, the harder the coal, the lower the index number.

Since the grindability index varies, not only from seam to seam but within the same seam, grindability data are of utmost economic importance to the users of commercial grinding and pulverizing equipment.

The results of grindability measurements by the Hardgrove machine are affected by several factors, among them the ash and moisture content, temperature, and the presence of different petrographic constituents (organic components distinguishable by microscopic inspection). Chapter 12 has more information.

ITEMS OF ULTIMATE ANALYSIS

Ultimate analysis is needed for the computation of air requirements, weight of products of combustion, and heat losses, on boiler tests. The air requirements and the weight of products of combustion determine fan sizes. The following are items of ultimate analysis as determined by *ASTM Standards* D 3176.

TOTAL CARBON

Total carbon includes both the carbon in the fixed carbon and in the volatile matter, and will be proportionately greater than the fixed carbon as the volatile content of the coal increases. All this carbon appears in the products of combustion as CO_2 when the fuel is completely burned.

HYDROGEN

All hydrogen in the fuel is burned to water and, together with the moisture in fuel, appears as water vapor in the waste gas. In the publications of the U.S. Bureau of Mines, ultimate analysis of coal on as-received basis includes moisture in the hydrogen and oxygen items. The weight of the water vapor in the products of combustion is nine times the weight of the hydrogen item.

NITROGEN

Nitrogen in most solid fuels is low and of no importance in combustion calculations, as it is incombustible.

OXYGEN

The oxygen content of fuels is a guide to the rank of the fuel. The amount of oxygen is high in low-rank fuels like lignite. Oxygen in fuels is in combination with carbon or hydrogen and, therefore, represents a reduction in the potential heat of a fuel. High-oxygen fuels have low heating values.

As there is no direct ASTM method of determining oxygen, it is calculated by subtracting from 100 the sum of the other components of the ultimate analysis. Any errors incurred in the other determinations are placed on the oxygen, and a material balance cannot be obtained to aid in checking the accuracy of the ultimate analysis.[7]

WASHABILITY

The washability characteristic of a coal is the most important tool available to determine the extent to which a coal may be cleaned. Examination of washability data for a particular coal or a particular size of coal will reveal the quality of coal which may be obtained by mechanical cleaning, as well as the quantity of coal of a particular quality. Further examination of the data will indicate the ease or difficulty with which the coal may be cleaned and will give valuable information concerning the type of commercial cleaner most suitable for that particular coal.

The ash, sulfur, or Btu specifications of all of the final product generally dictate whether or not cleaning is necessary. After technical considerations are evaluated with the help of washability characteristics and if the cleaning is technically sound, then the economic decisions are made. These considerations include the value of the final product and the cost of obtaining it.

Float-and-sink separation is quite effective for determining the washability characteristics of coarse coal, but the problems associated with cleaning of extremely fine sizes dictate other methods. Froth flotation is an increasingly important method for cleaning fines. The process consists of passing air through a suspension of fine coal in water. The coal particles attach themselves to the air bubbles and are removed in the froth on top of the pulp. The refuse particles remain in the pulp. Chemicals are added to the pulp to help produce the froth.

Although washability data may be used to determine the quantity and the quality of the coal theoretically possible from a flotation process, a more realistic method has been developed. This method consists of splitting up the original flotation froth into several fractions and refloating the fractions two or three times. Each refloating fraction is then analyzed to determine the quantity and quality of the products. In actual plant operation, the first float is referred to as a "rougher" operation, and the subsequent flotations as "cleaner" and "recleaner" operations. The cleaning and the recleaning are required at times to meet specification grade.

TYPICAL COAL ANALYSES

Table IV shows the form in which coal analyses are given in the U.S. Bureau of Mines publications.[8] Such publications contain the proximate and ultimate analyses and softening temperatures of ash of several coals from various states. The coals are identified by county, mine, coal bed, and rank.

Table V gives analyses of several typical U.S. coals and coke, classified by the ASTM system of Table II. Besides proximate and ultimate analyses, higher heating value and theoretical combustion-air requirements "A" (on a pounds-per-million-Btu basis) are given. Table VI presents an overview of coals from outside the continental U.S.

Appendix A gives extensive data on both United States coals and coals from all the major producing areas of the world. Also, in Appendix A, the International Systems for Classification of Hard Coals, Brown Coals and Lignites are discussed in detail. Additional analyses of American, European, and Asian coals are given, along with international classifications.

BURNING CHARACTERISTICS OF COALS

A significant burning characteristic of coal is the property of caking exhibited by some coals and its opposite, free-burning, shown by others. As important as this characteristic is, it must be admitted that there is no test which will permit its precise evaluation in the laboratory. While no difficulty exists in distinguishing between caking and free-burning coals, there are many shades and gradations of difference between the two extremes, and frequently these gradations are of the greatest interest to the consumer. The free-swelling index test described earlier is an approach to the problem.

CAKING VERSUS FREE-BURNING

When heated in a furnace, caking coals pass through a plastic state during which the individual pieces fuse together into large masses of semi-coke, which is impervious to flow of air. In free-burning coals, the individual pieces do not fuse together but burn separately, or after fusion the mass breaks up quickly into fragments. Subbituminous coals and the lignites

Table IV. Coal Chemical Analyses

Condition or Basis	% Proximate Analysis				% Ultimate Analysis*					HHV, Btu/Lb
	H2O	VM	FC	Ash	C	H2	O2	N2	S	
As-received	3.39	20.61	66.53	9.47	77.29	4.59	5.61	1.73	1.31	13,619
Dry		21.33	68.87	9.80	80.00	4.36	2.69	1.79	1.36	14,098
Moisture- and ash-free	...	23.65	76.35	...	88.69	4.83	2.99	1.98	1.51	15,629

Pennsylvania, Somerset County, Upper Kittaning Bed, No. 3 Mine
*In the ultimate analysis, moisture on an as-received basis is included in the hydrogen and oxygen.

Table V. Analyses of Typical U.S. Coals, as Mined

State	Rank	% Proximate Analysis				% Ultimate Analysis						HHV, Btu/Lb	A at Zero Excess Air, Lb/10^6 Btu*
		H_2O	VM	FC	ASH	H_2O	C	H_2	S	O_2	N_2		
RI	A	13.3	2.5	65.3	18.9	13.3	64.2	0.4	0.3	2.7	0.2	9,313	808
CO	B	2.5	5.7	83.8	8.0	2.5	83.9	2.9	0.7	0.7	1.3	13,720	787
NM	B	2.9	5.5	82.7	8.9	2.9	82.3	2.6	0.8	1.3	1.2	13,340	786
PA **	B	5.4	3.8	77.1	13.7	5.4	76.1	1.8	0.6	1.8	0.6	11,950	791
***	B	2.3	3.1	87.7	6.9	2.3	86.7	1.9	0.5	0.9	0.8	13,540	794
****	B	4.9	3.7	82.2	9.2	4.9	81.6	1.8	0.5	1.3	0.7	12,820	788
AR	C	2.1	9.8	78.8	9.3	2.1	80.3	3.4	1.7	1.7	1.5	13,700	770
PA	C	3.0	8.4	78.9	9.7	3.0	80.2	3.3	0.7	2.0	1.1	13,450	777
VA	C	3.1	10.6	66.7	19.6	3.1	70.5	3.2	0.6	2.2	0.8	11,850	782
AR	D	3.4	16.2	71.8	8.6	3.4	79.6	3.9	1.0	1.8	1.7	13,700	774
MD	D	3.2	18.2	70.4	8.2	3.2	79.0	4.1	1.0	2.9	1.6	13,870	761
OK	D	2.6	16.5	72.2	8.7	2.6	80.1	4.0	1.0	1.9	1.7	13,800	775
WV	D	2.7	17.2	76.1	4.0	2.7	84.7	4.3	0.6	2.2	1.5	14,730	767
PA	E	3.3	20.5	70.0	6.2	3.3	80.7	4.5	1.8	2.4	1.1	14,310	765
VA	E	3.1	21.8	67.9	7.2	3.1	80.1	4.7	1.0	2.4	1.5	14,030	778
AL	F	5.5	30.8	60.9	2.8	5.5	80.3	4.9	0.6	4.2	1.7	14,210	768
CO	F	1.4	32.6	54.3	11.7	1.4	73.4	5.1	0.6	6.5	1.3	13,210	763
KS	F	7.4	31.8	52.4	8.4	7.4	70.7	4.6	2.6	5.0	1.3	12,670	769
KY	F	3.1	35.0	58.9	3.0	3.1	79.2	5.4	0.6	7.2	1.5	14,290	758
MO	F	5.4	32.1	53.5	9.0	5.4	71.6	4.8	3.6	4.2	1.4	12,990	769
NM	F	2.0	33.5	50.6	13.9	2.0	70.6	4.8	1.3	6.2	1.2	12,650	766
OH	F	4.9	36.6	51.2	7.3	4.9	71.9	4.9	2.6	7.0	1.4	12,990	762
OK	F	2.1	35.0	57.0	5.9	2.1	76.7	4.9	0.5	7.9	2.0	13,630	757
PA	F	2.6	30.0	58.3	9.1	2.6	76.6	4.9	1.3	3.9	1.6	13,610	773
TN	F	1.8	35.9	56.1	6.2	1.8	77.7	5.2	1.2	6.0	1.9	13,890	767
TX	F	4.0	48.9	34.9	12.2	4.0	65.5	5.9	2.0	9.1	1.3	12,230	767
UT	F	4.3	37.2	51.8	6.7	43	72.2	5.1	1.1	9.0	1.6	12,990	758
VA	F	2.2	36.0	58.0	3.8	2.2	80.6	5.5	0.7	5.9	1.3	14,510	764
WA	F	4.3	37.7	47.1	10.9	4.3	68.9	5.4	0.5	8.5	1.5	12,610	758
WV	F	2.4	33.0	60.0	4.6	2.4	80.8	5.1	0.7	4.8	1.6	14,350	768
IL	G	8.0	33.0	50.6	8.4	8.0	68.7	4.5	1.2	7.6	1.6	12,130	766
KY	G	7.5	37.7	45.3	9.5	7.5	66.9	4.8	3.5	6.4	1.4	12,080	774
MO	G	10.5	32.0	44.6	12.9	10.5	63.4	4.2	2.5	5.2	1.3	11,300	773
OH	G	8.2	36.1	48.7	7.0	8.2	68.4	4.7	1.2	9.1	1.4	12,160	762
WY	G	5.1	40.5	49.8	4.6	5.1	73.0	5.0	0.5	10.6	1.2	12,960	757
IL	H	12.1	40.2	39.1	8.6	12.1	62.8	4.6	4.3	6.6	1.0	11,480	769
IN	H	12.4	36.6	42.3	8.7	12.4	63.4	4.3	2.3	7.6	1.3	11,420	758
IA	H	14.1	35.6	39.3	11.0	14.1	58.5	4.0	4.3	7.2	0.9	10,720	754

Table V. Analyses of Typical U.S. Coals, as Mined — *Continued*

State	Rank	% Proximate Analysis				% Ultimate Analysis						HHV, Btu/Lb	A at Zero Excess Air, Lb/10⁶ Btu*
		H₂O	VM	FC	ASH	H₂O	C	H₂	S	O₂	N₂		
MI	H	12.4	35.0	47.0	5.6	12.4	65.8	4.5	2.9	7.4	1.4	11,860	762
CO	I	19.6	30.5	45.9	4.0	19.6	58.8	3.8	0.3	12.2	1.3	10,130	756
WY	I	23.2	33.3	39.7	3.8	23.2	54.6	3.8	0.4	13.2	1.0	9,420	757
ND	J	34.8	28.2	30.8	6.2	34.8	42.4	2.8	0.7	12.4	0.7	7,210	750
TX	J	33.7	29.3	29.7	7.3	33.7	42.5	3.1	0.5	12.1	0.8	7,350	752

*A is the theoretical air required for combustion under stoichiometric conditions (no excess air).
**Orchard Bed, ***Mammoth Bed, ****Holmes Bed, RANK KEY: A-Meta-anthracite, B-Anthracite, C-Semianthracite, D-Low-Vol. Bituminous, E-Med.-Vol. Bituminous, F-High-Vol. Bituminous A, G-High-Vol. Bituminous B, H-High-Vol. Bituminous C, I-Subbituminous, J-Lignite

are classed as free-burning coals. They lack the fusion property of the caking coals.

Another term for caking is *agglomerating*, and the agglomerating index is used in classification of coals to indicate the dividing line between *noncaking* coals and those having *weakly caking* properties. The test is essentially the same as the free-swelling index already discussed, the noncaking designation being applied only to coals that produce a noncoherent residue which can be poured out of the crucible as a powder or flakes that will pulverize easily with thumb and finger pressure. In practice, coals that approach this borderline will be free-burning.

Both caking and free-burning coals can be burned without difficulty and equally well in pulverized form. In general, the caking coals fall within the range of the high-volatile A, medium-volatile and low-volatile bituminous coal groups. Within these groups, wide variations in behavior will be found.

COKING VERSUS CAKING

Coking coals are those which make good coke suitable for metallurgical purposes. Coke is produced when coking coal is heated in a coke oven, out of contact with air, and the greater part of the volatile matter is driven off. It consists mostly of the fixed carbon and ash of the original coal.

The term *coking coals* is sometimes used in-

stead of *caking coals*. The caking process in a boiler furnace is confused with the coking process in the coke oven. There are many caking coals which do not make good coke in a coke oven, and there are some free-burning coals that make good coke.

Caking and coking coals have generally lower oxygen content than free-burning and noncoking coals. This, however, is true only to a certain extent.

When a caking coal is exposed to the action of air over a long period of time, it picks up

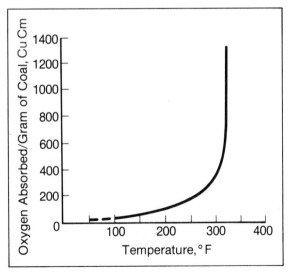

Fig. 2 **Chart showing an increase in rate of oxygen pickup which results from heating coal while it is exposed to air**

Table VI. Typical Analyses of Coals of the World

Country	District or Mine	H₂0	TYPICAL ANALYSIS—AS RECEIVED				Cal/kg	HHV, Btu/Lb
			Vol	FC	Ash	Sul		
Argentina	Turbio River	8.6	34.8	40.9	15.7	0.9	5755	10,360
Australia	New South Wales							
	Western Field	2.6	30.0	52.8	14.6	0.7	6455	11,620
	Southern Field	0.6	23.29	65.08	11.0	3.7	7275	13,090
	Queensland	1.5	37.0	49.9	11.6	. . .	6835	12,300
	Victoria (Brown Coal)	66.3	17.7	15.3	0.7	0.1	2055	3,700
Belgium	Batterie and Vidette	1.0	8.5	63.5	27.0	. . .	595	10,710
Brazil	Sao Jeronimo	13.8	24.7	27.1	34.4	3.0	3665	6,600
	Sao Jeronimo-							
	Washed	16.0	23.1	32.9	28.0	0.9	4205	7,570
	Butia	11.5	32.0	42.9	13.6	1.3	. . .	. . .
Canada	Alberta-Drumheller	20.0	28.0	41.0	11.0	. . . .	5010	9,020
	Saskatchewan-Souris	35.0	23.4	34.6	8.0	. . .	4050	7,290
	British Col.-Crows Nest	1.4	24.5	61.8	12.3	0.5	7420	13,360
	Nova Scotia-Emery	4.0	33.7	51.6	10.7	2.5	7000	12,600
Chile	Schwager	2.9	41.3	52.2	3.6	0.9	7950	14,310
	Lota	3.4	39.6	55.4	1.6	0.7	7900	14,220
	Mafil	12.6	35.6	40.0	11.8	0.6	5620	10,120
China	Kailin	2.5	29.9	44.4	25.7	0.66	5720	10,300
	Kew Loong Kieng	5.4	29.7	45.0	19.9	. . .	6040	10,870
	Kiaping	3.5	24.4	41.1	31.0	. . .	5160	9,290
Colombia	Bogota	5.3	23.4	63.7	7.6	0.8	7900	14,220
France	Bethune	8.0	18.0	39.0	35.0	. . .	4670	8,410
	Anzin	1.6	9.2	44.3	44.9	. . .	4275	7,690
Germany	Frimmersdorf-							
	Westfield	60.7	20.0	16.7	2.6	0.2	2355	4,240
	Saar	9.7	31.8	48.7	9.8	. . .	6130	11,040
	Saxony	53.1	25.3	18.1	3.5	0.9	2500	4,500
	Westphalia	1.7	23.7	69.2	5.4	. . .	7760	13,970
	Lower Silesia	4.5	25.6	56.1	13.8	. . .	6540	11,770
United Kingdom								
Wales	Cardiff	1.5	11.0	85.5	2.0	0.8	8000	14,400
	Arley	1.1	36.3	59.0	3.6	2.3	8155	14,680
England	Durham	1.5	34.7	60.0	3.8	0.87	7410	13,340
Scotland	Lanark	7.5	31.8	56.7	4.0	0.2	7600	13,680
Greece	Aliveri	31.0	30.0	21.0	18.0	. . .	3130	5,640

Table VI. **Typical Analyses of Coals of the World — *Continued***

Country	District or Mine	H₂0	TYPICAL ANALYSIS—AS RECEIVED				Cal/kg	HHV, Btu/Lb
			Vol	FC	Ash	Sul		
India	Bermo Seam	1.9	21.1	50.4	26.6	0.9	6010	10,820
	Damodar Valley	4.0	12.8	41.1	42.1	0.3	4365	7,850
	Trombay	7.2	20.8	44.7	27.3	1.0	5315	9,560
	Umaria Field	5.3	27.1	47.8	19.8	. . .	6100	10,980
	Palana	41.4	29.2	23.8	5.6	. . .	3730	6,710
Italy	Sardinia	3.6	39.8	33.0	23.6	6.5	5670	10,210
Japan	Hiyoshi-Anthracite	2.7	5.8	75.0	16.5	. . .	6960	12,540
	Hukuho	8.6	33.8	44.5	13.1	. . .	6830	12,300
	Niiura	19.0	24.8	31.2	25.0	. . .	4730	8,520
Mexico	Palu	1.3	21.0	59.0	18.7	0.7	6780	12,200
Peru	Chimbote	4.4	4.4	77.5	13.7	. . .	4150	7,470
	Goyllarisquisga	4.0	35.3	29.5	31.2	. . .	4950	8,910
Poland	Katowice	17.0	21.0	40.0	22.0	. . .	4500	8,100
	Upper Silesia	4.0	31.6	58.4	6.0	. . .	7500	13,500
Russia	Donetz Anthracite	2.0	3.5	83.0	11.5	0.8	7170	12,910
	Donetz Med. Vol.	3.5	21.0	71.0	4.5	3.6	8070	14,530
	Donetz Long Flame	7.0	40.0	31.5	21.5	5.7	6280	11,300
Spain	Asturias	10.2	11.9	47.6	30.3	0.8	4960	8,930
	Asturias	5.9	20.0	60.5	14.0	. . .	6120	11,020
	Zaragoza	19.5	34.6	25.4	20.5	. . .	4000	7,200
Turkey	Raihenburg	17.1	34.9	24.8	23.2	0.5	3700	6,660
South Africa	Natal	4.2	16.6	70.5	8.7	4.18	. . .	. . .
	Orange Free State	5.6	28.4	50.4	15.6	1.5	5910	10,640
	Transvaal	2.2	27.0	57.5	13.3	0.7	6730	12,120
Venezuela	Barcelona	3.0	36.1	57.5	3.4	1.4	7600	13,680
Yugoslavia	Anatolia	1.4	29.4	51.3	17.9	1.0	6510	11,720

oxygen and loses much of its caking property. It is known that the outcrop coal of a caking-coal seam shows little of the caking property. The rate of oxygen pickup increases rapidly as the temperature is raised, as shown in Fig. 2.

The caking characteristic is more pronouned when the coal contains a large proportion of fines than it is with screened or lump coal. Some of the caking coals could pass as noncaking if the slack were screened out.

SOLID FUELS
OTHER THAN COAL

Many solid or semisolid fuels other than coal are used in the steam-generating process. As described in this section, the majority of these fuels result from the production of primary industrial goods; some are waste fuels that depend upon local economic conditions for their use as sources of energy. They occur in many different forms (most of them not capable of being pulverized like coal), have a wide range of calorific content, and many require special equipment for efficient burning.

COKE AND COKE BREEZE

Coke is the fused solid residue left when certain coals, petroleum, or tar pitch are heated in an atmosphere excluding oxygen, so as to expel their volatile content. The process of thus decomposing these fuels into their gaseous and solid fractions is known as destructive distillation or carbonization.

When anthracite is rapidly heated out of contact with air to, say, 1600°F, it will evolve some volatile matter, but remain essentially unchanged in form. Lignites, when subjected to the same treatment, give off a large amount of gas, while their solid, charry residue cracks and shrinks, but does not fuse together to form

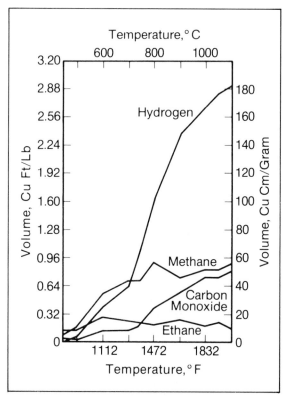

Fig. 3 **Gaseous products of distillation of Silkstone coal (Great Britain) at high temperatures**

"coke." Many varieties of bituminous coals, on the other hand, become plastic and "melt" when heated to only 500–700°F. Due to the resinous substances in these coals, the particles of the molten mass stick together, forming a porous coke which varies in color from dull gray to light silvery gray.

The character of the coke residue is dependent on the kind of fuel distilled, the temperature and pressure to which the fuel is exposed, and the type of oven used.

When the distillation process is carried on in temperatures over 700–900°F, it is called high-temperature carbonization, whereas low-temperature carbonization takes place below 700–900°F. Both the character and relative quantity of solid and gaseous distillation products depend on the temperature employed. This is best illustrated by a comparison between Fig. 3 which shows the volume and kind of gas evolved by an English coal at high temperatures and Fig. 4 which shows the same relation for a U.S. coal at low temperatures. With an increase in temperature, there is a corresponding increase in the evolution of hydrogen and carbon monoxide, at the expense of methane and the higher hydrocarbons. Because of its greater yield of gas, the high-temperature process is preferred for fuel-gas-making purposes and for metallurgical coke. Low-temperature distillation, on the other hand, requires less heat per ton of coke produced and is, therefore, more economical for making domestic coke.

Good coke from this process is shiny, hard, and uniformly porous. It has little volatile matter and is smokeless. If used for metallurgical purposes, it must not have too much sulfur; in foundry work, not much moisture; for domestic use, as little ash as possible; and for making blue-water gas, as high an ash-fusion temperature as possible. The proportion of ash in coke is seen from Fig. 4 to be higher than coke ash content the original coal.

For firing steam generators, good coke is normally considered uneconomical. But "coke breeze," degraded-size coke with as much as 40 percent passing through a ⅛-inch mesh screen, is advantageously burned on certain types of

Fig. 4 Gaseous products from distillation of Pittsburgh coal at low temperatures

stokers. As the typical analyses of Table VII indicate, coke breeze usually has a higher ash content than the rest of the coke.

Nearly all coke produced now is carbonized at high temperatures in byproduct ovens of the slot type; these have largely displaced the older "beehive" ovens. The volatile products of the process, consisting essentially of gas, ammonia, tar and light oil, are recovered and separated into their various fractions. Fig. 5 shows diagrammatically the fuels taking part in and resulting from the coke-making process, together with their respective typical analyses.

PETROLEUM COKE

Petroleum coke is a byproduct of a process in which residual hydrocarbons are converted to lighter, more highly valued distillates. Two processes that produce these byproducts are in use: delayed coking and fluid coking.

DELAYED COKING

In this process, the reduced crude oil is heated rapidly and flows to isolated coking

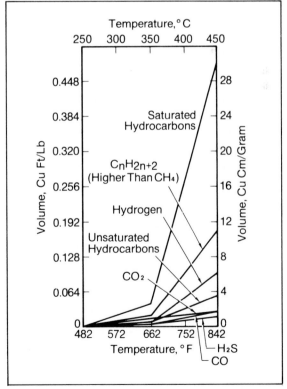

Fig. 5 Typical analyses of fuels involved in the manufacture of byproduct coke

drums where it is coked by its own contained heat. The process requires several drums to permit removal of the coke in one drum while the others remain on stream. The residual product which solidifies in these drums is termed *delayed coke*. When first removed from the drum, it has the appearance of run-of-mine coal, except that the coke is dull black.

The analysis of the coke varies with the crude from which it is made. The components range as follows:

Moisture	3–12%
Volatile matter	10–20%
Fixed carbon	71–88%
Ash	0.2–3.0%
Sulfur	2.9–5.4%
Btu/lb, dry	14,100–15,600

FLUID COKING

Two large vessels are used in fluid coking. One is known as a reactor vessel, and the other, a burner vessel. In this process, fluid coke is both the catalyst and secondary product. The seed coke is first heated in the burner vessel, either by adding air and burning a portion of the coke, or by burning an extraneous fuel such as oil. The heated seed coke then flows into the reactor vessel where it comes in contact with the preheated residual oil and the lighter fractions of the oil are flashed off. The coke which is produced both deposits in uniform layers on the seed coke and forms new seed coke. Thus there is a constantly accumulating coke reservoir which is tapped off and is available as a boiler feed.

The coke thus formed is a hard, dry, spherical solid resembling black sand. It is composed of over 90-percent carbon with varying percentages of sulfur and ash, depending on the source of the crude oil. Typical analyses are

Fixed carbon	90–95%
Volatile matter	3–6.5%
Ash	0.2–0.5%
Sulfur	4.0–7.5%
Btu/lb, dry higher	14,100–14,600

COAL TAR

Coal tar is a byproduct in the carbonization of coal. The tar compounds are extremely complex and number in the hundreds. The solid material which is insoluble in benzene is contained as colloidal and coarse dispersed particles and is known as "free carbon." The composition of the tar is dependent on the temperature of carbonization and, to a lesser extent, on the nature of the coking coal. The following is an example of a coal tar analysis.

Carbon	89.9%
Hydrogen	6.0%
Sulfur	1.2%
Oxygen	1.8%
Nitrogen	0.4%
Moisture	0.7%
Gravity, Baumé	1.18 °
Viscosity at 122°F, SSF	900
Flash point	156° F
Heating Value, Btu/lb, dry	16,750

Coal tar is burned in boilers only when it cannot be sold for other purposes at a higher price than its equivalent fuel value. At ordinary temperature, the viscosity of tar is very high and must be heated for pumping. It burns like a fuel oil and the same equipment can be used.

COAL TAR PITCH

Coal tar pitch is used to a small extent for generation of steam. It is the residue resulting from the distillation and refining of coal tar. The pitch is solid at ordinary atmospheric temperature but becomes liquid at about 300°F. Generally, it is burned in pulverized form; in a few cases, it is melted and burned like oil or coal tar. When it is burned in pulverized form, it must be kept cool during pulverization and during delivery to the furnace. In some cases, it is preferred to coal. Because of its very low ash content, the stack gas is practically free from dust, and therefore there is no flue dust nuisance. When burned in liquid form, it must be kept very hot to prevent congealing. Table VIII shows analyses of coal tar pitch.

Table VII. Analyses of Typical Cokes, as Fired

	% Proximate Analysis					% Ultimate Analysis					HHV, Btu/Lb	A at Zero Excess Air, Lb/10⁶ Btu
	H_2O	VM	FC	ASH	H_2O	C	H_2	S	O_2	N_2		
Kind												
High-temperature coke	5.0	1.3	83.7	10.0	5.0	82.0	0.5	0.8	0.7	10.0	12,200	798
Low-temperature coke	2.8	15.1	72.1	10.0	2.8	74.5	3.2	1.8	6.1	10.0	12,600	763
Beehive coke	0.5	1.8	86.0	11.7	0.5	84.4	0.7	1.0	0.5	11.7	12,527	807
Byproduct coke	0.8	1.4	87.1	10.7	0.8	85.0	0.7	1.0	0.5	10.7	12,690	802
High-temperature coke breeze	12.0	4.2	65.8	18.0	12.0	66.8	1.2	0.6	0.5	18.0	10,200	805
Gas Works Coke:												
Horizontal retorts	0.8	1.4	88.0	9.8	0.8	86.8	0.6	0.7	0.2	9.8	12,820	808
Vertical retorts	1.3	2.5	86.3	9.9	1.3	85.4	1.0	0.7	0.3	9.9	12,770	809
Narrow coke ovens	0.7	2.0	85.3	12.0	0.7	84.6	0.5	0.7	0.3	12.0	12,550	802

WOOD

Wood is a complex vegetable tissue composed principally of cellulose, an organic compound having a definite chemical composition. It would, therefore, seem reasonable to assume that equal weights of different dry wood species will have practically the same heat content. However, owing to the presence of resins, gums and other substances in varying amounts, heat content is not uniform.

Ultimate analyses showing the chemical composition of several different wood species are given in Table IX. Because the substances making up these fuels are complex organic chemical compounds, and complex thermodynamic changes take place when they are burned in a furnace, it is not possible to make use of formulas such as the Dulong type to predict their heating values. These analyses do not indicate the amount of resins or similar substances present. But note that the heat content, on the dry basis, is greatest in the cases of highly resinous woods as fir and pine.

The moisture content of freshly cut wood varies from 30 to 50 percent. After air drying for approximately a year, this is reduced to between 18 and 25 percent.

Table VIII. Coal Tar Pitch

Proximate Analysis

Moisture	2.2%
VM	48.2%
FC	48.9%
Ash	0.7%

Ultimate Analysis

Carbon	90.1%
Hydrogen	4.9%
Sulfur	0.9%
Oxygen	0.6%
Nitrogen	0.6%
Moisture	2.2%
Ash	0.7%
HHV, Btu/lb, dry	16,200

Most wood as commercially available for steam generation is usually the waste product resulting from some manufacturing process. Its moisture content as received at the furnace will depend on (1) extraneous water from source or storage or handling in the rain and (2) whether it is "sap wood" or "heart wood," as well as on the species and on the time of year it is cut.

The use of wet refuse wood for steam generation falls into three broad classifications, each with its own specific combustion problems. As both producer and user of byproduct fuel, sawmills are in the first category. Byproduct fuel for in-plant use is usually made up of sawdust, shavings, bark and other wood waste in varying percentages dependent on the nature of the mill operation, the methods of storage and disposal of waste wood as well as the arrangement of available fuel burning equipment.

In the second classification are those plants which purchase their wood fuel supply, usually composed of chips with little or no sawdust and shavings.

Paper mills are in the third classification, as they must dispose of the wet wood refuse produced in their wood preparation plants. Their principal problem is one of wet bark disposal.

BARK

A common waste product in paper mills, bark results from debarking tree trunks used in making paper. The bark is peeled off the trunks in long rope-like strips. This shape and size, combined with the high moisture content, make the handling of the fuel difficult.

Bark as received from the barking drums contains 80 percent or more moisture, and in this condition is of no value as a fuel. This fact is best illustrated by Table X, the data for which have been prepared on the basis of a dry bark

Table IX. Typical Analyses of Dry Wood

	C	H₂	S	O₂	N₂	Ash	HHV, Btu/Lb	A at Zero Excess Air, Lb/10⁶ Btu
Softwoods†								
Cedar, white	48.80	6.37	...	44.46	...	0.37	8400*	709
Cypress	54.98	6.54	...	38.08	...	0.40	9870*	711
Fir, Douglas	52.3	6.3	...	40.5	0.1	0.8	9050	720
Hemlock, western	50.4	5.8	0.1	41.4	0.1	2.2	8620	706
Pine, pitch	59.00	7.19	...	32.68	...	1.13	11320*	702
white	52.55	6.08	...	41.25	...	0.12	8900*	723
yellow	52.60	7.02	...	40.07	...	0.31	9610*	710
Redwood	53.5	5.9	...	40.3	0.1	0.2	9040	722
Hardwoods†								
Ash, white	49.73	6.93	...	43.04	...	0.30	8920*	709
Beech	51.64	6.26	...	41.45	...	0.65	8760*	729
Birch, white	49.77	6.49	...	43.45	...	0.29	8650*	712
Elm	50.35	6.57	...	42.34	...	0.74	8810*	715
Hickory	49.67	6.49	...	43.11	...	0.73	8670*	711
Maple	50.64	6.02	...	41.74	0.25	1.35	8580	719
Oak, black	48.78	6.09	...	44.98	...	0.15	8180*	714
red	49.49	6.62	...	43.74	...	0.15	8690*	709
white	50.44	6.59	...	42.73	...	0.24	8810*	715
Poplar	51.64	6.26	...	41.45	...	0.65	8920*	716

*Calculated from reported high heating value of kiln-dried wood assumed to contain 8-percent moisture.
†The terms "hard" and "soft" wood, contrary to popular conception, have no reference to the actual hardness of the wood. According to the *Wood Handbook*, prepared by the Forest Products Laboratory of the U.S. Department of Agriculture, hardwoods belong to the botanical group of trees that are broad-leaved whereas softwoods belong to the group that have needle or scalelike leaves, such as evergreens: cypress, larch, and tamarack are exceptions.

heating value of 8750 Btu per lb. Thus, at 80 percent moisture the heating value is only 1750 Btu per lb (as received), and for every pound of dry substance there are 4 lbs of water which must be evaporated before any heat is available. Under these conditions, the bark will not support its own combustion, and it will be necessary to supply heat from some other source if the wet material is to be disposed of in the furnace of any steam generating unit.

HOG FUEL

In the manufacture of lumber, the amount of material removed from the log to produce sound lumber is approximately as follows: 18 percent in the form of slabs, edging and trimming; 10 percent as bark; and 20 percent as sawdust and shavings. While the total waste material will usually average 50 percent, distribution of different types of waste may vary widely from the approximations given above, owing to mill conditions as well as to the ultimate finished product.

The mills frequently use either the sawdust or a mixture of sawdust and shavings for steam production because these can be burned without further processing. The remainder of the so-called waste products requires further size reduction in a "hog" to facilitate feeding, rapid combustion, transportation and storage. These newly sized products, together with varying percentages of sawdust and shavings present, constitute *hog fuel*.

The percentage of sawdust and shavings present may be quite high if the fuel is to be burned at the sawmill. Table XI shows typical analyses of hog fuel.

A large paper producer conducted a series of tests to determine the moisture content, as well as the unit weight, of waste wood produced in its mill. The results of these tests, shown in Table XII, illustrate the wide variation in weight that will exist between units of hog fuel because of moisture and different wood-species content.

Hog fuel, as normally delivered to the furnace, contains variable amounts of moisture, averaging approximately 50 percent, most of which is in the cellular structure of the wood. Storage of logs in the mill pond, water lubrication of saws, and exposure to rain because of outdoor storage of the hog fuel all contribute to the high total moisture content. In addition, the hog fuel, on dry-wood basis, contains approximately 81 percent volatile matter and somewhat less than 18 percent fixed carbon. The noncombustible residue, in the form of wood ash, is only a small fraction of 1 percent.

Table X. Relationship of Bark Moisture to Heat Content

% H$_2$O	HHV, Btu/Lb	Lb water/ lb dry Substance
0	8750	0.00
20	7000	0.25
40	5250	0.67
50	4375	1.00
60	3500	1.50
70	2625	2.30
80	1750	4.00
90	875	9.00

Table XI. Analyses of Hog Fuels

Kind of Fuel	Western Hemlock	Douglas Fir	Pine Sawdust
H$_2$0 As Received	57.9	35.9	. . .
H$_2$0 Air Dried	7.3	6.5	6.3
Proximate Analysis, Dry Fuel			
VM	74.2	82.0	79.4
FC	23.6	17.2	20.1
Ash	2.2	0.8	0.5
Ultimate Analysis, Dry Fuel			
Hydrogen	5.8	6.3	6.3
Carbon	50.4	52.3	51.8
Nitrogen	0.1	0.1	0.1
Oxygen	41.4	40.5	41.3
Sulfur	0.1	0	0
Ash	2.2	0.8	0.5
HHV, Btu/lb, dry	8620	9050	9130

BAGASSE

Bagasse is a waste fuel produced when sugar is extracted from cane. The cane stalks grow in the field from 10 to 12 ft high. In Latin America, it is customary to cut the stalks again into smaller pieces, 2 to 3 ft long, before sending them through shredding machines or rotary knives. The shredding, or cutting operation, is called "disintegration" or "defibration," and serves to open up the hard rind and thereby facilitate the squeezing out of juice in the cane.

As in the case of wood, sugar cane consists of cellulose fiber which makes up the tissue enclosing such sugars as sucrose ($C_{12}H_{22}O_{11}$) and glucose ($C_6H_{12}O_6$). Water and small quantities of mineral ash are also present. On a moisture- and ash-free basis, the cane contains from 10 to 17 percent cellulose fiber and from 83 to 90 percent sugar.

To separate the juice from the fiber, the disintegrated cane is crushed between rollers. After this primary pressing, the issuing fiber, or "bagasse," is sent through more roller mills for further extraction. At the same time that the bagasse undergoes additional squeezing, it is sprayed, or "imbibed," with plain water or diluted juice to help dissolve more of the sugar. When hot water, generally taken from the boiler feed line, is used to soak the bagasse, the operation is known as "maceration." On leaving the last mill, a typical bagasse might have 40 percent fiber, 2.5 percent sugar, 55 percent moisture and 2.5 percent ash. The relatively high ash content in many bagasse samples is because of trash and dirt picked up in harvesting.

Table XIII shows typical ultimate analyses of bagasse from different countries, on a dry basis. (As-received bagasse contains 40 to 60 percent moisture by weight.) Carbon content is slightly lower; oxygen a little higher than in wood, possibly due to the extraction of sugar.

The size of bagasse pieces depends on the machinery employed to disintegrate the cane. A simple crusher will produce coarser bagasse than is obtained by adding a shredder ahead of the crusher. Aside from the special case where grindstones defibrate the cane, the finest size is obtained with rotating knives replacing both shredder and crusher.

FOOD-PROCESSING WASTES

The production of food from many fruits and vegetables results in burnable solids that are available for in-plant energy production. Among these are nut hulls, with a fuel value of about 7700 Btu/lb as fired; rice hulls, with 5200

Table XII. Unit Weight and Moisture Content of Wood (as-received basis)

Type of Wood	% H2O	Weight-lb/cu ft
Drum Barker (pressed)	63.4	19.3
Regular paper mill waste wood	56.9	21.5
Hemlock	53.7	19.4
Douglas fir	44.4	17.4

Table XIII. Typical Analyses of Bagasse, Dry

	% by Weight					HHV, Btu/Lb	A at Zero Excess Air, Lb/10⁶ Btu
	C	H₂	O₂	N₂	Ash		
Cuba	43.15	6.00	47.95	. . .	2.90	7985	629
Hawaii	46.20	6.40	45.90	. . .	1.50	8160	687
Java	46.03	6.56	45.55	0.18	1.68	8681	651
Mexico	47.30	6.08	45.30	. . .	1.32	8740	646
Peru	49.00	5.89	43.36	. . .	1.75	8380	700
Puerto Rico	44.21	6.31	47.72	0.41	1.35	8386	627

to 6500 Btu/lb; corn cobs, with 7500 to 8300 Btu/lb; and coffee grounds, with between 4900 and 6500 Btu/lb.

MUNICIPAL AND INDUSTRIAL REFUSE

Solid residential, commercial, and industrial waste is a fuel having some of the characteristics of wood, bagasse, and other "young" fossil fuels. It derives most of its heating value from its cellulosic content. In most cities today, this material is collected and transported to central points for disposal through landfilling or incineration. When shredded and separated into light and heavy fractions, a fuel can be produced having thermal energy equal to lignitic coals, with high ash, but low sulfur, content.

The technical aspects of recovery of the energy from this resource, as opposed to its simple disposal, are well documented. (See references 9 through 19.)

Refuse is a highly time-, geography-, and weather-dependent fuel. Its character varies widely with the economic status of the people generating it. It is extremely heterogeneous but, in general, has increased in paper and plastic content and, therefore, heating value, through the years. The garbage fraction has decreased, as has the quantity of ash from coal-fired household furnaces. In suburban areas, it will have greater or lesser content of leaves and grass as a function of the day in the week, and more or less moisture content as a function of the weather. Urban refuse is characterized by large quantities of paper bags, cardboard, and similar dry combustible material.

Similarly, industrial refuse has higher thermal value today than earlier, because of the increased use of plastics and other synthetic materials, many of which have high heating values with little or no moisture or ash. Typical high-calorific-value components of industrial waste are rubber, wood, sawdust, fats, oils, waxes, solvents, paints, and other organic materials, many of them with heating values of 10,000 to 19,000 Btu per pound.

Raw municipal refuse will be typically from one-third to one-half paper; 2 to 12 percent textiles, rubber, plastics, and leather; 7 to 24 percent food waste; 1 to 7 percent wood; 5 to 12 percent glass and ceramics; 7 to 11 percent metal; and 1 to 33 percent grass, leaves and dirt. Proximate and ultimate analyses of residential solid waste with magnetic metals removed are given in Table XIV. Further separation of heavy-density materials (nonferrous metals, stone, masonry, and glass) can increase refuse heating value to between 7,000 and 8,000 Btu per pound.

LIQUID FUELS

Fuel oil used for steam generation purposes may be defined as petroleum or any of its liquid residues remaining after the more volatile constituents have been removed.

Petroleum is sometimes burned in its crude form. In this condition, most of it will contain lighter gasoline fractions which lower the flash point and present a fire hazard. Through limited fractional distillation, or topping, the lighter gasoline can be removed and a safe fuel oil can be produced. If the refining process is carried through extended fractional distillation and cracking, such fuels as gasoline,

Table XIV. Analyses of Typical Residential Solid Waste With Magnetic Metals Removed

Proximate Analysis	% As Received
H_2O	19.7–31.3
Ash	9.4–26.8
VM	36.8–56.2
FC	0.6–14.6
HHV, Btu/lb	3100–6500
Ultimate Analysis	
H_2O	19.7–31.3
Ash	9.4–26.8
Carbon	23.4–42.8
Hydrogen	3.4–6.3
Nitrogen	0.2–0.4
Chlorine	0.1–0.9
Sulfur	0.1–0.4
Oxygen	15.4–31.9

Table XV. Detailed Requirements for Fuel Oils[A]

Grade of Fuel Oil	Flash Point, °C (°F)	Pour Point, °C (°F)	Water and Sediment Vol %	Carbon Residue on 10 % Bottoms %	Ash Weight %	Distillation Temp. C (°F) 10% Point	90% Point	
	Min	Max	Max	Max	Max	Max	Min	Max
No. 1 Distillate oil intended for vaporizing pot-type burners and other burners requiring this grade	38 or legal (100)	−18[C] (0)	0.05	0.15	. . .	215 (420)	. . .	288 (550)
No. 2 Distillate oil for general purpose heating for use in burners not requiring No. 1	38 or legal (100)	−6[C] (20)	0.05	0.35	. . .	. . .	282[C] (540)	338 (640)
No. 4 Preheating not usually required for handling or burning	55 or legal (130)	−6[C] (20)	0.50	. . .	0.10	. . .	. . .	. . .
No. 5 (Light) Preheating may be required depending on climate and equipment	55 or legal (130)	. . .	1.00	. . .	0.10	. . .	. . .	. . .
No. 5 (Heavy) Preheating may be required for burning and, in cold climates, may be required for handling	55 or legal (130)	. . .	1.00	. . .	0.10	. . .	. . .	. . .
No. 6 Preheating required for burning and handling	60 (140)	[G]	2.00[E]	. . .	. . .	. . .	. . .	. . .

[A] It is the intent of these classifications that failure to meet any requirement of a given grade does not automatically place an oil in the next lower grade unless in fact it meets all requirements of the lower grade.

[B] In countries outside the United States other sulfur limits may apply.

[C] Lower or higher pour points may be specified whenever required by conditions of storage or use. When pour point less than −18°C (0°F) is specified, the minimum viscosity for Grade No. 2 shall be 1.8 cSt (32.0 SUS) and the minimum 90 % point shall be waived.

[D] Viscosity values in parentheses are for information only and not necessarily limiting.

[E] The amount of water by distillation plus the sediment by extraction shall not exceed 2.00 %. The amount of sediment by extraction shall not exceed 0.50 %. A deduction in quantity shall be made for all water and sediment in excess of 1.0 %.

[F] Where low sulfur fuel is required, fuel oil falling in the viscosity range of a lower numbered grade down to and including No. 4 may be supplied by agreement between purchaser and supplier. The viscosity range of the initial shipment shall be identified and advance notice shall be required when changing from one viscosity range to another. This notice shall be in sufficient time to permit the user to make the necessary adjustments.

[G] Where low sulfur fuel oil is required, Grade 6 fuel oil will be classified as low pour +15°C (60°F) max or high pour (no max.) Low pour fuel oil should be used unless all tanks and lines are heated.

Excerpted from *ASTM Standards* D 396, Specifications for Fuel Oils.

Table XV. Detailed Requirements for Fuel Oils[A] — *Continued*

Saybolt Viscosity, s[D]				Kinematic Viscosity, cSt[D]				Specific Gravity 60/60°F (deg API)	Copper Strip Corrosion	Sulfur, %
Universal at 38°C (100°F)		Furol at 50°C (122°F)		At 38°C (100°F)		At 50°C (122°F)				
Min	Max	Min	Max	Min	Max	Min	Max	Max	Max	Max
. . .	. . .	. . .	. . .	1.4	2.2	. . .	. . .	0.8499 (35 min)	No. 3	0.5 or legal
(32.6)	(37.9)	. . .	. . .	2.0[C]	3.6	. . .	. . .	0.8762 (30 min)	No. 3	0.5[B] or legal
(45)	(125)	. . .	. . .	5.8	26.4[F]	. . .	. . .	. . .	. . .	legal
(>125)	(300)	. . .	. . .	>26.4	65[F]	. . .	. . .	. . .	. . .	legal
(>300)	(900)	(23)	(40)	>65	194[F]	(42)	(81)	. . .	. . .	legal
(>900)	(9000)	(>45)	(300)	>92	638[F]	50°C	(122°F)	. . .	. . .	legal

kerosene, gas oil, light fuel oils, lubricating oil, heavy fuel oil, residual tar, pitch and petroleum coke are produced.

PROPERTIES OF FUEL OIL

The term *fuel oil* may conveniently cover a wide range of petroleum products. It may be applied to crude petroleum, to a light petroleum fraction similar to kerosene or gas oil, or to a heavy residue left after distilling off the fixed gases, the gasoline, and more or less of the kerosene and gas oil. To provide standardization, specifications have been estab-

lished, Table XV, for several grades of fuel oil.

Sometimes designated as light and medium domestic fuel oils, Grades No. 1 and No. 2 are specified mainly by the temperature of the distillation range. Grade No. 6, designated as heavy industrial fuel oil and sometimes known as Bunker C oil, is specified mainly by viscosity. The specific gravities of Grades 4, 5, and 6 are not specified because they will vary with the source of the crude petroleum and the extent of the refinery operation in cracking and distilling.

Despite the multiplicity of chemical compounds found in fuel oils, the typical analyses of these fuels, as shown in Table XVI, are fairly constant.

SPECIFIC GRAVITY

This is the ratio between the weight of any volume of oil at 60°F and the weight of an equal volume of water at 60°F. The common designation is *Sp Gr 60/60°F* and is expressed as a decimal carried to four places.

Gravity determinations are readily made by immersing a hydrometer into the sample and reading the scale at the point to which the instrument sinks in the oil. The specific gravity is either read direct or the gravity is measured in degrees API.

Formerly, the gravity of oil was measured in degrees Baumé but confusion developed over the use of the two so-called Baumé scales for light liquids. To overcome this, the American Petroleum Institute, the U.S. Bureau of Mines, and the U.S. Bureau of Standards agreed to recommend, in 1921, that only one scale be used in the petroleum industry, and that it be known as the API scale. The relation between specific gravity and °API is expressed by

$$\text{Sp Gr 60/60°F} = \frac{141.5}{131.5 + \text{°API}} \tag{1}$$

HEATING VALUE

This may be expressed in either Btu per gallon at 60°F or Btu per pound. The heating value per gallon increases with specific gravity, because there is more weight per gallon, and ranges from about 135,000 to 150,000 Btu. The heating value per pound of fuel oil varies inversely with the specific gravity, because lighter oil contains more hydrogen; it ranges from 18,300 to 19,500 Btu.

The exact determination of the heat content of fuel oil is made in a bomb calorimeter. However, there is an approximate relationship between specific gravity and higher heating value. For an uncracked distillate or residue,

$$\text{Btu/lb (High)} = 17,660 + (69 \times \text{API gravity}) \tag{2}$$

For a cracked distillate,

$$\text{Btu/lb (High)} = 17,780 + (54 \times \text{API gravity}) \tag{3}$$

VISCOSITY

This is defined as the measure of the resistance to flow. The greater this resistance, the longer it takes a given volume of oil to flow through a fixed orifice. The Saybolt Universal viscosity is expressed in seconds of time that it takes to run 60 cc through a standard size orifice at any desired temperature. Viscosity is commonly measured at 100°F, 150°F and 210°F. The oil is held at constant temperature within ± 0.25°F during the test period.

Fuel oil is very viscous, and it takes a long time to make a determination with the Saybolt Universal viscosimeter. For this reason, the viscosity of fuel oil is usually measured with a Saybolt Furol viscosimeter, which is the same as the Saybolt Universal except that the orifice is larger. Viscosity of 62 seconds Saybolt Furol is 600 seconds Saybolt Universal.[20]

Another measure of viscosity sometimes used is the so-called Engler degree or specific viscosity. The Engler degree is the quotient of time of outflow of 200 cc of oil, divided by the time of flow of 200 cc of water; that is, the viscosity of oil is compared with that of water.

Viscosity of fuel oil decreases as the temperature rises and becomes nearly constant above about 250°F. Therefore, when fuel oil is heated to reduce the viscosity for good atomization, there is little gain in heating the oil beyond 250°F. Moreover, since burners operate most efficiently with oil of constant viscosity, it is desirable to operate in the viscosity range where temperature variations have the least effect. This is illustrated in Fig. 6 for No. 6 Bunker C oil. Fig. 7 shows the viscosity-temperature relationships for the several grades of fuel. Table XVI shows typical analyses.

The relationship among specific gravity, deg

API, density in lb per gal, Btu per lb, and Btu per gal for petroleum products is graphically shown in Fig. 8. Also included are the ranges in deg API for gasoline, kerosene, gas oil and fuel oils. Knowing the value of any one of these characteristics, it is possible to determine all the others quickly. For example, assume the deg API to be 75, then the intersection of this value with the deg API curves is at a point A, through which a horizontal line is drawn to intersect the remaining curves. Then, by referring to their respective scales, it is possible to read the specific gravity B as 0.685, the density C as 5.675 lb per gal, and the higher heating value at D as 20,550 Btu per lb, or at E as 116,800 Btu per gal. Of particular interest is the fact that, although the high specific gravity fuel oils (15°API) have a lower heating value per pound than the lower specific gravity gasoline (60°API), the total heat per gallon, the basis on

which they are purchased commercially, is considerably greater.

FLASH AND FIRE POINT

Flash point of fuel oil is the lowest temperature at which sufficient vapor is given off to

Fig. 6 **Viscosity versus temperature, No. 6 fuel oil**

Table XVI. Typical Analyses and Properties of Fuel Oils*

Grade	No. 1 Fuel Oil	No. 2 Fuel Oil	No. 4 Fuel Oil	No. 5 Fuel Oil	No. 6 Fuel Oil
Type	Distillate (Kerosene)	Distillate	Very Light Residual	Light Residual	Residual
Color	Light	Amber	Black	Black	Black
API gravity, 60°F	40	32	21	17	12
Specific gravity, 60/60°F	0.8251	0.8654	0.9279	0.9529	0.9861
Lb/U.S. gallon, 60°F	6.870	7.206	7.727	7.935	8.212
Viscos., Centistokes, 100°F	1.6	2.68	15.0	50.0	360.0
Viscos., Saybolt Univ., 100°F	31	35	77	232	. . .
Viscos., Saybolt Furol, 122°F	. . .	. . .	. . .	. . .	170
Pour point, °F	Below zero	Below zero	10	30	65
Temp. for pumping, °F	Atmospheric	Atmospheric	15 min.	35 min.	100
Temp. for atomizing, °F	Atmospheric	Atmospheric	25 min.	130	200
Carbon residue, %	Trace	Trace	2.5	5.0	12.0
Sulfur, %	0.1	0.4–0.7	0.4–1.5	2.0 max.	2.8 max.
Oxygen and nitrogen, %	0.2	0.2	0.48	0.70	0.92
Hydrogen, %	13.2	12.7	11.9	11.7	10.5
Carbon, %	86.5	86.4	86.10	85.55	85.70
Sediment and water, %	Trace	Trace	0.5 max.	1.0 max.	2.0 max.
Ash, %	Trace	Trace	0.02	0.05	0.08
Btu/gallon	137,000	141,000	146,000	148,000	150,000

* Courtesy Exxon Corporation

form a momentary flash when flame is brought near the surface. The values vary with the apparatus and procedure; both must be specified. Flash point specifications for the several grades of fuel oil are given in Table XV. Fire point is the lowest temperature at which the oil gives off enough vapor to burn continuously.

SULFUR AND ASH

Sulfur is a very undesirable element in fuel oil because its products of combustion are acidic and cause corrosion in economizers, air heaters and gas ducts. Because of the high hydrogen content in fuel oil, and the resulting high water vapor content in the products of combustion, a given amount of sulfur in fuel oil has the potential of doing more damage than the same amount of sulfur in coal.

Fuel oil contains all the solid impurities originally present in the crude oil. If these solids contain a large proportion of salt, they are very fusible and can cause considerable trouble.

OIL REFINERY REFUSE FUEL

Byproducts from refinery operation consist of a wide variety of refuse fuels. There are solids, such as asphaltic pitch and petroleum coke. The liquids, termed *sludge,* often have a high specific gravity and contain variable amounts of solid matter in suspension.

The characteristics of the sludge are governed by those of the crude oil used and the manner in which it is processed. Many of the suspended solids may be carbonaceous, in the form of small particles of oil coke.

Perhaps the most troublesome of sludges, because of its frequent and widely varying characteristics, is *acid sludge.* Its gravity may range between 5 and 14°API, and its viscosity is indeterminate. It contains changing quantities of weak sulfuric acid that may run as high as 40 percent, and this, together with the suspended carbonaceous material and flux, which must be added to make the sludge flow, causes heat

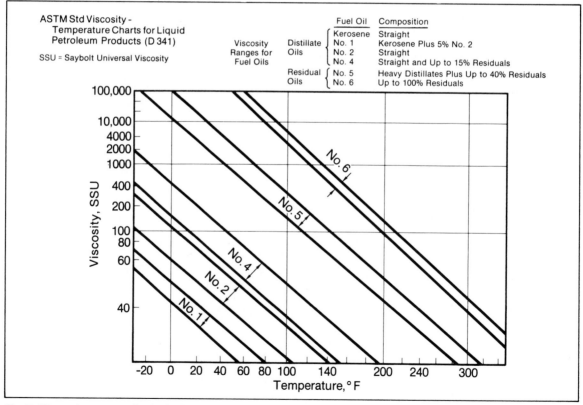

Fig. 7 **Viscosity ranges for fuel oils**

values to vary between 8,000 and 17,500 Btu/lb.

Alkaline sludges, such as soda tar and neutralized sludge, are less troublesome to fire since they are less variable in character than acid sludge.

GASEOUS FUELS

Gaseous fuels, when available, are ideal for steam generation because of the ease of control, the presence of little or no solid residue, and the low excess-air requirement, which contributes to high efficiency.

Properties of fuel gas considered to be of prime importance are composition, heating value, and specific gravity.

ANALYSIS

The analysis of fuel gas is expressed in terms of volume percentages of the component gases.

Determinations can be made by selective absorption in chemical solutions, by separation of components through distillation, by infrared or mass spectrometry, or by means of gas chromatography. Typical analyses of various gases are given under their specific headings.

HEATING VALUE

The heating value refers to the quantity of heat released during combustion of a unit amount of fuel gas. Determinations are made with a continuous flow (constant pressure) gas calorimeter. The heating value as determined in calorimeters is termed *high heating value* and is the quantity of heat evolved when the products of combustion are cooled to 60°F and the water vapor produced is completely condensed to a liquid at that temperature. The *low heating value* differs from the high heating value by the latent heat of evaporation of water

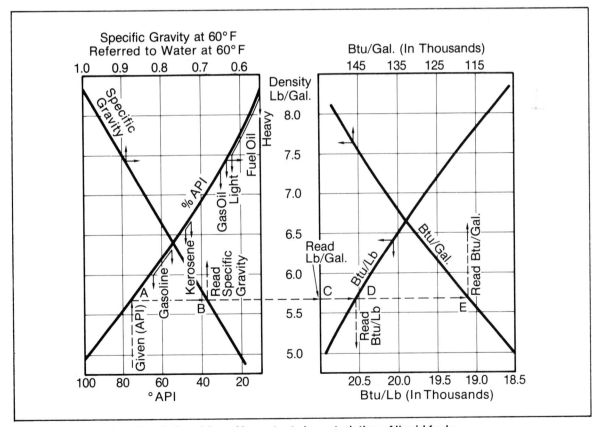

Fig. 8 Chart showing the relationships of important characteristics of liquid fuels

formed in the combustion process, as described on Page 2–12.

The heating value of manufactured gas is expressed as Btu per cu ft when measured at 60°F and 30 in. Hg, saturated with water vapor. The values for natural gas, however, are commonly reported at a pressure of 14.7 psia (pounds per square inch absolute) or 30 in. Hg, at a temperature of 80°F, and generally on a dry basis.

The heating value of gaseous fuels varies considerably, depending on the constituents present. When not obtainable by test, H_f can be calculated by summing up the heat evolved by the individual combustible fractions of the gas.

In Table XVII are shown the principal components, together with their properties at 60°F and 30 in. Hg, moisture-free. When present in different proportions, these make up various fuel gases.

ANSI/ASTM Standards D 3588 gives a method for calculating calorific value and specific gravity of gaseous fuels and includes a method for determining the repeatability and reproducibility of the calculated values.

SPECIFIC GRAVITY

Various methods for determining the specific gravity of a fuel gas are available but three

Table XVII. Combustion Constants of Dry Gases at 60°F and 30 In. Hg

Gas	Chemical Formula	O₂ Reqd./Cu Ft of Dry Gas, Cu Ft	CO₂ Formed/Cu Ft of Dry Gas, Cu Ft	H₂O Formed/Cu Ft of Dry Gas, Cu Ft	Density of Dry Gas, Lb/Cu Ft	HHV of Dry Gas Btu/Cu Ft*	Btu/Lb
Oxygen	O₂	...	...	...	0.08461	...	...
Nitrogen (atmospheric)	N₂	...	...	...	0.07439	...	...
Air	...	...	...	...	0.07655	...	...
Carbon dioxide	CO₂	...	...	...	0.1170	...	...
Water vapor	H₂O	...	...	...	0.04758	...	...
Hydrogen	H₂	0.5	...	1.0	0.005327	325	60,991
Hydrogen sulfide	H₂S	1.5	1.0**	1.0	0.09109	647	7,100
Carbon monoxide	CO	0.5	1.0	...	0.07404	321	4,323
Saturated Hydrocarbons							
Methane	CH₄	2.0	1.0	2.0	0.04246	1014	23,896
Ethane	C₂H₆	3.5	2.0	3.0	0.08029	1789	22,282
Propane	C₃H₈	5.0	3.0	4.0	0.1196	2573	21,523
Butane	C₄H₁₀	6.5	4.0	5.0	0.1582	3392	21,441
Pentane	C₅H₁₂	8.0	5.0	6.0	0.1904	4200	22,058
Unsaturated Hydrocarbons or Illuminants							
Ethylene	C₂H₄	3.0	2.0	2.0	0.07421	1614	21,647
Propylene	C₃H₆	4.5	3.0	3.0	0.1110	2383	21,464
Butylene	C₄H₈	6.0	4.0	4.0	0.1480	3190	21,552
Pentylene	C₅H₁₀	7.5	5.0	5.0	0.1852	4000	21,600
Acetylene	C₂H₂	2.5	2.0	1.0	0.06971	1488	21,344
Benzene	C₆H₆	7.5	6.0	3.0	0.2060	3930	19,068
Toluene	C₇H₈	9.0	7.0	4.0	0.2431	4750	19,537

* If gas is saturated with moisture at 60°F and 30.0 in. Hg, reduce by 1.74%.
** SO₂ rather than CO₂

methods have been adopted as *ASTM Standards D 1070*, Test for Gravity, Specific, (Relative Density) of Gaseous Fuels.

DIRECT WEIGHING METHOD

This involves the determination of the weight differential between two equal volumes of gas and air, both at identical conditions of temperature and pressure.

PRESSURE BALANCE METHOD

In this method, a flask containing the gas is counterbalanced on a beam enclosed in a container. The beam is brought to balance by adjusting the air pressure within the container which varies the buoyancy of the flask. The procedure is repeated with air in the flask and the specific gravity determined from the ratio of the required absolute pressures.

DISPLACEMENT BALANCE METHOD

The instrument consists of a balance beam on each end of which two bells are suspended in a sealing liquid. One bell, containing air, is open to the atmosphere through holes in its top; the other bell, containing the gas, is open to the atmosphere through a 59-in. gas column connected to the space under the bell. An unbalanced force is produced which is equal to the pressure differential above and within the gas-filled bulb. The magnitude of this force is an indication of the specific gravity.

NATURAL GAS

Natural gas is perhaps the closest approach to an ideal fuel because it is practically free from noncombustible gas or solid residue. It is found compressed in porous rock and shale formations, or cavities, which are sealed between strata of close-textured rocks under the earth's surface. When these so-called gas-bearing sands of a pool are tapped by drilling wells, the gas is found to be under rock pressure, which may be as high as 2000 psig (pounds per square inch gage). As gas is withdrawn, this pressure gradually decreases until the field must be abandoned.

Natural-gas fields frequently exist in the neighborhood of oil deposits. Usually natural gas occupies the space above the oil and the oil,

in turn, lies over salt water. The relative density of these substances accounts for their segregation, natural gas being lightest, water heaviest, and oil in between. But not all natural gas is associated with oil. At times it is found by itself, or directly in contact with salt water, hermetically sealed by the rock.

Although whenever possible natural gas is delivered at the required destination under well pressure, it is also frequently transported over long distances by means of pipelines and compressors. Thus, the furnace which uses this gas may be close to the well or at the end of a pipeline and the conditions in the pipelines may change the composition of natural gas going to the furnace. For instance, aside from the effect of compression, which liquefies the heavy members of the hydrocarbon family, water and oil are sometimes sprayed into the gas to keep it "moist." For this reason, any natural-gas analysis, as fired, should be taken at the point of use rather than at the well.

COMPOSITION OF NATURAL GAS

The characteristics of natural gas, as it comes out of the earth's surface, depend to some extent on its underground conditions. Generally, it is odorless and colorless. It burns with a blue flame and is highly explosive when mixed with air in the correct proportions. The range in its chemical composition is indicated by Table XVIII, where it is seen that methane, CH_4, and ethane, C_2H_6, are its principal combustible components. This is because in natural-gas analyses it is customary to report the heavier hydrocarbons in terms of CH_4 and C_2H_6, or if this grouping is not satisfactory, in terms of C_2H_6 and C_3H_8 (propane).

When sulfur is present in the oil deposit, the analysis of natural gas associated with this oil often includes hydrogen sulfide. This hydrogen sulfide is removed in most instances before distributing the gas because it is a potential source of pipeline corrosion.

In addition to its combustible constituents, natural gas may contain considerable amounts of carbon dioxide, CO_2, or nitrogen, N_2. It sometimes happens that gas is drawn from wells under suction and that, because of this, air will leak into the lines. The analysis of natural gas will then show the presence of oxygen.

DRY AND WET NATURAL GAS

If natural gas has been in contact with oil, it will be impregnated with varying amounts of heavy hydrocarbon vapors, such as pentane, C_5H_{12}, and hexane, C_6H_{14}, which are liquid at ordinary pressure and temperature. Known as "wet" natural gas, it is usually economical to dry it by liquefying the heavy vapors, which are then collected and called *casing-head gasoline*. In a complete chemical analysis of natural gas, a certain fraction of a heavy hydrocarbon is sometimes preceded by the letter "n," such as "n-butane," which means "normal" butane, and the remainder uses the prefix "iso," meaning "equal," as, for example, "iso-butane." The chemical formula is the same in both cases as the prefix merely denotes a different arrangement of the atoms in the hydrocarbon molecule. However, the physical and chemical properties of these so-called "isomers" are not usually the same.

"Dry" natural gas comes from wells away from oil deposits and is, therefore, comparatively devoid of heavy hydrocarbons.

Natural gases are also classified as either "sweet" or "sour." The *sour* gas is one which contains some mercaptans and a high percentage of hydrogen sulfide while the *sweet* gas is one in which these objectionable constituents have been removed. Analysis of sour and sweet gases are shown in Table XIX.

HEATING VALUE

The higher or gross heating value of natural gas is usually about 1000 Btu per cu ft, and it can be computed by adding together the heat contributed by volumetric percentages of the various component gases. This method will usually result in a lower value per cubic foot than that obtained by calorimetric determinations, because the unsaturated hydrocarbons are frequently grouped and reported with C_2H_6. For the same reason, the corresponding density, under standard conditions of 60°F and 30 in. Hg, will also be lower. The calculated Btu per pound, however, will be close to its actual value, because of the compensating effect of the lower calculated density.

LIQUEFIED PETROLEUM GAS (LPG)

The term *liquefied petroleum gas, LPG*, is applied to certain hydrocarbons which are gaseous under normal atmospheric conditions, but can be liquefied under moderate pressure at normal temperatures. LPG is derived from natural gas and from various petroleum-refinery sources such as crude distillation and cracking. The hydrocarbons in LPG are mainly of the paraffinic (saturated) series, principally propane, isobutane and normal butane.

The California Natural Gasoline Association has divided LPG mixtures into six standard

Table XVIII. Characteristics of Typical Natural Gases at 60° F and 30 In. Hg, Dry

% by Volume								Density, Lb/Cu Ft	HHV		A at Zero Excess Air, Lb/10^6 Btu
CO_2	N_2	H_2S	CH_4	C_2H_6	C_3H_8	C_4H_{10}	C_5H_{12}		Btu/Cu Ft**	Btu/Lb	
5.50	...	7.00	77.73	5.56	2.40	1.18	0.63*	0.05621	1061	18,880	738
3.51	32.00	0.50	52.54	3.77	2.22	2.02	3.44*	0.06610	874	13,220	729
26.2	0.7	...	59.2	13.9	...	...	...	0.06747	849	12,580	732
0.17	87.69	...	10.50	1.64	...	...	...	0.07120	136	1,907	732
0.20	0.60	...	99.20	...	...	...	...	0.04491	1006	22,410	732
...	0.60	...	...	79.40	20.00	...	...	0.08812	1935	21,960	735
...	0.50	...	...	21.80	77.70	...	...	0.11079	2389	21,560	738

*All hydrocarbons heavier than C_5H_{12} are assumed to be C_5H_{12}
**If gas is saturated with moisture at 60°F and 30.0 in. Hg, reduce by 1.74%.

grades based on physical properties such as vapor pressure and specific gravity, as shown in Table XX.

The greatest use of LPG is as a domestic fuel with an appreciable amount being consumed in synthetic rubber production and chemical industries. It has a limited use in steam-generating units as an ignition and warm-up fuel but is generally prohibited for economic reasons from being a primary fuel.

REFINERY AND OIL GAS

Both refinery gas and oil gas may be defined as gaseous fuels composed of uncondensed distillation fractions. Aside from differences in composition, refinery gas is distinguished commercially as a byproduct, whereas oil gas is a main product of distillation.

A brief review of the methods of treating crudes will give a better understanding of the nature of oil and refinery gases.

Like coal, petroleum is the source of various solid, liquid, and gaseous products which are used as fuels and for other purposes. Among the solid fuels derived from it are the heavy tars, pitches, and cokes which are collected at the bottom of stills; the liquid products comprise gasoline, kerosene, gas oils, and various

grades of fuel oils, as well as semifluid sludges left over from refinery operations. Finally, petroleum yields a variety of gaseous fuels, some of which are purposely manufactured for sale, such as oil gas and carburetted water gas, and others in the nature of waste products, known as refinery gases.

There are two basically different ways of processing crudes. The first and older is distillation; the second and more recent is cracking. Frequently, in modern refinery practice, both methods are combined into the same or successive operations.

DISTILLATION VERSUS CRACKING

In a typical continuous distillation process, the crude oil is first preheated in a tube still to a temperature of about 600°F. The charge is then sent to a fractionating tower, or column, where it is flashed at atmospheric pressure and separated into its various components according to their specific gravities.

In addition to distillation being carried out at atmospheric pressure or under vacuum, it may take place in the presence of steam or other inactive gas. Both vacuum and steam distillation permit fractionation at lower temperature.

Cracking is the thermal decomposition of petroleum. In a typical cracking process, the crude oil is heated in tube coils to a temperature of 850 to 1000°F and discharged, under a pressure of perhaps 750 psi, first into separators which eliminate the tar and heavy oil, and then into a fractionating tower.

PRODUCTION OF REFINERY FUELS

As a fuel, refinery gas is withdrawn from whatever point in the refining system it is found economical. It may come from raw gasoline tanks, from stabilizers, from cracking stills, or from adsorbers used in purifying operations. Likewise, depending on the process and the point of origin in the system, the fuel gas may be at, or below, or above atmospheric pressure; if it comes from a condenser, it may be at room temperature, but its temperature may be much higher if taken directly from a cracking still or fractionating tower. Often, refinery

Table XIX. Natural Gas from Arkansas Fields

Constituents	Raw-sour gas*	Sweetened-sour gas**
Carbon dioxide	5.50	0.00
Methane	77.73	88.83
Ethane	5.56	6.35
Propane	2.41	2.75
Butane	1.17	1.34
Pentane	0.39	0.45
Hexane and higher	0.24	0.28
Hydrogen sulfide	7.0	0.0004
HHV	. . .	. . .
Btu/cu ft at standard conditions	. . .	1159

*From Big Creek field
**From McKamie field

gases from various sources in the plant are blended together before being burned.

Because it is specifically manufactured for commercial purposes, oil gas deserves special mention, as the heat value standard for the locality where it is sold governs its final composition.

Oil gas is produced by spraying oil into a retort heated to about 1300°F, causing thermal decomposition. Cracking of the oil is then completed by passing the gas through a second retort, which converts the unstable hydrocarbons of low molecular weight into permanently gaseous hydrocarbons. In this manner about 85 percent of the oil is recovered as gas.

The wide range of characteristic analyses of these gases is given in Table XXI. The last two analyses are of oil gases; the others represent refinery gases.

COKE-OVEN GAS

As its name implies, coke-oven gas is a by-product of the destructive distillation of bituminous coal in the manufacture of coke. The raw coal is placed in ovens, which are externally heated until practically all the volatile matter is driven out. The coke-oven gas is made up chiefly of hydrogen, methane, ethylene, and carbon monoxide, with small percentages of carbon dioxide, nitrogen, oxygen, and heavy hydrocarbons or illuminants. The character of the raw coal and the length of time taken in the roasting operation influence the exact composition of coke-oven gas.[21]

As the coke-oven gas comes from the oven at high temperatures, it frequently contains various impurities in the form of tarry particles, dust, benzol, and hydrogen sulfide. With rare exceptions, however, it is always washed and cooled before being sent to a storage tank and distributed for burning.

Because of a breaking down of the heavy hydrocarbons, carbonization at high temperatures generally results in calorific values varying from 400 to 600 Btu per cu ft. On the other hand, low-temperature carbonization gives a smaller yield of coke-oven gas, but a higher heating value, ranging from 600 to 1000 Btu per cu ft. Table XXII indicates a spread between 477 and 829 Btu per cu ft in the high heating value of the analyses selected. The heating value of a coke-oven gas, when not given, may be accurately determined by a summation of the heats evolved by the individual combustible constituents of the gas.

PRODUCER GAS

Producer gas is formed through the partial combustion of coal or coke by passing less than stoichiometric air through a hot fuel bed. Because of the use of air, the nitrogen content of the gas is high, generally 50 to 55 percent by

Table XX. CNGA Standard Grade for LPG Mixture

CNGA Standard Grade	Max Vapor Pressure Psig at 100°F	Range of Allowable Sp Gr 60/60°F $H_2O = 1.0$	Composition
A	80	0.585–0.555	Predominantly butanes
B	100	0.560–0.545	Butane-propane mixture, largely butanes
C	125	0.550–0.535	Butane-propane mixture, proportions approximately equal
D	150	0.540–0.525	Butane-propane mixture, propane exceeds butane
E	175	0.530–0.510	Propane-butane mixture, largely propane
F	200	0.520–0.504	Predominantly propane

volume, and the heating value is rather low, ranging from about 140 to 180 Btu per cu ft. The ranges of component gases in this fuel are

CO	20–30%
H_2	8–20%
CH_4	0.5–3 %
CO_2	3–9 %
N_2	50–56%
O_2	0.1–0.3%

WATER GAS (BLUE GAS)

Water gas is made in a cyclic process, in which coke is "blown" with air to raise its temperature and then "blasted" with steam. The steam reacts with the hot carbon endothermally as follows:

$$C + H_2O \rightarrow CO + H_2$$

(4)

The gas is sometimes called "blue gas" because of the characteristic blue flame with which it burns, the color resulting from the high percentage of hydrogen and carbon monoxide. A typical analysis shows this gas consists of the following components:

Table XXI. Characteristics of Typical Refinery and Oil Gases at 60°F and 30 In. Hg, Dry

% by volume								
O_2	. . .	. . .	. . .	. . .	. . .	2.3	0.9	0.1
N_2	. . .	. . .	. . .	. . .	. . .	8.7	8.4	2.7
CO_2	. . .	. . .	. . .	. . .	3.3	. . .	2.2	1.0
CO	. . .	. . .	. . .	. . .	1.5	. . .	14.3	6.8
H_2	. . .	. . .	. . .	. . .	5.6	. . .	50.9	59.2
H_2S	2.18	. . .	. . .	. . .	. . .	. . .	. . .	. . .
CH_4	41.62	4.30	92.10	5.0	30.9	30.3	15.9	25.4
C_2H_6	20.91	82.70	1.90	12.0	19.8	13.4	5.0	. . .
C_3H_8	19.72	13.00	4.50	30.0	38.1	19.1	. . .	. . .
C_4H_{10}*	9.05	. . .	1.30	34.0	0.0	14.7	. . .	. . .
C_5H_{12}†	6.52	. . .	0.02	19.0	. . .	1.8	. . .	. . .
$C_3H_3H_6$‡	. . .	. . .	. . .	. . .	0.2	9.7	2.4	4.8
Density Lb/Cu Ft	0.08676	0.08377	0.04845	0.13760	0.08102	0.09232	0.03631	0.02756
HHV Btu/Cu Ft**	1898	1858	1136	2988	1696	1844	519	586
Btu/Lb	21,880	22,170	23,460	21,720	20,930	19,970	14,300	21,270
A at Zero Excess Air Lb/10^6 Btu	722	725	723	717	725	715	648	657
CO_2 at Zero Excess Air %	13.3	13.4	12.1	13.9	13.4	13.6	12.2	10.6

*Includes both iso-C_4H_{10} and n-C_4H_{10}.

†Includes all saturated hydrocarbons heavier than C_5H_{12}, also both iso-C_5H_{12} and n-C_5H_{12}.

‡Includes all illuminants.

**If gas is saturated with moisture at 60°F and 30.0 in. Hg, reduce by 1.74%.

Table XXII. Characteristics of Typical Coke-Oven Gases at 60°F and 30 In. Hg, Dry

CO_2	O_2	N_2	CO	H_2	CH_2	C_2H_4	C_6H_6	Density, Lb/Cu Ft	HHV Btu/Cu Ft*	Btu/Lb	A at Zero Excess Air, Lb/10⁶ Btu
1.8	0.2	3.4	6.3	53.0	31.6	2.7	1.0	0.0298	596	20,010	674
1.4	0.5	4.2	5.1	57.4	28.5	2.9	...	0.0263	539	20,490	664
2.6	0.6	3.7	6.1	47.9	33.9	5.2	...	0.0316	603	19,070	676
3.13	...	...	11.93	42.16	37.14	4.76	0.88	0.0359	663	18,500	684
0.1	...	2.4	6.8	27.7	50.0	13.0	...	0.0393	829	21,100	700
0.75	...	12.1	6.0	53.0	28.15	...	...	0.0291	477	16,390	668

% by Volume

*If gas is saturated with moisture at 60°F and 30.0 in. Hg, reduce by 1.74%.

CO_2	5.6%
CO	37.0%
H_2	47.3%
CH_4	1.3%
N_2	8.8%
HHV, Btu/cu ft	287

CARBURETTED WATER GAS

Water gas enriched with fuel oil to raise its heating value is called *carburetted water gas*. The process involves the injection of oil into the carburetting chamber during the steam blow; the water gas, passing into the carburetor, picks up the oil vapor which is then cracked into gases. The composition and heating value of the carburetted water gas varies with the amount of oil used, the latter property varying between 400 and 700 Btu per cu ft. Table XXIII shows typical analyses of this gas.

REGENERATOR WASTE GAS

The lighter hydrocarbons or gas oils produced in the petroleum coking processes are further refined in catalytic-cracking units. These units fall into two general types: fluid units, in which fine powdered catalyst flows through the equipment with flow characteristics resembling a liquid, and moving-bed units, which use either spherical or pelleted catalyst circulated by elevators or gas lifts.

The cracking of the feed takes place in a chemical reactor vessel. The preheated catalyst is maintained in a fluid state, and during the cracking reaction the catalyst becomes coated with a coke deposit. To maintain catalyst activity, this material must be removed.

The spent catalyst is continuously removed from the reactor and transported to a regenerator vessel. In this unit compressed air fluidizes the catalyst and burns off the carbon. To keep compression costs to a minimum, as well as to keep the temperature inside the regenerator restricted to a level which will not destroy catalyst activity, the smallest amount of air is used that will effectively clean the catalyst.

Table XXIII. Analyses of Carburetted Water Gas

Component	From Coke %	From Anthracite %
Carbon dioxide and hydrogen sulfide	0.9	3.3
Nitrogen	6.8	4.2
Hydrogen	37.4	38.4
Carbon monoxide	35.0	31.0
Methane	8.1	12.7
Ethane	1.30	1.05
Ethylene	6.7	6.9
Propane	0.25	0.08
Propylene	1.5	0.87
Butane	0.0	0.0
Butylene	0.75	0.45
Liquid hydrocarbons	1.30	1.05

This combustion process, therefore, normally produces an appreciable percentage of carbon monoxide.

The gas, although at temperatures as high as 1125°F, has a heating value of not over 40 Btu per cu ft. A typical analysis of the constituents in regenerator waste gas follows:

CO	6.9%
CO_2	8.1%
O_2	0.8%
N_2	65.8%
H_2O	18.4%

BLAST-FURNACE GAS

Since blast-furnace gas is one of the most important byproducts in the smelting of iron ore to obtain pig iron, its characteristics are best understood by examining what takes place in a blast furnace when in operation.

Iron ore, coke, and limestone are alternately charged into the furnace from the top at the same time that air, previously heated to between 1100 and 1300°F, is blown into it through openings at the bottom. In moving down through the furnace, the mass of solid raw materials is vigorously scrubbed by air which sweeps upward at velocities up to 450 ft per sec. The process of extracting iron from its ore begins when carbon in the coke unites with oxygen in the air to form carbon monoxide, CO, with the liberation of heat. Next, the presence of more carbon together with this heat reduces the iron oxide and converts some of the carbon monoxide to carbon dioxide, CO_2. To facilitate removal of impurities from the molten mass, limestone is added and more CO_2 is formed.

Besides carbon monoxide and carbon dioxide, blast-furnace gas contains nitrogen, hydrogen, and sometimes, small amounts of methane (Table XXIV). The last two are the result of high-temperature dissociation of moisture which enters the furnace with the materials charged, whereas the nitrogen in the analyses is almost exclusively derived from the air blast.

While at one time iron and steel producers concentrated their entire attention on getting the highest yield of pig iron per ton of coke burned, now they are much more aware of the economic value of a quality blast-furnace gas.

Present-day furnaces burn this fuel in any one of three different states: (1) as raw gas with some of the dust and dirt removed; (2) after the gas has had a "primary" cleaning or washing; and (3) after it has been thoroughly dedusted or washed by means of "final" as well as "primary" cleaners.

DUST

The high velocity at which blasts of air sweep through the alternate layers of coke, iron ore, and limestone causes many fine particles, and some fairly large lumps, to be carried along in suspension as dust. In some cases, as much as 50 grains of dust per standard cubic foot (at 60°F and 30 in. Hg) have been measured in the gas leaving the top of the blast furnace. Burned in this state, the gas would quickly plug the firing equipment and boiler passages, and require almost continuous shutdown for cleaning. Generally, therefore, many of the suspended solids are removed, before firing, by passing the blast-furnace gas through a dry dust catcher. On exiting from this dust catcher as "raw gas," it still contains 3 to 15 grains of dust per standard cu ft, and, in this condition, it is sometimes burned under steam-generating units.

More often, however, before being delivered to a boiler furnace, the gas is given an additional, or primary, cleaning by means of either a dry separator or a washer, to reduce the dust content to 0.1–0.8 grain per standard cu ft. As desired, following the "primary" cleaners, either dry or wet final cleaners further remove remaining dust content to 0.005–0.05 grain per standard cu ft. When washed, blast-furnace gas can carry a considerable amount of water in suspension as fine droplets as well as water vapor.

TEMPERATURE

The temperature at which blast-furnace gas reaches the boiler depends on the kind of cleaning apparatus employed. As raw gas coming from the dust catcher, its temperature may be anywhere from 300 to 800°F. If the subsequent cleaning is done with dry separators, the drop

Table XXIV. Characteristics of Typical Blast-Furnace Gases at 60°F and 30 In. Hg, Dry

% by Volume					Density, Lb/Cu Ft	HHV		A at Zero Excess Air, Lb/10⁶ Btu
CO₂	N₂	CO	H₂	CH₄		Btu/Cu Ft*	Btu/Lb	
14.5	57.5	25.0	3.0	. . .	0.0779	90.1	1150	576
13.0	57.6	26.2	3.2	. . .	0.0771	94.6	1219	575
15.59	59.28	23.35	1.7	0.08	0.0792	81.4	1021	577
8.7	56.5	32.8	1.8	0.2	0.0762	113.3	1478	579
5.7	59.0	34.0	1.3	. . .	0.0753	113.6	1498	576
6.0	60.0	27.0	2.0	5.0	0.0734	144.0	1950	631

* If gas is saturated with moisture at 60°F and 30.0 in. Hg, reduce by 1.74%

in gas temperature through each separator may be only 30 to 50°F. On the other hand, washers, using sprays of water to precipitate the dust, lower the temperature of the gas to 70–120°F. Furthermore, in some cases the distance from blast furnace to boiler is sufficiently great to cause a drop in temperature from radiation losses in the connecting piping.

REFERENCES

[1] George Frederick Gebhardt, *Steam Power Plant Engineering*, Chapter II "Fuels," 6th ed. New York: John Wiley and Sons, 1925.

James A. Kent, ed. *Riegel's Handbook of Industrial Chemistry*, 7th ed. New York: Van Nostrand Reinhold Co. 1974.

[2] Sam H. Schurr and Bruce C. Netschert, *Energy in the American Economy, 1850–1975: An Economic Study of Its History and Prospects*. Originally published by John Hopkins Press, 1960. Reprinted 1977 by Greenwood Press, Inc., Westport, CT; pp 57–83 and 302–346.

A. J. Johnson and G. H. Auth, ed., *Fuels and Combustion Handbook*. New York: McGraw-Hill, 1951.

National Coal Association, *Coal Facts*. Washington: National Coal Association, 1979.

[3] William Kent, "Classification and Heating Value of American Coals," *Transactions of the ASME*, 36: 189–209, 1914.

A. C. Fieldner, "Constitution and Classification of Coal," *Transactions of the ASME*, Paper FSP 50–51: 49–50, 1927–1928.

Henry Kreisinger and B. J. Cross, "Burning Characteristics of Different Coals," *Transactions of the ASME*, Paper FSP 50–52: 49–50, 1927–1928.

[4] Illinois University at Urbana-Champagne. Engineering Experiment Station. Bulletin Series no. 37, "Unit Coal and the Composition of Coal Ash," by S. W. Parr and W. F. Wheeler, 1909.

Illinois University at Urbana-Champagne. Engineering Experiment Station Bulletin Series no. 180, "The Classification of Coal," by S. W. Parr, 1928.

[5] W. H. Ode and F. H. Gibson, "Effect of Sulfur Retention on Determined Ash in Lower Rank Coals," U. S. Bureau of Mines, Report of Investigation 5931. Washington: U. S. Bureau of Mines, 1962.

[6] H. Kreisinger, "High and Net Heat Values of Fuel," *Combustion*, 2(2): 25–26 and 47, Aug. 1930.

[7] National Research Council. Committee on Chemistry of Coal. *Chemistry of Coal Utilization*, Supplementary Volume, ed. by H. H. Lowry. New York: John Wiley, 1963. Chapter 5, "Coal Analysis and Mineral Matter," by W. H. Ode.

[8] Roy F. Abernethy and Elsie M. Cochrane, "Fusibility of Ash of United States Coals," U. S. Bureau of Mines, Information Circular 7923. Washington: U. S. Bureau of Mines, 1960.

Roy F. Abernethy and Elsie M. Cochrane, "Free-Swelling and Grindability Indexes of United States Coals," U. S. Bureau of Mines, Information Circular 8025. Washington: U. S. Bureau of Mines, 1961.

[9] F. Nowak, "Considerations in the Construction of Large Refuse Incinerators," *Proceedings of the 1970 National Incinerator Conference*, Cincinnati, May 17–20, 1970. Sponsored by ASME Incinerator Division. New York: American Society of Mechanical Engineers, 1970, pp 86–97.

[10] J. W. Regan, "Generating Steam from Prepared Refuse," *Proceedings of the 1970 National Incinerator Conference*, Cincinnati, May 17–20, 1970. Sponsored by ASME Incinerator Division. New York: American Society of Mechanical Engineers, 1970, pp 216–223.

[11] ASME 71–WA/Inc–1

by A. D. Konopka—Systems Evaluation of Refuse as a Low Sulfur Fuel: Pt. 3–Air Pollution Aspects.

/Inc–2

by R. E. Sommerlad, et. al.—Systems Evaluation of Refuse as a Low Sulfur Fuel: Pt. 2—Steam Generator Aspects.

/Inc–3

by A. M. Roberts and E. M. Wilson—Systems Evaluation of Refuse as a Low Sulfur Fuel: Pt. 1—The Value of Refuse Energy and the Cost of Its Recovery.

Presented at the ASME Winter Annual Meeting, Washington, D. C., Nov. 28–Dec. 2, 1971. New York: American Society of Mechanical Engineers, 1971.

[12] John T. Pfeffer, *Reclamation of Energy from Organic Waste: Final Report.* Report No. PB-231-176 (EPA-670/2-74-016), prepared under EPA grant No. EPA-1P-80766, Department of Civil Engineering, University of Illinois, Urbana, Illinois, Mar. 1974. Springfield, Va.: National Technical Information Service.

[13] W. E. Franklin, D. Rendersky, L. J. Shanon, and W. A. Park, *Resource Recovery: Catalogue of Processes*, Report No. PB-214 148, Midwest Research Institute, Kansas City, Mo., Feb. 1973. Springfield, Va.: National Technical Information Service.

[14] W. E. Franklin, D. Bendersky, L. J. Shannon, and W. R. Park, *Resource Recovery: The State of Technology*, Report No. PB-214 149, Midwest Research Institute, Kansas City,

February, 1973. Springfield, Va.: National Technical Information Service.

[15] Gerald E. Dreifke, David L. Klumb, and Jerrel D. Smith, "Solid Waste as a Utility Fuel," *Proceedings of the American Power Conference*, Vol. 35: 1198–1206. Chicago: Illinois Institute of Technology, 1973.

[16] D. Joseph Hagerty, et al., *Solid Waste Management.* New York: Van Nostrand Reinhold Co., 1973.

[17] Joseph G. Singer and Joseph F. Mullen, *Closing the Refuse Power Cycle*, presented at the ASME–IEEE Joint Power Generation Conference, New Orleans, Sept. 16–19, 1973, ASME Paper-73-PWR-18.

[18] Robert A. Lowe, *Energy Recovery from Waste: Solid Waste as Supplementary Fuel in Power Plant Boilers*, Report No. PB-256 494 (EPA-SW-36d. ii), Grant No. S-802255, prepared by the City of St. Louis, Mo. in cooperation with Union Electric Co., St. Louis, Mo., 1973.

[19] John H. Fernandes and R. C. Shenk, "The Place of Incineration in Resource Recovery of Solid Waste," *Proceedings of the 1974 National Incinerator Conference*, Miami, May 12–15, 1974: Resource Recovery Through Incineration, 1–10, sponsored by the ASME Incinerator Division. New York: American Society of Mechanical Engineers, 1974.

[20] *ASTM Standards*, Parts 15, 24, and 140, D 2161, "Standard Method for Conversion of Kinematic Viscosity to Saybolt Universal Viscosity or to Saybolt Furol Viscosity." Philadelphia: American Society for Testing and Materials, latest edition.

[21] C. E. Lucke, *Engineering Thermodynamics.* New York: Columbia University Press, 1941.

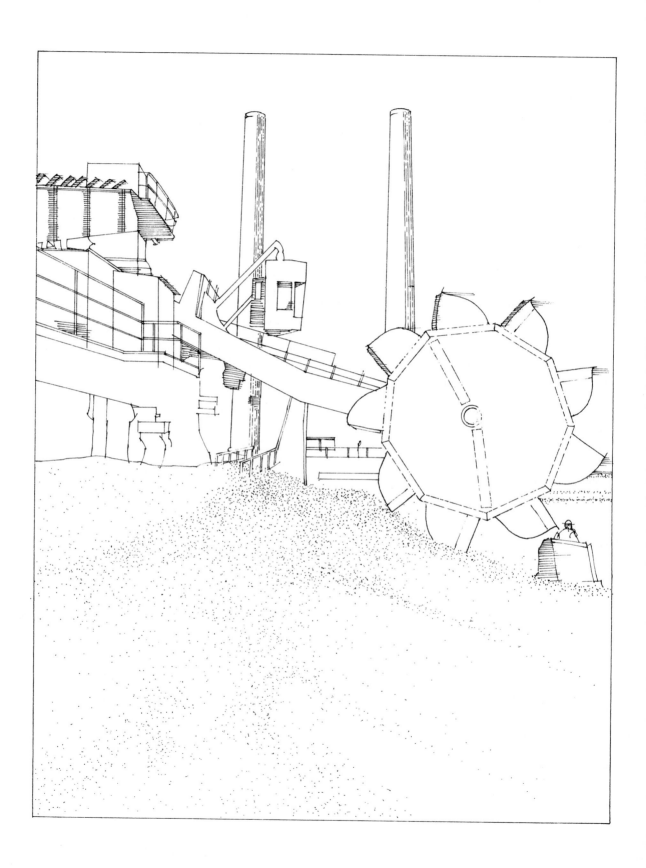

CHAPTER 3

Properties of Coal Ash

As mined, coal contains varying quantities of mineral matter which, when the coal is burned, results in the incombustible residue known as ash. Most of this mineral matter was carried in by wind and water; only a small fraction was inherent in the original vegetation. The mineral matter from which ash is formed is an undesirable substance in the coal. An inert material on which freight must be paid, it must be removed from the furnace as fast as it accumulates; otherwise, it may cause interruption in operation. Also, provision must be made for handling and disposing of the ash, both functions representing items of cost.

The mineral matter of coal cannot be completely separated by any physical method to identify fully the individual minerals or to determine them quantitatively. Therefore, to assess the amounts of the major elements present in coal, an analysis is made to determine the percentages of the oxides of these elements present in the coal ash.

The ash analysis does not indicate the nature or distribution of the mineral matter but, nevertheless, provides information which is useful in both the study and the utilization of coal. Examination of many coal-ash analyses shows, in almost all cases, that oxides of silicon, aluminum, iron, calcium and magnesium account for 95 percent or more of the ash. Of the other components present, oxides of sodium and potassium are important only as they act as fluxes in fusing the ash.

ASH IN COAL: PRINCIPAL DESIGN FACTOR

The management of this coal ash is one of the major considerations in the design of a pulverized-coal steam generator. The behavior of the mineral matter in a coal, as it influences slagging reactions during the combustion process, is a significant factor in furnace sizing in terms of volume, plan area, and fuel-burning zone. Mineral matter formed as tenacious deposits on waterwall surfaces insulates the heat-transfer portions of the furnace—thus, the ash properties affect the disposition of both radiant and convective heating surface, as well as the number of furnace-wall cleaning devices usually known as sootblowers.

The behavior of this mineral matter, as it influences fouling of convection-type surfaces, affects the amount of such surfaces, their spacing, and the quantity of sootblowers for cleaning these heat transfer surfaces.

And the percentage of this mineral matter in the coal is significant because of the amount of slagging and fouling that it can cause, the burden that it places on ash-handling equipment and disposal facilities, the frequency and length of sootblowing, and the rate of wear of pulverizer parts. Thus, for any given chemical and physical properties of coal ash, their net effect on the boiler during a given time period will be directly proportional to the amount fired in the furnace.

A corollary of this observation on the management of ash is that completely de-ashed coal of any type or rank can be burned in a furnace designed specifically for oil or gas firing. That is to say, ash is what gives a coal its "character." Without ash, *all* furnaces could easily be designed on the basis of heat transfer only.

Students, designers, and users of large pulverized-coal boilers must realize that since the 1920's, substantial work has been done to establish "scientific" methods for the sizing of furnaces. Further, during these years, much has been learned about the ways in which certain coals (and their ash) act in different sizes and types of furnaces.

But it must be understood and accepted that, as the art exists today, engineering judgment, based upon what we know about the ash in a coal (based on ASTM analyses and other parametric data) and how that ash has "behaved" in actual furnace operation, is the only guide to sizing new and larger furnaces.

In this chapter, then, most of the useful physical and chemical properties of ash are given. Useful parameters for categorizing ash also are

Table I. Coal-Ash Chemical Composition Ranges

Oxide Component	Percentage
SiO_2	10–70
Al_2O_3	8–38
Fe_2O_3	2–50
CaO	0.5–30
MgO	0.3–8
Na_2O	0.1–8
K_2O	0.1–3
TiO_2	0.4–3.5
SO_3	0.1–30

presented and discussed—all as they relate to slagging and fouling of boiler surfaces. Methods of ash analysis that have been developed recently are described; and the mechanism of fire-side metal loss by either corrosion or erosion caused by fuel ash is covered. Appendix C contains additional engineering data on other significant ash properties. All such information is of vital concern to engineers making decisions about furnace size and heating-surface arrangements.

COMPOSITION OF COAL ASH

Coal ash consists almost entirely of metal oxides. The composition varies over a wide range, and there is no "typical" ash analysis.

CHEMICAL ANALYSES

Chemical analyses of coal ash provide data from which to estimate coal-ash and slag characteristics, as well as calculate various correlation parameters. Analyses are generally performed on ash prepared to *ASTM Standards D 3174, Ash in the Analyses Sample of Coal and Coke.* Pulverized coal is burned in a ceramic crucible, in air, at 1290–1380°F, to completion (except for the ash residue).

Chemical analyses of coal ash are reported as the mass percent of each equivalent oxide and are generally expressed as:

$$SiO_2 + Al_2O_3 + Fe_2O_3 + CaO + MgO + Na_2O + K_2O + TiO_2 + P_2O_5 + SO_3 = 100\%$$

(1)

Because it is usually present in insignificant quantities, P_2O_5 is sometimes omitted.

Table I gives the ranges of the chemical composition of most coal ash.[1]

Research has shown that the chemical composition of coal ash prepared to *ASTM Standards D 3174* is different from that of flyash, bottom ash, or waterwall slag as they occur in actual boiler furnaces. However, because few adequate alternatives have been established, coal ash and slag behavior commonly are estimated using the chemical composition of the ash. Methods involving gravity separation of pulverized-coal fractions can be used in an effort to simulate the segregation effects in an actual furnace. (See the section of this chapter on Selective Deposition of Ash Constituents.)

MINERALOGICAL ANALYSES

Mineralogical analyses of coal ash attempt to identify the original mineral-matter forms in coal. The thermal behavior of coal ash in an operating furnace largely depends on the reactions between the ash-forming minerals, which cannot be detected by the ordinary chemical analyses. Accordingly, it can be argued that coal-ash and slag behavior should be characterized by its mineralogical composition and not by its chemical composition. However, to date, neither a standard procedure for the low-temperature ashing technique nor a criterion for mineral detection has been established.

Mineralogical analyses of coal ash can be performed either on ash prepared according to *ASTM Standards* D 3174 or, preferably, on ash prepared according to the low-temperature ashing technique. Low-temperature ash is produced by placing pulverized-coal samples in an oxygen plasma at approximately 400°F. The oxygen will gradually break down the organic matter without excessive thermal decomposition of the inorganic mineral species.

At least a hundred mineral species are associated with coal. Table II lists the more abundant mineral forms.

Thermal reactions among ash-forming minerals are an important, although very complex, subject. Fig. 1 gives an overview of important steps during the heating of mineral matter.

CHEMICAL REACTIONS DURING COMBUSTION

Most ash constituents will not be in the form shown in Table I when the coal goes to the fur-

Table II. Typical Mineral Species Found in Coal

Mineral Species	Formula
Kaolinite	$Al_2O_3 \cdot 2SiO_2 \cdot H_2O$
Illite	$K_2O \cdot 3Al_2O_3 \cdot 6SiO_2 \cdot 2H_2O$
Muscovite	$K_2O \cdot 3Al_2O_3 \cdot 6SiO_2 \cdot 2H_2O$
Biotite	$K_2O \cdot MgO \cdot Al_2O_3 \cdot 3SiO_2 \cdot H_2O$
Orthoclase	$K_2O \cdot Al_2O_3 \cdot 6SiO_2$
Albite	$Na_2O \cdot Al_2O_3 \cdot 6SiO_2$
Calcite	$CaCO_3$
Dolomite	$CaCO_3 \cdot MgCO_3$
Siderite	$FeCO_3$
Pyrite	FeS_2
Gypsum	$CaSO_4 \cdot 2H_2O$
Quartz	SiO_2
Hematite	Fe_2O_3
Magnetite	Fe_3O_4
Rutile	TiO_2
Halite	$NaCl$
Sylvite	KCl

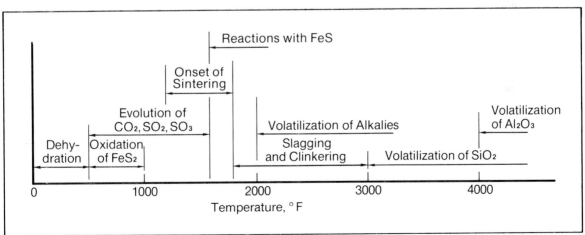

Fig. 1 Effect of heating on coal mineral matter

nace. As has been pointed out, the bulk of the ash is mineral matter brought in by water, and is largely a mixture of the various compounds. These compounds change considerably as they pass through the furnace and are subjected to high furnace temperature. Chemical reactions take place among these substances, and also between them and the reducing gases and hot carbon. They form new and more complex compounds, usually containing less oxygen than the original constituents, because the oxygen is taken away by the reducing gases and hot carbon. This is particularly true of the ferric oxide, Fe_2O_3, which occurs in the coal largely as pyrites, FeS_2. This may be reduced to FeS or to the lower oxides, Fe_3O_4 and FeO, or even metallic iron, Fe. The lower sulfide and oxides have lower softening and fusion temperatures. While going through the fusion state, the new compounds form solutions, and this change further lowers the fusion temperature.

As a rule, ash high in SiO_2 or alumina has high softening temperature, and this temperature is not greatly affected by reducing atmosphere. The alkali metal compounds Na_2O and K_2O, as well as the alkaline earth, magnesium oxide, tend to lower the softening temperature of the ash.

IRON IN COAL ASH

Iron compounds are responsible for much of the misbehavior of coal ash. Therefore, coals with ash high in iron are always suspected of causing trouble. If the ash, and particularly the iron, is uniformly distributed through the coal, difficulties are more likely to occur than if the iron compounds are in large pieces, separated from the coal. When the coal is pulverized, the larger and heavier pieces of ash are rejected by some pulverizers and do not go through the furnace. In screenings with a high percent of fines, the ash is uniformly distributed through the coal, and therefore compounds of iron are likely to cause trouble.

In pulverized-coal firing, there may be a considerable separation of the different constituents of the ash. The ash deposited at the furnace bottom will have chemical composition and physical properties different from those of the ash carried by the gases.

In slagging- or wet-bottom pulverized-coal furnaces, a considerable part of the iron compounds in the slag may be reduced to metallic iron, which sinks to the bottom of the molten slag and is difficult to remove in either hot or cold state.

In some coals, the iron is in the form of pyrite, FeS_2, which, while passing through the furnace, undergoes various changes. Both the iron and the sulfur may combine with oxygen, iron forming the lower oxides and sulfur, SO_2 or SO_3. Sulfur may also combine with the alkaline metals, Na and K, to form sulfur compounds, which have very low fusion temperature. In slagging-bottom furnaces, where the molten ash remains in a liquid state over extended periods of time, some of these sodium and potassium sulfur compounds are vaporized, then condensed on watercooled furnace walls, and may become an important factor in external corrosion of furnace-wall tubes.

COAL-ASH SLAGGING AND DEPOSITION

A number of parameters are used for evaluating coal-ash behavior as they affect furnace slagging and deposition on both the furnace walls and convection surfaces. Some of these parameters are

- ash-fusibility temperatures
- base/acid ratio
- iron/calcium ratio
- silica/alumina ratio
- iron/dolomite ratio
- dolomite percentage
- ferric percentage.

Such indices help organize the ash composition into "building blocks" that lend insight to expected behavior under burning conditions.

Some confusion exists between the terms *slag* and *deposits* (or deposition). Definitions as they apply to pulverized-coal firing are:
1. *Slag*—fused deposits or resolidified molten

material that forms primarily on furnace walls or other surfaces exposed predominately to radiant heat or excessively high gas temperatures.

2. *Deposits*—bonded (sintered or cemented) ash buildup that forms primarily on such convection surfaces as superheater and reheater tubes but also on furnace walls at lower than slag-producing temperatures.

A summary of ash properties in terms of slagging and deposition is given in the following sections of this chapter.

MEASURING ASH-FUSIBILITY TEMPERATURES

Ash fusibility has long been recognized as a tool for measuring the performance of coals related to slagging and deposit buildup. It is still perhaps the most basic means for predicting coal-ash performance. Other parameters are used primarily to explain or amplify ash-fusibility temperatures. In general, high fusion temperatures result in low slagging potential in dry-bottom furnaces, while low fusion temperatures are considered mandatory for wet-bottom (slag-tap) furnaces.

Many experimental methods have been developed for measuring the fusion temperatures of coal ash. Most tests are based on the gradual thermal deformation of a coal-ash sample, and the characteristic fusion temperatures are reported when the sample fuses into certain distinctive shapes or heights. Most test methods are strictly empirical and have little theoretical basis. The following descriptions characterize some of the methods.

ASTM STANDARDS METHOD

ASTM Standards D 1857, Fusibility of Coal Ash, gives the experimental procedure for one method of testing. The test is based on the gradual thermal deformation of a pyramid-shaped ash sample, 3/4 inch in height and 1/4 inch in equilateral-triangular base width. Mounted on a refractory substrate, the sample is heated at a prescribed rate in a gas or electric furnace. A controlled atmosphere (reducing or oxidizing, depending upon the tests to be per-

formed) is maintained inside the furnace. During the heating process, changes in the shape of the pyramid are observed, Fig. 2, and the following four characteristic deformation temperatures are reported:

1. Initial Deformation Temperature (IT): The temperature at which the tip of the ash pyramid begins to show any evidence of deformation. Shrinkage of the cone is ignored if the tip remains sharp.

2. Softening Temperature (ST), H = W: The temperature at which the ash sample has fused into a spherical shape in which the height is equal to the width at the base. The H = W softening temperature in a reducing atmosphere frequently is referred to as the "fusion temperature."

3. Hemispherical Temperature (HT), H = 1/2W: The temperature at which the ash sample has fused into a hemispherical shape where the height is equal to 1/2 the width at the base.

4. Fluid Temperature (FT): The temperature at which the ash sample has fused down into a nearly flat layer with a maximum height of 1/16 inch.

Prior to the revision of *ASTM Standards* D 1857, only three characteristic deformation temperatures (initial deformation, softening, and fluid) were observed with no dimensional (height-to-width) specifications for the softening and fluid points. Because of such differ-

1.		Cone Before Heating
2.	IT (or ID)	Initial Deformation Temperature
3.	ST	Softening Temperature (H=W)
4.	HT	Hemispherical Temperature (H=½W)
5.	FT	Fluid Temperature

Fig. 2 Critical temperature points as defined in *ASTM Standards* D 1857

ences in definitions, earlier investigations have reported the softening temperatures without distinguishing between their being spherical or hemispherical. Unless specified otherwise, the softening temperature may be assumed to represent the spherical point, where H = W.

Although the earlier standard procedure used only reducing atmospheres for the tests, many studies give the ash-fusion temperatures without specifying the atmosphere; it thus must be assumed that the tests were carried out in a reducing atmosphere.

BRITISH STANDARD METHOD

In principle, the British standard method is similar to the ASTM method, but differs from it in several experimental specifications. B.S. 1016, Part 15, gives the procedure for this method of testing. The British method specifies that the ash sample be a pyramid of 8 to 13 mm in height with the height 2 to 3 times the width of the triangular base. Mounted on a refractory substrate, the sample is heated at a prescribed rate in an electric furnace with a controlled atmosphere (either reducing or oxidizing) maintained inside the furnace. During the heating process, changes in the sample shape are observed through a magnifying optical instrument and the following three characteristic deformation temperatures are reported:

1. Initial Deformation Temperature: The temperature at which the tip of the ash pyramid begins to show any evidence of deformation.
2. Hemispherical Temperature: The temperature at which the ash sample has fused into a hemispherical shape where the height is equal to ½ the width.
3. Flow Temperature: The temperature at which the ash sample has fused into a flattened disk shape such that the height is ⅙ the width.

GERMAN STANDARD METHOD

German Standard DIN 51 730 describes the procedure for this method of testing. The test is based on the gradual thermal deformation of a cylindric sample of coal ash, 3 mm in height and 3 mm in diameter, or a cubic sample of coal ash with 3 mm edges. The sample is mounted on a platinum-covered refractory substrate, which is placed on an electric heating element. The heating element, together with the ash sample, is inserted into a small furnace and heated at a prescribed rate. A controlled atmosphere (either reducing or oxidizing) is maintained inside the furnace. An image of the sample is projected onto a graduated screen so that changes in the shape of the ash can be observed. The following three characteristic temperatures are reported:

1. Softening Temperature: The temperature at which the first indication of softening appears, mainly in the form of rounding of the edges or swelling of the sample.
2. Hemispherical Temperature: The temperature at which the ash sample has fused into a hemispherical shape where the height is equal to ½ the base width.
3. Flow Temperature: The temperature at which the ash sample has fused into a flattened disk such that the height is reduced to ⅓ the original sample height.

OTHER METHODS

Similar to the German method in experimental procedure and specifications, the International Standard Method, ISO 540, requires the observation of three characteristic temperatures—initial deformation, hemispherical, and flow. However, a greater latitude is allowed in the shapes and dimensions of the ash sample, because it has been shown that geometrical variations in the sample, within certain limits, have little influence on the observed results.

The Russian experimental procedure (GOST 2057–68) is similar to the German; characteristic deformation temperatures reported during the heating of the sample are the deformation temperature, the softening (hemispherical) temperature, and the temperature of beginning of liquid fused state.

RELATION BETWEEN CHEMICAL AND MINERALOGICAL COMPOSITION

Barrett[2], Estep et al[3], and Thiessen et al[4] have shown that the fusion behavior of coal ashes is quite similar to that of the corresponding oxide mixtures. Barrett concluded that, if coal ashes are finely ground, intimately mixed, and brought to the same standard state before the fusion tests are made, then, (1) the fusion temperatures depend only on the composition and not on the manner in which the composition is obtained; and (2) the softening temperature is closely related to the equilibrium phase diagram of the corresponding oxide components which make up the ashes.

ASH-SOFTENING TEMPERATURE RELATIONSHIP TO DEPOSIT REMOVAL

If ash arrives at a heat-absorbing surface at a temperature near its softening temperature, the resulting deposit is likely to be porous in structure. Depending on the strength of the bond, it may fall off the metal surfaces from its own weight or it can be removed by sootblowing. If such a deposit is permitted to build up in a zone of high gas temperature, its surface (because of the insulating properties of the ash) can reach the melting point and then run down the wall surfaces in the furnace.

If ash particles arrive at the heat-absorbing surface at temperatures below the softening temperature, they will not form a bonded structure, but instead, will settle out as dust. As such, removal is comparatively simple.

On the other hand, if ash particles have been subjected to temperatures higher than the softening temperature for a sufficient time to become plastic or liquid, the resulting deposit will be a coarse, fused mass condensed on the cooler metal surface. The resolidified material is tightly bonded and difficult to remove. As this material builds up on itself, its insulating properties continuously increase the surface temperatures until the fluid temperature is reached and slag runoff results.

INITIAL DEFORMATION-FLUID TEMPERATURE DIFFERENTIAL

The temperature differential between initial deformation and fluid temperatures gives an insight as to the type of deposit formation to expect on furnace tube surfaces. A small tem-perature spread from initial deformation to fluid temperatures indicates that the wall slag will be thin, running and tenacious. This type of slag is extremely difficult to control by sootblowing. As the range from initial deformation to fluid temperature increases, the resulting slag deposit will build up to thicker proportions before the surface becomes sufficiently liquid to run. The tube-ash bond is less adhesive and therefore responds better to removal by sootblowing.

PROPERTIES OF COAL-ASH COMPONENTS

The acidic oxide constituents SiO_2, Al_2O_3, and TiO_2 found in coal ash are generally considered to produce high melting temperatures. Temperatures will be lowered proportionally by the relative amounts of basic oxides, Fe_2O_3, CaO, MgO, Na_2O, and K_2O available in the ash for reaction. Minerals associated with coals consist of multiple combinations of elements listed in the first column of Table III. If these elements were each exposed to air under the proper heat conditions, each would be converted to its highest form of oxide. Individual melting temperatures of these oxides are listed in the third column, and, assuming no interaction between them, the melting temperature of the ash would be represented by the weighted average of the oxides. But an interaction takes place at elevated temperatures that produces complex salts having entirely different physical constants. Among other changes, the melting temperatures of the compounds are usually lowered. The table lists some of the combinations, with melting temperatures.

The sum of the noted acidic components can range from 20 to 90 percent of the ash. Generally, highly acid coal ashes have high ash-fusion temperatures and high slag viscosities.

The sum of the basic components can be between 5 and 80 percent. Either high or low basic values can result in high fusion temperatures. Minimum fusion temperatures occur at about 30 to 40 percent basic component.

BASE/ACID RATIO

This index is defined as:

$$\frac{B}{A} = \frac{Fe_2O_3 + CaO + MgO + Na_2O + K_2O}{SiO_2 + Al_2O_3 + TiO_2} \tag{2}$$

Because most elements combine with each other according to their acidic or basic properties, the base/acid ratio reflects a potential for ash-containing metals to combine in the combustion process to produce low melting salts. Extremes at either end of the base/acid ratio indicate a minimum potential for forming combinations with low fusibility temperatures. Note that the alkaline metals, sodium and potassium, are exceptions in that they form low-melting ash regardless of the base/acid combinations: therefore, their presence in an ash composition in sufficient concentrations significantly alters base/acid influences.

Although the base/acid ratio is an indication of the fusion characteristics and slagging potential of a coal ash, it should not be used as the sole criterion of evaluation. A simple ratio such as the base/acid ratio does not take into account differences in fluxing action among the several bases nor does it recognize the degrees of interaction with the acidic components. (*Fluxing property,* in this connotation, is defined as a property of the component or substance which lowers the fusion temperature of the mixture; the terms *flux* and *fluxing property* are also used to describe the lowering in viscosity of a liquid mixture.)

Also, an ash in which the major constituents are alumina and iron will have different slagging characteristics from an ash in which the components include higher percentages of silica and calcium and yet both can have the same base/acid ratio.

In any case, the base/acid ratio is a valuable supplement to ash-fusibility temperatures and other data in predicting the relative performance of coal ash in the furnace. With most ash, a base/acid ratio in the 0.4 to 0.7 range manifests low ash-fusibility temperatures and a higher slagging potential.

SILICA/ALUMINA RATIO

The silica/alumina ratio is defined as:

$$\frac{SiO_2}{Al_2O_3} \tag{3}$$

The general range of values is between 0.8 and 4.0.

The silica/alumina ratio can provide additional information relating to ash fusibility. As both of these constituents are acidic and are, therefore, considered high melting as oxides, silica is more likely to form lower melting species (silicates) with basic constituents than is alumina. For two coals having equal base/acid ratios, the one with a higher silica/alumina ratio should have lower fusibility temperatures.

Table III. Properties of Coal-Ash Components

Element	Oxide	Melting Temp (°F)	Chemical Property	Compound	Melting Temp (°F)
Si	SiO_2	3120	Acidic	Na_2SiO_3	1610
Al	Al_2O_3	3710	Acidic	K_2SiO_3	1790
Ti	TiO_2	3340	Acidic	$Al_2O_3 \cdot Na_2O \cdot 6SiO_2$	2010
Fe	Fe_2O_3	2850	Basic	$Al_2O_3 \cdot K_2O \cdot 6SiO_2$	2100
Ca	CaO	4570	Basic	$FeSiO_3$	2090
Mg	MgO	5070	Basic	$CaO \cdot Fe_2O_3$	2280
Na	Na_2O	Sublimes at 2330	Basic	$CaO \cdot MgO \cdot 2SiO_2$	2535
K	K_2O	Decomposes at 660	Basic	$CaSiO_3$	2804

Effects of increasing amounts of alumina on the formation of the silicates depend on the amount and the combination of bases present, temperature and time of reaction, and other factors. A finite evaluation is virtually impossible because of the complex interactions. Fig. 3 illustrates the effect of silica/alumina ratios on ash-fusibility temperatures. In laboratory investigations, varying proportions of silica and alumina were mixed with an Illinois coal and then burned in a muffle furnace used to prepare ash for fusibility determinations. Fusibility temperatures were determined in a reducing atmosphere. According to these data, no appreciable change is noted between silica/ alumina ratios of 1.7 and 2.8. At ratios less than 1.7, the softening and fluid temperatures both increase; at ratios greater than 2.8, the fluid temperature decreases. Initial deformation temperatures were not affected by any wide changes in ratios.

Fig. 3 Ash-fusibility temperatures as affected by silica/alumina ratios (C-E laboratory data)

IRON/CALCIUM RATIO

This parameter, also known as the iron-oxide/calcium-oxide ratio, is defined as:

$$\frac{Fe_2O_3}{CaO}$$

(4)

As indicated, the base/acid ratio does not account for differences in fluxing action. Among the five basic-oxide components, iron and calcium are the most important, primarily because they make up the largest amount of the basic constituents. Iron oxides comprise 5 to 40 percent of the ash and calcium oxides make up 2 to 30 percent. The following statements, extracted from ref. 5, relate the iron-calcium relationship to the fusibility of ash.

"1. In the absence of lime, iron oxides do not make the most fusible slags."

"2. Ferric oxide, up to about 20 percent, has a fluxing effect which increases with the percentage, but above 20 and up to 40 percent it does not materially increase the fusibility."

"3. The combined fluxing effect of iron oxides and lime has a complex relation to the percentage of the two fluxes present. For ashes in which the percentage of iron oxide is over 14 percent, the addition of a given percentage of lime produces a lowering of the fusion temperatures greater than the same additional percentage of iron oxide."

"4. The quantity of magnesia present in coal ashes is usually smaller than the lime; its fluxing effect with lime present is greater than that of an equal additional amount of lime in about the ratio of 3:2."

Comparisons such as the following confirm this decrease.

Coal	Fe_2O_3	CaO	Fe_2O_3/CaO Ratio	Softening Temperature, °F
(1)	31.8	0.3	106.0	2360
(2)	24.8	2.0	12.4	2270
(3)	21.3	4.8	4.4	2130

The iron/calcium ratios of the three examples are 106, 12.4 and 4.4 respectively. Fig. 4 shows the effect of limestone addition to fusibility temperatures on an Eastern U.S. coal. Based on these two data sources as well as observation of other fusibility-ash composition relationships, Fe_2O_3/CaO ratios between 10 and 0.2 have a marked effect on lowering the fusibility temperatures of coal ash. Extreme effects are evident between ratios of 3 and 0.3.

IRON/DOLOMITE RATIO

The iron-oxide/dolomite ratio is defined as:

$$\frac{Fe_2O_3}{CaO + MgO} \quad (5)$$

This parameter is essentially identical to the Fe_2O_3/CaO ratio. CaO and MgO have been

found to have similar fluxing properties, and the use of this ratio is recommended when the MgO content of the ash is high.

Bituminous-type ash is characterized by an iron-oxide/dolomite ratio greater than one, while lignitic ash has $Fe_2O_3/CaO + MgO$ in a ratio that is less than one.

DOLOMITE PERCENTAGE (DP)

This is defined as:

$$DP = \left(\frac{CaO + MgO}{Fe_2O_3 + CaO + MgO + Na_2O + K_2O} \right) \times 100 \quad (6)$$

This parameter is used primarily for coal ashes with a basic-oxide content over 40 percent. It has been empirically related to the viscosity of coal-ash slags.[6] Its general range is from 40 to 98 percent. At a given percent basic, a higher DP usually results in higher fusion temperatures and higher slag viscosities.

EQUIVALENT Fe_2O_3 AND FERRIC PERCENTAGE (FP)

These parameters describe the degree of iron oxidation in coal-ash slags. They are defined as:

$$Equiv.\ Fe_2O_3 = Fe_2O_3 + 1.11\ FeO + 1.43\ Fe,\ \text{and}$$

$$FP = \left(\frac{Fe_2O_3}{Equiv.\ Fe_2O_3} \right) \times 100 \quad (7)$$

These terms were introduced when it was observed that the ash-fusion temperatures and slag-crystallization temperatures were lower in a reducing atmosphere than in an oxidizing atmosphere. Experiments showed that this deviation was due to the different forms of iron oxide that could exist depending on the surrounding atmosphere. It was concluded that FeO and Fe are stronger fluxing agents than Fe_2O_3 and result in depression of ash-fusion and slag-crystallization temperatures. Thus, equivalent Fe_2O_3 and FP depend on combus-

Fig. 4 Ash-fusibility temperatures of an Eastern coal as affected by limestone addition

tion conditions and are usually determined by chemical analysis of actual furnace slags.

In *ASTM Standards* D 1857, it has been specified that a reducing atmosphere should contain a mixture of oxidizing and reducing gases in which the content of the oxidizing gas is within the limits 20 to 80 percent by volume. In this range of gaseous composition, the iron is mainly in the ferrous state, FeO. Under stronger oxidizing conditions, the iron is mainly in the ferric state, Fe_2O_3; under more reducing conditions, the iron is mainly in the metallic state, Fe.

SILICA PERCENTAGE (SP)

This relationship is defined as:

$$SP = \left(\frac{SiO_2}{SiO_2 + Equiv.\ Fe_2O_3 + CaO + MgO} \right) \times 100$$

$$(8)$$

SP, which has a range of 35 to 90 percent, has been empirically correlated with the viscosity of coal-ash slags. As SP increases, the slag viscosity increases. (Silica percentage is also occasionally referred to as silica ratio or equivalent silica content.)

TOTAL ALKALIES (Na₂O + K₂O)

As previously noted, sodium and potassium metals join with other elements in combinations that produce low fusibility temperatures. The influence of alkalies on fusibility and slagging potential in the furnace is proportional to the quantity in the ash.

With sodium-containing coals, the rate of buildup and the ability to control deposits effectively seem to be related to the amount of sodium present. This is particularly true of coals with lignitic-type ash (low iron, high alkali, and high-alkaline earths) as found primarily in U.S. coals west of the Mississippi. The ash of such coals will contain CaO as high as 40 percent and the sodium oxide may range from 1 to 15 percent, as extremes.

DEPOSITS: WESTERN-TYPE ASH

Fouling studies at the U. S. Bureau of Mines, Grand Forks, North Dakota have shown a relationship of the sodium in the ash and the fouling rate; those coals with less than 3 percent sodium oxides in the ash were found to be "low fouling" and as the sodium increased above this figure, the fouling rate increased proportionately.[7]

Most sodium compounds melt at temperatures below 900°C (1650°F). In addition, sodium solids manifest a property beyond melting temperatures alone that contributes to deposit building. Besides low melting temperatures, some sodium compounds volatilize at relatively low temperatures. These disperse throughout the gas stream and subsequently condense on other ash particles and on metal surfaces as heat is absorbed and gas temperatures are lowered. The condensed sodium provides a binding matrix for ash particles to fuse together and build up on tube surfaces.[8, 9]

Sodium oxide is transformed directly from a solid to a gaseous state at 2350°F. Because certain lignites and low-rank coals may have sodium that is organically bound, they are particularly susceptible to the formation of sodium oxide and consequent vaporization in the combustion zone. The sodium is released to a free state as the organics are consumed in the flame and are immediately available for vaporization into the gas stream. On the other hand, sodium tied up as mineral salts must be first decomposed to a free state before it is available for vaporization and, therefore, may not be as proportionally active.

A widespread distribution of sodium vapor in the combustion gases assures contact with ash particles and metal surfaces as the gas cools and the sodium condenses. Thus, particle surfaces are "conditioned" for bonding and the resulting deposit forms rapidly. The rate of buildup is proportional to the amount of active sodium in the coal. This phenomenon applies particularly to high-alkali ash defined as Western U.S. type ash. Because deposit buildup is rapid with such coals, tube spacing in convective passes must be maintained on wide centers to minimize bridging.

DEPOSITS: EASTERN-TYPE ASH

Because ash compositions differ, criteria for evaluating Eastern-type coals are somewhat different from those for Western coals. Eastern coals are characterized as high iron and low-alkali/alkaline-earth content; the ash composition of such coals reflects an Fe_2O_3 level exceeding the combined CaO, MgO, Na_2O and K_2O percentage. In addition, sulfur percentages are higher than Western coals and lignites. Superheater-reheater bonded deposits from such coals are primarily complex alkali-iron sulfates. These are generally tightly bonded, more dense, more corrosive, and less receptive to removal by sootblowing. Again, alkaline compounds (chiefly sodium) are a contributing factor to the buildup. Volatile sodium, in particular, contributes to furnace fouling, even at levels of less than 2 percent of the ash. The presence of both iron and sulfur to combine with volatile sodium is conducive to the formation of complex iron-alkali sulfates.

Sodium present in the form of silicates has less tendency to cause fouling. H. E. Crossley in his Melchett lecture to the Institute of Fuels in 1962 had this to say about alkalies in coal:

"It was known that alkalies existed in coal in two forms: chlorides and complex silicates. The chlorides could be expected to volatilize readily during combustion but the silicates could be expected to retain alkali in the ashes. Thus, if an attempt was made to relate the forms of alkali-rich deposits with alkali in coal, there could be presence of the complex silicates. It was decided instead to use the amount of chlorine as the index of volatile alkalies and this has been standard practice ever since. In consequence, the determination of chlorine has become an important item in the ultimate analysis of coals."[10] (This statement does not include or describe the mechanism of volatile sodium as found in lignitic-type coals.)

The chlorine content itself can be used as an indication of the fouling tendency of a coal, a fact which has been recognized not only in this country, but in England. Crossley classifies coals as follows:

Fouling Potential	Chlorine %, Coal Basis
High	Greater than 0.3
Medium	0.3 to 0.15
Low	Less than 0.15

American experience confirms that tightly bonded deposits in the convection areas can be expected when the chlorine level exceeds 0.30. Rather than depend on the measurement in the coal as the yardstick for evaluating the volatile or "active alkali," another approach is to measure the soluble sodium in the coal. The relationship of soluble sodium as measured and the chlorine, interpreted as sodium, is shown in the following table:

Fouling Potential	Cl%, Coal Basis	Equiv. Na %
High	Greater than 0.5	Greater than 0.33
Medium	0.3	0.2
Low	Less than 0.1	Less than 0.07

FORMS OF ALKALIES IN COAL

Alkalies can be present in coal in various forms. Alkalies which vaporize during combustion are often classified as active alkalies, because they are free to react or condense subsequently in the boiler. Active alkalies consist primarily of simple inorganic salts and organically bound alkalies. More stable forms of alkalies exist in impurities such as the clay and shale minerals which remain relatively inert during combustion, and therefore are less influential in the ash deposition process. Fig. 5 summarizes the different categories in which various alkali forms can be associated.

A TECHNIQUE FOR DISTINGUISHING ACTIVE FROM INACTIVE ALKALI

To segregate the different categories of alkalies, a technique has been developed utilizing a dilute acetic-acid medium. Leaching coal samples in a dilute acetic-acid solution exposes the coal to a source of hydrogen ions. It appears that an ion exchange possibility exists in which the hydrogen ions (H^+) of the acid displace or exchange with metallic elements associated with the organic coal molecules. These elements include sodium, potassium, calcium, and magnesium.

The weak acid used during leaching provides the hydrogen-ion source necessary to displace organically bound elements, but does not have the strong dissolving powers which would be necessary to break down the complex extraneous minerals. The constituents (in particular alkalies) removed from the coal essentially consist of the organically bound material along with the simple inorganic compounds. Alkalies present either in organic fractions or in simple inorganic salts can be expected to volatilize during combustion, and are therefore of primary interest.

RESULTS OF WEAK-ACID ANALYSIS

Analysis of acetic acid-soluble alkalies has been conducted on a cross-section of U.S. coals for which performance characteristics are well established through commercial operation.

Detailed data comparing the alkali contents of the ash of seven U.S. coals are summarized in Table IV. The ash varies in fouling tendencies from severe to low or minimal. Values presented for sodium in the ash were determined by the conventional ashing and lithium tetraborate fusion procedure.

In general, the coals containing high alkali contents and, in particular, high sodium contents had the most severe fouling tendencies. This is the expected trend. However, after studying the acetic-acid-soluble alkaline contents of the coals, one is better able to relate their fouling behavior. Past work has primarily focused on sodium as the bad-acting constituent responsible for fouling. It is possible to understand why sodium is frequently more influential than potassium by comparing the relative quantities of acetic-acid-soluble sodium and potassium in Table IV.

What is believed to be the primary reason that sodium has a greater influence is that sodium is frequently present in an active form, whereas potassium is typically contained in a less active form. Values for acetic-acid-soluble sodium in U.S. coals frequently range up to 10 times more than the soluble-potassium values. In many U.S. coals, much of the potassium appears to be tied up in extraneous clay minerals

Fig. 5 **Manner in which alkalies are contained in coal**

which do not break down readily when heated, making the potassium in this form less reactive. Although the potassium contents of these coals range from 0.5 to 1.9 percent K_2O in the ash, the acetic-acid-soluble potassium generally is equivalent to less than 0.1 percent K_2O in the ash. Conversely, the acetic-acid-sodium content of the high-fouling coals represents virtually all of the Na_2O detected in the ash.

The coals containing the most soluble alkali were low-rank coals (subbituminous coals and lignites). It is believed that such coals can contain substantial quantities of alkali (as well as alkaline-earth constituents) present as organi-

Table IV. Comparative Alkali Content of U.S. Coals

Rank Region	Lignite ND	Sub B MT	Lignite TX (Yegua)	Lignite TX (Wilcox)	hvBb UT	hvAb PA	Lignite TX (Wilcox)
HHV, Btu/lb, Dry Basis	10640	12130	7750	9710	12870	13200	8420
Ash Composition (%)							
SiO_2	20.0	33.9	62.1	52.3	52.5	51.1	57.9
Al_2O_3	9.1	11.4	15.1	17.4	18.9	30.7	21.8
Fe_2O_3	10.3	10.8	3.5	5.3	1.1	10.0	3.9
CaO	22.4	21.0	6.2	9.4	13.2	1.6	7.1
MgO	6.4	2.7	0.7	3.2	1.3	0.9	2.1
Na_2O	5.0	5.8	3.6	0.9	3.8	0.4	0.7
K_2O	0.5	1.6	1.9	1.2	0.9	1.7	0.8
TiO	0.4	0.7	0.9	1.2	1.2	2.0	1.1
SO_3	21.9	12.0	6.1	9.6	6.2	1.4	4.4
Fouling Potential	Severe	High	High	Moderate	Moderate	Low	Low
Lb Ash/10^6 Btu, Dry Basis	9.0	4.6	43.3	20.1	7.9	10.2	34.4
Acetic-Acid-Soluble							
Sodium (Na, ppm)	3980	2680	9650	1030	1120	250	340
Potassium (K, ppm)	. . .	. . .	1230	85	85	. . .	110
Alkali in Ash, % Wt.							
Na_2O	5.0	5.8	3.6	0.9	3.8	0.4	0.7
K_2O	0.5	1.6	1.9	1.2	0.9	1.7	0.8
Equiv. Sol. Alkali in Ash, % Wt. of Ash							
Na_2O	5.58	6.45	3.88	0.71	1.49	0.15	0.16
K_2O	. . .	. . .	0.44	0.04	0.08	. . .	0.05
% Sol. Alkali of Total (Equiv. Sol. Na_2O)/ (Na_2O in Ash)	112	111	108	79	39	38	23
(Lbs Sol. Na)/ (10^6 Btu Fired)	0.374	0.221	1.245	0.106	0.087	0.018	.040
(Lbs Sol. Na)/(lb Ash/ 10^6 Btu Fired)	0.044	0.048	0.223	0.005	0.014	0.002	0.001

cally bound humates. It appears that the potential for having organically bound metallic compounds decreases as the coal rank increases. The Utah high-volatile bituminous illustrates this tendency. This fuel contains a relatively high sodium content (3.8 percent Na_2O in ash). But the soluble sodium content is only about 40 percent of the "total" sodium and the overall fouling potential is low to moderate.

In the case of the particular coals selected, all of the high-fouling coals had quantities of soluble sodium greater than the "total" quantity of sodium detected in the ash by the conventional technique. The lower values for "total" sodium may be the result of a slight loss of organically bound material during the ashing process.

RELATION OF FOULING POTENTIAL TO ALKALI FORM

The data in Table IV indicate that fouling potential of coal ash is related to both total quantity of acetic-acid-soluble alkali and to the equivalent percentage of soluble alkali in ash. The total volatile alkali is believed to be reflected by furnace input of soluble alkali listed in Table IV as pounds of soluble sodium per million Btu fired. It is postulated that the deposition mechanism could involve the condensation of the gaseous alkali species which provides the sticky, bonding matrix to build convection-pass deposits. The greater the quantity of this "glue," the more severe the deposition. Conversely, the greater the quantity of ash particles, the thinner this "glue" would be spread. Because this bonding matrix is a surface phenomenon, it would depend on both the total quantity of vapor species and the diluting influence of the ash. Therefore, a combination of pounds of soluble sodium per million Btu fired and pounds of soluble sodium per pound of ash per million Btu fired should be used when evaluating the fouling potential of a fuel. (See Table IV, bottom two entries.)

VARIATION OF ASH PROPERTIES WITHIN A COAL SEAM

Note that it is possible to experience vastly different ash properties within the same coal seam. This point is illustrated with the two comparative lignites mined in Eastern Texas from the Wilcox formation. The sodium contents of the two lignites are very similar (0.9 percent and 0.7 percent Na_2O in ash respectively). However, the ash-fouling behavior of these fuels is significantly different, as vividly illustrated by the acetic-acid-soluble sodium contents of the coal. Roughly 80 percent of the sodium in the moderate-fouling Wilcox lignite could be considered active compared to only 23 percent for the low-fouling lignite. On a concentration basis (pounds of sodium per pound of ash per million Btu fired), the moderate-fouling lignite has more than 10 times that of the low-fouling lignite because of the ash dilution.

The acetic-acid-soluble technique is relatively new, such that the limited data thus far accumulated neither allow development of quantitative relationships nor define the reliability of the analysis. But the major value of the technique is the apparent sensitivity to the "active alkalies" present, which seem to be a predominant factor in high-fouling behavior.

SELECTIVE DEPOSITION OF ASH CONSTITUENTS

Several slagging and fouling indexes to predict the behavior of coal ash in furnaces during the combustion of coal have been reviewed in preceding text. These analyses consider a homogeneous distribution of the mineral matter throughout the coal matrix. Such an assumption may be applicable to stoker firing, where the coal particles, as fired, are relatively large, but may not be applicable in pulverized coal where the composition of mineral matter of individual particles can be quite different.[11, 12, 13] Because the behavior of an individual coal-ash particle depends upon its composition, *average* properties may not be an accurate index of the slagging and fouling potential of a coal.

Most evaluations of coal ash, including the determination of fusibility temperatures, do not consider the phenomenon of selective deposition when attempting to predict slagging and fouling behavior. The fractionation of a coal prior to a determination of fusibility temperatures can provide a better insight into what occurs within the furnace; i.e., individual particles of ash can act independently of one another with respect to their physical state and reactions in the flame. [14-17]

THE DISTRIBUTION OF MINERAL MATTER IN THE COAL MATRIX

Ash-fusibility temperatures as determined by ASTM procedures are the temperatures at which the composite ash sample initially deforms, softens, and becomes fluid. These values, as well as such ratios as base/acid, iron/calcium, and silica/alumina, provide a guide to the slagging and fouling characteristics of the coal being burned. But they do not predict how the various minerals behave during the combustion process. Ash deposits on furnace walls differ significantly from the ash of the as-fired coal. Use of the coal-ash fusibility values and the coal/ash ratios does not explain the selective deposition of ash constituents noted on furnace walls.

Table V shows the composition of deposits collected from a boiler burning a high-volatile bituminous coal and compares it with the composition of the as-fired ash. The most notable difference in the composition of these two samples is the iron content, the ash deposit having an iron content over three times as great as the coal ash as-fired. The amount of difference between as-fired ash and that taken from tube surfaces is a function of the distribution of mineral matter in the coal matrix.

These data suggest a mechanism that can explain why some coals slag more than conventional analysis would indicate. Coal is a heterogenous substance in terms of its organic and inorganic content. The coal-preparation engineer makes use of this knowledge in most beneficiation processes. Density differences or surface property differences are exploited when separating clean coal from the refuse or high-ash-containing parts of the coal. Also the potential for liberating the inorganic material increases as the coal is ground finer.

The pulverization of coal, then, increases the potential for liberating inorganic particles. It has been estimated by Moody and Langan[18] that 40 to 70 percent of the particles are pure coal (containing inherent mineral matter only), 20 to 40 percent occur as coal and mineral matter (extraneous as well as inherent), and 10 to 40 percent are pure mineral matter (extraneous only).

Comparing the composition of particles that result from pulverization can show an extreme difference in constituents. Because these particles are fired in suspension, the behavior of the mineral matter in a given particle will depend on the composition of that particle alone and, of course, the makeup of the surrounding gases. Each particle will reach a physical state (sticky, sintered, or molten) related to its *own* composition and reaction with surrounding gases; it will not be affected by the composition or physical state of other particles in suspension.

Fig. 6 illustrates a hypothetical breakdown of a lump of coal during pulverization. Certain portions of the coal may be enriched with specific minerals. When the parent lump has been pulverized, the composition of any given particle will depend on the local composition of the lump and is not representative of the average composition of the lump. When these particles are fired in a furnace, their propensity for depo-

Table V. Comparison of Ash Deposit Composition with As-Fired Coal Ash Composition

Ash Composition	As-Fired Coal Ash	Lower Furnace Ash Deposit
SiO_2	47.0	33.3
Al_2O_3	26.7	18.0
Fe_2O_3	14.6	43.5
CaO	2.2	1.2
MgO	0.7	0.5
Na_2O	0.4	0.2
K_2O	2.3	1.6
TiO_2	1.3	0.8
P_2O_5	0.9	0.4
SO_3	1.1	0.5

sition will be a function of their individual physical states, aerodynamic properties, and adhesive properties (or wettability). Ash particles with a high propensity for deposition are probably molten, high-density, spherical particles that do not follow gas stream-lines, and that readily wet the heat-transfer surfaces they contact. Ash particles with a low propensity for deposition are probably dry (high-melting temperature), irregularly shaped particles that are more likely to follow gas stream-lines than to contact the furnace walls.

As discussed earlier, iron compounds are among the materials having the lowest fusing temperatures found in coal ash.[5, 19] It is postulated that particles high in iron form high-density molten spheres that have low drag coefficients, thereby facilitating their penetration through the gas stream to the tube wall. Ash particles that have very high fusing temperatures do not melt to form spheres; their irregular shapes give higher drag coefficients and allow them to follow gas stream-lines. Some particles having low melting temperatures contain carbonate compounds whose gaseous evolution of CO_2 generates cenospheres, which, being hollow, are low in density and also follow gas stream-lines.

COAL ANALYSIS AS A FUNCTION OF PARTICLE SIZE

In predicting behavioral tendencies of mineral matter during combustion, it is important to analyze coal in the size range at which it is being used, because segregation of mineral matter is a function of particle size. As each particle is different, it would be ideal to analyze and quantify individual particles; however, this could prove to be difficult and costly. As a practical alternative to analyzing individual particles, a gravity fractionation technique has been developed.[20]

PROCEDURE FOR GRAVITY FRACTIONATION

The procedure requires that the coal be pulverized to the same fineness as that during firing; the coal particles then are separated by density, using various mixtures of organic liquids having specific gravities of 1.3, 1.5, 1.7, 1.9, 2.1, 2.5, and 2.9. Fewer separations might be adequate, but as the procedure was being developed a finer resolution of gravity fractions was found desirable. A 1-pound sample is normally used and is well stirred into the 1.7 gravity liquid using conventional separatory funnels. After separating the 1-pound sample into the fraction that sinks and the fraction that floats in the 1.7 liquid, each fraction is filtered and washed with a low-density organic solvent. The float fraction is then taken to the next lighter gravity liquid; the sink fraction is taken to the next heavier gravity liquid as shown in Fig. 7. After separation, the eight fractions are air-dried at 250°F and submitted for the following analyses: percent ash, ash composition, ash fusibility, and, optionally, X-ray diffraction.

Fig. 6 **Segregation of mineral matter during grinding**

RESULTS OF ANALYSES

Table VI shows the analyses of three coals selected for the gravity fractionation technique.

Tables VII through IX present data for each of the coal gravity fractions. Compositional differences among the gravity fractions are thought to represent the most important data obtained; fusibility temperatures of ash contained in the gravity fractions would be controlled by composition, for instance. Results here primarily compare composition and behavior of the ash deposit.

SLAGGING INFLUENCED BY IRON CONTENT OF ASH

The role of iron is one of the more important factors in assessing slagging potential. Frequently, investigators use the total iron concentration in a coal ash to assess the slagging potential; however, this iron value could be misleading as it does not account for distribution of iron compounds in the coal matrix. In addition to the importance of the distribution

of mineral matter within the coal matrix, the type of minerals also plays a role in the ash deposition process. For example, iron is frequently present as pyrites (FeS_2) and carbonates ($FeCO_3$) and/or as an impurity in calcite and dolomite, and less frequently as prochlorite ($Fe_2Mg_2Al_2Si_2O_{11}$), hornblende ($CaFe_3Si_4O_{12}$), hematite (Fe_2O_3), and others.[21] Pyrites will more likely exist as discrete particles within the heavier gravity coal fractions whereas carbonates are more likely to be disseminated throughout the coal matrix and not show a concentration with gravity fractionation. The occurrence of these and other iron-containing minerals and their degree of segregation in the coal matrix are functions of coalification.

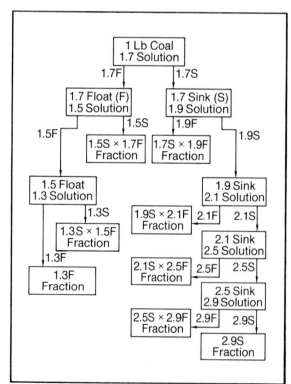

Fig. 7 Gravity separation procedure

Table VI. ASTM Properties of Test Coals

Coal*	A	B	C
ASTM RANK	hvA	hvC	Subbit C
Proximate Analysis			
Moisture	0.7	2.7	10.2
Volatile Matter	32.3	41.7	31.5
Fixed Carbon	54.4	46.4	42.8
Ash	12.6	9.2	11.9
Fusibility Temperatures (°F)			
IT	2430	2080	2130
ST	2510	2140	2170
HT	2560	2170	2210
FT	2660	2300	2310
Ash Composition			
SiO_2	50.7	52.0	50.2
Al_2O_3	30.2	17.5	16.9
TiO_2	1.9	1.3	0.8
Fe_2O_3	9.5	15.5	8.9
CaO	1.6	4.5	11.5
MgO	0.9	1.1	3.5
Na_2O	1.0	0.6	1.8
K_2O	2.7	2.8	1.7
P_2O_5	< 0.1	< 0.1	...
SO_3	1.4	4.2	4.3

*Reporting Basis: As-fired (pulverized)

Table VII. Gravity Separations—Coal A

Gravity Fraction:	1.3F	1.3 × 1.5	1.5 × 1.7	1.7 × 1.9	1.9 × 2.1	2.1 × 2.5	2.5 × 2.9	2.9S
Wt% of Coal	11.32	56.92	9.79	13.33	1.08	2.05	4.05	1.46
% Ash	2.3	7.4	20.4	14.6	51.1	79.1	88.2	71.0
Fusibility Temperatures (°F)								
IT	2420	2700+	2700+	2700+	2520	2320	2420	2010
ST	2520	2700+	2700+	2700+	2670	2400	2510	2040
HT	2690	2700+	2700+	2700+	2700+	2470	2660	2070
FT	2700+	2700+	2700+	2700+	2700+	2610	2700+	2130
Ash Composition								
SiO_2	44.2	52.8	53.7	52.5	53.7	50.6	58.0	26.6
Al_2O_3	36.3	29.9	27.1	27.9	27.1	24.9	22.4	8.6
TiO_2	1.7	1.6	1.1	1.3	1.0	0.8	0.9	0.8
Fe_2O_3	7.0	6.4	6.8	7.2	7.2	5.3	6.7	59.3
CaO	4.7	2.2	1.7	1.6	1.4	5.1	1.3	1.2
MgO	1.2	1.1	1.1	1.1	1.2	1.1	1.1	0.6
Na_2O	0.7	1.2	1.1	1.2	1.2	1.0	1.0	0.8
K_2O	2.9	0.4	3.1	3.1	3.3	3.0	3.1	1.2
SO_3	1.0	0.4	0.4	0.4	0.4	6.2	0.8	0.8

Table VIII. Gravity Separations—Coal B

Gravity Fraction:	1.3F *	1.3 × 1.5	1.5 × 1.7	1.7 × 1.9	1.9 × 2.1	2.1 × 2.5	2.5 × 2.9	2.9S
Wt% of Coal	0.13	45.45	45.52	3.87	2.83	1.20	0.44	0.56
% Ash	1.0	3.2	6.9	32.5	41.3	53.4	78.7	64.3
Fusibility Temperatures (°F)								
IT		2030	2150	1950	1900	1930	2050	2020
ST		2110	2240	2060	1950	1960	2100	2040
HT		2230	2420	2150	1970	2010	2150	2050
FT		2470	2500	2230	2140	2150	2210	2210
Ash Composition								
SiO_2		55.1	57.7	50.1	44.4	39.3	22.4	12.7
Al_2O_3		19.0	21.5	15.2	13.3	11.8	6.8	4.3
TiO_2		2.1	1.2	1.0	0.6	0.6	0.4	0.5
Fe_2O_3		13.2	13.5	24.9	30.5	26.0	22.0	57.3
CaO		2.3	1.9	1.7	3.7	9.5	20.1	9.7
MgO		1.1	1.2	0.9	0.7	0.5	0.3	0.2
Na_2O		0.5	0.4	0.4	0.3	0.3	0.3	0.3
K_2O		2.1	2.2	1.8	1.4	1.1	0.4	0.3
SO_3		0.6	0.3	0.7	2.7	9.3	26.1	12.3
P_2O_5		< 0.1	< 0.1	. . .	. . .	. . .	. . .	< 0.1

*Insufficient sample

Initial stages of the reaction of mineral matter in the flame can influence ash deposition. Physical differences (such as density and size) and, more importantly, melting temperatures (and thus shapes of particles), are determined by the products of transient reactions in the flame, depending on the type of mineral:

	FeS_2	FeS	$FeCO_3$	FeO
Specific Gravity	5.02	4.62	3.96	5.70
Melting Temp (°F)	1382(d)	2182	1112(d)	2511

Where d indicates that the compound decomposes at the temperature shown. The compounds that reach the walls control the type of deposit formed. The reactions below illustrate this point:

$$FeS_2(c) + O_2 \xrightarrow[\text{oxidation}]{\text{initial}} FeS(l) + SO_2(g) \tag{9}$$

$$FeCO_3(c) \xrightarrow[\text{reaction}]{\text{initial}} FeO(c, l) + CO_2(g)$$

where c = crystalline, g = gaseous, and l = liquid

$$\tag{10}$$

The first reaction, the oxidation of iron pyrite initially to pyrrhotite and SO_2, is one of the more significant reactions the mineral matter experiences in the combustion zone. The product FeS forms molten spheres which, through less drag and higher density (compared to most other particles in the fireball) are more likely to contact the walls of the furnace. Depending on the composition of ash deposits already present on the furnace wall, subsequent reactions involving FeS may form a material that melts at a relatively low temperature. The reactions in (11), (12A) and (12B) illustrate two possible products with significantly different melting temperatures. Reaction 11 shows the formation of magnetite (Fe_3O_4) which will tolerate a rela-

Table IX. Gravity Separations—Coal C

Gravity Fraction: Wt% of Coal % Ash	1.3F * 0.2	1.3 × 1.5 62.76 6.1	1.5 × 1.7 32.28 6.4	1.7 × 1.9 1.56 21.8	1.9 × 2.1 1.09 39.9	2.1 × 2.5 0.62 82.6	2.5 × 2.9 0.45 84.0	2.9S 1.05 68.3
Fusibility Temperatures (°F)								
IT		2230	2260	2240	2310	2180	2350	2210
ST		2290	2370	2340	2380	2230	2440	2250
HT		2310	2390	2400	2430	2280	2490	2380
FT		2340	2420	2630	2550	2420	2530	2530
Ash Composition								
SiO_2		41.1	43.7	54.5	53.4	51.0	37.0	6.8
Al_2O_3		18.5	24.2	25.7	20.7	10.3	3.0	0.7
TiO_2		0.8	0.8	0.6	0.8	0.4	0.3	0.3
Fe_2O_3		3.2	2.0	7.1	5.9	3.5	3.7	79.0
CaO		19.6	16.1	7.0	8.2	11.9	22.8	3.9
MgO		5.1	4.3	1.4	1.0	0.6	0.8	0.3
Na_2O		0.3	0.5	0.3	0.2	0.2	0.2	0.2
K_2O		0.3	0.3	0.4	0.2	0.4	0.4	0.2
SO_3		9.5	7.7	2.7	6.5	9.6	11.0	6.2
P_2O_5	< 0.1	< 0.1	< 0.1	< 0.1		0.2	0.3	0.2

*Insufficient sample

$$FeS(l) + Fe_2O_3(c, l) + 3/2\ O_2(g) \rightarrow Fe_3O_4(c, l) + SO_2(g) \tag{11}$$

$$2FeS(l) + 3O_2(g) \rightarrow 2FeO(c, l) + 2SO_2(g) \tag{12A}$$

$$FeO(l) + SiO_2(c, l) \rightarrow FeSiO_3(c, l)$$
$$\text{(melting temp 2095°F)} \tag{12B}$$

***Table X.* Total Iron Compared with Segregated Iron**

Coal	% Iron in Entire Coal Ash	Total % Iron in 2.9 Sink Fraction
A	9.5	39.9
B	15.5	11.9
C	8.9	69.7

tively high melting temperature before decomposing to FeO and O_2. The presence of Fe_3O_4 in the deposit would contribute toward a "dry" deposit. Reaction 12A shows the formation of FeO as an intermediate product which can react with silica to form a low-melting iron silicate (shown in 12B). The presence of iron silicate would contribute toward a molten deposit.

Iron compounds in the "2.9 sink" are given special emphasis as they often contain mostly pyrites, which can cause slagging. The bar charts depicted in Fig. 8 show that iron compounds in coal B are more uniformly distributed throughout the coal matrix than in coal C. Thus, coal C has the high potential for slagging. This agrees with observations made in the field; a furnace burning coal C had more slagging problems than a unit burning coal B.

Table X shows that the degree of segregation of iron compounds within the coal matrix has no bearing on the total percentage of iron in the raw coal. If the coals are ranked solely by iron content, there is a significant difference between the orders of ranking, influenced by measurements of total or segregated iron.

FOULING AS INFLUENCED BY ALKALINE CONTENT OF ASH

As described earlier in this chapter, the alkalies sodium and potassium are important when an assessment of ash fouling is required. But, the total quantity of alkalies is not necessarily an accurate index of fouling potential, as was the case with total iron versus slagging potential. Rather, fouling may well be related to the quantity of "active alkalies." Other investigations show that vapor pressures of gaseous sodium and potassium compounds at temperatures present in coal flames can account for significant evaporation of these materials.[22] Recondensation of these gases constitutes an important mechanism of deposition.

Organically bound alkalies have the potential to form very reactive species in the combustion zone (as transient elements or compounds) which exist as gases; these can condense subsequently in the boiler as gas temperatures decrease. More stable forms of alkalies (such as feldspars and impurities in clay minerals) liberate less of these reactive species and are less influential in the ash-deposition process.[20]

It is reasonable to expect that alkalies found

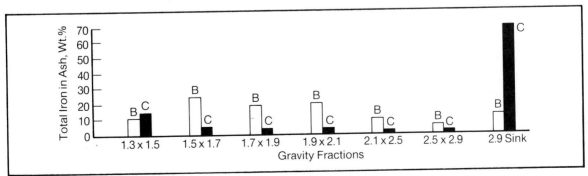

***Fig. 8* Iron content of various gravity fractions, coal B vs coal C**

in the low-density coal fractions (lighter than 1.7 specific gravity) are largely present as organically bound minerals. Alkalies found in heavier gravity coal fractions (greater than 1.7) are less likely to be organically bound.

Examination of coals A and C shows coal A to have 3.7 percent total alkalies and coal C to have 3.5 percent total alkalies. A judgment made on this basis alone would indicate similar fouling potential for both of the coals. But experience with these coals has shown a unit burning coal C has considerably more fouling problems in the convection passes than a unit burning coal A. Fig. 9 shows coal C to have considerably more alkalies in the lower gravity fractions than coal A.

Table XI shows the percentage of alkali in the entire coal ash in each of the three raw coals versus the percentage of total alkali in the 1.7 float fraction. If the coals are ranked solely on the basis of the alkali in the entire coal ash, there is a significant difference compared with the order indicated by the alkali content of the 1.7 float.

Table XI. Total Alkali Compared with Segregated Alkali

Coal	% Alkali in Entire Coal Ash	Total Alkali in 1.7 Float Fraction
A	3.7	30.0
B	3.4	66.2
C	3.5	76.2

CORROSION BY FUEL ASH

During normal operation of utility boilers, metal wastage has occurred primarily (Fig. 10)

- on waterwalls near the firing zone
- in the high-temperature superheater and reheater sections
- in the low-temperature gas passes and air heaters.

To reduce failures in these areas, C-E has established the underlying causes of major types of corrosion and has developed practical procedures for the control of waterwall and low-temperature wastage.

In recent years the most common temperature for the main steam and reheat on larger steam-generating units has been 1005°F. As a result, fundamental studies of high-temperature corrosion begun in the 1960's have been discontinued. Except for some very promising work in identifying the corrosive constituents in coals,[23] little new information concerning high-temperature coal ash corrosion is available.

CONCLUSIONS FROM SERVICE EXPERIENCE OF COAL-FIRED UNITS

Although the U.S. utility industry has, in general, abandoned the 1050°F and higher steam temperatures, there are a number of steam generators operating at those temperatures from which the following has been established:

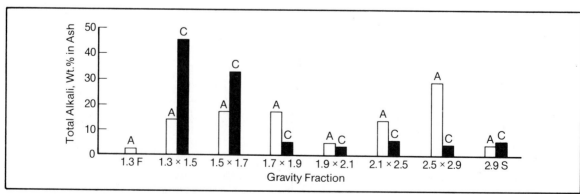

Fig. 9 Alkali content of various gravity fractions, Coal A vs Coal C

1. All coals do not produce an ash that is "corrosive." Only a small percentage of coal-fired units experienced serious corrosion requiring major operating or maintenance corrections. Although the percentage is small, the actual numbers of units that experienced serious corrosion problems were substantial, and the concern and attention given to the coal-ash corrosion problem are certainly warranted. But it is important to know that many coal-fired units operate at steam temperatures of 1050°F with essentially no corrosion, or at acceptably low corrosion rates.

2. For coals that are "corrosive," metal temperature is an important corrosion-rate variable. As surface metal temperatures increase to about 1200°F, corrosion rates increase significantly. A unit delivering steam at temperatures of 1050°F or higher will have a greater corrosion problem than a 1005°F steam unit *if* the coal is corrosive. The corrosion rates will be higher, and the amount of material undergoing corrosion will be significantly increased. For the types of coal that can be classified as noncorrosive, however, temperature does not appear to be an important variable with regard to corrosion. If the coals are non-corrosive, there need not be a greater corrosion concern as steam temperatures are increased above 1005°F.

3. The molten ash produced by corrosive coals is highly aggressive and corrosion is not easily prevented.

a. All potentially viable pressure-part materials corrode at unacceptable rates. Currently, no tube material has an adequate high-temperature strength to resist corrosion if the coal ash is corrosive.

b. Various tube coatings have been tried. Electroplated chromium has proven effective in preventing corrosion, but it is an expensive solution with an indeterminate adherence life. Bi-metal tubes with an outer corrosion-resistant clad high in chromium, such as alloy IN 671 (50 Cr-50 Ni), show promise of having adequate corrosion resistance, but the cost of such tubing is high. In addition, these alloying

elements are expected to be in critically short supply in the future. Other less expensive corrosion-resistant coatings have been tried without success.

The high-temperature corrosion that did occur was a liquid-phase coal-ash attack under tightly bonded deposits that was observed when surface metal temperatures exceeded 1100°F. This attack affected superheaters and reheaters made of austenitic (stainless) and ferritic steel.[23-39]

CONCLUSIONS FROM RESEARCH ON COAL-ASH CORROSION

Research programs have attempted to determine causes and suggest remedies for this type of wastage. Both austenitic (stainless) and ferritic steel are subject to this wastage, which takes place under tightly bonded deposits. While this excessive deposit-type wastage of ferritic alloys increases with increasing tem-

Fig. 10 **Steam-generator side elevation showing areas where wastage has occurred**

perature, wastage of austenitic alloys is characterized as a function of temperature by the "bell-shaped" curve shown in Fig. 11. Careful inspection at various temperatures reveals a thin white or yellow layer next to the tube surface. This layer, which is molten within the 1000° to 1300°F temperature range, contains a high concentration of alkali and sulfur (Fig. 12).

Simultaneous field and laboratory investigations, including chemical and X-ray diffraction analyses, have shown that complex alkali-iron-trisulfates are major constituents of the white inner layers associated with wastage on both superheater and reheater tubes and on corrosion probes, as well as in controlled laboratory wastage experiments. By means of laboratory weight-loss tests, the "bell-shaped" corrosion curve has been reproduced under the same conditions needed for synthesis of the complex sulfate.[28] As noted earlier, this same complex sulfate was formed as a byproduct of waterwall wastage.[24, 33]

With the principal corrosive defined, efforts turned toward establishing the mechanism of complex sulfate formation to assist in recommendation of adequate protective measures. It is significant that the concentration of compounds thought to be responsible for corrosion is considerably greater in probe and tube deposits, as a result of selective deposition, than in the coal ash or flyash from which these compounds originate.

An important explanation advanced by early investigators is that the initial deposits may be a powderlike material containing alkalies and iron oxide which react with sulfur trioxide to form alkali-iron-trisulfates.[40] Concentration of alkalies on the tube surface may also occur by thermal migration of molten material through the deposits to the tube surface.[28]

On the basis of the selective deposition observed, it was felt that individual particles of flyash vary in composition and, therefore, have different fusion temperatures. Some of the particles that are molten or semimolten at relatively low temperatures continue to stick to the tubes. Sodium and potassium compounds released during the combustion process in a form capable of reaction with SO_3 in the flue gas, may condense or deposit on the tubes as the initial layer. This explains the formation of bonded deposits in regions where the gas temperature is significantly lower than the fusion temperature of the total coal ash.

Fig. 11 also shows a comparison of the equilibrium curves and the "bell-shaped" wastage curve for austenitic stainless steel. It has been suggested that the potassium/sodium ratio in the coal ash or tube deposit is significant. The molar ratio of alkalies determines the

Fig. 11 Physical state of complex alkali-iron-trisulfates as a function of temperature and the corrosion of austenitic alloys

Fig. 12 Effect of steam temperature on deposit structure

temperature range over which the complex sulfates are molten. The equilibrium concentration of sodium-iron-trisulfate was not molten from 1150°F to 1275°F. The greatest fluid range appears to be the 1:1 molar sodium/potassium ratio. This corresponds to the 1030° to 1275°F region where corrosion was observed. This is to be expected because a molten corrosive is generally more reactive than its solid counterpart. Consequently, an alkaline molar ratio of about 1:1 in a deposit is corrosive over a wider temperature range than any other combination because of the greater range of fluidity of the complex sulfate.

The roles of the various compounds necessary to form a corrosive deposit are placed in proper perspective by the equilibrium curve. The steps that influence formation and growth of deposits from combustion products of coal may be summarized as follows:

1. During combustion, pyrite (FeS_2) and organic sulfur react with oxygen:

$$2FeS_2 + 5\tfrac{1}{2}O_2 \rightarrow Fe_2O_3 + 4SO_2$$
$$RS \text{ (organic sulfide)} + O_2 \rightarrow SO_2$$
$$SO_2 + \tfrac{1}{2}O_2 \rightarrow SO_3$$

2. In the high flame temperature, the Na and K in the clays and shales react to form Na_2O and K_2O.

3. The Na_2O and K_2O then react with SO_3 either in the gas stream or after deposition on the tube:

$$(Na_2 \text{ or } K_2)O + SO_3 \rightarrow (Na_2 \text{ or } K_2)SO_4$$

4. The alkali sulfates, iron oxide, and SO_3 then react to form the complex sulfate:

$$3(K_2 \text{ or } Na_2)SO_4 + Fe_2O_3 + 3SO_3 \rightarrow 2(K_3 \text{ or } Na_3)$$
$$Fe(SO_4)_3$$

When the tube deposit contains a sufficiently high potassium-sulfate/sodium-sulfate ratio, formation of liquid pyrosulfate could occur. SO_3 reacts directly with the alkali-sulfate mixture forming pyrosulfate, which, in turn, at-

tacks the oxide to form complex sulfate at a higher rate than in the case of the dry reaction.

The melting point of a mixed alkali pyrosulfate ($K_{1.5}Na_{0.5}S_2O_7$) is 535°F when SO_3 is above 7 ppm. The low-melting pyrosulfates, as well as the complex sulfates, are considered primary agents in superheater corrosion, as was previously noted.

5. The complex sulfate in the molten phase then reacts with the tube metal:

$$2(K_3 \text{ or } Na_3)Fe(SO_4)_3 + 6Fe \rightarrow$$
$$\tfrac{3}{2}FeS + \tfrac{3}{2}Fe_3O_4 +$$
$$Fe_2O_3 + 3(K_2 \text{ or } Na_2)SO_4 + \tfrac{3}{2}SO_2$$

The reaction products shown in item 5 above tend to slow down the corrosion rate, but if the deposit spalls, the reaction begins anew. The rate of spalling, then, affects the overall rate of corrosion.

PREDICTION OF COAL-ASH CORROSIVITY

Based on an understanding of the corrosion process outlined above, work has been done to quantify the effects of specific coal-ash constituents on high-temperature corrosion.[41, 42]

Certain relationships were developed between coal-ash constituents and the degree to which they affect corrosion rates. The study has shown that the alkalies, alkaline earths, iron, and sulfur are the most significant constituents relative to high-temperature corrosion. It is significant that the alkali concentration had been measured by an acid leaching process. Such a procedure gives a better measure of the simpler forms of sodium and potassium than total alkali measurements. These simpler forms of the alkalies are thought to be more available for reaction in forming alkali-iron-trisulfate, K_3 or $Na_3 Fe(SO_4)_3$, the species directly responsible for tube wastage according to previous investigation by C-E and others. Because the alkalies are generally the least plentiful of the four constituents mentioned, they are usually the most sensitive corrosion indicators.

The alkaline-earth materials are important as they may preferentially retain the alkalies as sulfates or double salts of the type $K_2Ca_2(SO_4)_3$, thus preventing formation of the aggressive compound $K_3Fe(SO_4)_3$.[43]

SHORT-TERM PROBES AS CORROSION INDICATORS

During the study noted, probes were inserted for periods of five minutes for purposes of measuring the acid-soluble sodium and potassium during each test firing.[23] These probes were inserted during tests in which raw coals and prepared coals were burned as well as during tests in which additives were used. Acid-soluble sodium and potassium values were expressed as a ratio and plotted against measured corrosion rate and they showed a remarkably good correlation (Fig. 13). It was noted that the acid-soluble Na_2O/K_2O ratio measured from probe deposits is probably a closer approximation of the relative concentration of sodium and potassium-iron-trisulfate than that measured from the coal, for the following reason:

The many physical and chemical phenomena that cause changes in the coal constituents during combustion have already taken place when the resultant probe deposits are measured for sodium and potassium content. Therefore, an acid-soluble measure of the alkalies in the *deposit* rather than in the *coal* would automatically consider the effects of combustion on the mineral matter in the coal.

This short-term acid-soluble-alkalies meas-

Fig. 13 Acid soluble Na_2O/K_2O molar ratio vs observed corrosion rate

urement approach is a simple and accurate way of assessing the corrosive potential of coal ash.

METHODS OF MINIMIZING THE CORROSIVE POTENTIAL OF COAL ASH

Addition or removal of certain constituents may modify a potentially corrosive coal. The entire operating system at the supplier facility should be examined from the seam face, where mining is begun, to the point of loading for shipment. These operations may be summarized as follows:

1. Mining: the coal is removed from the ground by one of several mining methods and transported from the mine.

2. Coal preparation: the run-of-mine (raw) coal may now be processed by any combination of many preparation procedures.

3. Coal additives and blending: additives or other coals may be blended with the original coal prior to shipment.

MINING

Analysis of channel samples of coal removed from a seam enclosed on two sides by "barren" material showed that the corrosion-affecting minerals, as well as other mineral matter, originated primarily from the roof, floor, or partings in the seam.[23] Therefore, the corrosiveness of a coal may be reduced by mining so that the concentration of alkaline-earth materials is increased with respect to the alkalies. This can be accomplished by inclusion or exclusion of seam roof material, floor material, and material contained in partings.

COAL PREPARATION

The procedures used to prepare coals for market should be examined. The results of bench-scale chemical and physical tests revealed that the individual chemical constituents of coal mineral matter often concentrate in specific size and/or weight fractions of the coal. Thus, preparation practices which employ sizing and gravity concentrating techniques can be used to alter the chemical composition of the coal product. Because high-temperature corrosion can be related to coal mineral-matter properties, it is possible to reduce corrosive potential of many coals through the judicious application of conventional coal-preparation methods. In one case, the corrosiveness of the coal was reduced from 10.2 mg/cm²-300 hr to 2.9 mg/cm²-300 hr because of the benefits derived from a beneficiation process.[23]

COAL ADDITIVES AND BLENDING

Adding materials such as dolomite and limestone or blending two or more coals, can counteract the corrosive nature of a coal.

The use of additives results in the preferential formation of sulfates or double salts of the type $K_2Ca_2(SO_4)_3$. Additives can also have beneficial effects in reducing problems from slagging and fouling. Tests have showed that, in most cases, ash deposits become more friable when an additive was used and deposits become easier to remove.[23]

CHLORIDE AS A FACTOR IN CORROSION

The research establishing the mechanism of the liquid-phase-deposit high-temperature corrosion has not shown any significant corrosion at the chloride levels of 0.1 to 0.2 percent normally encountered in coal firing.[44]

Investigations at C-E showed that the probe corrosion rate for clean coal increased by a factor of 3.3 when firing raw and clean coals from the same mine source. In this case, the coal had been cleaned by a gravity separation in carbon tetrachloride. Therefore, the residual chloride in the cleaned coal was 1.3 percent as opposed to a 0.05-percent level in the raw coal. This corrosion rate was confirmed by subsequent testing.[23]

Chloride concentrations in American coals range from 0 to 0.6 percent while coals from the United Kingdom peak at 0.8 percent. The 0.6 percent high for U.S. chloride levels is somewhat misleading in that the majority of U.S. coals have chloride levels less than 0.2 percent. Because of this, chlorine thus far has not been implicated by U.S. investigators as a major contributing factor to tube wastage.[45]

The role of chloride in increased corrosion may take several paths. Chloride naturally occurs in coal as an inorganic material and may be carried over with the flyash or released by strong sulfur acid as HCl. It can also be volatilized as NaCl. In addition, chloride can enter with refuse in either an organic or inorganic form. The resulting chloride compounds usually are concentrated on cooled tube surfaces where additional reactions may occur.

It is thought that two major adverse mechanisms are involved in the potential increase in corrosion rate in incinerators and/or fossil fuel-fired boilers in the presence of chloride. One involves formation of eutectics or complexes resulting in a lowering of melting point of deposits. This phenomenon is of particular concern in waterwall wastage where the temperature of molten salts would increase.

The second mechanism, probably of greater concern in the superheater, involves the reaction of gas-phase sulfuric acid with deposit chloride to release HCl near the heated tube surface. Subsequent reaction may involve stepwise formation of volatile ferric chloride [46, 47] and/or unstable chloride or oxychlorides of other alloy components.

Heat-transfer surfaces installed in incinerators in both Europe and the U.S. have excessive corrosion rates.[48] It has been judged that combinations of sulfur, chlorine, lead, tin and zinc have been the corrosive agents. In these studies, where raw unprepared refuse is fired, it has been thought that the concentration of lead, tin, and zinc deposits results in a lowering of the deposit melting point with an acceleration of liquid-phase corrosion.

Battelle researchers have conducted investigations that show opposing effects of chlorine and sulfur in refuse.[49, 50] An increase in chlorine increases the corrosion rates of low-alloy steels while an increase of sulfur decreases the corrosion rates of all the steels investigated. They reported that the major contribution to the corrosion reaction is in the type of compounds that are deposited on the corrosion probe. Their investigation confirms the importance of the chloride reaction as reported by other investigators of the corrosion process.

CORROSION PROBLEMS FROM OIL ASH

Although this chapter focuses primarily on the physical and chemical properties of coal ash as they relate to slagging and fouling of boiler surfaces, fuel oil can also cause problems of corrosion.

Burning residual-fuel oil in utility steam generators has not resulted in wastage of *waterwall* tubes. The principal wastage problems associated with boilers firing high-sulfur oils are (a) high-temperature corrosion of superheater and reheater tubes by low-melting-ash deposits, and (b) low-temperature corrosion of air heater, ducts, and dust-collector equipment by condensed sulfuric acid in the flue gas.

Analyses of typical residual oil ash as recorded in Table XII show that the composition of oil ash varies widely, and indicate that many elements may be found in the ash. However, the bulk of the ash contains compounds of vanadium, iron, nickel, sulfur, and alkali metals. The compounds of particular interest are those of vanadium, sodium, and sulfur which are associated with deposit formation and accelerated corrosion at high temperatures. The ash content of heavy-residual oil varies considerably, but is usually not over 0.1 percent. Concentration of vanadium in the ash is related to the source of the crude.

Vanadium content of residual-oil ash may vary from a trace to 30 percent or more. Similar variations occur in sodium content. Sulfur contents in oil have been reported from 0.7 to more than 5 percent.

HIGH-TEMPERATURE CORROSION BY OIL ASH

Opinion varies considerably on the exact mechanism of oil-ash corrosion, but most investigators agree that accelerated corrosion occurs by the fluxing action of molten sodium-vanadium complexes on the protective oxide scale on the tube. Various compounds containing different sodium/vanadium ratios frequently considered oxygen carriers, have been mentioned as participating in such corrosion.

Both melting and liquid temperatures on heating and cooling have been determined for several sodium-vanadium compounds and sodium sulfate.[51, 52, 53] The data in Table XIII show differences between the two liquidus curves for vanadium compounds, but not sodium sulfate. These differences are considered to be results of the absorption and evolution of oxygen by the complexes when heated to the melting point or cooled to the solidification point. These temperature differences could be of importance both to the formation of deposits and subsequent high-temperature corrosion by such deposits. Sulfur trioxide and nascent oxygen have also been suggested as corrodents.

A review of the work on this subject results in a curve relating metal wastage to the phase diagram of Na_2O versus V_2O_5.[54] Fig. 14 plots the results for an iron-base alloy. It can be seen that the greatest wastage occurs at a Na_2O/V_2O_5 ratio of about 1:5. Molten-temperature range of this ratio is 1150° to 1200°F. However, as was noted previously, eutectics occur at temperatures considerably lower; metal wastage would be possible at lower temperatures if the corresponding ratio of Na_2O/V_2O_5 is present. In ac-

Table XII. Analyses of Ash from Heavy Fuel Oils

	Mid-Cont.	% by Weight		
		Texas	Iran	Venezuela
SiO_2	31.7	1.6	12.1	2.4
Fe_2O_3 ⎫				
Al_2O_3 ⎬	31.8	8.9	18.1	18.4
TiO_2 ⎭				
CaO	12.6	5.3	12.7	2.9
MgO	4.2	2.5	0.2	2.6
MnO	0.4	0.3	TR	. . .
V_2O_5	TR	1.4	38.5	50.5
NiO	0.5	1.5	10.7	. . .
Na_2O	6.9	30.8	. . .	12.7
K_2O	. . .	1.0	. . .	0.5
SO_3	10.8	42.1	7.0	8.6
Chloride	. . .	4.6	. . .	. . .

tual practice, diluents in the ash usually raise the melting point to 1100°F or higher; corrosion of metal surfaces below 1100°F is not usually a problem.

Boilers operating at steam temperatures of 1005°F or higher will have some superheater and reheater tubes operating at temperatures above 1100°F and will, therefore, be subject to corrosion. Field measurements of superheater and reheater tubes wastage have indicated corrosion rates of as much as 0.030 in. per year.

Many approaches have been taken to prevent high-temperature oil-ash corrosion. These include oil treatment to remove vanadium, sodium, and sulfur from the oil[55, 56]; the use of corrosion-resistant alloys and protective coatings; low-excess air operation; and the use of magnesium metal, magnesium oxide, or dolomite additives.

LOW-TEMPERATURE CORROSION FROM OIL ASH

The greater part of the sulfur released in the combustion of fuel oil appears in the products of combustion as SO_2. A small percentage is oxidized to SO_3 which, in the cooled flue gas, reacts with water in the vapor phase to form sulfuric acid. The formation of SO_3 in boilers is a complex process which is not thoroughly understood. Three possible mechanisms have received the most attention: (1) oxidation of SO_2 by molecular oxygen, (2) oxidation of SO_2 in the flame by atomic oxygen, and (3) catalytic oxidation of SO_2. Various authors have considered these mechanisms,[57-59] but extensive field tests have indicated that catalytic oxidation in the convection pass is a major source of SO_3.

If metal temperature is below the acid dew point, the sulfuric acid condenses on and corrodes it. If the gas temperature falls below the dew point, the sulfuric acid condenses on flyash particles which can agglomerate to form acid smuts. It follows that low-temperature corrosion and acid smuts will be eliminated by maintaining both metal and gas temperatures above the acid dew point or by the reduction of SO_3 in the flue gas.

The relation of SO_3 concentration to acid dew

point temperature was established in a laboratory investigation.[60] In this study a direct determination was made of SO_3 in the gas stream. By maintaining a specially designed condenser at a temperature between the acid dew point

Table XIII. Liquidus/Melting Points Sodium and Vanadium Oil-Ash Constituents

Compound	Melting Point	Liquidus Temp		Ref.
		Heating	Cooling	
V_2O_5	1247, 1274°F	1220°F	1165°F	51, 52
$Na_2O \cdot 6V_2O_5$	1255	185	1060	52
$5Na_2O \cdot V_2O_4$ $\cdot 11V_2O_5$	995	984	922	51, 53
$Na_2O \cdot 3V_2O_5$	1220	1040	1020	52
$NaVO_3$ $(Na_2O \cdot V_2O_5)$	1140	1040	1020	52
Na_2SO_4	1625	1625	1625	52

Fig. 14 Effect of Na_2O/V_2O_5 mixtures on oil-ash corrosion

and the water dew point, sulfuric acid is condensed while all other flue-gas constituents remain in the gas phase.

Acid dew point is defined as "the temperature at which the combustion gases are saturated with sulfuric acid" and the dew-point/ acid concentration relationship was determined using the condensation sampling method. Fig. 15 graphically illustrates the agreement of dew-point determination of this type with thermodynamically calculated data, and shows electrical dew-point meter measurements. In view of the uncertainties involved with using dew-point meters, it is preferable to use the condenser analytical method together with dew-point curves to predict the temperatures at which the corrosive sulfuric condensate will first appear.

Although the low-temperature sections of a boiler can be protected against acid corrosion, and acid-smut fallout eliminated by maintaining metal and gas temperatures above the dew point, it is readily recognized that a more positive solution to these problems is the reduction

Fig. 15 Dew point as a function of
$H_2SO_4 /(SO_3)$ **concentration**

of sulfur-trioxide in the flue gas. Firing with low excess air plus alkaline additives to reduce SO_3 concentration has been done extensively in the United States and Europe.[61]

REFERENCES

[1] W. A. Selvig and F. H. Gibson, "Analyses of Ash from United States Coals," *U. S. Bureau of Mines Bulletin 567*. Washington: U.S. Bureau of Mines, 1956.

W. A. Selvig and F. H. Gibson, "Analyses of Ash from Coal of the United States," *U. S. Bureau of Mines Technical Paper 679*. Washington: U. S. Bureau of Mines, 1945.

[2] Elliott P. Barrett, "The Fusion, Flow, and Clinkering of Coal Ash: A Survey of the Chemical Background," Chapter 15 of *Chemistry of Coal Utilization*, Vol. I, edited by H. H. Lowry, pp. 496–571. New York: John Wiley and Sons and London: Chapman and Hall, Ltd., 1945.

[3] Thomas G. Estep, Harry Seltz, and William J. Osborn, "Determination of the Effect of Oxides of Sodium, Calcium, and Magnesium on the Ash Fusion Temperatures by the Use of Synthetic Coal Ash," *Mining and Metallurgical Investigations, Carnegie Institute of Technology, Mining and Metallurgical Advisory Boards, Bulletin 74*, 1937.

[4] G. Thiessin, C. G. Ball, and P. E. Grotts, "Coal Ash and Coal Mineral Matter," *Industrial and Engineering Chemistry*, 28: 335–361, 1936.

[5] P. Nicholls and W. A. Selvig, "Clinker Formation as Related to the Fusibility of Coal Ash," *U. S. Bureau of Mines Bulletin 364*. Washington: U. S. Bureau of Mines, 1932.

[6] A. F. Duzy, "Fusibility-Viscosity of Lignite-Type Ash," *ASME Paper No. 65—WA/FU-7*. New York: American Society of Mechanical Engineers, 1965.

[7] G. H. Gronhovd, et al., "Study of Factors Affecting Ash Deposition from Lignite and Other Coals," *ASME Paper No. 69–WA/C1-1*. New York: American Society of Mechanical Engineers, 1969.

[8] W. Beckering, et al., "Examination of Coal and Coal Ash by X-Ray Techniques," *Technology and Use of Lignite, Proceedings*; by James L. Elder and Wayne R. Kube. Co-sponsored by the U.S. Bureau of Mines and the University of North Dakota, Grand Forks, N.D., May 1–2, 1969, pp. 89–102. (U.S. Bureau of Mines Information Circular 8471). Washington: U.S. Bureau of Mines, 1970.

[9] J. R. Partington, *Textbook of Inorganic Chemistry*, 6th edition, p. 689. London: MacMillan Co., 1950.

[10] H. E. Crossley, "The Melchett Lecture for 1962: A Contribution to the Development of Power Stations," *Institute of Fuel. Journal*, 36 (269): 228–239, June 1963.

[11] James V. O'Gorman and Philip L. Walker, Jr., "Mineral Matter Characteristics of Some American Coals," *Fuel*, 50 (2): 135–151, April 1971.

[12] James V. O Gorman and Philip L. Walker, Jr., "Thermal Behavior of Mineral Fractions Separated from Selected American Coals," *Fuel*, 52 (1): 71–79, January 1973.

[13] J. E. Payner and W. G. Marskell, "The Distribution of Mineral Matter in Pulverized Fuel and Solid Products of Combustion," *The Mechanism of Corrosion by Fuel Impurities*, proceedings of the International Conference held at the Marchwood Engineering Laboratories, Marchwood, near Southampton, Hampshire, England, May 20–24, 1963, H. R. Johnson and D. J. Littler, general editors. London: Butterworths, 1963, pp. 113–136.

[14] G. B. Gould and H. L. Brunjes, "Proportions of Free Fusible Material in Coal Ash, as an Index of Clinker and Slag Formation," *American Institute of Mining and Metallurgical Engineers Technical Publication 1175*; New York: American Institute of Mining and Metallurgical Engineers, 1940.

[15] R. W. Borio and R. R. Narciso, Jr., "The Use of Gravity Fractionation Techniques for Assessing Slagging and Fouling Potential of Coal Ash," *Transactions of the ASME Journal of Engineering for Power*, 101, Series A (4): 500–505, October 1979; also in Combustion Engineering publication TIS-5823; and in *ASME Paper No. 78–WA/CD-3*. New York: American Society of Mechanical Engineers, 1978.

[16] R. W. Bryers, "Influence of the Distribution of Mineral Matter in Coal on Fireside Ash Deposition," *Transactions of the ASME Journal of Engineering for Power*, 101, Series A (4), 506–515, October 1979; also in *ASME Paper No. 78–WA/CD-4*. New York: American Society of Mechanical Engineers, 1978.

[17] H. R. Hazard, et al., "Coal Mineral Matter and Furnace Slagging," proceedings of the American Power Conference, 41: 610–617, 1979. Chicago: Illinois Institute of Technology, 1979.

[18] A. H. Moody and D. D. Langan, Jr., "Fusion Characteristics of Fractionated Coal Ashes," *Combustion*, 5 (4): 15–17, October 1933.

[19] R. W. Bryers, "The Physical and Chemical Characteristics of Pyrites and Their Influence on Fireside Problems in Steam Generators," *ASME Paper No. 75–WA/CD-2*. New York: American Society of Mechanical Engineers, 1975.

[20] See Reference 15.

[21] William T. Reid, *External Corrosion and Deposits; Boilers and Gas Turbines*. New York: American Elsevier Pub. Co., 1971.

[22] Leo Brewer, "The Thermodynamic Properties of the Oxides and Their Vaporization Processes," *Chemical Reviews*, 52: 1–75, 1953.

[23] R. W. Borio, et al., "The Control of High-Temperature Fire-Side Corrosion in Utility Coal-Fired Boilers," *U. S. Department of the Interior, Office of Coal Research, Research and Development Report No. 41*, April 1969. Washington: U. S. Department of Interior, Office of Coal Research, 1969.

[24] A. C. Corey, H. A. Grabowski, and B. J. Cross, "External Corrosion of Furnace-Wall Tubes—III. Further Data on Sulfate Deposits and the Significance of Iron Sulfide Deposits," *Transactions of the ASME*, 71: 951–963 November 1949.

[25] A. L. Plumley, J. Jonakin, and R. E. Vuia, "A Review Study of Fireside Corrosion in Utility and Industrial Boilers. Part I—How to Lower Corrosion in Boilers," *Canadian Chemical Processing*, 51:52, June, 1967. Based on Combustion Engineering publication TIS-2775.

A. L. Plumley, J. Jonakin, and R. E. Vuia, "A Review Study of Fireside Corrosion in Utility and Industrial Boilers. Part II—M.G.O. Injection Flow Boiler Corrosion," *Canadian Chemical Processing*, 51:70, July, 1967. Based on Combustion Engineering publication TIS-2775.

[26] J. G. Koopman, et al., "Development and Use of a Probe for Studying Corrosion in Superheaters and Reheaters," *Proceedings of the American Power Conference*, 21: 236–245, 1959.

[27] James Jonakin, G. A. Rice, and J. T. Reese, "Fireside Corrosion of Superheater and Reheater Tubing," *ASME Paper No. 59-FU-5*. New York: American Society of Mechanical Engineers, 1959.

[28] Wharton Nelson and Carl Cain, Jr., "Corrosion of Superheaters and Reheaters of Pulverized-Coal-Fired Boilers," *Transactions of the ASME. Journal of Engineering for Power*, 82, Series A: 192–204, 1960

[29] J. T. Reese, James Jonakin, and J. G. Koopman, "How Coal Properties Relate to Corrosion of High Temperature Boiler Surfaces," *Proceedings of the American Power Conference*, 23: 391–399, 1961.

[30] Carl Cain, Jr. and Wharton Nelson, "Corrosion of Superheaters and Reheaters of Pulverized-Coal-Fired Boilers II." *Transactions of the ASME. Journal of Engineering for Power*, 83, Series A: 468–474, October 1961.

[31] Wharton Nelson and E. S. Lisle, "A Laboratory Evaluation of Catalyst Poisons for Reducing High-Temperature Gas-Side Corrosion and Ash Bonding in Coal-Fired Boilers," *Journal of the Institute of Fuel*, 37 (284): 378–384, September 1964.

[32] Wharton Nelson and E. S. Lisle, "High Temperature External Corrosion on Coal-Fired Boilers: Siliceous Inhibitors," *Journal of the Institute of Fuel*, 38 (291): 179–186, April 1965.

[33] R. C. Corey, et al., "External Corrosion of Furnace-Wall Tubes—II. Significance of Sulfate Deposits and Sulfur Trioxide in Corrosion Mechanism," *Transactions of the ASME*, 67: 289–302, 1945.

[34] H. R. Johnson and D. J. Littler, general editors, *The Mechanism of Corrosion by Fuel Impurities*, proceedings of the International Conference held at the Engineering Laboratories, Marchwood, near Southampton, Hampshire, England, May 20–24, 1963. London: Butterworths, 1963.

[35] S. A. Goldberg, J. J. Gallagher, and A. A. Orning, "A Laboratory Study of High Temperature Corrosion on Fireside Surfaces of Coal-Fired Steam Generators," *Transactions*

of the *ASME. Journal of Engineering for Power*, 90, Series A: 193–212, 1968.

[36] M. Weintraub, S. Goldberg, and A. A. Orning, "A Study of Sulfur Reactions in Furnace Deposits," *Transactions of the ASME. Journal of Engineering for Power*, 83, Series A: 444–450, October 1961.

[37] P. Sedor, E. K. Diehl, and D. H. Barnhart, "External Corrosion of Superheaters in Boilers Firing High-Alkali Coals," *Transactions of the ASME. Journal of Engineering for Power*, 82, Series A: 181–193, July, 1960.

[38] H. E. Crossley, "External Boiler Deposits," *Journal of Institute of Fuel*, 25 (145): 221–225, September, 1952.

[39] P. H. Crumley, A. W. Fletcher, and D. S. Wikon, "The Formation of Bonded Deposits in Pulverized-Fuel-Fired Boilers," *Journal of the Institute of Fuel*, 28 (170): 117–120, March 1955.

[40] C. H. Anderson and E. Diehl, "Bonded Fireside Deposits in Coal-Fired Boilers; A Progress Report on Manner of Formation," *ASME Paper No. 55-A-200*. New York: American Society of Mechanical Engineers, 1955. Abstracted in *Mechanical Engineering*, 78: 271, 1956.

[41] R. W. Borio and R. P. Hensel, "Coal-Ash Composition as Related to High-Temperature Fireside Corrosion and Sulfur Oxides Emission Control," *Transactions of the ASME. Journal of Engineering for Power*, 94, Series A: 142–148, April 1972; also in. *ASME Paper No. 71-WA/CD-4*. New York; American Society of Mechanical Engineers 1971; and in Combustion Engineering publication TIS-3019.

[42] R. W. Borio, et al., "Control of High-Temperature Metal Wastage in Pulverized Coal-Fired Steam Generators," Combustion Engineering publication TIS-5055.

[43] A. Rahmel, "Influence of Calcium and Magnesium Sulfates on High Temperature Oxidation of Austenitic Chrome-Nickel Steels in the Presence of Alkali Sulfates and Sulfur Trioxides," *Mechanism of Corrosion by Fuel Impurities;* proceedings of the International Conference held at the Marchwood Engineering Laboratories, Marchwood near Southhampton, Hampshire, England, May 20–24, 1963. H. R. Johnson and D. J. Littler, general editors. London: Butterworths, 1963.

[44] A. L. Plumley, "Incinerator Corrosion Potential," *ASME Incinerator Division Corrosion Symposium*. New York: American Society of Mechanical Engineers, 1970.

[45] A. J. B. Cutler, et al., "The Role of Chloride in Corrosion Caused by Flue Gases and Their Deposits," *ASME Paper No. 70 WA/CD-1*. New York: American Society of Mechanical Engineers, 1970.

[46] K. Fassler, H. Leib, and H. Spaun, "Corrosion in Refuse Incinerators," *Mittelungen der VGB*, 48 (2): 126–139, 1968.

[47] R. Baum and C. H. Parker, "Incinerator Corrosion in the Presence of Poly- (Vinyl Chloride) and Other Acid-Releasing Constituents," *Plastecology 1972*, Society of Plastic Engineers, Regular Technical Conference, Rosemont, Illinois, October 11–12, 1972, pp. 44–51.

[48] R. E. Summerlad, R. W. Bryers, and J. D. Shenker, "Systems Evaluation of Refuse as a Low Sulfur Fuel: Part 2—Steam Generator Aspects," *ASME Paper No. 71-WA/INC-2*. New York: American Society of Mechanical Engineers, 1971.

[49] H. H. Krause, D. A. Vaughan, and W. K. Boyd, "Corrosion and Deposits from Combustion on Solid Waste. Part III—Effects of Sulfur on Boiler Tube Metal," *Transactions of the ASME. Journal of Engineering for Power*, 97 (3), Series A: 448–452, July 1975. Also published as *ASME Paper No. 74-WA/CD-5*. New York: American Society of Mechanical Engineers, 1974.

[50] H. H. Krause, D. A. Vaughan, and W. K. Boyd, "Corrosion and Deposits from Combustion of Solid Wastes. Part III—Effects of Sulfur on Boiler Tube Metals," *Transactions of the ASME. Journal of Engineering for Power*, 97 (3), Series A: 448–452, July 1975.

[51] A. T. Bouden, P. Draper, and H. Rowling, "The Problem of Fuel Oil Ash Deposition in Open Cycle Gas Turbines," *Proceedings of the Institution of Mechanical Engineers*, 167: 291–300, 1953.

[52] Norman D. Phillips and Charles L. Wagoner, "Use of Differential Thermal Analysis in Exploring Minimum Temperature Limits of Oil Ash Corrosion," *Corrosion*, 17 (8): 102–106, August 1961.

[53] T. Widell and I. Juhasz, "Softening Temperature of Residual Fuel Oil Ash," *Combustion*, 22 (11): 51, May 1951.

[54] J. J. MacFarlane and N. Stephenson, "Communication," pp. 30T–31T of article by S. H. Frederick and T. F. Eden, "Corrosion Aspects of the Vanadium Problem in Gas Turbines," *Corrosion*, 11: 19T–33T, 1955.

[55] A. Voorhies, Jr., et al., "Improvement in Fuel Oil Quality, I—Demetalization of Residual Fuels II—Desulfurization of Residual Fuels." *Mechanism of Corrosion by Fuel Impurities*, proceedings of the International Conference held at the Marchwood Engineering Laboratories, Marchwood, near Southampton, Hampshire, England, May 20–24, 1963. H. R. Johnson and D. J. Littler, general editors. London: Butterworths, 1963.

[56] C. J. A. Edwards, *Literature Survey Primarily Covering Fireside Deposits and Corrosion Associated with Boiler Superheater Tubes in Oil-Fired Naval Steam-Raising Installation with Some References Also to Similar Problems in Land-Based Installations and Gas Turbines*. British Petroleum Research Centre, 1964.

[57] G. Whittingham, "The Oxidation of Sulfur Dioxide in the Combustion Process," *Third Symposium on Combustion, Flame, and Explosion Phenomena*, sponsored by the Combustion Institute and held at the University of Wisconsin, 1949, pp. 453–459. Pittsburgh: The Combustion Institute, 1971.

[58] A. B. Hedley, "Sulfur Trioxide in Combustion Gases," *Fuel Society Journal*, 43: 45–54, 1962.

[59] Arthur Levy and E. L. Merryman, "SO_3 Formation in H_2S Flames," *Transactions of the ASME. Journal of Engineering for Power*, 87, Series A: 116–123, January 1965.

Ibid., 374–378, October 1965.

[60] E. S. Lisle and J. D. Sensenbaugh, "The Determination of Sulfur Trioxide and Acid Dew Point in Flue Gases," *Combustion*, 36 (7): 12–16, January 1965.

[61] J. T. Reese, J. Jonakin, and V. Z. Caracristi, "Prevention of Residual Oil Combustion Problems by Use of Low Excess Air and Magnesium Additive," *ASME Paper No. 64-PWR-3*. New York: American Society of Mechanical Engineers, 1964.

BIBLIOGRAPHY

Bassa, G. and B. Bator, "The Influence of Distribution of Minerals in Pulverized Coals with High Mineral Contents on the Working Conditions of Steam Generators," *The Mechanism of Corrosion by Fuel Impurities*, proceedings of the International Conference held at the Marchwood Engineering Laboratories, Marchwood, near Southampton, Hampshire, England, May 20–24, 1963, H. R. Johnson and D. J. Littler, general editors. London: Butterworths, 1963, pp. 90–101.

Bishop, R. J. and J. A. C. Samms, "Pilot Scale Investigations of the Formation of Bonded Deposits," *The Mechanism of Corrosion by Fuel Impurities*, proceedings of the International Conference held at the Marchwood Engineering Laboratories, Marchwood, near Southampton, Hampshire, England, May 20–24, 1963, H. R. Johnson and D. J. Littler, general editors. London: Butterworths, 1963, pp. 155–172.

Boow, J., "Sodium/Ash Reactions in the Formation of Fireside Deposits in Pulverized-Fuel-Fired Boilers," *Fuel* 51(3): 170–173, July 1972.

Bryers, R. W., "The Physical and Chemical Characteristics of Pyrites and Their Influence on Fireside Problems in Steam Generators," *ASME Paper No. 75-WA/CD-2*. New York; American Society of Mechanical Engineers, 1975.

Bryers, R. W., and T. E. Taylor, "An Examination of the Relationship Between Ash Chemistry and Ash Fusion Temperatures in Various Coal Size and Gravity Fractions Using Polynomial Regression Analysis," *Transactions of the ASME. Journal of Engineering for Power*, 98, Series A: 528–539, October 1976.

Crossley, H. E., "External Boiler Deposits. Paper 4—Special Study of Ash and Clinker in Industry," *Journal of the Institute of Fuel*, 25(145): 221–225, September 1952.

Dundersdale, J., et al., "Studies Relating to the Behaviour of Sodium During the Combustion of Solid Fuels," *The Mechanism of Corrosion by Fuel Impurities*, proceedings of the International Conference held at the Marchwood Engineering Laboratories, Marchwood, near Southampton, Hampshire, England, May 20–24, 1963, H. R. Johnson and D. J. Littler, general editors. London: Butterworths, 1963, pp. 139–144.

Garner, L. J., "The Formation of Boiler Deposits from the Combustion of Victorian Brown Coals," *Journal of the Institute of Fuel*, 40(314): 107–116, March 1967.

Hedley, A. B., et al., "Available Mechanisms for Deposition from a Combustion Gas Stream," *ASME Paper No. 65-WA/CD-4*. New York: American Society of Mechanical Engineers, 1965.

Khrustalev, B. A., "Spectral Radiation Properties of Some Materials at High Temperatures and Their Influence on the Integral Absorption and Radiation Properties," *Heat Transfer-Soviet Research*, 5(2): 60–64, March/April 1973.

Krzhizhanovskii, R. E., et al., "Influence of Particle Size of Ash on the Structure and Effective Thermal Conductivity of Loose Deposits," *Thermal Engineering* (translation of *Teploenergetika*), 19(10): 36–39, 1972.

Kuleshova, I. A., et al., "Investigation of Fraction Composition and Properties of Pulverized Coal," *Thermal Engineering* (translation of *Teploenergetika*), 17(6):33–38, 1970.

Littlejohn, R. F., "Mineral Matter and Ash Distribution in 'As-Fired' Samples of Pulverized Fuels," *Journal of the Institute of Fuel*, 39(301): 59–67, February 1966.

Littlejohn, R. F. and J. D. Watt, "The Distribution of Mineral Matter in Pulverized Fuel," *The Mechanism of Corrosion by Fuel Impurities*, proceedings of the International Conference held at the Marchwood Engineering Laboratories, Marchwood, near Southampton, Hampshire, England, May 20–24, 1963, H. R. Johnson and D. J. Littler, general editors. London: Butterworths, 1963, pp. 102–112.

Marskell, W. G. and J. M. Miller, "Some Aspects of Deposit Formation in Pilot-Scale Pulverized-Fuel-Fired Installations." *Journal of the Institute of Fuel*, 29(188):380–387, September 1956.

Moody, A. H. and D. D. Langan, Jr., "Fusion Characteristics of Fractionated Coal Ashes," *Combustion*, 5(4):15–17, October 1933.

Moody, A. H. and D. D. Langan, Jr., "Fusion Temperature of Coal Ash as Related to Composition," *Combustion*, 6(8):13–20, February 1935.

Mulcahy, M. F., et al. "Fireside Deposits and Their Effect on Heat Transfer in a Pulverized-Fuel-Fired Boiler, Part I: The Radiant Emittance and Effective Thermal Conductance of the Deposits," *Journal of the Institute of Fuel*, 39(308):385–394, September 1966.

National Research Council. Committee on Chemical Utilization of Coal. Chemistry of Coal Utilization, prepared by the Committee on Chemical Utilization of Coal, Division of Chemistry and Chemical Technology, National Research Council, H. H. Lowry, chairman, Supplementary volume. New York: John Wiley and Sons, Inc., and London: Chapman and Hall, Ltd., 1963.

Raask, E., "Reactions of Coal Impurities During Combustion and Deposition of Ash Constituents on Cooled Surfaces," *The Mechanism of Corrosion by Fuel Impurities*, proceedings of the International Conference held at the Marchwood Engineering Laboratories, Marchwood, near Southampton, Hampshire, England, May 20–24, 1963, H. R. Johnson and D. J. Littler, general editors. London: Butterworths, 1963, pp. 145–154.

Smith, R. A. and L. R. Glicksman, "Radiation Properties of Slag," *ASME Paper No. 69-WA/PWR-7*. New York: American Society of Mechanical Engineers, 1969.

Tufte, Philip H., et al., "Ash Fouling Potentials of Western Subbituminous Coals Determined in a Pilot-Plant Test Furnace," *Proceedings of the American Power Conference*, 38:661–671, 1976. Chicago: Ill. Institute of Technology, 1976.

CHAPTER 4

Combustion Processes

This chapter includes the many fundamental equations used to describe how the fuel and air injected into a furnace are transformed into gaseous products of combustion. A major section is devoted to the "theory behind the hardware"—the mathematical background and experiential basis for reactions in both laboratory and power-plant ("commercial") furnaces. The discussion concludes with the theoretical and empirical criteria for the formation of nitrogen oxides during combustion, and methods for reducing their emission from a furnace.

All the material is closely related to the design of furnaces for both utility and industrial steam generators, and to the sizing of boiler and air heater heat-transfer surfaces, dust-collection and flue-gas desulfurization equipment, and mechanical draft fans.

HISTORICAL INTRODUCTION

Although from his earliest existence on earth man has been fascinated by fire, he did not achieve a quantitative understanding of the combustion process until about the year 1880. Prior to that date, one can trace the development of many hypotheses concerning the nature and properties of fire, including some that were expressed in supernatural terms of fear and awe. However, even the existence of the now discredited phlogiston theory of combustion did not prevent enterprising engineers from designing and constructing boilers to generate steam for the earliest steam engines.

Phlogiston was a hypothetical mysterious substance which sometimes was presumed to have the property of negative weight and which combined with a body to render it combustible. First proposed by G. E. Stahl in 1697, the phlogiston theory dominated the chemical thought of the 18th century. Even such a perceptive observer as Joseph Priestly, who in 1774 discovered the unique power of oxygen for supporting combustion, accepted the phlogiston theory. In the years between 1775 and 1781, Antoine L. Lavoisier substituted for it the theory of oxygenation and provided experimental evidence that combustion was the union of the substance burned with the oxygen of the atmosphere.

In 1755 Joseph Black discovered carbon dioxide, and in 1781 Henry Cavendish demonstrated the compound nature of water. At about this same time Lavoisier made the precise measurements and formulated the volume and weight relationships that underlie the modern theory of combustion.

Beyond this, in 1811 Amedeo Avogadro established that the number of molecules in a unit volume under standard conditions is the same for all gases. During this same period John Dalton enunciated the law of partial pressures, and in 1803 his study of the physical properties of gases led to formulation of the atomic theory, including the law of combining weights. A related observation was made by Gay-Lussac in 1808 that gases always combine in volumes that bear simple ratios to each other.

COMBUSTION FUNDAMENTALS

To the engineer concerned with boiler design and performance, combustion may be considered as the chemical union of the combustible of a fuel and the oxygen of the air, controlled at such a rate as to produce useful heat energy. The principal combustible constituents are elemental carbon, hydrogen, and their compounds. In the combustion process, the compounds and elements are burned to carbon dioxide and water vapor. Small quantities of sulfur are present in most fuels. Although sulfur is a combustible and contributes slightly to the heating value of the fuel, its presence is generally detrimental because of the corrosive nature of its compounds.

Air, the usual source of oxygen for combustion in boilers, is a mixture of oxygen, nitrogen and small amounts of water vapor, carbon dioxide, argon and other elements. The composition of dry atmospheric air is given in Table I.

In an ideal situation, the combustion process would occur with the exact proportions of oxygen and a combustible that are called for in theory (the stoichiometric quantities). But it is impracticable to operate a boiler at the theoret-

---

Table I. Composition of Combustion Air

Dry Atmospheric Air

The volumetric composition of dry atmospheric air given in NACA Report 1235 (Standard Atmosphere—Tables and Data for Altitudes to 65,800 feet, November 20, 1952),[1] and the molecular weights of the gases constituting dry air are as follows:

	Volume %	Mol. Wgt.
Nitrogen	78.09	28.016
Oxygen	20.95	32.000
Argon	0.93	39.944
Carbon dioxide	0.03	44.010

(Neon, helium, krypton, hydrogen, xenon, ozone, and radon, combined, are less than 0.003%.)

Dry air with this composition has an apparent molecular weight of 28.97 lb/lb mol and a density at 32°F and 14.7 psia of 28.97 ÷ 359 = 0.0807 lb/ft³. The oxygen content is 23.14% by weight. The lb dry air/lb oxygen = 1 ÷ 0.2314 = 4.32.

Wet Atmospheric Air

Wet atmospheric air is defined in this text as the above air plus 0.013 lb of water vapor/lb of dry air. (Air at 80°F, 60% relative humidity, and 14.7 psia pressure contains 1.3% water vapor by weight. See Fig. 1.)

Wet air with this amount of water vapor has an apparent molecular weight of 28.74 lb/lb mol and a density at 32°F and 14.7 psia of 0.0801 lb/ft³. The oxygen content is 22.84% by weight. The lb wet atmospheric air/lb oxygen = 1 ÷ 0.2284 = 4.38.

The mass of nitrogen, argon, carbon dioxide and water/lb oxygen = 77.16/22.84 = 3.38 lb.

---

ical level of zero percent excess oxygen. In practice this condition is approached by providing an excess of oxygen in the form of excess air from the atmosphere. The amount of excess air varies with the fuel, boiler load, and the type of firing equipment.

COMBUSTION EQUATIONS

For combustion calculations, however, it is customary to write the combustion reaction equations on the basis of theoretical oxygen only, notwithstanding the presence of excess air and nitrogen. A partial list of these combustion equations and the approximate heat released in the reactions are given in Table II.

All combustion calculations are based on fundamental chemical reactions shown in Table II. Not only do the equations indicate what substances are involved in the reaction, but they also show the molecular proportions in which they take part.

Each molecule has a numerical value that represents its relative weight or molecular weight. This molecular weight is the sum of the atomic weights of the atoms composing the molecule. For example, carbon, C, has a molecular weight of 12; oxygen, O_2, has a molecular weight of $2 \times 16 = 32$; and carbon dioxide, CO_2, has a molecular weight of $12 + (2 \times 16) = 44$. These molecular weights are only relative values and may be expressed in any units. Note that the molecular weights in Table II are the whole-number values of the main isotopes of each substance.

It has been established that a molecular weight of any substance in the gaseous state and under the same conditions of temperature and pressure will occupy the same volume. This relationship is very significant. The volume will, of course, vary numerically for different units of weight and for different conditions of temperature and pressure. For combustion calculations, the pound and the cubic foot are the units commonly used in the U.S. and, unless otherwise stated, the temperature and pressure are understood to be 32°F and 14.7 psia. Thus a molecular weight of 32 lb of oxygen at 32°F and atmospheric pressure will have the same volume as a molecular weight of 44 lb of carbon dioxide under the same conditions. This volume is 359 cu ft.

CONCEPT OF THE MOL

A molecular weight expressed in pounds is called a *pound mol*, or simply a *mol*, and the volume that it occupies is called a *molal volume*. Molal volume varies with changes in temperature and pressure according to Boyle's and Charles' laws and may be corrected to any desired conditions. Volume is directly proportional to the absolute temperature and inversely proportional to the absolute pressure.

Table II. Combustion Equations

Combustible	Molecular Weight	Reaction	Heat Release,* Btu/lb
Carbon	12	$C + O_2 \rightarrow CO_2$	14,100
Hydrogen	2	$H_2 + 0.5\,O_2 \rightarrow H_2O$	61,000
Sulfur	32	$S + O_2 \rightarrow SO_2$	4,000
Hydrogen sulfide	34	$H_2S + 1.5\,O_2 \rightarrow SO_2 + H_2O$	7,100
Methane	16	$CH_4 + 2\,O_2 \rightarrow CO_2 + 2H_2O$	23,900
Ethane	30	$C_2H_6 + 3.5\,O_2 \rightarrow 2CO_2 + 3H_2O$	22,300
Propane	44	$C_3H_8 + 5\,O_2 \rightarrow 3CO_2 + 4H_2O$	21,500
Butane	58	$C_4H_{10} + 6.5\,O_2 \rightarrow 4CO_2 + 5H_2O$	21,300
Pentane	72	$C_5H_{12} + 8\,O_2 \rightarrow 5CO_2 + 6H_2O$	22,000

*Higher heating value/lb of combustible

Because combustion processes in steam boiler furnaces usually take place at practically constant atmospheric pressure, pressure corrections are seldom necessary.

Returning to the combustion equation for carbon and oxygen and applying these concepts, it is now possible to write this reaction in several ways. For purposes of molar analysis carbon may be treated as a gas.

$$(1)\, C + (1)\, O_2 = (1)\, CO_2 \tag{1}$$

$$1\, mol\, C + 1\, mol\, O_2 = 1\, mol\, CO_2 \tag{2}$$

$$12\, lb\, C + 32\, lb\, O_2 = 44\, lb\, CO_2 \tag{3}$$

Dividing through by 12,

$$1\, lb\, C + 2.67\, lb\, O_2 = 3.67\, lb\, CO_2 \tag{4}$$

$$1\, volume\, C + 1\, volume\, O_2 = 1\, volume\, CO_2 \tag{5}$$

Because there are 4.32 lbs of dry air/lb of oxygen, the stoichiometric combustion of 1 lb of carbon requires 11.52 lb of dry air, or 11.68 lb of wet air (with 1.3 percent water vapor).

Each equation balances; there are the same number of atoms of each element and the same weight of reacting substances on each side of the arrow but not necessarily the same number of molecules, mols or volumes. Thus, one atom of carbon combined with one molecule of oxygen gives only one molecule of carbon dioxide; two mols of hydrogen plus one mol of oxygen yield two mols of water vapor.

It will be evident from a consideration of the mol-volume relationship that percent by volume is numerically the same as mol percent.

Because a mol represents a definite weight as well as a definite volume, it is a means of converting analyses by weight into analyses by volume and vice versa. Volumetric fractions of the several constituents of a gas can be multiplied by their respective molecular weights, with the sum of the products then being equal to the apparent molecular weight of one mol of gas. The percent by weight of each component can then be determined. Finally, the density of any gas at any temperature is found by dividing the molecular weight of the gas by the molal volume at that temperature, Fig. 2.

Fig. 1 Moisture content of dry air as a function of dry-bulb temperature and relative humidity

Fig. 2 Gas density determination

METHODS OF COMBUSTION CALCULATIONS

Two methods of combustion calculations are presented in this text. The first is known as the mol method and is based on the chemical relationships previously explained. The second method uses the firing of a million Btu as a basis for calculation.

THE MOL METHOD

Table II gives the basic combustion reactions for the carbon, hydrogen, and sulfur in coal.

Assume a high-volatile bituminous coal of the following analysis, burned at 23 percent excess air; perform calculations on the basis of 100 lb of as-fired fuel. The fuel analysis as fired is the following

	% by Weight	Mol Weight
C	63.50	12
H_2	4.07	2
S	1.53	32
O_2	7.46	32
N_2	1.28	28
H_2O	15.00	18
Ash	7.16	
HHV	11,200 Btu/lb	

The calculation of air weight for combustion must be made on the basis of an oxygen balance because oxygen is the only element common to all oxidizing reactions. Oxygen contained in the fuel must be deducted from the calculated quantity needed because it is already combined with carbon, hydrogen, or other combustible constituents of the coal.

The molar relations are as given in Table II:

Mol	Mol O_2	Mol CO_2	Mol H_2O	Mol SO_2
C	1	1		
H	0.5		1	
S	1			1

AIR FOR COMBUSTION

O_2 for C	63.5/12	= 5.29 lb mol
O_2 for H	4.07/2 × 2	= 1.02 lb mol
O_2 for S	1.53/32	= 0.05 lb mol
	Total	6.36 lb mol

Less O_2 in fuel	7.46/32	= 0.23 lb mol
O_2 required		= 6.13 lb mol
O_2 in excess air	6.13 × 0.23	= 1.41 lb mol
	Total O_2 required	= 7.54 lb mol

Dry air required = (7.54 lb mol O_2)

$$\frac{(100 \text{ lb mol air})}{(20.95 \text{ lb mol } O_2)} = 36.0 \text{ lb mol}$$

36.0 × 28.97 = 1043 lb dry air/100 lb fuel

WEIGHT OF DRY PRODUCTS OF COMBUSTION

The weight of gaseous products of combustion can be calculated from the volumetric analysis of flue gas. Not only the weight of the flue gas/100 lb of coal but its analysis and volume can be calculated from the information given in the preceding example.

To obtain the wet products of combustion, or total wet gas when a fuel burns completely, the weight of the fuel is added to the weight of atmospheric air supplied for its combustion. If some of the fuel is ash or, if because of incomplete combustion, some of the fuel does not leave the furnace with the gases, then there will be less burned-out fuel in the products.

The wet products of combustion in the above example then, are the fuel (100 lb − 7.16 lb ash = 92.84 lb/100 lb) plus the air required for combustion or (rounded) 93 + 1043 = 1136 lb/100 lb of fuel.

THE MILLION-BTU METHOD

This method for combustion calculations is based on the concept that the weight of air required in the combustion of a unit weight of any commercial fuel is more nearly proportional to the unit heat value than to the unit weight of the fuel. Consequently, the weights of air, dry gas, moisture, wet gas, and other quantities are expressed in pounds per million Btu fired.

In connection with this calculation method, the following items will be discussed:

1. Fuel in products, F
2. Atmospheric air for combustion, A
3. Effect of unburned combustible
4. Products of combustion, P
5. Moisture in the combustion air, W_a

6. Moisture from fuel in products of combustion, W_f

7. Dry gas content of combustion products, P_d

The first four items are necessary for the calculation of the gas and air quantities. Items 5 to 7 form the basis of heat balance calculations, either in the design or testing of a steam generating unit.

FUEL IN PRODUCTS, F

As defined earlier, F is that portion of the fuel fired which appears in the gaseous products of combustion. Because all quantities are to be those required for, or resulting from, the firing of 1,000,000 Btu, F must be calculated on that basis. If a fuel contains no ash, F is obtained by dividing 1,000,000 by the as-fired heating value of the fuel. For solid fuels where ash and/or solid combustible loss must be considered,

$$F = \frac{10^4(100 - \% \text{ ash} - \% \text{ solid combustible loss})}{\text{fuel heat value}}$$

where:

F = lb/10^6 Btu fired

% ash = percent by weight in fuel as fired

% solid combustible loss = percent by weight in fuel as fired

fuel heat value (HHV) = high heat value as fired, Btu/lb

$$(6)$$

ATMOSPHERIC AIR FOR COMBUSTION, A

In accordance with the molar method, the theoretical weight of dry air (zero excess) may be calculated from the fuel analysis and the formula:

$$A_{dry} = \left[\frac{11.52\,(\%C) + 34.57\,(\%H - \%O/8) + 4.32\,(\%S)}{\text{HHV}} \right] \times 10^4$$

$$(7)$$

in which numerator and denominator are on the same basis—as-fired, moisture-free, or

moisture-and-ash free—and A_{dry} is in lb/10^6 Btu fired.

For air with 1.3-percent moisture by weight (80°F and 60-percent relative humidity), the formula becomes

$$A_{wet} = \left[\frac{11.68\,(\%C) + 35.03\,(\%H - \%O/8) + 4.38\,(\%S)}{\text{HHV}} \right] \times 10^4$$

$$(8)$$

Values of A_{wet} range from 570 lb/10^6 Btu for pure hydrogen to above 800 lb/10^6 Btu for certain cokes and meta-anthracite coals, as shown in Fig. 3 for various fuels burned in steam generators. Any calculated values of wet air for combustion differing substantially from these values should lead to a cross-verification of the ultimate analysis and the observed high heating value. The analysis and HHV of the fuel have to be from the same sample to avoid errors in air and gas weight determinations.

EFFECT OF UNBURNED COMBUSTIBLE

In the combustion of solid fuels, even in pulverized form, it is not feasible to burn the available combustible completely. Thus, the

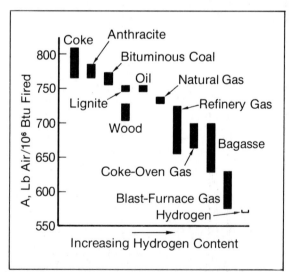

Fig. 3 Combustion-air requirements for various fuels at zero excess-air—a range of values as an approximate function of hydrogen content

air requirement per million Btu *fired* has to be reduced to the air required per million Btu *burned*. This is done by multiplying the combustion air A by the combustible-loss correction factor C.

The unburned combustible loss can be expressed either as percent carbon heat loss or the percent combustible weight loss. These are related by the expression:

$$\% \text{ Carbon heat loss } = \frac{14{,}600}{\text{HHV}} \times \% \text{ solid comb. wgt. loss} \qquad (9)$$

in which 14,600 is the heat value for combustibles in refuse recommended by *A.S.M.E. Performance Test Code*, and HHV is the high heating value of the as-fired fuel.

If a fuel has carbon as its only combustible constituent, the factor C equals

$$1 - \frac{\% \text{ solid combustible weight loss}}{100} \qquad (10)$$

If, however, all heat in the fuel does not come from carbon alone (so that the air is not strictly proportional to carbon burned), the factor C

will not be exact. For high-carbon, low-volatile fuels it will be nearly exact and will result in only a small error even for fuels low in fixed carbon and high in hydrogen. The error involved by using Eq. 10 in all cases is quite within the limits of accuracy of all other combustion calculations.

Finally, C can be expressed as a function of percent heat loss by combining the above relationships:

$$C = 1 - \frac{\% \text{ carbon heat loss}}{100} \times \frac{\text{HHV}}{14{,}600} \qquad (11)$$

Fig. 4 is a graphical solution of this equation.

PRODUCTS OF COMBUSTION, P

The total gaseous products of combustion, P, become the sum of F and A (as corrected for combustible loss). Thus,

$$P = F + CA \qquad (12)$$

where:
  P = total gaseous products of combustion, lb/10^6 Btu fired
  F = fuel fired exclusive of ash or solid carbon loss, lb/10^6 Btu fired
  A = atmospheric air consumed, lb/10^6 Btu fired
  C = combustible loss correction factor

MOISTURE IN COMBUSTION AIR, W_a

For heat-balance calculations, the moisture in air will be 1.3 percent of the air weight/10^6 Btu, or $W_a = 0.013A$, for ambient conditions of 80°F and 60-percent relative humidity. For air at a higher or lower temperature or relative humidity, the moisture content will be as shown in Fig. 1; air per million Btu, A, and W_a must be adjusted appropriately.

MOISTURE FROM FUEL, W_f

This item is separately reported both in an *ASME Performance Test Codes* heat balance

Fig. 4 Graphical solution of equation 11

and in a predicted heat balance. In the case of some fuels (such as natural and refinery gases), the heat loss because of this moisture may be the largest single item in the heat balance. W_f includes the combined surface and inherent moisture, W_c, from a fuel, plus the moisture formed by the combustion of hydrogen, W_h. W_c will vary from zero, or a mere trace in fuel oil, to over 115 lb/10^6 Btu fired in the case of green wood; W_h will vary from zero or a trace in lamp-black to 100 lb/10^6 Btu fired in the case of some refinery gases. Thus,

$$W_f = W_c + W_h, \text{ where}$$
$$W_c = H_2O \times \frac{10^4}{\text{HHV}}$$
$$\text{and } W_h = 9 \times H \times \frac{10^4}{\text{HHV}}$$

$$(13)$$

W_c and W_h are in lb/10^6 Btu fired, H_2O is the percent water by weight in the as-fired fuel, H is the hydrogen in the fuel (percent by weight as fired) and HHV is the high heating value of the as-fired fuel, Btu/lb.

DRY GAS, P_d

The dry-gas content of the combustion products is used in the calculation of the dry-gas-loss item of a boiler heat balance.

The dry gas may be determined by subtracting the water vapor from the total products, thus,

$$P_d = P - (W_a + W_f)$$

where

P_d = dry gas, lb/10^6 Btu fired
P = total products of combustion
W_a = moisture in air
W_f = moisture from fuel

COMBUSTION CALCULATIONS BY GRAPHICAL METHODS

In Appendix D, we present a convenient graphical system for solving the equations of this million Btu method, for coal and most other power plant fuels. Examples of all the significant combustion calculations are included to reinforce the above information.

In the event that an ultimate analysis of a given coal is not available, the curves and data in Appendix D can be used to arrive at close approximate solutions.

One of the principal purposes of Appendix D is to enable an engineer required to perform combustion calculations to obtain a "visual feel" for the order of magnitude of the calculated values. Engineering judgments about such concepts are very difficult to make based on calculations done on electronic computing equipment. When used in commercial problem solving, the answers obtained from computers stand alone, with no reference to physical input parameters. Thus, there is a lack of the judgmental development that can be gained from using graphical devices and one's skills may be limited to computer inputting.

THERMOCHEMISTRY

Energy is associated with the forces which bind atoms together to form a molecule. A rearrangement of the atoms to form new molecules, such as occurs in a chemical reaction, entails the liberation or absorption of energy. The branch of thermodynamics which deals with this subject is referred to as *thermochemistry*. Unfortunately, the working definitions regarding this aspect of thermal analysis are often obscurely stated and contradictory between authors. The definitions which follow are therefore not universal nor subscribed to by all authors in this field. In the main they will rely on the authoritative treatises by Wark[2], Reynolds and Perkins[3], and Van Wylen and Sonntag[4].

DEFINITIONS OF TERMS

Before proceeding, it is necessary to remark here that the reference datum for chemical thermodynamic tabulations is usually taken to be 1 atm pressure and 25°C (298°K, 77°F, or 537°R). This is called the *standard reference state* and, by convention, the enthalpy of every elemental substance (such as H_2, O_2, N_2, Cl) is defined to be zero at the standard reference state. We will briefly review several other definitions concerned with the emission or consumption of energy accompanying a thermochemical reaction.

INTERNAL ENERGY OF REACTION

If a chemical reaction occurs at constant volume and at 25°C initial temperature and the products of reaction are returned to 25°C, then the energy excess (liberated) or deficit (absorption) required to meet the conditions of this system is known as the internal energy of reaction. The symbol assigned this energy is ΔU_R. Heat of reaction at constant volume is an alternate for the internal energy of reaction. By first law analysis, we can write for this item $Q - \Delta U$.

ENTHALPY OF REACTION

If a chemical reaction is initiated at 25°C and the products are returned to 25°C and this process is carried out at constant pressure, then the energy supplied or disposed of is referred to as the enthalpy of reaction. The symbol assigned this energy is ΔH_R. Heat of reaction at constant pressure is an alternate term for the enthalpy of reaction. Although both ΔU_R and ΔH_R can be found tabularly listed, ΔH_R is the more commonly encountered as it is conveniently measured in a steady-flow device. Heat of reaction is a short form for heat of reaction at constant pressure, and is tabulated on a basis of Btu per mol of fuel burned. Heating value is synonymous with the heat of reaction, except that it is always taken as being positive.

ENTHALPY OF COMBUSTION

This is defined, sometimes, as the negative of the heating value. The symbol assigned the enthalpy of combustion is ΔH_C.

HIGHER HEATING VALUE; LOWER HEATING VALUE

If water in the products of combustion of a fossil fuel is taken as being condensed and lowered in temperature to 77°F at 1 atm, the condensation heat release h_{fg} is added to ΔH_C and this is called the higher heating value (HHV). If the H_2O remains as a vapor, then h_{fg} (1050.3 Btu/lb$_m$ at 25°C) is not added to ΔH_C depending on whether the enthalpy of combustion tabulation is on a liquid or vapor (H_2O) basis.

EXOTHERMIC HEAT

A chemical reaction which liberates energy (heat) is called exothermic and is denoted by ΔH_R (see heat of reaction at constant pressure). The sign convention adopted for the liberated energy is negative. This sign convention is not universal (not used in all textbooks).

Use of the negative convention invariably is justified by the argument that heat is removed from the system in order to return it to 25°C. The negative convention for exothermic reactions is, in fact, physically correct and can be justified on a more convincing basis. For example, in thermochemical terms:

H_2 (gas) + ½ O_2 (gas) → H_2O (liquid):

ΔH_R, 25°C = $-122,970$ Btu/lb mol

ΔH_R, 25°C = -68.137 kcal/g mol

a reaction which is also the HHV for the combustion of hydrogen. Fig. 5 demonstrates the principles introduced, on the basis of the formation of a lb-mol of H_2O, where one mol of a substance whose molecular weight is M is defined as M unit masses of that material.[5]

Fig. 5 Exothermic enthalpy of reaction for formation of H_2O at 1 atm, constant pressure

ENTHALPY OF FORMATION

Although the internal energy and enthalpy of reaction are basic quantities in the solution of thermochemical problems, the myriad chemical reactions effectively prohibit the overwhelming task of tabulating ΔU_R and ΔH_R values. Therefore, the concept of the enthalpy of formation was introduced. Applying the first law to a chemical reaction in a closed system at constant pressure, we write

$$\underset{i \text{ reactants}}{\Sigma(\nu_i H_i)} + \Delta H_R = \underset{i \text{ products}}{\Sigma(\nu_i H_i)}$$

where H_i is the molar enthalpy of any product or reactant at the pressure and temperature of the reaction, and ν_i again is the stoichiometric coefficient for each, based on the balanced chemical equation. It is clear that many sensible enthalpy tables for various gases account for changes in temperature at constant composition, whereas the thermochemical process being considered is defined in terms of constant temperature with variable composition. It follows that sensible enthalpy tables are not sufficient for evaluating energy transformations resulting from chemical reactions.

To circumvent this difficulty, the concept of an enthalpy of formation ΔH_f, is introduced. This is defined as the energy released or absorbed when a specific chemical compound, such as CO_2 or H_2O, is formed from its elements. The reactions, again, are such that initial reactant temperature and final product temperature are the same; written symbolically

$$Q = \Delta H_f = H_{compound} - \underset{i}{\Sigma(\nu_i H_i)}_{elements}$$

In this case the reactants are taken arbitrarily as the stable form of the elements at the given initial state. For example, the stable forms of gases such as hydrogen, nitrogen, and oxygen at 1 atm pressure and normal temperatures are $H_2(g)$, and $O_2(g)$. On the other hand, the stable form of carbon under these same conditions is $C(s)$. Because a value of zero has been assigned

to the enthalpy of all stable elements at 1 atm and 25°C, the enthalphy H_i of any compound at the same state is simply the enthalpy of formation of that substance, or

$$\Delta H_f = H_{compound} - zero = H_{compound}$$

Because the chemical enthalpy of a stable element is always zero, by definition, the enthalpy of any compound is composed of two parts: that associated with its formation from elements and the sensible enthalpy associated with a change of state at constant composition. The sum of these two parts is called the absolute enthalpy of a substance.

The foregoing is illustrated by the reaction

$$C(s) + O_2(g) \rightarrow CO_2(g)$$

As solid carbon and gaseous diatomic oxygen are the stable forms of these elements at 25°C and 1 atm, their chemical enthalpies are chosen to be zero. The enthalpy of reaction is easily measured experimentally for this reaction, and it is found to be $-169{,}290$ Btu/lb mol, or -94.054 kcal/g mol. These values are also the enthalpy of formation of carbon dioxide. From which it follows that ΔH_R, ΔH_C, and ΔH_f are related but not synonymous. This is shown somewhat more clearly by Table III.

The usefulness of ΔH_f values is based on the assumption that the enthalpy of any compound is equal, arbitrarily, to its enthalpy of formation from stable elements, we may substitute ΔH_f values for H_i values. Therefore

$$\Delta H_r = \underset{i}{\Sigma(\nu_i \Delta H_f)}_{products} - \underset{i}{\Sigma(\nu_i \Delta H_f)}_{reactants}$$

This equation is completely general for any reaction as long as the enthalpies of formation for all products and reactants are measured at the same temperature and pressure. This equation is widely used in thermochemistry. Its principal merit is, instead of requiring tabulations of thousands of values of ΔH_R for all conceivable reactions of interest, it is necessary only to tabulate ΔH_f values for compounds of interest. From the knowledge of ΔH_f values, applying this equation leads directly to any desired enthalpy of reaction.

We have briefly presented several different definitions or labels, but giving something a label does not necessarily constitute a satisfactory explanation. If, in addition, we literally interpret the words of Van Wylen[4] "The justification of this procedure of arbitrarily assigning the value of zero to the enthalpy of the elements at 25°C, 1 atm rests on the fact that, in the absence of nuclear reactions, the mass of each element is conserved in a chemical reaction. No conflicts or ambiguities arise with this choice of reference state, and it proves to be very convenient in studying chemical reactions from a thermodynamic point of view", then we are in a quandary regarding the origin of the energy we are tabulating.

Obviously, no one is going to abandon the law of conservation of mass as it is far too useful. On the other hand, we do not create energy out of thin air. The problem is resolved if we recognize that the law of conservation of mass is a near exact approximation which has been replaced by the law of conservation of mass-energy. There is nothing in Einstein's equation that prohibits or invalidates it outside the world of nuclear transition. For the HHV to be extracted from the reaction and do work, some-

thing else must disappear . . . that something is a minute amount of mass. We can quite readily calculate a conversion constant on a per Btu and on a per kcal basis. We write the well known Einstein relation as:

$$\delta m = E/C^2$$

where[5]

$$C = 2.99793 \times 10^5 \text{ km/sec}$$
$$= 1.86282 \times 10^5 \text{ miles/sec}$$

For a ΔE of 1 Btu, C of 9.8357×10^8 ft/sec, the gravitational constant of 32.174 ft-lb_m/lb_f-sec^2 and the relationship for the mechanical-equivalent of heat, 1 Btu = 778.16 ft-lb_f[6]

$$(1 \text{ Btu}) \times \frac{778.16 \text{ ft-}lb_f \times}{\text{Btu}}$$

$$\frac{32.174 \text{ ft-}lb_m}{lb_f\text{-sec}^2 \, 96.741 \times 10^{16}\frac{\text{ft}^2}{\text{sec}^2}}$$

yields 2.588×10^{-14} lb_m/Btu

Using the more recent value of 777.649 for J (see ref 6), we get 2.586×10^{-14} lb/$_m$/Btu. On a metric basis, we get 4.655×10^{-4} kg/kcal. It follows that we adopt 2.586×10^{-14} lb_m/Btu and 4.655×10^{-14} kg/kcal as the mass equivalency

Table III. Enthalpy of Formation vs. Enthalpy of Combustion[1] at 25°C and at 1 atm Pressure

Substance	Chemical Formula	$\Delta H_f(25°C)$ kcal/g mol	$\Delta H_f(25°C)$ Btu/lb mol	$\Delta H_c(25°C)$ kcal/g mol	$\Delta H_c(25°C)$ Btu/lb mol
Carbon	C (solid)	0	0	−94.054	−169,290
Hydrogen	H_2 (gas)	0	0	−68.317	−122,970
Oxygen	O_2 (gas)	0	0	0	0
Carbon Monoxide	CO (gas)	−26.417	−47,540	−67.636	−121,750
Carbon Dioxide	CO_2 (gas)	−94.054	−169,290	0	0
Water	H_2O (vapor)	−57.798	−104,040	0	0
Water	H_2O (liquid)	−68.317	−122,970	0	0
Methane	CH_4 (gas)	−17.895	−32,210	−212.80	−383,040
Propane	C_3H_8 (gas)	−24.82	−44,680	−530.60	−955,070
Methyl Alcohol	CH_3OH (gas)	−48.08	−86,540	−182.61	−328,700

For ΔH_c the water in products of combustion is assumed to be liquid. The ΔH_c values are therefore also HHV values (except that HHV values are always given as positive).

constants. In the case of a power plant which averages a heat fired of, say, 3000×10^6 Btu/hr then, over a 25-year operating lifetime we find that

$$3 \times 10^9 \times 24 \times 365 \times 25 \times 2.586 \times 10^{-14} \cong 17 \, lb$$

So about 17 lb of matter have been converted into energy, of which roughly 6.8 lb became electrical energy. This loss of mass is true only, of course, in the case where we transfer energy out of the system. In an adiabatic process where the system is not cooled down to the standard reference state, then no mass is lost because no energy is transferred.

THE GIBBS AND HELMHOLTZ FUNCTIONS

The enthalpy of formation concept we have just discussed implies that the reaction under consideration goes to completion. The disruptive energies available in a flame as, for example, temperature, are sufficiently high that this is not strictly true; thus, the reaction goes to completion in a somewhat cooler region adjoining the bulk flame volume. This is commonly referred to as residual combustion. The bulk flame composition in terms of the established product constituents (O_2, O, H_2O, OH, CO, CO_2, N_2, N, SO_2, SO, NH, NH_3, CN, HCN) attains some equilibrium composition consistent with the prevailing temperature.

By thermodynamic calculations it is possible to predict how far a reaction need go to reach equilibrium at a specified temperature by considering the thermodynamic potential of the reaction according to the Gibbs Free Energy Change ΔG.[7,8] Because this includes entropy in its determination, it is appropriate at this point to dispel some of the confusion that historically has attended this quantity. In physics a system is said to be in its most probable configuration when the number of accessible states is a maximum.

This is defined as follows[9]:

> u = system energy
> N = number of atoms in the system

The number of accessible states is called the degeneracy function g (not to be confused with the Gibbs function g) and is written as g(N, U). For any meaningful system this is a very large number and therefore the physicist defines for convenience a smaller number σ such that

$$\sigma(N,u) = \ln g(N,u)$$

This definition is called the *Entropy* or *Fundamental Entropy* and is related to the thermodynamic entropy S by the definition

$$S = K_B \sigma$$

where
K_B = the Boltzmann constant = 1.381×10^{-16} erg/°K

Taking two systems, not in contact, we define system 1 to have accessible states g_1 and system 2 to have accessible states g_2. Then the combined accessible states are $g_1 g_2$. The physicist's entropy of the combined system is

$$\sigma = \ln(g_1 g_2) = \ln g_1 + \ln g_2 = \sigma_1 + \sigma_2$$

The total entropy is, thus, the sum of the entropies of the separate systems. From statistical mechanics we find that a quantity called the *Fundamental Temperature* is defined in terms of the fundamental entropy as

$$\frac{1}{\tau} = \left(\frac{\partial \sigma(N,u)}{\partial u} \right)$$

Performing the operation,

$$\frac{1}{\tau} = \frac{\partial \sigma(N,u)}{\partial u} = \frac{\partial \ln g(N,u)}{\partial u} = \frac{1}{g} \frac{\partial g}{\partial u}$$

$$= \frac{1}{g(N,u)} \lim_{\Delta u \to 0} \frac{g(N,u + \Delta u) - g(N,u)}{\Delta u}$$

As $N \to 0$, we conclude that $g(N,u) \to 0$ because for zero atoms we have zero accessible states, or $\frac{1}{\tau} \to \infty$ from which $\tau \to \infty$. It follows that

$$\frac{K_B}{\tau} = K_B \frac{\partial \sigma}{\partial u} = \frac{\partial K_B \sigma}{\partial u} = \frac{\partial S}{\partial u}$$

We now define a quantity T such that $\tau = K_B T$. Then

$$\frac{1}{T} = \frac{\partial S}{\partial u}$$

which we write in engineering form as

$$dS = \frac{du}{T}$$

In a more restricted sense, this is generally encountered as

$$S = \int \frac{dq}{T}$$

and is the entropy associated with the Gibbs equation. We can write the first law in the form (per unit mass)

$$dq = dU + Pdv \tag{15A}$$

$$dq = dh - vdP \tag{15B}$$

where h is the usual classical thermodynamic enthalpy function, defined as $U + Pv$, but is evaluated in terms of T and P. By taking $h = h(T,P)$, we write

$$dh = \left(\frac{\partial h}{\partial T}\right)_P dT + \left(\frac{\partial h}{\partial P}\right)_T dP$$

which introduces the definition for the specific heat at constant pressure as:

$$C_P = \left(\frac{\partial h}{\partial T}\right)_P$$

We can write the second law in the Clausius form as:

$$dq = TdS \tag{16}$$

Combining (16) and (Eq. 15A), we get

$$dS = \frac{1}{T} dU + \frac{P}{T} dv \tag{17A}$$

which is called the Gibbs equation. Writing Eq. 17A as:

$$TdS = dU + Pdv \tag{17B}$$

and assuming a system at constant volume ($dv = 0$), we get the definition

$$T = \left(\frac{\partial u}{\partial S}\right)_v \tag{17C}$$

Writing Eq. 15B as

$$TdS = dh - vdP \tag{18a}$$

and taking a system at constant pressure ($dP = 0$) we also get the definition

$$T = \left(\frac{\partial h}{\partial S}\right)_P \tag{19}$$

Writing Eq. 15A as

$$TdS = dU + Pdv$$

Then at constant u ($du = 0$) it follows that

$$\frac{P}{T} = \left(\frac{\partial S}{\partial V}\right)_u \tag{20}$$

We can then show the Gibbs equation from

$$S = S(u, v)$$

$$dS = \left(\frac{\partial S}{\partial u}\right)_v du + \left(\frac{\partial S}{\partial v}\right)_u dV \tag{21}$$

Substituting Eqs. 17c and 20 into 21, we get

$$dS = \frac{1}{T} du + \frac{P}{T} dV$$

Now differentiate TS

$$d(TS) = TdS + SdT$$

or

$$TdS = -SdT + d(TS)$$

Since (15B) can be written as

$$TdS = dh - vdP$$

we get

$$dh - vdP = d(TS) - SdT$$

then

$$dh - d(TS) = d(h - TS) = VdP - SdT = d(g)$$

The definition

$$g = h - TS \tag{22}$$

is known as the Gibbs function (Fig. 6) and is the *Free Enthalpy* but is also commonly called the Gibbs free energy. The equation

$$d(h - TS) = VdP - SdT \tag{23}$$

gives

$$\left(\frac{\partial(h - TS)}{\partial P}\right)_T = v \text{ at constant T} \tag{24}$$

and

$$\left(\frac{\partial(h - TS)}{\partial T}\right)_P = -S \text{ at constant P} \tag{25}$$

Taking $\frac{\partial}{\partial T}$ of Eq. 24 and $\frac{\partial}{\partial P}$ of Eq. 25, we get

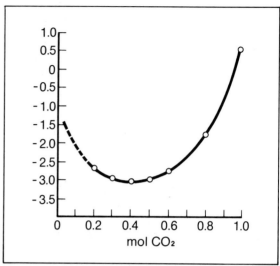

Fig. 6 The Gibbs function calculation shows that equilibrium is established at about 0.4 mol CO_2

$$\frac{\partial(h - TS)}{\partial T \partial P} = \left(\frac{\partial v}{\partial T}\right)_P, \ \frac{\partial(h - TS)}{\partial P \partial T} = -\left(\frac{\partial S}{\partial P}\right)_T$$

from which

$$\left(\frac{\partial S}{\partial P}\right)_T = -\left(\frac{\partial v}{\partial T}\right)_P \tag{26}$$

Returning to Eq. 15B we write classic definition of C_P

$$C_P = \left(\frac{\partial h}{\partial T}\right)_P \text{ or } dq = C_P (dT)_P = dh$$

Then Eq. 15B becomes

$$C_P (dT)_P = Tds - \cancel{vdP}_o$$

which yields an alternate definition for C_P as

$$C_P = T\left(\frac{\partial S}{\partial T}\right)_P \tag{27}$$

For engineering applications the entropy S is given as a function of temperature and pressure. (See Properties of Steam, Appendix F.)

Taking $\quad S = S(T,P)$, then

$$dS = \left(\frac{\partial S}{\partial T}\right)_P dT + \left(\frac{\partial S}{\partial P}\right)_T dP$$
(28)

Substituting Eqs. 26 and 27, we get

$$dS = \frac{C_P}{T}dT - \left(\frac{\partial v}{\delta T}\right)_P dP$$
(29)

where Eq. 29 is a convenient form for calculating change in entropy at constant pressure.
If we combine Eq. 15A with the differential of TS, we get

$$d(TS) - SdT = du + Pdv$$

or

$$d(u - TS) = -Pdv - SdT = d(f)$$
(30)

In Eq. 30 the definition

$$f = u - TS$$
(31)

is called the Helmholtz function and is also known as the free energy property of the system. To distinguish this from Gibbs free energy, it is customary to call this the Helmholtz free energy.

From the classical definition of enthalpy as h = u + Pv, we write the Gibbs function as

$$g = h - TS = u + Pv - TS$$
(32)

Combining Eqs. 32 with 31, we find that the Gibbs and Helmholtz functions are related as

$$g = f + Pv$$
(33)

Eq. 33 possibly accounts for the fact that the Gibbs function is also referred to as the Gibbs-Helmholtz equation.

Differentiating the enthalpy, h = u + Pv, we get

$$dh = du + Pdv + vdP$$
(34)

and writing the Gibbs Eq. 17A as

$$du = TdS - Pdv$$
(35)

we get upon combining Eqs. 34 and 35

$$dh = TdS + vdP$$
(36)

Differentiating the Gibbs function Eq. 22

$$dg = dh - TdS - SdT$$
(37)

and combining Eqs. 36 and 37, we get a differential equation of state

$$dg = vdP - SdT$$
(38)

At constant pressure we write Eq. 38 as

$$dg = -SdT$$
(39)

In the JANAF[10] form, this is written as

$$\frac{d(\Delta G^\circ)}{dT} = -\Delta S^\circ$$
(40)

where the circular superscript ° indicates the thermodynamic standard of 1 atm. and 25°C.

The Gibbs and Helmholtz functions have negative values since TS is greater than u or h.

On a T-S diagram for steam, this is clearly illustrated as shown (g = h − TS) (Fig. 7).

The equilibrium composition of a mixture reacting in an isothermal constant volume enclosure is the composition with the least absolute value of the Helmholtz function (f = u − TS) (Fig. 8).

A chemical reaction proceeding at constant temperature and pressure has the Gibbs function of the mixture decreasing to a minimum at the equilibrium composition. The Gibbs function (Fig. 9) allows us to determine the equilibrium composition of any reactive mixture of known pressure and temperature, regardless of whether these were constant during the reaction or not.

The Equilibrium Coefficient and the van't Hoff Equation

Eq. 38 is written as

$$dg = vdP$$

(41)

for a constant-temperature process. We are interested in this, as the Gibbs function criterion for equilibrium is based on constant temperature and total pressure.

Assuming ideal gases, we replace v in Eq. 41 by v = RT/P, giving

$$dg = RT \frac{dP}{P}$$

(42)

Integrating from standard state T° to T for the Gibbs differential and from standard state pressure of 1 atm to partial pressure P_i at Gibbs condition g_T at temperature T, and for any i^{th} component of a multicomponent gas, we get

$$g_T - g_{T°} = RT \ln \frac{P_i \, atm}{1 \, atm}$$

Taking R to be the universal gas constant, ft-lb/lb-mol-°R, and taking J as 778 ft-lb = 1 Btu (mechanical equivalent of heat), then

$$g_T - g_{T°} = \frac{RT}{J} \ln \frac{P_i}{1} \quad Btu/lb\text{-}mol$$

Writing this in terms of component i of a mixture

$$g_{i,T} = g_{i,T°} + \frac{RT}{J} \ln P_i$$

(43)

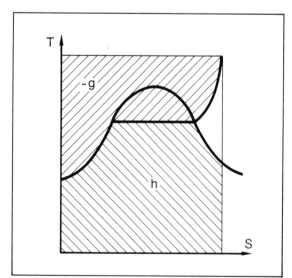

Fig. 7 Enthalpy h and free enthalpy g (Gibbs function).

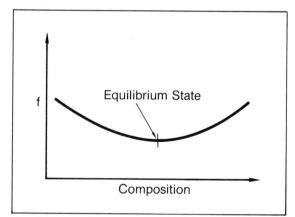

Fig. 8 Equilibrium at isothermal and constant volume conditions (Helmholtz function)

In Eq. 43, the value of g_i of the ith component at temperature T is found from the Gibbs function of the component at temperature $T°$ (25°C) and its partial pressure P_i (atm.) in the mixture.

STOICHIOMETRIC COMBUSTION OF GAS

To introduce the next step, we consider the combustion of natural gas and assume it to be 100 percent CH_4.

$$CH_4 + 2O_2 \rightarrow CO_2 + 2H_2O \tag{44}$$

or in symbolic form

$$\nu_A A + \nu_B B \rightarrow \nu_E E + \nu_F F \tag{45}$$

where the ν_i are called the stoichiometric coefficients. Because we normally burn with air, we can assume air to be 21 percent by volume oxygen and take the balance as nitrogen.

$$21\% \ O_2 + 79\% \ N_2 \rightarrow 100\% \ air$$

or

$$1 \ mol \ O_2 + 3.76 \ mol \ N_2 = 4.76 \ mols \ air$$

We rewrite Eq. 44 as

$$CH_4 + 2O_2 + 7.52 N_2 \rightarrow CO_2 + 2H_2O + 7.52 N_2$$

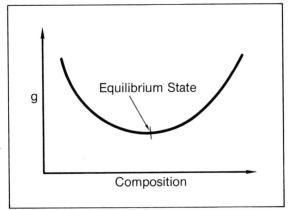

Fig. 9 Equilibrium at isothermal and constant pressure conditions (Gibbs function)

The values of ν_i are, of course, always known when the reaction is known. For an ideal gas the properties of the components are independent of one another (Gibbs-Dalton Law), wherefore the Gibbs function of the mixture is just the sum of the Gibbs functions of the i components. Then

$$G_{mix} = \sum N_i \, g_{i,T} = \sum N_i \left(g_{i,T°} + \frac{RT}{J} \ln P_i \right) \tag{46}$$

where N_i is the number of mols of each constituent present in the enclosure. If a differential amount of reactants A,B are combusted in time $d\gamma$ to form products E,F (see Eq. 45) and writing these mol amounts as dN_A, dN_B, dN_E, dN_F, then the change in the Gibbs function according to Eq. 46 is

$$dG_M = \left(g_{E,T°} + \frac{RT}{J} \ln P_E \right) dN_E + \left(g_{F,T°} + \right.$$
$$\left. \frac{RT}{J} \ln P_F \right) dN_F - \left(g_{A,T°} + \frac{RT}{J} \ln P_A \right) dN_A$$
$$- \left(g_{B,T°} + \frac{RT}{J} \ln P_B \right) dN_B \tag{47A}$$

$$= g_{E,T°} \, dN_E + g_{F,T°} \, dN_F - g_{A,T°} \, dN_A - g_{B,T°} \, dN_B$$
$$+ \frac{RT}{J} \ln \frac{P_E^{dN_E} P_F^{dN_F}}{P_A^{dN_A} P_B^{dN_B}} \tag{47B}$$

From Eq. 45, we realize that the stoichiometric coefficients specify the number of mols of reactants and products that are involved in the process. For differential amounts of reaction, we write

$$dN_A + dN_B \rightarrow dN_E + dN_F \tag{48}$$

which implies that instead of ν_A mols disappearing, we have $k\nu_A$ mols disappearing. Or

$$k\nu_A + k\nu_B \rightarrow k\nu_E + k\nu_F \tag{49}$$

Here k is referred to as a proportionality constant. Substituting Eq. 49 (that is, $k\nu_E = dN_E$ and so on) into Eq. 47A, we get

$$k\left[\nu_E\left(g_{E,T^\circ} + \frac{RT}{J}\ln P_E\right) + \nu_F\left(g_{F,T^\circ} + \frac{RT}{J}\ln P_F\right)\right.$$
$$- \nu_A\left(g_{A,T^\circ} + \frac{RT}{J}\ln P_A\right)$$
$$\left. - \nu_B\left(g_{B,T^\circ} + \frac{RT}{J}\ln P_B\right)\right] = dG_M \tag{50}$$

We are interested in the case of chemical equilibrium (Fig. 9) and assume an infinitesimal reaction around equilibrium to result in a net Gibbs function change of zero. For this event we write Eq. 50 as

$$O = \nu_E\, g_{E,T^\circ} + \nu_F\, g_{F,T^\circ} - \nu_A\, g_{A,T^\circ} - \nu_B\, g_{B,T^\circ}$$
$$+ \frac{RT}{J}\ln\frac{P_E^{\nu E} P_F^{\nu F}}{P_A^{\nu A} P_B^{\nu B}} \tag{51}$$

The quantity $\nu_E\, g_{E,T^\circ} + \nu_F\, g_{F,T^\circ} - \nu_A\, g_{A,T^\circ} - \nu_B\, g_{B,T^\circ}$ is known as the standard-state Gibbs function change for a reaction and is usually written as ΔG_{T°. Or, in general,

$$\Delta G_{T^\circ} = \sum_{i=1}^{n} \nu_i\, g_{i,T^\circ}\Big/ products$$
$$- \sum_{j=1}^{m} \nu_i\, g_{j,T^\circ}\Big/ reactants \tag{51}$$

Eq. 51 now is therefore written as

$$- \Delta G_{T^\circ} = \frac{RT}{J}\ln\frac{P_E^{\nu E} P_F^{\nu F}}{P_A^{\nu A} P_B^{\nu B}} \tag{52}$$

EQUILIBRIUM CONSTANT

For ideal gas reactions, it is customary to define an *equilibrium constant*, K_P, such that

$$K_P = \frac{P_E^{\nu E} P_F^{\nu F}}{P_A^{\nu A} P_B^{\nu B}} \tag{52A}$$

Or, in general (i refers to products, j to reactants)

$$K_P = \frac{\prod_1^n P_i^{\nu_i}}{\prod_1^m P_j^{\nu_j}} \tag{52B}$$

Dropping the conversion constant J to obtain the usual textbook form, Eq. 52, then becomes

$$\Delta G_{T^\circ} = - RT \ln K_P \tag{53}$$

We now recast Eq. 22, taking into account the constant temperature assumption, in the form

$$\Delta G_{T^\circ} = \Delta H_{T^\circ} - T\Delta S_{T^\circ} \tag{54}$$

Substituting Eq. 54 into Eq. 53, we get

$$- R \ln K_P = \frac{\Delta H_{T^\circ}}{T} - \Delta S_{T^\circ} \tag{55}$$

Differentiating Eq. 55 with respect to T, we get

$$- R \frac{d(\ln K_P)}{dT} = - \frac{\Delta H_{T^\circ}}{T^2} + \frac{1}{T}\frac{d(\Delta H_{T^\circ})}{dT} - \frac{d(\Delta S_{T^\circ})}{dT} \tag{56}$$

Now Eq. 15C for the case of constant pressure is

$$TdS = dh \tag{57}$$

Writing Eq. 57 as $T\Delta S_{T^\circ} = \Delta H_{T^\circ}$ and differentiating with respect to T, keeping in mind that T itself is held constant, we get

$$\frac{Td(\Delta S_{T^\circ})}{dT} = \frac{d(\Delta H_{T^\circ})}{dT}$$

As these terms in Eq. 56 cancel, we get

$$\frac{d(\ln K_P)}{dT} = \frac{\Delta H_{T^\circ}}{RT^2}$$

(58)

Since $d(1/T) = -dT/T^2$, Eq. 58 can also be written as

$$\frac{d(\ln K_P)}{d(1/T)} = -\frac{\Delta H_{T^\circ}}{R}$$

(59)

as well as

$$\Delta H_{T^\circ} = RT^2 \frac{d(\ln K_P)}{dT}$$

(60)

Eqs. 58, 59, and 60 are known as the van't Hoff equation. Generally the enthalpy of reaction is approximately independent of temperature. If such is the case, then Eq. 59 can be integrated as

$$\int_{K_{P_1}}^{K_{P_2}} d \ln (K_P) = \int_{1/T_1}^{1/T_2} -\frac{\Delta H_{T^\circ}}{R} d(1/T)$$

or

$$\ln \frac{K_{P_2}}{K_{P_1}} = -\frac{\Delta H_{T^\circ}}{R}\left(\frac{1}{T_2} - \frac{1}{T_1}\right)$$

(61)

For exothermic reactions ΔH_{T° is negative by convention (heat or radiation is carried away from the system). By second law considerations one expects $T_2 > T_1$. Therefore the right hand side of Eq. 61 is negative. This requires that $K_{P2} < K_{P1}$. Thus for exothermic reactions the equilibrium constant K_P decreases with increasing temperature. For endothermic reactions one expects the opposite to be the case. Eq. 61 also tells us, as well as the van't Hoff equation in general, that K_P is a function of temperature, but that this is physically meaningless unless the reaction is also specified. How the stoichiometric equation is specified is, unfortunately, also important. This is illustrated by the following identical reactions

(a) $\quad CO + \frac{1}{2}O_2 \rightarrow CO_2$

(b) $\quad 2CO + O_2 \rightarrow 2CO_2$

The standard state Gibbs function change for the preceding reaction is

$$\Delta G_{T^\circ} = \nu_{CO2} g_{CO2} - (\nu_{CO} g_{CO} + \nu_{O2} g_{O2})$$

or

$$\Delta G_{T^\circ}/_{(a)} = 1g_{CO_2} - 1g_{CO} - \tfrac{1}{2}g_{O_2}$$

$$\Delta G_{T^\circ}/_{(b)} = 2g_{CO_2} - 2g_{CO} - 1g_{O_2}$$

Thus $\Delta G_{T^\circ}/_{(b)} = 2\Delta G_{T^\circ}/_{(a)}$. Writing Eq. 53 as

$$K_P = e^{-\Delta G_{T^\circ}/RT}$$

(53A)

and taking the ratio of K_P's, we get

$$\frac{(K_P)_b}{(K_P)_a} = \frac{e^{-2\Delta G_{T^\circ}/_{(a)}/RT}}{e^{-\Delta G_{T^\circ}/_{(b)}/RT}} = \frac{e^{-2x}}{e^{-x}}$$

If we now square $(K_P)_a$, we get the ratio to be equal one

$$\frac{(K_P)_b}{[(K_P)_a]^2} = \frac{e^{-2x}}{(e^{-x})^2} = 1$$

(62)

or

$$(K_P)_b = (K_P)_a{}^2$$

Thus by doubling the stoichiometric equation, we have squared the equilibrium coefficient. If we take the "backward rate" or dissociation reaction for $(a)_1$ we write

$$CO_2 \to CO + \tfrac{1}{2} O_2$$

and

$$\Delta G_T /_{(c)} = 1g_{CO} + \tfrac{1}{2}g_{O_2} - 1g_{CO_2} = - \Delta G_T /_{(a)}$$

Similarly, we take

$$\frac{(K_P)_c}{(K_P)_a^{-1}} = \frac{e^{-(-x)}}{(e^{-x})^{-1}} = 1 \tag{63}$$

or

$$(K_P)_c = 1/(K_P)_a$$

With the useful result that the backward rate equilibrium coefficient is simply the reciprocal of the forward rate equilibrium coefficient. By use of the perfect gas law, the equilibrium constant, K_P, can be put in somewhat more useful form than is given by Eqs. 52A and 52B. Realistically speaking, if one had a cylinder containing a mixture of gases at a total pressure of 1000 psig, it would be difficult to invent a pressure gage that would sequentially read the partial pressures and identify the corresponding components. An Orsat analysis identifying the components and the volumetric composition is a more practical method.

For component i in volume v, we write by the perfect gas law

$$P_i = \frac{M_i R_i T}{v} \frac{(lb\text{-}ft/°R)\,°R}{ft^3}$$

$$= \frac{M_i \dfrac{\mu_i R_i}{\mu_i} T}{v} \frac{lb}{ft^2} = \frac{M_i}{\mu_i} \frac{R_o T}{v} \frac{lb}{ft^2}$$

Since $P_{total} = \sum P_i$,

then $\dfrac{M_i\,lb}{\mu_i\,lb/mol} = N_i$

where:

N_i is the number of mols of each constituent present in volume v

Taking the ratio P_i/P_T, we get

$$\frac{P_i}{P_T} = \frac{M_i/\mu_i R_o T/v}{\sum (M_i/\mu_i R_o T)/v} = \frac{N_i}{\sum N_i} = \frac{N_i}{N_{mT}}$$

where

M_T = mols total (products)

Then

$$P_i = \frac{N_i}{N_{mT}} P_T = x_i P_T \tag{64}$$

Substituting Eq. 64 into Eq. 52B, we get

$$K_p = \frac{\prod\limits_1^n \left(\dfrac{N_i}{N_{mT}} P_T\right)^{\nu_i}}{\prod\limits_1^m \left(\dfrac{N_j}{N_{mT}}\right)^{\nu_j}}$$

$$= \frac{\prod N_i^{\nu i} (P_T/N_{mT})^{\nu i}}{\prod N_j^{\nu j} (P_T/N_{mT})^{\nu j}}$$

$$= \frac{\prod\limits^n N_i^{\nu i}}{\prod\limits^m N_j^{\nu j}} \left(\frac{P_T}{N_{mT}}\right)^{\Sigma \nu i - \Sigma \nu j}$$

$$= \frac{\prod\limits^n N_i^{\nu i}}{\prod\limits^m N_j^{\nu j}} \left(\frac{P_T}{N_{mT}}\right)^{\Delta \nu} \tag{65}$$

Using reaction 45 as an example, we would write Eq. 65 as

$$K_P/_{(31)} = \frac{N_E^{\nu E} N_F^{\nu F}}{N_A^{\nu A} N_B^{\nu B}} \left(\frac{P_T}{N_{mT}}\right)^{\nu E + \nu F - \nu A - \nu B} \tag{66}$$

APPLICATION TO COMBUSTION CALCULATIONS

The following calculations demonstrate the application of the foregoing discussion.

BURNING PROPANE

Burn propane (C_3H_8) stoichiometrically (0% excess air). The reaction on a molar basis is, assuming dry air,

$$C_3H_8 + 5O_2 + 18.8N_2 \rightarrow 3CO_2 + 4H_2O + 18.8N_2 \tag{67}$$

The air-to-fuel ratio therefore is

$$\frac{5 \text{ mol O}_2 \times \dfrac{32 \text{ lb}}{\text{mol}} + 18.8 \text{ mol N}_2 \times \dfrac{28 \text{ lb}}{\text{mol}}}{1 \text{ mol C}_3H_8 \times \dfrac{44 \text{ lb}}{\text{mol}}} = 15.7$$

or, equivalently

$$\frac{23.8 \text{ mol air} \times 29 \text{ lb air/mol air}}{1 \text{ mol C}_3H_8 \times 44 \text{ lb C}_3H_8/\text{mol C}_3H_8}$$

$$= 15.7 \text{ lb air/lb C}_3H_8$$

Now suppose that we burn the propane substoichiometrically at 80 percent theoretical dry air. To solve the problem of insufficient air, we make the assumption that H_2 will always go to H_2O in favor of C going to CO_2. (On the basis of reaction kinetics this is a valid assumption.) Reaction 67 now becomes

$$1C_3H_8 + 4O_2 + 15.04N_2 \rightarrow$$
$$aCO + bCO_2 + 4H_2O + 15.04N_2 \tag{68}$$

This reaction solves as

$$C_3H_8 + 4O_2 + 15.04N_2 \rightarrow$$
$$2CO + 1CO_2 + 4H_2O + 15.04N_2 \tag{68A}$$

Reaction 68A is an approximation as we have implicitly assumed that the reaction goes to completion. Continuing with the combustion of propane, we may assume, say, 150 percent theoretical dry air and consequently write reaction 67 as

$$C_3H_8 + 7.5O_2 + 28.2N_2 \rightarrow$$
$$3CO_2 + 4H_2O + 2.5O_2 + 28.2N_2 \tag{69}$$

Products $= 3 + 4 + 2.5 + 28.2 = 37.7$ mols.
The product mol fractions are

$$CO_2 = \frac{3}{37.7} \cong 0.08 \quad H_2O = \frac{4}{37.7} \cong 0.106$$

$$O_2 = \frac{2.5}{37.7} \cong 0.066 \quad N_2 = \frac{28.2}{37.7} \cong 0.748$$

Then $P_{H_2O} = 0.106 \times 14.7 = 1.56$ psia with a corresponding dew point (saturation temperature) of 117°F. Converting this to a wet-air basis of 80°F, 1 atm, 1.013 lb. wet air/lb dry air we calculate

$$\frac{0.013 \text{ lb H}_2O}{\text{lb dry air}} \times \frac{29 \text{ lb dry air}}{\text{mol air}} \times \frac{1 \text{ mol H}_2O}{18 \text{ lb H}_2O}$$

$$= 0.021 \frac{\text{mol H}_2O}{\text{mol air}}$$

From the left-hand side of (69), we have 35.7 mols air used in the reaction or 35.7 mol air $\times$ 0.021 mol H_2O/mol air $= 0.75$ mol H_2O introduced with the air. Wherefore the products (right-hand side of (69)) now contain $4 + 0.75 = 4.75$ mol H_2O. Thus,

$$P_{H_2O} = \frac{4 + .75}{37.7 + .75} = 0.1235 \text{ atm.} = 1.816 \text{ psia}$$

Now suppose that we have a volumetric (Orsat) analysis of the products ($CO_2 = 11.5$ percent, $O_2 = 2.7$ percent, and $CO = 0.7$ percent) and we know we are burning propane. We then write reaction (67) as

$$xC_3H_8 + aO_2 + a3.76N_2 \rightarrow 11.5CO_2 +$$
$$0.7CO + 2.7O_2 + 85.1N_2 + bH_2O \tag{70}$$

The carbon balance for reaction 70 is

$$3X = 11.5 + 0.7 \quad X = 4.0667 \quad \cong 4.07$$

The hydrogen balance for reaction 70 is

$$8X = 8 \times 4.0667 = 2b \quad b \cong 16.25$$

The oxygen balance for reaction 70 is

$$2a = 2 \times 11.5 + 0.7 + 5.4 + 16.25$$

$$a \cong 22.65$$

Substituting for x, a, b in reaction 70 and dividing through by 4.07, then we get

$$C_3H_8 + 5.56O_2 + \frac{85.1}{4.07}N_2 \rightarrow \frac{11.5}{4.07}CO_2$$

$$+ \frac{0.7}{4.07}CO + \frac{2.7}{4.07}O_2 + \frac{85.1}{4.07}N_2 + \frac{16.25}{4.07}H_2O$$

$$\text{(70A)}$$

Comparing reaction 70A with the stoichiometric reaction (70), it follows that the excess air determined by Orsat analysis is

$$\frac{5.56}{5} \times 100 \cong 111 \text{ percent theoretical air}$$

or 11 percent excess air.

BURNING HYDROCARBON FUEL

Next we suppose that we have an Orsat analysis ($CO_2 - 12.1\%$, $O_2 - 3.8\%$, $CO - 0.9\%$) and we suspect we are burning some hydrocarbon fuel. We then write

$$C_xH_y + aO_2 + a3.76N_2 \rightarrow 12.1CO_2 + 0.9CO +$$

$$83.2N_2 + 3.8O_2 + bH_2O$$

$$\text{(71)}$$

"a" from the nitrogen component is

$$a\,3.76N_2 = 83.2N_2, a = 83.2/3.76 = 22.1$$

Then, from the oxygen balance

$$2 \times 22.1 = 2 \times 12.1 + 0.9 + 2 \times 3.8 + b$$

$$b = 11.5$$

From the carbon balance, we write

$$x = 12.1 + 0.9 = 13.0$$

For the hydrogen balance, we write

$$y = 2b = 2 \times 11.5 = 23.0$$

wherefore reaction (71) becomes

$$C_{13}H_{23} + 22.1O_2 + 83.2N_2 \rightarrow 12.1CO_2 + 0.9CO +$$

$$83.2N_2 + 3.8O_2 + 11.5H_2O$$

$$\text{(71A)}$$

Here the formula $C_{13}H_{23}$ is an average composition of the fuel components.

From reaction 71A the combustion air is $22.1 + 83.2 = 105.3$ mols per mol fuel. To convert reaction (57a) to a stoichiometric basis we realize that, ideally, 0.9 CO should be 0.9 CO_2 and that 3.8 O_2 goes to zero and that 0.9 oxygen supplies 0.45 O_2 to the 0.9 CO_2 so an additional 0.45 O_2 must be supplied by the left-hand side.

Therefore, the O_2 requirement on the left-hand side of reaction 71A is

$$22.1\,O_2 - 3.8\,O_2 + 0.45\,O_2 = 18.75\,O_2$$

Hence, reaction 71A becomes

$$C_{13}H_{23} + 18.75\,O_2 + 3.76 \times 18.75N_2$$

$$\rightarrow 13\,CO_2 + 11.5\,H_2O + 3.76 \times 18.75\,N_2$$

$$\text{(72)}$$

from which it follows that the excess air percent is

$$\frac{22.1 - 18.75}{18.75} \times 100 \cong 17.9\%$$

GIBBS FUNCTION CALCULATION

Consider the water-gas reaction

$$CO + H_2O \rightarrow CO_2 + H_2$$

and apply the Gibbs function to the total system. First, we assume the following reactions

$$1\,CO + 1\,H_2O \rightarrow 1\,CO_2 + 1\,H_2$$

$$1\,CO + 1\,H_2O \rightarrow 0.8\,CO_2 + 0.8\,H_2 +$$
$$0.2\,CO + 0.2\,H_2O$$

$$1\,CO + 1\,H_2O \rightarrow 0.6\,CO_2 + 0.6\,H_2 +$$
$$0.4\,CO + 0.4\,H_2O$$

$$1\,CO + 1\,H_2O \rightarrow 0.5\,CO_2 + 0.5\,H_2 +$$
$$0.5\,CO + 0.5\,H_2O$$

The Gibbs function for the total system is Σ products $- \Sigma$ reactants

$$= \sum_i (h_i - T\Delta S_i)_{products} - \sum_j (h_j - T\Delta S_j)_{reactants}$$

To apply the above to the postulated reactions, we use Eq. 29. From $Pv = mR_oT = RT$, we write

$$v = \frac{R}{P} T$$

then

$$\left(\frac{\partial v}{\partial T}\right)_P = \frac{R}{P}$$

Substituting in Eq. 29

$$dS = \frac{C_p}{T} dT - \frac{R}{P} dP \tag{73}$$

Then, for component i,

$$(S_i)_{T.P} = S_i^o + \int_{T_o}^T C_P \frac{dT}{T} - R \ln \frac{P_i}{P_o} \tag{74}$$

In the JANAF tables, the entropy at temperature T for component i is tabulated at 1 atmosphere and we therefore make a "correction" for component i at partial pressure P_i starting at pressure $P_o = 1$ atm. Hence,

$$(S_i)_{T.Pi} = S_{i.1}^o + \int_{T_o}^T C_P \frac{dT}{T} - R \ln \frac{P_i}{1}$$

$$= S_{i.T.1} = R \ln P_i \tag{75}$$

From the JANAF tables, we tabulate the following values at 1000°K and 1 atm, Table IV. We assume the reaction to proceed at 1000°K for convenience, to simplify the calculations.

HEAT GAS-PHASE REACTION

Consider the gas-phase reaction

$$1CO + \tfrac{1}{2}O_2 \rightleftharpoons 1CO_2 \tag{76}$$

and assume the reaction is in equilibrium at 1 atm and 3000°K. Assume negligible tempera-

Table IV. Gibbs Function Calculation—Step 1

Component	$H^\circ_{1000} - H^\circ_{298}$ kcal/mol I	$H^\circ_{298} - H^\circ_0$ kcal/mol II	$H^\circ_{1000} - H^\circ_0$ $\Sigma(I + II)$ Sensible Enthalpy	ΔH°_F (1000°K) Enthalpy of Formation kcal/mol	S°_{1000} Entropy at 1 atm. cal/mol-°K
CO_2	7.984	2.238	10.222	−94.321	63.444
H_2	4.944	2.024	6.968	0.000	39.702
CO	5.183	2.072	7.255	−26.771	56.028
H_2O	6.209	2.367	8.576	−59.246	55.592

Table V. Gibbs Function Calculation—Step 2

$H_{products}$ at 1 mol each

10.222	CO_2
6.968	H_2
17.190	kcal/mol

$H_{reactants}$ at 1 mol each

7.255	CO
8.576	H_2O
15.831	kcal/mol

$H_{sensible} = H_{at\ 1\ mol} \times$ fractional mol

Table V. Gibbs Function Calculation—Step 2 — *(Continued)*

Mol	0.8	0.6	0.5	0.4	0.3	0.2
CO_2	8.17	6.133	5.111	4.089	3.067	2.044
H_2	5.574	4.181	3.484	2.787	2.090	1.394
Σ	13.752	10.314	8.595	6.876	5.157	3.438
Mol	0.2	0.4	0.5	0.6	0.7	0.8
CO	1.451	2.902	3.627	4.353	5.078	5.804
H_2O	1.715	3.430	4.288	5.145	6.003	6.861
Σ	3.166	6.332	7.915	9.498	11.081	12.665
$\Sigma_{Products}$	16.918	16.646	16.510	16.374	16.238	16.103

$$H_{products} - H_{reactants} \text{ vs. mols } CO_2$$

Mol CO_2	1.0	1.08	0.6	0.5	0.4	0.3	0.2
Products	17.190	16.918	16.646	16.510	16.374	16.238	16.103
Reactants	−15.831	−15.831	−15.831	−15.831	−15.831	−15.831	−15.831
Σ	1.359	1.087	0.815	0.679	0.543	0.407	0.272

Table VI. Gibbs Function Calculation—Step 3

Calculating entropies according to Eq. 75, we get (at 1000°K)

S_{CO_2}	=	$1.0(63.444-1.986 \ln 0.5)$	=	64.821
S_{H_2}	=	$1.0(39.702-1.986 \ln 0.5)$	=	41.079
Total		$S_{products}$ at 1 atm (& 1 mol CO_2)	=	105.900 cal/mol-°K

S_{CO}	=	$1.0(56.028-1.986 \ln 0.5)$	=	57.405
S_{H_2O}	=	$1.0(55.592-1.986 \ln 0.5)$	=	56.969
Total		$S_{reactants}$ at 1 atm	=	114.374 cal/mol-°K

S_{CO_2}	=	$0.8(63.444-1.986 \ln 0.4)$	=	52.211
S_{H_2}	=	$0.8(39.702-1.986 \ln 0.4)$	=	33.218
S_{CO}	=	$0.2(56.028-1.986 \ln 0.1)$	=	12.120
S_{H_2O}	=	$0.2(55.592-1.986 \ln 0.1)$	=	12.033
Total		$S_{products}$ at 0.8 mol CO_2	=	109.582 cal/mol-°K

S_{CO_2}	=	$0.6(63.444-1.986 \ln 0.3)$	=	39.501
S_{H_2}	=	$0.6(39.702-1.986 \ln 0.3)$	=	25.256
S_{CO}	=	$0.4(56.028-1.986 \ln 0.2)$	=	23.690
S_{H_2O}	=	$0.4(55.592-1.986 \ln 0.2)$	=	23.515
Total		$S_{products}$ at 0.6 mol CO_2	=	111.962 cal/mol-°K

Table VI. Gibbs Function Calculation—Step 3 — *(Continued)*

Calculating entropies according to Eq. 75, we get (at 1000°K)

S_{CO_2}	=	$0.5(63.444-1.986 \ln 0.25)$	=	33.099
S_{H_2}	=	$0.5(39.702-1.986 \ln 0.25)$	=	21.228
S_{CO}	=	$0.5(56.028-1.986 \ln 0.25)$	=	29.390
S_{H_2O}	=	$0.5(55.592-1.986 \ln 0.25)$	=	29.173
Total		$S_{products}$ at 0.5 mol CO_2	=	112.890 cal/mol-°K
S_{CO_2}	=	$0.4(63.444-1.986 \ln 0.2)$	=	26.656
S_{H_2}	=	$0.4(39.702-1.986 \ln 0.2)$	=	17.159
S_{CO}	=	$0.6(56.028-1.986 \ln 0.3)$	=	35.051
S_{H_2O}	=	$0.6(55.592-1.986 \ln 0.3)$	=	34.790
Total		$S_{products}$ at 0.4 mol CO_2	=	113.656 cal/mol-°K
S_{CO_2}	=	$0.3(63.444-1.986 \ln 0.15)$	=	20.163
S_{H_2}	=	$0.3(39.702-1.986 \ln 0.15)$	=	13.041
S_{CO}	=	$0.7(56.028-1.986 \ln 0.35)$	=	40.679
S_{H_2}	=	$0.7(55.592-1.986 \ln 0.35)$	=	40.374
Total		$S_{products}$ at 0.3 mol CO_2	=	114.257 cal/mol-°K
S_{CO_2}	=	$0.2(63.444-1.986 \ln 0.1)$	=	13.603
S_{H_2}	=	$0.2(39.702-1.986 \ln 0.1)$	=	8.855
S_{CO}	=	$0.8(56.028-1.986 \ln 0.4)$	=	46.278
S_{H_2O}	=	$0.8(55.592-1.986 \ln 0.4)$	=	45.930
Total		$S_{products}$ at 0.2 mol CO_2	=	114.666 cal/mol-°K

$$S_{products} \times 1000°K = S_{products} \text{ in kcal/mol}$$

$$(-S_{products} + S_{reactants})T = -T \Delta S$$

$$\Delta = \Sigma \text{ products} - \Sigma \text{ reactants}$$

Mol CO_2	1.0	0.8	0.6	0.5	0.4	0.3	0.2
$S°_{products}$	−105.900	−109.582	−111.962	−112.890	−113.656	−114.257	−114.666
$S°_{reactants}$	114.374	114.374	114.374	114.374	114.374	114.374	114.374
Σ	+ 8.474	+ 4.792	+ 2.412	+ 1.484	+ 0.718	+ 0.117	− 0.292

Table VII. Gibbs Function Calculation—Step 4

For the heat of formation (exothermic), we get, at 1000°K & 1 atm. total pressure

Mol CO_2	1.0	0.8	0.6	0.5	0.4	0.3	0.2
H_{FCO_2}	−94.321	−75.457	−56.593	−47.160	−37.728	−28.296	−18.864
H_{FH_2}	0	0	0	0	0	0	0
Σ	−94.321	−75.457	−56.593	−47.160	−37.728	−28.296	−18.864

Table VII. Gibbs Function Calculation—Step 4 — *(Continued)*

For the heat of formation (exothermic), we get, at 1000°K & 1 atm. total pressure

Mol_{H_2O}	0	0.2	0.4	0.5	0.6	0.7	0.8
H_{FCO}	0	− 5.354	−10.708	−13.385	−16.062	−18.740	−21.417
H_{FCO_2}	0	−11.849	−23.698	−29.623	−35.548	−41.472	−47.397
Σ	0	−17.203	−34.406	−43.008	−51.610	−60.212	−68.814
$\Sigma_{H_F}{}^{prod}$	−94.321	−92.660	−90.999	−90.168	−89.338	−88.508	−87.678
$\Sigma_{H_F}{}^{reac}$	+85.017	+85.017	+85.017	+85.017	+85.017	+85.017	+85.017
Σ	− 9.304	− 7.643	− 5.982	− 5.151	− 4.321	− 3.491	− 2.661

Finally

$$(\underset{products}{\Sigma\ H_S + H_F - TS}) - (\underset{reactants}{\Sigma\ H_S + H_F - TS}) \text{ is tabulated in Table VIII}$$

as

$$\Sigma\left[H_S{}_{\ products} - H_S{}_{\ reactants}\right] + \Sigma\left[H_F{}_{\ products} - H_F{}_{\ reactants}\right] - \Sigma\left[TS{}_{\ products} - TS{}_{\ reactants}\right]$$

where Δ means Σ products $-$ Σ reactants

Table VIII. Gibbs Function Calculation—Final Step

Mol CO$_2$	1.0	0.8	0.6	0.5	0.4	0.3	0.2
$\Delta S°$	+8.474	+4.792	+2.412	+1.484	+0.718	+0.117	−0.292
$\Delta H_S°$	+1.359	+1.087	+0.815	+0.679	+0.543	+0.407	+0.272
$\Delta H_F°$	−9.304	−7.643	−5.982	−5.151	−4.321	−3.491	−2.661
Gibbs	+0.529	−1.764	−2.755	−2.987	−3.060	−2.967	−2.681

ture dissociation for O_2. For the reaction

$$CO_2 \rightleftharpoons 1CO + \tfrac{1}{2}O_2$$

at 1 atm and 3000°K, Ref. 2 gives the equilibrium coefficient as

$$Log_{10} K_P = -0.485$$

The equilibrium coefficient we need, according to Eq. 63, is therefore

$$(K_P)_a = 1/(K_P)_b$$

$$(K_P)_a = \frac{1}{10^{-0.485}} = 10^{0.485} = 3.055$$

From Eq. 65, we have for (a)

$$K_P = \frac{\prod_n^{} N_i{}^{\nu_i} \left(\frac{P_T}{N_{mt}}\right)^{\Sigma \nu_i - \Sigma \nu_j}}{\prod_m^{} N_j{}^{\nu_i}}$$

or

$$K_P = 3.055 = \frac{(N_{CO_2})^1}{(N_{CO})^1 (N_{O^2})^{\frac{1}{2}}} \left(\frac{1\ \text{atm.}}{N_{mT}}\right)^{1-(1+\frac{1}{2})}$$

(77)

As we anticipate that the reaction does not go to completion, we rewrite reaction (76) with CO and O_2 also on the right-hand side. We note in Eq. 65 that the stoichiometric coefficients appear as exponents only; there are therefore no restrictions on the mols. We can therefore consider the case of an equimolal reaction (for convenience) and write

$$1CO + 1O_2 \underset{EQUIL.}{\rightarrow} x\,CO + YO_2 + zCO_2$$

(78)

In this reaction the product mols are

$$N_{mT} = x + y + z$$

Substituting the mixture [the right-hand side of reaction 78] into reaction 77 we get

$$\frac{z^1}{x^1y^{\frac{1}{2}}}\left(\frac{1}{x+y+z}\right)^{-\frac{1}{2}} = \frac{z\,(x+y+z)^{\frac{1}{2}}}{xy^{\frac{1}{2}}}$$

(79)

In addition, the carbon balance demands that $1 = x + z$ and the oxygen balance requires that $3 = x + 2y + 2z$, then

$$z = 1 - x \text{ and } y = \frac{1}{2}\,(3 - x - 2z)$$
$$= \frac{1}{2}\,(3 - x - 2 + 2x) = \frac{1+x}{2}$$

Thus

$$N_{mT} = x + y + z = x + \frac{1+x}{2} + 1 - x = \frac{3+x}{2}$$

Substituting into Eq. 79, we get

$$3.055 = \frac{(1-x)\left(\dfrac{3+x}{2}\right)^{\frac{1}{2}}}{x\left(\dfrac{1+x}{2}\right)^{\frac{1}{2}}} = \frac{(1-x)\,(3+x)^{\frac{1}{2}}}{x\,(1+x)^{\frac{1}{2}}}$$

Squaring both sides and simplifying

$$8.3x^3 + 8.3x^2 + 5x - 3 = 0$$

By inspection $x = \frac{1}{3}$ is an approximate solution. By additional calculation we find that x is close to 0.34. Then

$$z = 1 - x = 1 - .34 = .66$$

and

$$y = \frac{1+x}{2} = \frac{1.34}{2} = .67$$

and it follows that the equilibrium reaction is

$$1\,CO + 1\,O_2 \rightarrow 0.34\,CO + 0.67\,O_2 + 0.66\,CO_2$$

which is the equilibrium composition we would expect for the specified reaction.

CALCULATION WITH AIR

Now let us do a more realistic calculation using air instead of oxygen. We write Eq. 78 as

$$CO + O_2 + 3.76\,N_2 \rightarrow x\,CO + y\,O_2 + z\,CO_2 + 3.76\,N_2$$

The mols of mixture at equilibrium are

$$N_{mT} = x + y + z + 3.76$$

We also note that N_2, carried along as an inert, has no effect in Eq. 65, that is,

$$K_P = \frac{\prod N_i{}^{\nu_i}N_{N_2}{}^{3.76}}{\prod N_j{}^{\nu_j}N_{N_2}{}^{3.76}}\left(\frac{P_T}{N_{mT}}\right)^{\nu_i + 3.76 - \nu_j - 3.76}$$

and, as before,

$$3.055 = \frac{z^1}{x^1\,y^{1/2}}\left(\frac{1\text{ atm.}}{x+y+z+3.76}\right)^{-\frac{1}{2}}$$

The carbon and oxygen balances remain the same

$$1 = x + z, \quad 3 = x + 2y + 2z$$

and

$$z = 1 - x, \quad y = \frac{1+x}{2}$$

then

$$3.055 = \frac{(1-x)\,(1)^{-\frac{1}{2}}}{x\left(\dfrac{1+x}{2}\right)^{\frac{1}{2}}(x+y+z+3.76)^{-\frac{1}{2}}}$$

Substituting for y and z

$$3.055 = \frac{(1-x)\left(\dfrac{10.52+x}{2}\right)^{\frac{1}{2}}}{x\left(\dfrac{1+x}{2}\right)^{\frac{1}{2}}}$$

squaring both sides and simplifying

$$8.3x^3 + .78x^2 + 20.04x - 10.52 = 0$$

By inspection, it is clear that $\frac{1}{3} < x < \frac{1}{2}$; by successive approximations we determine that

$$x = 0.46, z = 1 - x = 0.54, y = \frac{1+x}{2} = 0.73$$

$$1CO + 1O_2 + 3.76N_2 \rightarrow 0.46CO + 0.73O_2$$
$$+ 0.54CO_2 + 3.76N_2$$

Comparing this with the previous solution

with the inert nitrogen constituent dropped.

$$1\ CO + 1\ O_2 \rightarrow 0.34\ CO + 0.67\ O_2 + 0.66\ CO_2$$

We see that the presence of an inert (nitrogen) decreases the amount of CO_2 formed. If we now take a less drastic temperature, say 1000°K, and perform the equilibrium calculation, we find that for the reaction

$$CO_2 \rightarrow CO + \tfrac{1}{2}\ O_2$$

Reference (2) gives the equilibrium constant as $\text{Log}_{10} K_P = -10.221$. Then

$$(K_P)_a = \frac{1}{(K_P)_b} = \frac{1}{10^{-10.221}} = 10^{10.221}$$

Taking K_P as 10^{10} (for convenience) we get

$$(10^{10})^2 = 10^{20} = \frac{(1-x)^2(3+x)}{x^2 + x^3}$$

Hence

$$10^{20}x^3 + 10^{20}x^2 = 3 - 5x + x^2 + x^3$$

which can be rewritten closely as

$$10^{20}x^3 + 10^{20}x^2 + 5x - 3 = 0$$

We can conclude that the x value is effectively zero. Thus,

$$1\ CO + 1\ O_2 \rightarrow \tfrac{1}{2}\ O_2 + 1\ CO_2$$

At 1000°K, therefore, the reaction effectively goes to completion which is far from being the case at 3000°K.

We used a K_P for the reaction $1\ CO + \tfrac{1}{2}\ O_2 \rightarrow 1\ CO_2$ of 3.055 at 3000°K. To estimate the K_P for the same reaction at 2000°K, we use the van't Hoff isobar Eq. 61.

$$\ln\frac{K_{P_2}}{K_{P_1}} = -\frac{\Delta H_{T_o}}{R}\left(\frac{1}{T_2} - \frac{1}{T_1}\right)$$

The universal gas constant, R, has units of

$$1.986\ ^{cal}/_{g-mol \times k} \quad \text{or} \quad 1.986\ ^{Btu}/_{lb-mol-\,°R}$$

The enthalpy of reaction, $\Delta H_T°$, is given by reference (2) as $-119,500$ Btu/mol at 2000°K and $-117,200$ Btu/mol at 3000°K. Taking a numerical average of $-118,350$ Btu/mol, we get

$$\ln\frac{K_{P_2}}{K_{P_1}} = \frac{118350}{1.986}\left(\frac{1}{3600} - \frac{1}{5400}\right) \cong 5.54,\ \text{then}$$

$$e^{\ln\frac{K_{P_2}}{K_{P_1}}} = e^{5.54} \cong 255 = \frac{K_{P_2}}{3.005},\ \text{or}$$

$$K_{P_2} = 778$$

which compares reasonably well with the value of 766 given by Wark[2]. The van't Hoff equation therefore gives a fair value in the absence of experimental data.

CHARACTERISTICS OF FLAME

Although the foregoing elements of combustion thermodynamics give an overall appreciation of combustion as a chemical reaction, nothing was said in regard to the flames themselves. Flames can be broadly classified in two distinctly different types: laboratory flames and industrial flames. The implication of the distinction is that data obtained from one are not necessarily transferable to the other.

SPECTRA

Enabling investigators to study spectra is the major function the laboratory flame performs. Over the years, investigators[11] have established the following from the study of various flame configurations in the laboratory.

DISCRETE OR DISCONTINUOUS

Line spectra are produced by discharges in monatomic gases or vapors. Bright lines appear at definite wavelengths separated by intervals in which no energy appears. These correspond to stationary energy state transitions of electrons in free atoms. In this connection, it may be mentioned that free atoms give rise to the production of free radicals by a flame referred to as the atomic flame. That is, atomic hydrogen or oxygen (or nitrogen) interacts with molecules to give light emission due to free radicals. Specific reactions[12] observed are

$$NO + H \rightarrow HNO + h\nu$$
$$NO + O \rightarrow NO_2 + h\nu$$

Band spectra (diatomic) are produced by discharges in polyatomic gases. With greater spectroscopic resolution, these are a regular series of lines at very close spacing. In the visible and ultraviolet, band spectra are due to electronic state transitions for the molecules. Simultaneous changes in the rotational and vibrational states accompany them as well. The rotation-vibration change gives rise to the fine structure (lines) within the band. For diatomic molecules, the band spectra are regular and of sharply defined appearance. Diatomic free radicals which have been identified in laboratory flames and which contribute to band systems in the visible and ultraviolet are CH (blue-violet radiation), OH (strong ultraviolet spectrum with peak at 3064 Å), C_2 (Swan's green bands), CN (violet bands as well as red and near infrared), and NH (identified by the 3360 Å peak) where resonance transition from electronic ground state to lowest excited states requires low energy. The subsequent emission has a very high transition probability (electronic transition lifetimes in the visible and ultraviolet from about 10^{-6} to 10^{-8} sec) coupled with a high probability that these excited electronic states are formed in excess of the equilibrium concentration (chemiluminescence).

In the infrared, spectra are generally due to vibration-rotation transitions without changes in the electronic quantum states. The vibration-rotation transitions have much smaller transition probabilities than electronic transitions (ν-r transition lifetimes in the infrared are between about 10^{-3} and 10^{-1} sec) which limits observation to molecules of large concentrations. Briefly, the optical spectra are determined by the outer orbit electrons (outside the closed, or filled, electron shells). The shifts in orbit give lines in the visible and ultraviolet. Electronic energy charge determines the position of the band system as a whole, along the wavelength (a) axis.[13]

The gross structure of the band system (splitting into a number of bands within the system) is due to energy changes of the molecule by changes in atomic vibration along the internuclear axis. By assuming the molecule to be a harmonic oscillator, it can be shown that the vibrational energy is quantized by half integral values, 1/2, 3/2, 5/2, and so forth. The fine structure of the band (lines within a band) which can be clearly seen, for example, in the CH or OH spectrum are from changes in rotational state of the molecule about its mass center.

Identifying species from the spectrum is not a simple task. CH, OH, C_2, CN, NH have the strongest band systems in the visible and near-ultraviolet, whereas CO, O_2, and N_2 do not show emissions of appreciable strength in the visible and ultraviolet region.

Unlike the diatomic spectra, the band spectra due to polyatomic molecules are much more complex and of diffuse appearance. Band systems in the visible and ultraviolet (due to electronic transitions) include emission systems from HCO, NH_2, and HCHO. Other polyatomic products of partial combustion are CH_3, C_2H_2, CH_4, and CH_2, although these have not been definitely identified. The spectra definitely established for hydrocarbon laboratory flames have identified CO, OH, CN, C_2, NH_2, CO_2, H_2O, and NO_2.

In the infrared, the main contributors are CO_2 (in the 4.4 μ and 2.8 μ bands) and H_2O (in the 1 to 2.8 μ band). Other contributors to the infrared bands are CO, OH, and CH. The OH radical has an appreciable equilibrium concentration in hot gases, whereas the CH radical has very low concentrations and is essentially an insignificant component. Produced by carbon-rich flames, CN is characterized by its main contribution in the violet bands, but also contributes to the red and near-infrared. Note that available energy is not necessarily always converted into radiant energy. In flame gases, a molecule suffers about 10^9 collisions/sec and requires on the order of 10^3 collisions to remove excess vibrational energy or 10^{-6} sec to attain equipartition of vibrational and translational energy, which implies a travel distance of approximately 10^{-5} meter. This has been measured for sodium in a nitrogen atmosphere at 2000°F. Quenching the N_a fluorescence by N_2 indicates that N_a undergoes about 3.1×10^9 collisions/sec, with a collision lifetime of 3.2×10^{-10} sec, which compares with a free radiative lifetime of about 1.6×10^{-8} sec; we can thus expect a deactivation by radiation about 2 percent of that due to collisions.

CONTINUA

Energy is required to transform a molecule into, for example, a radical plus an atom or ion plus an electron. This energy is supplied by light absorption and, in the case of dissociation, is referred to as photodissociation and photoionization. This leads to regions of continuous absorption spectra in molecules. In molecules, it is not unusual to find that discrete excited states lie above the first dissociation limit and are in an overlap condition with the continuum energy-level range. The molecules therefore undergo radiationless transitions to the continuum, resulting in dissociation. The process of radiationless transition from the discrete state into the continuum without change in energy level and leading to a decomposition is called an AUGER process. These processes occur in the optical region of atomic and molecular spectra, among others. This is also referred to as predissociation. It is possible for the dissociation process to lead to an emission continuum, such as the H_2 continuum.

In this case, molecules in a highly excited state undergo transition to a much less excited unstable state which dissociates to two hydrogen atoms with emission of a strong ultraviolet continuum. This process is used as a background source for absorption spectroscopy. It is uncertain whether the hydrogen continuum has been identified in flames. In the case of photoionization, the absorption spectra of atoms consist of a series of lines (the Rydberg series) which converge to a limit. Beyond the limit the absorption region is continuous. The Rydberg series reflects electron excitation in the outer orbits and the continuum corresponds to electron ejection resulting in a positive atomic ion.

The inverse process of recombination leading to a continuous emission spectrum inverse to the continuous absorption spectrum occurs, for example, by a radiative transition from an upper state in the continuous range to a lower discrete state. This is referred to as the two-body recombination problem. In this case, the upper state corresponds to a two-body collision (of either atoms or radicals) or a recombination between an electron and ion. The collision time is about 10^{-13} second and the electronic transition probability (radiative lifetime) is approximately 10^{-8} seconds. The probability that a collision leads to stable molecule formation with light emission is thus about one in 10^5.

Radiative two-body recombination is also possible by the mechanism of the inverse AUGER process. In this situation, two particles collide with an energy equal to some discrete state of the compound system. If during the collision time a transition to a lower stable state takes place, a recombination to form a molecule or radical with emission of radiation occurs. It is thought that this is the applicable process for the reaction

$$NO + O \rightarrow NO_2 + h\nu$$

where the emission spectrum is nearly continuous and extends from approximately 4000 Å to the near infrared and is strongest in the yellow-green.

Retardation Continua

The process of photoionization results in a population of fast electrons and slow positive ions. The electron retardation due to the positive field results in continuous emission radiation. In flames this is believed to be a negligible contributor to the spectrum.

Particle Continua

In the solid phase (particles), the molecules are closely bound to other molecules, which results in the loss of rotation with intermolecularly coupled vibrations. The consequence is that we no longer obtain well-defined band systems, but only regions of continuous absorption and emission. In the case of heavy atoms, such as uranium, the inner-shell electron transitions are shielded from external effects so that a diffused line spectrum from these systems is possible. In flames, the most important continuum is from hot carbon particles. Particles of carbon and ash are already in existence in pulverized-fuel-fired systems, which tends to obscure the fact that solid carbon particles are formed also in liquid- and gas-fired flames. In laboratory flames, the carbon particles are from 100 Å to 2000 Å in size and are, therefore, smaller in diameter than the wavelength of visible light. The consequence is that these carbon particles act as scattering kernels with the result that, although the carbon is itself quite black, the emissivity increases towards the shorter wavelengths (i.e., the ultraviolet). The color temperature is, therefore, higher than the thermodynamic gas temperature. The mechanism of carbon particle formation even from premixed hydrocarbon laboratory flames is not fully established, and conflicting theories exist.

LABORATORY FLAMES

In the case of laboratory flames generated for the purpose of spectroscopic observations, the primary characteristic is that these are stationary, whether they are of the diffusion or premixed variety. These flames generally exhibit distinct flame zones which can be separately studied. That is, the investigator can focus upon a zone to record and study the detailed flame structure in the zone.

Laboratory flames for spectroscopic study lend themselves to the introduction of metals or metal compounds which generate strong lines of resonance excitation; a well-known example of this is the yellow sodium "D" lines (5890 Å and 5896 Å). This may be used to estimate the flame temperature (e.g., sodium line-reversal technique) or to study the metal spectrum. The laboratory flame spectrum (for spectroscopic study) is well defined and can be highly transparent over large regions of wavelength. The distinction is drawn here between flames generated by the spectroscopist and turbulent flames generated in combustion laboratories for purposes of estimating such factors as fuel burnout times and completeness of combustion, where the investigator, for good reason, has little interest in the spectrum.

INDUSTRIAL FLAMES

Flames in industrial (power-plant) furnaces are characterized by being turbulent; in the case of tangentially fired furnaces, these can be described as forced-vortex turbulent diffusion flames. The spectrum of these flames is continuous, tends to be black, and is consequently spectroscopically indistinct. That is, the spectrum varies with the flame conditions and is difficult to identify with an industrial fuel. This is in contradistinction to laboratory fuels which are mono-component and maintain a high degree of purity.

There is no characteristic spectrum that can be associated with the flame of a given industrial fuel. It has been shown that the spectrum is very dependent on the flame conditions, such as the fuel/air ratio and the temperature. This has been shown in tests where major changes in spectrum were demonstrated simply by manipulating the secondary air dampers.

As we progress from optically thin stationary laboratory flames to optically opaque turbulent industrial flames, we find that the strength of emission of a particular band depends on the concentration of the appropriate radiating species in the excited state and on the rate or, more precisely, the transition probability, at which the species radiates. The observed strength is reduced by self-absorption. For small optically thin flames, the self-absorption is very weak and the intensity loss in laboratory flames for the CH, C_2, and HCO bands is not appreciable. In the infrared and for OH at 3064 Å (ultraviolet), the self-absorption becomes appreciable, which reduces the intensity and modifies the appearance of those bands.

If we consider the main band of OH in a flame, we find that, as we increase the thickness of the flame layer, for the stronger lines the increase in intensity is restrained to a limiting emissivity value of 1 (black body limit at that wavelength and temperature). The weakest lines (band fine structure) are initially little affected by increasing self-absorption and increase in intensity in nearly direct proportion to the increase in flame thickness. With increasing flame thickness, these, in turn, have their intensity restrained to the black-body limit. The consequence is, that for a large coal- or oil-fired tangential furnace, the spectrum of the bulk flame is a near-black continuum spectrum. In this case, the lines from metallic impurities or from "seeding" the flame cannot be distinguished in a continuum spectrum. Differential brightness (intensity) in the wavelength interval under examination is possible if the metallic contribution is of a higher color temperature than the flame temperature (the black-body-spectrum radiating temperature). It is not clear why this should be expected in a utility furnace with the attendant implied second-law violation.

Since fossil-fuel flames are spectroscopically rather indistinct, that is to say, more or less Planckian in their spectral distribution it follows that the ultraviolet region would come into consideration for scanning purposes.

Ultraviolet radiation[14] which is defined to lie in the wavelength range of 40 to 4000 Å is generally divided into three regions: Near ultraviolet (3000 to 4000 Å), far ultraviolet (2000 to 3000 Å), and extreme ultraviolet (40 to 2000 Å). As the extreme ultraviolet is strongly absorbed by air (O_2, N_2), it is not a first-choice selection for flame-scanning purposes. It follows that the main interest would be in the 2000 to 3500 Å range. Here, the concern is a sufficiency of photon flux for scanner activation. We, therefore, perform the following black-body calculations:

Define

$$\frac{\int_0^\lambda E(\lambda)d\lambda}{\int_0^\lambda E(\lambda)/d\lambda = \sigma T^4}_{black} \qquad \text{(Assume Planckian distribution)}$$

then

$$\int_0^{2000\,\text{Å}} E(\lambda)d\lambda = 4.96 \times 10^{-13}\sigma T^4$$

$$\int_0^{3500\,\text{Å}} E(\lambda)d\lambda = 8.565 \times 10^{-7}\sigma T^4$$

$$\int_{2000\,\text{Å}}^{3500\,\text{Å}} E(\lambda)d\lambda = (8.565 \times 10^{-7} - 4.96 \times 10^{-13})\sigma T^4$$

$$\cong 8.565 \times 10^{-7}\sigma T^4$$

where

$$\sigma = 0.17134 \times 10^{-8}\,\text{Btu/hr-ft}^2\text{-}^\circ R^4$$

Assume 3000°F as typical mean tangentially fired flame temperature

$$\sigma T^4 \cong 246,000\,\text{Btu/ft}^2\text{-hr}$$

thus

$$q' = 0.2107\,\text{Btu/ft}^2\text{-hr}$$

$$h_v = 0.538 \times 10^{-21}\,\text{Btu/photon, at 3500 Å}$$

$$\phi \cong 4 \times 10^{17}\,\text{photons/cm}^2\text{-sec}$$

This is a generous flux for sensing provided that a scanner is able to detect it. In this regard, it is possible to postulate some concern about "shielding absorption" by O_2, H_2O, CO_2, N_2 and CO gases in the furnace and consequent flux attenuation.

THE FORMATION AND CONTROL OF NO$_x$ IN STEAM-GENERATING EQUIPMENT

Nitrogen monoxide (NO) and nitrogen dioxide (NO_2) are byproducts of the combustion process of virtually all fossil fuels. Historically, the quantity of these inorganic compounds in the products of combustion was not sufficient to affect boiler performance, and their presence was largely ignored. In recent years, oxides of nitrogen have been shown to be key constituents in the complex photochemical oxidant reaction with sunlight to form smog. Today, the presence of NO_2 and NO (collectively referred to as NO_x) is regulated by both state and federal authorities and has become an important consideration in design of fuel-firing equipment.

THERMAL NO$_x$

The formation of NO_x in the combustion process is often explained in terms of the source of nitrogen required for the reaction. The N_2 can originate from the atmospheric air, in which case the product is referred to as "thermal

NO$_x$" or from the organically bound nitrogen components found in all coals and fuel oils which are termed "fuel NO$_x$." It is important to note that even though NO$_x$ consists usually of 95 percent NO and only 5 percent NO$_2$, the normal practice is to calculate concentrations of NO$_x$ as 100 percent NO$_2$.

The mechanisms involving thermal NO$_x$ were first described by Zeldovich[15] and later modified to what is referred to as the extended Zeldovich mechanism.

$$N_2 + O \rightleftharpoons NO + N \tag{80}$$

$$N + O_2 \rightleftharpoons NO + O \tag{81}$$

$$N + OH \rightleftharpoons NO + H \tag{82}$$

As the equilibrium values predicted by this mechanism are higher than those actually measured, it is generally assumed that Eq. 80 is rate-determining due to its high activation energy of 317 kJ/mol. A better understanding of thermal NO$_x$ can be derived from bench-scale tests that measure NO$_x$ in a heated mixture of N$_2$, O$_2$, and argon[16]. These tests show that thermal NO$_x$ can be predicted by the following equation:

$$|NO| = K_l e^{(-K_2/T)} |N_2||O_2|^{1/2} t$$

where $|\quad|$ = mol fraction
T = temperature
t = time
K, K$_2$ = constants $\qquad$ **(83)**

From this equation, it can be seen that thermal NO can be decreased by reducing time, temperature, and concentrations of N$_2$ and O$_2$. The fact that temperature in this equation is an exponential clearly demonstrates its importance in the control of thermal NO$_x$. In practice, the Zeldovich mechanisms demonstrated by Eq. 83 are sufficient for predicting NO$_x$ only in regions that are downstream of the flame front.

Fenimore[17] coined the phase "prompt NO" to describe the NO generated within the flame front region for which, because of the very short residence time, the Zeldovich reactions proved inadequate. Subsequent investigation by DeSoeto[18] showed that, as in Zeldovich's reactions, temperature in all cases reduced prompt NO; however, additional O$_2$ increased NO for fuel-rich flame fronts but decreased NO for fuel-lean flame fronts.

The effects of fuel-rich vs. fuel-lean flame fronts on prompt NO can be seen from the formation of NO from diffusion vs. premixed gas flame. As shown in Fig. 10, the stoichiometry at the premixed flame front is the same as the overall stoichiometry of the flame, since all the air is mixed with all the fuel. In the diffusion

Fig. 10 Diffusion-flame and premixed-flame mechanisms

Fig. 11 NO$_x$ versus stoichiometry for premixed and diffusion flames

flame, fuel and air are introduced separately and mixed by burner-induced turbulence. The flame front forms before mixing is complete and is, therefore, fuel-rich even though the total fuel/air mixture may be air-rich. Tests by Takahashi[19] et al., Fig. 11, show the bell-shaped curve characteristic of prompt NO for premixed flames, but the diffusion flame does not show decreasing NO with increasing O_2 because the actual flame front is never air-rich.

It is interesting to note that Takahashi has shown that two separate flames, one fuel-lean premixed flame, plus one fuel-rich diffusion flame (points C_1 and C_2, Fig. 11) can be combined to produce a lower NO(at C') than either type flame with the same overall stoichiometry (points A or B).

FUEL NO$_x$

Although the kinetics involved in the conversion of organically bound nitrogen compounds found in fossil fuels are not yet well understood, numerous investigators have shown fuel NO$_x$ to be an important mechanism in NO$_x$ formation from fuel oil, and the dominant mechanism in NO$_x$ generated from the combustion of coal. Bench-scale tests, Fig. 12, burning fuel oils in a mixture of oxygen and carbon dioxide (to exclude thermal NO$_x$) have shown a remarkable correlation between the percent N_2 in the fuel oil versus NO$_x$.[20] Fig. 12 also illustrates the fact that the percent of fuel-nitrogen conversion is not constant, but decreases with increasing fuel nitrogen.

Similar bench-scale tests run for various coals have not produced similar results. Fig. 13 illustrates the large contribution of fuel NO$_x$, yet there is no apparent correlation between the quantity of fuel-bound nitrogen and fuel NO$_x$. Clearly, the fuel-nitrogen conversion rate is not constant, but will vary widely depending more on coal rank than on actual nitrogen content.

One explanation of the fuel-nitrogen conversion rate is shown in Fig. 14 which was obtained by subtracting a calculated Zeldovich thermal-NO$_x$ value from total NO$_x$ measured in large tangentially fired utility units. The resultant fuel-NO$_x$ correlated well with the fuel nitrogen/oxygen ratio which suggests that fuel-bound oxygen, or some other fuel property that correlates with fuel oxygen, influences the percent conversion of fuel nitrogen to fuel NO$_x$.

Although there is little doubt that fuel-bound

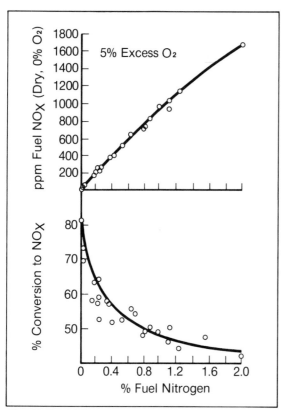

Fig. 12 Fuel NO and percent conversion of fuel nitrogen to Fuel NO—liquid fuels

Fig. 13 Fuel NO and percent conversion of fuel nitrogen to fuel NO—pulverized coal, premixed

nitrogen is an important contributor to total NO$_x$ emissions from coal and oil, the mechanisms involved in the transformation of fuel nitrogen to NO appear to be every bit as complex as the combustion process itself. On the other hand, several investigators have made quantitative measurements in laboratory tests that provide valuable insight to the potential control of fuel NO$_x$.[21]

Pershing[22] isolated fuel NO$_x$ by burning coal in a synthetic oxidant mixture that had a specific heat similar to air, containing 21 percent O$_2$, 18 percent CO$_2$, and 61 percent argon. On the basis of four different coals, the studies showed that fuel NO$_x$, unlike thermal NO$_x$, was relatively insensitive to the range of temperatures found in most flames. Levy[23] et al. found that, under pyrolysis, 65 percent of the fuel nitrogen remained in the char after all the volatile matter had evolved at the 1380°F used in the ASTM proximate-analysis test, and 90 percent had evolved by 2400°F. These tests, then, suggest that the fuel-bound nitrogen begins to evolve in the later stages of devolatization of coal and that subsequent high temperatures do not significantly affect the conversion to NO.

A most significant property of fuel nitrogen conversion that affects the design of fuel-firing equipment relates to the availability of oxygen to react with the fuel-nitrogen compounds in their gaseous state. Simply stated, the compounds that evolve from a coal particle such as NCH and NH$_3$, are relatively unstable and will reduce to harmless N$_2$ under fuel-rich conditions, or to NO under air-rich conditions. The technique used to demonstrate this is staging.

In staging, a portion of the total air required to complete combustion is withheld initially and the balance of the air is mixed with the incomplete products of combustion only after the oxygen content of the first-stage air is consumed. By varying the quantity of air introduced as first-stage air, the combustion of a coal particle or oil droplet can be interrupted at different stages of the reaction because of lack of oxygen, and allowed to proceed further at such time as the balance of air (second-stage air) is introduced. For NO$_x$ control, the ideal quantity of first-stage air would be that which is sufficient to only generate the temperatures necessary to drive the gaseous state, but insuf-

Fig. 15 The effect of liquid fuel composition on emissions—staged

Fig. 14 Fuel-bound nitrogen conversion to NO$_x$ in pulverized-coal combustion; the influence of the coal-oxygen to coal-nitrogen ratio

ficient to provide sufficient oxidant to complete a reaction to NO.

Fig. 15 shows the effect of first-stage stoichiometric ratio on outlet NO_x levels for liquid fuels with various nitrogen levels. Even though the tests used air for an oxidant and the total NO_x levels represent both thermal and fuel NO_x, the increased effectiveness of staging with higher fuel-nitrogen content is clear. Fig. 16 shows a similar but less dramatic effect on a Utah bituminous coal. This and other tests have shown that for coal, unlike oil, decreasing the first-stage stoichiometric air below an optimum level will increase NO_x levels, which suggests the possible requirement of an oxidant to reduce the intermediate HCN, NH_3, and other radicals.

Because coal is the primary fuel used in utility and large industrial steam generators, the most important design criteria relevant to the control of both thermal and fuel NO_x for coal firing can be summarized as follows:

■ Coals with the lowest fuel-nitrogen and the lowest fuel oxygen/nitrogen ratios generally will produce the lowest NO_x.

■ The fuel NO_x can be minimized by controlling the quantity of air permitted to mix with the fuel in the early stages of combustion.

■ The thermal-NO_x contribution to total NO_x can be reduced by operating at low excess-air

percentages, as well as by minimizing gas temperatures throughout the furnace through the use of low-turbulence diffusion flames and large water-cooled furnaces.

Chapter 13 describes the equipment used in large steam generators to minimize NO_x formation in the fuel burning process in a furnace. In Chapter 17, several methods of chemically reducing the amount of NO_x passing to the atmosphere are reviewed. Such methods make no attempt to affect oxide formation in the furnace, but only convert it before the gases enter the stack.

Fig. 16 **The effect of initial fuel/air mixing— staged, Utah bituminous coal**

REFERENCES

[1] "Standard Atmosphere Tables and Data for altitudes to 65,800 feet," National Advisory Committee for Aeronautics Report 1235 International Civil Aviation Organization (ICAO), Montreal, Canada and Langley Aeronautical Laboratory, Langley Field, VA. 1952.

[2] Kenneth Wark, *Thermodynamics*, 2nd ed., McGraw-Hill, 1971.

[3] William C. Reynolds and Henry C. Perkins, *Engineering Thermodynamics*, 1st ed., McGraw-Hill, 1970.

[4] Gordon J. Van Wylen and Richard E. Sonntag, *Fundamentals of Classical Thermodynamics*, 2nd ed., John Wiley & Sons, Inc., 1973.

[5] E. U. Condon and Hugh Odishaw, *Handbook of Physics*, 2nd ed., New York: McGraw-Hill, 1967.

[6] R. E. Bolz and G. L. Tuve, eds., *Handbook (of Tables for) Applied Engineering Science*, Publ. by the Chemical Rubber Co., Cleveland, Ohio, Copyright 1970.

[7] It may be noted that the term *Gibbs Free Energy* is in common use. Strictly and historically speaking it is incorrect. The Gibbs function of the system is termed the "Free Enthalphy" property. The Helmholtz function of the system is more properly called the "Free Energy" property. See, for example, E. Schmidt[8].

[8] E. Schmidt, *Thermodynamics*, translated from 3rd German edition, Oxford University Press, London, England, 1st English ed., 1947.

[9] C. Kittel, *Thermal Physics*, John Wiley & Sons., New York, 1969.

[10] JANAF (Joint Army, Navy, Air Force Project), *Thermochemical Tables*, 2nd ed., 1970 issued 1971, NSRDS-NBS 37, U.S. Government Printing Office, Washington, D.C.

[11] A. G. Gaydon and H. G. Wolfhard, *Flames: Their Structure, Radiation, and Temperature*, 4th ed. (revised), John Wiley & Sons Publ. Co., Halsted Press, 1979.

[12] Gerhard Herzberg, *The Spectra and Structures of Simple Free Radicals*, 1st ed., Cornell University Press, 1971.

[13] M. Orchin and H. H. Jaffe, *Symmetry, Orbitals and Spectra*, 1st ed., John Wiley & Sons Publ. Co., Wiley-Interscience Division, 1971.

[14] L. R. Koller, *Ultraviolet Radiation*, 1st ed., John Wiley & Sons, Inc., 1952.

[15] Ya. B. Zel'dovich, "The Oxidation of Nitrogen in Combustion and Explosions," *Acta Physicochimica U.S.S.R.*, 21:577–628, 1946.

[16] D. J. MacKinnon, "Nitric Oxide Formation at High Temperature," *Air Pollution Control Association Journal*, 24(3): 237–239, March 1974.

[17] C. P. Fenimore, "Formation of Nitric Oxide From Fuel Nitrogen in Ethylene Flames," *Combustion and Flame*, 19(2): 289–296, October 1972.

[18] G. DeSoete, "Mechanism of Nitric Oxide Formation From Ammonia and Amines in Hydrocarbon Flames," *Revue de L'Institut Francais du Petrole et Annuales Des Combustibles Liquides*, 28(1): 95–108, 1973.

[19] Yasuro Takahashi, et al., "Development of Super-Low NO_x PM Burner," *Mitsubishi Technical Bulletin No. 134*. Mitsubishi Heavy Industries, Ltd., 1979.

[20] W. W. Habelt, "The Influence of Coal Oxygen to Coal Nitrogen Ratio on NO_x Formation," Presented at the 70th Annual AIChE Meeting, New York, November 13–17, 1977; Published as Combustion Engineering publication TIS-5140, Windsor, CT: Combustion Engineering, Inc., 1977.

[21] W. W. Habelt and B. M. Howell, "Control of NO_x Formation in Tangentially Coal-Fired Steam Generators," *Proceedings of the NO_x Control Technology Seminar*, San Francisco, February 5–6, 1976. Special Report. Report no. PB-253 661 (EPRI SR-39). Springfield, VA: National Technical Information Service, 1976.

[22] D. W. Pershing and J. O. L. Wendt, "The Effect of Coal Composition on Thermal and Fuel NO_x Production from Pulverized Coal Combustion," *Central States Section, The Combustion Institute Spring Meeting*, Columbus, Ohio, April 5–6, 1976. Pittsburgh: The Combustion Institute, 1976.

[23] J. M. Levy, et al., *Combustion Research on the Fate of Fuel-Nitrogen Under Conditions Of Pulverized Coal Combustion*. Final Task Report. Report no. PB-286 208 (EPA-600/7-78/165). Springfield, VA: National Technical Information Service, 1978.

[24] M. P. Heap, et al., "The Influence of Fuel Characteristics on Nitrogen Oxide Formation—Bench Scale Studies," *Proceedings of the Third Stationary Source Combustion Symposium: Volume II, Advanced Processes and Special Topics*. Report no. PB-292 540 (EPA-600/7-79/050B), pp. 3–39. Springfield, VA: National Technical Information Service, 1979.

CHAPTER 5

Steam Generation

revious chapters have covered the steam power-plant cycles, general engineering and economic decisions related to the purchase of a steam-generating unit. Also discussed were fuels and their evaluation for use in a boiler furnace. The characteristics of coal ash were covered in great detail to emphasize the significant influence of mineral matter in solid fuels on the sizing and satisfactory operation of a large boiler. This earlier material, which also "burned" the fuel and determined the products of combustion, as well as presenting some of the principles of combustion in a furnace, established the theory behind the hardware.

This chapter will cover *steam generation* by considering the roles of the different components that make up a steam generator.

Included are the *properties of steam* used to perform basic heat-balance and sizing calculations. Also examined are the criteria involved in the *configuration of boiler pressure parts and auxiliaries* as a function of system pressures and temperatures. Generically introduced are the various parts of a reheat-cycle steam generator and an explanation of their functioning as heat-absorbing apparatus. (More specific information in the following four chapters will supplement and amplify these descriptions.) Also presented is the vital function of *water-steam circulation* in a modern high-pressure furnace, along with the basic principles of thermally induced and pumped circulation. The important aspects of the *separation of steam* from the steam-water mixture entering the upper drum of a subcritical-pressure boiler and the general types of mechanical drum internals used are covered.

STEAM AS A WORKING FLUID

The theoretical amount of work that can be obtained from steam used in a prime mover is equivalent to the change in its total heat content from its condition at the entering state to that at the exhaust state.

The efficiency of the prime mover in converting the heat energy to mechanical effort governs the actual work obtained.

For economic studies involved in the selection and design of all steam- and power-generation equipment, it is necessary to understand thoroughly the properties of steam, the use of steam tables and the use of superheat. A brief review of these fundamentals that apply to the generation of steam will be helpful.

PROPERTIES OF STEAM

Steam results from adding sufficient heat to water to cause it to vaporize. This vaporization occurs in two steps: first, by adding heat to the water to raise it to the boiling temperature; second, by continuing the addition of heat to change the state from water to steam.

When heated at average atmospheric pressure at sea level, each pound of water increases in temperature about 1°F for each Btu added until 212°F is reached. Additional heat does not cause the temperature to rise but, if continued, results in boiling, and the water changes its state from a liquid to a vapor.

When water is heated to the boiling point in a closed vessel, the vapor released causes the pressure in the vessel to rise. With the rise in pressure, the temperature at which the water boils also will rise. It has been determined experimentally that during the change in state of any substance from a liquid to a vapor at constant pressure, the vapor in contact with its liquid will remain at constant temperature until the vaporization has been completed. Thus, the temperature at which boiling occurs for any given pressure is constant and is called the *saturation temperature*. This temperature is the same for the water as it is for the vapor with which it is in contact.

DEFINITIONS

The heat of the liquid is the heat used to raise a unit weight of water, normally one pound, from 32°F to the saturation temperature corresponding to a given pressure. Also called the enthalpy of the saturated liquid, this is stated in Btu per lb.

The latent heat of vaporization is the heat added to a unit weight of water at saturation temperature to vaporize it completely and produce dry saturated steam. This is the enthalpy of evaporation or vaporization.

Dry saturated steam contains no moisture, and is at saturated temperature for the given pressure. Its total heat content, or enthalpy of the saturated vapor, is equal to the heat of the liquid plus the heat of vaporization.

Steam which contains water in any form, either as minute droplets, mist, or fog, is called wet steam. Wet steam may result from the entrainment of water in boiling or from partial condensation. In either case, the total heat content of the mixture is less than that of dry

saturated steam, because vaporization is incomplete. The percentage of dry vapor by weight in the mixture is known as the quality of the steam. Thus, with 3-percent moisture in steam, the quality is 97 percent. The total heat of wet steam is equal to the heat of the liquid plus the percentage of latent heat of vaporization represented by the steam quality. The temperature of wet steam is the same as dry steam at the corresponding pressure.

Steam with a temperature higher than that of saturated steam at the same pressure is called superheated. Accomplished by maintaining the pressure and adding heat to the steam after its removal from contact with water, superheating results in an increase in temperature and volume. The total heat of superheated steam, or its enthalpy, is equal to the total heat of dry saturated steam plus the heat of superheating. The term total heat is the general engineering expression applicable to any steam condition, whether wet, dry saturated, or superheated. Also known as the enthalpy of steam, it is the amount of heat that must be added to a unit weight of water at 32°F to produce the end state under consideration.

The properties of steam have been the subject of considerable research in many of the countries of the world for many years, as stated in Appendix F. The Mollier diagram, constructed as an enthalpy-entropy chart to show the steam tables graphically, is particularly useful in the analysis of power-plant cycles. It visualizes the process of expansion of steam through the various sections of a steam turbine and helps in the quick but approximate solution of many other thermodynamic problems. Appendix F tells how to obtain a C-E Mollier chart based on steam tables available from C-E.

SUPERHEATED AND SATURATED STEAM

The properties of superheated steam approximate those of a perfect gas. One important characteristic is the dependence of internal energy on temperature; thus, the closer steam approaches a perfect gas, the better it does its work. In addition, it contains no moisture, nor can it condense until its temperature has been lowered to that of saturated steam at the same pressure. This particular characteristic is of considerable value because, with the correct amount of superheat, it is possible to eliminate condensation in steam lines and to decrease the moisture in the turbine exhaust.

With saturated steam, the heat available depends entirely upon pressure, while with superheated steam there is additional heat, proportionate to the degree of superheat. This additional heat is obtained through increased expenditure of fuel, but the economic benefits derived result in a net efficiency gain of considerable magnitude (see Chapter 1). By using a comparatively small amount of superheat, it is possible to reduce moisture at exhaust conditions and to effect an increase in the percentage of heat utilized.

LIMITS OF STEAM TEMPERATURE AND PRESSURE

The materials of superheater construction govern the practical limits of steam tempera-

ture and pressure. There has been considerable development in the metallurgy of steel alloys and in the manufacturing of both the tubing and the finished sections of the superheater. These have made possible the design of superheaters and reheaters for high-temperature and high-pressure boiler installations, as have improvements in the art of welding. While those installations which border on the limitations of available materials may be more interesting, and perhaps more sensational, the large majority is in the 750° to 1050°F temperature range. Although commonplace, they represent the places where the greatest savings are made.

A study of steam temperatures accompanying installations using 2400 psig throttle pressures discloses that in the 1950's, 1050°F was overwhelmingly selected as the primary temperature. The trend since that time has been in the direction of 1000°F primary temperature, and is a well established—but surely not exclusive—pattern. Again, experience has proved to be the arbiter. First, the initial cost of

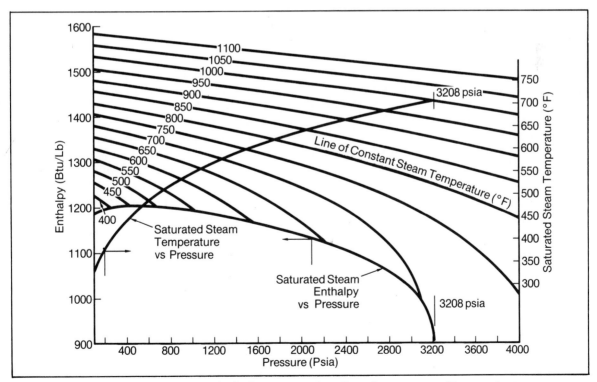

Fig. 1 Variation in heat content (enthalpy) of steam as a function of pressure and temperature

boilers and turbines for the higher temperature level proved to be less attractive as experience accumulated. In addition, even though accurate and conservative methods of superheater metal selection are used, problems do arise during sustained elevated temperature operation because of the adverse effects of certain fuel constituents on unit availability. Some owners therefore decided to reduce primary steam temperatures while continuing to lower capital cost through larger units. Other utilities chose to take advantage of the thermal gain from higher primary steam temperature and maintained the established 1050°F level.

Units employing the nominal 3500-psi cycle most commonly use 1000°F superheat and 1000°F reheat. About 30 percent of existing supercritical-pressure units have a second reheat stage at 1000°F, justified by high fuel cost and high anticipated load factor.

The curves in Fig. 1 show the variation in heat content of steam at different pressures. Also included are the heat of the liquid and the temperature of saturated steam. The values used in plotting these curves are from the 1967 ASME Steam Tables in Appendix F. When using the steam tables, or charts prepared from them, note that pressure is stated as absolute (psia). The steam gage on a boiler indicates the pressure in the vessel above that of the atmosphere. For these conditions, the absolute pressure is equal to atmospheric pressure plus gage pressure. Condensers and similar equipment operate under vacuum, and their gages usually read in inches of mercury (in. Hg). For these conditions, absolute pressure is equal to atmospheric pressure minus vacuum.

REDUCING STEAM CONSUMPTION BY SUPERHEATING

Previous paragraphs have touched on the value of superheated as compared with saturated steam. A further discussion will serve to illustrate more clearly the manner in which superheating reduces steam consumption, particularly in regard to industrial and marine-boiler installations.

In the case of a steam turbine, high super-

heat is of utmost importance as the absence of moisture in steam decreases friction losses and erosion of turbine blades. If dry saturated steam is used in a turbine, condensation rate increases as the steam passes through the succeeding stages. The friction losses increase rapidly, because the condensate is actually inert material which acts to check the speed of the turbine rotors. By using superheated steam, the condensation can be limited to a relatively few stages in the turbine discharge end, thus reducing windage loss and friction between rotor and vapor because of lower density and absence of moisture in the initial stages.

Pipelines carrying steam lose heat by radiation. Thus, if steam entering a line is dry saturated, any loss in heat will immediately cause condensation which is usually discharged from the line through traps, and is frequently wasted. So, in addition to the heat loss from radiation, there is also loss of the heat in the condensate. Of course, if the condensate is returned to the hotwell, a portion of the heat in the liquid is recovered. By adding a sufficient amount of superheat to the steam, it can be piped without condensation loss.

Using saturated steam in industrial processes often results in minute quantities of moisture in the steam at the point of use. The use of dry saturated steam translates into a considerable savings in steam consumption and frequently increased output. As explained previously, these advantages accrue from sufficiently superheating the steam to overcome condensation in process-steam pipelines.

The installation of a superheater in a boiler has the effect of reducing the amount of work that must be done by the evaporative surfaces to produce the same power. In other words, installing a superheater has the effect of increasing plant capacity. In addition, a properly designed superheater increases the thermal efficiency of the steam-generating unit.

FUNDAMENTALS OF STEAM-GENERATOR DESIGN

Water-tube boilers range in capacity from

small low-pressure heating units generating a few thousand pounds of steam per hour to large reheat steam generators operating in the supercritical pressure region and serving turbine-generators in the million kilowatt range. In slightly different terms, capacity may be magnified more than a thousand times from the smallest to the largest, pressure may extend from just above atmospheric to values as high as 5000 psig, and steam temperatures may vary from the boiling point to a highly superheated condition at 1050°F or above.

What are the common elements in boilers having such a diversity of design parameters? To answer this question it may be well to define the primary function of a boiler which is simply *to generate steam at pressures above the atmospheric*. Steam is generated by the absorption of heat produced in the combustion of fuel. In some instances, such as waste-heat boilers, heated fluids serve as the heat source.

Generation of steam by heat absorption from products of combustion suggests that a boiler must have a pressure-parts system to convert incoming feedwater into steam; a structure within which the combustion reaction may take place, at the same time facilitating heat transfer and supporting boiler components; a means of introducing fuel and removing waste products; and controls and instruments to regulate and monitor operation. A boiler designer has to work with such things as drums, headers and tubing, which make up the pressure-parts system and enclose the furnace in which combustion takes place; burners and related fuel and ash-handling equipment; and fans to supply combustion air and exhaust waste gases. Various types of instruments and controls link these elements together in a physical and an operational sense.

A BRIEF HISTORY OF STEAM GENERATION

A furnace for firing a fossil fuel is a device for generating controlled heat with the objective of doing useful work. The work application may be *direct*, as with rotary kilns, or *indirect*, as in boilers for industrial or marine use, or for the generation of electric power. A further differentiation is whether the furnace enclosure is cooled, such as with *waterwalls*, or uncooled, with a refractory lining.

Furnaces developed originally from a need to fire pottery (4000 B.C.) and to smelt copper (3000 B.C.). Hastening and improving combustion by the use of bellows to blow air into the furnace was used about 2000 B.C.

Closely associated with the furnace is the corresponding steam boiler. Such boilers appear to be of Greek and Roman origin and were employed for household services. The Pompeiian water boiler, incorporating the water-tube principle, is one of the earliest recorded instances of boilers doing mechanical work (130 B.C.). It sent steam to Hero's engine, a hollow sphere mounted and revolving on trunnions, one of which permitted the passage of steam, which was exhausted through two right-angled nozzles that caused the sphere to rotate. This was the world's first reaction turbine.

For the next 1600 years, furnaces in general and waterwall furnaces in particular were essentially a neglected technology. This can be partly ascribed to the fact that steam as a working fluid had no application until the invention of the first commercially successful steam engine by Thomas Savery in 1698. In 1705, Newcomen's engine followed and by 1711, this engine was in general use for pumping water out of coal mines. Self-regulating steam valves were incorporated in 1713.

Many varieties of firetube boilers were invented in the second half of the 18th century, culminating with the Scotch marine boiler described in Chapter 9. As the name implies, in the firetube boiler the tubes may be considered to be a component part of the furnace, with the combustion process completed within the tube bundles. But such units were limited to operating pressure of about 150 psig, again as discussed in Chapter 9. The development of the modern water-tube furnace for steam generation at higher pressures and in larger sizes than available with firetube boilers is the subject of the various chapters of book.

BOILER OUTPUT

The output or capacity of a steam generator is often expressed in pounds of steam per hour or in the power output of a turbine generator in those cases where a single boiler provides the entire steam supply for an electric generating unit. Neither term is a true measure of the thermal energy supplied by the boiler.

Actual boiler output in terms of heat energy depends on several factors other than quantity of steam. These include temperature of feedwater entering the economizer, steam pressure and steam temperature at the superheater outlet, and the quantity, temperature and pressure of steam entering and leaving the reheater. Similarly, because turbine and generator efficiencies affect the boiler output, the generator output in kilowatts is not entirely a true measure of the energy output of the boiler alone.

These elements vary with the size and purpose of the power plant in which the boiler is installed. A large central station in which high thermal efficiency is a primary requisite has many more refinements and auxiliaries than a small heating plant in which minimum capital investment may be an important criterion. No matter how many of these elements may be present, however, the boiler designer must integrate them so that the boiler as a whole can function as a carefully adjusted, complex system which is capable of efficient operation over a wide load range.

STEAM-GENERATOR FUNCTIONS

In addition to its primary function of evaporating water to steam at high pressure, the modern boiler has to

■ produce that steam at exceptionally high purity, using stationary mechanical devices to remove impurities in the boiling water

■ superheat the steam generated in the unit to a specified temperature, and maintain that temperature over a designated range of load

■ re-superheat (reheat) the steam which is returned to the boiler after expanding through the high-pressure stages of the turbine, and maintain that reheat temperature constant over a specified range of load

■ reduce the gas temperature leaving the unit to a level that satisfies the requirement for high thermal efficiency and at the same time is suitable for processing in the emission-control equipment downstream of the boiler

BOILER EFFICIENCY

A diagram is one of the best ways to comprehend the significance of boiler efficiency as it is affected by the heat absorption pattern in a steam generator. Fig. 2 shows the distribution of heat energy in a reheat boiler for utility use. It is apparent that the primary source of heat is the fuel (supplemented by thermal energy from fans, pumps, and pulverizers), but that the preheated air for combustion adds directly to the total heat in the furnace. The amount of heat in the preheated air corresponds to that extracted from the exhaust gases by the air heater. This concept is discussed further in both this chapter and Chapter 6.

Of the total heat entering the furnace, the major portion is absorbed as sensible and latent heat of vaporization in the heating surfaces of the economizer, furnace, superheater and reheater. This absorbed heat represents the boiler output in the form of superheated and reheated steam. Losses which account for the remainder of the heat supplied to the furnace consist of the heat contained in the flue gas leaving the air heater (principally the sensible and latent heat in the moisture from the fuel), smaller losses from less-than-perfect combustion and radiation from the boiler and its ancillary equipment. A description of these losses and how they are calculated is given in Chapter 6.

HEAT-ABSORBING SURFACES

The objective of the boiler designer is to arrange heat-transfer surface and fuel-burning equipment to optimize thermal efficiency and economic investment. He or she may select from waterwalls, superheaters, and reheaters, each of which absorbs heat from the furnace gas as it performs its respective function of heating water to the saturation point and of superheating and resuperheating steam. On the other hand, air heaters and economizers recover heat from the furnace exit gases to preheat combustion air and increase the temperature of incoming feedwater.

The boiler designer must proportion heat-absorbing and heat-recovery surfaces to make best use of the heat released by the fuel. Waterwalls, superheaters, and reheaters are exposed to convection and radiant heat, whereas convection heat transfer predominates in air heaters and economizers.

The relative amounts of such surfaces vary with the size and operating conditions of the boiler. A small low-pressure heating plant with no heat-recovery equipment has quite a different arrangement from a large high-pressure unit operating on a reheat regenerative cycle and incorporating heat-recovery equipment.

Fig. 3 shows how the proportion of energy absorbed varies with different types of boilers.

In a heating-plant boiler operating with a minimum of feedwater heating and no superheater it is evident that most of the heat absorbed is utilized in evaporating water to steam. In a large reheat unit with feedwater heaters and heat-recovery equipment, heat for evaporation is comparatively small, whereas heat for superheating and reheating accounts for more than half of the total input.

Fig. 4 is a plot of temperature vs. heat absorption for four different high-pressure steam cycles: the single-reheat 1800 psig cycle at 5 percent overpressure; the 2400 psig, 1000°F cycle with single reheat to 1000°F, again in 5 percent overpressure (2620 psig at the superheater outlet); and a single-reheat and a double-reheat supercritical cycle, both at 1000°F at the turbine throttle. Such heat-absorption profiles will vary with entering feedwater temperature, cold-reheat temperature, and relative size of furnace and economizer.

FACTORS INFLUENCING BOILER DESIGN

In addition to the basics of unit size, steam pressure, and steam temperature, the designer must consider other factors that influence the overall design of the steam generator.

FUELS

Coal, although the most common fuel, is the most difficult fuel to burn. The types of coal and their characteristics are covered thoroughly in Chapter 2 and Appendix A.

As described in Chapter 3, the ash in coal consists of a number of objectionable chemical elements and compounds. Because of the high percentage of ash that can occur in coal, it has a serious effect on furnace performance.

At the high temperatures resulting from the burning of fuel in the furnace, fractions of ash can become partially fused and sticky. Depend-

Fig. 2 **Steam generator energy flow**

ing on the quantity and fusion temperature, the partially fused ash may adhere to surfaces contacted by the ash-containing combustion gases, causing objectionable buildup of slag on or bridging between tubes. Chemicals in the ash may attack materials such as the alloy steel used in superheaters and reheaters.

In addition to the deposits in the high-temperature sections of the unit, the air heater (the coolest part) may be subject to corrosion and plugging of gas passages from sulfur compounds in the fuel acting in combination with moisture present in the flue gas.

THE FURNACE

Heat generated in the combustion process appears as furnace radiation and sensible heat in the products of combustion. Water circulating through tubes that form the furnace wall lining absorbs as much as 50 percent of this heat which, in turn, generates steam by the evaporation of part of the circulated water.

Furnace design must consider water heating and steam generation in the wall tubes as well as the processes of combustion. Practically all large modern boilers have walls comprised of water-cooled tubes to form complete metal coverage of the furnace enclosure. Similarly, areas outside of the furnace which form enclosures for sections of superheaters, reheaters and economizers also use either water- or steam-cooled tube surfaces. Present practice is to use tube arrangements and configurations which permit practically complete elimination of refractories in all areas that are exposed to high-temperature gases.

Waterwalls usually consist of vertical tubes arranged in tangent or approximately so, connected at top and bottom to headers. These tubes receive their water supply from the boiler drum by means of downcomer tubes connected between the bottom of the drum and the lower headers. The steam, along with a substantial quantity of water, is discharged from the top of the waterwall tubes into the upper waterwall headers and then passes through riser tubes to the boiler drum. Here the steam is separated from the water, which together with the incoming feedwater, is returned to the waterwalls through the downcomers.

Tube diameter and thickness are of concern from the standpoints of circulation and metal

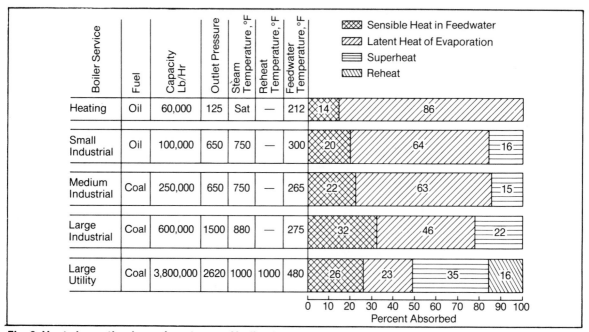

Boiler Service	Fuel	Capacity Lb/Hr	Outlet Pressure	Steam Temperature, °F	Reheat Temperature, °F	Feedwater Temperature, °F	Percent Absorbed
Heating	Oil	60,000	125	Sat	—	212	14 / 86
Small Industrial	Oil	100,000	650	750	—	300	20 / 64 / 16
Medium Industrial	Coal	250,000	650	750	—	265	22 / 63 / 15
Large Industrial	Coal	600,000	1500	880	—	275	32 / 46 / 22
Large Utility	Coal	3,800,000	2620	1000	1000	480	26 / 23 / 35 / 16

Legend: Sensible Heat in Feedwater; Latent Heat of Evaporation; Superheat; Reheat

Fig. 3 **Heat absorption by various types of boilers**

temperatures. Thermo-syphonic (also called thermal or natural) circulation boilers generally use larger diameter tubes than positive (pumped) circulation or once-through boilers. This practice is dictated largely by the need for more liberal flow area to provide the lower velocities necessary with the limited head available. The use of small-diameter tubes is an advantage in high-pressure boilers because the lesser tube thicknesses required result in lower outside tube-metal temperatures. Such small-diameter tubes are used in recirculation boilers in which pumps provide an adequate head for circulation and maintain the desired velocities. Circulation of water and steam in both subcritical and supercritical boilers are discussed further in other sections of this chapter.

SUPERHEATERS AND REHEATERS

The function of a superheater is to raise the boiler steam temperature above the saturated temperature level. As steam enters the superheater in an essentially dry condition, further absorption of heat sensibly increases the steam temperature.

The reheater receives superheated steam which has partly expanded through the turbine. As described earlier, the role of the reheater in the boiler is to re-superheat this steam to a desired temperature.

Superheater and reheater design depends on the specific duty to be performed. For relatively low final outlet temperatures, superheaters solely of the convection type are generally used. For higher final temperatures, surface requirements are larger and, of necessity, superheater elements are located in very high gas-temperature zones. Wide-spaced platens or panels, or wall-type superheaters or reheaters

of the radiant type, can then be used. Fig. 5 shows an arrangement of such platen and panel surfaces. A relatively small number of panels are located on horizontal centers of 5 to 8 feet to permit substantial radiant heat absorption. Platen sections, on 14″ to 28″ centers, are placed downstream of the panel elements; such spacing provides high heat absorption by both radiation and convection. These modes of heat transfer are discussed further in Chapter 6. Convection sections are arranged for essentially pure counterflow of steam and gas, with steam entering at the bottom and leaving at the top of the pass, while gas flow is opposite. As explained in Chapter 6, this arrangement allows a maximum mean temperature difference between the two media and minimizes the heating surface in the primary sections.

Metallurgy

Superheaters and reheaters designed for high pressures and temperatures above 1000°F require high-strength alloy tubing. Besides selection of materials for strength and oxidation resistance, the use of high steam pressure requires greater tube thicknesses in all tubes subject to steam pressure. Further, thicker tubes are subject to higher outside metal temperatures and, because chemical action is accelerated at higher temperatures, the tube metal is more subject to external corrosion. This is of particular concern when burning fuels containing objectionable impurities. The designer takes account of such conditions in selecting material and tube sizes. See Chapters 3, 6, and 10 for information relating to corrosion from coal ash, selection of superheater and reheater surface, and materials used for commercial construction of this equipment.

Fig. 4 **Heat absorption variation with cycle pressure**

ECONOMIZERS

Economizers help to improve boiler efficiency by extracting heat from flue gases discharged from the final superheater section of a radiant/reheat unit (or the evaporative bank of an industrial boiler). In the economizer, heat is transferred to the feedwater, which enters at a temperature appreciably lower than that of saturated steam. Generally economizers are arranged for downward flow of gas and upward flow of water.

Water enters from a lower header and flows through horizontal tubing comprising the heating surface. Return bends at the ends of the tubing provide continuous tube elements, whose upper ends connect to an outlet header that is in turn connected to the boiler drum by means of tubes or large pipes. Tubes that form the heating surface may be plain or provided with extended surface such as fins. Frequently, they are arranged in staggered relationship in the gas pass to obtain high heat transfer and to lessen the space requirements.

Designing the economizer for counterflow of gas and water results in maximum mean temperature difference for heat transfer. (See Chapter 6 for more on the temperature difference.) Upward flow of water helps avoid water hammer, which may occur under some operating conditions. To avoid generating steam in the economizers, the design ordinarily provides existing water temperatures below that of saturated steam during normal operation.

As shown in Fig. 5, economizers of a typical utility-type boiler are located in the same pass as the primary or horizontal sections of the superheater, or superheater and reheater, depending on the arrangement of the surface.

Tubing forming the heating surface is generally low-carbon steel. Because steel is subject to corrosion in the presence of even extremely low concentrations of oxygen, it is necessary to provide water that is practically 100 percent oxygen-free. In central stations and other large plants it is common practice to use deaerators for oxygen removal.

Small low-pressure boilers may have economizers made of cast iron, which is not as sub-

Fig. 5 Arrangement of superheater, reheater and economizer of a large coal-fired steam-generator

ject to oxygen corrosion. However, the design pressure for this material is limited to approximately 250 psig. Whereas cast-iron tubes find little application today, cast-iron fins shrunk on steel tubes are practical and can be used at any boiler pressure.

AIR HEATERS

Steam-generator air heaters have two important and concomitant functions: they cool the gases before they pass to the atmosphere, thereby increasing fuel-firing efficiency; at the same time, they raise the temperature of the incoming air of combustion. Depending on the pressure and temperature cycle, the type of fuel, and the type of boiler involved, one of the two functions will have prime importance.

For instance, in a low-pressure gas- or oil-fired industrial or marine boiler, combustion-gas temperature can be lowered in several ways—by a boiler bank, by an economizer, or by an air heater. Here, an air heater has principally a gas-cooling function, as no preheating is required to burn the oil or gas.

If the boiler is a high-pressure reheat unit burning a high-moisture subbituminous or lignitic coal, high preheated-air temperatures are needed to evaporate the moisture in the coal before ignition can take place. Here, the air-heating function becomes primary. Without exception, then, large pulverized-coal boilers either for industry or electric-power generation use air heaters to reduce the temperature of the combustion products from the 600°-800°F level to final exit-gas temperatures of 275°F to 350°F. In these units the combination air is heated from about 80°F to between 500°F to 750°F, depending on coal calorific value and moisture content.

In theory, only the primary air must be heated: that is, air used to actually dry the coal in the pulverizers. Ignited fuel can burn without preheating the secondary and tertiary air. But there is considerable advantage to the furnace heat-transfer process from heating *all* the combustion air; it increases the rate of burning and helps raise adiabatic temperature.

Chapter 12 presents the various uses of air

heaters in the pulverization process. Some of the available types of air heaters are described in Chapter 15. Establishing inlet air and outlet gas temperatures to minimize corrosion of air-heater surface is considered in Chapter 6.

In sizing air heaters, note that, while the cost of pressure parts of a unit increase as the steam pressure increases, the air-heater cost is independent of pressure. Consequently, it is not difficult to justify the cost of larger air heaters on boilers operating at higher pressure levels.

CONTROL OF STEAM TEMPERATURE

To maintain turbine efficiency over a wide load range and to avoid fluctuations in turbine metal temperatures require constant primary steam and reheat temperatures over the anticipated operating load range. To satisfy this requirement, a boiler must be equipped with means for controlling and maintaining such steam temperatures over the desired range. If uncontrolled, steam temperatures will rise as the steam output increases. This is particularly characteristic of convection-type superheaters, which account for the major share of heat absorbed by the superheater.

To provide an economical installation that operates at minimum metal temperatures, superheaters and reheaters should be designed to provide exactly the specified steam temperature at maximum output. An optimum design is one in which *all* the gas leaving the furnace passes over *all* the installed superheater and reheater surface at 100 percent boiler rating, without need of either superheater or reheater spray-water. To satisfy this the *means of control* must maintain full steam and reheat temperatures over the total control range.

TECHNIQUES OF STEAM-TEMPERATURE CONTROL

Steam-temperature control devices must be incorporated in the original design of a boiler firing system, in the superheater or reheater circuitry, or in arrangements of dampers for gas bypass. The following are the most frequently used means of control.

■ Firing-system manipulation, in which the effective release of heat from the fuel-burning process is made to occur at a higher or lower portion of the furnace; this affects the heat absorption pattern in the furnace and, consequently, the furnace exit-gas temperature.

■ Desuperheating by water sprayed into piping ahead of, in between, or following superheater or reheater sections.

■ Recirculation of gas, in which a portion of the combustion gases are brought back to the furnace and are added to the "once-through" flow of gas passing over superheater and reheater.

■ Gas bypass around some of the installed heating surface that is "excess" in certain parts of the load range; the purpose is to prevent such surfaces from absorbing heat from the bypassed gas so that the desired steam temperature is achieved without using any other means.

Subsequent sections describe in more detail these different methods of control, used in one form or another by all manufacturers.

Firing-System Manipulation

There are two common ways to vertically displace the zone of highest heat release in a furnace to achieve a change in the outlet gas temperature. The first, often used with front- or rear-wall fixed burners, is to insert or withdraw levels of burners as a function of load; removing lower levels and firing through the remaining upper levels effectively moves the high-heat-release zone higher in the furnace. This method necessitates backup by spray desuperheating for vernier control.

Tilting fuel and air nozzles, used in corner (tangential) firing systems are a positive means of controlling outlet gas temperature smoothly without cycling equipment in and out of service. Superheater or reheater steam temperatures are regulated by changes in nozzle position. Directing the flame toward the upper part of the furnace maintains a higher gas outlet temperature during light load—or when the walls are clean—than is the case if the flame were directed horizontally into the furnace. At higher loads, or when the walls are coated with ash or slag, nozzles can be positioned horizontally or angled downward.

Desuperheating Control

Desuperheating is the reduction of temperature of superheated steam accomplished by spraying water into the piping either ahead of or behind a superheater or reheater section. To minimize the amount of water used in the process, most large boiler installations use desuperheating in combination with one of the other temperature-control methods. This is because of water-treatment and pumping-power considerations.

Rising temperature with increasing output characterizes the performance of a superheater or reheater which receives its heat by convection from gas flowing over it. With desuperheating control *only*, the superheater must be designed for full temperature at some partial load. As a result, there is excessive heat-transfer surface, with corresponding excess temperatures, at higher loads. A desuperheater can be used to remove this excess in temperature. If located beyond the outlet of the superheater, a desuperheater will condition the steam before it is passed along to the turbine. Although this arrangement is practical for steam temperatures of 825°F and lower, the preferred location of the desuperheater, especially for temperatures above 850°F, is *between* sections of the superheater. In such interstage installations, the steam is first passed through one or more primary superheating sections, where it is raised to some intermediate temperature. It is then passed through the desuperheater and its temperature controlled so that, after continuing through the secondary or final stage of superheating, the required constant temperature condition is maintained.

Desuperheating of reheat steam is generally not desirable because of the effect on plant heat rate. To evaporate the water that is added to the reheat flow (usually ahead of the point where the reheat steam is introduced into the steam generator) requires firing additional fuel in the boiler. There also results an increased condenser loss for the same primary steam flow. Consequently, reheat outlet temperature is best controlled using some means other than water spray, unless it is unavoidable.

The heat given up by the steam during a temperature reduction is picked up by the cooling water in three steps. First, its temperature is raised to that of saturated water; then the water is evaporated; and finally, the steam thus generated is raised to the final condition of temperature at the desuperheater outlet. By setting up a simple heat balance, it is possible to determine quickly the quantity of water required to desuperheat for any given set of conditions.

Desuperheaters are either the indirect or direct (mixing) type. The water available for use as the temperature-regulating medium governs the selection for any specific installation. This is not so important with the indirect non-contact type, where a tubular heat exchanger is used, since the steam to be desuperheated is separated from the cooling medium, and the heat is transferred through the separating tube wall. In the direct type, however, the cooling medium is injected into, and mixed with, the superheated steam to reduce the temperature. To be used for this purpose, the cooling medium must be of condensate quality, containing very few solids.

In industrial or marine practice, to help reduce costs, non-contact desuperheating coils may be installed in one of the boiler drums. The principal objection to this design is its relatively low capacity. Through necessity, all parts must be sufficiently small to be conveniently handled through the boiler-drum access opening. The coils must therefore be compact, and made in sections to permit assembly and installation within the drum space limitations. If large or bulky, and if the number of parts are many, the assembly of the coils may become almost impossible.

Gas Recirculation

In this temperature-control means, described further in Chapter 6, a portion of the flue gas is diverted from the main stream at a point following the superheater and reheater (usually between the economizer outlet and the air-heater inlet) and is recirculated to the furnace. The gas passes through a recirculating fan and mixes with the gas in the furnace, causing a reduction

in heat absorption. The heat available to the superheater and reheater increases, as does the quantity of gas passing over the surfaces. Both of these factors increase steam temperature.

Bypass-Damper Control

An arrangement of bypass dampers in a relatively cool gas zone downstream of superheater or reheater sections provides an acceptable means for maintaining constant steam temperature; automatic controllers adjust the dampers to provide the required degree of temperature control. If load changes are abrupt, frequent, and of considerable magnitude, there is likely to be some hunting in positioning the damper. As there is also some lag in the response to temperature changes, final temperature varies over a plus or minus 10°F range. This variation is characteristic where the regulation of steam temperature depends solely on control of gas flow through bypass-damper operation.

During the early damper-opening periods, the gas flow rapidly increases and then falls off as the full-open position is approached (see Fig. 6). The data were taken from an operational test during which the capacity of the unit was held constant and the effect of variable bypass-damper opening against steam temperature was recorded. There is an increase of 15°F in steam temperature for a change in damper from 100 percent to 40 percent open. However, the temperature increase from 40 percent open to fully-closed damper is 50°F. It is apparent

Fig. 6 **Chart illustrating steam temperature change with respect to damper opening**

that sensitive responses, resulting in more uniform temperatures, are obtainable when the regulator operation is confined to the early stages of damper opening. In other words, any changes in capacity that would normally require the bypass damper to operate above 50 percent open should be compensated for by other adjustments so as to keep within the sensitive control range.

WATER/STEAM CIRCULATION

The term circulation, as applied to steam generators, is the movement of water, steam, or a mixture of the two, through heated tubes. The tubes can be in furnace walls, boiler banks, economizers, superheaters, or reheaters. Adequate circulation results in the cooling fluid absorbing heat from the tube metal at a rate which maintains the tube temperature at or below design conditions. Adequate circulation also keeps the tube within the other physical and chemical limitations required by the inside and outside environment. In boilers, circulation through the varied systems of heated tubes can involve just the flow entering and leaving the system (called the once-through flow), a means of recirculating the fluid, or some combination of these two circulation concepts.

Steam generators of all manufacturers have similar pressure-part systems. For any given steam-power cycle, the economizer contains fluid in the lowest temperature range, with its inlet temperature being that leaving the top feedwater heater. The superheater contains fluid in the highest temperature range, with its outlet temperature essentially fixed. The evaporator contains the middle range of fluid temperatures.

Circulation in economizers, superheaters and reheaters is most commonly of the once-through type. The furnace-wall system of high-pressure units uses either once-through or recirculation flow, or some combination. By convention, these modes of circulation have become terms of reference for the complete steam generating unit.

At pressures below the 3208-psia critical point, the major portion of the evaporator operates at a saturation temperature established by the pressure of the furnace-wall system. At supercritical pressures, the wall system has no fixed fluid temperature; a continuous temperature increase occurs in the furnace-cooling fluid between the furnace-wall inlet and outlet.

The most critical circulating system in a large boiler is that of the furnace walls; they are at the same time the area of highest heat-absorption rates and a major structural component of the unit. This section, and Chapter 7, discuss the various types of furnace-wall circulation that the designer can use, their differences and the advantages of each.

CIRCULATION IN FURNACE WALLS

There are four types of furnace-wall circulation systems used for present-day steam generators. Their application depends on pressure, unit size and planned operating mode, required maneuverability, and the manufacturer's design philosophy. Fig. 7 shows the four types diagrammatically; they are:

■ thermally induced, also called thermal, thermo-syphonic, or "natural", with inherent recirculation

■ thermally induced, pump-assisted, with recirculation

■ once-through, with no recirculation

■ once-through, with superimposed pumped recirculation

Because of the influence that pressure has on the behavior of water in the steam-generating process, it is necessary to distinguish between the different circulation systems at subcritical and supercritical pressures.

THERMAL CIRCULATION

The first type, thermal circulation, is a recirculating system at subcritical pressure. It depends on the static-head difference between the water in the downcomers (usually unheated) and the steam-water mixture in the heated generating tubes to produce circulation and maintain sufficient mass velocity and mixture quality for adequate furnace-wall cooling. Circulation begins only after heat is applied to the generating or "riser" tubes and, when once begun, is proportional to the amount of heat locally supplied. To maintain the overall system pressure drop as low as possible, boilers using this principle for cooling the furnace enclosure need large flow areas in downcomers, supply tubes, generating tubes, and relief tubes to the drum.

Thermal-circulation boilers are the dominant choice of all manufacturers for low and medium subcritical-pressure operation, as they have been since the early development of the water-tube boiler. Theoretically, thermal circulation can be used at any waterwall operating pressure below the critical pressure of 3208 psia, as long as there is some finite density difference between the water in the downcomers and the saturated steam-water mixture in the heated circuits. Practically, the maximum furnace-wall pressure that has been used is about 400 psi below the critical pressure.

Later in this chapter are discussed the principles of thermal circulation including some of the mathematical bases for subcritical-circulation calculations in this mode. Also covered is the design background for different types of drum internals used to separate steam from the recirculating water so that it can proceed on to the superheater as a heatable vapor.

PUMP-ASSISTED THERMAL CIRCULATION

This type of subcritical-boiler recirculation system uses an external mechanical force, produced by one or more low-pressure-differential pumps located in the downtake system to supplement the thermal head. The thermal-circulation circuitry now includes pumps, isolating valves and, in many designs in this category, waterwall-circuit flow-control orifices. The orifices are varied in size to insure uniform circulation under changing furnace conditions. In general, waterwall tubes of boilers having positive-circulation systems of the type described are smaller than those of thermal circulation units; in the latter circuitry, large tubes minimize friction losses and take maximum advantage of the limited head provided by density difference.

Pump-assisted thermal circulation units find particular application at the high subcritical-pressure levels, where there is reduced fluid static-head energy available to recirculate the furnace-wall fluid. The reduced driving force is of concern where a very large number of parallel tube circuits makes heat distribution a problem, such that some tubes can overheat under certain operating conditions; also, if there is less circulation-energy available it limits the boiler maneuverability.

Note that the only difference between the straight thermally induced boiler and the pump-assisted is in the circulating systems. Otherwise, both types share the same kind of firing methods, means of superheating and reheating and controlling superheater and reheater outlet temperatures, heat-recovery

Fig. 7 **Steam-generator circulation systems**

equipment and structural support. A C-E developed positive-circulation design is described in Chapter 7.

ONCE-THROUGH CIRCULATION

In a once-through boiler, there is no recirculation of water within the unit. In elemental form, the boiler is merely a length of tubing through which water is pumped. Heat is applied, and the water flowing through the tube is converted into steam and superheated to the desired temperature at the outlet. In actual practice, the single tube is replaced by numerous small tubes arranged to provide effective heat transfer similar to the arrangement in drum type boilers. Note that the economizer and superheater operate on the once-through principle even in drum-type boilers. The fundamental differences lie only in the heat-absorbing circuits or evaporating portion of the unit. The word *evaporating* includes boiling at subcritical pressures and heating into the compressible vapor region at supercritical pressures.

In the typical reheat unit, the evaporating surface consists of waterwalls which form the major part, if not all, of the furnace enclosure. The principal distinguishing features of a once-through boiler are related to the design and operation of the waterwalls.

The distinctive design requirements stem partly from the temperatures that may exist in the waterwalls of a once-through unit, in which there is a considerable rise in temperature from waterwall inlet to outlet. Even greater differences may exist during start-up or upset conditions. And there can be significant differences between adjacent individual tubes. The furnace design and construction must take into account the relative thermal expansions produced by these temperature differences in various parts of the furnace and between tubes, casing, and buckstays. The first distinguishing characteristic of once-through boilers, then, is their furnace-wall temperature patterns.

The second principal characteristic concerns means of preserving furnace tubing integrity. Unlike a drum-type boiler, in which circula-

tion of the working fluid is provided whenever the unit is fired, the once-through cooling flow is essentially proportional to the firing rate and is inadequate to provide waterwall tube protection during startup and at low loads. That is, in an elemental once-through unit, the design does not permit internal recirculation; nevertheless, a through flow has to be established at least in the highly heated portions of the circuitry. The operation of the power-plant feedwater system, including the boiler feed pump, is needed to produce the through flow, and suitable means must be provided to dispose of the circulated flow without incurring loss of heat or working fluid. This is normally done with a steam-turbine bypass system.

The once-through design has been successfully applied to both the high-subcritical and supercritical pressure ranges. In this connection, it is useful to point out some differences in boiler operation in the two pressure regimes.

Supercritical Versus Subcritical Once-Through Operation

When water is heated at a pressure above 3208 psia it does not boil. Therefore, it does not have a "saturation temperature", nor does it produce a two-phase mixture of water and steam. Instead, the fluid undergoes a transition in the enthalpy range between 850 and 1050 Btu/lb (Fig. 1). In this range its physical properties (including density, compressibility and viscosity) change continuously from those of a liquid (water) to that of a vapor (steam). The temperature rises steadily; the specific heat and rate of rise varies considerably during the process. The nature of supercritical steam generation rules out the use of a boiler drum to separate steam from water; drumless units are universal for supercritical operation.

During the boiling process at subcritical pressure, individual molecules break out of the dense liquid clusters and, as the physical surroundings permit, form a separate vapor phase. At supercritical pressure, as heat is added to the liquid, the clusters gradually divide into smaller clusters and the spacing of the molecules gradually becomes less dense until the transition to the wide-spaced, random arrangement of a vapor is completed.

The most important result of this situation is that all impurities in the feedwater must either be deposited in the furnace and superheater surfaces or must be carried over into the turbine. As described in Chapter 11 only the best possible feedwater treatment can be considered acceptable. Because blowdown from the drum and furnace walls (as is possible with drum-type units) is not available to remove impurities from the system, not only the makeup water but also a portion of the condensate must be purified. Otherwise the concentration of impurities in the system will build up gradually until intolerable conditions or tube failures will force an outage for cleaning or repairs.

More information on the development of the once-through boiler and its operation at both subcritical and supercritical pressures can be found in the 1967 edition of this text.[1]

ONCE-THROUGH FLOW
WITH SUPERIMPOSED RECIRCULATION

This fourth common type of boiler circulation, used for supercritical service, involves the superposition of pump-assisted circulation, as previously described, on the once-through flow. *Superposition* means that the pumps are permanently installed, but with a local bypass system, to allow them to be in-line or in the bypassed position as a function of load. The pumps then operate to assist circulation as required, on start-up and at low loads.

By adding to the once-through flow as necessary, the boiler-water circulating pumps act to protect the furnace-wall system from excessive metal temperatures. At loads that are above 60 percent of maximum, and 100 percent maximum continuous rating, the pumps are no longer needed for wall-tube protection, and the unit operates on once-through flow.

With this type of unit, it is usual to supply a start-up system that contains shutoff and throttling valves (arranged between the furnace wall and the superheater) which can be bypassed through a low-pressure system with a water separator. This arrangement permits the furnace wall to operate at a pressure above the 3300 psig level while allowing the superheater to operate at a subcritical pressure level during start-up. The system also lends itself to variable-pressure operation through the superheater and steam turbine over any specified load range. More detail on such start-up equipment is presented in Chapter 7.

COMPARISON
FOR SUBCRITICAL STEAM CYCLES

Turbines for 2400 psig operation are usually designed for steam pressures of 2520 psig at the turbine throttle—a condition of 5 percent overpressure. A boiler-drum *operating* pressure of between 2750 and 2850 psig is required to allow for pressure drop through the superheater and the main steam line. As indicated earlier, with the densities of steam and water rapidly approaching each other above this pressure level, it represents an approximate limit for a drum-type boiler incorporating steam separation and recirculation.

An advantage of drum-type units over once-through designs is their ability to operate with marginal quality feedwater. Steam separation permits elimination of undesirable solids by blowdown without affecting steam purity. The tendency of solid constituents to remain with the water phase makes this possible.

Because water is converted completely to steam in a once-through unit, solids in the feedwater must ultimately deposit in either the boiler, the superheater, or the turbine. Although high-quality makeup water can be provided consistently, the condenser always represents a possible threat of contamination. Demineralization of the condensate is necessary in systems with once-through boilers if power production is not to be curtailed during condenser leaks.

The furnace-wall tubes of the majority of coal-fired, drum-type, steam generators are virtually always some type of carbon steel. Its use is possible because the waterwalls are used exclusively for steam generation (evaporation). As a result, the fluid temperature in these tubes is constant and predictable. Even with very high furnace heat-transfer rates, mean-wall tube-metal temperatures seldom exceed 800°F.

TWO-PHASE FLOW

The design of boiler furnaces in the subcritical pressure range requires close attention to the adequacy of coolant flow necessary to keep the evaporative process in waterwall tubes within the nucleate boiling range. The importance of this aspect of two-phase flow has been brought about by the elevated steam pressures and better steam qualities for which boilers are being designed. Conditions are aggravated by the increased and varying absorption rates to which some furnaces are subjected.[2]

In simplest terms, the design problem centers on the choice of a physical arrangement that provides the coolest waterwall at minimum pump power. To accomplish this the designer must know the conditions under which the evaporative process passes from nucleate to transitional and finally to film boiling. Also necessary is information on the manner in which waterwall metal temperature can be expected to change as these phases occur.

An understanding of what is involved in two-phase flow under these conditions is possible from observing the changes that are produced in the film conductance, as indicated most directly by the inside tube-metal temperature when the heat flux, coolant mass flow, enthalpy and pressure are varied.

If a tube were heated uniformly along its length while water at a sufficiently high mass flow were passed through it at a given pressure, the inside metal temperature would follow a plot as described by the solid line in Fig. 8. If the flow rate were reduced, a point would be reached along the mixed or quality phase section of the plot where the metal temperature rises, as indicated by the dashed line in the illustration. The point of departure from the horizontal is known as DNB or the point of departure from nucleate boiling. The maximum point on the curve can be referred to as the point of film boiling or the minimum conductance point. Between DNB and the film-boiling point is the region of transitional boiling.

At DNB, the bubbles of steam forming on the hot tube surface *begin* to interfere with the flow of water to the tube surface, and eventually coalesce into a film of steam which effectively blankets the hot tube surface. The indication of this departure is defined as tube metal temperature fluctuations of 20°F or greater at frequencies of 10 seconds per cycle or slower. The transition from this point of departure from nucleate boiling to the point of steady-state film boiling is unstable because of the sweeping away of the coalescing bubble groups. This unstable phenomena exhibits itself first with cyclical tube-metal temperature fluctuations of 10° to 20°F at a frequency appreciably slower than that of nucleate boiling bubble generation (something in the order of seconds per cycle versus tens of cycles per second for nucleate boiling). As this unsteady transition approaches full film boiling, metal temperature fluctuations of 50° to 100°F at even slower frequencies are observed. Fig. 9 is another way of illustrating the phenomenon.

CIRCULATION IN A SUBCRITICAL WATER-TUBE CIRCUIT

In recirculation-type boilers, the difference in density between steam and water is utilized to provide (or assist in providing) water circulation. (See Fig. 10) Generally, the downtakes

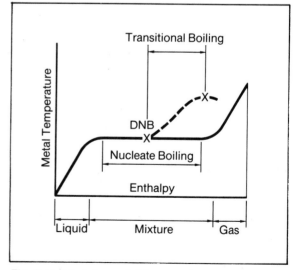

Fig. 8 **Inside tube-metal temperature as a function of two-phase flow conditions**

external to the furnace serve as the high-density leg of the system. The heated furnace walls or the forward portion of a boiler bank, containing a mixture of steam and water, constitutes the low-density leg. The available head to promote circulation is reduced by frictional and entrance and exit losses in the several circuits. The "adequate circulation" referred to earlier can be achieved only if the losses are low and make available a sufficient circulating head.

Before proceeding to the analytical and quantitative calculations of boiler circulation, consider what happens in a water-tube of a subcritical boiler. A steam-generating circuit (Fig. 11), for the velocity and resistance involved will circulate as much water as the differential head will allow. The resistance is the sum of that due to steam flow and that due to water flow. Because the downcomer head is constant, the downcomer flow is a function of the sum of the downcomer head and the riser tube losses. Steam flow is a function of the firing rate, and the water-to-steam ratio in the riser circuit will vary for each operating condition.

The water in the mixture does not necessarily flow uniformly or at the same velocity as the steam, as most riser tubes are more or less vertical, and the flow is against gravity. Because the water is heavier, it tends to separate and recirculate. The degree of such steam-water slippage and consequent recirculation depends on: the relative densities of steam and water, the relative amounts of steam and water in the mixture, the steam flow velocity, and the internal area of the riser tube. As might be expected, maximum slippage is found in boilers having large-diameter tubes, high ratios of water to steam, and low flow velocities.[3]

CIRCULATION RATIO

Circulation ratio is defined as the mass rate of water fed to the steam-generating tubes divided by the mass rate of steam generated. If steam is condensed in the drum by coming in direct contact with the feedwater, the mass of steam for the above calculation will be greater than the net output of the steam drum. In a boiler with drum internals capable of separating steam from water without condensing steam in the drum, the circulation ratio is the total circulation mass rate divided by the total steam mass rate leaving the steam drum.

The average mass of water per pound of steam leaving the steam-generator circuits and entering the steam drum, then, is the circulation ratio minus one.

Fig. 9 **Effect of DNB on tube metal temperature**

Fig. 10 Chart showing relationship of steam and water mixtures

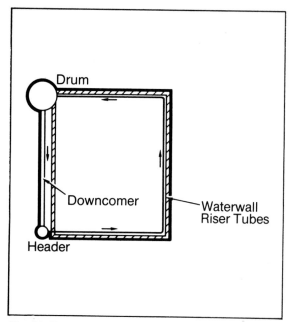

Fig. 11 **Typical steam generating circuit in a subcritical-pressure water-tube boiler**

GENERAL BOILER CIRCULATION

There are two distinct but related ways to consider boiler circulation. The primary view sees circulating fluid transmitting heat from an external source to a machine for conversion of thermal energy into mechanical energy. In this view the boiler is regarded as a thermal transformer in which heat-transfer functions are of first importance and are controlled essentially through fluid circulation.

A second viewpoint emphasizes circulation as a means of protecting the structure of the boiler by rapidly moving fluid through its drums, tubes and headers to prevent overheating. This places circulation also in the role of a structural-protective mechanism.

Ideally these viewpoints are combined in a design in which efficiency of heat transfer is maximized while cost is minimized.

From a physical standpoint, there are three principles involved in the study of thermally induced circulation of fluid.

■ pressure from expansion of a fluid by the application of heat to some portion of a circuit causes circulation

■ with equilibrium established, the work available from expansion balances the work done against resistances to flow in the circuit

■ mass flow of fluid in a closed circuit is constant throughout the circuit and unaffected by volume expansion resulting from a steady-state heat input

A unified analysis of subcritical-pressure boiler circulation proposed by R. W. Haywood in 1951 incorporated revisions of the hydraulic theory proposed by W. Y. Lewis and S. A. Robertson in 1940, the thermodynamic approach proposed by R. S. Silver in 1943, and the expansion approach set forth by R. F. Davis in 1947. Following the Haywood analysis with changes in wording and terminology.[4]

FLUID FLOW IN HEATED PIPES

The classical analysis of frictional flow of a homogeneous fluid along a heated pipe must be understood before it can be applied to the special case of circulation, without bubble slip, in a subcritical boiler U-tube circuit.

The general energy equation relating to a unit mass of a homogeneous fluid in steady flow in a heated pipe is:

$$Jdq = Jdh + d\left(\frac{V^2}{2g_o}\right) + \frac{g}{g_o}dZ \tag{1}$$

$$= JdE + pdv + vdp + \frac{VdV}{g_o} + \frac{g}{g_o}dZ \tag{2}$$

where q is heat flow into the fluid; h is enthalpy of the fluid; V is velocity of the fluid; Z is height above a datum level; J is mechanical equivalent of heat; g_o is standard gravitational acceleration; g is acceleration; E is internal energy; p is pressure and v is specific volume.

This equation applies whether the flow is frictional or frictionless. To develop from it the equation for frictional flow the equation of state for the fluid is needed, namely,

$$dE + \frac{pdv}{J} = TdS \tag{3}$$

and the fact that for frictional flow

$$TdS = dq + \frac{dW_f}{J} \tag{4}$$

where S is entropy of the unit, and W_f is the mechanical work dissipated by friction per unit mass of fluid.

The substitution of Eq. 3 and Eq. 4 in Eq. 2 gives

$$dW_f + vdp + \frac{VdV}{g_o} + \frac{g}{g_o}dZ = o \tag{5}$$

All the terms in Eq. 5 represent energy quantities per unit mass of fluid, and dW_f is that part of the available mechanical energy which is dissipated by friction. In the simple case of skin friction in a straight pipe

$$dW_f = \frac{4f}{d}\frac{V^2}{2g_o}dl \tag{6}$$

where f is a dimensionless friction coefficient; d is the inside diameter of the pipe and l is length of pipe.

The substitution of this in Eq. 5 would give the momentum equation for frictional flow in a straight pipe, but this is only a special case of the more general equation. For other "losses", such as in bends, etc., dW_f may usually be expressed as some function of the kinetic energy at the point, namely,

$$dW_f = K\frac{V^2}{2g_o} \tag{7}$$

where K is friction loss coefficient for a particular point.

It is important to note that the units of dW_f are ft-lb-weight of energy/lb mass of fluid.

The Simple U-Circuit

To show the equivalence of the different theories of circulation, the idealized simple U-circuit shown in Fig. 12 is considered. In these circumstances the following simplifying assumptions are justified where in other circumstances they might be questionable:

The pressures at points A and F, just outside the tubes, are assumed to be the same, and equal to p_s, and the kinetic energy of the fluid is assumed to be negligible at A and F.

D-E is a heated riser, in which the steam and water are assumed to move together as a homogeneous mixture, and in which there is a uniform increase in specific volume of the mixture with distance along the tube from D to E. Thus in DE, $dZ = dl = adv$, where $a = l/[v_1 (v_2/v_1 - 1)]$.

Frictional effects in the portion of the circuit from C to D are neglected.

HYDRODYNAMIC PRINCIPLES OF CIRCULATION

The hydrodynamic analysis is concerned

Fig. 12 **Simple U-circuit,
subcritical drum-type boiler**

with the variation of *pressure*, not "head", the condition to be fulfilled being that

$$\int_A^F dp = 0$$

around the circuit. Hence Eq. 5 is applied in the form

$$-\int dp = \int \frac{g}{g_o} \frac{dz}{v} + \int \frac{VdV}{g_o v} + \int \frac{dW_f}{v} \tag{8}$$

from which

$$\int_C^B \frac{g}{g_o} \frac{dz}{v} - \int_D^E \frac{g}{g_o} \frac{dz}{v}$$
$$= \int_A^F \frac{dW_f}{v} + \int_A^F \frac{VdV}{g_o v} \tag{9}$$

All the terms in Eq. 9 represent pressures (e.g. lb/sq ft), so that the hydrodynamic analysis of circulation may be verbally expressed as:

Circulation rate adjusts itself until a state of equilibrium has been reached such that the difference between the hydrostatic pressures at the feet of the downcomer and riser legs is equal to the sum of the total pressure drops due to friction and acceleration in the circuit.

Hydrostatic pressure is the pressure which would exist at the point if there were a stationary column of liquid above the point, whose density varied in the same way as it would under the actual dynamic conditions of circulation. Pressure rise due to deceleration is included within the meaning of the term *pressure drop due to acceleration*.

By carrying out these integrations for the circuit of Fig. 12, the respective terms of Eq. 9 are readily shown to be

$$\int_B^C \frac{g}{g_o} \frac{dz}{v} - \int_D^E \frac{g}{g_o} \frac{dz}{v}$$
$$= \frac{g}{g_o} \frac{l}{v_1} \left[1 - \frac{1}{v_2/v_1 - 1} \log_e v_2/v_1 \right] \tag{10}$$

$$\int_A^F \frac{dW_f}{v} = \frac{V_1^2}{2g_o v_1}$$
$$\times \, [K_A + (v_2/v_1)\, K_F + (2f\, l/d)\, (v_2/v_1 + 3)] \tag{11}$$

$$\int_A^F \frac{V dV}{g_o v} = \frac{V_1^2}{2g_o v_1} (v_2/v_1 - 1) \tag{12}$$

from which the velocity of circulation is given nondimensionally by the expression

$$\frac{V_1^2}{2gl} = \frac{1 - \dfrac{1}{v_2/v_1 - 1} \log_e v_2/v_1}{C} \tag{13}$$

where

$$C = [(K_A + (v_2/v_1)K_F)$$
$$+ (2fl/d)\,(v_2/v_1 + 3) + (v_2/v_1 - 1)] \tag{14}$$

THERMODYNAMIC (EXPANSION) METHOD OF CIRCULATION

For the case in which fluid is assumed to flow as a homogeneous mixture, the thermodynamic (or expansion) analysis of circulation is of interest. Resulting from an essentially thermodynamic approach, it is at the same time very expressive of the physical nature of the process to describe it as an expansion theory. Its development depends on an understanding of the significance of the expansion work term, pdv, in the frictional, steady-flow process. This is found by substituting in Eq. 5 the relation

$$vdp = d(pv) - pdv \tag{15}$$

giving

$$pdv = dW_f + d(pv) + d\left(\frac{V^2}{2g_o}\right) + \frac{g}{g_o}\, dz \tag{16}$$

All the terms in Eq. 16 represent energy quantities (e.g. ft lb force of energy/lb$_m$ of fluid).

For integration round the circuit, Eq. 16 may be written

$$\int pdv = \int dW_f + \Delta FE + \Delta KE + \Delta PE \tag{17}$$

where ΔFE is increase in flow energy pv; ΔKE is increase in kinetic energy and ΔPE is increase in potential energy.

Applying this to the circuit of Fig. 12

$$\Delta FE = p_s(v_2 - v_1), \quad \Delta KE = 0, \quad \Delta PE = 0$$

Also, $p = p_s + p'$, where p' is the local excess of pressure at any point above the drum pressure. Substitution of these relations in Eq. 17 gives

$$\int_A^F p'dv = \int_A^F dW_f \tag{18}$$

The thermodynamic or expansion analysis of circulation may thus be expressed as:

When unit mass of fluid flowing round the circuit expands by an amount dv at a point where the pressure is $(p_s + p')$, it does an amount of work $(p_s + p')\, dv$ against the surrounding fluid, but the work done at the boundaries of the system in consequence of this expansion is only $p_s dv$.

Thus an excess of mechanical work equal to $p'dv$ is available for overcoming friction (or which, in the more general case, would also be available for imparting increased kinetic and potential energy to the fluid). This excess of mechanical work may be termed the *work available for circulation*, and the rate of circulation adjusts itself until a state of equilibrium is established between the work available for circulation and the mechanical energy dissipated by friction in the circuit.

As they are derived from a common equation, it is evident that both thermodynamic and hydrodynamic analyses give the same answer for the rate of circulation. But the hydrodynamic approach is simpler to apply because the thermodynamic approach requires a knowledge of the pressure at all points in the circuit where expansion is taking place, and this pressure must first be calculated by the procedure used in the hydrodynamic method. The steps involved are outlined as follows:

In evaluating $\int_A^F p' dv$, the integration only is necessary over that part of the circuit with a change in volume, namely, in the heated riser. Thus

$$\int_A^F p' dv = \int_D^E p'' dv + (p_E - p_3)(v_2 - v_1)$$

$$(19)$$

where $p'' = (p - p_E)$, and is evaluated from Eq. 8 to give

$$p'' = \frac{g}{g_o} a \log_e \frac{v_2}{v} + \frac{G^2}{g_o}(v_2 - v)$$
$$+ \frac{aB}{2}(v_2^2 - v^2)$$

$$(20)$$

where $B = 2fG^2/g_o d$ and G is mass velocity, V/v. Also

$$(p_E - p_s) = -v_2/v_1(1 - K_F)\frac{V_1^2}{2g_o v_1}$$

$$(21)$$

Substituting Eqs. (20) and (21) in Eq. (19) and integrating,

$$\text{"work available"} = \int_A^F p' dv = \frac{g}{g_o} l$$
$$\times \left[1 - \frac{1}{v_2/v_1 - 1}\log_e v_2/v_1 \right] + \frac{V_1^2}{2g_o}$$
$$\times \left[(v_2/v_1 - 1)^2 + \frac{2fl/d}{3}(2\{v_2/v_1\} + 1) \right.$$
$$\times (v_2/v_1 - 1) \times v_2/v_1$$
$$\left. \times (v_2/v_1 - 1)(1 - K_F) \right]$$

$$(22)$$

The mechanical energy dissipated in friction in the whole circuit is given by

$$\int_A^F dW_f = K_A \frac{V_1^2}{2g_o} + 4fl/d \frac{V_1^2}{2g_o}$$
$$+ aB \int_{r1}^{r2} v^2 dv + K_F \frac{V_2^2}{2g_o}$$

where $a = \frac{1}{(v_2 - v_1)}$.

Thus

$$W_f = \frac{V_1^2}{2g_o}\left[K_A + (v_2/v_1)^2 K_F + \frac{4fl/d}{3} \right.$$
$$\left. \times ((v_2/v_1)^2 + (v_2/v_1) + 4) \right]$$

$$(23)$$

Equating (22) and (23) results again in Eqs. (13) and (14) thus giving the same answer for the rate of circulation as was given by the hydrodynamic method. Although the thermodynamic analysis may clarify the physical processes involved in circulation, evaluating the rate of circulation by this means is considerably more complicated than by the hydrodynamic method, and the latter is therefore much preferred for practical use.

SEPARATION OF STEAM AND WATER

Water technology for steam generators is not limited to conditioning or treatment of makeup and feedwater, as discussed in detail in Chapter 11. It is also concerned with the phase transformation of water to steam, and the separation of liquid and gaseous constituents. The study of these phenomena considers physical chemistry, fluid flow and mechanical design.

Despite many theoretical analyses of steam and water separation and a great number of hypotheses to explain these phenomena, steam and water separation in boilers retains many aspects of an engineering art and has thus far defied completely rational understanding. Experimental work on both model and full-scale apparatus continues to provide useful information. Engineering criteria for the design of separators for subcritical-pressure steam and water separation, require correlation of these laboratory results with widely varied experience, as evidenced by the successful operation for many years of effective and efficient separation devices. But the challenge remains to develop a verifiable theoretical structure that provides an analytically rigorous explanation of the phenomena of steam and water separation in terms of the mass flows and physical equipment size found in large boilers.

THE REQUIREMENT FOR STEAM SEPARATION

Steam generated in a subcritical-pressure recirculation-type boiler is intimately mixed with large and variable amounts of circulating boiler water. Before the steam leaves the boiler and enters the superheater, practically all of this associated boiler water must be separated from the steam. This separation must be done within a limited space in the drum, within a matter of seconds and under a variety of velocity, pressure and other operating conditions. The pressure drop across the steam and water separators must not be sufficient to affect boiler circulation or water-level control.

Nearly all of the liquid and solid impurities in the steam and water mixture must be separated from the steam before it is suitable for use. Any unseparated liquid in the steam contains dissolved and suspended boiler-water salts which appear as a solids impurity in the steam when the moisture is evaporated in the superheater or directed to a turbine or other steam driven apparatus.

The moisture content in a saturated steam is defined by its quality, which is a measure of the percent by weight of dry steam or moisture in the mixture. The solids content in a saturated steam is defined by its purity, a measure of the parts per million of solids impurity in the steam. Solids content in steam from high subcritical-pressure or supercritical boilers is measured in parts per billion.

The relationship between moisture carry-over, solids carryover and boiler-water concentration is best illustrated by an example. For a 0.01 percent moisture carryover of boiler water having 1000 ppm concentration, the solids in the steam would be 1000×0.0001 or 0.1 ppm. Conversely, the moisture carryover can be calculated if the boiler-water concentration and the steam impurity content are known.

BOILER DRUM

The drum of a subcritical boiler serves two functions, the first being that of separating steam from the mixture of water and steam discharged into it. Second, the drum houses equipment to purify steam after being separated from the water.

As the quantity of water contained in the boiler below the water level is relatively small compared to the total steam output, the matter of water storage is not significant. Primarily, the space required to accommodate steam-separating and purifying equipment determines drum size. Drum diameter and length should be sufficient to provide accessibility for installation and inspection. Length generally depends on furnace width; in the case of high-capacity units, it is controlled by the space required for the steam-separating devices.

The weight of water in the mixture delivered to the drum for separation depends on the circulation and may range from less than two to over 25 times the weight of steam. To reduce this water to the small fraction found in the steam requires a high efficiency of water separation. The equation indicating the percent of water separation necessary to give a steam impurity may be expressed as:

$$\text{Percent of water separation} = 100 - \frac{100\,P_s}{NC_b}$$

$$\textbf{(24)}$$

where
P_s = ppm of impurity in steam
N = circulation ratio, lb of water/lb of steam
C_b = boiler-water concentration

DRUM INTERNALS

Drum internals in subcritical-pressure boilers separate water from steam and direct the flow of water and steam to establish an optimum distribution of drum metal temperature during boiler operation. Such apparatus may consist of baffles which change the direction of flow of a steam and water mixture, separators which use a spinning action for removing water from steam, or steam purifiers such as washers and screen dryers. These devices are used singly or in consort to remove impurities from the steam leaving the boiler drum.

Numerous factors affect the separation of water from steam in a boiler, among which are

■ the density of water with respect to the steam

■ the available pressure drop for drum-internal design

■ the amount of water in the mixture delivered to the steam drum

■ the quantity or total throughput of water and steam to be separated

■ viscosity, surface tension and other such factors affected by pressure

■ water level in the drum

■ the concentration of boiler-water solids

There is a considerable difference in the density of water and steam as pressure increases toward the critical point. This relationship is shown in Fig. 13 which is a plot of the ratio of the density of water to the density of steam as a function of pressure. The density of water at 1200 psia is approximately 16 times that of steam. At 2800 psia, the density of water is about three times that of steam. Thus, as pressure increases, separating water from steam with simple devices becomes more difficult and requires more efficient apparatus to achieve primary separation in a confined area.

WATER SEPARATION STAGES

The stages of water separation are designated as primary separation, secondary separation, and drying. The devices used are primary separators, secondary separators and dryers. The term dryer was established during the course of development of water-tube boilers on the basis that the final stage of separation delivered a "dry" and saturated steam.

PRIMARY AND SECONDARY SEPARATORS

Primary and secondary separation reduces the water content of the steam from the boiler tube circuits to a moisture level that a final-stage dryer can handle. Frequently, the design of equipment for primary and secondary separation is influenced as much by the boiler design as by the basic function of separating the water from the steam.

Practically all drum internals consist of plate baffles, banks of screens, arrangements of corrugated or bent plate, and devices using radial acceleration of water from steam.

Baffle plates are generally used to change or reverse a flow pattern to assist gravity separation in the open drum space. Fig. 14 illustrates

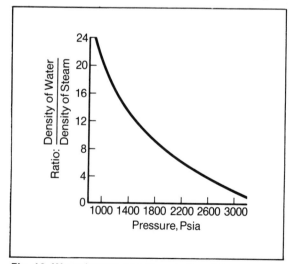

Fig. 13 **Water/steam density relationship**

Fig. 14 **Baffle plates in a steam drum**

examples of simple baffle arrangements. Baffle plates change flow direction of water and steam and act as impact plates. Water separating out on such plates normally will drain off through or adjacent to the steam flow, and a controlling factor in design and operation is the steam flow velocity through such drainage. Areas under and around baffles must be sufficient to prevent excessive re-entrainment of spray. Limited in their impact-separating capacity, the chief purpose of plate baffles is to direct flow to make maximum use of the gravity separating capacity available from any low-velocity steam space in the drum.

Screens of wire mesh material are generally satisfactory for secondary separators or dryers. The limiting factor for screen separators is the steam flow velocity through the free area of the screen and the water drainage capacity of the screen. Screens are effective in separating spray. Riser mixtures normally have too much water in them for screens to handle as primary separators. Other factors affecting performance of screens as primary separators are circulation ratio, size of screen, and steam flow velocity through the screen. Examples of screen arrangements as primary or secondary separators in boiler drums are shown in Fig. 15.

Bent and corrugated plates are commonly used for all three stages of separation. Fig. 16 illustrates an example of a corrugated plate assembly which has the advantage of a higher ratio of free area to projected area than do

screens. This equipment can be relatively small for the same steam flow velocity.

Bulk separators, Fig. 17, deflect large quantities of water directed into the drum from active risers. The apparatus reduces the bulk water entrained with the steam and directs it below the water level. This design has allowed higher evaporation rates per foot of furnace width since it satisfactorily removes the bulk of the spray water from the steam. The bulk separator reduces moisture by providing impact surface, a change of direction for the mixture, a drain trough and a screen layer for reduction of fine spray.

Reversing hoods, shown in Fig. 18, combine all the desirable design features of baffle and change-of-direction principles. As indicated, steam and water from the active generating tubes are directed behind a baffle into the slotted reversing hoods. These primary separators are simply an arrangement of baffle plates to guide steam and water in a manner to give maximum utilization of gravity separation in open drum space. By accelerating the gravity flow of water and by reversing the flow of steam, normal gravity potential is increased and separation enhanced.

At higher pressures, water and steam are separated most efficiently in a drum internal utilizing radial acceleration to disengage the entrained particle from the steam. Guide vanes impart spinning action to the turbulent mixture, and the circular motion causes the heavier

Fig. 15 Use of screens for secondary separation

Fig. 16 Corrugated-plate assembly

Fig. 17 Bulk separators for removal
of spray water from steam

Fig. 19 Turbo separators followed by
corrugated-plate assembly

water particles to move radially outward
through the steam and to impinge upon the
outer wall of the separator where they can be
collected. The efficiency of separation is related to pressure in that the relative densities
of water and steam determine the resistance
to particle motion due to buoyant effects. As
operating pressure is increased, and as the density of saturated steam approaches that of water, relative motion is more difficult to achieve
and separation efficiency is decreased.

The turbo separator, shown in Fig. 19 uses
the radial acceleration principle. Equipped
with a corrugated plate assembly at the outlet
of the separator, it provides primary and secondary separation of water from steam at pres-

sures up to the critical operating point.

As the water and steam mixture circulated
from the waterwalls is introduced into the
drum, it sweeps the drum shell on its path to
the bottom. The confining baffle concentric
with the drum shell creates effective velocities
and rapid heat transfer. The mixture enters the
separators arranged along the length of the
drum. Vanes spin the mixture as it travels upward through the separators and thus create a
separating force. The concentrated layer of
water flowing upward along the surface of the
primary tube is skimmed off and directed
downward through an outer concentric tube for
discharge below the waterline with minimum
disturbance to the water level.

Fig. 18 Reversing-hood primary separators

Fig. 20 Screen dryer for removal of
residual moisture from steam

The steam and the remaining entrained water continue upward through a steam collector nozzle and turn horizontally into the secondary separator. The velocity at this point is low and water cannot be re-entrained from wetted surfaces and runs off the plates. Leaving the separator, the steam flows upward into the final dryer which facilitates handling of spray and dehydration of foam. The turbo separator has no inherent capacity limit because there is no water seal under a high differential pressure. Changes in water level do not affect the efficiency of the turbo separator[5].

DRYERS

A component of internals, dryers function to remove residual moisture from steam after primary and secondary separators have eliminated most of the circulating water. They are designed to have a large surface area on which moisture can deposit and from which it can drain back into the drum by gravity. Flow velocity through the free area of a dryer must be restricted to limits above which deposition or drainage may be inhibited.

Closely spaced corrugated or bent plates, screens or matts of woven wire mesh can be used as dryer surface materials. The screen dryers are a practical compromise of performance and drainability that have given satisfactory service for years.

The design of dryers requires consideration of a number of factors. Space limitation in the drum restricts the dryer size. Other factors as sturdiness, leak-proof installation, drainage facilities and provision for cleaning due to possible plugging of dryer free areas must also be considered when selecting a steam dryer. The pressure drop across a dryer is normally low because of the low flow velocities and relatively small amounts of water involved.

Dryers operate on a low-velocity deposition principle, not on a velocity separation principle. Formation of insoluble residues on the dryers from boiler water entrained with the steam decreases the free area, increases the local velocity, and promotes carryover. Similar results are noted by the filming action of foamy boiler water in the dryer. The free surface areas are reduced significantly, increasing the local velocity and facilitating re-entrainment of boiler water and carryover. Dryers in boilers operating with foamy boiler water or high suspended matter in the boiler water should be inspected periodically and cleaned as necessary. Fig. 20 is a simplified representation of a screen dryer for final drying of steam.

AUXILIARY DRUM INTERNALS

Feedwater lines, blowdown lines and chemical feed lines are also installed in the boiler drum. In some marine boilers, desuperheaters may also be installed. Although feedwater, blowdown and chemical feed lines normally do not take up much drum space, their location can be a minor complication in the overall internals arrangement. To give satisfactory distribution of flow, these lines are usually run to the center of the drum where they feed other branch lines that are perforated.

Feedwater lines are submerged in the drum water but must be arranged so as to avoid discharge of cold feedwater against the bare drum shell as temperature variations can cause severe thermal stress in the thick drum shells. In some cases, it is desirable to concentrate the colder feedwater flow into the downcomer tubes to condense steam entrained in the downcomer flow and improve boiler circulation. It is also necessary to prevent water hammer which can occur readily if steam leaks back into the feedwater system. The inflow of cold water may suddenly condense the steam and create a vacuum. Water hammer results when water rushing into the vacuum stops suddenly.

To control scale, sludge and corrosion chemical feed lines introduce chemicals in a manner which insures rapid mixing with the feedwater. The chemicals are generally added in a concentrated form, and it is necessary to flush the lines periodically with clean water to prevent plugging due to reaction and deposition.

Blowdown lines periodically or continuously remove a portion of water from the boiler. Sufficient concentrated boiler water is removed and replaced by low-concentration

Fig. 21 **Dry-box construction**

Fig. 23 **Relationship of silica in boiler water to operating pressure**

feedwater to maintain a desired concentration in the boiler water. These lines are located to minimize the occlusion of feedwater and chemical feed, and are designed to prevent entrainment of steam.

Perforated plates or tapered-plate restrictions at the top of the drum distribute steam flow. Not a steam dryer, this dry-box arrangement distributes the flow to allow a minimum of steam outlets to assure a satisfactory velocity distribution to a steam dryer. Fig. 21 shows a dry box construction.

STEAM WASHERS

Steam washers are special drum internals in which low-concentration feedwater is sprayed into the steam space to dilute the solids content in the moisture being carried over to the steam dryer. Originally used in multiple-drum boil-

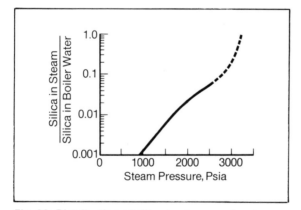

Fig. 22 **Distribution of silica in steam and water**

ers at pressures from 600 to 1200 psig. they became obsolete as water treatment improved and pressures increased. Interest in steam washers has been renewed however because of their potential for reducing the amount of silica vaporized with the steam. This reduction is not possible with mechanical devices used for steam separation.

Vaporization of silica increases with pressure, as illustrated in Fig. 22. At 2500 psia, the silica in the steam is about 10 times the quantity at 1500 psia, for the same concentration in the boiler water.[6] Boiler-water pH affects the vaporization of silica, as shown in Fig. 23. Controlling silica at recommended values such as these will assure less than 20 ppb in the steam.

Laboratory results and field data conclusively indicate that silica reduction by steam washing in boilers above 1800 psig is ineffective. Improving the quality of makeup water is the only effective means of controlling the silica problem.[7]

VAPOROUS CARRYOVER

As operating pressures increase, the steam phase exhibits greater solvent capabilities for the salts that may be present in the water phase. These salts will be partitioned in an equilib-

TABLE I. SUMMARY OF LABORATORY RESULTS

	2600	2800	3000
Drum pressure (psig)	2600	2800	3000
Concentration in boiler water, ppm	15	15	15
Sodium sulfate, %	0.02	0.04	0.28
Disodium phosphate, %	0.01	0.03	0.41
Trisodium phosphate, %	0.02	0.04	0.35
Sodium chloride, %	0.04	0.09	0.39
Sodium hydroxide, %	0.02	0.08	0.55

rium between the steam and water. Known as vaporous carryover, this phenomenon will contribute additional boiler-water solids directly to the steam, independent of the efficiency of steam-water separation components.[8]

Although silica was the first material found to exhibit significant vaporous carryover, it is now realized that such carryover contributes a major proportion of total solids in the steam as drum operating pressures increase above 2600 psig. And it is recognized that controlling the amount of vaporous solids in the boiler water will be required for these other salts as it was for silica.

Table I shows results of a laboratory experiment conducted in 1973-1974 to study vaporous carryover.[9] For various salts, it lists percent vaporous carryover, which is the ratio of the salt concentration in the steam and boiler water. In each case, sodium was measured and then converted to the concentration value.

REFERENCES

[1] Glenn R. Fryling, ed., *Combustion Engineering: A Reference Book on Fuel Burning and Steam Generation*, Rev. ed. New York: Combustion Engineering, Inc., 1966, pp. 25-1–25-27.

[2] Warren M. Rohsenow and H. Choi, *Heat, Mass and Momentum Transfer*. Englewood Cliffs, NJ: Prentice-Hall, 1961, pp. 211–236.

Samson S. Kutateladze, *Fundamentals of Heat Transfer*, 2nd rev. and augm. ed. Translated by Scripta Technica, Inc., and edited by Robert D. Cess. New York: Academic Press, 1963, pp. 342–379 and 380–398.

[3] G. A. Nothman and R. C. Binder, "Slip Velocity in Boiler-Tube Circuits," *Combustion*, 14(12): 40–42, June 1943.

[4] R. W. Haywood, "Research into Fundamentals of Boiler Circulation Theory," *Proceedings of the General Discussion on Heat Transfer*, jointly sponsored by the American Society of Mechanical Engineers and the Institution of Mechanical Engineers, London, Sept. 11–13, 1951, and Atlantic City, Nov. 26–28, 1951, pp. 63–65. London: Institution of Mechanical Engineers, 1951.

W. Yorath Lewis and S. A. Robertson, "The Circulation of Water and Steam in Water Tube Boilers and the Rational Simplification of Boiler Design," *Proceedings of the Institution of Mechanical Engineers*, 143: 147–178, 1940.

S. A. Robertson, "Communication on the Circulation of Water and Steam in Water Tube Boilers and the Rational Simplification of Boiler Design," *Proceedings of the Institution of Mechanical Engineers*, 144: 184–190, 1940.

R. S. Silver, "A Thermodynamic Theory of Circulation in Water Tube Boilers," *Proceedings of the Institution of Mechanical Engineers*, 153: 261–281, 1945.

R. F. Davis, "Expansion Theory of Circulation in Water Tube Boilers," *Engineering*, 163: 145–148, 1947.

[5] T. Ravese, "The Application and Development of the Turbo Steam Separator," *Combustion*, 26(1): 45–47, July 1954.

E. M. Powell and H. A. Grabowski, "Drum Internals and High-Pressure Boiler Design," *ASME Paper No. 54-A-242.* New York: American Society of Mechanical Engineers, 1954.

[6] F. G. Straub and H. A. Grabowski, "Silica Deposition in Steam Turbines," *Transactions of the ASME*, 67: 309–316, May 1945.

[7] H. A. Klein, "Evaluation of Steam Washers in Power-Plant Boilers," *Transactions of the ASME. Journal of Engineering for Power*, 83, Series A: 343–353, October 1961.

[8] F. Gabrielli and H. A. Grabowski, "Steam Purity at High Pressure," Presented at the ASME-IEEE-ASCE Joint Power Generation Conference, Charlotte, NC, Oct. 8–10, 1979; Published as Combustion Engineering publication TIS-6329. Windsor, CT: Combustion Engineering, Inc., 1979.

[9] S. L. Goodstine, "Vaporous Carryover of Sodium Salts in High-Pressure Steam," *Proceedings of the American Power Conference*, 36: 784–789, 1974. Chicago: Illinois Institute of Technology, 1974.

CHAPTER 6

Designing for Performance

To design a large steam generator, manufacturers follow a step-by-step process that begins with establishing basic output-steam conditions and systematically building to the structural design of furnace walls, headers and supporting steel.

So that each manufacturer can develop a competitive bid that will give reasonably similar steam- and water-side performance, owners issue a set of design criteria that form the basic ground rules. Generally, the scope-of-supply specifications issued to a boiler manufacturer cover the pressure parts, the pulverizing and fuel-burning equipment, the air heaters, the sootblowers, the furnace containment and ductwork, and the furnace safeguard supervisory system. "Standard versions" of specifications include

■ primary-steam and reheat-steam pressures and temperatures
■ feedwater temperature
■ complete fuel and ash analyses
■ ambient-air and outlet-gas temperatures

Often, the mechanical-draft fans, structural steel, and furnace-bottom ash-handling equipment are also part of the scope of supply. But even if these items are not included, their required performance and physical characteristics must be defined because of their important role in performance, accessibility, and maintenance of the boiler and because they directly interface with the primary steam-generating equipment. Only when the owner asks for expanded-scope "boiler islands" will the manufacturer design such peripherals to the steam generator as walkways and stairs, steam and feedwater piping, the boiler building, and the coal silos or bins. The steam-generator supplier can also be responsible for the design of precipitators, flue-gas desulfurization systems, and complete ash-handling equipment.

AN OVERVIEW OF DESIGN BASICS

One of the first steps in the boiler design process is to calculate boiler efficiency by using the required excess-air percentage for the fuel to be burned. Working in a systematic fashion, the designer next determines fuel, air and gas quantities, selects pulverizers, and establishes a preliminary configuration of furnace windboxes.

From analysis of pulverizing-air requirements, the feedwater temperature, and the variation of these and other factors over the normal operating range of the unit, the designer arrives at air-heater inlet and outlet gas and air temperatures. In turn, this determination allows calculation of net heat input, furnace size, and outlet gas temperature.

SELECTING HEAT-ABSORBING EQUIPMENT

Having settled on the basic "box size" and gas temperature leaving the furnace, the designer now calculates the gas-temperature drops for all of the superheater, reheater and economizer sections up to the air-heater inlet. A graphic representation of the design calculations to this point gives the skeleton unit shown in Fig. 1.

By an iterative process, the several high-pressure heat-transfer components are "surfaced." That is, the designer assumes a total physical configuration, including tubing diameters and spacings, then defines the net area for gas flow between the tubes (called the *free gas area*) and determines heat-transfer rates for each section. When a satisfactory arrangement of surface is determined, the designer calculates the steam- and water-side pressure drops, and gas-side pressure losses (also referred to as *draft losses*). Finally, metal temperatures are calculated and tubing diameters, materials, and thicknesses are chosen.

With the overall steam-generating unit shape now developed, the cut-and-try strategy can be applied to the circulation-system design for which a general approach was outlined in Chapter 5. Usually, the waterwall tubing diameter, spacing and thickness are predetermined from design experience with units of the same size and pressure level. To arrive at the desired system performance, therefore, the designer's effort centers on proper sizing of downtakes, supply tubes, risers, and circulating pumps.

SELECTING NON-HEAT-ABSORBING EQUIPMENT

At this point the design of the basic heat-absorbing circuitry is complete and the design engineer proceeds with specifications for

■ drums, headers, desuperheaters, and connecting piping (discussed later in this chapter)

■ the ignition system (see Chapter 13) air heaters, pumps, and sootblowers (see Chapter 15)

■ ductwork and fans (the sizing of which are covered in this chapter and the mechanical features of which are described in Chapter 15)

■ the furnace-wall structure, which has to consider both explosive and implosive forces (see Chapter 14)

■ ash-handling equipment (see Chapter 16)

■ the structural support system, including hanger rods, columns, girders, and beams

■ platforms, walkways, and stairs

■ other balance-of-boiler-island items, such as specialized chemical-recovery-boiler auxiliaries, emission-control equipment, and stacks.

Except in the case of marine boilers and some retrofit situations, an owner usually does not severely restrict the physical space made available for a major boiler installation. Although the designer has a free hand to establish an optimum configuration by using existing company's standards, costs of building volume and auxiliary-equipment power consumption will often lead to consideration of several options in both basic pressure-part and pulverizer arrangement as well as the selection of the boiler-related auxiliaries. The process of selecting the equipment will be described in greater detail in subsequent sections.

Fig. 1 Skeleton arrangement of radiant-reheat unit showing superheater, reheater and economizer downstream of furnace

This introductory look at the design process has viewed its basis, its scope, and its sequence. The next section explains step-by-step how to calculate unit heat absorption, efficiency, and fuel fired.

HEAT ABSORPTION AND EFFICIENCY CALCULATIONS

The first calculation in the boiler-design process is that of the heat absorbed by the working fluids—the primary steam flow and the reheated-steam flow. The purchaser establishes these flows at one or more load points, and gives the steam-generator supplier the pressures and temperatures at the inlets and outlets of the primary and reheat headers.

Boiler capacity is given in terms of the mass flow of primary steam at maximum continuous rating (MCR). In this and other texts, nominal boiler size is commonly expressed in "megawatts", an approximation used for convenience—steam-turbine generators are rated in

electrical output on the basis of stated condensing conditions. Boilers are properly rated on their steam output(s) at certain pressures and temperatures.

HEAT ABSORBED

With the outlet steam conditions identified, the heat content or enthalpy, h, in Btu per lb, is read from steam tables (Appendix F) by interpolating as necessary. The heat in the feedwater, h_f, is read from tables or charts for compressed water such as Fig. 2. For a nonreheat unit, if W_s represents the steam produced in pounds per hour, the total boiler output or heat absorbed, Q_{abs}, will be

$$Q_{abs} = W_s(h - h_f)$$

(1)

For a unit with one or more stages of steam reheating, the heat absorbed in the reheater(s) is added to the primary-steam heat absorption to arrive at the total Q_{abs}. Fig. 3 emphasizes that this total heat absorption takes place between point A, where the fuel and preheated combustion air enter the furnace and burn, and point B, where the gases leave the economizer, which is usually the final primary-working-fluid heat absorber. The heat of the products of combus-

Fig. 2 **Enthalpy of Compressed Water (to obtain enthalpy in Btu/lb (above 32°F) for any water temperature and pressure, add or subtract the value on the ordinate from the water temperature. Example: 400°F water at 4000 PSIG, read – 20 from curve. h_f = (400 – 20) = 380 Btu/lb)**

Fig. 3 **Total heat absorption by the primary working fluids in a steam generator—the water and steam—takes place between points A and B. The theoretical or adiabatic temperature at point A includes the heat added to the combustion air in the air heater. (Heat is not *absorbed* in the air heater, but is transferred only.)**

tion passing through the air heater is picked up by the air and transferred immediately to the furnace, essentially without loss.

HEAT FIRED

The fuel fired, Q_f, in Btu's per hour, is given by the relation

$$Q_f = \frac{Q_{abs}}{\eta}$$

$$(2)$$

where η is the overall chemical efficiency of the steam generator. (See Chapter 21, Testing and Measurements, for more information on the definition of chemical-heat efficiency.)

The quantity of fuel to be burned, the amount of air to be supplied, and the products formed are all calculated from Q_f. These three quantities largely determine the size of the furnace and the other components.

The amount of fuel fired, sometimes called the combustion rate, is found by dividing Q_f by the high heating value of the fuel (to give the mass of fuel fired per hour) or, for gaseous fuels, the volumetric rate which is the cubic feet of gas fired per hour.

STEAM-GENERATOR EFFICIENCY

The efficiency of a boiler is most frequently taken to be the ratio of the heat absorbed by the water and steam to the chemical heat in the fuel fired. It is not a measure of the efficiency with which the coal or other fuel is fired into the combustion chamber or onto a grate, although the carbon heat loss item in a heat balance will account for this. Modern suspension-burning systems reduce this carbon heat loss inefficiency to minimal amounts. Nor is boiler efficiency the net rate at which an electrical generating plant produces power, called the net plant heat rate in Btu/kWhr. But boiler efficiency must be known to determine the "Btu" consumed so that the net plant heat rate can be established for a given boiler turbine unit.

Simplistically, a boiler absorbs most of the heat in the fuel fired but is unable to "capture"

the heat in the gases going to the stack. Included in that lost heat to the stack is the latent heat of vaporization of the water in the fuel and the water formed by the combustion of hydrogen, which is impossible for the boiler to absorb. Thus, efficiency becomes a function of the type and analysis of fuel fired, the excess air at which it is burned, the air temperature entering and the gas temperature leaving the air preheater, and several other factors described later. Based on the fuel and the above temperatures, heat losses and credits are calculated as a percent of the heat input, and the efficiency becomes

$$\eta = 100 - \%\text{Losses} + \%\text{Credits}$$

$$(3)$$

The process of accounting for all the heat losses, as well as the heat available in the steam, is known as a *heat balance*. The heat balance method is frequently used to test for the efficiency of an operating unit. Unlike the test engineer who can measure these losses accurately, the designer must assign to some of them values based on experience (see Chapter 21, Testing and Measurements).

The following losses are those which must be known before the efficiency can be determined.

- loss in dry products of combustion
- loss due to moisture in air
- loss due to moisture from fuel
- loss due to water vapor in gaseous fuels
- loss due to moisture from hydrogen in fuel
- loss due to unburned combustible
- loss due to radiation
- losses unaccounted for

COMBUSTION CALCULATIONS

With the fuel analysis given, the excess-air percentage decided on (see subsection Excess Air for Combustion, which follows), and the moisture content of the air stated or assumed, the designer can perform the combustion calculations as delineated in Chapter 4. By using the combustion equations or the graphical methods presented in Appendix D, the air for combustion, the dry weight of products, the weight of water resulting from burning the fuel, and the other items required for heat-balance work are determined. Also, a check is made of the ultimate fuel analysis supplied versus the high heating value, to discover early any discrepancy in this correlation (see Chapter 4 for more on that aspect of the calculation).

EXCESS AIR FOR COMBUSTION

Perfect or stoichiometric combustion is the complete oxidation of all the combustible constituents of a fuel, consuming exactly 100 percent of the oxygen contained in the combustion air. Excess air is any amount above that theoretical quantity.

Commercial fuels can be burned satisfactorily only when the amount of air supplied to them exceeds that which is theoretically calculated as required from equations showing the chemical reactions involved. The quantity of excess air provided in any particular case depends on

■ the physical state of the fuel in the combustion chamber

■ fuel particle size, or oil viscosity

■ the proportion of inert matter present

■ the design of furnace and fuel burning equipment

For complete combustion, solid fuels require the greatest, and gaseous fuels the least, quantity of excess air. Fuels that are finely subdivided on entering the furnace burn more easily and require less excess air than those induced in large lumps or masses. Burners, stokers and furnaces having design features producing a high degree of turbulence and mixing of the fuel with the combustion air require less excess air.

Table I indicates the range in values for the excess-air percentage commonly employed by the designer. These are expressed in percent of theoretical air, and are understood to be at the design load condition of the boiler. (At lower loads, both in design and in operation, higher percentages are sometimes used.)

Table I. Excess Air at Furnace Outlet

Fuels		% Excess air
Solid	Coal (pulverized)	15–30
	Coke	20–40
	Wood	25–50
	Bagasse	25–45
Liquid	Oil	3–15
Gaseous	Natural gas	5–10
	Refinery gas	8–15
	Blast-furnace gas	15–25
	Coke-oven gas	5–10

AIR TEMPERATURE FOR COMBUSTION, t_a

Efficiency calculations are based on the air temperature that will actually be entering the air heater, not on the ambient temperature (t_{aa}) nor the specified reference air temperature (t_{ra}). The increase in temperature of the air as it passes through the forced-draft (FD) fan and the steam or hot-water air heater must be added to t_{aa} to arrive at t_a.

A function of the power consumed by the fan, air temperature rise through an FD fan can be calculated from

$$\Delta T_{fd} \simeq \frac{10,300(HP)}{W_a}$$

(4)

where ΔT_{fd} is in °F, HP is the brake horsepower to the fan shaft, and W_a is the weight of air being handled in lb/hr. The relation is based on conversion to heat of the air horsepower and the horsepower corresponding to the inefficiency of the fan. This heat must be stored in the air. The formula includes a small correction required for velocity pressure at the fan outlet but the formula cannot be used to predict the temperature rise at the no-flow or shut-off condition.

AIR TEMPERATURE RISE
BY STEAM OR HOT-WATER HEATING

It is common in power plants to provide heating coils ahead of the main air heater inlets to preheat the air entering those heaters. Although primarily used to reduce the potential for corrosion on the heating surfaces of the air heater, preheating air with steam or hot water can substantially improve the overall plant efficiency. Preheating increases the heat content of the incoming combustion air which helps increase unit efficiency and thereby decrease the fuel that is fired in the boiler.

The economic and practical limits to improved boiler efficiency by lowering the unit's exit-gas temperature, have essentially been reached. Corrosion and/or plugging of air heaters and dust-collection equipment generally determine the lower temperature limit, which depends largely on the sulfur content of the fuel being burned. Efforts to design and operate modern units for sustained periods with 250°F final flue-gas temperature at full load generally have been unsuccessful with many fuels, and usually the design objective[1] is at least 25°F higher, or 275°F. Extraction-steam air preheating has both increased the efficiency and protected air heater surfaces because the steam

flow through the high-pressure turbine blading can be greater for a given electrical output. Thus, steam-turbine efficiency is improved by extracting steam for air heating just as it is improved with feedwater heating.

AIR HEATER COLD-END PROTECTION

The part of an air heater called the *cold end* is the section in which the incoming "cold" air meets the exiting cooled products of combustion. The sum of these temperatures divided by 2 is called the average cold-end temperature (ACET). Since cold-end fouling and corrosion can be related to the ACET level, it is usual practice to work to such a temperature to establish the exit-gas temperature and the required air temperature leaving the steam or hot-water heater. A guide for setting the cold-end temperature is given in Fig. 4.[2]

For subbituminous and lignitic coals having the sum of the lime (CaO) and magnesia (MgO) greater than the ferric oxide (Fe_2O_3) in the ash, the sulfur content used for reading the curve should be adjusted to *equivalent sulfur*, ES.

$$ES = 14{,}000 \times S/HHV$$

(5)

where S is the percent sulfur in the coal as fired and HHV is the high heating value of the coal as fired.

Thus, for a low-rank coal with an HHV of 7,000 Btu/lb and an as-fired sulfur content of 1 percent, the curve must be read at an ES of 2 percent, for an ACET of 163°F.

EXIT GAS TEMPERATURE—
CORRECTED VS. UNCORRECTED

Note that the ACET in Fig. 4 is termed "uncorrected". That means that the gas temperature used in the averaging calculation is not adjusted for the leakage from air- to gas-side of the air heater. Because of the differential pressure between the air entering and the gases exiting an air heater (the latter being below atmospheric pressure in most instances), there is a flow of cooling and diluting air over to the gas-side of the heater.

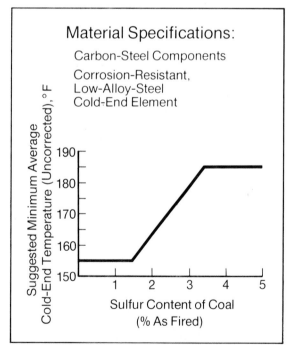

Fig. 4 Recommended minimum average cold-end temperature for coal firing

The dilution raises the excess-air percentage that is measured in the exiting flue gases. The measured exit temperature at the preheater is lower than the uncorrected (actually un-measurable) temperature because of this air leakage. In efficiency calculations, designers use the uncorrected (theoretical) temperature and the excess-air percentage *entering* the air preheater as the basis for the heat losses. The result would be the same if the corrected temperature and the corrected excess air were to be used in the calculations.

It is important to realize that the more input parameters specified, the less the potential for differences in fuel fired and air and gas quantities when bids are taken. The preceding groundwork is fundamental to the calculation of the several heat losses.

LOSS IN THE DRY PRODUCTS OF COMBUSTION

Frequently the largest of all, the loss in dry products of combustion represents the difference between the heat content of the dry exhaust gases and the heat content these gases would have at the temperature of the ambient air. The dry gas (P_d) is calculated by subtracting the water vapor in the products from the total products of combustion (P) with all quantities expressed in pounds per million Btu input (see Chapter 4). Knowing P_d, the percent dry-gas loss is found from

$$L_{dg} = \frac{P_d \times 0.24\,(T_g - T_a)}{10^4}$$

(6)

LOSS DUE TO MOISTURE IN AIR

The moisture in the combustion air (W_a) is determined for specified conditions of temperature and relative humidity, as described in Chapter 4. For an atmospheric air requirement (A) in pounds per million Btu fired and typical conditions of 80°F and 60-percent relative humidity, W_a will be 0.013 CA, where C is the combustible-loss correction factor.

The heat loss, in percent of heat input, equals

$$L_a = \frac{W_a\,(0.46)\,(T_g - T_a)}{10^4}$$

(7)

LOSS DUE TO MOISTURE IN FUEL

This loss represents the difference in the heat content of the moisture in the exit gases and that at the temperature of the ambient air. If H_2O includes both the surface and hygroscopic moisture in percent by weight of fuel fired, then

$$W_c = H_2O\,(10^4)/HHV$$

(8)

For T_g higher than 575°F, the loss due to fuel moisture equals

$$L_f = \frac{W_c\,(1066 + 0.5T_g - T_f)}{10^4}$$

(9)

and for T_g lower than 575°F,

$$L_f = \frac{W_c\,(1089 + 0.46T_g - T_f)}{10^4}$$

(10)

in which T_f corresponds to the temperature of the fuel received at the pulverizers or the oil or gas guns. This temperature is ordinarily taken as 80°F or the reference air temperature if the actual temperature is not known.

It should be understood that W_c does not include water vapor as found in gaseous fuels.

LOSS DUE TO WATER VAPOR IN GASEOUS FUELS

Moisture is also present in many gaseous fuels, particularly in blast-furnace gas and coke-oven gas, which are frequently dedusted by passing them through sprays of water. This moisture exists in the gas in two separate forms, each requiring different treatment in calculating the heat balance.

Washed gas contains *entrained* water in the form of suspended globules. Generally where exceptionally clean gas is not required, the entrained moisture, W_c averages 7 lb per million Btu. No entrained water is in unwashed gas.

In addition to the visible moisture in a liquid state, nearly all gaseous fuels contain some water vapor. In natural gas, the water vapor is there because of salt water that has been in contact with the gas in the ground, or because of *rehydration*. In refinery gas, blast-furnace gas, and coke-oven gas it is present either owing to the nature of the process of which these gases are byproducts, or because of subsequent cleaning operations.

The water vapor (W_s) in pounds per million Btu is of such magnitude that it can usually be neglected in heat-balance calculations for natural gas, refinery gas, or coke-oven gas. For blast-furnace gas saturated with moisture at 60°F, W_s may be taken as 8 lb per million Btu without serious error.

In a heat balance for gaseous fuels W_s must be considered separately from W_h and W_c, since it exists as a vapor which already has the latent heat of vaporization, and therefore requires no heat evolved by the fuel to vaporize it. In every respect it is similar to W_a so that the percent loss due to its presence is

$$L_s = \frac{W_s\,(0.46)\,(T_g - T_a)}{10^4}$$

$$(11)$$

LOSS DUE TO MOISTURE FROM HYDROGEN IN FUEL

This loss includes the sensible and latent heats of the moisture from the combustion of the hydrogen in the fuel above the ambient or reference air temperature. The water from hydrogen (W_h) equals $9 \times H \times 10^4/HHV$, as previously defined. When only the proximate analysis is available, it is necessary to resort to an empirical relation between the hydrogen in the fuel and the volatile matter, such as is found in Appendix D. But remember that, in deriving the hydrogen moisture from a proximate analysis, the loss due to the water loss may be in error as much as 1.5 percent—equal to or greater than some other items in the heat balance.

For T_g higher than 575°F, the loss due to moisture from hydrogen in fuel equals

$$L_h = W_h\,(1066 + 0.5\,T_g - T_a)/10^4$$

$$(12)$$

and for T_g lower than 575°F, the loss equals

$$L_h = W_h\,(1089 + 0.46\,T_g - T_a)/10^4$$

$$(13)$$

in which T_a is the air temperature entering the air preheater; that is, the ambient air temperature plus the FD fan and steam-air-heater temperature rises. The above relationships apply to solid, liquid and gaseous fuels.

LOSS DUE TO UNBURNED COMBUSTIBLE

This loss represents the unliberated thermal energy occasioned by failure to oxidize completely some of the combustible matter in the fuel. There are two possible sources of such unburned material.

The first and most important is the one due to solid fuel which is trapped in the ash deposited in the bottom-ash hopper or the various flyash hoppers. The loss can vary considerably according to the character of the fuel and its ash content, and the design of burning equipment and furnace. Considerable judgment is required on the part of the designer to interpret test data for this loss.

The second source of unburned combustible is the incomplete combustion of the carbon in the fuel as evidenced by the presence of carbon monoxide (CO) in the products leaving the furnace. This loss is usually negligible in well-operated boilers, but when it occurs, it is not confined to any particular type of fuel. Usually it is assumed that the CO loss is zero, regardless of the fuel.

For purposes of design calculations only, liquid and gaseous fuels are presumed to burn with no combustible loss.

LOSS DUE TO RADIATION AND CONVECTION

This loss is a comprehensive term used in a heat balance calculation to account for heat losses to the air through conduction, radiation, and convection. The heat emanates from the boiler, ductwork, and pulverizers. Because it is very difficult to measure in existing units, this is the only significant loss for which computation is not based on test measurements in the *Performance Test Code* for boilers.

Fig. 5, used for both design work and performance tests on fully watercooled furnaces,

was extrapolated by the American Boiler Manufacturers Association from data obtained from some relatively small boilers. The curve values were later checked by the ASME Test Code committee against actual measured losses on several large boilers and were found to be conservatively high.[3] Note that this item does not account for or include radiation, convection, or infiltration losses from a precipitator located ahead of the air heater(s).

SENSIBLE HEAT LOSS IN ASH

The *ASME Performance Test Code PTC 4.1* provides for the measurement of the sensible heat lost in the ash leaving through the furnace bottom, and the ash collected from the hoppers under the economizer, air heaters, precipitators or fabric filters. Bottom-ash heat loss is determined by measuring the temperature increase and flow of the cooling water in and out

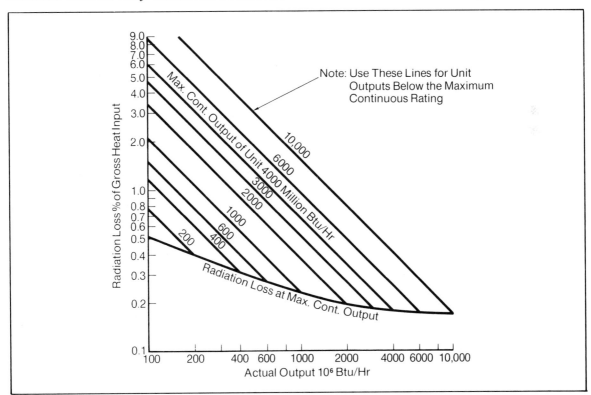

Fig. 5 Radiation loss for completely water cooled furnaces. The radiation loss values obtained from this curve are for a differential of 500°F between surface and ambient temperature and for an air velocity of 100 feet per minute over the surface. The curve is based on an analysis done by the American Boiler Manufacturers Association (ABMA), and is published in the original format in the *ASME Performance Test Code* PTC-4.1.

of the bottom-ash hopper, and making the specified corrections for evaporation and sluice-gate leakage. Flyash heat is Code-designated as L_d, the heat loss due to sensible heat in the flue dust; this is different and distinct from any loss attributed to unburned carbon in the ash.

Because its measurement is extremely difficult, the sensible heat lost in the ash leaving a unit is not shown as a separate item in either predicted heat balances or in ASME Short Form efficiency tests. It most often is considered to be included as part of the ½ percent "unaccounted-for" loss discussed next.

UNACCOUNTED-FOR LOSSES

This item represents unclassified and difficult-to-measure losses that are included in a heat balance to arrive at a guaranteed contractual efficiency.

The value used consists of three components, of unstated weight. First, there are the unmeasured losses which, because of the difficulty or the great expense of measurement, are best included in a convenient margin. Typical is the sensible-heat-in-ash loss of the previous section. Approximation of such a loss by calculation frequently will be a more satisfactory approach than setting up and operating the very complicated testing equipment and instrumentation to obtain meaningful results.

Second, the loss includes some unstated tolerance for instrument error. Whether the short form performance test is made, or the fully detailed and very costly long-form procedure is followed, it is important to arrive at an efficiency that can be accepted both by the owner and the supplier. Chapter 21 on field testing and measurements covers the probable, and rather large, measurement error that can be expected in performance testing. Having some "room for error" will often eliminate the need for retests on the basis of faulty instrumentation, poor placement or operation of probes, and other potential areas of disagreement.

The third component, grouped with instrument-error, is the manufacturer's tolerance in making an efficiency guarantee.

HEAT CREDITS

A heat credit is any energy obtained from outside the envelope of the steam generator (see Fig. 7, Chapter 21) and added to the working fluid or fluids, the air, or the gas inside the envelope boundary. This is over and above the chemical heat in the fuel fired and is usually in the form of electrical energy.

As a practical matter only major credits are considered in most heat-balances. These include the heat from the power conversion in pulverizer motors, primary-air-fan motors, gas-recirculating-fan motors, and circulating-pump motors.

Credits are calculated by determining the power input to the motor (or steam turbine if the steam is supplied from outside the envelope) and dividing by the heat fired (Q_f) if the power is applied to the air or gas, or by the heat absorbed (Q_{abs}) if the power is applied directly to the working fluid; the quotient is then expressed in percent of fuel fired for use in the heat-balance calculation.

HEAT LOSS IN INTEGRAL PRECIPITATOR

It has been demonstrated that there is a substantial gas-temperature drop in the ductwork and through the walls of a precipitator located between the boiler economizer and the air heater(s). This temperature drop results from radiation, convection, and air inleakage. No tests have been performed to categorize these contributors to the problem.

Logically, there is a loss of energy which has to be charged someplace. Because the precipitator is not part of the steam-generator circuitry and because the heat is not returned to the air or gas, the loss should not be charged to the boiler.

The most satisfactory approach is to consider the integral precipitator as another "heat absorber", similar to a second reheater, and take the energy absorbed as an additional output. Using the higher Q_{abs} will give the correct Q_f and the correct air and gas weight without penalizing the steam-generator efficiency.

The heat "lost" or "absorbed" in such a precipitator can be calculated by

$$L_{ip} = \frac{W_g \times c_p \times \Delta T_g}{Q_f} \times 100$$

$$(14)$$

where

W_g is the gas flow through the precipitator, lb/hr

c_p is the specific heat of the gas, Btu/lb-°F

ΔT_g is the gas-temperature drop through the precipitator, °F, and

Q_f is the heat fired, Btu/hr

Note that this method does not take into account the air leaking into the precipitator. If such leakage can be anticipated and quantified, it should be given special consideration because of its effect on air-heater heat transfer (the lower gas temperature entering the air heater reduces the heat head for thermal transfer) and its effect on the ID-fan performance and power consumption.

HEAT-BALANCE CALCULATION

The heat balance of Table II for a boiler to serve a 500-MW turbine is based on firing a bituminous coal of the analysis given in Chapter 4, page 4–5 at an excess-air percentage of 23 percent. The carbon loss, FD-fan temperature rise, and heat credits are assumed for this example, and will vary from case to case. Combustion air has 0.013 lb of water vapor per lb of air (80°F and 60 percent relative humidity). Fuel temperature is taken as equal to ambient air temperature.

FIRING SYSTEM DESIGN

With combustion and heat-balance calculations completed, and the overall steam-generator heat absorption fixed, the designer can now arrive at the weight of fuel fired.

$$\text{Fuel fired, lb/hr} = \frac{Q_f}{\text{HHV}}$$

$$(15)$$

where Q_f is in Btu/hr and the high heating value, HHV, is in Btu/lb.

PULVERIZER SELECTION

It is customary in pulverizer selection to provide one or two "spare" or standby mills to allow for on-line maintenance at boiler full load. (See Chapter 22 for more comments on pulverizer maintenance with the unit in operation.) If there are "n" number of pulverizers installed then (n-1) mills will be capable of full boiler load grinding the worst fuel that the unit must handle; with an average or more

---

Table II. **Heat-Balance Calculations**

Exit gas temperature, uncorrected for leakage, t_g, °F		285
Ambient air temperature, t_{aa}, °F		80
Temperature rise, FD fan, Δt_{fd}, °F		10
Air temperature entering air heater, T_a, °F		90
Solid combustible loss, % by weight		0.20
Combustible loss correction factor, C		0.9985
Fuel in products, F, lb/10^6 Btu		83
Air for combustion, A, lb/10^6 Btu		936
Air in products, C × A, lb/10^6 Btu		934
Total products, P = (F + CA) lb/10^6 Btu		1017
Water in air, W_a lb/10^6 Btu		12.1
Water in fuel, W_c lb/10^6 Btu		13.4
Water formed in combustion, W_h lb/10^6 Btu		32.7
Dry gas in products, P_d lb/10^6 Btu		959

Heat loss in dry gas	%	4.49
Heat loss from water in fuel	%	1.53
Heat loss from combustion of H_2	%	3.70
Heat loss from moisture in air	%	0.11
Heat loss from unburned carbon	%	0.20
Radiation and convection loss	%	0.18
Unmeasured losses*	%	1.50
Total losses,	%	11.71
Less heat credits**	%	0.49
Net losses,	%	11.22
Efficiency (100 − net losses)	%	88.78

*Unmeasured losses include tolerance for instrument error and manufacturer's margin.

**Heat credits here are the sum of motor inputs to pulverizers, primary-air fans, and boiler-water circulating pumps, determined in a separate calculation.

favorable fuel, (n-2) mills can accommodate the maximum load. In either case, pulverizer selection is done using capacity curves similar to those given in Chapter 12, allowing for the wearing parts being in worn condition.

The capacity of a given size pulverizer varies significantly with coal moisture, the grindability of the coal (its "ability to be ground"), and the fineness required for satisfactory, low-carbon-loss burning. Chapter 12, Pulverizers and Pulverized-Coal Systems, covers these parameters and their effects on pulverizer performance. The wider the range in coal calorific value, moisture content and grindability, the greater must be the overall pulverizer capacity.

The statistical probability of all the unfavorable characteristics occurring at the same time, and the total possible period of operation at full boiler load with the worst fuel, have to be weighed against the cost and complexity of multiple installed-spare pulverizers.

WINDBOX DESIGN

With tangential or corner firing, each pulverizer installed delivers ground coal to a row of fuel nozzles located at different levels in the furnace. A row will contain 4 or 8 nozzles depending upon whether the furnace is of the *open type* or of the divided type; the latter usually has a full or partial centerwall between the two firing chambers, with 4 nozzles per horizontal row in each of the two chambers. In an open furnace with six pulverizers, there will be four fuel nozzles arranged in six horizontal rows for a total of 24. Further detail about tangential windboxes and associated ignition equipment is given in Chapter 13, Fuel-Burning Equipment.

With front- or rear-wall firing using fixed round burners, the piping from the pulverizers to the burners is configured in various ways depending upon the manufacturer's preference, steam-temperature control means, and nitrogen-oxide reduction strategy.

Windbox sizing for either tangential or wall firing must recognize the effect of plant altitude on airflow velocity, both in primary-air/ fuel piping and in secondary-air compart-

ments. Air volume and corresponding velocity vary linearly with the *elevation correction factor* (barometric pressure at sea level divided by the barometric pressure at altitude; see Fig. 6). Pressure drop through a given windbox opening or burner throat varies as the square of the actual velocity divided by the elevation correction factor; this must be taken into account in fan sizing, covered later in this chapter.

AIR-HEATER DESIGN

Having designed the windbox and selected the pulverizers to accommodate the least favorable present or future fuel, the designer now has sufficient information to define the air preheater requirements.

The gas flow is the primary determinant in sizing an air heater, since the pressure drop through the gas side varies predictably with load (being essentially proportional to the square of the gas flow and linear with absolute gas temperature). Primary and secondary airflows are additive to the total airflow required, but each will change with fuel moisture, load, and the number of pulverizers in operation. The maximum primary airflow and pressure required by a certain size air

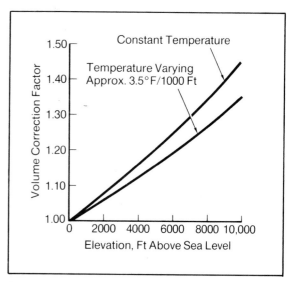

Fig. 6 Volumetric correction for elevation above sea level (Calculated from the data of Standard Atmosphere—Tables and Data to 65,800 Feet, NACA Report 1235)

heater will be important factors in primary-air fan and motor selection.

Air heater design is covered in detail in Chapter 15. The use of the trisector and other air-heater configurations is treated in connection with pulverizing systems in Chapter 12.

FURNACE PERFORMANCE

The following section deals with the thermal performance of a large steam-generator furnace. Although the determination of furnace exit-gas temperature is the key to the performance of all the very expensive superheater and reheater surfaces installed behind it, that temperature is not amenable to calculation. Only through field experience with similar fuels and generally the same mode of furnace operation can such temperatures be determined with confidence. And despite using the most sophisticated computer techniques in the analysis of the upper and lower furnace regions as heat-transfer entities, the data input to those computers is based on a subjective judgment of the slagging character of every coal burned.

We will discuss heat transfer in general as a brief introduction to the subject of furnace heat transfer. We will then show a portion of the analytical approach we take to furnace performance, and will refer to other published material for the interested reader.

Finally, we leave the reader with the perception that furnace outlet temperature determination, while not a secret process, is certainly and necessarily a proprietary one.

HEAT TRANSFER

A necessary step in the design of boilers is a detailed engineering analysis of heat transfer to estimate the cost, practicability and size of equipment to interchange a specified amount of heat in a given time. A steam-generating-unit furnace wall, for example, can be operated successfully over extended periods only if surface temperatures can be maintained within acceptable limits by removing heat continuously and at rapid rates. The size and geometry of a boiler furnace depend not only upon the amount of heat to be transmitted but also on the rate at which it can be absorbed or transferred.

MODES OF HEAT TRANSFER

Most textbooks on heat transfer define three modes of heat flow: *convection, conduction* and *radiation.* These three encompass much of the field of physics including mechanics, heat, acoustics, optics and electricity. For gases, conduction takes place by elastic impact; for solid nonconductors, in longitudinal vibration; and for metals, in electronic movement. The laws of aerodynamics and hydrodynamics govern convection which involves the transportation and exchange of heat due to the mixing motion of different parts of a fluid.

Radiative heat transfer is an electromagnetic event which in fossil-fuel-fired furnaces occurs mainly in the infrared range.

Usually, heat is transferred simultaneously by more than one of these modes.

Convection

Authorities differ as to whether Sir Isaac Newton formulated a definition of convection or a law of cooling when he first expressed the following relationship in 1701:

$$q = hA_s\Delta T \tag{16}$$

where q denotes the time rate of heat flow, h is the surface or film coefficient of heat transfer, A_s is the heat-transfer-surface area and ΔT is a temperature difference between a surface and a fluid in contact with it.

Conduction

More than a century later, in 1828, the French physicist and mathematician J. B. J. Fourier formulated the basic law of heat conduction, which may be expressed as follows:

$$q = -kA_c\frac{dT}{dx} \tag{17}$$

where k is the thermal conductivity, A_c is a constant cross-sectional area, and dT/dx is the temperature gradient at the section. The minus sign signifies that the heat is flowing in the direction of decreasing temperature, in accordance with the second law of thermodynamics.

Radiation

In 1879, Joseph Stefan empirically discovered the third fundamental law of heat transfer, the basic equation for total thermal radiation from an ideal radiator or black body. It was derived theoretically by Ludwig Boltzmann in 1884, and may be expressed as follows:

$$q = \sigma A_s T^4$$

(18)

where σ is the Stefan-Boltzmann constant for total black radiation, A_s is the heat-transfer-surface area, and T is the absolute temperature. (See equations 23 and 23A.)

The Stefan-Boltzmann equation represents the total radiant energy emitted by a black body in all directions, but it does not reveal the distribution of energy in the spectrum. The distribution of emissive power among the different wave lengths was derived by Max Planck in 1900, using the quantum concept.[4]

Heat transfer in boilers will be covered in more detail after furnace performance is discussed. In a later section this chapter covers fluid-to-fluid transfer rates and convection heat-transfer in detail.

FURNACE DESIGN CONSIDERATIONS

The furnace in a modern steam generator is a large water-cooled chamber in which fuel and air are mixed and burned in suspension. Its purpose is to generate heat under controlled conditions with the objective of doing useful work in a steam turbine or other machine. In a thermal-circulation (non-pumped circulation) furnace, some of the heat absorbed is used to move the water-steam mixture against the internal frictional resistance of the 1-in. to 3-in. diameter furnace-wall tubing.

FURNACES FOR PULVERIZED COAL FIRING

Furnaces for burning coal are more liberally sized than those for oil or gas firing. This is necessary to complete combustion within the confines of the furnace and to prevent the formation of objectionable ash or slag deposits. Furnace-wall heat-absorption rates are low enough that tubing metal temperatures do not greatly influence the furnace size.

The furnace dimensions of a unit to fire pulverized fuel have a major influence on the arrangement of firing equipment, the location and quantity of convective heat-transfer surfaces, the quantity and length of soot blowing equipment, the amount of supporting structural steel, the extent of platforms and stairways, and the arrangement of ductwork. A furnace must be properly proportioned, with adequate height between the top row of coal nozzles and the furnace arch, to assure adequate retention time for the gaseous combustion products. The upper furnace area uses widely spaced superheater or reheater panels and platens to further cool the gases. These measures insure that the furnace outlet temperature at the entrance to the close-spaced convection surfaces will be sufficiently low to avoid excessive ash accumulations.

A designer determines the furnace plan area by carefully studying all of the coals anticipated to be burned and arriving at an appropriate value of net heat input to plan area (NHI/PA). Values presently used for a wide range of coals are from 1.4 to 2.0 million Btu/hr-sq ft.

FURNACES FOR OIL AND NATURAL-GAS FIRING

Oil does not require, at what has been normal excess-air requirements, as large a furnace volume as coal to achieve complete combustion. However, the rapid burning of and high radiation rate from oil results in high heat-absorption rates in the active burning zone of the furnace. The furnace size must, therefore, be increased above the minimum required for complete combustion, to reduce heat-absorption rates and avoid excessive furnace-wall metal temperatures.

Natural-gas firing permits the selection of smaller furnaces than for oil firing primarily because a more uniform heat-absorption pattern is obtained.

This brief discussion of furnace sizing relates primarily to tangential firing. Some of the statements made do not necessarily apply to furnace and firing-system combinations employed by manufacturers other than C-E.

Once the furnace size has been established, (based principally on experience with similar fuels burned in other units), and the windboxes have been located in relation to the panels and platens in the upper furnace, an analysis is made to arrive at the outlet gas temperature.

FURNACE ANALYSIS

Analysis here means the engineering solution to yield the information required by an engineer for the design of tangentially fired utility furnaces. The gas-side requirement is two-fold: (1) selection of the requisite grade of water-wall steel requires, quantitatively, the axial absorption profile, and (2) the furnace outlet temperature must be known to within about ±50°F to correctly size the sequence of superheaters, reheaters, economizers and air heater.

Since analysis of radiative transfer between parallel planes is not trivial, study of a vortex-fired utility furnace becomes a project of fair magnitude. This may be verified by a scan of the family of "Parallel Plate" papers[5-59]. Thus, the analysis of industrial furnaces has developed on an overall phenomenon basis. An early example of this is the Rosin Equation (1925) for coal dust flames, discussed by Essenhigh (see Appendix B).

DEFINITIONS USED IN FURNACE DESIGN

Effective Projected Radiant Surface (EPRS)

Effective projected radiant surface is the total projected area of the planes which pass through the centers of all wall tubes, plus the area of a plane which passes perpendicular to the gas flow where the furnace gases reach the first convection superheater or reheater surface. In calculating the EPRS, the surfaces of both sides of the superheater and reheater platens extending into the furnace may be included.

Furnace Volume

The cubage of the furnace within the walls and planes defined under EPRS.

Volumetric Heat Release Rate

The total quantity of thermal energy above fixed datum introduced into a furnace by the fuel, considered to be the product of the hourly fuel rate and its high heat value, and expressed in Btu per hour per cubic foot of furnace volume. This value, does not include the heat added by preheated air nor the heat unavailable through the evaporation of moisture in fuel and that from the combustion of hydrogen.

Heat Available or Net Heat Input

The thermal energy above a fixed datum that is capable of being absorbed for useful work. In boiler practice, the heat available in the furnace is usually taken to be the higher heating value of the fuel corrected by subtracting radiation losses, unburned combustible, latent heat of the water in the fuel or formed by the burning of hydrogen, and adding sensible heat in the air (and recirculated gas if used) for combustion, all above an ambient or reference temperature.

Furnace Release Rate

Furnace release rate is the heat available per sq ft of heat absorbing surface in the furnace (the EPRS).

Furnace Plan Heat-Release Rate

Furnace plan heat-release rate is usually based on the net heat input at a horizontal cross-sectional plane of the furnace through the burner zone, expressed in million Btu/hr-sq ft. The area of the plan is calculated from the horizontal length and width of the furnace taken from the centerline of the waterwall tubes.

The engineering approach to various aspects of furnace behavior, as distinguished from the theoretical approach, is reasonably well characterized by[20-27] and also well represented by Thekdi et al.[28] An excellent survey of the current state-of-the-theoretical-art is given by Beer and Siddall.[29]

A promising approach is the Hottel zoning method,[30-32] which is intended as a realistic scheme for calculating radiant heat exchange with respect to volume-distributed heat release. Although from the literature it is clear that the zoning method has gained widespread acceptance, rigorous solutions for utility furnaces are not yet available.[33]

EMISSIVITY OF THE COMBUSTION PRODUCTS

Furnace heat-transfer calculations, must deal on a quantitative basis with the emissivity of the gaseous products of combustion, gas-to-gas absorptivity, and metallic-surface-to-gas absorptivity.

Because about 95 percent of the heat transfer in large combustion chambers is by radiation, it is important to evaluate the radiative power of the gas/fuel/flame media. If heat transfer requires quantification, the emissivity of the radiating components in the furnace must be known. To make this identification, however, demands the capability to predict the formation, space-dependent concentration, and lifetime of transient species such as OH, C, CO, CN, HCN, N, NO, HCO, H, C_2, CH and other radicals which may be present. Not the least problem in the determination is predicting soot formation (size, distribution, and density) in hydrocarbon flames or particle radiation in coal flames.

Similarly, the radiation contribution by the unburned fuel itself, if the ignition temperatures are high, may not be insignificant either. At this time, neither the chemical and reaction kinetics nor the individual spectra are established or even known completely.

Only the main products of combustion, CO_2 and H_2O, have accepted emissivity values. An engineering approach based on CO_2 and H_2O radiation with an allowance for other contributors constitutes an acceptable alternative because the design engineer is interested in the effective overall gas emissivity as it results from the interacting radiating components. This requires establishing a relation by which the total effect can be expressed in terms of known components.

MODIFIED EMISSIVITY AND ABSORPTIVITY FACTORS

An assumption that fuel and air are ideally and instantaneously converted to CO_2 and H_2O seriously underestimates the waterwall heat-absorption rates. That is, the Hottel emissivities[34] used for calculating radiative transfer, even though they have been confirmed time and time again (see Ref. 35), constitute only a partial contributor to the emissivity in a tangentially fired furnace. It is clear that an additional emissivity factor is necessary. Bueters[36,37] showed that the source condition required "blackening", which led to the development and use of the "F_E operator".

Taking the definition of gas emissivity as

$$\epsilon = \frac{\text{energy actually radiated by the system}}{\text{energy radiated if the system were black}},$$

the combustion-product emissivity is related to Hottel emissivity according to the equation

$$\bar{\epsilon} = \frac{F_E - 1 + \epsilon_H}{F_E}, \quad 1 \le F_E < \infty \tag{19}$$

It follows that the wall-to-gas re-radiation absorptivity is blackened accordingly, or

$$\alpha_{w \to g} = \frac{F_E - 1 + \alpha_H}{F_E} \tag{20}$$

where,

$\bar{\epsilon}$ = combustion products emissivity

F_E = a value which modifies Hottel emissivities to yield combustion-products emissivity

ϵ_H = the combined emissivity for CO_2 and H_2O as given by Hottel[34]

$\alpha_{w \to g}$ = gas absorptivity with respect to bounding-surface radiation

α_H = gas absorptivity as given by Hottel[34]

The gas-to-gas absorptivity, $\alpha_{g \to g}$, is analogously defined as

$$\alpha_{g \to g} = \frac{F_A - 1 + \alpha_H}{F_A} \quad (21)$$

where F_A is the gas-to-gas radiation factor for combustion products.

The F_E factor, as defined, is not related to factors published elsewhere.[38] The behavior of F_E is physically what one would expect for a transition region from a Hottel radiation, $F_E = 1$, dependent on beam length, pressure, and temperature, to the black-body limit, $F_E \to \infty$, where emissivity is independent of beam length, temperature, and pressure. This is illustrated by Fig. 7 where $\epsilon(F_E = 1)$ is taken at typical Hottel values for industrial furnaces of 0.2, 0.3, and 0.4, all at temperature T. The F_E "operator" has therefore been adopted as being fundamentally preferable to using a multiplying factor or corrective addition on ϵ_H.[36]

To determine and correlate source descrip-

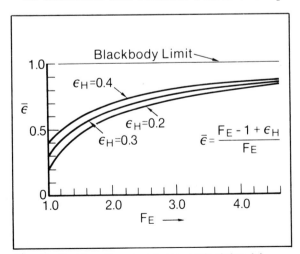

Fig. 7 Combustion products emissivity ($\bar{\epsilon}$) (for radiating components) vs F_E

tors such as F_E, the heat-absorption profile and furnace outlet temperature are measured on operating steam-generating units. The resulting data is processed by a computer which uses it as a boundary condition to solve for source descriptors.[37]

F_E values for large natural-gas-fired furnaces are about 1.2. Applying this to a Hottel emissivity of about 0.34 for gas temperatures in the range of 3000°F, one arrives at $\bar{\epsilon} = 0.45$. This accounts for additional contributions by convection, transient species, and soot. An altered Hottel emissivity of about 0.39 would be estimated from the work of Ludwig and Boyton on water vapor.[39] Assuming that this is a more exact value and that convective transfer is 4 to 5 percent, we can postulate roughly

$$0.45\sigma T^4 = \text{Hottel radiation} + \text{convection} + \text{additional radiation}$$
$$= 0.39\sigma T^4 + 0.02\sigma T^4 + 0.04\sigma T^4 \quad (22)$$

For a rather typical temperature of 3500°R, we would arrive at a convective coefficient of

$$0.02\sigma T^4 = h \Delta T, \Delta T \approx 2000°F$$
$$h = \frac{.02 \times .17134 \times 10^{-8} \times 3500^4}{2000}$$
$$\cong 2.6 \text{ Btu/ft}^2\text{-hr-°F}$$

This value is in the range of values for combustion chambers given by Steward and Cannon.[40]

When quantitative convective correlations for tangentially-fired furnaces have been determined along the lines established by Hottel, the F_E value for fuels on which no operating experience is available may be predetermined.

RADIATION FORMULATION

Hottel and Egbert[41] give a Stefan-Boltzmann form of equation for net radiation as

$$q = 0.1723 \text{ A } \bar{\epsilon}_{surf} \left[\epsilon_g \left(\frac{T_g}{100}\right)^4 - \alpha \left(\frac{T_s}{100}\right)^4 \right] \quad (23)$$

Modified by F_E, this equation becomes

$$q = 0.17134 \, A_s \, \acute{\epsilon}_s \left[\epsilon_g \left(\frac{T_g}{100} \right)^4 - \alpha_{w \to g} \left(\frac{T_w}{100} \right)^4 \right]$$

$$(23A)$$

where

q = heat given up by flame Btu/hr

0.17134×10^{-8} Btu/ft²-hr-(°R)⁴ is the Stefan-Boltzmann constant,

$\acute{\epsilon}_s$ = effective exchange factor to account for infinite number of reflections and re-radiations; written in terms of surface emissivity (dimensionless)

ϵ_g = radiative (combustion products) emissivity, dimensionless

A_s = effective surface area of flame envelope and receiving surface when equal, sq ft

$\alpha_{w \to g}$ = fraction of bounding-surface radiation which is absorbed by the gas, as above

T_g = gas temperature, °R

T_w = cold-surface temperature, °R

This equation is used to formulate the gas-to-gas radiation exchange and gas-temperature distribution inside a furnace by means of a horizontal slicing technique.[37]

In Eq. 23A, the area of the flame will vary substantially with furnace design and fuel fired. The type of firing used affects the rate at which gas sweeps over heating surface, and the area of the flame varies with the rate of firing, other things being constant. Flame emissivity depends on many factors including

■ flame luminosity due to burning particles

■ the concentration of water vapor and carbon dioxide in the flame

■ the volume of flame and its temperature.

The temperature of the flame envelope will be neither constant nor uniform in a watercooled furnace of a steam-generating unit. Combustion characteristics of different firing equipment vary widely. Some produce a short, but intense and highly turbulent flame, while combustion with others is relatively slow, thereby producing a comparatively long flame of greater volume.

Although for any given furnace the area of cold surface is fixed, slag accumulation may influence its effectiveness. The emissivity of the watercooling installed depends on the material used and its condition. For an oxidized steel furnace, however, the emissivity will approach unity at high temperatures.

Generally, the temperature of the cold surface may be taken as that of the water and steam inside the tube, without introducing an appreciable error. But depending on its area, thickness and density, slag accumulation will affect not only the area but also the temperature of the cold or receiving surface. (See Appendix C, Determinations of Coal-Ash Properties.)

DESIGN APPROACH

From the foregoing discussion of the variables affecting the temperature field and radiant heat transfer in the boiler furnace, the reasons why the designer does not usually approach the problem in a purely theoretical manner should be apparent. In practice, the designer resorts to the use and interpretation of empirical data collected from boilers of similar design operating under similar conditions. Known theories of heat transfer are applied to the empirical data so that they may be used for conditions differing from those tested. This is necessary to improve and advance the art of designing boiler furnaces. Furthermore, to predict the temperature of flue gas leaving a given furnace in advance of actual operation requires a background of accumulated data, experience and judgment generally possessed only by manufacturers of the equipment involved.

In the simplified empirical design approach, traverses are made of the gas stream leaving the furnace to determine the weighted average temperature. Such measurement of boiler furnace performance is simple in principle but difficult to attain in practice. There are many problems in taking measurements at high temperature in a complex equipment configuration of large size.

The average outlet temperature, along with

the calculated weight of the products of combustion and the mean specific heat above an arbitrary datum, will give the heat content of the gas leaving the furnace above the datum. This may be done according to the following equation:

$$q = Wc_p(T_l - 70) \qquad (24)$$

where c_p is the mean specific heat at constant pressure from 70°F to the leaving temperature, T_l is the gas temperature leaving the furnace, and W is the weight flow rate of gas.

The heat absorbed by the radiant heating surface exposed to the furnace gas is the difference between the net heat liberated in the furnace available for absorption and the heat content of the gas leaving the furnace.

TYPICAL FIELD TEST RESULTS

Reference 42 reports a full scale field study of the foregoing design approach. The study involved a 600-MW tangentially-fired boiler burning a highly slagging high-volatile bituminous coal.

The boiler furnace, shown in outline in Fig. 8, is 56-ft wide, 49-ft deep, and 183-ft high. During the tests the net heat input on the plan area was 2.1×10^6 Btu/sq ft-hr. Furnace temperatures were measured using aspirating, single-shielded high-velocity thermocouples on 15-ft water-cooled probes extending 14 ft into the furnace.

Table III summarizes the gas temperatures measured at the 138-ft level through 7 sighting ports opposite the furnace nose. The average gas temperature reported in this test program for the 7 traverse lines is 2232°F, with a maximum variation of ± 150°F. (Temperatures measured in ports 2, 3, and 4 were done on one day, and are higher than those measured in ports 5, 6, 7, and 8 on the next day.) As is to be expected, temperature levels anywhere in a large furnace firing pulverized coal will vary throughout a day, and through a week. This occurs as a function of the thickness of slag and ash on the furnace walls, the sootblowing pattern, slag falls during the night, and burner flow and mixing patterns.[42]

ELEMENTS OF BOILER HEAT TRANSFER

Earlier, this chapter introduced the concepts of heat transfer by various modes. Ref. 43 gives much of the historical background of their development. From an understanding of these concepts, it is apparent that the calculation of heat transfer occurring in superheater, reheater, and economizer sections downstream of the furnace has a first-order dependence on the furnace-outlet gas temperature. And, after the different types of surfaces are installed and the unit goes into operation, the furnace leaving temperature has a similarly significant effect on how they perform.

Table III. **Gas temperatures at elevation 138 ft**

Traverse Distance[a]	Temperature,°F						
	2[b]	3	4	5	6	7	8
2	2239	2249	2313	2225	2130	2170	2165
4	2263	2296	2290	2165	2090	2080	2200
6	2290	2315	2305	2165	2115	2080	2260
8	2340	2340	2310	2155	2100	2100	2260
10	2366	2379	2330	2165	2130	2145	2220
12	2384	2374	2318	2240	2100	2155	2255
14	2377	2375	2300	2230	2060	2180	2290

(a) Distance in feet from boiler inside wall.
(b) Port number (typical).

FLOW OF HEAT THROUGH FURNACE TUBES

The heat which is given up by the furnace gas, and which results in the generation of steam within the tube exposed to that gas, must pass through a series of resistances: the gas film adjacent to the tube; slag on the tube surface; tube wall; internal scale deposited by the water evaporated; the water and steam film. If the slag and scale are not bonded intimately to the tube surface, two more resistances may be added: the gas film between the slag and tube, and the steam film between the internal scale and the tube wall. Fig. 9 illustrates the temperature gradient resulting from the flow of heat through some of these series resistances.

Heat transfer through the gas film and the evaporating film does not follow the simple equation for conduction. The temperature gradient through the other resistances, however, is inversely proportional to the thermal conductivity. For conductance through a body having flat parallel plane surfaces, the following equation may be used:

$$\Delta t = \frac{(q/A_s)\, x}{k}$$

(25)

where

Δt is the temperature drop across any single thermal resistance,

q/A_s is the heat flux per unit of surface area,

x is the thickness of the resistance, and

k is the thermal conductivity for unit thickness,

all expressed in consistent units.

For radial heat flow in a tube wall we write:

$$\Delta t = \frac{q/A_s}{k}\, r_2 \left[\log_e \frac{r_2}{r_1} \right]$$

(26)

where r_2 is the outside radius, r_1 is the inside radius, and q/A_s is the heat flux at the outside tube surface, again in consistent units.

The temperature gradient shown in Fig. 9 is typical of furnace tubes exposed to radiant heat. From inspection, the resistance having the dominating influence on heat-transfer rate is that through the gas film. Thus, for many practical purposes, the temperature of the receiving surface may be taken as equal to that of the water and steam within the tube. This approximation can be closer to fact when studying transfer in convective zones than it is for furnace-wall tubes. Accumulations of slag or flyash on the outside surface, or scale on the inside, may easily become the controlling resistance to any heat transfer if allowed to form unchecked.

As described in Chapter 11, Water Technology, inside scale can cause sufficient increase in tube metal temperature to produce overheating and rupture.

Fig. 8 Test furnace outline, showing test-probe elevation 138 ft.

Fig. 9 Temperature gradient for furnace-wall tubes exposed to radiant heat, with slag accumulation

FLUID-TO-FLUID HEAT-TRANSFER RATES

The fundamental theory of heat-transfer in the steady state is analogous to, and based on, the same concept as Ohm's law, namely: *That flow varies directly as the potential and inversely as the resistance.* Thus in Fig. 9, the potential between the two fluids is the temperature difference $(t_6 - t_1)$, and there are five resistances in series—the hot fluid (gas) film, the slag or ash layer, the metal separating the fluids, the internal scale or sludge layer, and the cold-fluid evaporating film.

Applying the Ohm's law analogy, the flow of heat, Q, will equal the temperature difference divided by the resistance. In each instance, as with Ohm's law the resistance is the reciprocal of the thermal conductance.

In a boiler bank or economizer the temperature difference, Δt_s, between cold fluid and clean heating surface will be very small compared to Δt_g, because the thermal conductance of the water film is high. But in a superheater or reheater the air or dry steam becomes the cold fluid, and the temperature gradient across the film will be higher because the thermal conductance of these films is lower.

The designers of boiler banks and economizers, therefore, are interested only in the overall thermal conductance or heat-transfer rate, and are not greatly concerned with the intermediate rates or temperatures, because the metal temperature will be close to that of the cold fluid. On the other hand, designers of superheaters, furnace waterwalls, and reheaters are also concerned about the metal temperatures.

EFFECT OF GAS-FLOW DIRECTIONALITY

Whether the gas flows parallel or transverse to the tube-bank axis has a major effect on the rate of heat transfer. When gas flows through tubes, the flow is parallel to the axes for their entire length. When flowing outside tubes, however, there is usually a combination of parallel-flow convection and cross-flow convection, in addition to local radiation.

Equations for heat transfer with parallel flow contain a factor for inside tube diameter, but the actual tube diameter can be used only when the gas actually flows through the tubes. For flow outside the tubes, an *equivalent diameter* is used:

$$d_e = \frac{4A_c}{P}$$

$$(27)$$

where d_e is the equivalent diameter, A_c is the free gas passage area and P is the gas-touched perimeter of tubes, all in consistent units.

When calculating the heat transfer in a parallel-flow pass of a boiler, coefficients for flow parallel to the axis of the tubes should be applied only to those portions where the gas is confined between parallel baffles and forced to travel with minimal turbulence along the axis of the tubes. For the portions at the ends of such passes, cross-flow transfer rates may be used for the effective surface opposite the entrance and exit openings. Consideration should be given to the variation of mass velocities in those portions, if any.

In general, the convective heat-transfer coefficient with flow across tube banks is considerably higher than with parallel flow. Under some conditions it is twice as much for comparable velocities. Fig. 10 shows the approximate variation. The upper limit represents flow across small diameter tubes, and the lower limit, flow parallel to tubes that are spaced on relatively wide centers.

FACTORS AFFECTING CONVECTION HEAT TRANSFER FROM GAS

Among most designers of steam-generating equipment, the convection heat-transfer rate in those parts of the apparatus not exposed to luminous radiation is the overall rate between the fluid giving up and the fluid receiving the heat. It has been shown that the gas film conductance may be used instead of the overall rate without much error in certain parts of the equipment. But even the gas film conductance must include a factor or an addition to allow for nonluminous radiation from hot gases, such as carbon dioxide and water vapor, both of which are present in the products of combustion of all common fuels. Therefore, when we speak of the *convection* rate, it will be understood to include this radiation, and the expression *pure convection* will be used in connection with all data or curves not including this allowance.

An analysis of pure convection will show that the heat-transfer rate per unit area of heating surface will be affected by numerous variables given in the following expression.

$$R_c = f(D, V, \rho, \mu, c_p, k, a)$$

where:

R_c = film conductance fluid to solid for pure convection

D = linear dimension of solid surface

V = linear velocity of fluid stream

ρ = density of fluid

μ = viscosity of fluid

c_p = specific heat of fluid at constant pressure

k = conductivity of fluid

a = geometric relation ratio or combined ratios to cover the effect of spacing, width, depth and length

Investigators have found that good correlation of test data has resulted when these variables are combined into dimensionless groups or ratios, as follows:

Nusselt number or group = $Nu = R_c D/k$

Reynolds number or group = $Re = DV \rho/\mu$

Prandtl number or group = $Pr = c_p \mu/k$

Fig. 10 Chart showing the range of convective heat-transfer rate between conditions of parallel- and cross-flow of gas

For forced convection it may, therefore, be written that

$$R_c D/k = f[(DV \, \rho/\mu), (c_p \, \mu/k), (a)] \tag{28}$$

Expressed in terms of power functions, this becomes

$$R_c D/k = k F_a (DM/\mu)^n (c_p \, \mu/k)^m \tag{29}$$

in which

k   = constant proportionality factor to be experimentally determined

F_a = arrangement factor replacing a, to be experimentally determined

M   = $V \times \rho$ = mass velocity of fluid

m, n = power functions to be experimentally determined

The factor, a, and F_a in the two foregoing equations could probably be eliminated if all parts and dimensions of all heat-transfer apparatus were geometrically similar. This is impossible in commercial practice, and has not always been done in designing apparatus for research purposes. Therefore, where D in these equations is merely taken as tube diameter, complete agreement between data from different sources is not to be expected. This may partly explain the disagreement in values of m, n and k as determined by different investigators. Higher values for n have been found for flow parallel to the axis of tubes than for flow transverse to the axis.

The numerical value of the Prandtl group, c_p μ/k, is nearly the same for all the constituents of flue gas, and, therefore, is practically constant for all flue gas at a given temperature. There is little opportunity to determine by experiment to what extent this group enters into heat transfer from gas, and some investigators do not include it in their equations. However, there is considerable variation in the specific heat of gases at high temperature, and there is no certainty that proper correction for gas temperature has been allowed when this group is omitted. In general, heat-transfer equations containing no temperature term, or containing none of the fluid properties which vary with temperature, are to be considered only for limited application in the range for which the heat-transfer equations are derived.

In regard to tube arrangement and spacing, it has been definitely established that, in banks of tubes, the depth of the bank affects the heat-transfer rate. There is a marked increase for each row up to about the fifth, and gradually less and less increase to the tenth. This is caused by increased turbulence from row to row. For one particular Reynolds number, and other variables kept constant, Pierson[44] found approximately 25 percent lower cross-flow heat-transfer rate for two rows than for ten rows for both *in-line-* and *staggered-tube* arrangements, but the difference between five rows and ten rows was about 9 percent. Experiments of others would indicate that a very turbulent gas stream, on approaching the bank, may affect these comparisons and produce higher heat-transfer rates for shallow banks than indicated in previous text.

It is obviously incorrect to expect staggered tube rows to give better cross-flow heat transfer than tubes in line without considering the effect of depth spacing in the direction of flow.

When the depth spacing is great in both cases, so that the stream has a chance to expand fully after passing each row, there can be no possible advantage with staggered rows, and the two should be equal. The method used by Grimison[45] for correlation of Pierson's and Huge's[46] data indicates this to be true under certain conditions, but it is also affected by the gas velocity when tube diameter and temperature are maintained constant.

CONVECTIVE HEAT-TRANSFER RATES

In day-to-day calculations of superheater and reheater heat transfer, it is convenient to work from curves that synthesize the above factors. For convection transfer, the general equation forming the basis for either curves or computational programs is

$$R_c = k\, c_p\, M^x/D^y \tag{30}$$

where

R_c = pure convection heat transfer, gas to metal

k = a constant

c_p = specific heat of gas at constant pressure

M = gas mass velocity through the free area between the tubes

D = tube diameter, all being in consistent units

and x and y are exponents; the constant and the

Fig. 11 Convection transfer rate

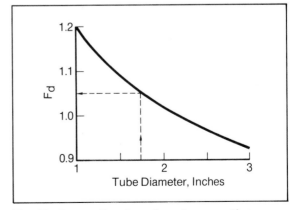

Fig. 12 Convection transfer-rate correction factor for tube geometry

Fig. 13 Convection transfer-rate correction factors, Reynolds number and tube geometry

exponents must be determined empirically and depend on tube arrangement and spacing.

From tests on large steam-generating units or other heat-recovery equipment, it is difficult to ascertain the precise effect on heat transfer of variations in velocity, tube diameter, distribution and direction of flow, tube spacing, or gas temperature. But it is, nevertheless, necessary to adjust the various coefficients and exponents in such basic relations as Eq. 30 to reflect operational experience.

Typical parametric curves based on test data are shown in Figs. 11, 12, and 13. The overall convection rate is $R_c = R'_c \times F_d \times F_a$.

THE EFFECT OF NONLUMINOUS RADIATION

Carbon dioxide and water vapor are the principal radiating components of boiler flue gas; their combined radiating effect has historically been referred to as nonluminous radiation. Transfer rates and radiant beam lengths for nonluminous radiation are to a great extent

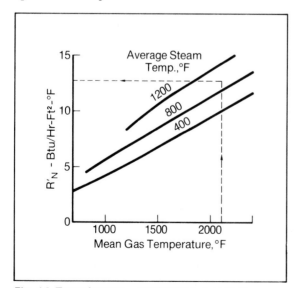

Fig. 14 Transfer rate—nonluminous radiation

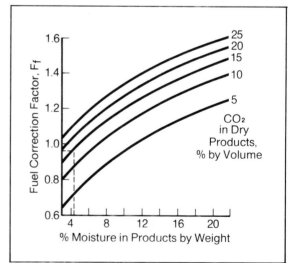

Fig. 15 Fuel correction factor for nonluminous radiation

based on work done by Hottel and others previously referenced.

In all cases where the flue-gas temperature is high and the tube spacing relatively great, the nonluminous radiation will be of considerable magnitude and should be added to the pure convection rate. Figs. 14 through 17 show typical rates and correction factors. The radiant beam length is calculated according to Fig. 16 and is entered into Fig. 17 to obtain the beam-length correction factor, F_b. The basic nonluminous rate from Fig. 14 is multiplied by F_f (Fig. 15) and F_b to get a corrected rate to be used in subsequent calculations.

EFFECT OF VARIATION IN TEMPERATURE DIFFERENCE

The temperature difference between gas and steam, water, or air produces the flow of heat; the logarithmic temperature difference (LMTD) represents the effective difference between two fluids. The LMTD depends on the relative directions of flow of the fluids as they pass through or over the surface. That is, do they flow counter to, parallel to, or across one another. For parallel or counter flow

$$\text{LMTD} = \frac{\text{greatest difference} - \text{least difference}}{\log_e\left(\dfrac{\text{greatest difference}}{\text{least difference}}\right)}$$

or,

$$\text{LMTD} = \frac{\Delta T_1 - \Delta T_2}{\log_e\left(\dfrac{\Delta T_1}{\Delta T_2}\right)}$$

(31)

where ΔT_1 and ΔT_2 are given in Fig. 18. These figures show that for a given heat recovery the greatest temperature difference will be obtained, and the least heating surface required, when the two fluids flow counter to each other. Furthermore, with parallel flow, the highest temperature of the heated fluid can only approach but not equal the lowest temperature of the heating fluid.

In waterwalls or economizer surface, the temperature difference between cold fluid and clean heating surface will be very small compared to the temperature difference between the clean surface and the mean gas temperature because the thermal conductance of the water film is high. In a superheater or reheater, on the other hand, the temperature gradient across the cold film will be higher because the thermal conductance of these films is lower.

In the design and proportioning of waterwall and economizer surface, interest is primarily in the overall thermal conductance or heat-transfer rate. The intermediate rates or temperatures are of secondary concern because the metal temperature will be close to that of the cold fluid. Design of superheaters, reheaters and waterwalls must also consider the metal temperatures. In the case of superheaters, knowledge of metal temperature is necessary for the most economical use of alloy material. The designer of a heat-transfer device such as a tubular air heater, on the other hand, must know the temperature of the metal separating the two fluids to combat condensation of

Fig. 16 Radiant beam length, in-line tubes

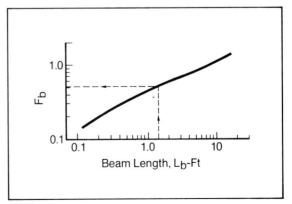

Fig. 17 Correction factor, radiant beam length

moisture and acid vapors, or to minimize the effect by selection of noncorrosive materials.

APPLICATION OF HEAT-TRANSFER RATES TO BOILER CALCULATIONS

As discussed, superheater and reheater tubular surfaces in the upper furnace and beyond, (loosely termed the "convection pass") absorb heat in three ways: by direct radiation from the flame; by nonluminous radiation, chiefly from the carbon dioxide and water vapor in the combustion gases; and by heat transfer through pure convection.

The contributions from these sources are additive and directly affect both heat absorption and metal temperatures. That is, a superheater in a high-temperature gas zone that "sees" the fireball may have the same convection rate, R_c, as a low-temperature superheater section in a 1000°F zone. But the effective overall transfer rate, in this instance including the long-beam-length-radiation, may be double the R_c.

From the second law of thermodynamics, we know that a given surface will absorb heat proportionally to the temperature difference and the transfer rate.

$$q/A_s = R_t \quad (\text{LMTD}) \tag{32}$$

where q is the heat absorbed per unit time, A_s is the area of the heating surface, R_t is the overall transfer rate, and LMTD is as previously defined—all in consistent units.

The logarithmic mean temperature difference must be used in Eq. 32 because the reduction in temperature between T_1 and T_2 is not directly proportional to the amount of surface passed over. For small surfaces, and for values of ΔT_2 greater than half ΔT_1, the arithmetic mean temperature difference can be used without appreciable error.

Also, for a closed system in which the weight of gas entering is equal to the weight leaving,

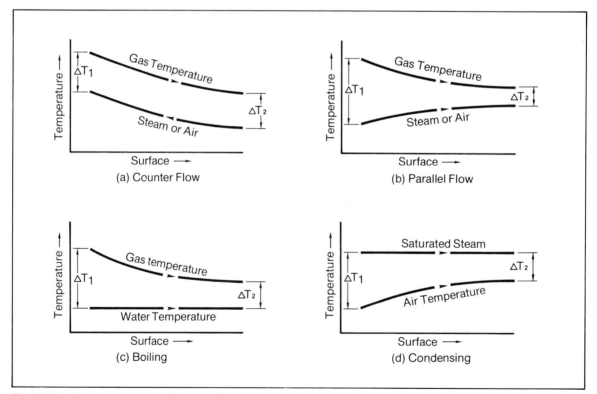

Fig. 18 **Fluid temperatures in heat exchangers**

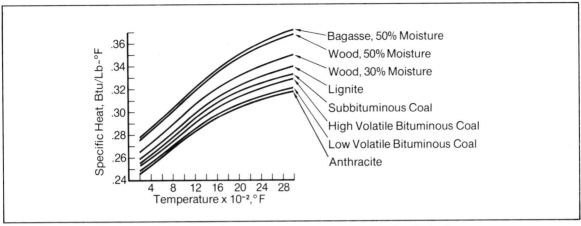

Fig. 19 **Specific heat at constant pressure for products of combustion of solid fuels**

and in which losses due to radiation and convection from the boundary walls can be neglected, the quantity of heat absorbed by the surface will equal the heat given up by the gas:

$$q = W_g c_p \, \Delta T \tag{33}$$

where W_g is the mass flow-rate of gas, c_p is the mean specific heat at constant pressure, and ΔT is the gas temperature drop, all in consistent units. Figs. 19 and 20 give specific heats at constant pressure of the products of combustion of several solid, liquid, and gaseous fuels, burned at usual excess-air percentages. Fig. 21, with specific heats of air at varying moisture contents, is useful for air-heater calculations.

When heat transfer in commercial apparatus is calculated from changes in fluid temperature determined by test measurements on similar apparatus, several additional errors may be introduced. In taking the temperature readings, the gas stream is large, and simultaneous readings at many points are necessary. If there is stratification or nonuniform flow, the arithmetic average of these readings may introduce an error which may be much larger than any error in the temperature readings themselves. An incorrect specific heat value will introduce another error which can be eliminated in the research laboratory by supplying the heat in some way which can be measured with a high degree of accuracy.

For any heat-transfer surface, then, the gas temperature drop is

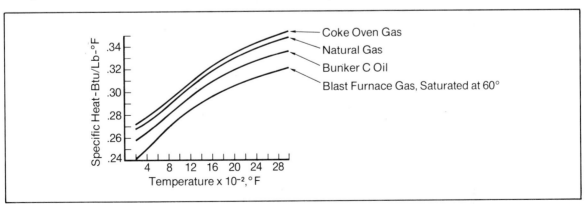

Fig. 20 **Specific heat at constant pressure for products of combustion of liquid and gaseous fuels**

Curve No.	Moisture Lb H₂O/Lb Dry Air	Approximate Atmospheric Equivalent at 29.92 In. Hg
1	Dry Air	
2	0.013	60% Rel. Humidity at 80° F
3	0.025	60% Rel. Humidity at 100° F
4	0.043	100% Rel. Humidity at 100° F

Fig. 21 Specific heat at constant pressure of air at varying moisture contents

$$\Delta T_g = \frac{R_t A_s}{W_g c_p} \text{(LMTD)}$$

$$(34)$$

where the transfer rate and the heating surface are defined on the same basis—tubing inside diameter, outside diameter, or mean-wall diameter. R_t is the total rate, equal to pure convection rate plus nonluminous transfer rate.

Where luminous or "long-beam" radiation from the fireball is to be taken into account, curves such as in Fig. 22 are used to give radiant-heat absorption on flat projected areas of banks of tubing; they are to be corrected for view factor and depth of tube bank.

CALCULATION OF A REHEATER

An over-simplified example of a single-section reheater will tie together much of the preceding discussion. Assume the section is located in a moderately high gas-temperature zone, with both inlet and outlet steam conditions known. It is then possible to calculate in one step without assumption of intermediate temperatures.

KNOWN DATA

Tube diameter	2⅛ in. OD
Free gas area, FGA	1675 sq. ft.
Number of assemblies, N	90
Steam temperature leaving, t_2	1005 °F
Steam pressure leaving, P_2	488 psig
Steam temperature entering, t_1	680 °F
Steam pressure entering P_1	500 psig
Steam flow, W.	3,500,000 lb/hr
Gas weight, W,	4,600,000 lb/hr
Gas temperature entering T_1	2000 °F

CALCULATION OF HEATING SURFACE

The reheater section is counter flow and its entering gas temperature, T_1, is the same as the gas temperature, leaving the superheater previously calculated.

To find gas temperature leaving reheater, T_2, and heating surface, S, required to raise steam temperature from 680°F to 1005°F, the following steps are required.

The amount of direct furnace radiation which passes through superheater surfaces ahead of the reheater is first determined using the projected area of the tubing and a correlation such as Fig. 22. Assume that the direct radiation absorbed by the reheater is 25 million Btu per hour. The total heat to be absorbed is now established from the steam conditions in and out of the reheater. The direct radiation is deducted to obtain the convective plus non-luminous heat transferred, q_c.

Enthalpy of steam at 1005°F and 488 psig =
$H_2 = 1523$ Btu/lb

Enthalpy of steam at 680°F and 500 psig =
$H_1 = 1345$ Btu/lb

Heat absorbed by reheater per lb of steam =
$\Delta H = 178$ Btu

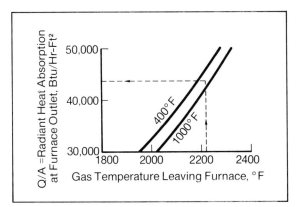

Fig. 22 Radiant heat absorption at furnace outlet

Total heat absorbed by reheater $= W_s \Delta H =$ $3,500,000 \times 178 = 623 \times 10^6$ Btu/hr. Subtracting the radiant heat absorbed (25 million Btu/hr.),

$$q_c = 598 \times 10^6 \, \text{Btu/h}$$

Since q_c is also the heat absorbed from the gas, the following relationship, leading to the solution of T_2, may be expressed.

$$q_c = W_g c_p \Delta T_g$$

$$\Delta T_g = \frac{q_c}{W_g c_p} = T_1 - T_2$$

For solution of T_2 all values are known in the above equations except c_p which for an assumed temperature of 1790°F, firing high-volatile bituminous coal, is 0.308 (from Fig. 19)

$$\Delta T_g = \frac{598 \times 10^6}{4,600,000 \times 0.308} = 422°F$$

$$T_2 = 2000 - 422 = 1578°F$$

Heating surface, A_s, is the only remaining unknown in connection with this reheater section. This can be determined from

$$A_s = \frac{W_g c_p \Delta T_g}{R_t (\text{LMTD})}$$

From Fig. 23, which shows the temperature gradient across the reheater, we calculate the LMTD.

$$\text{LMTD} = \frac{(T_1 - t_2) - (T_2 - t_1)}{\text{Log}_e \dfrac{T_1 - t_2}{T_2 - t_1}} =$$

$$\frac{995 - 898}{\text{Log}_e \dfrac{995}{898}} = 946°F$$

$$
\begin{aligned}
R_t &= R_n + R_c \\
R_n &= R'_n \times F_b \times F_f \\
T_m &= t_{avg} + \text{LMTD} \\
T_m &= \frac{1005 + 680}{2} + 946 = 1789°F
\end{aligned}
$$

Assume a radiant beam length of 1.2 ft

$$
\begin{aligned}
R'_n &= 10.5 \, \text{Btu/hr-sq ft-°F} \\
&\quad (\text{from Fig. 14}) \\
F_b &= 0.45 \, (\text{from Fig. 17}) \\
F_f &= \text{Use } 1.05 \\
R_n &= 10.5 \times 0.45 \times 1.05 = 5.0 \, \text{Btu/hr-sq ft-°F} \\
R_c &= R'_c \times F_d \times F_a \\
&\quad \text{Mass velocity, G, is required to evaluate} \\
R'_c &\\
G &= \frac{W_2}{FGA} = \frac{4,600,000}{1675} \\
&= 2750 \, \text{lb/hr-sq ft} \\
R'_c &= 9.5 \, \text{Btu/hr-sq ft-°F} \\
&\quad (\text{from Fig. 11 based on } T_m = 1789°F) \\
F_d &= 1.0 \, (\text{from Fig. 12})
\end{aligned}
$$

Use 0.95 (Fig. 13 would be used for actual tube spacings.)

$$
\begin{aligned}
R_c &= 9.5 \times 1.0 \times 0.95 \\
&= 9.0 \, \text{Btu/hr-sq ft-°F} \\
R_t &= R_n + R_c = 5.0 + 9.0 \\
&= 14.0 \, \text{Btu/hr-sq ft-°F} \\
S &= \frac{W_g \times c_g \times \Delta T_g}{R_t \times \text{LMTD}} \\
&= \frac{(4,600,000)(0.308)(422)}{(14.0) \quad (946)} \\
&= 45,100 \, \text{sq ft}
\end{aligned}
$$

DRAFT LOSSES AND THE SPECIFICATION OF FANS

Intimately tied to the physical arrangement of tubular heating surfaces and the determination of convective and nonluminous heat-transfer rates is the draft loss, or pressure drop, of the gases passing over them.

Although there is no direct mathematical relationship between heat transfer and draft loss, it can be said in general that convection transfer rates and draft losses are directly proportional, but to an unknown power function. That is, the rate of heat transfer can seldom be increased without producing an increase in pressure differential.

The engineer designing superheater, reheater, boiler bank, economizer, and air heater surfaces has to balance the cost of heating surface against the power penalty for pressure drop and draft loss to arrive at an economic configuration. And because the several different transfer surfaces (depending on their design pressure level and operating temperature) have widely varying costs per unit of surface area, they too have to be evaluated carefully to arrive at the optimum mix. It is because of this correlative relation of transfer rate and draft loss that it is necessary to include terminology and calculation methods for draft losses through tube banks and power-plant stacks.

DRAFT

Although often used in many ways, the term *draft* is defined here as pressure difference *below* that of the atmosphere. The absolute pressure of the atmosphere at mean sea level is 29.9 in. Hg, or 14.7 psia under conditions referred to as *normal barometer*. Without any change in elevation above sea level, barometric pressure may vary as much as 3 in. Hg from weather conditions. Thus, as the absolute pressure corresponding to zero, or balanced draft, is quite variable, it is customary, and more convenient, to express draft values in terms of gage pressure rather than absolute pressure.

For example, a simple U-tube half filled with water may be used as a draft gage, by connecting one leg to a duct or furnace in which the pressure of draft is to be measured, and leaving the other leg open to atmospheric pressure. If the absolute pressure in the furnace is exactly equal to the absolute atmospheric pressure outside the furnace, the water level in the two legs of the U-tube will remain at the same elevation. This is known as a balanced-draft condition, and the draft is said to be zero. On the other hand, if the absolute pressure in the furnace is less than that of the outside atmosphere, the level in the tube leg exposed to the atmosphere will move down, and the level in the other leg will move up. The difference in level is then the draft measured in inches of water, and generally written inches water gage (″WG).

In recording draft readings it is not necessary to place a minus sign ahead of the numerical value of draft when the pressure at point of measurement is lower than that of the atmosphere. But if the absolute pressure at the point of measurement is greater than that of the atmosphere, it should preferably be called *pressure*. If it is called draft, the numerical values should be preceded by a plus sign.

FORCED AND INDUCED DRAFT

The term *forced draft* is indicative of an absolute pressure higher than that of the

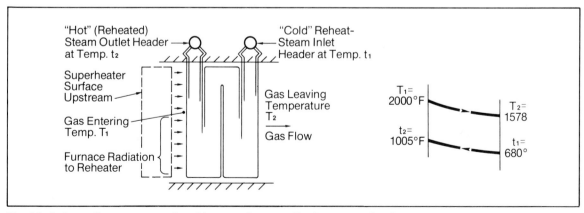

Fig. 23 **Schematic arrangement and temperature gradient across reheater**

atmosphere, and this expression is therefore not consistent with the word *draft* as previously defined. The term *induced draft* is indicative of an absolute pressure lower than that of the atmosphere, but the word induced is somewhat superfluous when using the previous definition of draft. Nevertheless, these expressions are in common usage and are used in this text, despite these inconsistencies.

PRESSURE DROP AND DRAFT LOSS

The difference between pressure gage readings in parts of a system operating with a positive pressure relative to that of the atmosphere, is generally called *pressure drop;* whereas the difference between gage readings in parts of a system operating with a negative pressure relative to that of the atmosphere, is generally called *draft loss.* The actual gage readings are referred to as pressure or draft, as the case may be, except that in reporting data taken at a point where there is normally a draft, it is called draft even when there is a pressure, but a plus sign should be used as a prefix to the figures given.

PRESSURE

When the fluid to be measured has motion, it has a *velocity pressure* in addition to its *static pressure.* The *total pressure* is the algebraic sum of velocity pressure and static pressure. Static pressure is the force per unit area exerted on a wall by adjacent fluid which is at rest, or which is flowing without disturbance along the wall of a conduit. To obtain the static pressure of a fluid at rest, use any pipe or tube having an opening at the point in question. Generally, a tube with a special construction at the end, called a "static tube," is used to determine the static pressure of fluid moving in a straight conduit of sufficient length. Sometimes, a static hole in the wall of the conduit is used.

In the case of fluids flowing in curved paths, such as near elbows, centrifugal force of the fluid affects the pressure. Care must be taken to locate static holes and impact tubes so that they are not affected by curved paths, eddies, or turbulence; otherwise the determination of static pressure or total pressure will be inaccurate.

MEASUREMENT OF TOTAL PRESSURE

Total pressure is measured with an open-ended tube (known as an impact tube) pointed upstream. The excess of total pressure as shown by the impact tube over the static pressure is the exact equivalent of the energy represented by the velocity. This difference is known as velocity pressure or velocity head. When static pressure is below atmospheric, and therefore negative, the total pressure will be a numerically smaller negative number, or may even be positive, depending on the magnitude of the draft and the fluid velocity.

Any statement of pressure should be accompanied by an indication of whether it is static or total, whether it is gage or absolute, and at what base plant altitude, if greater than 1000 ft above sea level. After correction for difference in local elevation, the difference in total pressure between two points in a closed system is a measure of the pressure loss between them; the difference in static pressure between the same points will give the same result only if the fluid velocities at both points are the same. When the velocity of a fluid stream in a horizontal conduit is decreased by a diverging section, the velocity head is decreased and the static head increased. Thus it is quite possible to have a downstream static pressure that is higher than upstream, even though there is a loss in total pressure in the direction of flow.

See Chapter 21, Testing and Measurements, for draft-loss observations in the field.

STACK EFFECT

Flow of hot gas or hot air in a vertical duct introduces a factor of correction for elevation. Because the fluid in the duct has a lower density than the outside air, *stack or chimney effect or thermal static draft* exists. The pressure drop for downward flow increases, and it decreases for upward flow, compared to what the pressure drop would normally be under the same conditions in a horizontal duct. This stack-effect correction may be of considerable magnitude when determining the true pressure drop or draft loss in a tall piece of apparatus, and can be of particular significance in a series of boiler passages and flues, with the direction of the gas flow alternately up and down.

The static draft, as this difference in pressure can be properly called, must be calculated, since simple draft-gage readings indicate the combined values of stack-effect and frictional flow losses. The calculation is done using the following formula:

$$p = 27.7 \, Z_c \left(\frac{P_a}{R_a T_a} - \frac{P_c}{R_c T_c} \right) \tag{35}$$

where the height under consideration is Z_c feet, p_a and p_c are the absolute pressures (psia) of the ambient atmosphere and the combustion gas, respectively, T_a and T_c are the average absolute temperatures, and R_a and R_c are the respective gas constants. The value of R_a is 53.3, while that of R_c depends upon the composition of the gases. At usual excess-air percentages, R_c is 52.2 for bituminous coal, 53.2 for fuel oil, 55.6 for natural gas, and 49.3 for blast-furnace gas.[47]

Note that the equation for static draft involves only one dimension, the height of the gas pass or stack, and that the static draft is the maximum that can be produced by any such pass of a given height when filled with stationary gases of a given density and surrounded by a still atmosphere of a given density.

DRAFT-LOSS CALCULATIONS

The variables in the pressure differential across the convection surface of a steam-generating unit include friction due to flow across tubes; loss of head in turns; friction due to flow through, or parallel to, tubes; and stack effect. Named in order of magnitude, they occur in practically all steam generating units.

Gas and air velocities in steam-generating units will always be such as to produce turbulent flow, particularly at the high ratings. Under these conditions friction loss, when measured in terms of inches of water, will vary directly as the square of the mass velocity, and inversely as density, which also means directly with the absolute temperature. Eqs. 36, 37, and 38 show the mechanics of friction loss for the three types itemized above.

Flow across tubes	$PD = fN H_v$	(36)
Turn loss	$PD = K \times H_v$	(37)
Flow along tubes	$PD = f \dfrac{L}{D} \times H_v$	(38)

where:

PD = pressure drop, "WG

f = friction factor, dimensionless

N = number of restrictions

K = constant, depending on type of turns

L = length of tube in ft

D = inside diameter, or equivalent diameter in ft

H_v = velocity head, "WG

The velocity head is calculated from Eq. 39.

$$H_v = 0.0002307 \frac{(G/1000)^2}{d} \tag{39}$$

where:

G = mass velocity, lb/hr-sq ft free area

d = density lb/cu ft

For flow across tubes, the friction factor will

Fig. 24 Mass flow versus Reynolds number

depend on the tube diameter and arrangement, and on the Reynolds number, which is in turn directly proportional to velocity and tube diameter, and inversely proportional to the viscosity of the gas. Of the two main variables, the tube arrangement is by far the more important. Generally the friction loss from flow across staggered tubes is considerably greater than for tubes in a line. When tubes are in line, however, the friction loss will increase as the spacing in the direction of gas flow is increased. When that spacing reaches approximately four times the tube diameter, the friction loss will be the same, whether the tubes are in line or staggered. It is not within the scope of this text to discuss in detail the variation of friction factor with tube arrangement. A close approximation, however, is 0.24 when the tubes are in line, and 0.36 for staggered tubes.

The number of restrictions will be equal to the number of tube rows crossed over, unless the tubes are so staggered that the minimum free area for the passage of air or gas is determined by the diagonal clearance between adjacent tubes. If that is the case, the number of restrictions will be the number of tube rows minus one.

A calculation of draft loss across 22 rows of tubes in a convection bank, with the tubes on a square pitch of 3½" is as follows:

$$\frac{S_T}{D} = \frac{\text{Transverse Spacing}}{\text{Outside diameter of tube}} = \frac{3\frac{1}{2}''}{2\frac{1}{2}''} = 1.4$$

$$\frac{S_L}{D} = \frac{\text{Longitudinal Spacing}}{\text{Outside diameter of tube}} = \frac{3\frac{1}{2}''}{2\frac{1}{2}''} = 1.4$$

Reynolds number (from Fig. 24)

$$20,000 \times \frac{2\frac{1}{2}''}{10''} = 5000$$

Friction factor, f (from Fig. 25) = 0.092

Draft loss per restriction (from Fig. 26) = 0.027

Draft loss through

bank $(0.027) \dfrac{(0.092)}{(0.100)} (22) = 0.55''$ WG

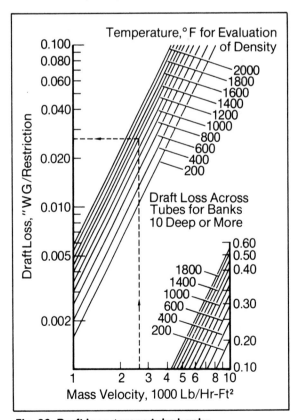

Fig. 25 Friction factors for in-line tube banks

Fig. 26 Draft loss across tube banks

DRAFT LOSSES IN DUCTWORK

Ductwork systems form a substantial part of a pulverized-coal steam generator, both in physical size and in cost. The principal elements are (a) the main cold- and hot-air ducts from the forced-draft fans to the air preheaters, and then to the furnace; (b) the hot gas ducts from the economizer to the air heater(s) and then to the emission-control equipment and on to the induced-draft fans; and (c) the high-pressure primary-air ducts from the primary-air fans to the air heaters and on to the pulverizers. Smaller ducts are needed for sealing air to pulverizers and other equipment, and ignitor and scanner cooling air.

To determine the size and performance of these ducts, the designer must first establish the predicted maximum flows, the allowable duct velocities (based on company standards and parasitical-power costs), and both the ambient barometric pressure and the effect of localized pressures in the ducts above or below the ambient barometric pressure.

AIR AND GAS VOLUME CALCULATIONS

Air and gas weights result from the combustion calculations plus considerations of tempering air, air-heater leakage, and casing infiltration. To convert gas weight to cubic feet per minute (CFM) at sea level (14.7 psia), use this relation.

$$CFM = \frac{W_g (T + 460)}{(MW)_g \, 82.2}$$

(40)

where CFM is the cu ft/min of air or gas at temperature T in °F, W_g is the air or gas weight in lb/hr, and MW is the apparent molecular weight of the air or gas mixture in pounds.

This volumetric flow rate at 14.7 psia has to be corrected for plant elevation above sea level using Fig. 6 and for local pressure in the ductwork system. Fig. 27 illustrates the varia-

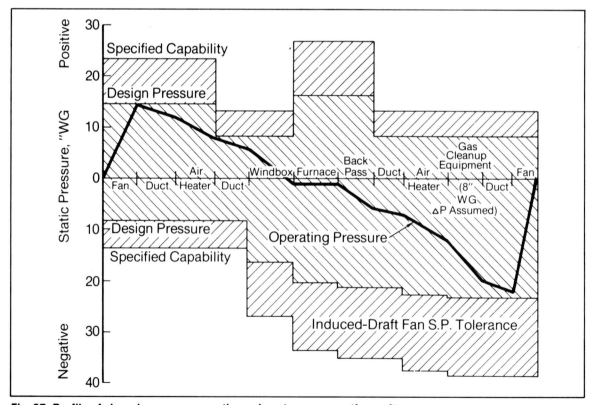

Fig. 27 **Profile of air and gas pressures through a steam generating unit**

tion in pressure that exists in a ductwork system from FD-fan inlet to ID-fan outlet. Actual gas volumes at each point of interest must be calculated using a correction curve like Fig. 28.

VELOCITIES IN DUCTS

As a general rule, the following velocities are used in arriving at the cross-sectional flow areas of boiler ducts.

Cold-air ducts	2000 to 2500 ft/min
Hot-air ducts	3000 to 3500 ft/min
Gas ducts	3500 to 4000 ft/min

Velocities can be higher at higher temperatures because the gas is less dense and therefore has less impact energy; lower static-pressure loss results for a given temperature.

DUCT-LOSS DETERMINATION

Air pressure and gas draft losses are a power function of velocity (approximately the square) and an inverse fuction of the specific volume of the fluid. The most significant losses occur in turns and at abrupt changes in flow area. Vaning is often necessary to reduce losses where there are tight turns or large variations in cross-section, such as between an air-heater outlet and a precipitator inlet (where the gas velocity drops below 10 ft/sec).

Curves such as those in Figs. 29 and 30 are used to proportion ductwork for desired pressure or draft losses. They show that, for very large ducts, the resistance may be practically independent of length and almost wholly dependent on the design of bends.

DRAFT LOSS IN STACKS

A stack can operate to produce a net static draft or flow of gas because it contains a column of heated gas and is connected at its base, indirectly through the breeching and boiler, to the cooler outside air. To do so, the acceleration loss of the gas and the friction loss from boiler, ductwork, and stack must be overcome by the theoretical differential static head between the hot and cold column, which in turn depends on the height of the hot column and the density of the gas. (See Eq. 35.)

Stack performance curves are usually plotted for sea-level gas density, and corrections are made for elevations above sea level. It is obvious, however, that weather conditions which reduce barometric pressure have the same effect in reducing the capacity of a stack as if it were located at a higher altitude. Stack selection, or calculation of its performance, requires the determination of:

- gas weight to be handled
- mean gas density within stack at elevation
- air density outside the stack, at elevation

Fig. 28 Volumetric correction factor for negative pressure below the local barometric pressure. This provides an additional correction to the basic elevation correction curve, Fig. 6, to adjust for pressures in a steam generator that are below the local atmospheric pressure. Calculated from the data of Standard Atmosphere—Tables and Data to 65,800 feet, NACA Report 1235

The gas quantity calculation must make allowance for the number of boilers connected to the stack, the maximum excess air at which they may be operated, and the air leakage through idle units as well as through the many duct connections.

The gas-density calculation involves a knowledge of the gas temperature from each unit, and the effect of air leakage on the total mixture temperature. Heat losses in emission-control equipment, ductwork, and the stack itself must also be considered, because it is the *mean* density in the stack that must be calculated.

The barometric pressure at plant elevation must be taken into account, because it affects the density of both the heated column inside the stack and the cold column of outside air.

Fig. 31 is a convenient graphical method of analyzing a stack of given diameter and height for the net effect of thermal draft versus friction loss. It is plotted for an 80°F ambient temperature and sea level pressure of 29.92 in. Hg. The net gain or loss must be divided by the elevation correction factor (Fig. 6) for elevation above sea level, or for a depressed barometer from atmospheric conditions that have to be taken into account.

The effective height of the stack, rather than the actual height, is used with Fig. 31 as in any stack-effect calculation. If allowance has been made for static draft in all apparatus and connections between the boiler and the stack, then the effective height is the distance between the top of the stack and the centerline of the opening in the stack where the gas enters.

SPECIFYING POWER-PLANT FANS

Specifying the required operating conditions for fans at various load points is generally left to the boiler manufacturer. The fan manufacturer assumes responsibility for producing the volume and pressure specified although limited by the fact that standard fan test codes specify certain conditions which can be maintained in a formal testing setup but which are seldom if ever duplicated in an actual installation. It is thus practically impossible, or at least very expensive, to determine comparable performance of laboratory and field conditions. Furthermore, the connections made to a fan may affect its performance to such an extent that it would be unwise to select it without reasonably large pressure and volume tolerances unless it were shop tested with inlet and outlet connections identical to those to be used under service conditions. In this connection it is always desirable to submit the layout of ductwork connected to fans to the fan manufacturer for evaluation and comments.

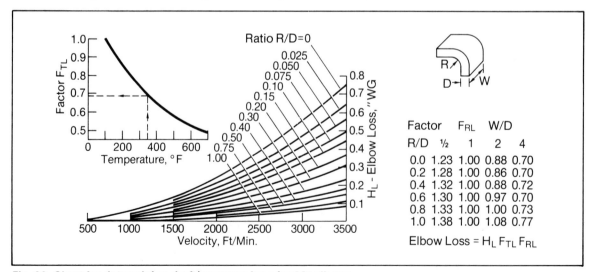

Fig. 29 **Chart for determining draft/pressure loss for 90° elbows**

FORCED DRAFT FANS

The requirements of FD fans are calculated from the fuel fired and the excess air. For pressurized firing, the calculation is quite accurate as all air passes through the FD fans. For balanced-draft units, the calculation is more complicated as the excess air measurement does not usually correspond to the air through the FD fans. Other sources of airflow into the unit are setting infiltration and tempering air.

Infiltration and Tempering

Determined by tightness of expansion joints, observation and access doors and other penetrations of the boiler casing infiltration varies with life, operation and maintenance of the unit. Moisture in the fuel determines tempering air which is high with dry coal and low with wet coal. In assigning values for infiltration and tempering note that too high an estimate of airflow through fan and air preheater results in low predicted exit-gas temperature.

Effect of Air Temperature

The temperature and elevation of the fan above sea level both affect the density of the air, which in turn affects the capacity of the fan. The moisture content of the air, especially for tropical conditions, also has to be taken into account.

If air preheater protection such as a steam coil is provided *ahead* of the fan, the air temperature leaving must be considered. If hot-air recirculation is used for air preheater protection, then both temperature and extra volume must be considered.

Pressure Specification

On balanced-draft units the required static head is the sum of all series resistances in the secondary air system, including cold air duct, steam air heater, air preheater, air metering device, hot air duct, dampers and burner pressure drop. On pressure-fired units the additional loss from the furnace to the stack outlet must also be included in determining total system resistance. Where stack effect is present, it must also be considered in determining total head requirement of the fan.

Selection

The volume and static pressure calculated according to the foregoing give the actual required fan capacity under predicted operating conditions. The calculation assumes excess air, steady load, tight casing, normal fuel and commercially clean surfaces as might be expected during an acceptance test. These actual conditions are needed to evaluate power consumption at the various loads, select the control equipment and provide a fan that will operate at maximum efficiency at the desired normal output of the steam-generating unit.

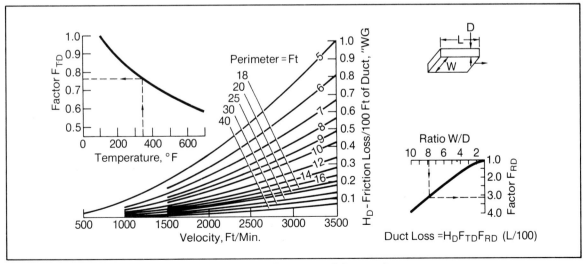

Fig. 30 **Chart for determining friction loss for straight runs of ductwork**

Fig. 31 **Net draft (thermal static draft minus friction loss) versus gas velocity and stack diameter at 80°F ambient temperature and 29.92″ Hg**

Fig. 32 **Typical gas-recirculation system**

These actual calculated operating conditions should not be used as maximum requirements in purchasing the fan. At times it may be necessary and desirable to operate with more excess air, or the actual temperature at the fan may be higher than anticipated, or the fan may not be up to expectations because of poor inlet and discharge conditions. Therefore, when specifying conditions for fan selection, liberal excess factors such as the following are generally applied to both volume and pressure:

■ balanced-draft unit, 25 percent excess volume, 50 percent excess static pressure

■ pressure-fired unit, 20 percent excess volume, 25 percent excess static pressure

These values may, of course, be modified if extreme conservatism was used in arriving at the so-called actual requirements, or if they were calculated for an unusual peak load well above the desired MCR of operation.

INDUCED-DRAFT FAN

The induced-draft fan is usually positioned at the outlet of the terminal heat recovery apparatus. It may be located either ahead of, or after, the dust collector. Sometimes it is an integral part of, and built into, the stack base. This fan therefore must handle the gas resulting from combustion of the fuel as well as all infiltration occurring up to the fan inlet, including leakage in the air preheater.

Volume Specifications

The volume requirements of ID fans are figured at the calculated density existing at the fan inlet. Based on the flue-gas temperature entering the fan, density should also be corrected for elevation above sea level and, of course, be based on the actual specific volume of the products of combustion at the excess air percentage leaving the last piece of heat-transfer or emission-control equipment.

Flue-gas weight on which the volume is based is calculated from the fuel requirements and excess air. This gas weight should include moisture from fuel, from combustion of hydrogen, and from the air or any other source.

The flyash carried in the flue gas from a pulverized-coal fired unit does not appreciably increase the total volume of the mixture handled, even though it does increase density. The presence of ash may increase the power requirements of the drive for a given speed and capacity. But since ash will generally be less than five grains/cu ft, no allowance need be made other than for fan excess factors recommended in "Selection" subsection below.

Pressure Specification

The ID-fan must provide a static head equal to the series resistance from the furnace to stack outlet, including resistance of superheater, reheater, boiler bank, economizer, air preheater, dust collector and all ductwork. Besides resistances, the net stack effect must be included together with required furnace draft in arriving at the total draft requirement of the ID fan.

Selection

The volume and static pressure calculated in accordance with the foregoing give the actual required fan capacity under good operating conditions, with assumed excess air, commercially clean surfaces and normal leakage values. As with the FD fan, such conditions are needed for evaluating power, setting controls and providing a fan that will operate at maximum efficiency at desired normal output of the boiler, but the actual calculated operating conditions should not be used as maximum requirements in purchasing the fan. Operation at higher excess air may be advisable; higher amounts of gas recirculation may be used; leakage and infiltration may be higher than estimated; surfaces may be dirty, which will increase temperature as well as resistance; and the fan may not perform to expectations because of poor inlet and discharge connections. Therefore, in specifications for ID fans, liberal excess factors are generally applied to both volume and pressure, as follows: 20 percent excess volume and 30 percent excess static pressure. As with the FD fan, these figures may be modified if extreme conservatism was used in arriving at the so-called actual requirements, or if they were calculated for an unusual peak load well above the desired maximum continuous rate of operation.

GAS RECIRCULATION FAN

For the same size unit and the same amount of heat released by the fuel, oil firing requires much larger heating surfaces in the superheater and reheater than for coal firing. Much of this relatively expensive surface can be eliminated by increasing the gas mass flow through the convection passes, using gas recirculation. This is common on straight oil-fired units and is a good solution for combination coal and oil units. The gas recirculating duct system is shown in Fig. 32. Gas is tapped off the main gas duct at point A, passes through the gas recirculating fan and enters the bottom of the furnace at B. Damper C controls the flow and is part of the steam temperature control system.

The gas recirculation fan is necessary to overcome the pressure differential between the furnace and the economizer outlet. If for any reason the fan is shut down while the boiler is in operation, high temperature furnace gas would flow backward through the fan and ducts, which are not designed to withstand such temperatures. Therefore shutoff damper D, automatically closes when the fan stops. However, even the best shutoff damper has some leakage, so higher pressure air is tapped off the main duct at point E. The shutoff damper F is ordinarily shut, but opens automatically with closing of the other shutoff damper. There will then be a small flow of air in both directions from point G thus protecting all equipment that might be damaged.

Volume Specifications

The amount of recirculation needed to make steam temperature at the control load determines the volume requirements of the GR fan. Specifying the flue-gas volume to be handled together with the gas temperature is a matter for the superheater designer to determine. However, it must be given at both the upper and lower end of the operating range of the gas-recirculation requirement.

Pressure Specifications

Gas-recirculation flow results in pressure drops throughout the GR system, including ducts, dampers and dust collector. Because the amount of gas recirculated adds to and is common with the main gas flow through the superheater, reheater and economizer, it also increases the drops through these. It is these latter resistances which generally dominate in establishing the total head requirements of the recirculation fan.

At control load or some other partial boiler load, GR requirements are maximum. But because the main gas flow is low, the total head requirements of the recirculation fan are moderate. At full boiler load, little or no gas recirculation may be required. However, since the main gas flow through the boiler is high, the pressure differential across the superheater, reheater and economizer is high and the recirculation fan must produce a high static head to balance this differential. In selecting the fan, the relationship of fan head to the differential is a critical factor to consider.

If at any point over its operating range the fan could not develop enough head to overcome the differential developed by the boiler, backflow of furnace gas will result through the fan with very serious consequences.

To protect against this condition, it is usual to specify as a minimum point on the fan characteristic a pressure at least 2 in. wg. above the maximum superheater-reheater-economizer differential at full load on the boiler. Normally, control-load requirements dictate fan size. The following are usual excess percentages applied to the calculated requirements at this load: 15 to 20 percent volume excess, with the static pressure boost adjusted to accommodate the increased volume.

STRESS ANALYSIS AND STRUCTURAL DESIGN OF STEAM GENERATOR COMPONENTS

In a steam generator design, the structural integrity of the pressure parts and their supports is of major concern. Not only must the drums, headers, and tubing withstand all the pressure stresses under hostile conditions of high temperature and, frequently, corrosive atmospheres, but they must also retain their positions, contour, and roundness under a variety of externally imposed loads. Extremely sophisticated analyses of the involved stresses must be made of both the pressure-retaining parts and their supporting hanger rods, U-bolts, lugs, and structural members.

This section describes the important aspect of the boiler design engineer's work that can be called "designing for structural performance."

MATERIALS SELECTION FOR SUPERHEATERS AND REHEATERS

From the view point of thermodynamics, the power-plant cycle efficiency is related to primary and reheat steam temperatures. A steam temperature increase improves the cycle efficiency, everything else being the same. However, superheater and reheater outlet conditions are limited by the ability of materials to withstand physical stress and by economic breakeven points.

In the high temperature region of boilers, allowable stress goes down as materials are exposed to high flue-gas temperatures necessary to superheat and reheat steam to high temperatures. At the same time, more costly grades of alloy steel are required to withstand the physical stress imposed by elevated temperatures and pressures.

As an example of temperature increase effect, the allowable stress for a material known as SA-213 T-11 drops from 11,000 psi at 950°F to 6600 psi at 1000°F. Up to 850°F it is usually possible to specify carbon steel, but beyond this point more costly alloys are required.

In view of these facts, selection of materials is a most important consideration in superheater and reheater design. Proper material selection requires knowledge not only of metal temperature conditions but also of the economics of manufacture and fabrication of various steel alloys. These aspects are amplified in Chapters 10 and 18 on materials and metallurgy, and manufacturing. A systematic procedure to calculate the metal temperatures of super-

heater and reheater tubing is explained in the following subsection.

SUPERHEATER AND REHEATER METAL TEMPERATURES

Before proceeding to make metal temperature calculations, the designer assumes the following data to be known for the point in question:

- gas temperature, T_g
- steam temperature at the point in question, t_s
- mass velocity of gas, G_g
- mass velocity of steam, G_s
- tubing size and estimated thickness
- tubing material
- steam pressure
- heat absorbed, q, Btu/hr.

(1) Total heat-transfer rate, R_t (as defined in previous section on boiler calculations):

$$R_t = R_c + R_n \tag{41}$$

(2) Total heat absorption rate per unit area, $\frac{q}{A_o}$ is calculated from

$$\frac{q}{A_o} = R_t (T_g - t_s) \tag{42}$$

By knowing R_t, t_s and T_g the localized heat absorption rate per unit area can be obtained.

If the superheater or reheater tube in question is subject to direct furnace radiation, this should be taken into consideration in Eq. 42. Fig. 33 is a polar plot of a reheater tube facing the furnace, showing the higher metal temperature rise on the front face of the tube compared to the back or downstream side.

(3) Steam side film conductance of heat transfer h_c:

After the heat absorption per unit area is determined, the next step is to establish steam side film conductance of heat transfer, h_c. By dimensional analysis and experimental work, a general relationship is developed to calculate the film conductance for forced convection in fluids. This may be evaluated from the equation $(Nu) = a(Re)^b(Pr)^c$, where $a \doteq 0.023$, $b = 0.8$, $c = 0.4$ and the terms are respectively Nusselt, Reynolds and Prandtl numbers. The correlation may then be expressed as follows.

$$\frac{h_c D}{k} = 0.023 \left(\frac{DG}{\mu}\right) 0.8 \left(\frac{c_p \mu}{k}\right) 0.4 \tag{43}$$

where D is an expression of applicable diameter, k is the thermal conductivity of the fluid, G is the mass velocity, μ is the absolute viscosity of the fluid and c_p is the specific heat at constant pressure. The values of a, b and c are determined experimentally and should be used with discretion, taking into consideration results available in heat-transfer literature.

(4) Steam side film temperature drop, Δt_s:

By knowing the heat absorption rate per unit area and steam side film conductance of heat transfer, the steam side film temperature drop can be obtained from the following relationship.

$$\Delta t_s = \frac{q}{A_o} \frac{1}{h_c} \frac{D_o}{D_i} \tag{44}$$

where D_o is the outside diameter of tube and D_i is the inside diameter of tube. The D_o/D_i term appears in the above formula because q/A_o was based on outside diameter of tube.

(5) Tube wall temperature drop, ΔT:

Temperature drop through tube can be calculated from the conduction equation:

$$\Delta T = \frac{q}{A_o} D_o \log_e \frac{D_o}{D_i} \frac{1}{2k} \tag{45}$$

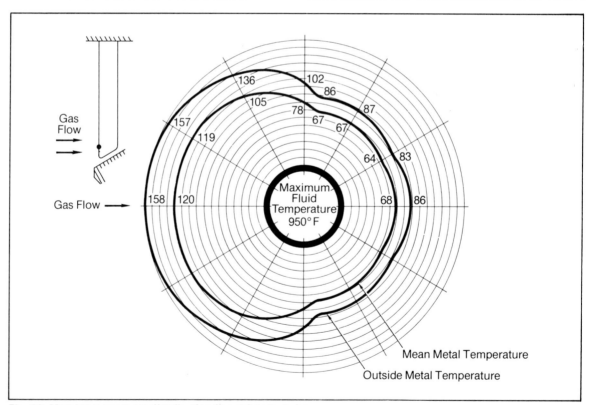

Fig. 33 Metal temperature distribution in a reheater tube

where k is the thermal conductivity of the tube for which the temperature is being calculated.

The tube metal temperature at any given point in the tubing will be the sum of the steam temperature, film temperature drop and average tube wall temperature drop.

METAL TEMPERATURE TOLERANCES

The preceding represents an ideal case based on the assumptions that the steam flow rate and temperature and gas flow rate and temperature are uniform for all the elements. These conditions actually are never experienced in the performance of the steam generator. It is necessary therefore to provide so called "unbalances" or tolerances that are anticipated. These include the following:

■ Desuperheater allowance which is the number of degrees that the steam temperature will rise at the particular point upstream of the superheater when the full use of the desuperheater is made. Usually the design is such that little or no desuperheating is required. However, when a desuperheater is installed all pressure parts ahead of the desuperheater are designed to include the desuperheater allowance.

■ Steam temperature unbalance which allows for the increase in average steam temperature at a given point caused by the unbalanced distribution in steam flows, gas flows and gas temperatures.

■ Film and metal drop unbalance which is considered to be the increase in the calculated average film and metal temperature drop caused by the unbalanced distribution in the gas flows and gas temperatures.

The maximum metal temperature at any given point in the tubing will be the sum of the steam temperature, film and metal temperature drops, desuperheater allowance—if any, steam temperature unbalance and film and metal drop unbalance.

After the metal temperature is established, the selection of material may be made in accordance with the *ASME* Boiler and Pressure Vessel Code. Section I of the Code covering power boilers gives details for calculating tube wall thickness and the allowable stress values for the various materials. In superheater and reheater design it has been found desirable to limit the use of various materials according to the oxidation-resistance limits in Table IV.

They are in all cases lower than maximum permissible metal temperatures established by the *ASME* Boiler and Pressure Vessel Code.

PRESSURE-DROP CALCULATIONS

Another aspect of the design of superheaters, reheaters and economizers, that relates to the selection of materials in previous paragraphs is the steam or water pressure drop that occurs in operation. Just as there is a semi-proportional relationship between transfer rate and draft loss, as previously explained, there is a similar connection between pressure drop and metal temperature. That is, the fluid film thickness inside a heated tube is affected by the mass flow of fluid through the tube. And pressure drop is roughly a square function of the mass flow.

In evaluating whether a given pressure drop is too high through any proposed circuitry, the principal concerns most often are (a) the design

Table IV. Maximum Outside-Surface Metal Temperatures

ASME Code Alloy Specification	Nominal Composition	Oxidation Limit, °F
SA-213	Carbon Steel	850
SA-213 T-1	Carbon- ½ Mo	900
SA-213 T-11	1¼ Cr- ½ Mo	1025
SA-213 T-22	2¼ Cr- 1% Mo	1075
SA-213 T-9	9 Cr- 1 Mo	1175
SA-213 TP 304H	18 Cr- 8 Ni	1300
SA-213 TP 347H	18 Cr-10Ni	1300

pressure of upstream pressure parts, and (b) the power penalty for any increment of pressure drop versus the cost of using more expensive alloys in superheater or reheater tubing to reduce wall thickness and, thereby, the pressure drop. An example of the first situation is the influence on boiler drum and waterwall tubes and headers of the superheater pressure drop: the superheater drop is added to the required superheater-outlet pressure to arrive at the operating pressure in the drum, the furnace walls, the risers, and the downtakes. With tolerances specified by the *ASME Code*, the actual design or working pressure of the steam generator is established. The higher the superheater pressure drop, the higher the ASME design pressure for the entire unit, which has a direct effect on the thickness and cost of the pressure parts.

Basic Pressure-Drop Equations

The following equations are used for water and steam pressure-drop calculations on subcritical-pressure boilers, and are similar to those for supercritical units.

Water flowing through pipes and tubing:

$$\Delta P = \frac{1.4 \times F^{1.85} L}{10^3 D^{4.85}}$$

$$\text{(46)}$$

where

F = flow per path, 1000 lb/hr

L = length of tube plus equivalent length of bends, ft

D = inside diameter in inches

Steam flowing through tubing, up to 6″ O.D.:

$$\Delta P = \frac{4.11 \times F^{1.85} V L}{10^4 D^{4.97}}$$

$$\text{(47)}$$

Steam flow through pipes:

$$\Delta P = 1.306 \left(1 + \frac{3.6}{D}\right) \frac{L V F^2}{D^5}$$

$$\text{(48)}$$

where

F = flow per path, lb/min

V = specific volume, cu ft/lb

and L and D are as defined above.

For determining the total equivalent length of a circuit, the following factors are used, where the equivalent length is equal to the factor multiplied by the inside diameter (ID) of the tubing. Thus, a 180° bend in a tube with 2 in. ID has an equivalent length (for use in Eq. 46, 47, 48) of 30 × 2 = 60 in. = 5 ft.

Equivalent Lengths

	MULTIPLYING FACTOR ON ID
Entrance loss	30
Exit loss	30
Squeezed return bend	50
180° bend	30
90° bend	25
45° bend	15
90° short radius elbow	24
90° long radius elbow	12

Entrance and exit losses are applied to the junctions between tubes and headers. A squeezed

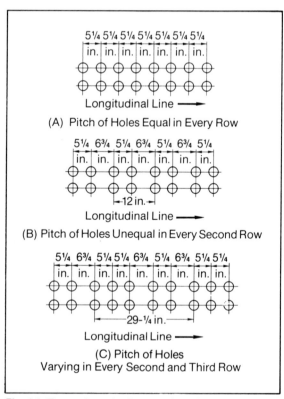

Fig. 34 Examples of tube spacings in drums or headers

return bend is one with a bend radius less than the tube outside diameter (OD). A 90° short-radius elbow is defined as having a bend radius less than 3 times the pipe OD. Anything greater is considered a long-radius elbow.

MECHANICAL STRESSES IN DRUMS, HEADERS AND PIPING

Industrial safety codes, such as the *ASME Code*, provide the designer with acceptable formulas for sizing various components of a pressure vessel. Typical formulas making use of equations from the basic theory of elasticity for specific shells of revolution presented here are taken from Section I, Rules for Construction of Power Boilers, of the *ASME Code*.[48]

SPHERICAL SHELL

The minimum thickness, t, of a spherical shell of inside radius, R, for a design maximum allowable working pressure, P, and a maximum allowable working stress, S, all in consistent units, is

$$t = \frac{P\,R}{2 \times S \times E - 0.2\,P}$$

(49)

on an elastic shell basis.

In this equation, E is the efficiency of the weakest joint used in forming the shell, expressed as a decimal, and called the ligament efficiency. It is based on the pitch, diametral size, and configuration of the holes in a drum or header. For openings that form a definite pattern in pressure parts, the efficiency of ligament between the tube holes is determined per paragraph PG-52 of Section I of the Code.

When the pitch of the tubes on every tube row is equal, as in Fig. 34, the formula is

$$E = \frac{p - d}{p}$$

(50)

where p is the longitudinal pitch of adjacent openings and d is the diameter of the openings, in consistent dimensions, and E is the efficiency of ligament, as a decimal. For a pitch of 5¼ in. and tube-hole diameter of $3^9/_{32}$ in., efficiency is $(5.25 - 3.28)/5.25 = 0.375$.

When the pitch of the tube holes on any one row is unequal, the formula is

$$E = \frac{p_1 - n\,d}{p_1}$$

(51)

where p_1 is the pitch between corresponding openings in a series of symmetrical groups of openings and n is the number of openings in length p_1. The pitch in these equations is measured either on the flat plate before rolling or on the median surface after rolling.

For the spacing shown in Fig. 34 B, the efficiency is $(12 - 2 \times 3.281) / 12 = 0.453$. For the spacing in Fig. 34 C, ligament efficiency is $(29.25 - 5 \times 3.281)/29.25 = 0.439$.

The strength of those ligaments between tube holes that are subjected to a longitudinal stress shall be at least one-half the required strength of the ligaments coming between the tube holes which are subjected to a circumferential stress. When tubes or holes are arranged in a drum or shell in symmetrical groups along lines parallel to the axis and the same spacing is used for each group, no group efficiency shall be less than that on which the maximum allowable working pressure is based.

Eq. 51 gives the correct thickness for thin-walled shells, but when the thickness of the shell is greater than about 0.36 R, the elastic theory requires that thickness be calculated on a thick-wall basis. The formula for thickness is

$$t = R \left[\sqrt[3]{\frac{2(SE + P)}{2SE - P}} - 1 \right]$$

(52)

CYLINDRICAL SHELL

The minimum thickness for a thin-wall cylindrical shell for piping, drums, and headers in the steam generator is

$$t = \frac{PR}{SE - (1 - y)\,P} + C$$

(53)

where C is an additional allowance for threading and structural stability and y is a temperature coefficient, as in Table V.

For thick-wall cylinders, in which the thickness is greater than one-half the inside radius, the elastic theory requires that the shell wall thickness be determined from

$$t = R \left(\sqrt{\frac{SE + P}{SE - P}} - 1 \right)$$

(54)

HEMISPHERICAL HEAD

The formulas for a hemispherical head are identical to those for a spherical shell. Either industrial-code rules or the theory of elasticity give the required thicknesses for these shells.[49] If a pressure vessel consists of a cylindrical shell capped with a hemispherical head, the component sizes can be determined by codes or by the theory of elasticity using the simple membrane formulas.

SEMIELLIPSOIDAL HEAD

The standard semiellipsoidal head recognized by the *ASME* Code has half the minor axis, or the depth of the head, at least equal to one-quarter the inside diameter of the head. By elastic theory this head requires a thickness of

$$t = \frac{PR}{SE - (1 - y) P}$$

(55)

The R in the above equation is either the length of the major axis, or the diameter of the mating cylinder.

Table V. Temperature Coefficient y used in Design Calculations

Design Temperature	Up to 900°F	901° to 950°F	Above 950°F
y factor for ferritic steels	0.40	0.50	0.70

From Section I, *ASME* Boiler Code. Between temperatures listed, determine y by interpolation.

TORISPHERICAL HEAD

A torispherical head is a shell which combines part of a torus with a spherical cap. In the *ASME* Code the knuckle, or torus, radius is required to be 0.06 times the radius of the crown, or spherical cap, and the crown radius may not exceed the diameter of the pressure vessel. There are no directly applicable formulas based on elastic theory but any given head shape can readily be calculated from basic equations. The *ASME* Code specifies the thickness to be

$$t = \frac{5PL}{4.8SE}$$

(56)

where L is the radius to which the head is dished, measured on the concave side.

FLAT HEAD

A flat head can be considered as a circular plate which is uniformly loaded by pressure. The amount of end fixity depends on the method of mounting and the stiffness of the cylindrical shell to which the flat head is attached. If the plate is assumed to be simply supported, then no moments are transferred to the shell, and the maximum plate stress occurs at the center of the plate. The stress is:

$$S_{max} = \frac{3(3 + v)P\,R^2}{8t^2}$$

(57)

The degree of end fixity is determined by applied edge moments,

$$M_o = C_1 P\,R^2$$

and superposed stresses,

$$S_s = \frac{6M_o}{t^2}$$

By substituting allowable stresses in these equations, the required thickness of the plate can be expressed as:

$$t = d \sqrt{\frac{C_2 P}{S}}$$

(58)

where d is the inside diameter of the header at the flat end plate, and C_2 is a factor that depends on the method of attachment of the head and other items in Code paragraph PG-31.4.

Eq. 58 gives the thickness of a flat head as required by the *ASME* Code. The constant C_2 in the equation is a factor depending on the method of attachment of the head, and on the shell, pipe or header dimensions. It must be found from appropriate tables in the Code, and these tables usually specify the end fixity of the flat plate. In the industrial code, the constant is usually greater than that required by elastic theory, thereby adding another factor of safety to the code design.

DISCONTINUITY STRESSES

When a pressure vessel is subjected to internal pressure, redundant forces and moments are induced in areas of structural discontinuity such as the intersection of a cylindrical shell and a hemispherical head. This can best be visualized, Fig. 35, by assuming that the shell and head act as separate units with internal pressure applied to the individual, simply supported parts. Because the deflections of the components differ, shear forces and moments must be applied at the edges to rejoin the components for a compatible structure. The resulting stresses (usually bending stresses) induced by these shear forces and moments are called discontinuity stresses. The bending stresses reach a maximum at, or near, the dis-

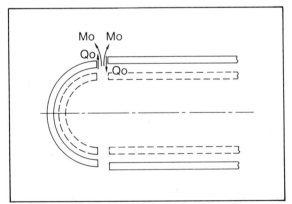

Fig. 35 Discontinuity forces at a head-cylinder junction under internal pressure

continuity, but they attenuate with distance from the joint.[50] A commonly accepted approach to the derivation of these discontinuity stresses is the theory of beams on an elastic foundation.[51]

If a pressure vessel with a hemispherical head is designed for minimum thickness of the mating components, then the maximum stress in the pressure vessel will be 27 percent higher than the circumferential stress in the cylindrical shell away from all discontinuities. On the other hand, for a vessel of uniform thickness, the maximum stress is only 3 percent higher than in the same size cylindrical shell.

A pressure vessel with a standard semiellipsoidal head of the same thickness as a mating cylindrical shell exhibits a maximum stress 13 percent higher than the circumferential membrane stress in the cylinder.[52] Unfortunately, membrane stresses and discontinuity stresses are very sensitive to changes in curvature.

REINFORCED OPENINGS

For very small unreinforced circular holes, the theory of elasticity shows that a stress concentration factor of three will exist around the hole under an uniaxial tension. The stress concentration is reduced to two for the state of biaxial tension. In a cylindrical shell under pressure, the state of stress is such that the circumferential stress is twice the longitudinal stress. Under this condition the stress concentration at an unreinforced penetration would reach a peak of 2.5. The stress concentration effect would be localized at the edge of the hole and could cause some plastic deformation with an inherent redistribution of stresses.

The *ASME* Code requires that, for holes larger than a certain diameter, reinforcement to the opening should be added by the nozzle attachment, increased shell thickness, or the pad for a cover plate if the opening is to be used for future servicing operations.

The Code's rules specify that the area removed for the penetration in a given cross section be reinforced within specified boundaries. At best this is a crude method; however, experience has shown that the stresses do not cause failure at nozzles if the level of stress in the shell is at a reasonable limit.[53] The best type of reinforcement is one in which the reinforcement is equally distributed on each side of the shell, that is, equal amounts of reinforcement extend inside and outside the shell.[54] This method of reinforcement is not always practical; most commonly, then, it is necessary that all the reinforcement must be on the outside of the shell.

STRESS ANALYSIS AND STRUCTURAL DESIGN OF FURNACE WALLS

Welded furnace walls are one of the most important components of boilers. They may be incorporated into the design of small shop-assembled boilers as well as in the largest utility-type units. Furnace walls, also frequently referred to as waterwalls, provide the enclosure around the major parts of a boiler and are integrally concerned with all of its essential functions. As a link in the steam generating cycle, they are components of the pressure parts system. The support of the furnace-wall system is linked to that of other components and will be discussed in the final section of this chapter dealing with structural design of boilers.

Welded furnace walls must be safe and reliable over a range of operating conditions. The furnace-wall tubes have the highest heat-flux rates in the boiler and are subjected to the most extreme fluctuations in temperature and pressure. During boiler startup the walls experience considerable overfiring and variable pressure conditions are encountered as the unit is brought up to its normal operating level. The furnace-wall enclosure must be designed to withstand both positive and negative inside pressures. In addition, special conditions sometimes occur in which the enclosure must withstand wind and earthquake loadings.

The crucial feature in the protection of a furnace-wall tube against failure is the assurance of adequate circulation of fluid within the tube under all operating conditions. For this reason, the thermodynamic requirement for the particular type of furnace determines the internal diameter of the wall tube. For some furnaces the wall will contain small-diameter tubing with thick walls while for other furnaces the tubing will be large diameter and relatively thin walls. Thus, mechanical behavior of furnace walls will vary greatly for different types of furnaces.

MECHANICAL LOADING OF FURNACE WALLS

Analytical and experimental techniques make it possible to determine the stresses in the furnace wall in considerable detail. With this knowledge and the realization that different stresses have different degrees of significance, the furnace walls are designed to give the desired thermal behavior, at the same time being safe and reliable.[55]

As a starting point, the tube thickness is determined to give the required internal diameter for proper thermal performance of the furnace. Since the tubes are a part of the pressure system of the steam generator, the determination of wall thickness is within the jurisdiction of Section I of the *ASME* Code.[48] Thus the equation used for tube thickness is

$$t = \frac{PD}{2S + P} + 0.005D$$

(59)

where t is thickness, P is fluid pressure, D is outside tube diameter and S is the allowable stress according to Table PG 23.1 of Section I, *ASME* Boiler and Pressure Vessel Code.

Following this procedure satisfies the *ASME* Code requirements for minimum tube wall thickness and gives a wall panel with the required flexibility to keep the thermal stresses within reasonable limits on severe thermal transients. Except under special conditions, a thicker wall tube does not improve the overall stress condition. As the pressure stress becomes smaller because of thicker tube, the thermal stress increases rather rapidly with greater wall thickness. A change to a better material is the most satisfactory method of gaining improvement in strength requirements.

Other mechanical loads also act on the furnace wall and must be analyzed to assure its reliability. Some of these additional loads are furnace firing pressure, dead weight loads, wind loads, earthquake loads and reactive loads that exist between the furnace wall and the rigid buckstay system.

DETERMINATION OF FURNACE STRESSES

The straight analytical determination of stresses in the furnace walls is difficult because of the complex geometry of the panel. To begin the calculation, it is necessary to assume a fin size. For a furnace panel with normal heat-absorption rates, the fin width will be about one half inch. With this close tube spacing, the wall can be considered a stiffened orthogonal plate. Using the notation of Timoshenko,[56] the differential equation of equilibrium for small displacements of an orthotropic plate is

$$D_x \frac{\partial^4 W}{\partial x^4} + 2(D_1 + 2D_{xy}) \frac{\partial^4 W}{\partial x^2 \partial y^2}$$

$$+ D_y \frac{\partial^4 W}{\partial y^4} = q \tag{60}$$

where W is the lateral displacement,

$$D_x = \frac{E_x' h^3}{12}, \quad D_y = \frac{E_y' h^3}{12},$$

$$D_1 = \frac{E'' h^3}{12}, \quad D_{xy} = \frac{G h^3}{12},$$

q is uniform lateral load, E is the modulus of elasticity and h is wall thickness.

The numerical computer techniques of finite elements are used to solve Eq. 60. The tube and fin geometry of the furnace wall is transformed into an equivalent orthotropic plate by the use of equivalent load functions as developed by C-E engineers. The mechanical loads such as furnace pressure, dead weight, buckstay loading, wind and earthquake and the thermal loads from temperature distributions are applied to an orthotropic finite element plate model of the furnace walls. The transformed equivalent orthotropic plate elements are used to model the furnace wall and beam elements are used for the buckstay system. The finite element mathematical model of the furnace is solved using one of the finite element computer programs such as "MARC-CE Nonlinear Finite Element Program" or the "STRUDL Finite Element Program". The computer program findings are resultant forces and moments acting on the various equivalent orthotropic plate elements of the furnace-wall model (Fig. 36).

BALANCED THERMAL LOADING

Balanced thermal loading is defined as that condition of balanced heat absorption from one side of the wall which will result in local variation of temperature that produce thermal stresses in tubes and fins. The local metal temperatures existing in a tube and fin depend on the panel geometry, the heat flux, inside film coefficient and the type of boiler. Fig. 37 gives an example for a Controlled Circulation® boiler of the performance of the four critical temperatures; at the outside, mean and inside diameter on the crown of the tube and at the fin tip, as a function of inside film coefficient. The curves illustrate the importance of maintaining a minimum inside film coefficient to keep the tube cool. Using the relationship between heat flux and nucleate boiling coefficient shown in Fig. 38, the actual maximum temperatures in

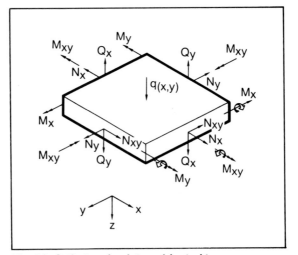

Fig. 36 **Orthotropic plate subjected to in-plane and lateral loads**

Fig. 37 **Furnace-wall tube temperature plot**

the tube and fin above the saturation temperature are plotted against flux rate in Fig. 39. This relationship is essentially proportional and demonstrates the range of absorption to which tubing and fin material may be exposed.

Temperature Distribution

The first step in determining the thermal stress in the fin and tube is to obtain a temperature distribution, T. The tube and fin respond with sufficient speed so that, at any given condition, this relationship can be approximated by the steady state.

Thus $\quad \nabla^2 T = 0$

where $\quad \nabla^2 T = \dfrac{\partial T^2}{\partial x^2} + \dfrac{\partial T^2}{\partial y^2}$

$$(61)$$

Numerical computer techniques are used to solve this differential equation. The CEWIND computer program for calculating temperature distributions is based on the finite difference method and provides directly the surface temperature and the internal temperature distributions. Fig. 40 shows some thermal isotherms generated by this program. Often a special computer tape will be made of the thermal results so that temperatures may be directly input to computer thermal stress programs.

The MARC-HEAT Computer Program will solve the same equation with a finite element type of analysis and has the advantage that the same finite element model may be used for both the thermal and stress analysis programs. However, stresses or strains require an extrapolation procedure.

The CE-NOAXCYL Nonlinear Axisymmetric Finite Element Analysis Program is a special purpose computer program which will provide a transient heat transfer analysis with non-axisymmetric loading on a symmetric tube and fin cross section. This program has the capability of making plastic and creep strain calculations if they are required.

Thermal Stresses

Thermal stresses occur in the tube and fin because the elements cannot deform freely. Some of the thermal stress results from differences between the mean temperature of the section and the local temperature. The remaining thermal stress is imposed on the tube and fin by the comparatively stiff buckstay system.

Fig. 38 **Correlation between heat flux and nucleate boiling**

***Fig. 39* Temperatures above saturation versus reheat flux**

A finite element model is made of the tube and fin geometry as shown in Fig. 41. If the temperature distributions of the tube and fin (Fig. 40) are input into one of the finite element computer programs such as "MARC-CE Nonlinear Finite Element Program" or "STRUDL" with proper boundary conditions, the computer will calculate thermal stresses and strains in the tube and fin geometry.

The forces and moments from the computer solution of the orthotropic furnace walls (Fig. 36) are applied to the tube and fin geometry as shown in Fig. 42. These forces and moments when used with the finite element model shown in Fig. 41 will generate additional local

stresses in the tube and fin geometry. The same finite element model is used to calculate the stresses and strains from the internal pressure applied to the tube. Combining and evaluating these stresses is covered later in this chapter.

UNBALANCED THERMAL LOADING

Unbalanced thermal loading is defined as temperature distribution which varies in either direction along the furnace wall. The variation in heat-absorption rates longitudinally and transversely across the wall is one reason for unbalanced temperature distribution. Fig. 39 shows how the metal temperatures vary with different heat absorption rates. Unbalances in the flow rate either in neighboring tubes or in different areas of the wall will give unbalanced temperatures. Flow rates in some boilers are very dependent on the heat absorption for a given tube. Further investigation reveals a very complex interplay between heat absorption and flow rates for some types of furnaces with conditions that can lead to large temperature unbalances. Fig. 40 shows temperature distributions for three different inside-film coefficients, which are strongly dependent upon flow rates. A third condition that will result in temperature variations in a furnace wall is that of varying fluid temperatures. In boilers of the

***Fig. 40* Temperature distribution in finned furnace-wall tubes**

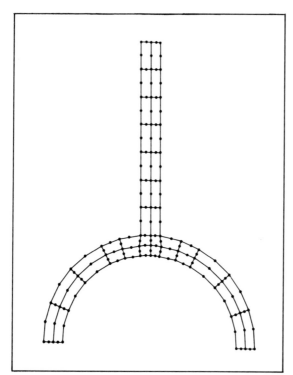

Fig. 41 **Finite element model of tube and fin**

once through type, the fluid temperature continually varies as the fluid progresses from inlet to outlet. In each case there is a very complex interaction between these conditions, and it is the responsibility of the boiler designer to select a suitable set of parameters so that the temperature unbalances will be within reasonable limits.

An experimental technique has been used to determine the stresses from the unbalanced thermal loadings. As an example, Fig. 43 shows a furnace wall panel under test at C-E's Kreisinger Development Laboratory. In this test controlled temperature distributions were imposed on the panel. To identify the influence of each type of discontinuity, electric strain gages placed on the outside surface of the panel, at its end, at its center, at the top bend, and at the soot blower opening determined the resulting strains.[57]

This experimental data has been used to evaluate the procedures for the equivalent orthotropic plate modeling of the furnace walls.

Unbalanced thermal distributions are applied to the furnace model and the resultant forces and moments determined with finite element analysis. Local effects of the resultant forces and moments on the tube and fin geometry are obtained by using the tube and fin finite-element model shown in Fig. 41.

SIGNIFICANCE OF CALCULATED STRESSES

The accurate and detailed determination of the mechanical and thermal stresses in the furnace wall is of little value until the designer knows how these stresses affect wall failure. A measured value of stress or strain has little meaning until it is associated with location and distribution in the panel and with the type of loading which produced it. For example, the average hoop stress in the tube from internal pressure has a different influence on the life of the panel than that of the peak stress at the intersection of the fin and tube from a redundant moment. An excessive hoop stress produces an instability in the tube which continues to grow and get thinner and thinner until rupture. On the other hand, the peak stress at the notch will relieve itself by yielding and only has a bearing on fatigue life or stress-rupture life.

To help evaluate the different types of stresses that may act on the wall, the various stresses are classified as primary, secondary, and local or peak stresses.

Fig. 42 **Geometrical configuration of tube and fin**

Primary Stress

A primary stress is a normal or shear stress developed by the imposed mechanical loading which is necessary to satisfy the laws of equilibrium of external and internal forces and moments. The basic characteristic of a primary stress is that it is not self-limiting. Primary stresses which exceed the yield strength will result in failure or gross distortion.

Secondary Stress

A secondary stress is a normal or shear stress developed by the constraint of an adjacent part or by self-constraint of a structure. The basic characteristic of a secondary stress is that it is self-limiting. Local yielding and minor distortion can satisfy the conditions which cause the stress. Thermal stresses which produce gross distortions are secondary stresses.

Local or Peak Stress

Local or *peak stress* is a normal or shear stress which is the highest in the region under consideration and is developed by changes in geometry such as a notch. Thermal stresses which are caused by self-constraint are treated as local stresses. The basic characteristic of a local or peak stress is that it causes no significant distortion and is objectionable only as a possible source of either a fatigue failure, brittle fracture, stress-corrosion cracking or stress-rupture failure. These categories also differentiate between a membrane stress (average value across a section) and a bending stress (linearly variable across a section).

COMBINATION OF STRESSES

The characteristic material values on which strength calculations are based are determined under uniaxial tension. Usually this is the common tension test. The furnace walls are subjected to multiaxial stress, and a direct comparison of the stress in the wall with the characteristic strength value of the material is not directly admissible. Only with the aid of a strength hypothesis is it possible to calculate an equivalent stress for comparison with the characteristic strength value as determined by the conventional tension test.

Maximum Shear Theory

The maximum shear stress theory is used as the failure criterion for the furnace walls. The selection of the maximum shear stress theory is based on the use of a good ductile steel for the furnace walls. According to the maximum shear theory, if the principal stresses are σ_1, σ_2, σ_3 and further if $\sigma_1 > \sigma_2 > \sigma_3$, the maximum shear stress is

$$\tau_{max} = \frac{\sigma_1 - \sigma_3}{2}$$

(62)

The equivalent stress to that of a simple tension or compression test would be

$$S = \sigma_1 - \sigma_3 = 2\tau_{max}$$

Called stress intensity, the equivalent stress is not a single stress quantity. Rather, it represents the combined stress of the three principal stresses or their equivalent. The addition of

***Fig. 43* Furnace-wall test apparatus at C-E Kreisinger Development Laboratory**

stresses from different categories must be performed at the component level, not after translating the stress components into stress intensities. Similarly the calculation of membrane stress intensity involves the averaging of stresses across a section and this averaging must be performed at the component level.

The allowable stresses except for the membrane stress have been derived from the same considerations that were used in writing Div 2 of Section VIII of the *ASME* Boiler and Pressure Vessel Code. It is an application of limit design theory tempered by engineering judgment and some conservative simplifications.

Allowable Membrane Stress

The first stress limit to consider is primary membrane stress. In this case the value is limited to the values as given in Table PG 23.1 of the Section I Rules for Construction of Power Boilers of the *ASME* Boiler and Pressure Vessel Code, since the tubing is part of the pressure system in the boiler.

Stress intensities are not determined because this section of the *ASME* Code is based on maximum stress theory.

Allowable Local Membrane or Bending Stress

In the remaining evaluation, the stress intensities are determined for comparison with the stress limits. The next limit is the sum of the primary membrane stress plus the primary bending stress plus any local membrane stress. These stresses are combined at the component level and then the stress intensity determined. This limit is set at 1.5 times the stress limits as given in Table PG 23.1 of Section I of *ASME* Code. In addition, if the temperatures are at the level where stress rupture is the mode of failure, the combined value is limited to those values given in the Table.

Allowable Secondary Stress

In the next consideration, the primary stresses (membrane and bending) are combined with the secondary stresses at the component level and the stress intensities determined. These values are limited to three times the values from Table PG 23.1 for temperatures below 700°F.

If the temperature is greater than 700°F, the influence of creep strains must be considered. Control of the secondary stresses is to limit deformations and to provide a valid basis for the elastic procedure for the fatigue analysis. When creep alters the stress distribution and increases the strain range, a high-temperature design procedure is required. For the low-alloy ferric materials the temperature range may increase to 850°F without serious creep strain.

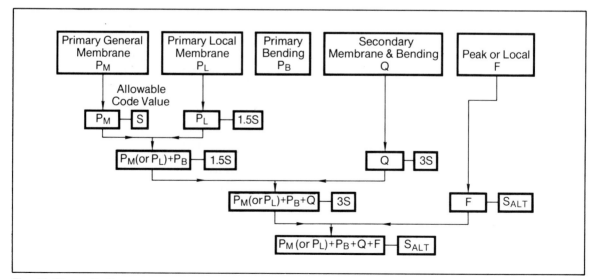

Fig. 44 **Stress limits**

Allowable Peak Stress

For the next evaluation all the stresses, primary, secondary and local are combined for both the maximum and minimum conditions of an operational cycle. From these values the maximum and minimum stress intensities can be determined. Using these stress intensities the alternating stress is calculated. These stresses are usually evaluated on a fatigue basis which will be discussed in the next section.

Where loads are at steady state or of very low cycle frequency and the temperatures are in the realm of stress rupture, the total stresses can be limited by yield stresses. In this region each material has a different behavior as influenced by notches and metallurgical changes. Therefore, a survey of the literature on the material should be made as an aid in the final evaluation. Fig. 44 summarizes the stress limits for the various stress categories.

FATIGUE ANALYSIS

The first step in the fatigue analysis is to estimate a stress history for the expected life of the unit. From this stress history, the different operating cycles, such as startups, shutdowns, load changes and other changes which cause the stress level in the wall to vary, can be determined. In each of these cases, the maximum and minimum stress intensities are determined. Alternating stress intensities can then be calculated by

$$S_{alt} = \frac{S_{max} - S_{min}}{2}$$

(63)

If these stresses are significant, they will use up part of the life of the unit. The number of times the significant alternating stresses can be repeated is determined from a design fatigue curve as shown in Fig. 45. In these curves the alternating stress is plotted as a function of the cycles to failure with suitable safety factors. Because safety factors vary considerably and are dependent upon the mechanical behavior of the material, the uncertainty of the assumed loads and the uncertainty in the material (scatter of data), specific values of the ordinate of typical curves are not given. Curves such as these are determined by experimental methods and may be found in the literature. Some fatigue curves for materials normally used in furnace design can be found in Section III of the *ASME* Boiler and Pressure Vessel Code. These are believed to reflect a conservative design.

In the furnace wall the stresses on both sides of the wall must be determined. The trend of the decrease in fatigue life as the temperature increases is shown in Fig. 46. Thus, because of the temperature influence on fatigue life, the hot face of the tube or fin may fail although the higher stresses may be calculated elsewhere.

CUMULATIVE DAMAGE

The furnace wall is subjected to a wide variety of operating conditions, some of which produce no significant stresses and some of which will produce stresses worthy of consideration. When a design is for either static loads or for a large number of cycles, it is sufficient to design for the condition which pro-

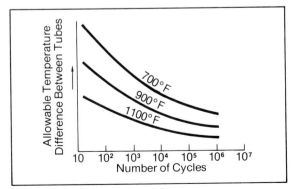

Fig. 45 Design fatigue curve

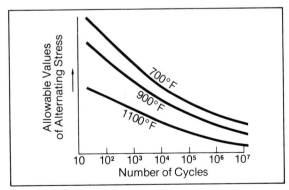

Fig. 46 Decrease in fatigue life

duces the highest stresses and ignore all others. In this case, design is for infinite life, and all stress must be below the damaging level.

Usually the number of operational stress cycles which the furnace wall must withstand is not large, but the value of the operational stress is large unless severe restrictions are imposed.

As soon as the existence of strains beyond the elastic limit is accepted, the design is based on finite life and the damaging effect of all significant strains must be considered. The relationship between the alternating stress and cycles to failure can be determined from the design fatigue curves, and the number of required cycles can be estimated from the anticipated stress history. With these relationships established, the expected life can be estimated with fair accuracy by adding together the "cycle ratios" produced by each operating condition.

$$\text{Cumulative Damage Index} = \sum_{i=1}^{i=n} \frac{P_i}{N_i}$$

(64)

where P_i is the number of times operating cycle will occur and N_i is the number of times alternating stress can be withstood, based on the fatigue design curve.

Fatigue tests have shown that the cumulative damage index can vary over a range of 0.6 to 5. If the most damaging stresses are applied first, the cycles ratio may be as low as 0.6. If the lower stress values are applied first and followed by progressively higher stresses, the cycles ratio can be as high as five. These are extreme conditions. For the case with random distribution of cycle ratio as for a furnace wall, the cumulative sum will be close to unity. Thus the imposed limiting condition is

$$\sum_{i=1}^{i=n} \frac{P_i}{N_i} = 1$$

(65)

Welded furnace walls must be safe and reliable for a wide range of boiler operating conditions. The analytical techniques and experimental procedures discussed in this section give the boiler designer the necessary tools to make an evaluation of the strength of furnace walls and to assess the suitability of furnace wall design to withstand any of the various operating conditions.

DESIGN OF BOILER STRUCTURAL SUPPORT SYSTEMS

Because the combustion process must be confined within a complex structure capable of supporting many static and dynamic loads, *structural design* is an important sector of overall boiler design. But it is unfortunately true that the fundamental importance of heat transfer and fluid flow tends to obscure the role of the boiler structural designer whose task is to analyze the many internal and external loads and to select suitable structural members.

Structural design of boilers shares much in common with bridge and building design. There is a long history of progressive advancement in this engineering art.[58] Yet there is little evidence of a specialized literature of boiler structural design, and almost no consideration is given to structural problems in the most widely used works on power-plant design.[59]

STRUCTURAL DESIGN CONDITIONS

Structural design of boilers involves the consideration of many factors. The type of boiler, its location, and its method of construction all have a bearing, as do design specifications, codes and ordinances, protective coatings, and type of structure, including choice of members and connections.

Supports for boilers vary greatly, depending upon size and function. Utility boilers and the larger industrial units, including recovery units for pulp and paper mills, are top-supported. Contrarily, shop-assembled boilers including those for waste-heat recovery and high-temperature water are bottom-supported, as are those for marine service. (See Chapters 8 and 9.) This section, however, will be specifically concerned with the structural design of a top-supported central-station boiler.

LOCATION OF INSTALLATION

Boiler location has various effects upon structural design. It may determine whether indoor or outdoor construction is used. It has a bearing on the specification of domestic or foreign steel shapes. It may require special consideration for climatic conditions, including both natural occurrences and those artifically induced, as in a chemical plant or oil refinery. It will establish wind loads, seismic conditions and soil bearing capabilities for foundations. Local ordinances and regulations may impose special requirements, including restrictions on materials and limitations of structural size.

Indoor boilers for utility service are a part of the power-plant structure, using the building columns for vertical support. Lateral support is provided by the bracing system of the building, which is completely enclosed and roofed. Boiler platforms for access and maintenance are coordinated with the elevations of power-plant floors.

Although outdoor units may have the boiler completely exposed to wind and weather, many are built with a full or partial roof and a protective enclosure around the fuel-firing equipment. Special consideration must be given to the waterproof design of casings and insulation for outdoor units.

SOURCES OF DESIGN INFORMATION

Many decisions must precede calculations for structural design. For example; will the unit be designed for indoor or outdoor construction? Should the frame be rigid, simple, or semirigid? Related to this is the choice of alternative connections: riveted, bolted, or welded. It is also wise at this time to consider protective coatings and their application.

There are many codes, standards and specifications pertinent to and helpful in making these decisions. One useful publication is *Minimum Design Loads in Buildings and Other Structures* [60] which lists design loads for many materials, gives estimated weights of snowfall and wind loads for practically all geographical areas of the United States, and includes seismic factors relating to the most common occurrences of earthquakes. Detailed information on protective coatings for steel may be found in the *Steel Structures Painting Manual.* [61]

The American Institute of Steel Construction's *Manual of Steel Construction* covers most routine design work. This manual includes the "AISC Specification for the Design Fabrication and Erection of Structural Steel for Buildings" plus an extended commentary. [62]

Structural design of a large boiler involves the solution of many simultaneous equations and can most efficiently be done by using a structural-design computer program such as STRUDL. [63] Such structures are very large, often exceeding 200 feet in height and involving the design and erection of several thousand tons of structural steel.

Top-supported boilers have many hangers which carry the loads of the various component pressure-parts to the structural steel framing. The boiler is allowed to expand downward from the main supports at the top of the structure; both structural-steel members and hanger rods are used. In high-temperature areas, the hangers may be water-cooled or steam-cooled tubing operating at high pressure and designed to the *ASME* Code.

A distinctive feature of boiler structural design is the buckstay system, which protects the pressure parts against transient internal or external forces. The pressure parts, including waterwall tubing and wall radiant surface, are attached to and must therefore deflect with the buckstays. Spacing of buckstays is determined from furnace pressure, tube diameter and spacing, and that part of the allowable stress in the tubing which can be allotted for bending.

REFERENCES

[1] M. K. Drewry, "Economy of Efficient Air Preheating with Extraction Steam," *Transactions of the ASME Journal of Engineering for Power,* 84:1–8, January 1962; also *ASME Paper No. 60-WA-94.* New York: American Society of Mechanical Engineers, 1960.

[2] "Cold-end Temperature and Material Selection Guide for Ljungstrom Air Preheaters," the Air Preheater Company, Inc., Wellsville, NY (request latest edition).

[3] "Steam Generating Units," *ASME Performance Test Codes, PTC No. 4.1.* New York: American Society of Mechanical Engineers, latest edition.

[4] Josef Stefan, "Uber Die Beziehung Zeischen der Warmestrahhung und der Temperatur," *Akademie der Wissenschaft. Sitzungs Berichte,* 79:391–428, 1879.

Ludwig Boltzmann, "Deduction of Stefan's Formula for Radiation from Maxwell's Electromagnetic Theory of Light," *Annalen der Physik und der Physikalischen Chemie,* 22:291–294, 1884.

Max Planck, *Theory of Heat Radiation,* 2nd ed. Translated by Morton Masius. New York: Dover Publications, 1959.

[5] C. M. Vsiskin and E. M. Sparrow, "Thermal Radiation Between Parallel Plates Separated by an Absorbing-Emitting Nonisothermal Gas," *International Journal of Heat and Mass Transfer,* 1(1):28–36, 1960.

[6] Thomas H. Einstein, *Radiant Heat Transfer to Absorbing Gases Enclosed Between Parallel Flat Plates with Flow and Conduction.* Report No. NASA-TR-R-154 (N64-11558). Springfield, VA: National Technical Information Service, 1963.

[7] J. R. Howell and M. Perlmutter, "Monte Carlo Solution of Thermal Transfer Through Radiant Media Between Gray Walls," *Transaction of the ASME Journal of Heat Transfer,* 86:116–122, February 1964. Also in: *ASME Paper No. 63-AHGT-1.* New York: American Society of Mechanical Engineers, 1963.

[8] J. R. Branstetter, *Radiant Heat Transfer Between Nongray Parallel Plates of Tungsten.* Report No. NASA-TN-D-1088 (N62-71662). Springfield, VA: National Technical Information Service, 1961.

[9] J. R. Branstetter, *Formulas for Radiative Heat Transfer Between Nongray Parallel Plates of Polished Refractory Metals.* Report No. NASA-TN-D-2902 (N65-27550). Springfield, VA: National Technical Information Service, 1965.

[10] J. D. Buckmaster, *Radiative Heat Transfer and Conduction Between Parallel Walls.* Report No. AD-619 419. Springfield, VA: National Technical Information Service, 1965.

[11] R. Viskanta, "Heat Transfer by Conduction and Radiation in Absorbing and Scattering Materials," *Transactions of the ASME Journal of Heat Transfer,* 87:143–150, February 1965. Also: *ASME Paper No. 64-HT-33.* New York: American Society of Mechanical Engineers, 1964.

[12] H. M. Hsia and T. J. Love, "Radiative Heat Transfer Between Parallel Plates Separated by a Nonisothermal Medium with Anisotropic Scattering," *Transactions of the ASME Journal of Heat Transfer,* 89:197–204, August 1967. Also: *ASME Paper No. 66-WA/HT-28.* New York: American Society of Mechanical Engineers, 1966.

[13] D. K. Edwards and K. E. Nelson, "Rapid Calculation of Radiant Energy Transfer Between Nongray Walls and Isothermal H_2O or CO_2 Gas," *Transactions of the ASME Journal of Heat Transfer,* 84:273-278, November 1962. Also: *ASME Paper No. 61-WA-175.* New York: American Society of Mechanical Engineers, 1961.

[14] Michael A. Lutz, *Radiant Energy Loss From a Cesium-Argon Plasma to an Infinite Parallel Enclosure; Avco-Everett Research Laboratory Report 175.* Report No. AD-431 640 (BSD-TDR-64-6). Springfield, VA: National Technical Information Service, 1963.

[15] Yuan-Siang Pan, *Temperature Discontinuities and Energy Transfer in One-Dimensional Problems.* Report No. AD-618 220. Springfield, VA: National Technical Service, 1965.

[16] T. J. Love and R. J. Grosh, "Radiative Heat Transfer in Absorbing, Emitting, and Scattering Media," *Transactions of the ASME Journal of Heat Transfer,* 87:161–166, May 1965. Also: *ASME Paper No. 64-HT-28.* New York: American Society of Mechanical Engineers, 1964.

[17] John R. Howell, *Radiative Interactions Between Absorbing-Emitting and Glowing Media with Internal Energy Generation.* Report No. NASA-TN-D-3614 (N66-36426). Springfield, VA: National Technical Information Service, 1966.

[18] E. M. Sparrow and A. Haji-Sheikh, "A Generalized Variational Method for Calculating Radiant Interchange Between Surfaces," *Transactions of the ASME Journal of Heat Transfer,* 87:103–109, February 1965. Also: *ASME Paper No. 64-HT-11.* New York: American Society of Mechanical Engineers, 1964.

[19] R. Viskanta and R. J. Grosh, "Heat Transfer in a Thermal Radiation Absorbing and Scattering Medium," *International Developments in Heat Transfer, Proceedings of the 1961–62 International Heat Transfer Conference,* Boulder, Colorado, August 28–September 1, 1961 and London, January 8–12, 1962, Part IV, Section B—Radiation, Thermal Properties and Instrumentation, Paper 99, pp. 820–828. New York: American Society of Mechanical Engineers, 1963.

[20] Masayoshi Kuwata and Robert H. Essenhigh, "Comparative Influence of Turbulence and Convention in Combustor Performance" *Proceedings of the Second Conference on Natural Gas Research and Technology,* Atlanta, June 5–7, 1972, Session IV, Paper 3. Chicago: Institute of Gas Technology, ND.

[21] Mehty A. E. Zeinalov, Masayoshi Kuwata, and Robert H. Essenhigh, "Stirring Factors in Combustion Chambers: A Finite-Element Model of Mixing Along an 'Information

Flow Path'," *Fourteenth Symposium (International) on Combustion*, University Park, PA, August 20–25, 1972, pp. 575–583. Pittsburgh: The Combustion Institute, 1973.

22 Satyanarayana T. R. Rao and R. H. Essenhigh, "Experimental Determination of Stirring Factors Generated by Straight and Swirling Jets in Isothermal Combustion—Chamber Models," *Thirteenth Symposium (International) on Combustion*, Salt Lake City, August 23–29, 1970, pp. 603–615. Pittsburgh: The Combustion Institute, 1971.

23 Robert H. Essenhigh, *A New Application of Perfectly Stirred Reactor (P.S.R.) Theory to Design of Combustion Chambers.* Report No. AD-812 114. (Pennsylvania State University, Department of Fuel Science Technical Report No. FS67-1(U)). (Contract 656(29)). Springfield, VA: National Technical Information Service, 1967.

24 A. M. Godridge, "Heat Transfer in the Furnace Chamber of Pulverized-Fuel-Fired Water-Tube Boilers," *Institute of Fuel Journal*, 40(318):300–310, July 1967.

25 V. A. Lokshin, I. E. Semenovker and Yu. V. Vikhrev, "Calculating the Temperature Conditions of the Radiant Heating Surfaces in Supercritical Boilers," *Thermal Engineering* [Translation of Teploenergetika], 15(9):34–39, September 1968.

26 S. S. Filimonov, et al., "Calculation of Average Temperature and Thermal Resistance of Heating Surfaces in Furnace Chambers," *Thermal Engineering* [Translation of Teploenergetika], 15(9):40–44, September 1968.

27 E. S. Karasina, "Allowance for Fouling of Radiant Heating Surfaces." *Thermal Engineering* [Translation of Teploenergetika], 15(6):17–22, June 1968.

28 R. H. Essenhigh, et al., *Furnace Analysis: A Comparative Study.* Pennsylvania State University, Department of Fuel Science Technical Report No. FS/CGSSC-12/69-4. University Park, PA: Pennsylvania State University, 1969.

29 J. M. Beér and R. G. Siddall, "Radiative Heat Transfer in Furnaces and Combustion," *ASME Paper No. 72-WA/HT-29.* New York: American Society of Mechanical Engineers, 1972.

30 H. C. Hottell and E. S. Cohen, "Radiant Heat Exchange in a Gas-Filled Enclosure," *ASME Paper No. 57-HT-23.* New York: American Society of Mechanical Engineers, 1957.

31 H. C. Hottell, "The Melchett Lecture for 1960: Radiative Transfer in Combustion Chambers," *Institute of Fuel Journal*, 34(245):220–234, June 1961.

32 H. C. Hottell and A. C. Sarofim, *Radiative Transfer.* New York: McGraw-Hill, 1967.

33 D. B. Spalding, "Mathematical Models of Continuous Combustion," *Emissions from Continuous Combustion Systems, Proceedings, Symposium*, Warren, MI, September 27–28, 1971. New York: Plenum, 1972.

34 William H. McAdams, *Heat Transmission*, 3rd ed. New York: McGraw-Hill, 1954.

35 S. S. Penner and P. Varanasi, "Simplified Procedures for Estimating Band and Total Emissivities of Polyatomic Molecules," *Eleventh Symposium (International) on Combustion*, University of California at Berkeley, August 14–20, 1966, pp. 569–576. Pittsburgh: The Combustion Institute, 1967.

36 K. A. Bueters, "Combustion Products Emissivity by F_E Operator," *Combustion*, 45(9):12–18, March 1974.

37 K. A. Bueters, J. G. Cogoli, and W. W. Habelt, "Performance Prediction of Tangentially Fired Utility Furnaces by Computer Mode," *Fifteenth Symposium (International) on Combustion*, Tokyo, August 25–31, 1974, pp. 1245–1260. Pittsburgh: The Combustion Institute, 1974.

38 H. F. Mullikin, "Evaluation of Effective Radiant Heating Surface and Application of the Stefan-Boltzman Law to Heat Absorption in Boiler Furnaces," *Transactions of the ASME*, 57:517–529, 1935.

39 Frederick P. Boynton and Claus B. Ludwig, "Total Emissivity of Hot Water Vapor-II. Semi-Empirical Charts Deduced from Long-Path Spectral Data," *International Journal of Heat and Mass Transfer*, 14(7):963–973, July 1971.

40 F. R. Steward and P. Cannon, "The Calculation of Radiative Heat Flux in a Cylindrical Furnace Using the Monte Carlo Method," *International Journal of Heat and Mass Transfer*, 14(2):245–262, February 1971.

41 H. C. Hottel and R. B. Egbert, "Radiant Heat Transmission from Water Vapor," *AIChE Transactions*, 38(3):531–568, June 1942.

42 H. R. Hazard, et al., "Field Studies of Slagging in Tangentially Fired Boiler Furnaces—Part I, Labadie Field Trial," *ASME Paper No. 78-Wa/Fu-10.* New York; American Society of Mechanical Engineers, 1978.

43 W. E. Dalby, "Heat Transmission," *Institution of Mechanical Engineers Proceedings*, Parts 3–4:921–1071, 1909.

W. J. Wohlenberg, et al., "An Experimental Investigation of Heat Absorption in Boiler Furnaces," *Transactions of the ASME*, 57:541–554, 1935.

Osborne Reynolds, "On the Extent and Action of the Heating Surface for Steam Boilers," *Manchester Literary and Philosophical Society Proceedings*, 14:7–12, October 6, 1874.

L. M. K. Boelter, R. C. Martinelli, and Finn Johanssen, "Remarks on the Analogy Between Heat Transfer and Momentum Transfer," *Transactions of the ASME*, 63:447–455, 1941.

W. F. Davidson, et al., "Studies of Heat Transmission Through Boiler Tubing at Pressures from 500 to 3300 Pounds," *Transactions of the ASME*, 65:553–591, 1943.

Max Jakob, *Heat Transfer*, Vol. II. New York: John Wiley and Sons, 1957, pp. 373–381.

44 Orville L. Pierson, "Experimental Investigation of the Influence of Tube Arrangement on Convection Heat Transfer and Flow Resistance in Cross Flow of Gases Over Tube Banks," *Transactions of the ASME*, 59:563–572, 1937.

45 E. D. Grimison, "Correlation and Utilization of New Data on Flow Resistance and Heat Transfer for Cross Flow of Gases Over Tube Banks," *Transactions of the ASME*, 59:583–594, 1937.

[46] E. C. Huge, "Experimental Investigation of Effects of Equipment Size on Convection Heat Transfer and Flow Resistance in Cross Flow of Gases Over Tube Banks," *Transactions of the ASME*, 59:573–581, 1937.

[47] Clarence F. Hirshfeld, William N. Barnard, Frank O. Ellenwood, *Elements of Heat-Power Engineering*, Part III; *Auxiliary Equipment, Plant Ensemble, Air Conditioning, and Refrigeration*, 3rd ed. New York: John Wiley and Sons, 1933.

[48] American Society of Mechanical Engineers, Boiler and Pressure Vessel Committee, *ASME Boiler and Pressure Vessel Code*. New York: American Society of Mechanical Engineers, latest edition.

[49] Stephen Timoshenko and S. Woinowsky-Krieger, *Theory of Plates and Shells*, 2nd ed. New York: McGraw-Hill, 1959.

[50] G. W. Watts and W. R. Burrows, "The Basic Elastic Theory of Vessel Heads Under Internal Pressure," *Transactions of the ASME Journal of Applied Mechanics*, 71:55–73, March 1949.

[51] Stephen Timoshenko and S. Woinowsky-Krieger, *Theory of Plates and Shells*, 2nd ed. New York: McGraw-Hill, 1959.

Miklos Hetenyi, *Beams on Elastic Foundation; Theory with Applications in the Fields of Civil and Mechanical Engineering*. Ann Arbor, MI: University of Michigan Press, 1946.

[52] G. K. Cooper and L. W. Smith, Final Report of PVRC Project of the American Welding Society, Purdue University, August 1952. This report can be obtained from Pressure Vessel Research Council, United Engineering Center, New York.

[53] Julien Dubuc and Georges Welter, "Investigation of Static and Fatigue Resistance of Model Pressure Vessels," *Welding Journal*, 35:329s–337s, July 1956.

[54] G. J. Schoessow and E. A. Brooks, "Analysis of Experimental Data Regarding Certain Design Features with Pressure Vessels," *Transactions of the ASME*, 72:567–577, July 1950.

[55] Miklos I. Hetenyi, *Handbook of Experimental Stress Analysis*. New York: John Wiley and Sons, 1950.

A. J. Durelli, E. A. Phillips, and C. H. Isao, *Introduction to the Theoretical and Experimental Analysis of Stress and Strain*. New York: McGraw-Hill, 1958.

Albert Kobayashi, ed., *Manual on Experimental Stress Analysis*, 3rd ed. Westport, CT: Society for Experimental Stress Analysis, 1978.

Society for Experimental Stress Analysis, *Experimental Stress Analysis; Proceedings of the Society for Experimental Stress Analysis*, V.1–. Westport, CT: Society for Experimental Stress Analysis, 1943.

[56] Stephen Timoshenko and S. Woinowsky-Krieger, *Theory of Plates and Shells*, 2nd ed., pp. 361–376. New York: McGraw-Hill, 1959.

[57] C. C. Perry and H. R. Lisner, *The Strain Gage Primer*, 2nd ed. New York: McGraw-Hill, 1962.

Frank G. Tatnall, *Tatnall on Testing: An Autobiographical Account of Adventures Under 13 Vice Presidents*. Metals Park, OH: American Society for Metals, 1966.

[58] L. E. Grinter, *Theory of Modern Steel Structures*, revised ed. New York: Macmillan, 1949.

H. M. Westergaard, "One Hundred Fifty Years Advance in Structural Analysis," *American Society of Civil Engineers Transactions*, 94:226–246, 1930.

Stanley B. Hamilton, "The Historical Development of Structural Theory," *Institution of Civil Engineers Proceedings*, 1, Part 3:374–419, 1952.

[59] A. H. Palmer, et al., "Integrated Structural Steel Design Program," *American Society of Civil Engineers Proceedings, Journal of the Power Division*, 89(PO-1):67–82, September 1963.

[60] "Building Code Requirements for Minimum Design Loads in Buildings and Other Structures," *ANSI Standard No. A58.1*. Sponsored by the National Bureau of Standards and approved by the American National Standards Institute. New York: American National Standards Institute, latest edition.

[61] "Steel Structures Painting Manual", Volume 1 covers methods of surface preparation and paint systems. Volume 2 lists all types of important paint systems used in various industries; it also includes a guide with indexes for selection of suitable systems for various structures ad exposures, specifications for surface preparation and pretreatment, paint application and paints. Obtained from the Steel Structures Painting Council, Pittsburgh, PA.

[62] "Manual of Steel Construction", latest edition; American Institute of Steel Construction, N.Y.

[63] Robert D. Logscher, et al., *ICES STRUDL-II: The Structural Design Language Engineering User's Manual*, Vol 1; *Frame Analysis*, 1st ed. Massachusetts Institute of Technology, Department of Civil Engineering, Structures Division and Civil Engineering Systems Laboratory Research Report R68-91. Cambridge, MA: Massachusetts Institute of Technology, 1968.

CHAPTER 7

Reheat Steam Generators

Most of the fundamentals on boiler design, fuels, ash, coal pulverization, materials selection, manufacture, field construction and operation in this book are common in whole or in part to the technology of boiler designers and manufacturers worldwide. The information in this chapter departs from that commonality.

This chapter presents the C-E design philosophy as it applies to large reheat steam generators for utility service. Specifically covered are tangentially-fired subcritical and supercritical equipment and the laboratory work required to develop this equipment.

Since WW II, manufacturers have developed diverse designs for generating steam at the high subcritical and supercritical pressures. The diversity is particularly apparent in large, high-pressure units for which the individual proprietary designs become both the hallmark and *raison d'être* for each manufacturer. Like fingerprints, the arguments made for the superiority of a circulation or firing system characterize and differentiate all boiler designers.

The C-E product line and C-E's desire for excellence extend from the utility designs to the industrial and marine boilers. But it is for the design and development of its high-pressure reheat steam generators that C-E has built and staffed some of the finest laboratories in the "unsubsidized" world. The C-E research facilities are dedicated solely to the development and improvement of equipment directly for, or related to, steam generation.

IMPACT OF FUEL ON BOILER DESIGN

The most important item to consider when designing a utility or large industrial steam generator is the fuel the unit will burn. The furnace size, the equipment to prepare and burn the fuel, the amount of heating surface and its placement, the type and size of heat-recovery equipment, and the flue-gas treatment devices are all fuel dependent.

The major differences among those boilers that burn coal or oil or natural gas result from the ash in the products of combustion. (See Chapter 3.) Firing oil in a furnace results in relatively small amounts of ash; there is no ash from natural gas. For the same output, because of the ash, coal-burning boilers must have larger furnaces and the velocities of the combustion gases in the convection passes must be lower. In addition, coal-burning boilers need ash-handling and particulate cleanup equipment that costs a great deal and requires considerable space.

Table I lists the variation in calorific values and moisture contents of several coals, and the mass of fuel that must be handled and fired to generate the same electrical-power output. These values are important because the quantity of fuel required helps determine the size of the coal storage yard, as well as the handling, crushing, and pulverizing equipment for the various coals.

FURNACE SIZING

As stated in Chapter 6, the most important step in coal-fired unit design is to properly size the furnace. Furnace size has a first-order influence on the size of the structural steel framing, the boiler building and its foundations, as well as on the sootblowers, platforms, stairways, steam piping, and ductwork.

The fuel-ash properties that C-E considers particularly important when designing and establishing the size of coal-fired furnaces include:

■ the ash fusibility temperatures (both in terms of their absolute values and the spread or difference between initial deformation temperature and fluid temperature)

■ the ratio of basic to acidic ash constituents

■ the iron/calcium ratio

■ the fuel-ash content in terms of lbs of ash/million Btu

■ the ash friability

Table I. Representative Coal Analyses

	Med.-Vol. Bituminous	High-Vol. Bituminous	Subbitum-inous C	Low-Sodium Lignite	Med.-Sodium Lignite	High-Sodium Lignite
Total H$_2$O, %	5.0	15.4	30.0	31.0	30.0	39.6
Ash, %	10.3	15.0	5.8	10.4	28.4	6.3
VM, %	31.6	33.1	32.6	31.7	23.2	27.5
FC, %	53.1	36.5	36.6	26.9	18.4	26.6
Btu/lb, as fired	13,240	10,500	8,125	7,590	5,000	6,523
Btu/lb, MAF	15,640	15,100	12,650	12,940	12,020	12,050
Fusion (reducing), °F						
Initial Def.	2,170	1,990	2,200	2,075	2,120	2,027
Softening	2,250	2,120	2,250	2,200	2,380	2,089
Fluid	2,440	2,290	2,290	2,310	2,700	2,203
Ash analysis, %						
SiO$_2$	40.0	46.4	29.5	46.1	62.9	23.1
Al$_2$O$_3$	24.0	16.2	16.0	15.2	17.5	11.3
Fe$_2$O$_3$	16.8	20.0	4.1	3.7	2.8	8.5
CaO	5.8	7.1	26.5	16.6	4.8	23.8
MgO	2.0	0.8	4.2	3.2	0.7	5.9
Na$_2$O	0.8	0.7	1.4	0.4	3.1	7.4
K$_2$O	2.4	1.5	0.5	0.6	2.0	0.7
TiO$_2$	1.3	1.0	1.3	1.2	0.8	0.5
P$_2$O$_5$	0.1	0.1	1.1	0.1	0.1	0.2
SO$_3$	5.3	6.0	14.8	12.7	4.6	17.7
Sulfur, %	1.8	3.2	0.3	0.6	1.7	0.8
Lb H$_2$O/million Btu	3.8	14.7	36.9	40.8	60.0	60.7
Lb Ash/Million Btu	7.8	14.3	7.1	13.7	56.8	9.7
*Fuel Fired, 1000 lb/hr	405	520	705	750	1,175	900

*Constant Heat Output, Nominal 600-MW Unit, Adjusted For Efficiency

These characteristics and others, (all discussed in detail in Chapter 3 and Appendix C) translate into the furnace sizes in Fig. 1, which is based on the six coal ranks shown in Table I. This size comparison illustrates the C-E philosophy of increasing the furnace plan area, volume, and the fuel burnout zone (the distance from the top fuel nozzle to the furnace arch), as lower grade coals with poorer ash characteristics are fired.

Fig. 1 is a simplified characterization of actual furnaces built to burn the fuels in Table I. Wide variations exist in fuel properties within coal ranks, as well as within several subclassifications (e.g., subbituminous A, B, C), each of which may require a different size furnace.

Among the most important design criteria in large pulverized-fuel tangentially-fired furnaces are net heat input in Btu/hr-sq ft of furnace plan area (NHI/PA) and the vertical distance from the top fuel nozzle to the furnace

arch. Furnace dimensions must be adequate to establish the necessary furnace retention time to properly burn the fuel as well as to cool the gaseous combustion products. This is to ensure that the gas temperature at the entrance to the closely-spaced convection surface is well below the ash-softening temperature of the lowest quality coal burned. Heat-absorption characteristics of the walls are maintained using properly placed wall blowers to control the furnace outlet gas temperature by removing ash deposited on the furnace walls below the furnace outlet plane.

To arrive at an appropriate value of NHI/PA and furnace plan area requires thorough evaluation of all fuels expected to be burned in the unit. Depending on the coal, large pulverized-fuel units have an NHI/PA that generally varies from 1.4 to 2.0 × 10⁶ Btu/hr-sq ft.

The distance from the upper fuel nozzle to the furnace arch is a function of furnace width

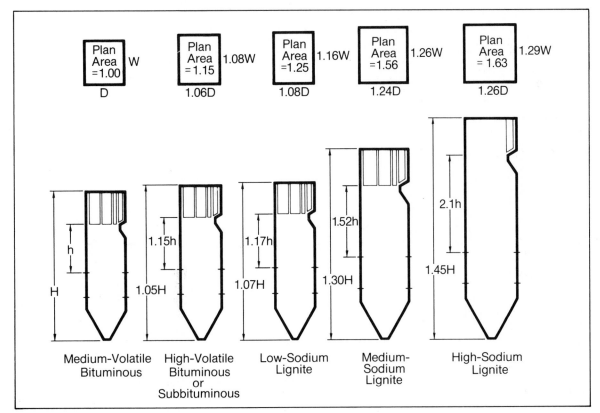

Fig. 1 **Effect of coal rank on furnace sizing (constant heat output)**

and depth but it also depends on the fuel-ash properties. The distance in current designs ranges from 45 ft to greater than 60 ft.

A furnace design parameter sometimes specified is burner-zone heat release. This term does not have the same significance in tangential firing as in other firing systems. In tangential firing not all of the fuel is consumed in the windbox zone because of the manner in which the fuel and air are introduced into the furnace. In a unit designed for wall firing, the fuel and air are intimately mixed at the burner throat and consumed directly in front of the burner.

With a face-fired boiler, burners can be moved farther apart or more burners can be added to give any value of burner-zone release rate as there is no interaction between rows of burners.

The vertical distance from the lowest coal nozzle to the point where the furnace walls are bent to form the hopper section of the furnace is a function of furnace width and depth and the slagging potential of the fuel. This dimension is generally between 12 and 30 feet in a tangentially-fired furnace. The hopper section typically slopes at 55° as shown in Fig. 2.

Panels and platens that are widely spaced

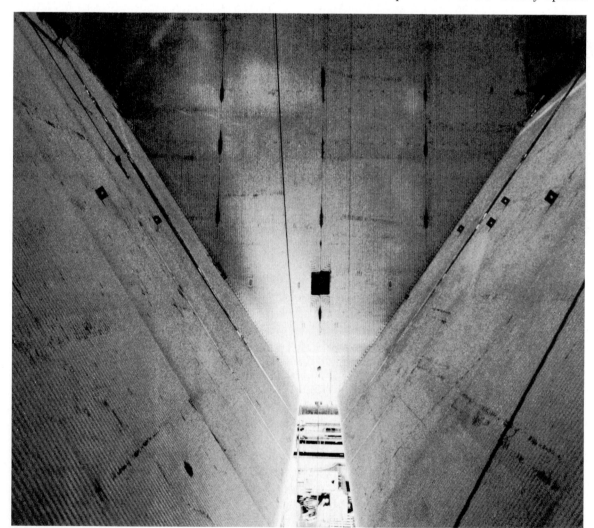

Fig. 2 Water-cooled hopper bottom of large pulverized-coal furnace. Hopper slopes typically are 55° from horizontal and openings about 4 ft. in width

may be required in the upper furnace to provide additional surface for radiant heat absorption. These sections potentially are subject to the most severe fouling conditions and wide spacing helps prevent ash plugging caused by bridging between adjacent assemblies. To perform satisfactorily in this environment, the platens are constructed with the tubes tangent to each other in the direction of gas flow.

With the exception of dry-bottom pulverized-coal units in sizes between approximately 50 and 100 MW, the furnace volumetric heat-release rate (in Btu/hr-ft³) generally is not a controlling design parameter. For such units, the release-rate limit is from 20,000 for very good bituminous coals to about 15,000 for lignites. Similarly, the burner-zone volumetric heat-release rate in Btu/hr-ft³ is not a meaningful design parameter for tangentially-fired boilers.

SUPERHEATER SURFACE ARRANGEMENT

The next consideration is the arrangement of the superheater, reheater and economizer heating surfaces in the upper portion of the furnace and in the convection pass (as described in Chapter 6). In locating these sections within the unit, a proper balance is required to maintain a thermal head with which to transfer heat from gas to steam as the heating-surface use is optimized and undesirably high metal temperatures are avoided. Also, to limit pressure-part erosion from flyash, the flue-gas velocity must not exceed reasonable limits. Depending upon the ash quantity and abrasiveness, the design velocity is generally 55 to 60 ft/sec. A furnace that burns coals yielding a heavy loading of erosive ash (usually indicated by a high silica/alumina content), may have a design velocity of approximately 50 ft/sec. Such velocities are based on the predicted average gas temperature entering the tube section, at the maximum continuous rating (MCR) of the steam generator fired at normal excess-air percentage.

SINGLE-FURNACE CAPABILITY

Between 1960 and 1965, C-E contracted for 51 units totaling 19,600 MW, the majority for medium- and high-volatile bituminous fuels.

Unit sizes ranged to 900 MW. All units over 300 MW had divided, twin open, or twin-divided furnaces with widths up to 90 ft. A two-firing-cell centerwall arrangement was used. During this time, C-E extended its single-firing-cell capacity 40 percent, to 450 MW from a previous high of 325 MW.

In the 1966 to '70 period, C-E built 56 coal-fired units totaling 32,000 MW. The average unit size was 575 MW, 50 percent larger than the 380-MW average of the early 60's and C-E's single-furnace capability increased to 600 MW, with open furnaces 61 ft wide.

Since then, more than 100 single-furnace units representing nearly 55,000 MW of generating capacity have been designed. In the early 1970's C-E introduced the 65 ft wide single furnace and, in 1980, contracted for 70-ft wide designs. These increases in four-corner open-furnace sizes are made in nominal increments of about 10 percent. Each increase is based on sound design and satisfactory operating experience with earlier units.

During the 1960 to 1980 period, C-E also designed units with centerwalls for those unit sizes not available with a single firing cell.

The more than 125 units with centerwall design have exceeded 1000 unit-years of operation. In large centerwall units, some of which have furnace widths greater than 100 feet, buckstay systems, supporting structural steel, and long-retractable sootblowers play a dominant role in the economics of the design.

CONVECTION-PASS DESIGN

A number of coal-ash properties have a significant influence on superheater, reheater, and economizer convection-surface design, and the associated considerations of fouling and erosion. Included are

- ash-softening temperature
- base/acid ratio
- iron/calcium ratio
- sodium and potassium content
- silica and alumina content of the ash
- chlorine content
- ash friability

Fig. 3 shows superheater and reheater spacings in convection passes as a qualitative function of flyash adhesion (fouling) rate.

Considering the above factors in furnace sizing and convection-pass design, it is impractical to propose a steam generator capable of burning any kind of coal, nor would such a unit be economically feasible. For example, consider the wide variation in pulverizer size and primary-air-temperature requirements for a high-calorific-value, low-moisture, low-ash coal versus a subbituminous coal or lignite with a high moisture and ash content. Selecting an optimum preparation and firing system for one rank of fuel can result in a much less favorable situation for some other rank of fuel.

Operating experience on units firing certain coals shows the need for wide transverse tube spacing throughout the unit to reduce the fouling rate and possible bridging of ash deposits between adjacent assemblies. This arrangement minimizes serious fouling problems which have an adverse effect on fan power requirements and unit availability.

As the gas temperature is reduced along its flow path to well below the ash-softening temperature of the worst coal expected to be burned, the transverse spacing of the convection pass tube banks is also reduced—depending on fuel type and the ash characteristics. The tube spacing selected at the entrance to the convection pass depends mainly on the maximum gas temperature possible in this zone under upset conditions and the propensity of the ash to adhere.

In the superheater and reheater sections beyond the ash-adhesion temperature zone, the tube spacing is further reduced to the minimum for effective penetration of sootblower jets. In addition, gas velocities are maintained sufficiently low to prevent erosion. To avoid serious plugging, the transverse spacing in this area must be wide enough to allow pieces of accumulated ash loosened by sootblowers to pass through the tube bank and not bridge the span between adjacent tube rows.

Table II is a guide for establishing transverse clearances for platen and spaced convection surfaces. The guide is based on fouling and nonfouling coals and gas temperatures at maximum boiler load.

COAL PROPERTIES USED FOR DESIGN

Coal properties to be used in a boiler design are established on the Purchaser's specifications. It is preferable for the specifications to use an analysis that represents a bona fide coal as the performance coal and include low, average, and high analyses to confirm limits for the boiler design. Important items of the analysis are calorific value, moisture and ash contents, grindability index, and the ash analysis. If the fuel specifications are stated as ranges, it is customary to consider the average as the performance fuel but to design the unit to handle fuels with the worst analysis.

Fig. 3 Superheater and reheater spacing as a function of adhesion (fouling) rate of flyash

If coals from two or more sources may be fired, individual analyses rather than a calculated average are desirable, with "low" and "high" representing the composite. Justification for using individual and separate analyses comes from the necessity to evaluate mill capabilities as well as eutectic ash influences on unit performance. The "worst" coal can become the design coal when there is a good probability that the power plant will use a significant amount of the "worst" coal. If the worst coal will be a small percent of the fuel supply, it may be more economical to accept a small reduction in load during those periods when such coal is fired.

DRY-BOTTOM VERSUS WET-BOTTOM

All current pulverized-coal reheat units are of the dry-bottom type; the ash dislodged from the furnace walls is below the ash-melting point and leaves the furnace bottom in a substantially dry condition. The wet-bottom or slagging-bottom furnaces are offered only for special applications, such as in furnaces for gasifying coal. (See Chapter 24.)

Factors influencing the acceptance of dry-bottom furnaces have been

■ the ability to burn a greater variety of coals with a wide range in fusibility temperature

■ the greater flexibility afforded in operating over wide load ranges

■ higher unit efficiency with the elimination of the latent-heat loss of the molten slag.

In the wet-bottom design, the lower part of the flame has to sweep the furnace floor at all

---

Table II. Transverse Clearance Guide

Temperature Range	Inches of Clearance	
°F	Nonfouling Coal	Fouling Coal
2000–2400	Platen –22	Platen –22
1750–2000	Spaced– 7	Platen –12
1450–1750	Spaced– 3	Spaced– 6
Up to 1450	Spaced– 2	Spaced– 3

---

loads to maintain fluidity of ash. This requirement imposes a definite limitation in the use of slag-tap furnaces. Slag-tap freezing can occur during operation at low load or with fuel fired only in the upper furnace for steam temperature control. In addition, wet-bottom units have higher nitrogen-oxide production.

The dry-bottom furnace, on the other hand, particularly those designs using tilting fuel nozzles, can provide a wider steam temperature control range and can handle many coals with varying ash characteristics. It is this latter characteristic, more than any other, that was originally responsible for greater application of dry-bottom units.

In the usual dry-bottom furnace, the hopper is formed by bending the front- and rear-wall tubes at their lower ends. The tube slope is greater than the angle of repose for ash, and thus forms a self-cleaning, watercooled hopper. Ash is discharged to the ash receiver through a transverse opening in the hopper, about 4-ft wide on large units. (Fig. 2).

FURNACE DESIGN FOR OIL & GAS FIRING

Selecting a furnace size, its wall tubing, and its circulating system is a function of two distinct design parameters: the complete combustion of the fuel and the preservation of satisfactory furnace-wall metal temperatures. To this end, furnaces for burning pulverized solid fuels must be configured to prevent the formation of objectionable slag deposits, which can increase the furnace outlet-gas temperature above design values. Generally, the large furnaces and the wall deposits associated with coal firing result in relatively low furnace-wall absorption rates, so that tube-wall metal temperature does not influence furnace size.

When firing oil, the larger amount of fuel reaction surface available for combustion produces complete combustion in a smaller furnace volume. The higher consequent heat-release rate per unit area of furnace-wall surface can cause high localized heat-absorption rates. Furnace sizing for oil burning, then, must account for the effect of high absorption rates on both metal temperatures and circulation, and these factors usually determine the dimensions of an oil-fired furnace.[1]

Gas-fired furnace design is similar to oil-fired, except for the fact that gas firing inherently results in lower localized heat-absorption rates. This allows designing somewhat smaller furnaces with even higher heat-release rates than used for oil firing.

BURNING REFUSE IN UTILITY BOILERS

Chapter 8 describes methods of burning municipal refuse and other cellulosic wastes in industrial boilers. In such units, large percentages of mixed commercial and household refuse are burned; in some, a small startup burner is the only fossil fuel consuming device.

For several important reasons large pulverized-coal units primarily generating electricity should limit refuse firing to 10 to 20 percent of the full-load fuel firing rate. The following are some of these reasons.

■ Even shredded and air-separated refuse is not completely homogeneous, because refuse composition and moisture content vary considerably from season to season, and day to day. This nonhomogeneity will result in much wider fluctuations in the heating value than that experienced with coal firing.

■ Fired alone, refuse is potentially more corrosive than most coals and fuel oils. It appears that the corrosion potential from burning refuse is nearly linear with the percentage burned. It seems prudent, therefore, to limit the amount of refuse burned in reheat units.

■ Generally speaking, the moisture content of prepared refuse will be more than triple that of bituminous coal (on a pounds-per-million-Btu basis) and will vary widely from day-to-day—as will its heating value. In addition the relatively high moisture content of refuse and the corresponding decrease in fuel-firing efficiency will increase the combustion gas mass compared to the primary fuels being burned in any given plant. Limiting the percentage of refuse burned minimizes the effect on superheater and reheater outlet steam temperatures, and on the air-heater exit gas temperature.

■ With coal-fired units in which the fuel being burned is of relatively high-sulfur content (1.5 percent or higher), precipitator collection efficiency will be adversely affected by a large contribution of low-sulfur refuse.

■ Often, moving large quantities of refuse to a 500-MW or larger steam generator poses a logistic problem that precludes the use of large percentages of refuse because of the traffic situation. Undoubtedly, a refuse collecting/preparing/burning system would be most economic using several units at different generating stations, rather than concentrating a single large system in one locaton.

■ Another important consideration is the effect a steam generator outage has on the ability of a utility to honor a commitment to handle a certain flow of refuse without interruption. Municipalities probably would not tolerate a stoppage in the "flow" of refuse. A weekday steam generator outage may result in the refuse piling up at the preparation facility or the power station. It is, therefore, mandatory that short-term storage or landfill sites be provided to handle refuse during steam generator outages. Conversely, if the flow of refuse to the steam generator is interrupted, the steam generator must be able to develop full load on the prime fuel.

LARGE HIGH-PRESSURE FURNACE-WALL SYSTEM DESIGN

The design of the various heat-absorbing equipment described in previous chapters involves a finite pressure drop or resistance to fluid flow. Air heaters, economizers, superheaters and reheaters all have a multiplicity of parallel flow paths or circuits through which the fluid being heated must pass; the uniformity of flow distribution depends largely upon the magnitude of the pressure drop across the apparatus.

The watercooled furnace, in general, handles the heated fluid by many more parallel circuits than are found in the other heat-transfer devices; therefore, the problem of distributing water to each tube and providing adequate circulation for cooling the tube is correspondingly more difficult.

The tubes which form the furnace walls are of different lengths and are subject to varying heat absorption rates. Great care must be exercised to insure that each tube receives a sufficient flow of water to prevent overheating individual waterwall tubes. Flow instability, which can occur in furnace circuits, is considerably more difficult to control when a large number of tubes operate in parallel. The designer must calculate the heat absorption per furnace tube from a forecast of the normal absorption pattern of the entire furnace. This forecast depends on the height and width of the furnace, but most of all, on the manner in which the fuel is fired.

The anticipated pattern of heat absorption may not, however, be reproduced in service; moreover, it will fluctuate from time to time due to load changes, transient conditions, and because the thickness of ash covering the walls will not always be the same. With some firing systems, the number of pulverizers and burners in service also will vary the pattern.

At intervals ash deposits will drop off, or be removed by sootblowing, and this will give rise to further considerable variations. Misjudging the intensity or distribution of heat absorption may cause circulation difficulties that are impossible to correct except by decreasing the rating and operating pressure of the boiler.

As the boiler operating pressure approaches the critical point (Chapter 5) the difference in the density of water and steam to produce circulation approaches zero. Designing tube circuits of low enough resistance to insure adequate velocities and adequate water-to-steam ratio in all tubes at all loads, with all fuels, under varying slagging conditions and at all firing rates becomes proportionately more difficult at the 2750 to 2850 psig drum and waterwell operating pressure level.

Achieving proper circulation becomes increasingly difficult not only with higher operating pressures, but also with increased unit capacity. In units with large megawatt ratings, the fuel fired per lineal foot of furnace perimeter increases markedly compared to earlier 100 to 200 MW units. This had led the boiler industry to adopt internally rifled tubes for furnace walls because higher percentages of steam can be tolerated in the steam-water mixture in rifled furnace tubes.

In any case, the difficulties of designing a satisfactory furnace-wall circulating system involve

- furnace configuration
- different tube lengths in parallel circuits
- the necessity to shield some tubes from heat near the fuel nozzles or burners
- manufacturing tolerances of commercially available tubing (which affect inside diameter and consequent pressure drop tube-to-tube)
- allowance for different heat pickup in different portions of the furnace
- the possibility of internal deposits
- provision for the necessary pressure drop for steam-water separation in the drum

TANGENTIAL FIRING AND CIRCULATION SYSTEM DESIGN

With C-E tangential firing and its mode of introducing the fuel, the furnace is used as the burner; thus, heat-absorption patterns are much more uniform and more definable than with any other type of firing. As further described and illustrated in Chapters 13 and 14, the fuel and combustion air are introduced in the corners of the furnace, but the actual burning process takes place in the main body of the furnace. Therefore, heat is not liberated in a concentrated form in the area of the fuel admission assemblies, nor is it concentrated on one side of the furnace.

As the load on the steam-generating unit varies, the amount of heat admitted into the furnace is either increased or decreased uniformly, and in such a manner that the heat absorption pattern remains basically unchanged. This is because each pulverizer feeds one horizontal level of fuel nozzles. These two features of C-E's tangential firing, coupled with inherently low flame temperatures, are an asset to the successful design of and operation of the furnace circulation system.

FURNACE-WALL CIRCULATION IN REHEAT UNITS

Through evolution and wide experience, Combustion Engineering has developed three types of circulating systems, each designed to meet specific requirements and provide certain advantages—thermal ("natural") circulation, Controlled Circulation® and Combined Circulation® (Fig. 4). Each is adapted to fit specific power-plant requirements.

THERMAL CIRCULATION

Thermally induced circulation, in theory at least, can be used in a boiler design that approaches the critical pressure of 3208 psia. This can be done only by going to extremely large diameter furnace-wall tubes of high-alloy materials and essentially zero pressure-drop downcomer systems, risers, and drum internals. The highest practical pressure that has been designed for is approximately 2800 psig in the drum and waterwall circuitry; this limits available pressure drop for superheater cooling to undesirably low values when required

superheater outlet pressure is above 2650 psig.

As furnace-wall operating pressures and furnace sizes increase, a designer must have substantially greater knowledge of waterwall heat-absorption patterns that result from firing system characteristics. Predictability and repeatability of such heat-flux patterns must be achievable on a positive, long-term basis. Operator intervention or equipment malfunction must not permit a different distribution of heat input to the furnace walls other than that for which the unit was designed.

CONTROLLED FORCED RECIRCULATION

In Chapter 5, the concept of subcritical-pressure controlled forced recirculation was introduced. It was stated that a boiler with such a circulation system incorporates a recirculating pump between the drum and waterwalls, thereby freeing the designer from dependence upon the difference in steam and water densities to provide circulating head. Using a recirculating pump means that the designer is assured of positive circulation even before heat is applied. Because the pump helps to overcome friction loss in the waterwall tubes, it's possible to substitute smaller diameter tubes for the larger diameter tubes required with a limited thermal circulation head. The net result is a lower-tube-weight, lower-metal-

Fig. 4 C-E circulating systems

temperature wall with lower thermal stresses.

Another advantage to incorporating a recirculating pump is the greater flexibility of boiler geometry and layout. Also, more freedom exists in the arrangement of boiler heating surface, for with assured positive circulation, horizontal evaporation surface may be used to any extent desired.

The C-E system for controlled, forced, recirculation at the high subcritical-pressure level is called Controlled Circulation. C-E does not presume to select that pressure which sharply differentiates between the possibility of using thermally induced circulation from the advisability of using Controlled Circulation. However, C-E designers believe that there is a throttle-pressure level above 2200 psig, particularly in large pulverized-coal units, where Controlled Circulation becomes prudent. A 2850-psig drum-pressure limit has been established for Controlled Circulation steam generators. This limit permits operation of the 2400-psig throttle pressure cycle at 5 percent overpressure, or 2520 psig at the turbine, and as high as 2680 psig at the boiler superheater outlet. Above the critical point, a combination of once-through and Controlled Circulation principles (Combined Circulation) is used.

COMBINED CIRCULATON

The Combined Circulation system is a once-through steam generator with a superimposed controlled, forced, recirculation system for the furnace walls, Fig. 4. The furnace-wall system is protected by recirculation of fluid with a boiler circulating pump when once-through flow is insufficient at low loads. The pump eliminates the need for a bypass system for furnace-wall protection, and still allows once-through supercritical flow at higher output. This type of design permits furnace-wall tubes of sufficient inside diameter so as to maintain an adequate mass flow through the tubes at all operating conditions. Fig. 4 indicates the furnace-wall fluid flow with recirculating pumps, which are in use from zero to about 60 percent load. In the Combined Circulation design, all furnace walls are single-pass upflow,

with no mixing headers. Proper design tolerances and the use of tube orifices allow for flow unbalance or uneven heat absorption. The mixing vessel or sphere is substituted for the conventional drum to properly mix the recirculated flow from the furnace walls with the unit throughput.

The furnace-wall arrangements are similar, with water flow being a single upflow pass in all cases. The tube outside diameter (OD) for thermal circulation boilers is generally 2½ to 3 inches, whereas Controlled Circulation units have smaller tubes, most frequently 1¾ to 2 in. OD in the outer furnace walls, depending upon the size and peripheral dimension of the unit. Furnace-wall tubing for high subcritical pressures is usually SA-192 or SA-210, low or medium-carbon steel. Combined Circulation units use 1¼-in. OD tubing in the furnace walls, of SA-213 Type T-11 (1.25-percent chrome alloy) furnace-wall tubing. Fusion-welded wall construction is used on all three of the circulating systems.

THERMAL-CIRCULATION FURNACE DESIGN

Thermal circulation results from a density difference between the mixture of saturated water and feedwater in the downcomers (downtakes) and the lighter steam-water mixture in the furnace-wall tubes. The temperature and corresponding density in the downtakes can be changed somewhat in the initial design of a unit by varying the water temperature leaving the economizer. Fig. 5 shows how the furnace-wall operating pressure and the percent steam in the mixture in the wall tube affect the available thermal head for circulation. The available head is the difference between the weight of water in the unheated downcomer and the static head of the steam-water mixture in the heated waterwall tubes.

Fig. 6 shows a typical thermal-circulation reheat steam generator for burning pulverized subbituminous coal. The boiler is designed to serve a 256,000 kW turbine-generator and generates 1,777,000 lb of steam per hour with superheater outlet conditions of 1990 psig and 1005°F.

Tangential fuel nozzles are located at five elevations in the four corners of the boiler furnace. Vertical downcomers connecting the steam drum to the bottom waterwall header system supply the boiler water. Lower ends of the front, rear, and side wall tubes connect to the bottom waterwall headers and the upper ends connect to the upper headers. Relief (riser) tubes transport the mixture of steam and water from the waterwalls to the drum, where the steam is separated from the boiler water. To insure uniform distribution of steam and water, the connecting tubes are spaced evenly along the drum and headers. Steam which has been separated from the steam-water mixture in the drum passes on to the first superheater stage.

The first superheater stage is located in the vertical gas pass to the rear of the furnace. Saturated steam from the drum passes through the roof of the furnace, then down the walls enclosing the rear pass to the lower ring header. From this point the slightly superheated steam flows through the horizontal superheater tubes in a generally counterflow direction to the downward flow of the products of combustion. From the first superheater stage, the steam passes to the finishing or outlet stage which is a platen section located at the gas outlet of the furnace. The reheater is located between the finishing platen superheater and the initial superheater stage. The flow of furnace gas over the reheater is essentially counterflow to the flow of steam.

The economizer is located directly below the first-stage superheater. Water flows upward in the economizer to provide counterflow of furnace gas and feedwater. Outlet tubes of the economizer section extend vertically upward to form the supporting hanger tubes for the horizontal superheater and the economizer. These tubes then connect to a header above the roof; connecting piping conducts the feedwater from this header to the drum.

This boiler is of the balanced-draft type. Pulverizers are pressurized by primary-air fans. Ljungstrom trisector air preheaters with vertical shafts are located at the economizer gas outlet. The gas ducts connecting the economizer to the air preheater and at the air preheater outlet are arranged with hoppers for ash collection as well as to collect the drain-off wash water.

With the exception of the air preheaters, the entire boiler is supported from steel located at the roof elevation. Expansion joints are provided in the gas duct below the economizer and

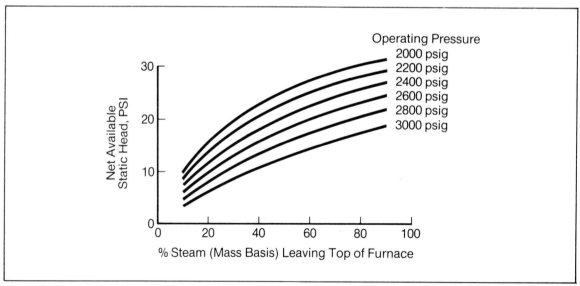

Fig. 5 **Typical available static head for circulation based on 200-ft. high furnace; this available head is independent of type of circulation**

in the air ducts between the air preheaters and the windboxes to accommodate the downward expansion of the boiler pressure parts in their heated condition.

Shown in Fig. 7 is a cross section of a drum used in C-E thermal-circulation boilers. In this drum, the steam-water mixture from the furnace passes through the centrifugal separators where a spin is imparted. This forces the water to the outer edge of the centrifugal separator where it is separated from the steam. Nearly dried, the steam passes through corrugated plates where, by low-velocity surface contact, the remaining moisture is removed by wetting action on the plates and final screen dryers.

The cross-sectional area of the drum limits the size and arrangement of the internal steam separators and dryers and, consequently, the acceptable rating in terms of lb/hr throughout per foot of length. A drum with a large diameter

Fig. 6 256-MW thermal-circulation tangentially fired pulverized-coal steam generator

affords more free area for water content at normal water level, and reduced moisture entrainment in the larger steam space. Within the limits of available pressure drop for steam/water separation, higher capacity separators and increased dryer surface can be provided to achieve a higher rating per foot of length.

For a specific diameter and arrangement of internal components, the drum capacity is proportional to length. The diameter and length, then, are determined by

■ unit generating capacity

■ the practical considerations of the spacing and arrangement of connecting tubes and piping with respect to drum-shell ligaments

■ the requirement to insure a uniform distribution of steam and water flow entering and leaving the drum

Vaporous carryover of certain boiler water constituents, such as silica and sodium, is determined by the respective volatility of these unwanted constituents, or their solubility in steam, as discussed in Chapter 5. They must be controlled by limiting the boiler-water solids concentration at high drum pressures. (See Chapter 11).

The percent of boiler-water solids that will be carried over by moisture entrained in the steam leaving the drum is proportional to the boiler-water solids concentration and to the percent moisture carried over. Moisture is removed sequentially by the steam separators, followed by gravitational separation of droplets in the steam space, and finally by the steam dryers, arranged to prevent moisture reentrainment.

A high water level in the drum reduces the steam space available for gravitational separation of moisture. An excessively high level can impair efficiency of primary and secondary separators, resulting in an increased moisture

Fig. 7 Steam-drum internals for C-E thermal-circulation reheat steam generators

content entering the dryers and a corresponding increase in carryover moisture in which there are entrained solids.

The dissolved solids in the boiler water should be held as low as practicable, consistent with the recommended chemical treatment for boiler-tube corrosion protection. This assures that solids carryover during high water-level excursions will be negligible (see Chapter 11).

CONTROLLED CIRCULATION

C-E's first Controlled Circulation boiler in an American central station went into service in 1942 at the Somerset Station of Montaup Electric Company. Since then, the principle of Controlled Circulation has been widely accepted for boilers ranging from waste heat, fluidized bed, marine and industrial units up to the largest power-plant installations. The reliability and safe operating records of Controlled Circulation boilers have justified their selection in power stations throughout the world.

THE CONTROLLED CIRCULATION SYSTEM

Water flow through the economizer is generally the same with either a thermal-circulation or a controlled recirculation boiler. Water from the economizer enters the drum, is mixed with the water discharged from the steam-water separators, and is directed to the large downcomers which are evenly spaced along the drum. From this point on, a C-E Controlled Circulation unit differs from a thermal-circulation boiler in five respects:

1. Circulating pumps are placed in the downtake circuit to provide sufficient head to insure adequate, positive upward circulation under all operating conditions.

2. Orifices are installed in the inlets of waterwall circuits to assist in obtaining a predetermined, proportioned flow of water to tubes of varying length and heat absorption.

3. Furnace-wall tubing is of smaller diameter and has lower metal temperatures than that for thermal circulation, all made possible by the head available from the pumps.

4. The drums are internally shrouded to provide uniform heating and cooling of the drum shell, for maximum maneuverability during startup, load changes, and shutdown.

5. Controlled Circulation boilers have an economizer recirculation line which provides a positive flow from the BWCP discharge through the economizer to the drum. Under start-up conditions, with the feedwater valve closed, this feature prevents steaming in the economizer and precludes the need for blowdown with its associated heat loss.

The boiler circulating pump suction is taken from a suction manifold, which is supplied by the downtakes. From the boiler circulating pumps the water discharges into the waterwall inlet ring header through the pump discharge lines. In the inlet header, the water passes through strainers and then through orifices feeding the furnace-wall tubes, the extended sidewall tubes and the water-cooled element spacers. The mixture of steam and water leaving the evaporative circuits is discharged into the upper drum, in which the steam is separated from the water.

In the drum of a Controlled Circulation unit, Fig. 8, the basic separation process is similar to that of thermal circulation drums except that the available pump head permits more efficient use of the centrifugal devices. One distinct advantage of the Controlled Circulation design is the internal shrouding of the drum. This watertight shrouding directs the flow of steam and water returning from the furnace around the inside surface of the drum, providing uniform heating. This uniform heating eliminates thermal stresses from temperature differences through the thick wall of the drum, between the submerged and unsubmerged portion of the shell, and from end to end. This facilitates rapid startups, shutdowns and cyclic operation.

In operation, a Controlled Circulation boiler has full-load circulation established before any heat is introduced into the furnace, which then permits rapid startup with virtually no time restrictions because of circulation in the pressure-part system.

CONTROLLED CIRCULATION PUMP AND PIPING SYSTEM

A water circulating system diagram (Fig. 9) shows the schematic arrangement of the boiler circulating pump and downcomer piping system. Downcomers installed on the steam drum carry the recirculated boiler water, mixed with the feedwater, into the circulating pumps. These pumps are connected through a common suction manifold that insures a flow through all the downcomers regardless of the number or location of the circulating pumps in service. This feature minimizes the water level difference along the length of the steam drum and contributes to good performance of the steam/water separation equipment independent of the number of pumps in service.

The schematic (Fig. 9) shows that the downcomers are straight vertical pipes connecting the steam drum and the suction manifold and that the circulating pumps are mounted on the suction manifold. Using the boiler as the support for the pumps is a feature that eliminates any need for external supports and prevents undue stresses which may affect the pump alignment.

The head developed by the circulating pumps is only that required to supplement the thermal head and, for a typical Controlled Circulation boiler is 25 psi or less; for this, a single-stage impeller is adequate. Boiler water circulating pumps (BWCP) are described further in Chapter 15.

STRAINERS AND ORIFICES FOR STEAM-GENERATING TUBES

Strainers or screens between the circulating pump discharge and the orifices prevent large particles of foreign material from plugging the orifices at the entrance to the generating cir-

Fig. 8 **Steam-drum internals for C-E Controlled Circulation reheat steam generators**

Fig. 9 **Furnace-wall system for C-E Controlled Circulation boiler**

cuits. Located in the inlet header to which the steam generating tubes are connected, the strainers may be installed in individual tubes or may provide for a group of tubes. Simplification dictates one strainer for a group of circuits whenever possible. This has the advantage that a fouled strainer will have less of an impact on flow through any particular orifice. Such an arrangement of strainers is shown in Fig. 10 for circuits with orifices contained in a waterwall supply header.

The strainers have small holes that, in number, are many times the area of the orifices. The holes also are smaller than the smallest orifice. This permits very fine particles to pass through the orifices without difficulty and also induces settling in the headers and drums of the larger particles. The strainers are made up in portable panels, permitting access to the orifices. As might be expected, the strainers are most important during the initial start-up of a new unit because, during this period of operation, in addition to crud originating in the boiler, foreign material is brought into the

Fig. 10 **Arrangement of orifices and strainers in lower ring header of C-E Controlled Circulation unit**

boiler from preboiler-cycle feedwater piping and auxiliary equipment.

Orifices are shop-fitted to adapters welded to the internal header wall. A keying arrangement insures that each orifice is installed in its proper tube circuit once the correctness of the initial installation of the orifice mount adapter has been established. Orifice size varies for different circuits or groups of circuits, depending on their length, arrangement and heat absorption.

DESIGN OF A CONTROLLED CIRCULATION FURNACE-WALL SYSTEM

The orificing and selection of pump head for a Controlled Circulation boiler are best understood by first reviewing a non-pump-assisted thermal circulation unit design.

The designer of a thermal circulation furnace of a given plan area determines the total number of parallel vertical tubes making up the outer walls of the furnace; a common selection is to use 2½-inch OD tubes on 3-inch centers. The next step, based on experience with units of similar physical size and heat duty, is to establish the size and number of unheated downcomers from the steam drum to the lower waterwall-header system. Along with this, it is necessary to establish the arrangement, diameter and number of relief tubes connecting the upper waterwall headers to the drum. An average overall percent steam leaving the furnace is then calculated, based on the heat absorbed by the "average" furnace tube and on the flow resistances in that tube, the downcomers, the relief tubes, the drum internals, and all associated entrance and exit losses.

Within the limits of available thermal head and physical space, adjustments in downcomer and relief-tube size and flow resistances can be made at this time to increase or decrease the average circulation to achieve satisfactory cooling of the furnace-wall.

Tubes in the furnace enclosure have different lengths, dissimilar configurations, and receive varying amounts of heat. Any tube absorbing more heat than the average tube has a *higher* circulating water flow, but probably also a high

percent steam leaving; typically, a 50-percent increase in absorption above the average, equally received throughout the length of a tube, produces a 10 to 20 percent increase in water flow entering. For every tube receiving *more* than the average tube, there is another tube receiving *less* water. Each tube must be analyzed on the basis of its individual heat absorption to arrive at its own mass percentage of steam (quality) leaving.

Realize that, in designing a waterwall section—a group of parallel tubes having a common (bottom) inlet header and a common upper (outlet) header, Fig. 11—the pressure drop or head loss between the headers has to be identical for every tube. This situation exists irrespective of any pump assistance. Flow in each tube, and percent steam in the mixture leaving, differs depending upon

- heat absorption (overall and local)
- effective inside diameter of tubing (as affected by manufacturing tolerances)
- effective tube length (accounting for bends)
- amount of tubing "shaded" from heat
- location relative to feeder tubes
- orifices (if used)

Tube A, for instance, may be longer, but have

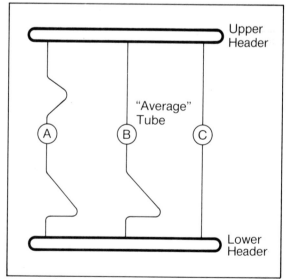

Fig. 11 **Schematic of furnace-wall section; head loss between headers is identical for each tube**

a lower overall heat absorption than the "average" tube B; without orificing, it will have a lower flow than B. Tube C, if shorter than B but fully exposed for its entire length to a high heat, will have a higher flow than the average tube (B). But *all* tubes must have the same differential pressure from header to header.

An equilibrium condition will always result in the flow-plus-orifice losses being additive to the weight of the saturated mixture in each tube, at any given moment. This is because the header-to-header differential is comprised of

■ the weight of the steam/water mixture in each tube

■ the pressure drop due to the resistance to flow of the steam/water mixture in each tube

■ orifice pressure drop (if any).

The flow may or may not be enough to cool the tube properly and it may even reverse (from upward to downward, and vice versa) from time to time, dependent upon the variables acting on it.

For unorificed parallel tubes, the flow-related pressure drop equality can be expressed approximately as

$$f\,L_A\,m_A{}^2 V_A = f\,L_B\,m_B{}^2 V_B = f\,L_C\,m_C{}^2 V_C$$

where f is a common friction factor, m_N is mass flow in the Nth tube, L_N is the effective length of any tube, and V_N is the average specific volume of the steam-water mixture in the Nth tube.

In tubes where mass flow is lower because of lower heat absorption, the specific volume is correspondingly higher to compensate for the flow resistance of a high-absorption tube with higher mass flow. For any given overall steam content, water between lower and upper headers redistributes from tube to tube according to the above relationships.

Fig. 12 gives a comparison between thermal-circulation and Controlled Circulation performance. In the upper curve, average mass flow in furnace-wall tubes is shown as a function of design heat absorption. Note that the circulating pumps move the maximum mass of water before firing commences, because the water is most dense at that time. The lower

curve shows that the designer of a Controlled Circulation unit can preferentially increase the flow in tubes with less favorable configurations to provide more cooling at all loads.

The orifice pressure drop designed into Controlled Circulation circuits is additive to the heated-circuit resistance loss and static head. Orificing individual tubes or groups of tubes provides either adequate mass flow or a desired exit quality under a wide range of postulated operating conditions.

The orifice pressure drop has a dampening effect on the almost random behavior of a purely thermal-circulation unit. Because the orifice drop occurs at the beginning of a circuit, before heat has been added in the furnace, the principal variable is mass flow through the opening, with no effect of differential specific volume. This is a very significant difference between pure *forced* circulation, in which most

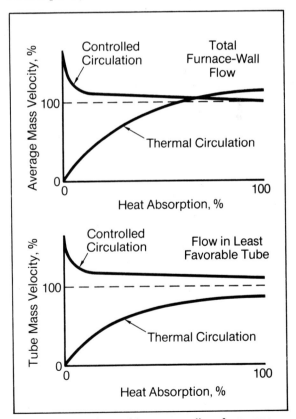

Fig. 12 Comparison of furnace-wall performance— thermal circulation versus Controlled Circulation

of the pressure drop is in the heated tube circuits themselves, and C-E's selectively orificed pump-assisted *controlled* circulation.

CONTROLLED CIRCULATION STEAM GENERATORS

Fig. 13 shows a Controlled Circulation reheat boiler designed to provide steam to a 500,000 kW turbine generator. This is a single open furnace. It has a superheater with both pendant and horizontal surfaces and a reheater with both radiant wall and pendant surfaces.

This boiler has a rated output of 4,100,000 lb of steam per hour with superheater outlet conditions of 2620 psig and 1005°F. It is designed to burn high-volatile bituminous coal and is of the balanced-draft type, with forced and induced draft and primary-air fans.

Six C-E pulverizers supply coal to tangential fuel nozzles located in the four corners of the furnace. The supply of water to the waterwalls begins with the steam drum. The water travels down through the downcomers to the suction manifold and into the circulating pumps from which it is discharged to the lower ring header which has flow-distributing orifices. The mixture of steam and water that flows up through the various heated circuits is collected in an arrangement of waterwall outlet headers located just above the furnace roof. The steam-water mixture passes through connecting tubes to the drum, where steam is separated from boiler water and passes on to the superheater.

The first-stage superheater is located in the vertical pass at the rear of the furnace. Saturated steam from the drum passes through the furnace radiant roof, backpass roof and walls, and then enters the lower inlet header of the first stage. The steam flows upward through the first-stage superheater and into the second stage, comprised of pendant double-loop panels located directly above the furnace. The final superheater is of the vertical pendant-platen type, and is also above the furnace, between the panels and the furnace nose.

Reheat steam enters the reheater radiant-wall inlet header and travels upward through the radiant wall tubes. After leaving the radiant-

wall outlet header, the reheat steam enters the low-temperature rear pendant, and continues into the finishing reheat pendant.

The plain-tube economizer is located directly below the first stage superheater. Vertical outlet tubes from the economizer serve to support both the economizer banks and first-stage superheater. The tubes then terminate in an economizer outlet header above the roof from which connecting piping transports the water to the drum.

Two vertical shaft regenerative type (Ljungstrom) trisector air preheaters are located beneath the economizer.

Fig. 14 shows a C-E Controlled Circulation boiler to serve a 714 MW turbine-generator; it has a rated output of 5,230,000 lb of steam per hour with superheater outlet conditions of 2620 psig and 1005°F. Again, tangential fuel nozzles at seven levels are located in the four corners of the open furnace. Each level is fed by its own pulverizer.

The circulation system supplies water to the waterwalls, with flow leaving the bottom of the drum through six 16-in. diameter downcomers and flowing to the circulation-pump suction manifold—the common suction for all three circulating pumps. Water discharged from the pumps flows through six 14-in. discharge lines to the lower front waterwall inlet ring header. Water travels upward through the furnace-wall tubes to the upper headers. Tubes between the upper headers and the drum (called risers or relief tubes) transport the mixture of steam and water from the waterwalls to the drum where the steam is separated from the boiler water and then passes to the first superheater section in the rear gas pass.

Saturated steam from the drum flows through the roof tubes and then cools the rear gas-pass walls (roof, side, front, and rear) before entering the first superheater section inlet header. From here, the slightly superheated steam travels counterflow to the gas to the outlet of the first section. It then passes to the panel section located at the top of the furnace. The finishing superheater is a pendant type. The pendant reheater is between the superheater

Fig. 13 Side elevation of 500-MW Controlled Circulation tangentially coal-fired steam generator

panel section and the final superheater section.

The tubes of the economizer, which is directly below the superheater, terminate in headers located between the top of the economizer and the first superheater section. Piping connected to the ends of these headers transports the heated water to the drum.

ADVANTAGES
OF CONTROLLED CIRCULATION

The C-E proprietary design of subcritical pump-assisted recirculation boiler, trade-marked Controlled Circulation, has many features that have made it a preferred choice of many electrical-generating utilities throughout the world.

Some of the advantages of Controlled Circulation are covered in Chapter 5; however, a primary reason for selecting a large coal-fired steam generator of the Controlled Circulation type in the 1980's and beyond, is its characteristic of *high dynamic maneuverability*. The fact that furnace-wall flow is positively estab-

Fig. 14 Open-furnace Controlled Circulation steam generator serving a 714-MW turbine-generator

lished, in an upward direction, *before* heat is applied enables an operator to fire such a furnace at any rate desired—that is, Controlled Circulation furnace walls and steam drums are never a limiting factor in building or changing load. Again, Controlled Circulation units are inherently better suited to operate under cycling conditions (particularly those demanded by two-shift operation) than other boiler types. This important aspect of the design is covered in depth in the subsection Design Features for Variable Load Operation of large steam generators later in this Chapter.

OPTIMUM CHEMICAL CLEANING

Circulating pumps on a boiler facilitate both pre-operational cleaning and operational scale removal. Laboratory testing with circulation at velocities of 0.5 to 1.0 ft/sec or greater has indicated that complete scale removal can be accomplished in 10 to 20 minutes following initial solvent contact. A significant reduction from the usual 4- to 6-hour hydrochloric-acid contact period can be obtained in pumped-circulation boilers where desired velocity conditions and uniform cleaning are assured in all tube circuits.

In a thermal-circulation boiler, solvent interchange or mixing from section to section is slow or does not occur, and significantly different levels of ion concentration can be noted in samples taken from various locations in a unit. A reasonably complete picture of what is occurring in a unit can be obtained by multipoint sampling. Although multisample monitoring is important during pre-operational cleaning to establish local ion equilibrium, it is of even greater interest in operational scale removal to guard against solvent depletion or hide-out in local areas. In units where recirculation can be maintained, uniform solvent concentration is rapidly established in all portions of a unit, and one sample point will give an indication of conditions throughout the unit.

Under a short solvent-contact procedure that is used with Controlled Circulation boilers, then, the solvent contact time is no longer than 30 minutes; with positive circulation, rapid and complete cleaning is assured with a minimum exposure time of pressure parts to the cleaning solvent. This also minimizes boiler downtime and, utilizing the rapid shutdown and startup capabilities of such boilers, it makes it possible to complete the entire procedure during a weekend outage.

DETECTING DETERIORATION OF FEEDWATER QUALITY

Carryover of metallic oxides and other impurities from the preboiler system may cause deposits on heated water circuits of any boiler. In severe cases such deposits can lead to tube failures.

The Controlled Circulation boiler offers an advantage for detecting deposits without removing the unit from service, by observing the circulating pump differential pressure between the pump suction manifold and either the discharge manifold or the waterwall lower header. Observation of the differential pressure provides a convenient external means of detecting internal waterwall system deposits and *anticipating* more serious operation difficulties.

The actual differential across the pump at normal full-load operation is established during initial operation, when the boiler is free of deposits. The differential pressure is then checked periodically at full-load operation. If there is an indicated difference between the baseline and later data, the boiler load may be reduced until an outage presents the opportunity to inspect and clean internal surfaces of water circuits, as described in Chapter 20.

OPERATION WITH WATERWALL TUBE LEAKS

Because of the available pump head, Controlled Circulation units use smaller diameter tubing than thermal circulation boilers, and incorporate orifices at the entrance to the tubes for optimum flow distribution. The two act to control and reduce the amount of water that can pass through a tube leak of a given size, resulting in a significantly lower damage potential to adjacent tubes than in a thermal unit; also, circulation in other waterwall tubes is not adversely affected and the makeup water system is not overloaded. This feature permits the operator to keep the unit in service until it is convenient to shut down. For example, operation can continue through a peak period or until a weekend. There have been many cases where a Controlled Circulation unit has been operated for several days with a waterwall tube leak. An additional capability is that of forced furnace-wall cooling with the pumps, which allows boiler cooldown with uniform stresses without using the feedwater pump or dumping feedwater to the condenser.

OPERATING-PRESSURE FLEXIBILITY

The curve in Fig. 15 shows that a Controlled Circulation steam generator can be operated through a wide range of pressure at full load. Operation within the permissible area allows great latitude in establishing a desirable sliding-pressure pattern.

WATER TREATMENT CONSIDERATIONS

In comparison to once-through boilers, Controlled Circulation boilers have numerous advantages in water treatment. Some important ones are described in the following text.

■ Drum boilers can remain "on line" during a condenser leak because the drum gives added

Fig. 15 Maximum permissible capacity as a function of operating pressure in drum, C-E Controlled Circulation boilers

protection. In the event of a condenser leak (greater than 0.5 ppm solids in the hot well), desuperheating must be discontinued and steam temperature limited by lowering fuel-nozzle tilt or possibly a drop in load. Under similar hot-well conditions, a once-through unit must be shut down. (See Chapter 11.)

■ During normal operation, polishers may leak small amounts of solids, which may be basic or acidic. In a once-through unit, these solids will continue to the turbine unchanged. There have been cases of turbine corrosion damage from these solids which are concentrated by the turbine. In a drum boiler, chemical treatment of the boiler water renders these solids harmless.

■ Chemical cleaning is facilitated with in-place pumps that can provide positive circulation as required by various solvents. This reduces the temporary piping required and eliminates the need for external pumps.

■ Base-loaded drum boilers are not as restricted on start-up as once-through units in regard to feedwater quality. Once-through units should have a cleanup loop associated with polishers to remove iron oxide and reduce silica in feedwater before start-up. Base-loaded drum boilers do not require this loop.

THERMAL CIRCULATION VERSUS CONTROLLED CIRCULATION

In choosing between thermally-induced circulation and Controlled Circulation, the following must be taken into account.

■ Although circulation does in fact increase in response to heat applied, the increase in flow is not directly proportional to the increase in heat flux. That is, although there is usually a larger amount of water circulated in an individual tube when more heat is applied, the increase may not be completely adequate to provide proper tube protection.

■ Slag can form heavily, and does form unpredictably, on different areas of the furnace at different times; it can be removed by sootblowers, or shed because of its mass, equally unpredictably. It is common to have a major part of the heat input to a furnace-wall tube in its upper half, because of sootblower cleaning or shedding, which can result in a calculable *decrease* in circulation rate in an individual tube or a group of tubes. Flow reversal can occur, with local overheating a possibility.

■ Controlled Circulation and thermal circulation boilers have the same thermal circulating head available if they have the same furnace height, the same economizer water-leaving temperature, and the same circulation ratio. (Fig. 5). The pumps and orifices incorporated in Controlled Circulation *do not destroy* the available thermal head or lessen the density difference between furnace-wall tube and unheated downcomer.

■ To assure there is adequate available head under all firing conditions and maneuvering the boiler, C-E adds orifices so that all tubes will receive water under all conditions and shrouds the thick-walled steam drum to cool it

or heat it in a controlled manner under all rates of load change. The circulating pumps complement these engineered modifications to the simple thermal-circulation design, and provide the pressure head to overcome the incrementally increased resistance. A most important point is that flow increases are created with pump assistance that are much greater than those available through the thermosyphonic phenomenon. This point is illustrated (Fig. 16) by comparing the pressure drops in the various components of typical thermal-circulation and Controlled Circulation steam generators.

■ The net power consumption of the circulating pumps is small compared to that in other circuitry of the boiler for accomplishing basically the same objective of equalized flow distribution with variation in load, firing conditions, and heat-absorption patterns. The

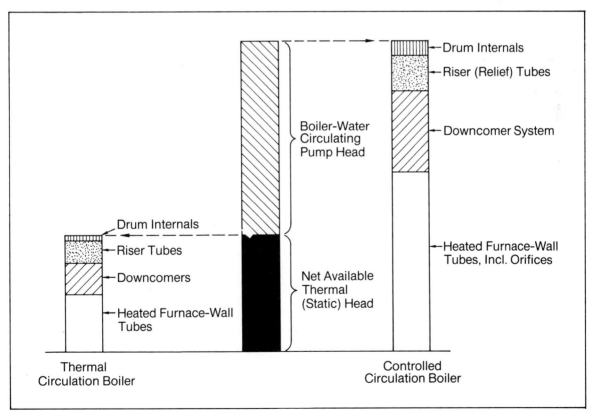

Fig. 16 Comparison of component pressure drops and available static head—thermal-circulation versus Controlled Circulation

feedwater-pump power charged to a unit, because of its superheater and economizer pressure drops, is substantially higher than the unrecovered power loss of the circulating pumps.

ACQUISITION OF CIRCULATION DESIGN DATA

The furnace enclosure is one of the most critical components of a steam generator and must be conservatively designed to assure high boiler availability. The *circulation objective* is to assure sufficient cooling of the furnace tubes during all operating conditions with an adequate margin of reserve for transient upsets. Adequate circulation prevents excessive metal temperatures or temperature differentials that could cause failures in the furnace-wall tubes due to overstressing or corrosion.

The design of a furnace-wall circulation system is a procedure requiring knowledge and data obtained both from field operating units and laboratory testing. The field data from operating units is required to understand and characterize the heat-absorption characteristics for a particular type of furnace configuration and firing system, throughout a wide range of load and water-side operating pressures, and the effect that fuel variation has on furnace heat absorption.

Furnace absorption/distribution standards are developed by correlating test data from many operating units. The following important parameters are considered in this work: furnace geometry, fuel, excess air, type of firing, disposition of fuel nozzles, heat input, and furnace-wall cleanliness. By using these standards, it is possible to calculate the vertical absorption-rate profile, the lateral heat-absorption distribution and other furnace heat accumulation patterns to properly engineer the furnace-wall circulation system.

The laboratory data is required for a knowledge of the physical properties of the furnace-wall tubing under actual furnace heat-transfer conditions. In the laboratory, flow versus qual-

Fig. 17 High-pressure heat-transfer loop, C-E's Kreisinger Development Laboratory

ity criteria have been established to predict DNB (departure from nucleate boiling) in a furnace tube containing boiling water. This has been done in C-E's high-pressure test loop at the Kreisinger Development Laboratory (KDL), Fig. 17. The allowable combinations of pressure, mass flow, local bulk quality, and local crown absorption rate have been calculated from the correlations based on the laboratory data. Additionally, the derived engineering standards take into account data scatter, dimensional tolerance, instrumentation error, and boiler water chemistry, all to provide sufficient margin to accommodate actual field operating conditions.

C-E researchers have tested both full-size smooth and rifled tubes; this forms the basis for the design engineering of high-pressure boilers using either type of furnace-wall tubing.

LABORATORY TEST PROGRAM

Tests on rifled tubing were conducted to determine the allowable quality without departure from nucleate boiling.

The C-E heat-transfer loop (Fig. 18) used for these tests consists of three principal parts:

■ the rifled-tube test sections, heated with sheathed heater elements either full or half circumferentially

■ the main loop, including drum, circulating pump, SCR-controlled electrical fluid preheaters, flow-control valves and orifices, and condenser (cooling) system consisting of a main condenser and a reflux condenser (for trapping non-condensable gases)

■ the temperature and flow measurement system, with its instrumentation and data acquisition and reduction equipment.

In the pressure range of 2700 to 2850 psig, the data relating mass flow to critical quality with constant heat flux shows

■ A high, constant-quality region at elevated mass flows, in which DNB qualities are independent of mass-flow rate

■ A low, variable-quality region at reduced mass flows, where DNB qualities depend greatly on the mass-flow rate

■ A transition region between them. Above 2850 psig, the transition region disappears. Below 2700 psig, DNB critical quality is independent of mass flow and only slightly influenced by incremental change in heat flux. The transition mass-flow rate may be considered a minimum allowable mass flow, above which DNB quality is determined by flux rate only.

DEVELOPMENT OF SUPERCRITICAL TECHNOLOGY

During the late 1920's the Swiss firm, Sulzer Brothers, Ltd. of Winterthur, became interested in once-through boiler design, and developed the Monotube boiler for application below the 3208 psia critical pressure. Their program included the installation of a laboratory boiler in

Fig. 18 Schematic arrangement of high-pressure heat-transfer loop shown in Fig. 17

1929. The first commercial installations were made about 1932. The decade of the 1930's marked the commercial acceptance of the once-through boiler in the European market for the pressure range of 1200 to 2400 psig. The development gathered strength, especially in Germany, and now a majority of the large, high-pressure steam-generating units installed are of the once-through type.

Combustion Engineering, Inc. entered into a license and technical assistance agreement with Sulzer Brothers, Ltd. in 1953 to benefit from their experience with the once-through Sulzer Monotube boiler and its controls. Marked advances in water technology, including ion exchange processes using demineralizing techniques, justified the confidence that continuous and reliable operation could be expected from large once-through boilers. Since that time, C-E and others have built a substantial number of once-through and other types of supercritical-pressure steam generators that have provided the utility industry with the ability to improve fossil plant efficiency.

The first of the second generation supercritical-pressure steam generating units designed and built by Combustion Engineering was the Combined Circulation unit for the Bull Run plant of the Tennessee Valley Authority. This unit began operation in late 1965 and demonstrated that the basic design principles of once-through flow supplemented by recirculated flow with circulating pumps, was well suited for large utility applications.[2]

For a detailed history of the development of the large supercritical steam generator, see Chapter 25 of the 1967 Combustion text[3] and the references therein.

Table III. Heat Rate Improvement —Net Plant—

Temperature, °F	2400 PSI	3500 PSI
	—Btu/kWhr—	
1000/1000	9,000	8,860
1050/1000	8,930	8,800
1000/1025/1050	—	8,630

HEAT RATE—THE WHY OF SUPERCRITICAL PRESSURE

The data in Table III give some insight into the relative improvement of net plant heat rate with several of the available cycles. Large incremental decreases in plant heat rate (improved efficiency) are very difficult to achieve. Increasing the superheat temperature of a subcritical unit to 1050°F, in lieu of 1000°F, provides only 0.8-percent improvement in the heat rate. Increasing pressure to 3500 psi at 1000°/1000°F, yields an improvement of 1.5 percent, and the double-reheat ramp cycle improves 4.1 percent above 2400 psi at 1000°/1000°F.

Many factors affect plant heat rate besides the cycle itself, such as load regime, forced-outage rate, fuel, condenser temperature, and boiler exit-gas temperature. These and other items noted in Chapter 1 must all be considered when selecting a pressure and temperature.

Fig. 19 shows the relative capital cost of a 750-MW supercritical steam generator to be about 3.5 percent greater than a subcritical drum-type unit serving a turbine-generator of the same capacity.[4]

The turbine generator and associated balance-of-plant equipment are approximately 1.5 percent lower in capital cost for the supercritical cycle, which offsets the higher cost of the supercritical steam generator. There is no significant difference in the erection costs for a drum type or supercritical unit. When considering the supercritical cycle, double reheat

Fig. 19 Cost comparison—drum-type boiler versus supercritical

should be investigated because the incremental increase in capital cost is relatively small—an increase in steam-generator capital cost of approximately 3 to 4 percent.

SUPERCRITICAL ONCE-THROUGH CIRCULATION

As discussed in Chapter 5, in a simple once-through boiler, circulation in any part of the unit can be established only by operating the feed pump and continuously admitting feedwater to the unit. To adequately cool the furnace-wall circuits in the vicinity of the firing equipment, it is necessary to establish a certain minimum water flow before the unit is fired. It has been normal practice to design once-through units so that the desired minimum velocity is obtained at a flow rate of approximately 30 percent of maximum flow. Although it is possible to obtain this minimum velocity with less than 30 percent flow, the result is an excessively high pressure drop at full load. On the other hand, a higher flow rate during start-up requires more extensive equipment for handling the start-up flow and also a higher firing rate and greater fuel cost during the starting procedure.

Because the feedwater must be very pure, it is expensive to produce and uneconomical to waste. A turbine bypass system is customarily provided to reclaim the water. For large supercritical-pressure units, the bypass system, sized for at least 30 percent of full-load flow, may be a serious economic handicap. Such a bypass system requires a major investment in equipment that may be seldom used, while it presents design, operating and maintenance problems.

C-E COMBINED CIRCULATION

Combined Circulation is a combination of once-through flow with recirculation, particularly developed by C-E for use at supercritical operating pressures (Fig. 20). Recirculation rather than feedwater flow protects the furnace walls during start-up and low loads. At high load levels, feedwater flow eliminates the need for recirculation.

Applying this concept to a steam generator involves two important characteristics. First, recirculation through the furnace-wall system is achieved by the flow from a single recirculating pump superimposed on the once-through flow. Regardless of load, it automatically, and without use of separate controls, produces required flows in the furnace-wall tubes. Second, the recirculating pump handles both recircu-

Fig. 20 **Development of Combined Circulation**

Fig. 21 C-E 770-MW Combined Circulation tangentially coal-fired steam generator

lated flow and feedwater flow and thereby assists the feedpump, reducing some of its power requirement.

Although Combined Circulation is a feature of the furnace-wall system only—flow through economizer and superheater being maintained by feedwater flow exclusively—it has a far-reaching effect on arrangement and operation of the whole plant cycle.

TYPICAL COMBINED CIRCULATION UNIT

The most common type of supercritical steam generator in operation in the United States is the C-E Combined Circulation design. About 75 pecent of the operating units are in the 600 to 900 MW size range, most having single reheat to 1005°F. A nominal 770-MW Combined Circulation boiler is shown in Fig. 21. It is designed for balanced-draft firing of sub-bituminous A coal. At maximum continuous steam flow of 5,400,000 lb/hr, with superheater outlet conditions of 3590 psig and 1005°F, net

turbine-generator output is 805 MW. The reheater flow is 4,850,000 lb/hr with an outlet temperature of 1005°F from inlet conditions of 583°F and 676 psig.

The furnace, of the centerwall or divided type, has an overall width of 83.5 feet, a depth of approximately 41 feet and a volume of 465,500 cubic feet. The outer walls are fusion-welded and consist of 1¼ in. OD tubes on 1¾ in. centers. The centerwall is comprised of 2 in. OD tubes on 2⅜ in. centers.

Seven C-E size 1003 pressurized pulverizers supply coal to the seven elevations of fuel nozzles; two centrifugal fans furnish the primary air to the pulverizers.

SYSTEM INTEGRATION

The simplified flow diagram (Fig. 22) illustrates several features that have significantly advanced system integration.

First, the supercritical once-through steam generator closes the steam and feedwater con-

Fig. 22 Simplified flow diagram of C-E Combined Circulation steam generator

nections of the steam-power cycle in a continuous heat-addition loop without the division established by the water level in the drum of subcritical recirculating units. This fact is recognized by an automatic, non-interacting, feed-forward control system, geared to the dynamic characteristics of the entire plant.

Second, system integration permits starting the turbine and steam generator simultaneously under conditions that provide an optimum of turbine protection for accelerated cold and hot starts. This facility is combined with unique features to remove solids and oxides from both preboiler and boiler systems.

Third, the principle of Combined Circulation eliminates the basic requirement of all other once-through systems for minimum feedwater flow through the furnace. Heat removed from the steam-generating system during any operation is determined only by functions other than furnace-wall protection. The feedwater heating system, therefore, need not be used to reduce start-up heat losses. This in turn avoids contamination of this system by start-up flow and makes the system very simple. Eliminating the minimum flow requirement also greatly facilitates use of the turbine-driven feedpumps for start-up and avoids complications from separate start-up pumps.

Finally, Combined Circulation benefits the steam generator by allowing for improved design and construction of the furnace-wall system which substantially reduces the boiler pressure drop bringing with it both first-cost and operating savings.

BOILER-TURBINE SYSTEM

A simplified arrangement of the steam generator and associated systems within the plant cycle is shown in Fig. 22. The feedwater enters the steam generator through the feedwater valve (FW). From the economizer the feedwater passes through the recirculating pump and its associated isolating valves to the furnace, where it flows in series through the centerwall and the outerwalls, then through the enclosure walls of the rear gas pass. At this point the steam passes through a system of

throttling valves (BTB and BT) and continues through four sections of horizontal and pendant superheater before reaching the steam leads to the turbine through an outlet piping system. Steam is returned to the steam generator for reheating in a two-section reheater, then returned to the turbine. The condensate passes through a demineralizer and a series of low-pressure heaters to an open deaerator. The turbine-driven feedpump then returns the feedwater through a string of high-pressure heaters to the feedwater valve.

The diagram also shows the main components of a very simple start-up system within which the throttling valves (BT and BTB) belong. Upstream of these valves, piping connects the furnace-wall system with the extraction valves (BE) and the start-up separator. The steam side of the separator is connected to the superheater system through a steam admission valve (SA) and to the condenser through a spillover valve (SP). Water from the separator is discharged to the condenser through the water drain valve (WD). The steam drain valve (SD), close to the turbine valve chest, discharges the steam for superheater cooling and heating of steam leads to the condenser and an injection valve (IC) regulates desuperheating water flow for condenser protection.

Auxiliary superheated steam is furnished to turbine seals, the deaerator, and the main feedpump turbine from separate start-up boilers.

COMBINED CIRCULATION RECIRCULATING SYSTEM

The components of the Combined Circulation recirculating system are shown in a simplified isometric view in Fig. 23. Mixing feedwater flow with recirculated flow (as takes place in the drum of a subcritical unit) occurs here in the spherical mixing vessel. A single downcomer brings the fluid to the two recirculating pumps which hang from a symmetrical tee connection on the downcomer. Only one pump is needed for low-load operation, the other being a spare on hot standby. Neither is required at high loads. The pumps discharge to a common header from which supply piping

Fig. 23 **Flow diagram of furnace-wall and startup system for Combined Circulation centerwall unit**

runs directly to the furnace-wall headers.

The subcritical drum (which functions to separate steam and water) is eliminated at supercritical pressure. The recirculated flow is returned from the outlet of the furnace-wall enclosure to the mixing vessel through a single recirculating line. A stop-check valve in this line automatically prevents bypassing the furnace-wall system when recirculation has ceased at the upper load range. Because downcomer, pumps, and piping to the centerwall handle mixed or through flow at low temperatures, they are all fabricated of carbon steel. The recirculating line and the mixing vessel use chrome-alloy material.

From the furnace-wall outlet headers, the fluid is piped to the backpass, where it cools the walls. From the backpass outlet header, the total boiler through-flow goes through the BT and BTB valve complex to the superheater. During waterwall recirculation conditions, a portion of flow in excess of the steam generator

through-flow is recirculated back to the mixing chamber—this flow is extracted ahead of the BT/BTB valve complex.

FURNACE-WALL SYSTEM

The arrangement of the Combined Circulation furnace-wall system (Fig. 24) has several characteristics:

■ Flow in all furnace and backpass enclosure walls is in the upward direction only.

■ With single-pass flow, all tubes in a welded panel have the same inlet temperature.

■ Centerwall flow and outerwall flow are in series on divided-furnace units.

■ All components of the recirculating system except the recirculating line are in series with the once-through flow.

■ All walls are formed by drainable, welded-tube panels.

These characteristics provide a number of important advantages, among which is the de-

Fig. 24 (a) Furnace-wall system flow diagram for Combined Circulation unit with centerwall
Fig. 24 (b) Furnace-wall system flow diagram for Combined Circulation open-furnace design

sign flexibility available from the presence of a circulating pump with which the flow quantity through the parallel tubes around the furnace periphery can be distributed. A better pressure drop performance through use of recirculation has already been noted. Other benefits are improved temperature performance over the entire load range and the elimination of the bypass system as a requirement of the furnace wall.

These advantages will be most clearly understood after considering the flow performance of a typical furnace-wall system with the volumetric flow at the furnace-wall inlet as a function of load (Fig. 25). The through-flow as maintained by the feedpump increases in direct proportion to load. The recirculated flow as maintained by the circulating pumps supplements the through-flow over the low load range in a manner which protects the furnace walls by raising the actual flow to a safe level regardless of feedwater flow.

At low loads the recirculated flow is great but decreases as the load increases. At about 60-percent load, the pressure drop through the furnace-wall system equals the head produced by the circulating pump; the stop-check valve in the recirculating line automatically closes. The circulating pump then ceases to add to the quantity of furnace flow but continues to contribute its positive head on the once-through flow and so acts as a booster to the feedpump. At this time, the pump may be shut down.

WELDED FURNACE ENCLOSURE

The furnace enclosure, including the outer furnace walls, the extended sidewalls and the backpass walls, is of welded tube panels, joined into a structure which requires the least amount of sealing (by a separate casing) against inside pressure. Because all outer furnace walls have a common inlet temperature and an outlet temperature with predictable tolerance around the perimeter, they may all be welded together.

Fig. 25 **Flow in Combined Circulation furnace-wall system**

The fluid temperature in the extended sidewalls and in the backpass enclosure is essentially that existing at the outlet of the other furnace walls. This makes it possible to weld these sections together.

PERFORMANCE

Fluid temperatures, both primary and reheat, throughout a typical supercritical steam generator at maximum continuous load are plotted against the percentage of heat absorption in Fig. 26.

The primary fluid takes about 83 percent of total output, showing a gradual and continuous rise of fluid temperature from the feedwater

inlet to the superheater outlet. The curve of these temperatures follows the characteristic line of supercritical fluid in which any heat absorption or change of heat content is accompanied by a change in fluid temperature.

Desuperheating occurring at the outlet of the panel superheater provides vernier control of average steam temperature. It also adjusts for unbalance of pickup across the width of the unit, as four individually temperature-controlled sections are installed in each furnace. The platen and finishing superheater sections add the balance of superheat.

SLIDING-PRESSURE COMBINED CIRCULATION

Existing supercritical designs with boiler throttle valves (to keep the furnace-wall system pressurized) can only operate in the sliding-pressure mode below approximately 30-percent rating (Fig. 27). Above this point, turbine load control is achieved through the turbine throttle valves. This causes the usual temperature changes in the first stage of the turbine and is a factor in permissible load-change rates.

Redesign of the boiler throttle valve arrangement (Fig. 28) results in a sliding-pressure turbine operation to 90-percent rating while maintaining the furnace walls in the supercritical mode. This design has the usual

Fig. 26 **Fluid temperatures through Combined Circulation steam generator at full load**

advantages for operation of the turbine in a sliding-pressure mode including increased reheat temperature control range and reduced thermal stress. Using the valves at all loads below 80 percent increases the valve wear and maintenance on these valves, but this additional wear does not present serious problems. Two-shifting operation, however, results in high wear and reduced life of some start-up-system valves.

To accommodate true variable-pressure operation of a supercritical system suitable for cycling duty, C-E has a unit similar to the basic Combined Circulation design that is capable of sliding-pressure operation throughout the total range of pressure. The furnace walls operate at subcritical pressure during low-load operation and supercritical pressure during high-load operation. This variable-pressure capability is available without the use of boiler throttling

Fig. 27 **Constant pressure program for Combined Circulation steam generators**

Fig. 28 **Sliding pressure operation of C-E Combined Circulation steam generators with throttling valves**

valves. Fig. 29 represents a typical operating-pressure regime for such a unit.

DESIGN FEATURES FOR VARIABLE-LOAD OPERATION

As pointed out in Chapter 1 and elsewhere, it is extremely important for large pulverized-coal-fired steam-generating equipment to have the capability to operate satisfactorily as the load varies widely.

Traditionally, electric utility companies purchased new boiler additions that were the largest and most efficient equipment available. These new units were base loaded for the first several years of use. But as capital became more difficult to acquire and requirements for emission control equipment increased, this pattern gradually changed.

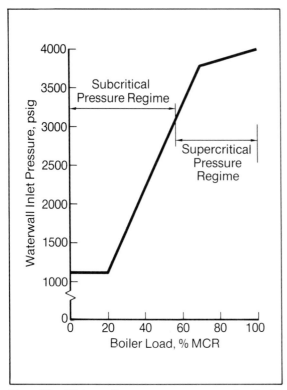

Fig. 29 Waterwall pressure versus load for sliding-pressure supercritical design without boiler throttling valves

As more of the older base-loaded plants are relegated to cyclic or low-load-factor operation, it is no longer valid to assume that new, large units are the most cost-effective to operate. On one hand, new units are designed with features for operating in the two-shifting and other cycling regimes. On the other hand, they may have parasitic environmental control equipment that impacts negatively on their overall plant efficiency. In any case, there is a need for maximum system flexibility and using the older equipment for peak loads is not completely reliable because there are strict limits to the cycling capability of any boiler not specifically designed for that kind of service. This section discusses such design limitations.

DEFINITION OF CYCLING

In the past, a conventional cycling unit (either an oil- or natural-gas-fired peaking unit) was described as one designed for rapid rates of load increase and a significantly larger number of start-up and shutdown cycles compared to conventional base load-operation.

A *coal-fired cycling boiler* is one that can operate for long periods of time at reduced capacities ($\cong$ 20 percent of MCR) and reduced pressures (such as 1000 psig) while burning only coal. Such a unit is also capable of base-load operation for extended periods. Operation (Fig. 30) is further defined.

■ Base-load mode—The unit is entirely base loaded.

■ Weekend mode—The unit is base loaded during weekdays and removed from service each weekend. In this mode, there is a cold start-up at the beginning of each work week.

■ Cycling mode—The boiler plant operates weekdays at full load during the day and at minimum load ($\cong$ 20 percent MCR) at night. It may be removed from service each weekend. This method of operation may also involve fast load changes.[15]

■ Two-shifting mode—The boiler plant operates weekdays at full load and is taken off line every night for 8 to 10 hours. In addition, the unit is removed from service each weekend.

After an 8- to 10-hour nonfiring period, start-ups on weekday mornings are usually categorized as "warm" starts.

To properly consider these operational modes during the design stage, it is necessary to take into account the effect of this type of boiler/turbine loading on furnace sizing, pulverizing and firing systems, operational control systems, turbine start-up systems, and water treatment.[6]

DESIGNING COAL-FIRED BOILERS FOR VARIABLE LOAD

The performance and cost of equipment for boilers dedicated to variable-load service are greatly influenced by the sizing of the furnace and the selection of the pulverizers.

FURNACE SIZING

In recent years, furnace sizing requirements for coal-fired boilers have become very conservative. This trend occurred to permit fur-naces to handle the worst possible ash-content coal that might become available at a particular site. When a conservatively designed furnace is supplied with coal that produces gas-side conditions much cleaner than anticipated by the design of the furnace, the result can be a lower-than-design steam temperature or reduced temperature control range.

Additionally, several days to several weeks normally are required to "season" the furnace of a coal-fired unit so that the unit can produce design outlet steam temperature(s). When load is reduced substantially, or when the boiler is taken off the line, the furnace sheds its accumulation of ash. After restart, additional time is required for the furnace to season.

PULVERIZER SELECTION

Designing a boiler for cycling operation requires special attention to select and properly size the pulverizing and firing-system components. Unless these components are flexible

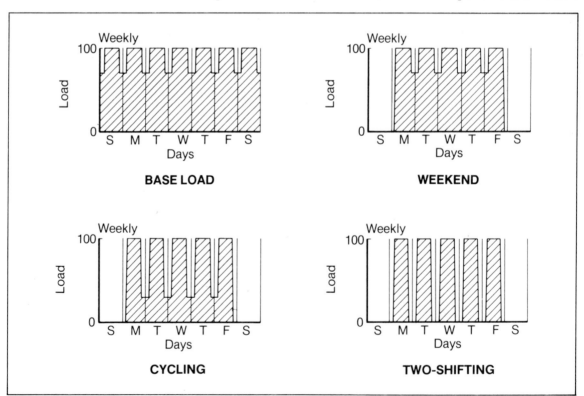

Fig. 30 **Modes of variable-load operation**

and reliable over a wide range of conditions, the boiler capability to cycle will be severely limited. Pulverizing equipment must be able to deliver fuel to the unit at low loads, as well as respond to the usual considerations of capacity, fineness and turndown. The alternative is to use large amounts of some stabilizing fuel such as oil or natural gas.

To obtain maximum flexibility and reliability, it is advantageous to use a greater number of pulverizers, of lower capacity, rather than use a smaller number of larger capacity pulverizers, thereby limiting the turndown ratio. The larger number of pulverizers, however, will generally increase initial capital costs.

The C-E system for the direct ignition of pulverized coal (Chapter 13) is well suited to provide the capability of starting up, shutting down, and operating at minimum loads without the use of stabilizing oil or gas fuels.

Air Temperature

Air temperature effect on the pulverizer performance is well known. Particularly during start-ups and low loads, primary air temperature can be a factor in the operation of the firing equipment. While a problem of low air temperature might be alleviated somewhat on warm restarts following overnight shutdowns, cold starts still are required after weekends and other outages. Therefore, in the selection and arrangement of the air-heating equipment, special consideration should be given to obtaining hot air as quickly as possible. This can be done either by direct firing supplemental fuel into the ducts to the pulverizers or preheating the air with steam heaters.

One factor that has a definite effect on the start-up characteristics of the boiler is the purge airflow requirements. Although purge airflow is essential it acts to cool furnace walls and reduce steam temperature; therefore, every attempt should be made to assure light-off and continued operation after the *first* purge.

UNIT START-UP

Start-up rates for generator-turbine units become increasingly important when system op-

eration departs from base loading. If a unit start-up from a cold condition takes eight hours, but the unit is started only two or three times a year, there is little economic impact from using the more expensive warm-up fuel and the direct labor cost also is minimal. But warm-up and stabilizing-fuel costs can be considerable if the unit is continually two-shifted or cycled at low loads.

The designs described in the following section can assist in matching superheat and reheat temperatures, and pressure ramp, to the turbine start-up requirements.

SUPERHEATER TEMPERATURE AND PRESSURE CONTROL

For a hot restart following an overnight outage, high-enthalpy steam is required. For a cold restart following a weekend outage, low-enthalpy steam is preferred to reduce thermal shock in the first stages of the high-pressure and intermediate-pressure turbines.

Although the steam-temperature control systems as designed for base-load operation generally have been adequate for such cycling, a simple start-up system can provide the necessary flexibility in steam temperature control. Fig. 31 shows an arrangement of valves and piping connecting the backpass ring header to the condenser. The arrangement is sized to pass approximately 5-percent flow at 1000 psig. This system controls pressure rise on start-up, permitting increased firing rates to achieve higher superheat and reheat temperatures. The motor-operated steam-drain bypass valve also preheats turbine leads *before* synchronization. A spray desuperheater in the line from the bypass valve to the condenser provides for thermal protection of the condenser.

REHEAT TEMPERATURE CONTROL

When high primary and reheat steam temperatures are required for hot-start conditions (to match turbine metal temperatures), valved connections from the saturated steam circuits to the reheat outlet are added to the backpass drain system, as shown in Fig. 32.

The system operates in the following man-

Fig. 31 **Backpass drain system for superheater temperature and pressure control**

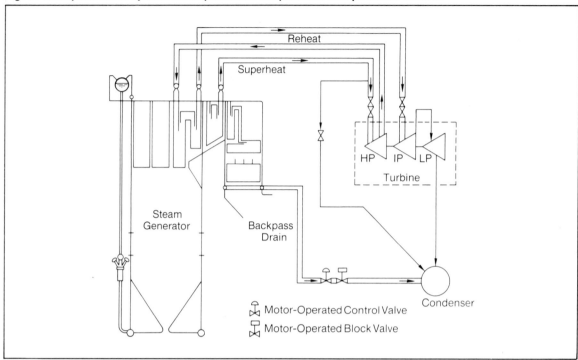

Fig. 32 **System for steam-temperature matching and reheat temperature control**

ner: Before the turbine is rolled, the unit is fired to achieve the desired primary steam temperature and pressure. The firing rate controls primary steam temperature, whereas pressure is controlled by the motor-operated valves.

Upon rolling the turbine and admitting steam to the reheater, high gas temperatures can produce higher-than-required reheat steam temperature. Reheater outlet temperature at start-up is then controlled by saturated steam from the drum. A line connects the drum to a desuperheater located at the reheater outlet. A motor-operated control valve regulates the flow of saturated steam from the drum to the reheater outlet. A block valve in this line prevents saturated steam from leaking into the interstage turbine when the unit is at full load.

Figs. 33 and 34 illustrate typical boiler start-up conditions for an overnight shutdown of eight hours and a weekend outage of 55 hours. From light-off to synchronization, the unit can be fired at a rate to produce gas temperatures necessary to develop the proper superheat temperature. At the same time the gas temperature at the first section of reheater is limited to approximately 1000°F until steam flow through the reheater is established. The gas-temperature probe in front of the reheater monitors the gas temperature.

Once the turbine is rolled, steam is passed from the high-pressure turbine exhaust to the reheater. Without saturated steam, the reheater outlet temperature would rapidly approach the gas temperature. Inputting such high-temperature steam to the cooler intermediate pressure turbine would cause high thermal stresses. With the described system, saturated steam can be directed from the drum to the desuperheater by activating the motor-operated control valve. In this manner it is possible to obtain the appropriate steam temperature for an optimum match with turbine metal temperatures.

ALLOWABLE START-UP AND LOAD-CHANGE RATES

Disregarding any firing limitations that may exist, the boiler component that limits start-up rate on Controlled Circulation units is the final

superheater outlet (SHO) header. There are several reasons why this header, rather than the thicker-wall steam drum, has such an effect on start-up rate.

■ SHO headers experience both fatigue and creep damage, while the drum experiences only fatigue damage due to its lower operating temperature.

■ There is a great difference in fatigue life at 1000°F and 680°F (the temperatures of SHO header and drum plate, respectively).

■ The temperature change the drum experiences on a typical hot start is approximately 400°F less than the SHO header.

Controlled Circulation drums have a nominal ramp-rate limit of 400°F/hr and a fast transient limit of 150°F temperature change during any 15-minute period. This fast transient limit is extremely important, as illustrated by the following example. If the unit is operated in a modified sliding pressure mode with approximately 1500 psig drum pressure at 50 percent load, a rapid increase from 50 percent to 100 percent load will increase the saturated temperature from approximately 600°F to 680°F, or a change of 80°F. During such transients, the drum can tolerate the rapid 80°F change an unlimited number of times.

The internal shroud in Controlled Circulation drums (Fig. 8) promotes heat transfer that is even around the circumference and along the length of the drum. This even heat transfer minimizes through-the-wall and top-to-bottom thermal gradients. Thermal-circulation boiler drums cannot tolerate such ramp rates because of the drum metal temperature differentials that would be generated. In actual practice, they are limited to less than one half the allowable rate of a Controlled Circulation unit. (Thermal-circulation units cannot use an effectively shrouded drum because the circulation system cannot accommodate the additional pressure drop.)

Although the superheater outlet header (SHO) usually is the limiting *boiler* component on Controlled Circulation units, it would be a mistake to assume that the SHO header always

Fig. 33 Start-up curves for operation following 8-hour shutdown. Hatched areas indicate temperature control achievable with the system shown in Fig. 32.

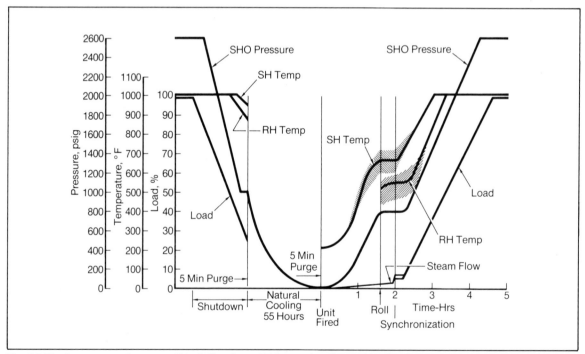

Fig. 34 Start-up curves for operation following a 55-hour shutdown. Hatched areas indicate temperature control achievable with the system shown in Fig. 32.

limits the boiler/turbine during cyclic operation and start-up. Large reheat turbines have start-up and loading rates compatible with reasonable cyclic life expenditure (CLE).

C-E has developed analytical procedures to generate CLE curves for boiler pressure parts. Fig. 35 shows a CLE curve for a 20″ OD, 4 in. wall-thickness 2¼ Cr-1 Mo superheater outlet header. The calculation procedures used to construct the SHO/CLE curve employ a cyclic elastic/plastic creep analysis of the SHO header tee. It is very imformative to compare CLE curves for a steam turbine (Fig. 36) and CLE curves for the SHO header tee (Fig. 35). The SHO header has much more cyclic capability than the turbine.

The start-up rates indicated for an overnight shutdown (8 hours) are approximately 55 minutes from synchronization to full load (Fig. 33). Start-ups after weekend or holiday shutdowns, in contrast to overnight shutdowns (Fig. 34), are generally limited by the steam turbine thermal stresses.

When lighting off a Controlled Circulation

Fig. 35 Cyclic life curves for typical superheater outlet header

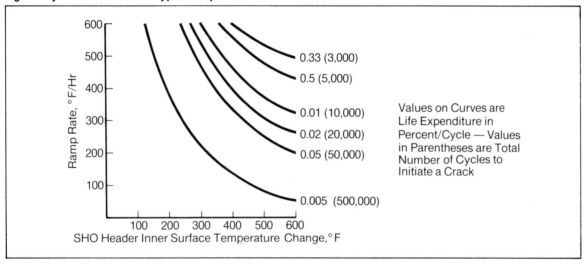

Fig. 36 Cyclic life curves for high-pressure steam turbine

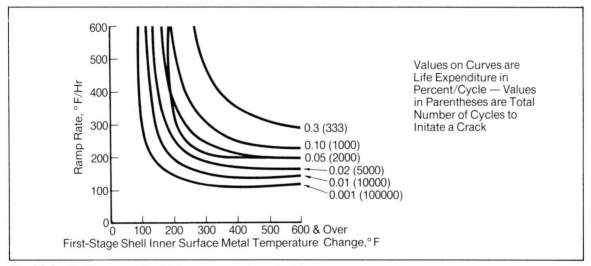

unit and raising the steam pressure, the saturated steam temperature increases about 100°F from first fire to synchronization, a period of approximately 30 minutes for a coal-fired unit. This time is not restricted by steam-generator pressure parts as the ramp rate is only 200°F/hr and can be readily increased provided the firing system and turbine conditions permit. From synchronization to full load in 55 minutes is an increase in saturation temperature of 130°F or a rate of 142°F/hr. This ramp rate is significantly less than that permitted by either the steam drum or SHO header.

TURBINE BYPASS SYSTEM

Bypassing the steam turbine requires the most expensive and complex start-up system. The turbine bypass system permits operation of the steam generator independent of the turbine at any rating up to the bypass capacity. This permits turbine start-up with essentially zero temperature mismatch. Bypass systems such as shown schematically in Fig. 37 are usually rated for 50 to 100 percent bypass flow under full-pressure conditions. The major advantages of a bypass system are its

■ flexibility of operation

■ ability to hold the generator output during start-up without undesirable turbine cooling

■ ability to recover following a load rejection before restarting or reloading the turbine

■ ability to match turbine metal temperatures on hot restart

Also, there is evidence that exfoliated superheater or reheater material bypassing the turbine during start-up greatly reduces exfoliation damage to turbine blading. The disadvantages of a turbine bypass system are

■ increased plant cost

■ complexity of control

■ additional valve maintenance

Fig. 37 **Steam-turbine bypass system**

Fig. 38 **Variable-pressure programs—drum boilers**

■ possibility of turbine or condenser damage due to malfunction or failure of components in the bypass system

■ increases in plant heat rate because of greater condenser heat loss during periods of bypass system operation

The temperature-matching potential of a bypass system depends upon its sizing; maximum steam temperature capability can be found from the steam temperature curves of the boiler at the maximum rating of the bypass system. If the desired temperature matches between the superheat and reheat steam and the turbine metals can be achieved with other start-up techniques, such as the C-E temperature matching system, no additional saving in start-up time on a hot start can be achieved with a bypass system.

Fig. 39 **Typical superheat and reheat temperatures in constant- and variable-pressure operation**

Supercritical units require a start-up system to protect the furnace walls during start-up and low loads as described in Chapter 5. These systems function as turbine bypass systems to varying degrees depending on their design.

VARIABLE-PRESSURE OPERATION

One operating regime that is useful to accommodate unit load changes and increased number of start-ups and shutdowns is variable-pressure operation.

For example, the boiler-turbine combination chosen has nominal steam conditions of 2400 psig, 1000°F/1000°F. The turbine has a partial-arc-admission first stage with 4 nozzle groups, each controlled by a separate valve. Three different operating-pressure programs are considered (Fig. 38). They are

■ full variable pressure: turbine control valves wide open

■ constant pressure when on control valve No. 4; variable pressure below the point where No. 4 valve closes

■ constant pressure when on valves Nos. 3 and 4; variable pressure below point where No. 3 valve closes

Operating with the first pressure program has the advantage of essentially eliminating first-stage temperature changes inside the turbine—as long as the initial and reheat temperatures are held constant. However, the response of the boiler-turbine combination to changes in load demand is relatively slow and may not satisfy the power-system control requirements. Some operating companies prefer to have the turbine speed governor contributing to system control, and therefore choose a hybrid pressure program such as shown by curves 2 or 3 in Fig. 38. This overcomes the main disadvantages of full variable-pressure operation, while still retaining most of the benefits. Five of these advantages are:

1. Extended control range (higher steam temperatures at low loads) of both the primary and reheat steam (Fig. 39).

2. Improved steam-flow distribution in the superheater at lower loads because of the

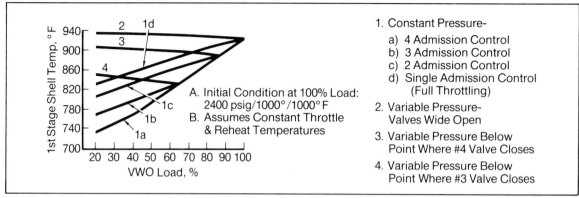

Fig. 40 **Typical steam-turbine first-stage shell temperature**

higher specific volume of the steam at lower pressures.

3. Minimal variation of first-stage shell temperature of the turbine under varying load conditions. Fig. 40 shows the change in first-stage shell temperature under a range of conditions involving constant and variable pressure, including different admission modes for the first stage ranging from partial-arc with four admissions to full-throttling control. By reducing the temperature difference that the first-stage components must endure during significant load changes, there are reduced thermal stresses within the turbine and operating constraints are appreciably reduced.

4. Improved overall power-plant heat rate considering boiler, turbine, feed pump, and other auxiliaries. Fig. 41 indicates the effect on turbine-generator heat rate of the various operating modes when the pressure in the entire boiler (superheater plus waterwalls) is allowed to vary. It can be seen that the two hybrid-pressure programs offer better heat rates over the load range than the others.

5. The reduced pressure level at lower loads unloads all cycle components between the feed pump and high-pressure turbine, thereby prolonging lifespan.

As their main goal these various start-up methods protect the turbine. The steam gen-

Fig. 41 **Effect of admission modes and throttle-pressure programs on heat rate—typical 2400 psig 1000°/ 1000° F turbine with 7-heater cycle and turbine-driven feedwater pump boiler feedwater pump (BFP)**

erator must also handle the thermal loads and ensuing thermal stresses that result from temperature differences and gradients imposed by start-up and shutdown, cyclic operations, and the heat-absorption process. As previously emphasized, Controlled Circulation furnace-wall systems provide protection throughout start-up and shutdown, pressure raising, and full-load operation by insuring positive water flow to all furnace-wall circuits independently of heat-input rate, thereby permitting accelerated start-ups and cool-downs.

Finally, regardless of whether variable pressure is used during normal operation, it can be advantageous for start-up and shutdown by providing better turbine temperature matching, especially with units subjected to cycling and two-shifting. It is normally unnecessary to go below half the maximum operating pressure to obtain the benefits of temperature matching.

DESIGN FOR CYCLIC DUTY

In addition to the design and performance requirements for which base-loaded units are selected, two additional requirements must be considered for the cycling boiler. These are rapid rates of load increase and a significantly greater number of start-up and shutdown cycles. The present rules of Section I of the *ASME Code* governing pressure-part design and fab-

rication do not provide specific guides for dealing with the thermal-stress and fatigue problems encountered in this type of unit. The *Code* does, however, charge the manufacturer with the responsibility of attending to and accounting for these effects.

The first step in an evaluation of this type of operation is making a conservative estimate of the number of operating cycles a plant must undergo; a review of unit operating experience has established a minimum life of 30 years. Further analysis indicates that start up and shutdowns affect the cyclic loading of boiler components (Fig. 42). The second step in evolving a good design is to develop and adopt a set of design criteria to allow the intelligent assessment of all types of loading (pressure, mechanical, thermal, and cycling) to insure long-term component integrity. This subject was discussed in Chapter 6. (See Fig. 6–44 and accompanying text.)

COMPONENT DESIGN AS INFLUENCED BY CYCLIC OPERATION

Understanding the definitions of cyclic requirements and boiler design criteria, the designer can assess the various temperature and loading conditions in terms of stresses, and can determine the capabilities of the steam-generator components to satisfy system re-

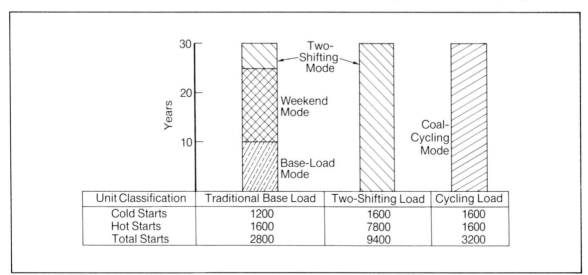

Unit Classification	Traditional Base Load	Two-Shifting Load	Cycling Load
Cold Starts	1200	1600	1600
Hot Starts	1600	7800	1600
Total Starts	2800	9400	3200

Fig. 42 **Fossil power-plant loading cycles**

quirements. The major factors affecting these design considerations are

- number of cycles
- heating and cooling rates
- component thickness, diameter and material
- operating temperature level

Analytical and test methods are used to evaluate specific performance capabilities of a variety of components such as

- drums, including downcomers
- headers, including tees and nipples
- furnace-wall tubes and attachments
- buckstays
- pumps and valves
- pulverizer structure and drive train
- duct expansion joints
- hanger rods and supports

Such components are evaluated using various factors, chief being the operating pressures and operating conditions that minimize thermal stresses in the steam-turbine rotor. Similarly, it is necessary to minimize thermal stresses in all boiler components.

Expansion stresses that result from steady-state operation are relatively simple to accommodate in a design, but thermal gradients produced by temperature transients greatly complicate the design. As faster start-up and shutdown rates become necessary, thermal gradients increase and the thermal design of a component may well run counter to the required design for mechanical loads, such as pressure and dead load. Attachments to pres-

sure parts normally are sized by the mechanical loads they carry. To reduce the size of such an attachment (so as to reduce a thermal difference) may invalidate its design. Heavy thick-walled components, such as the SHO tees or steam drums, are sized according to *pressure* requirements. Wall thicknesses, then, cannot be decreased to reduce thermal gradients and thermal stresses.

Pressure and thermal stresses combine to produce a total stress. Fig. 43 shows an ideal operational cycle in which the pressure and steam-temperature curves have the same rate for start-up as for shutdown. The stresses produced in a cylinder with the pressure and thermal loading cycle are shown in Fig. 44. Of interest is the relationship of the thermal and pressure stresses on the inside surface of the cylinder. During the entire cycle, the pressure stresses are tensile. Thermal stresses are compressive during start-up and tensile during shutdown. The pressure and thermal stresses oppose each other during start-up but are additive on shutdown.

The stress range shown in Fig. 44 determines the amount of fatigue damage represented by this cycle. The greater the stress range, the greater the fatigue damage. One possible way of reducing the stress range is to reduce pressure during a cooldown while maintaining the steam-temperature level.

Such a mode of operation (variable pressure) as depicted in Fig. 38 allows main steam and reheat steam temperatures to be maintained at a

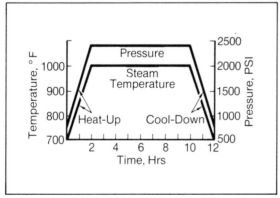

Fig. 43 Idealized operating cycle

Fig. 44 Combined pressure-/ thermal-stress cycle

given setpoint lower into the load range. Although it is for this reason and others discussed earlier that variable pressure is used, there is an added benefit. During a cooldown, the pressure stresses are additive as shown in Fig. 45. Therefore, the combined pressure and thermal stresses are lower than the stresses that would have been generated if pressure had been maintained and the temperature dropped.

CONTROL CONSIDERATIONS FOR VARIABLE-LOAD OPERATION

The thermal inertia of steam generating equipment relates directly to its size. It is necessary to understand when designing operational control equipment that, combined with increases in unit size, present practice is to design for variable-load operation. On constant-pressure units, it is only necessary to deal with the energy-storage changes associated with the changes in steaming rate. But, as previously discussed, turbine considerations virtually demand that variable-pressure operation be used on cycling units. This requirement places a special burden on the steam-generator control system, with the steam-temperature controls being the most severely affected.

The stored energy in a steam generator (metal temperature and steam enthalpy, both as a function of mass) is higher at full load than at any partial load. Increasing the load, therefore, requires temporarily raising the firing-ramp rate above the load ramp to provide the required increase in stored energy. During load increases on a variable-pressure unit, the slope

of the stored energy is substantially steeper than the load output curve.

Overfiring to satisfy the energy storage requirements of the waterwalls generally results in excessive heat pickup in the superheater and reheater, which have lower storage capacity. Further complicating the situation is the fact that the distribution of heat between waterwalls and superheater varies significantly with pressure because of changes in the vaporization heat of water and the specific heat of superheated steam as a function of pressure.

Traditional superheater temperature-control systems use cascade-type spray controls, in which the final-temperature error resets the setpoint for the desuperheater outlet temperature. This is a type of feedback control and is inadequate for even moderate rates of load change in a sliding-pressure mode. Any workable steam-temperature control configuration must include both careful timing of any overfiring and a sophisticated anticipation signal in the superheat and reheat control loops. Programming the desuperheater outlet temperature as a function of load and rate-of-change of load is one example of the use of feed-forward temperature control.

In a subcritical unit operating at constant pressure, shrink and swell of drum level occur during a load change because of the change in steaming rate. With sliding pressure, however, there is also a mass-inventory change associated with the pressure change. Feed-forward signals are used to help the drum-level controller distinguish between shrink and swell effects and feedwater/steam-flow mismatches. Regulating the speed of the boiler feed pumps is the most common control of feedwater flow rate. The reduced pressure at low loads with sliding-pressure operation requires that the stable speed control range on the pumps be significantly wider or that supplementary valve control be used.

The specific cycling mode that involves holding minimum load overnight presents some additional concerns associated with keeping supplementary-fuel use to an absolute minimum. Improved flame-scanning systems

Fig. 45 Pressure and thermal stress versus time

incorporating higher sensitivity scanners and/or increased quantities of scanners are mandatory. More precise control of fuel and air distribution to maintain the fuel ignition point at each fuel-admission location within the scanner viewing area is also essential.

In a two-shifting mode, the major impact on the control system is the need for more automation. Bringing in additional plant operators to control various subloops manually on every start-up may be acceptable on a base-load unit, but is not likely to be so for a two-shifting unit.

Traditional boiler-following control systems place too much of the burden on plant operators to coordinate both changing conditions of temperature, pressure and flow in the boiler and turbine. The use of a coordinated control system, with its plant-master concept, then, is virtually essential to satisfy the control requirements of cycling operation.

Using boiler start-up systems or turbine bypass systems adds an additional set of control loops that must also be carefully coordinated with the steam-generator and turbine-generator controls.

WATER TREATMENT FOR CYCLING UNITS

Any power plant operation that requires a great number of start-ups, shutdowns, and idle periods will be subject to inleakage of air, especially in the condensate and low-pressure feedwater systems. This increases the potential for preboiler and boiler internal corrosion and over-heating from deposition of corrosion products in internal tube surfaces. The mechanism by which this occurs is oxygen corrosion of feedwater heaters and interconnecting piping, plus the formation of corrosion byproducts such as iron-oxide and copper; these are subsequently transported to the boiler where they will deposit on the inside of the furnace-wall tubes. High oxygen concentrations in the feedwater and boiler water can also produce corrosion pitting, which can directly promote tube failures. Proper precautionary measures are necessary in cycling units to prevent corrosion damage.

Units for 2400 psi two-shifting and cycling operation, and *all* supercritical pressure units should have condensate polishing equipment to control corrosion-products, condenser in-leakage contaminants, and make-up water impurities. Its design and operation should keep feedwater contamination within boundaries of limiting criteria for all modes of operation. Ion exchange to process at least 25 percent of full-load condensate flow is required in two-shift drum-unit operation to process feedwater contaminants and impurities from the turbine and condenser. Cleanup of condensate will also facilitate reaching operating pressure without experiencing undue delays to control silica.

Detailed information on cycling-service pre-boiler cleanup, condensate deaeration, and condensate polishing is given in Chapter 11 and Chapter 21.

REFERENCES

[1] W. H. Clayton, J. G. Singer and W. H. Tuppeny, Jr., "Design for Peaking/Cycling" presented at the *Joint Power Generation Conference*, September, 1970 American Society of Mechanical Engineers Paper No. 70-PWR-9, New York.

[2] W. W. Schroedter, "A New Steam Generator for Supercritical Pressure", proceedings of the American Power Conference 24:301–316. Chicago; Illinois Institute of Technology, 1962

W. W. Schroedter, "Engineering The Bull Run Steam Generator," *Proceedings of the American Power Conference*, 25:359–385. Chicago: Illinois Institute of Technology, 1963

[3] G. R. Fryling, "Combustion Engineering," Revised Edition 1966. Library of Congress Catalog Number 66-23939, 1966

[4] H. E. Burbach and G. F. Shulof, "The Cycle Option," *Proceedings of the American Power Conference*, 42: Chicago, Illinois Institute of Technology, 1980

[5] L. W. Cadwallader, E. M. Powell, and J. G. Singer, "A New Look at Peaking Power," *Proceedings of the American Power Conference*, 28:413–421, 1966. Chicago: Illinois Institute of Technology, 1966

[6] H. E. Burbach, J. D. Fox, T. B. Hamilton, "Steam Generator Design Features for Variable Load Operations," *Proceedings of The American Power Conference*, 41: 561–579. Chicago, Illinois Institute of Technology, 1979

CHAPTER 8

Industrial Boilers

Industrial boilers are designed to fire many different fuels, each of which can affect the boiler design. In addition, the primary fuel may vary over the life of the boiler and many process plants produce byproducts that are valuable as fuel. Much of this chapter is dedicated to specific equipment for burning fuels other than coal, fuel oil, or natural gas.

Originally the term industrial boiler was applied only to steam generators in which evaporation occurred largely in a convective section (called the "boiler bank"). The term now includes units in which nearly all boiling takes place in the waterwall tubes, where heat transfer occurs principally through radiation. As size, available pressures, and steam temperatures changed, such units more commonly were used for electrical power generation by both municipal utilities and large industries and are being adapted to industrial uses.

Understandably, industrial boilers have preferably been designed to burn clean liquid and gaseous fuels when such fuels were available at reasonable cost. Unfortunately, world demand for such fuels has outpaced the supply. Thus, use of oil- and gas-burning steam-generating equipment will decline rapidly. The necessary shift to solid fuels will require use of boilers that are not only initially more expensive but also more difficult to operate. Such boilers also will require sophisticated ancillary equipment to control stack emissions.

As more coal and other solid fuels are used there will occur greater need for both stoker and pulverized-coal firing. Future legislation likely will prohibit the use of natural gas, and either prohibit or limit the use of oil as fuel in industrial boilers. Such restrictions will create an additional demand for new coal-fired boilers in the majority of installations. It is impractical to convert an oil-or gas-fired unit to coal.

PERFORMANCE REQUIREMENTS OF MODERN INDUSTRIAL BOILERS

Owners and operators of industrial boilers must consider such developments and adapt unit performance to:

■ Multifuel-Burning Capabilities: During the 70's some industrial concerns had to convert boilers from firing coal to gas, to oil, and back to coal as the environmental requirements, fuel costs, and fuel availability changed. To protect an investment in the steam-generating facility, the owner may more frequently request multiple-fuel capability in new units.

■ Waste-Fuel Utilization: Rising fuel costs plus a high cost to dispose of waste makes refuse, waste acids, and sludge more attractive as fuels for steam generation. A growing number of new boiler designs will use waste fuels.

■ Low Operating Costs: The cost of fuel and auxiliary power can, in a few years, exceed the original cost of a steam generator. Therefore, new equipment must be efficient and have a low auxiliary-power consumption.

■ Cogeneration Potential: Simultaneous generation of electrical power and low-pressure steam also is becoming more common as users strive to extract maximum heat from their fuel. Industrial firms will more frequently select the more efficient high pressure and temperature steam cycles to optimize the amount of electrical power and steam produced.

Radiant boilers will become more common because a conventional rolled-tube boiler bank using convective heat absorption at superheater outlet pressures above 1550 psig is not economical. Moreover, using steam reheat increases efficiency and consequently reduces fuel cost. Utilities have almost universally adopted the reheat cycle for power generation and large industrial plants also can benefit from steam reheat.

BOILER DESIGN AS A FUNCTION OF OPERATING PRESSURE

As Fig. 1 shows, the percentage of total heat absorbed in a boiler bank is reduced significantly at higher pressures by two factors:

1. In the superheater, the greater heat absorption required to heat the steam to a higher temperature reduces the gas temperature entering the boiler bank.

2. The water temperature in the boiler bank is essentially at the saturation temperature corresponding to the boiler operating pressure. As the operating pressure increases, the tempera-

Fig. 1 **Heat-absorption distribution for coal-fired boilers**

ture of the water inside the tubes rises thereby reducing the logarithmic mean temperature difference available for heat transfer.

DESIGN CRITERIA
FOR INDUSTRIAL BOILERS

Boiler designs are tailored to the fuels and firing systems involved. Some of the more important criteria are

- furnace heat release rates, both Btu/hr-cu ft and Btu/hr-sq ft of effective projected radiant surface (EPRS)
- heat release rates of grates
- flue-gas velocities through tube banks
- tube spacings

Table I gives typical values or ranges of these criteria for gas, oil and coal to illustrate the differences for the fuels and not necessarily to rep-

resent specific recommendations. The furnace heat-release rates are important from several viewpoints. The proper Btu/hr-sq ft of EPRS value, along with adequate flame to heat-absorbing-surface clearance, will keep maximum local absorption rates within safe limits and avoid "hot spots." Also, with coal firing, this aspect of design is important to prevent excessive slag accumulations on furnace walls and convection tube surface at the furnace outlet. The furnace heat release rate in Btu/hr-cu ft directly influences completeness of combustion. Limiting grate heat-release rates minimizes carbon loss, controls visible emissions, and avoids excessive flyash.

The need to limit draft loss usually controls flue gas velocities for gas or oil-fired boilers. On the other hand, with coal firing the design gas velocities, together with gas temperatures,

Table I. Some Typical Boiler Design Parameters

Furnace	Btu/hr-sq ft of EPRS	Btu/hr-cu ft
Natural gas	200,000	NA
Oil	175,000–200,000	NA
Coal-pulverized	70,000–120,000	15,000–22,000
Coal-spreader stoker	80,000–130,000	25,000–30,000

Stoker, coal-fired, grate heat-release rates	
Continuous discharge spreader	650,000–700,000 Btu/hr-sq ft
Dump grate spreader	450,000–550,000 Btu/hr sq ft
Overfeed traveling grate	400,000–550,000 Btu/hr-sq ft

Flue-gas velocity, ft/sec	Single-Pass Boiler	Baffled Boiler	Economizer
Gas or distillate oil	100	100	100
Residual oil	100	75	100
Bituminous coal			
Low ash	65–70	50	50–60
High ash	50	NA	40–50

Tube spacing, perpendicular to gas flow, inches clear	Superheater		Boiler		Economizer
	Front	Rear	Front	Rear	
Gas or distillate oil	2	2	1	1	1
Residual oil	4–6	2	1½	1	1
Bituminous coal					
Low ash/high fusion temperature	8	3–6	1½	1	1
High ash/low fusion temperature	10–16	4–6	2	1–2	1

influence the ability of the boiler to operate continuously without shutdown.

Although convection tube spacing is not critical in boilers designed to fire gas or distillate oil, it is very important when the fuel is a residual oil or coal. This is especially so with coals that have low ash-fusion temperatures or high ash-fouling tendencies and with low-rank coals such as subbituminous coals or lignite.

COAL-FIRING SYSTEMS

Many industrial boilers are designed for less than 250,000 lb steam/hr. For many years most of these units used a spreader stoker to fire coal because it was less expensive than installing pulverizers. In this size range the other benefits of pulverized-coal (PC) did not warrant the increased costs. Now, the advantages of each system must be evaluated thoroughly before selecting stoker or PC firing.

STOKER VERSUS PULVERIZED-COAL FIRING

A reduced efficiency due to the carbon loss is a major factor in comparing a stoker-fired boiler to a PC-fired boiler. A properly designed PC boiler can maintain an efficiency loss due to unburned carbon of less than 0.4 percent. On the other hand, a continuous-ash-discharge spreader-stoker-fired unit will typically have a carbon loss of 4 to 8 percent, depending on the amount of reinjection. The PC unit offers a lower carbon loss because of the increased combustion efficiency obtained with the finer coal particles that enter the furnace (normally 70 to 80 percent will pass through a 200-mesh screen). In contrast, the coal particles entering the furnace with a spreader stoker are much coarser. These coal particles have a ¾-inch top size and not more than 50 percent will pass through a ¼-inch screen.

The coal itself also affects the total fuel cost difference between these firing methods. Efficient operation of a spreader-stoker-fired boiler requires that the coal has the proper mixture of coarse and fine particles. Normally, double-screened coal is purchased to obtain the proper

mixture as run-of-the-mine coal generally does not have the optimum balance of coarse and fine material.

The fine coal particles are burned in suspension. If the amount of fine particles is too great, there will be excessive suspension burning which can produce

- higher stack particulate-matter loading

- furnace pulsations

- possible heat damage to the distributors

- higher carbon loss and visible emissions

If the amount of coarse coal is too great, there will be insufficient burning in suspension with the potential for loss of flame stability.

Most new surface mines are not adding the double-screening equipment required to produce stoker-quality coal. This means there are fewer potential coal suppliers for a spreader-stoker-fired plant. Mines that do produce sized coal for spreaders may charge considerably more for the extra preparation. This adds to the total fuel cost for this type of firing.

If double-screened coal is not used, the day-to-day efficiency of operation will be reduced as the coal sizing varies from optimum. The question of whether or not the higher cost for double-screened coal offsets the reduced efficiency with unsized coal cannot be answered on a general basis. The answer depends on the degree of coal sizing variation, quality of operators, and boiler or stoker size.

To accommodate unsized coal that has the proper amount of fines but an excess of coarse material, a plant can include a coal crusher and mixing equipment. A pulverized-coal-fired industrial boiler requires only that the coal entering the mill be 1½ in. top size. If the proper size is unavailable at the mine, coal of any size can be purchased and crushed at the plant site. Despite raw coal size, the pulverizer delivers the properly sized coal with the correct moisture content to the furnace. Another factor favoring PC firing is the fact that many high-ash coals with a low ash-fusion temperature create a clinkering problem when burned on a stoker. In Ref. 1, Pollock gives a detailed comparison of annual fuel costs for pulverized versus spreader-stoker coal firing.

EMISSIONS

Control of particulate emissions, sulfur oxides, and nitrogen oxides must also be evaluated in the comparative installed costs of different types of coal-fired equipment.

Formerly, a stoker-fired boiler had a definite advantage in controlling particulate-matter emissions. This type of firing produces larger particles that could be removed easily with inexpensive mechanical dust collectors. Current emission codes require an electrostatic precipitator or equivalent particulate-matter removal equipment on most new stoker-fired- and all pulverized-coal-fired boilers.

Sulfur-oxide removal equipment also may be required for industrial units and, when sized, must take into account that PC boilers with bowl mills can have less sulfur in the products of combustion than stoker-fired units. During the pulverizing process, the bowl-mill tramp-iron spout may reject up to 40 percent of the pyritic sulfur. Because pyritic sulfur may approach 60 percent of the fuel sulfur, a reduction of nearly 25 percent could be obtained under optimum conditions. With a stoker-fired unit, some pyritic sulfur may remain on the grate and be deposited in the stoker ash hopper.

Although the bulk of the data for NO_x emissions is for relatively small stoker-fired boilers, both firing systems appear equally capable of meeting NO_x emission levels.

FUEL FLEXIBILITY

Coal-fired boilers can be designed to burn a wide range of coals. For nonreheat units, boiler reliability or cycle efficiency will not be compromised because tilting tangential fuel nozzles and/or spray desuperheating can control the effect of varying furnace heat absorption on the superheater. But during design, coal and ash properties for all of the coals to be fired must be considered. The major factors in designing a boiler for a wide range of coals are

■ Furnace sizing, convective surface spacing, and sootblower coverage: Coals with a lower ash-softening temperature require a larger furnace to assure the ash is in solid form before it enters the convective tube surface. A furnace that is appropriately sized for the poorest ash properties will operate successfully with the better coals. In designing for multiple fuels, it is not uncommon for one fuel to set the furnace size while another dictates the minimum allowable convective-surface spacing and sootblower requirements.

■ Pulverizer requirements: The lowest heating-value coal with the lowest grindability will determine the pulverizer size. If the coals vary in moisture, the boiler convective surface (boiler bank, economizer, air preheater) must provide the proper air temperature to dry the coal in the pulverizer so it is surface-dry and can be transported pneumatically to the furnace. If, for example, the moisture ranges from 3 to 35 percent, the air temperature required by the pulverizer will vary from 300 to 700°F.

■ Superheater sizing: The specific fuel and ash components determine the heat-absorption characteristics of the furnace and superheater. But generally the best fuel, which produces the lowest gas weight and consequently the lowest heat-transfer rates and LMTD, will set the superheater size. A wide range of fuel moistures will require a spray desuperheater to control final steam temperature when firing high-moisture coal.

■ Fans and gas-cleaning equipment: The highest-moisture coal used in a boiler generates the largest volume of flue gas. The fans, ductwork and flue-gas cleaning equipment must be designed for these conditions. The fans will consume greater power at normal loads with low-moisture fuels because they are operating further from the high-efficiency design point. A variable-speed motor or turbine drive can minimize power loss due to such oversize fans.

PROVISIONS FOR A WIDE RANGE OF COALS

Some special considerations can be made in the original boiler design to accommodate a wide range of coals. With a 3 to 35 percent moisture variation in the coals to be fired, a primary air preheater may be used to preheat the mill air to 700°F from the nominal 550°F temperature leaving the secondary air preheater. When firing low-moisture coals, the primary air preheater is not used and there is a minimal requirement for parasitic cold tempering air at the pulverizer inlet. Fig. 2 shows a 650,000 lb/hr pulverized-coal-fired boiler designed using this principle for various coals.

Although increasing the pulverizer size to handle a wide range of coals is common, it has several drawbacks. The turndown capacity of a pulverizer is basically a function of the mill size. Enlarging the pulverizers reduces the mill turndown when firing a coal with a higher heating value and grindability than the mill design values. More pulverizers may be needed to obtain the required turndown with a system designed for a wide range of coals.

Except for the pulverizers and air temperatures, the design of stoker-fired boilers involves the same considerations for multiple-fuel firing. A stoker-fired boiler requires an air temperature of less than 400°F to maintain adequate grate cooling for high-moisture coals and less than 300°F for low-moisture coals. Because many high-ash coals with low ash-softening temperatures cause clinkering on the grate, they cannot be used efficiently. To maintain the required bed height, high-ash coals require a faster stoker speed which may increase the unburned carbon content of the stoker ash. Using a large quantity of ash reinjection also aggravates grate clinkering.

BURNING LIQUID, GASEOUS, AND OTHER FUELS

Besides a range of coals, an owner may consider firing other liquid, gaseous or solid fuels (present or future). Because pulverized coal is suspension-fired as are conventional liquid and gaseous fuels, the furnace is already proportioned for this function. Similarly, the required piping, combustion controls, and fuel-firing equipment are in place as part of oil or gas systems for unit warm-up. These fuels can be fired to carry load with little or no design or equipment modifications.

Up to 20 percent or more of the total heat input can be obtained from well-prepared solid wastes burned in suspension. Bark, bagasse, or refuse have all been successfully suspension-fired in a PC-fired boiler. These wastes are normally blown into the furnace pneumatically through ports located above the coal nozzles.

To burn liquid or gaseous fuels in a stoker-fired boiler, the firing equipment must be located relatively high above the grate surface to protect it from the radiant heat produced by the auxiliary burners. For long-term operation, it may be necessary to cover the stoker with refractory. For short-term operation, considerable quantities of air are used to cool the stoker; but firing with large quantities of excess air is inefficient.

The stoker is ideally suited for firing unsized solid fuels other than coal. Normally, bark, bagasse or refuse can supplement the coal with only a minimum amount of additional equipment. Also, in a stoker-fired boiler, the total heat input can come from a larger percentage of waste fuels than in a PC-fired boiler.

THE C-E VU-40 BOILER

The C-E Type VU-40 boiler (Fig. 2) is a field erected, top-supported, single-gas-pass, thermal circulation, two-drum boiler. Its features make it particularly suitable for the range of steam and fuel conditions of both large industrial and small central-station installations. Boiler applications cover steam capacities from 100,000 to 1,000,000 lb/hr, design pressures from 200 to 1800 psig, and design steam temperatures from saturated to 1005°F. Virtually any solid, liquid or gaseous fuel can be fired.

DESIGN FEATURES

The VU-40 is produced in sizes and types for every capacity, pressure, fuel, space condition or method of firing encountered in municipal and industrial power and steam plants. It can be arranged for tangential, horizontal, or stoker firing of single and multiple fuels.

FURNACE

Completely water cooled, the VU-40 furnace

uses welded tube panels which are constructed with 2½ in. outside-diameter tubes on 3 in. centers joined by ½ in. wide fins. These fins are cast integrally with the tube material to form an air-and gas-tight furnace enclosure that essentially eliminates refractory and its attendant maintenance problems.

Complete furnace sidewalls with inlet and outlet headers shop-welded to the fusion tube panels, are available whenever maximum shop assembly is desired. Also included are seal boxes, miscellaneous attachments, insulation pins, and castable refractory.

The drop-bottom furnace of the VU-40 may be designed for any vertical dimension and may include a corner tangential-firing system with either fixed or tilting nozzles, the latter to assist in achieving steam-temperature control. It also may have a horizontal fuel-firing system in the front or rear walls or may be fired by mechanical stokers, either alone or in combination with other types of fuel.

Fig. 2 A pulverized-coal-fired boiler rated 650,000 lb/hr, 1550 psig and 955°F at superheater outlet

CIRCULATION

Fig. 3 shows the circulation of water and steam in the VU-40 boiler. A high furnace and large unheated downcomer pipes provide a thermosyphonic circulation effect resulting in liberal water flow to the furnace waterwall tubes. The steam-water mixture from the waterwall tubes is conveyed to the steam drum through (1) the furnace roof tubes, (2) the relief tubes from the sidewall upper headers, (3) the boiler bank screen tubes and (4) the front row tubes in the main boiler bank.

Steam-drum sizes vary from 54 in. to 78 in. inside diameter, with suitable internals of the baffle or centrifugal type (Figs. 4 and 5) to separate the steam from the water. As it leaves the drum and flows to the superheater, or to the main steam line in the case of saturated-steam units, the steam has extremely low-moisture content and is consequently quite pure.

TOP SUPPORT

VU-40 boilers are top-supported from a structural-steel grid above the unit, with provision for lateral and downward expansion. The furnace section and superheater are suspended from the grid by hanger rods, while the boiler section is hung from two large-diameter U-bolts that cradle the upper drum. The structural steel which supports the grid also supports auxiliary equipment, platforms and walkways. Suspending the boiler from structural steel permits use of a drop-bottom furnace with a furnace height that is independent of the boiler-bank height.

The boiler size and structural support arrangement necessitate field erection. However, a number of components other than the waterwall panels, such as superheater assemblies, economizers, air heaters, fuel-burning equipment and ductwork, can be shipped with varying degrees of shop preassembly in order to facilitate erection and to reduce costs.

SINGLE-PASS CONVECTION SURFACES

Pendant platen and spaced superheaters in combination with the baffleless boiler bank result in a single-pass crossflow arrangement of heat-transfer surfaces. The vertical tubes are ar-

Fig. 3 Circulation system on a C-E VU-40 Industrial boiler

ranged in-line to facilitate inspection and cleaning. Tube sizes and spacings can be varied to achieve the highest possible heat-transfer rates with the least potential for gas-side fouling. This convection heating-surface arrangement is especially suitable where the flue gases contain high dust loadings. Because there are no baffles on which to concentrate and stratify the dust or fly-ash, the likelihood of gas-side plugging and tube erosion is substantially reduced as compared to multi-pass convection surfaces. It also has an inherent low draft-loss characteristic because of the lack of gas turns.

Installed across the entire furnace width, superheater surface takes advantage of the uniform distribution of combustion gases as they leave the furnace. Superheater assemblies are supported from their respective inlet and outlet headers located outside the gas stream above the furnace roof. The superheater headers, in turn, are supported by the furnace sidewalls and upper support steel.

FUELS AND FIRING EQUIPMENT

Diversity of fuels and fuel-firing systems typify industrial steam generation. All grades of conventional fossil fuels—plus numerous byproduct and/or waste fuels—have been fired in industrial units. The list of waste fuels is ever-growing with the decreasing availability and increasing cost of fossil fuels. The list also is affected by the increasing difficulty and expense in disposing of industrial and municipal waste materials in an ecologically acceptable manner. The versatility of the top-supported drop-bottom furnace to accommodate all types of fuel-burning equipment permits the burning of a wide variety of fuels as shown in Table II.

Table II. Fuels and Burning Equipment

	Fuel Burning Equipment		
Fuels	**Front Firing**	**Tangential Firing**	**Stoker**
Gases			
Natural gas	X	X	
Refinery gas	X	X	
**Carbon monoxide	X	X	
*Blast furnace gas	X	X	
Coke oven gas	X	X	
Hydrogen	X	X	
Liquids			
Oil	X	X	
Tars	X	X	
Pitch	X	X	
Waste sulfite liquor		X*	
Black liquor		X	
*Liquid wastes	X	X	
Solids			
Coal	X	X	X
Bark and hogged wood		X	X
Bagasse		X	X
Unsized refuse			X
Sized refuse		X	X

*Usually burned with supplementary fuel.
**Always burned with supplementary fuel.

Fig. 4 Steam drum internals—baffle type

Final Stage Screens

Deflection Baffle

Primary Screens

Normal Water Level

Feedwater Pipe

Continuous Blowdown Piping

Final Screen Dryers

Centrifugal Separators

Stationary Spinner Vanes

Normal Water Level

Continuous Blowdown Piping

Feedwater Pipe

Fig. 5 Steam drum internals—perforated centrifugal type

Fig. 6 illustrates lower-furnace variations for different types of fuel-burning equipment. The water-cooled furnace bottom can be equipped with a dump grate, as described in Chapter 13, to insure complete burnout of relatively large fuel particles of byproduct fuels such as bark, bagasse or sized refuse when these fuels are fired tangentially in suspension.

With the C-E tangential firing system, two or more of these fuels can be burned in combination, which is especially desirable if one fuel is a waste material of insufficient quantity to meet steaming requirements or is of a low calorific value or high moisture content so as to require supplementary firing.

Fig. 7 illustrates a 550,000 lb/hr VU-40 boiler installed in a paper mill. The boiler is capable of firing coal in pulverized form, bark on a grate and sawdust through its tilting tangential firing system. Nozzle tilts supplemented by an interstage spray desuperheater make it possible to achieve the design steam temperature of 950°F with any combination of fuels.

For auxiliary fuel, oil or gas nozzles are located in furnace sidewalls above the level of the bark distributors and are arranged for tangential firing. The elevations of the distributors and the auxiliary firing system are selected to compensate for the difference in the quantities and temperatures of gas from each fuel. Besides helping to maintain a more uniform steam temperature, positioning auxiliary fuel nozzles at high levels affords protection to the grates should there be occasion to burn oil or gas without firing bark.

THE C-E RADIANT BOILER

The C-E radiant boiler (Fig. 8) is a field-erected, top-supported, single-gas-pass, thermal circulation boiler designed for industrial and small central-station applications for the 1800-psig or higher-pressure steam cycle. The size ranges from 400,000 to over 4,000,000 lb/hr for nonreheat steam cycles requiring steam temperatures of 1000°F.

Fig. 6 Lower-furnace variations of the VU-40 boiler

Fig. 7 VU-40 boiler for a paper mill, for pulverized-coal, bark and sawdust firing

This radiant boiler is designed primarily for pulverized-coal firing but waste fuels such as sawdust, sewage sludge, or prepared municipal refuse can be fired in combination with the coal. An economizer section is substituted for the boiler bank section to facilitate efficient heat transfer when operating at 1850 psig or higher superheater-outlet pressure. Welded-wall construction and external pipe downcomers complete the circulation system.

There are, in addition to the above type of boiler, many reheat-cycle steam generators producing electricity for large industrial firms, particularly those involved in the production of basic metals. These units are identical to those described in the previous chapter and are found in sizes above 100 MW.

FIRING REFUSE IN INDUSTRIAL BOILERS

Chapter 2 included a discussion of municipal refuse as a fuel. Its value as an alternate energy source is proportional to the effort spent in "refining" or beneficiating it. And, to a certain extent, the cost of the boiler that can burn a prepared refuse will be inverse to the amount of money spent on the removal of metals and glass and on the size reduction and homogenization of the refuse.[2–14]

The following describes three distinctly different systems for handling and burning refuse, and the types of steam-generating equipment best suited for the specific method. The different systems are

- suspension firing of prepared refuse
- spreader-stoker firing of prepared refuse
- mass-burning of unprepared refuse

SUSPENSION FIRING OF PREPARED REFUSE

For suspension firing, refuse must be reduced to a maximum size of 2 in. × 2 in. so that it burns uniformly in suspension. Such size reduction also allows pneumatic conveying to the furnace.

Fig. 9 illustrates a typical preparation system for suspension firing. C-E uses its tangential system for 100-percent suspension firing. As described in Chapter 13, the refuse and heated air are directed tangent to a circle in the center of the furnace. Fuel and air are mixed in a single fireball aiding in the even distribution within the furnace. The lighter fraction of the refuse quickly burns in suspension. The larger and more dense refuse material will not remain suspended by the air and will fall to the furnace bottom, where a grate is provided to complete the combustion of this material. Several rows of tangentially-directed air nozzles are located between the fuel compartments and the stoker. These nozzles maximize the suspension burning of the heavier refuse material as it falls to the grate at the furnace bottom.

Suspension firing of prepared refuse has advantages over other systems. For example:

- faster boiler response rate
- smaller grate required
- normally can be retrofitted to a solid-fuel-fired boiler for heat inputs to 20 percent with pulverized coal firing
- higher thermal efficiency than the other systems due to the ability to use lower excess air
- the homogeneous nature of the fuel reduces the potential for furnace wall corrosion due to an alternating reducing/oxidizing atmosphere
- resource recovery potential

Disadvantages of this system include:

- the need for additional fuel-preparation and transport equipment
- higher auxiliary power requirements (due to the preparation system)
- higher flyash quantities leaving the furnace.

For this firing system, boilers able to burn up to 1500 tons/day of refuse can be designed for steam conditions to 825°F total steam temperature. The total-steam-temperature limitation avoids excessive superheater corrosion which increases significantly as the tube metal temperatures approach 900°F. As described in Chapter 3, it is believed that the chlorides in the refuse are the cause of this corrosion. The reaction of gas-phase sulfuric acid with deposited

Fig. 8 Pulverized coal-fired radiant boiler, rated 800,000 lb/hr, 1850 psig and 1005°F at superheater outlet

chloride releases HCl near the heated tube surface. A subsequent reaction may involve the stepwise formation of volatile ferric chloride and/or unstable chloride or oxy-chlorides of other alloy components.

The superheater-temperature limitation applies to 100 percent refuse-fired boilers regardless of the type of firing systems used. In units deriving 20 percent or less of the total heat from refuse in combination with pulverized coal, the superheater metal temperature may be higher without developing excessive corrosion rates. It is believed that the reduced corrosion rate with PC firing is a result of the neutralizing effect of the coal ash in combination with the reduced refuse fuel quantity.

FURNACE AND CONVECTIVE-SYSTEM DESIGN

The furnace of a suspension-fired boiler is sized for a maximum outlet temperature of 1600°F to avoid ash buildup and plugging of the convective heating surface. The convective surface must therefore be designed with wide tube spacing so ash buildup between sootblowing cycles cannot bridge from tube to tube.

A maximum flue-gas velocity in all convective areas of 25 ft/sec minimizes tube erosion. In-line tube arrangements assure the cleanability of all tube surfaces using retractable sootblowers. Precautions taken in the design to optimize the relationship between ash buildup and sootblowing will extend tube life as excessive tube wastage can occur with too frequent sootblowing.

When it is not possible to lower the flue-gas temperature of the boiler bank to about 600°F, an economizer cools the combustion gases.

The final heat-recovery equipment is normally a regenerative air preheater. Special precautions are necessary to minimize or eliminate corrosion of equipment located in the relatively cool gas temperature zone. Corrosion will increase significantly if the gas or metal temperature approaches 300°F.

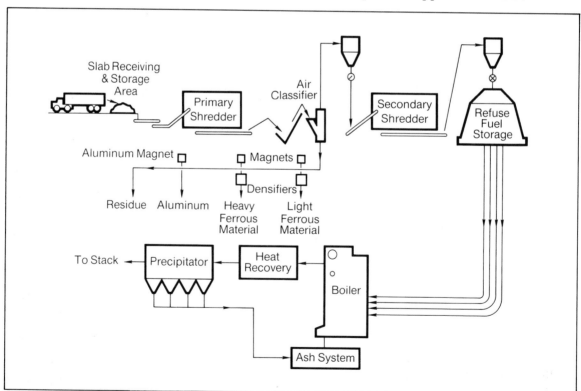

Fig. 9 Preparation system for suspension firing municipal refuse

In usual combustion processes, sulfur is released as SO_2, but a smaller percentage ($\sim$1%) is oxidized to SO_3. In the zones where the flue gas is cooler, this SO_3 reacts with water to form sulfuric acid. If the gas temperature is below the dew point, condensation occurs and the resulting acid attacks exposed metal surfaces in air heaters, fans, duct work and emission-control equipment.

Generally, refuse is a low-sulfur fuel; therefore, with proper design and operating procedures dew point wastage should be minimal. However, the presence of HCl in the effluent gas stream during refuse firing can increase corrosion potential due to general acid attack or stress-corrosion fatigue.

Proper operating procedures can help to minimize wastage. Experience at many plants, especially in Europe, indicates that less frequent use of sootblowers reduces the exposure of cleaned tube surfaces and makes the metal less vulnerable to attack. The ash deposits are protective unless the tube surfaces are at such a temperature that an accelerated molten phase or chloride attack can occur.

Provisions must be made to protect all cold-end surfaces from corrosion. The more common practices include

■ use of enameled or corrosion-resistant alloy steel in the regenerative air preheater

■ preheating the air entering the air preheater with steam coils to increase the minimum metal temperatures

■ insulation of all gas ducts to maximize the duct metal and flue gas temperatures.

The lower the stack temperature desired, the greater the precautions required to avoid cold-end corrosion. Most refuse plants in operation currently were designed when fuel was less expensive and, therefore, have stack temperatures in the 600°F range. Today, equipment is being designed for much lower stack temperatures, in the 350°F range.

SPREADER-STOKER FIRING OF PREPARED REFUSE

With this system, the raw refuse has a 6-in. top size with 95 percent being less than 4 in. In a typical preparation system (Fig. 10), the refuse is delivered on demand to small storage/metering bins at the boiler front where the refuse is delivered at a controlled rate to the pneumatic refuse distributors located in the furnace front wall. A screw feeder in the bottom of each bin is controlled by the combustion-control system to respond to the steam demand rate. High-pressure air is delivered to the pneumatic refuse distributors to assure even feed of the grate surface. The air quantity required for the refuse distributors is approximately 5 percent of the total air required for complete and efficient combustion.

Although the refuse delivered to the boiler has a greater percentage of large material that burns on the grate surface than does a full suspension system, there is sufficient light fraction to allow for suspension burning above the grate. The suspension burning, combined with the metering bins located near the boiler, produces fast boiler response to maintain stable operation when the fuel or steam demand quickly changes. The grate is a continuous-ash-discharge type which travels from the rear toward the front of the furnace. The stoker is almost identical to the continuous-ash-discharge machines currently used for stoker-firing coal or other waste cellulose fuels (Fig. 7).

With the spreader-stoker refuse-firing system, a single boiler can handle in excess of 1500 short tons of waste fuel a day. Total steam temperatures are limited to 825°F to avoid excessive corrosion when firing 100 percent refuse. The advantages of this system include

■ faster boiler response rate than mass-burning

■ the unit can be designed to burn other solid waste fuels or coal on the stoker

■ the homogeneous nature of the fuel reduces the potential for furnace-wall corrosion which can result from an alternating reducing/oxidizing atmosphere

■ high thermal efficiency due to the ability to use lower excess air than mass-burning

■ resource recovery potential

■ high sludge-disposal potential when compared to mass-burning.

The disadvantages of this system include

■ additional fuel-preparation-equipment when compared to mass-burning

■ higher auxiliary power requirements than mass-burning (due to the preparation system)

■ higher flyash quantities leaving the furnace than mass-burning.

All other design considerations are the same as those for prepared refuse for suspension burning previously covered.

MASS-BURNING OF UNPREPARED REFUSE

A third major refuse-firing system (Fig. 11) is the mass-burning of unprepared refuse in which raw refuse is discharged into a large pit. A bridge crane and clamshell are used for mixing the refuse as well as moving the material to the charging chute.

Typically, a hydraulic ram moves the refuse to the first grate which agitates and moves the refuse down a gentle slope. Agitation is re-quired to expose all of the refuse to the air in order to complete combustion. Because the refuse size is not reduced, the bulk of the combustion occurs at or near the grate surface.

Currently, mass-burning boilers (Fig. 12) are available in size ranges approaching 700 short tons of refuse per day.

FURNACE AND CONVECTIVE-SYSTEM DESIGN

The lower furnace must be necked out to accommodate the large grate area required for a mass-burning stoker but the total furnace must be sized to cool the gases to about 1300°F before they enter the first convective surface. Due to fluctuating furnace conditions from the non-uniform heat input rate, the steam temperature should be limited to 800°F for mass-burning in a boiler of the type shown in Fig. 12.

The nonhomogeneous nature of raw refuse can cause wide fluctuations in the steam flow, steam pressure and boiler water level. If the steam produced must be delivered at a uniform

Fig. 10 **Preparation system for spreader-stoker firing municipal refuse**

pressure and flow, special equipment such as accumulators and pressure-reducing stations must be designed into the system.

The constantly changing firing conditions in a mass-burning system require more conservative convective system design and sootblower coverage than that required by either the full-suspension or spreader-stoker type systems. Specific advantages of the mass system include:

■ lower auxiliary power consumption because the refuse preparation system is not required

■ requires less space than other systems

■ reduced flyash loading leaving the furnace

Disadvantages of the mass system include:

■ slower response rate to load changes

■ wide variation in steam flow and pressure make steady-state operation difficult

■ high excess-air requirement due to the non-homogeneous nature of the fuel resulting in lower thermal efficiency

■ corrosion potential of the lower furnace water-wall, which requires a protective coating

■ reduced resource-recovery potential.

Table III includes a comparison of the boiler performance of all three refuse systems when burning 600 short tons/day of refuse. This performance is for the boiler only. When comparing complete systems, the initial cost and

power requirements of all installed equipment must be evaluated. In addition, other factors such as revenue from electrical power generated and recovered products must be considered to determine the true cost-effectiveness of the various systems.

FIRING OTHER FUELS WITH REFUSE

When properly equipped, refuse-fired boilers can burn other solid, liquid, or gaseous fuels. With any of the three refuse systems, conventional fuel-firing assemblies can be included in the upper furnace for the suspension firing of another fuel. Common fuels that can be used in this manner include

■ pulverized coal

■ sawdust

■ fine bark or other small-size cellulose fuels

■ liquid and gaseous fuels

■ dried sewage sludge.

With spreader-stoker firing of prepared refuse, it is possible to design for stoker firing of other solid fuels such as coal, wood, bark, bagasse, or sludge in combination with the stoker-fired refuse. Although solid fuels can be mixed with refuse for mass burning, the maximum quantity of the supplementary solid fuel will generally be less than with the spreader stoker. As they were developed spe-

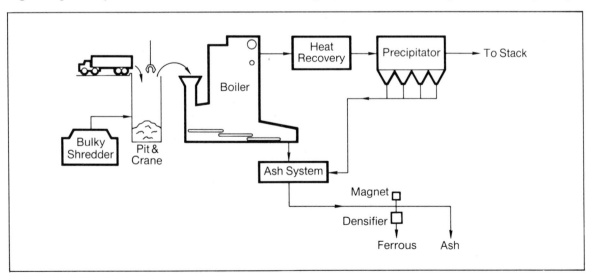

Fig. 11 **Preparation system for mass-burning municipal refuse**

Fig. 12 Side elevation of boiler for mass-burning of refuse

cifically for refuse, mass-burning stokers are less adaptable to other fuels.

Disposing of sewage sludge in refuse boilers will become more common because conventional sludge disposal methods are energy intensive. There are many varieties of sludge produced and it is possible to dispose of them in coal- or refuse-fired boilers. In most cases, there is even a net gain in heat delivered to the boiler; that is, the chemical heat in the sludge exceeds the latent heat of vaporization required to evaporate the moisture in the sludge. Removing as much moisture as possible before delivering the sludge to the boiler increases the quantity of sludge that can be disposed of. If the moisture is removed mechanically, the boiler thermal efficiency will be increased. Most sludges, however, contain large quantities of ash which must be handled by the boiler and particulate-removal equipment.

BOILERS FOR RECOVERY OF WASTE HEAT AND FIRING OF BYPRODUCT FUELS

For the purposes of this text, waste-heat boilers will be defined in two categories: those actually fired by waste and byproduct fuels and those unfired units which recover sensible heat from industrial processes and combustion gas turbines. This section covers only a few of the many waste heat processes.

CATEGORIZATION OF WASTE AND BYPRODUCT FUELS

Waste gases and byproduct fuels may be characterized as solid, liquid and gaseous in terms of the state in which they are fired. Information on their chemical composition and calorific value is included in Chapter 2. Solid waste fuels are generally handled and burned in stoker-fired or suspended-fuel-fired arrangements; liquids, in atomized form. Except for special cases, these do not differ appreciably from the handling of coal or oil. Gaseous waste and byproduct fuels, on the other hand, may require special treatment.

Relatively clean, and differing from natural gases mainly in volumetric heat content, refinery gas and coke-oven gas require only minor changes in burner design. In general, fuel gases with heat contents higher than 500 Btu/cu ft are easily handled by burners of the same type as used for natural gas. With gases of heating value less than 250 Btu/cu ft, consideration should be given to burning systems of high volumetric capacity, such as tangential firing.

The large percentages of inert gases or dust carryover differentiate waste gaseous fuels from natural gas. Most problems involved with these gases are typified in the handling of steel and copper reverberatory gases, blast-furnace gas, catalytic-cracker regenerator gas and gases from cement kilns. The degree to which the inerts are present, and the quantity, size and character of the solid, strongly influence the boiler design for a given application.

COPPER-REVERBERATORY GAS

Boilers fired with smelter gases are required to operate continuously for prolonged periods. These gases, which contain negligible amounts of combustible matter, are made available to the steam generator at a temperature of about 2200°F. They contain varying quantities of sulfur dioxide and sulfur trioxide as well as droplets of slag and metal that may be molten at temperatures as low as 1400°F.

To provide the maximum reduction in temperature of these hot gases with minimum contact with convection heating surface, boilers for this service have ample cooling chambers or furnaces. To further protect against plugging the narrower spaced convection bank, a wide-spaced platen bank is sometimes installed at the furnace outlet. Sufficient hopper capacity to catch the carryover is required in both the furnace and boiler bank. Because of the significant quantity of carryover, soot-cleaning devices must be judiciously located and systematically operated.

BLAST-FURNACE GAS

Blast-furnace gas is a dust-laden byproduct of the iron reduction process. It is valuable for its high carbon-monoxide content, which var-

Table III. Systems Comparisons*

	Suspension Firing of Prepared Refuse	Spreader Stoker Firing of Prepared Refuse	Mass Burning of Unprepared Refuse
	Prepared Refuse % WT	Prepared Refuse % WT	Raw Refuse % WT
Carbon	35.33	35.33	28.57
Hydrogen	3.60	3.60	2.91
Oxygen	21.60	21.60	17.46
Nitrogen	.45	.45	.36
Sulfur	.12	.12	.10
Moisture	25.90	25.90	28.80
Ash	13.00	13.00	21.80
Total	100.00	100.00	100.00
HHV	5690 Btu/Lb	5690 Btu/Lb	4600 Btu/Lb
Steam flow	128,586 Lb/Hr **	126,542 Lb/Hr **	124,171 Lb/Hr
Excess air	30%	40%	80%
Efficiency	76.12%	74.79%	69.74%
Stack temperature	350°F	350°F	350°F
FD fan horsepower	135	140	190
ID fan horsepower	110	120	145

*(600 Ton/Day 750°TST 300°F Feedwater)
**Assumes five percent combustible loss in preparation

ies widely with the furnace charge and affects the heating value of the gas, which can range from 65 to 110 Btu/cu ft.

The dust carried over is mostly iron oxide which can foul gas mains, firing systems, boiler furnaces and convection heating surfaces. To extend and improve availability of equipment, the blast-furnace gas may undergo as many as three stages of cleaning. The first stage is a simple mechanical separation; the second, a primary spray washing; and the third, either a more vigorous washing or an electrostatic separation. The dust load after the first stage of cleaning may range from 5 to 8 grains/cu ft. This is reduced to 0.3 to 1.0 grain/cu ft in the second stage and, in the final stage, to 0.005 to 0.01 grain/cu ft.

Boilers designed for steel-making service must be able to respond to very rapid load changes. When fired by blast-furnace or coke-oven gas, they are further subject to quick changes in the availability of these fuels. For this reason, a supplemental fuel is required.

The fuel must rapidly pick up load to maintain continuity of steam-generator operation.

Unlike designs for conventional fuels, the design of a boiler for blast-furnace-gas operation involves many variables. As a first consideration, the quantity of solid carryover in the gas may permit a unit which is as simple and as compact as those used exclusively for natural-gas or oil firing. Conversely, it may require a unit of larger size, freely hoppered and provided with as many soot-cleaning devices as a pulverized-coal-fired boiler.

Secondly, the low calorific value requires that 1500 to 1600 lb/hr of combustion products be generated for each million Btu fired. This compares with the 850 to 950 lb/hr of products per million Btu for such conventional fuels as oil and gas, and 950 to 1050 lb/hr of products per million Btu of coal fired. For a given evaporation, the quantity of products passing through a boiler varies considerably as fuels are changed. This means that the control of the steam temperature for units having high-temperature superheaters becomes a critical consideration. Design conditions are made more difficult because of the erratic availability of the blast-furnace gas, which creates the need to hold steam temperature constant under conditions in which it would tend to swing as much as 100°F in seconds. This problem is normally handled by steam temperature control devices such as spray or gas-recirculation.

There is an additional problem of handling the simultaneous burning of a number of fuels in the same furnace with blast-furnace gas. Tangentially-fired units of the type shown in Fig. 2 can be adapted easily to fire blast-furnace gas along with several other fuels.

OPEN-HEARTH FURNACE GAS

One of the common methods of producing steel from pig iron uses the open-hearth furnace. The exhaust gases leaving the furnace are passed through refractory checkerwork which serves as a regenerative heater for the combustion air required for direct firing of fuel into the furnace. Two sets of checkerwork are included with each furnace, and slide-gate dampers are used to exhaust air and gas alternately through the checkerwork. The reversals of checkerwork, plus variations in the operation of the open-hearth furnace itself, result in continuous changes of gas flow, dust loading and gas temperature. Ordinarily these gas temperatures range from 1000° to 1500°F, but may reach 2000°F where direct oxygen lancing of the furnace is used to increase steel output.

Steam demands in a steel mill make it practical to use waste-heat boilers for reducing the waste gas temperatures to about 600°F. This temperature reduction allows use of electrostatic precipitators to remove dust particles. Because the gases are dirty and offer only sensible heat, they present special requirements for the boiler designer. Heating surfaces must be arranged to minimize deposits and plugging of gas passages.

Fig. 13 shows a Controlled Circulation® boiler for the recovery of heat from open-hearth furnace gas. Tube spacing at the inlet section near the bottom of the unit is comparatively wide to prevent slag adherence and to mini-

Fig. 13 Controlled Circulation boiler for recovery of heat from open-hearth furnace gas

mize abrasion. As the gas is cooled in passing through the boiler, the tube spacing is decreased. The boiler circulating pumps not only permit flexibility in the choice of tube size and spacing but also assure positive and stable circulation under steady and variable load conditions.

Although originally applied to waste heat recovery from open-hearth furnace gas, this design of positive-circulation waste-heat boiler can be used wherever exhaust gas conditions and limited physical space justify the advantages of the pumped-circulation principle in reducing boiler size for a given steam output and waste heat throughput. Controlled Circulation waste-heat boilers find use in recovering heat from cement kilns and various metallurgical, mineral reduction and refining processes.

BASIC-OXYGEN PROCESS GAS

When compared with the open-hearth method, the basic-oxygen process for steel making has several advantages including reduction in time, increased rates of production and decreased costs. Oxygen is top-blown into a vessel similar to a Bessemer converter, and the products of this reaction, mainly CO gas, are collected in a fume hood. The total cycle time varies with the oxygen blowing rate, but usually a 20-minute oxygen blowing time is followed by a 25-minute charge time.

The fume hood reduces the temperature of the dust-laden gases and directs them to the cleaning equipment before discharge to the atmosphere. The unit designed for this service uses Controlled Circulation principles and can be combined with convection surface to constitute a waste-heat boiler as shown in Fig. 14. The unit is fabricated of small-diameter tubing with fins between adjacent tubes on the outside perimeter to form a continuous wall that is gas tight. The vessel cover is placed directly above the converter vessel and located so as to control entering ambient air. The ID fan controls the amount of air admitted to the hood for oxidizing the carbon-monoxide gas generated in the basic-oxygen process.

The dust from this steel-making process contains essentially Fe_2O_3 with small amounts of FeO and Mn_3O_4. There are also traces of silicon, calcium, aluminum and phosphorus oxides. As an indication of the minute particle size, consider that 85 percent by weight of the particles in the fume are less than one micron (1 μm), and 20 percent are less than half a micron. The dust loading varies considerably during the oxygen blowing period and reaches a maximum after carbon-monoxide evolution begins and temperature is highest.

The total weight of dust during a blowing cycle has been found to vary from one to two percent of the metallic charge weight. For standard designs, the dust loading from carry-over is 7 to 9 grains/standard cu ft.

The gas leaving the vessel is mainly carbon monoxide, and the total gas volume is directly related to the blowing rate. The carbon monoxide present must be totally burned in the hood to eliminate the possibility of an explosion in the associated duct work and dust collectors. An accepted design criterion is that the ratio of waste gas produced to oxygen blown is 25 to 1 under standard conditions. To insure complete oxidation of the carbon monoxide gas and more uniform heat absorption in the fume hood, a tangential overfire air system is used.

Controlled Circulation is necessary for this application because positive and complete circulation is required in areas of the furnace where high heat absorption takes place.

As shown in Fig. 14, feedwater is discharged into the steam drum where it mixes with circulated water from the unit. This water mixture

Fig. 14 **Fume hood for waste-heat recovery in the oxygen process for steel making**

enters the downcomers which are connected to circulating pumps that deliver water to a discharge manifold. The water then flows through supply tubes to the inlet headers of the fume hood and through the waterwalls to the outlet header. Risers from the outlet header to the steam drum complete the circuit. The unit has complete water cooling with convection surface located in the upper furnace area.

Cyclic operation presents many obstacles to the design of an acceptable system for continuous steam generation, and therefore, complicates the application of waste-heat boilers to the basic oxygen process. Obstacles include the fact that supplementary fuel must be fired during the charging period, and may sometimes be necessary during blowing and charging. The steam generated during the blowing cycle can be discharged into a header system and used elsewhere in the steel plant. One possibility of dampening the effect of the cyclic operations is to generate the steam at high pressure and store it in an accumulator. This steam can then be discharged at a constant rate and lower pressure during the charging cycle.

REFINERY REGENERATOR GAS

In the petroleum-refining industry, one of the major processes for producing gasoline is catalytic cracking. It is necessary to regenerate the catalyst continuously to maintain optimum output in steady-flow catalytic processes. The process of regeneration involves the removal of coke deposited on the catalyst in the cracking operation. It is accomplished in a regenerator, a large vessel in which compressed air circulates and scours the hot catalyst to burn off the coke and return the catalyst to the reactor for reuse. For this cleaning, large quantities of air must be raised to a pressure as high as 25 psig. At the same time, to minimize compression costs and to keep the temperature within the regenerator to a level which will not destroy catalyst activity, the quantity of air is limited to the smallest amount that will effectively clean the catalyst.

These combustion conditions produce an appreciable amount of carbon monoxide. This gas, which may leave the regenerator at tem-

peratures as high as 1125°F, contains a large amount of sensible heat, although it may have a heating value below 40 Btu/cu ft with a carbon monoxide content from 4 to 10 percent. Unable to support its own combustion under ordinary conditions, regenerator waste gas, also called "CO gas," requires a supplemental fuel such as refinery gas, oil or natural gas.

Boilers have been designed to burn this regenerator gas and to supply steam at pressures and temperatures suitable for power generation and process use. At the same time, these boilers reduce atmospheric pollution by oxidizing the carbon monoxide and hydrocarbon content of regenerator waste gas. A unit for burning this gas is shown in Fig. 15.

The main differences between boilers burning regenerator waste gas and conventional fuel-fired units stem from the nature of the gas and the fact that its full flow must be handled by the boiler at all times. A conventional boiler generally maintains a fixed fuel-air ratio throughout its load range and is capable of wide variation within this range. On the other hand, a boiler handling regenerator waste gas begins with a minimum steam output corresponding to the minimum fuel fired for stable and complete combustion. Steam output can be

Fig. 15 Tangentially fired VU-60 installation for burning refinery CO waste gas

varied from this minimum condition in only one direction, that is, upward.

An important feature of the waste-regenerator gas boiler is the use of *fixed* tangential firing. The waste gas, stabilizing fuel, and air are divided into several streams which are directed from the corners of the lower furnace. Concentration of the windboxes in the lower part of the furnace provides more heat for ignition as well as longer gas travel; location in quiescent corner positions assures positive ignition during all operating modes.

The impinging and scrubbing action of the streams upon one another produces the turbulence and mixing of fuel and air necessary for rapid and complete combustion.

Fig. 16 VU-60 unit with tangential firing system suitable for firing liquid and gaseous prime and waste fuels

THE C-E VU-60 BOILER

Fig. 16 shows a standardized field-erected boiler for firing clean liquid and gaseous fuels from coal, many of the waste and byproduct fuels previously discussed, as well as natural gas and fuel oil. Available in capacities from 100,000 lb/hr to 1,000,000 lb/hr, design pressures to 1800 psig and superheater-outlet steam temperatures to 1005°F, it is designed to make use of standardized modular components shop-assembled before field erection.

This boiler is most often designed for pressurized firing, without an induced-draft fan. The waterwalls consist of panels of 3-in. diameter tubes on 4-in. centers, between which metallic fins are placed and welded, produc-

Fig. 17 VU-60 unit with front-wall (round) burners for liquid and gaseous fuels

ing, a completely tight furnace enclosure. Insulation and lagging are applied directly over the tube panels. Fig. 17 shows the VU-60 arranged for front-wall round-burner firing.

This construction virtually eliminates refractory maintenance because the only refractory material is the floor tile; on front-fired units it is the burner throats. Both of these locations are water cooled. Also, tube replacement in the welded wall is simplified because the 1-in. fin between the tubes allows circumferential butt welding without springing adjacent tubes.

SUPERHEATER DESIGN

For steam temperatures above 825°F, the superheater is arranged in two stages, with interstage desuperheating for vernier control of outlet temperature. Multiloop pendant-type elements and a center connection in the large-diameter outlet header assure even distribution of steam throughout the superheater surface. The construction requires a minimum number of header joints. Superheater elements are supported from headers located out of the gas stream above the furnace roof; these headers are supported by furnace walls and drum.

When solid wastes must be burned along with gasecus or liquid wastes, a modification of the VU-60 modular boiler incorporates a continuous-ash-discharge spreader-type stoker and is bottom-supported like the basic VU-60. Its usual range of steam production is between 100,000 and 250,000 lb/hr, with operating pressures up to 1550 psig at the superheater outlet and total steam temperatures up to 955°F. Stoker coal, wood refuse, bark, bagasse or other cellulose fuels suitable for stoker firing can be burned. Supplemental oil, gas, or other waste fuels are fired with either a tangential firing system or front-wall round burners.

GAS-TURBINE HEAT RECOVERY

Gas turbines are widely used to provide standby or peaking power, and for unattended service in remote locations. But their thermal efficiency is low because of high exit-gas temperatures and the extremely high excess-air percentages in the combustion process. In many cases, the thermal efficiency of a gas-turbine plant can be improved by adding heat-recovery equipment. Frequently there have been economic benefits from adding either a fired or unfired steam generator to an existing gas-turbine installation.

Many combined gas-turbine/steam-turbine power plants have been conceived and designed on the basis of higher thermal efficiency than a conventional steam power-plant with the same steam conditions. Chapter 1 identified the four major classifications of combined cycles and their associated heat rates. The most commonly used cycles for industry are those with unfired and furnace-fired steam generators.

STEAM-GENERATOR DESIGNS

The basic principles for selecting the heat-recovery or steam-generation equipment for combined cycles are similar to those for conventional utility and industrial boilers. However, the designer must be more aware of the entire system arrangement in order to integrate the steam generator properly within the overall plant. Although overall cycle efficiency and economics generally determine the basic steam conditions, the designer should be involved in initial cycle considerations to provide maximum performance at least cost.

Despite a wide range of design criteria and arrangements, two denominators are common in all combined cycles. First, there is extensive use of externally finned pressure-part surfaces which provide for the most economic recovery of the gas-turbine exhaust heat. Second is the emphasis on low unit draft loss so as not to adversely affect gas-turbine performance.

Unfired Heat Recovery

Waste heat boilers for the recovery of sensible heat from gas-turbine exhaust are of either the natural or forced-circulation design. Such boilers can be built inside of what amounts to a continuation of the turbine exhaust duct. Gas velocities through these units are limited to about 100 ft/sec by reason of excessive back-pressure on the gas turbine.

Unfired boilers have been used mainly for the production of process steam. In some applications, they have been used for power generation or space heating. The simple-cycle, single-shaft gas turbine usually considered for this application produces substantially the same amount of exhaust gas at all loads. But exhaust temperatures drop sharply as turbine power-output decreases. The steam generated by a boiler following such a gas turbine is then nearly directly proportional to the turbine electrical output. A superheater installed in such a boiler also has a drooping characteristic with decreasing load.

Gas-turbine exhaust has often been used to add heat to the feedwater of a steam cycle by employing extended surface economizers of the same design as used in power boilers.[15]

Fig. 18 illustrates the temperature levels of a typical waste-heat application. The critical temperature differential which affects the steam generator and system design is the boiler "pinch point" or minimum differential between gas temperature and boiler saturated water temperature. For any given set of steam conditions and gas-turbine exhaust temperature, as the temperature differential is increased, the combined-cycle plant output will decrease and the plant heat rate will increase. In general, differentials of 40 to 50°F approach the minimum practical design.

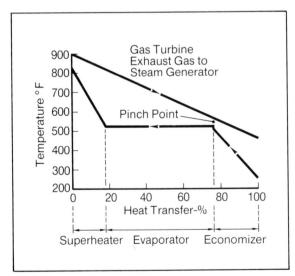

Fig. 18 Typical gas and steam temperatures—unfired steam generator

For these units, the quantity of installed heating surface is inversely proportional to the gas-side draft loss, but increases in gas-turbine back pressure will adversely affect gas-turbine performance. With these designs, fuel consumption will increase approximately 1 percent for each additional 4″ WG of draft loss.

Overall steam-generator design affects the choice of fluid circulation in the evaporator surface. For horizontal heating-surface arrangements, Controlled Circulation is used. This system incorporates a circulating pump in the evaporating loop to supply sufficient circulation to provide proper cooling and flow distribution within the evaporator tube banks.

Fig. 19 illustrates a typical unfired steam generator. The plant design incorporates a multiple of gas-turbine and steam-generator modules supplying a single steam turbine. The steam generator is Controlled Circulation and generates 210,000 lb/hr of steam at 400 psig and 730°F with 275°F feedwater temperature. The overall unit draft loss is maintained at 12″ WG. The gas temperatures entering and leaving the steam generator are 885° and 442°F, respectively. All economizer, evaporator, and superheater surfaces are spiral-finned carbon-steel material.

Boilers with Supplementary Firing

Normally containing 75 to 80 percent of the oxygen found in free atmospheric air, gas-turbine exhaust can concurrently supply to the furnace of a steam generator both sensible heat and oxygen for the combustion of a fuel. The design and operation of such boilers vary considerably, depending upon the ratio of the total exhaust flow to the amount necessary for oxidizing the supplementary fuel needed for a given evaporation. Combustion air preheaters are not used because of the already high level of preheat represented by the 700° to 900°F temperature of the exhaust gases.

Supplementary-fired steam generators (Fig. 20) using most of the oxygen in the turbine exhaust are of the same design and size as units using outside air through forced-draft fans. The stack temperature on such a unit can be dropped economically to within 100°F of the

Fig. 19 **Unfired steam-generator for recovering heat from gas-turbine exhaust**

— Economizer Section

— Evaporator Sections

— Superheater Section

Gas Turbine Exhaust

Fig. 20 **Boiler designed for supplementary firing in conjunction with gas-turbine combined cycle**

incoming feedwater temperature. In certain simple steam cycles where there is no lower feedwater temperature than that leaving the deaerator, and this temperature exceeds 300°F, the stack temperature can be dropped to within 50°F of this water temperature by an extremely large economizer. In such a cycle, gas turbine and boiler sizes must be matched closely to obtain a high ratio of feedwater flow to gas-turbine exhaust flow.

Because all gas-turbine/boiler applications involve the recovery of sensible heat, the usual concept of boiler efficiency loses its significance. Customary practice, therefore, is to evaluate performance of combined-cycle boilers on the basis of stack temperature. The overall station heat balance is determined using the calculated value of fuel fired in the boiler (rather than boiler efficiency as such), in addition to the fuel fired in the gas turbine.

SHOP-ASSEMBLED BOILERS

The growth of oil- and gas-fired shop-assembled boilers since their introduction in the early 1950's has paralleled industry's demand for higher capacities, pressures and temperatures. The evolution of the boiler line has been from 20,000 lb of steam per hour before 1950 to approximately 600,000 lbs/hr in the late 1970's. As an example, Fig. 21 shows the evolution of the VP (D type) boiler. Steam pressures and temperatures have kept pace with this capacity growth, from the saturated-steam conditions of the 1950's to today's operating pressures of 1650 psig and steam temperatures of 950°F.

As compared with a field-erected unit, the most significant advantage of the shop-assembled boiler is its lower installed cost. This differential comes from the development of standard designs with maximum use of standardized fabrication procedures and minimum field installation costs.

Shop-assembled boilers can be furnished with integrated auxiliary equipment. The lower capacity units are shipped completely packaged with fuel-burning equipment, safety and combustion controls, and boiler trim. Be-

Fig. 21 **Size and capacity growth of the VP boiler**

cause of shipping clearance limitations, it is not always possible or desirable to furnish the higher-capacity boilers in a single package. With higher capacity units it may also be desirable to use heat recovery equipment which is shipped as a separate, integrated, package.

The majority of shop-assembled water-tube boilers use thermal circulation and are designed for pressurized firing. Shipping clearances determine the allowable height-width dimensions of an assembled unit. Usually the allowable shipping depth is greater than can be effectively used. One of the problems of the designer, therefore, is to use the available height and width to best advantage.

The burner/furnace design must be properly coordinated, and burners have been developed specifically for shop-assembled boilers. Having a relatively narrow flame pattern, these burners are designed to burn the fuel completely within the necessarily limited, though sufficient, clearance dimensions from the burner centerline to the furnace walls.

Shop-assembled boilers typically use extensive water-cooled surface. This heat-absorbing surface that "sees" the flame determines the temperature of the combustion gases leaving the furnace. Liberal use of water cooling on the furnace walls, roof, and floor not only reduces the furnace temperature but also minimizes furnace refractory and its attendant maintenance. With a completely welded tube-wall enclosure, the result is uniform cubical thermal expansion superior to other construction.

The amount of furnace volume or heat release rate/cu ft of furnace volume bears no direct relationship to the furnace exit temperature; the amount of water-cooled furnace surface or the heat release rate/ft² is the valid criterion for determining furnace conditions. Typically, the furnace heat release rates when firing oil and gas range from 175,000 to 200,000 Btu/hr—ft² of EPRS (effective projected radiant surface).

Size and furnace configuration for these package boilers results in a ratio of radiant surface to furnace volume which is greater than for the larger field-erected units. This permits con-

siderably higher furnace liberation rates/cu ft of furnace volume.

The need to limit gas-side draft loss usually determines the flue-gas velocities for gas- or oil-fired shop-assembled boilers. On the other hand, with coal-fired, field-erected units, relatively low gas velocities are used to limit abrasion and erosion of tubes. Flue-gas velocities in shop-assembled units can go as high as 100 fps and result in draft losses of 10 to 15″ WG. This is acceptable when the unit is used in a capacity such as utility plant start-up.

Convection tube spacing is not critical in shop-assembled units as the fuels generally have little or no ash. However, the designer still must be cognizant of peculiarities in certain fuels such as high-sodium, high-vanadium residual oils which can form tacky deposits at approximately 1100°F. In this case, tube spacing and sootblower arrangement must be properly factored into the design.

The enclosing casing structure of shop assembled boilers, including the integral base plate, serves several functions. It is designed to eliminate objectionable gas leakage under maximum pressure conditions. Also, it must have sufficient structural strength for the necessary handling and lifting during manufacture, in transit and at the installation site. Permanent or detachable lifting lugs are provided to facilitate handling. Many oil- and gas-fired assembled units require only a suitably reinforced concrete slab or curb for foundation.

THE C-E "VP" AND "A" TYPE UNITS

A typical shop-assembled boiler configuration (Fig. 22) is the C-E VP, which is a D-shape design with a two-drum, vertical bent-tube boiler bank, and water-cooled furnace. These units can be designed to generate as much as 600,000 pounds per hour of steam. The VP has welded-wall construction, unheated downcomers, and a combination radiant-convection superheater which produces a flat steam temperature characteristic. It can be rail shipped in two sections for capacities up to 240,000 lb/hr; larger VP units are shipped over waterways on large barges.

Fig. 22 C-E VP, a D-type shop-assembled boiler

Another shop-assembled boiler is the A type (Fig. 23) which can generate as much as 300,000 pounds of steam per hour. The A-boiler is a three-drum design with one upper (steam) drum and two lower drums. Its symmetry makes the A design ideal for rail shipment because ballast is not needed. This simplifies off-loading and handling.

Both the A and VP designs have boiler banks with a multiplicity of simple tube circuits starting at the lower drum(s) and terminating in the steam drum. Expanded tube joints have proven most practical to connect these relatively close-spaced tubes into the drums. One factor which determines the thickness of drum tube sheets is the width of the ligaments between tube holes. To achieve the maximum ligament efficiency and minimum drum thickness with these close-spaced tubes, the tube ends are frequently swaged to a smaller diameter in order to reduce the required tube-hole size.

THE HU BOILER FOR PC FIRING

Responsive to fuel costs, fuel availability,

Fig. 23 C-E Type A shop-assembled boiler

and emission requirements, pulverized-coal-fired boilers are being used where only stoker-fired boilers were considered in the past. To provide the economy of installation of oil- and gas-fired shop-assembled boilers, C-E has developed the HU boiler (Fig. 24).

The bottom-supported HU boiler uses three drums, similar to the A boiler. A 100-percent, water-cooled, welded-wall, outer enclosure is combined with the three-drum construction to produce the inherent strength required for a shop-assembled boiler. Sizes range from approximately 30,000 lb/hr to 250,000 lb/hr steam capacity. Units having a capacity up to 80,000 lb/hr can be shipped by rail while larger units will require barge shipment or field erection of rail-shipped modular sections.

The HU design eliminates all gas turns with a straight-through gas flow pattern. The furnace cross section conforms to the shape of the flame envelope produced by the burners to allow maximum use of all furnace heating surface. To allow use of almost any type of coal, the generating bank is designed with wide tube spacing for extremely low gas velocities (less than 40 ft/sec).

The relatively long length of this unit results in an upper drum that is very conservatively sized. This and the quick response capabilities of pulverized-coal firing will accommodate any rapid load changes.

HEAT-RECOVERY EQUIPMENT

Most shop-assembled boilers include equipment to increase overall boiler efficiency and save substantial fuel by recovering heat from the flue gases leaving the generating equipment. In most cases this heat-recovery equipment can be shipped as a complete but separate package.

A counterflow arrangement of flue gas and feedwater for an economizer, or of flue gas and combustion air for an air preheater, results in the most effective use of the heat-recovery surface (see Chapter 6). With high-sulfur fuels, the possibility of corrosion of the cold-end surfaces should be considered with either an economizer or air preheater.

For either a regenerative or tubular-type air preheater, the operating temperature of the cold-end metal subjected to possible corrosion is essentially an average between the entering-air and leaving-gas temperatures. Bypassing some of the combustion air or preheating all of the combustion air to a limited degree will raise the metal temperature to eliminate or minimize corrosion.

The degree and frequency of partial load operation are most significant in establishing the optimum air heater selection. Packaged regenerative air preheaters are designed with reversible and replaceable cold-end layers fabricated of corrosion resistant material to minimize maintenance.

Because the gas-side transfer rate in an economizer is relatively low compared with water-side rate, the metal temperature of the cold-end of a counterflow economizer is only slightly above the entering feed temperature. With high-sulfur fuels, an economizer is usually not advisable unless the feedwater temperature exceeds 250°F.

SHOP-ASSEMBLED WASTE-HEAT BOILERS

Although applied primarily to fuel-fired boilers, shop assembly is also applicable to waste-heat boilers. Unless there is some special consideration, such as auxiliary firing, these units are built without a furnace preceding the boiler convection surface.

Other significant differences also exist between boilers designed to recover heat from waste gases and direct-fired boilers. The temperature and quantity of waste gas and the constituents in the gas vary widely depending on the source.

Because most oil- or gas-fired shop assembled boilers are pressure fired, the forced-draft fan overcomes resistances to gas flow throughout the boiler, whereas with many waste-heat units these resistances are overcome by an induced-draft fan. The relatively large volume of gases to be handled makes design for low draft losses desirable to minimize the horsepower requirements of the ID-fan driver.

The constituents in waste gases must be carefully evaluated in establishing the design of waste-heat boilers. The chemical analysis, dust loading, and slagging characteristics all affect arrangement of the boiler surface.

ECONOMICS OF SHOP-ASSEMBLY

Installation of two or more shop-assembled units instead of a single large field-erected unit aids in load flexibility and scheduling maintenance. Other factors such as limited available headroom for the installation of a field-erected boiler, or much shorter delivery time for a shop-assembled unit, are also important considerations. But the main reason to select a shop-assembled boiler is low installation cost.

Standardization is the key to reduced costs: standard boilers are pre-engineered. In setting up a line of standard boilers, it is necessary initially to consider all possible variables. Design conditions such as capacity and operating pressure are varied in increments. Physical variables such as terminal connection locations may be varied to some limited extent.

SAVINGS IN MANUFACTURING AND ERECTION

The greatest savings with standard shop-assembled boilers, however, is in manufacturing, which is far simpler and requires considerably less time to process the necessary fabricating information into the shop. Standard shop-assembled boilers are built under controlled conditions which permits a high-quality product at low cost (Fig. 25). The enclosed assembly area is arranged for optimum materials flow both of parts fabricated for individual units and for parts and materials to be taken from stock. Likewise, delays from adverse weather conditions are not encountered.

Aside from the obvious elimination of field erection costs, there are supplementary advantages that further reduce the installation costs and time. Most units require only a simple concrete slab foundation. And, as the boiler is shipped assembled, no erection space or material storage space is required at the site.

SHIPMENT

Smaller shop-assembled units have been shipped short distances by truck or in combination with rail. The development of new shipping methods contributed significantly to the rapid growth of large capacity shop-assembled boilers in the 1970's.

The first VP boilers had a fixed cross section and achieved size flexibility by varying the depth of the boiler. The cross section was limited to standard clearances for American railroads and permitted shipment in standard flat cars to almost any location. Further investigation determined that clearances to some locations were larger. In addition, special railroad cars were available or could be designed, among

Fig. 24 Arrangement of shop-assembled pulverized-coal boiler

Fig. 25 Shop-assembled units like this A boiler are manufactured under controlled indoor conditions .

Fig. 26 Type A boiler loaded on Schnabel car

which is the C-E patented Schnabel (Fig. 26) to accommodate boilers up to 20 ft high × 13 ft wide × 55 ft long.

Barge shipment has paved the way for delivery, to overseas and domestic markets, of shop-assembled boilers with steam flows as high as 600,000 lb/hr. Any shop-assembled boiler can be shipped by barge (Fig. 27) as equipment so delivered is generally not limited by physical dimensions. Boilers up to 30 ft wide × 35 ft high × 70 ft long weighing up to 950,000 lb can be shipped on virtually any existing commercial waterway with available barge equipment.

HIGH-TEMPERATURE-WATER BOILERS

Heating systems using high-temperature water (HTW) became popular after World War II. These systems usually operate in a pressure range from 120 to 300 psig with supply temperatures to the distribution system from 350° to 420°F. The higher temperature range affects cost because water flow rates and resulting pumping costs are reduced and system heat exchangers can be made smaller. On the other hand, the lower temperatures permit lighter and less expensive materials.

High-temperature water systems are closed systems with makeup required only to restore water that leaks out of the system at valve stems, pump shafts and similar packed joints. Obviously the average water temperature in the system varies depending on the load, and an expansion drum permits expansion or contraction of the water volume. A small makeup pump automatically adds the necessary makeup to hold the water level in the expansion drum above a predetermined level.

For heat consumers such as unit heaters, radiant panels, and coils of absorption refrigeration equipment, HTW may be used directly. As with steam, it is used indirectly for domestic hot water. Low-pressure steam or low-pressure hot water, if required, may be produced in suitable heat exchangers.

PRINCIPAL TYPES OF SYSTEMS

Both steam and gas pressurization have been used to maintain pressure in the system. Gas pressurization is commonly called "mechanical pressurization." *Gas* identifies the type of fluid used for pressurization, whereas *mechanical* indicates the pressurization method.

In the gas or mechanical pressurized system, nitrogen is used to maintain a pressure above the water level in the expansion drum. Controls to add or bleed off the gas as changes in water level occur maintain pressure independent of the heating load.

In a steam-pressurized system, the water is heated to the saturation temperature corresponding to the operating pressure. Reduction in pressure from the boiler outlet to the expan-

Fig. 27 Deep-water dockside facilities are used to ship large, shop-assembled boilers.

sion drum due to friction losses and drum elevation permits a small amount of water to flash into steam. The steam is collected in the upper part of the drum and maintains a pressure cushion on the entire system.

GAS-PRESSURIZED SYSTEM

Although the physical layout and size of individual installations vary, the basic components and usually the basic arrangement of the systems are similar (Fig. 28). Return water is heated in the boiler and delivered to the system at supply temperature. The water gives up its heat to the system load (usually divided in several zones) and is returned to the suction of the circulating pump. The circulating pumps are selected with sufficient head to overcome both the system and boiler resistance. Pressure higher than saturation pressure corresponding to the boiler outlet temperature is maintained in the system by means of gas pressure superimposed on the system at the expansion tank. The expansion tank floats on the line. Water temperature at the boiler outlet is used as an index for combustion control.

STEAM-PRESSURIZED SYSTEM

Fig. 29 shows the basic steam-pressurized system. Water at return temperature is heated in the boiler and delivered to the expansion drum at the supply temperature, essentially equal to the saturation temperature corresponding to operating pressure in the ex-

pansion drum. The circulating pumps taking suction from the drum circulate the hot water through the system. The water gives up its heat to the load and is returned to the boilers. The circulating pumps are selected for sufficient head to overcome any resistance encountered in both the system and boiler.

HIGH-TEMPERATURE WATER VERSUS STEAM

The choice of HTW or steam for heating or process work depends upon the size, arrangement and type of load. For large heating systems and certain process applications, HTW usually has certain advantages.

A steam heating system requires greater net plant output because of the losses associated with the change of phase of the heating medium, i.e., steam to condensate. Primarily trap and vent losses or flash-off from condensate, these losses can account for 10 to 25 percent of the net plant output. Because high-temperature water exists as a liquid throughout the system, these losses do not occur. As a result, the required capacity of hot-water boilers is less than steam boilers for a given system output.

As high-maintenance items such as steam traps, pressure-reducing valves and condensate equipment are eliminated, maintenance costs for high-temperature water systems are lower. In the closed HTW system, oxygen is eliminated on initial operation, and therefore

Fig. 28 **Schematic arrangement of gas-pressurized hot-water system**

the problem of pipe corrosion and replacement of return lines does not exist.

Because makeup for an HTW system is negligible, blowoff is unnecessary with normal operation. Makeup equipment can be very simple and inexpensive, and consists of a small water softener, a pair of makeup pumps and provision for intermittent addition of water-treatment chemicals to the heating system.

A high-temperature water system has substantially greater heat-storage capacity than a steam system. Therefore, fluctuating loads in the system tend to be damped out so that they do not directly or immediately affect boiler loads. The boilers operate at a more constant rate which improves their operating efficiency and the efficiency of the heating system as well.

Because of the heat storage capacity, the heating system acts as an accumulator, permitting extremely close control of temperature and the ability to readily meet infrequent peak loads. Close temperature control is often of considerable importance in process equipment, resulting in improved product quality or increased production. The ability to meet infrequent peak loads by utilizing this heat storage may allow the installed capacity of the heating system to be reduced.

BOILER DESIGN

The term boiler as applied to the hot-water heating units is a misnomer because under normal operating conditions very little or no steam is generated. However, these units are designed to meet the ASME Boiler Code and are operated in substantially the same manner as steam boilers. The absence of steam generation is noteworthy in that thermal circulation effects are negligible with respect to assisting boiler and overall system circulation. In effect the boiler has a forced circulation system of the once-through type.

Fig. 30 is a cross-section through a typical HTW boiler. In this design, water entering at the inlet nozzle (lower rear) is distributed, by a manifold outside the boiler casing, to two inlet headers, one located at the bottom of the rear wall for feeding the furnace rear and sidewall tubes and the other located immediately above the burner windbox for feeding the furnace front wall and roof tubes. The convection bank is formed by a continuation of the front and rear wall tubes, and all tubes terminate in the outlet header at the top. Orifice plates at inlets of all tubes control distribution within the boiler.

When the system is designed for a temperature drop of 125 to 175°F between supply and return temperatures, the boiler pressure drop can be held to 10 psi or less. This minimal pressure drop eliminates the need for separate boiler circulating pumps and results in a simpler and more economical arrangement.

Unlike a steam boiler, the once-through-type HTW boiler, with substantially no steam gen-

Fig. 29 **Schematic arrangement of steam-pressurized hot-water system**

eration, neither requires a steam drum nor does it trap dissolved solids entering with the feedwater. A blowdown connection on the boiler is therefore unnecessary. A strainer or sediment trap, located in the boiler inlet line, prevents solid impurities such as dirt or mill scale from entering the boiler. This is especially desirable during initial start-up or when cutting in new distribution zones.

FUEL-BURNING EQUIPMENT

Standardized HTW boilers can be used with oil or gas burners or can fire coal by means of spreader stokers. Fuel-burning equipment is substantially the same as for steam boilers except that, to minimize steam losses and makeup feed requirements, oil burners are usually of the mechanical instead of steam atomizing type. Air-puff sootblowers are usually used on hot-water boilers for the same reasons.

Fig. 30 Side elevation of fully water cooled high-temperature-water boiler for oil/gas firing

Pulverized-coal firing becomes more practical for boilers rated from 100 million Btu/hr upwards or where the coal is not suitable for stoker firing.

CONTROLS

As high-temperature water boilers are installed to meet space-heating requirements, rapid load changes are uncommon. A simple positioning-type combustion control suits the smaller single-burner shop-assembled boilers and stoker-fired units. For larger multiburner boilers, a metering system is preferable.

Because the boiler depends on a pump for circulation, a safety device should be provided to stop the fuel input in the event circulation drops below a predetermined point. This can be incorporated as a part of the boiler-water flow meter if installed, or can be actuated by the pressure drop within the boiler itself.

CIRCULATING PUMPS

The heart of HTW heating systems is the circulating pump. Standard horizontal process-type centrifugal pumps give reliable service under normal operating conditions. Economic considerations dictate that the friction loss in the pipe system be held to values which can be overcome by a single stage, 1750-rpm pump. At this pump speed, suitable packing is available for sealing the pump shaft. Mechanical seals also give satisfactory performance although it is essential that the mechanical seals be arranged for adequate cooling and to prevent the accumulation of sediment at seal faces.

In addition, to prevent vapor binding and cavitation at the pump inlet, the pump must have low net-positive-suction-head characteristics.

PULP AND PAPER INDUSTRY CHEMICAL RECOVERY BOILERS

Although the chemical recovery boiler shares its general appearance and many of its physical components with a power boiler, its distinctive process functions place it in a dif-

Boiler Bank

Economizer

Secondary-Air Fan

Steam-Coil Air Heater

Chemical Ash Tank

Salt-Cake Mixing Tank

Secondary (Indirect) Black-Liquor Heaters

Smelt Dissolving Tank

Superheater

Maintenance-Beam Openings

Tangential Secondary-Air Windbox

Black-Liquor Guns

High Primary-Air Ports

Low Primary-Air Ports

Furnace Hearth

Smelt Spouts

Fig. 31 **C-E chemical recovery unit**

ferent category (Fig. 31). Not only must it generate steam for paper-mill power and process demands, the recovery unit must also chemically restore the inorganic components of the black liquor to a form that can be subsequently reprocessed into the chemicals required by the digestor. The chemical recovery unit is an integral part of the kraft pulping process.

THE KRAFT PULPING PROCESS

This is a chemically closed process that produces pulp for paper making from a variety of organic materials. Wood is by far the most commonly used source of pulp used with the kraft process, although bagasse, straw and other nonwood fibers can also be used. The name *kraft*, from the Swedish and German meaning strength, is a term often applied to sulfate mills, which produce long-fiber pulp used for making high-strength paper.

PRODUCING PULP

Fig. 32 illustrates the paper making process. As the diagram shows, wood enters the kraft cycle at the digester for pulping. Although a batch-type digester is shown, many modern mills can also use a continuous digester. A batch-type digester is loaded with chips, and its top cover bolted down. It is then charged with chemical solution called white liquor, and steam at a pressure of about 150 psi is admitted. The charge is steamed or cooked for a period from two to six hours, depending on the grade of pulp desired.

Bringing a batch digester to cooking pressure requires large quantities of steam. As a result, there is a heavy intermittent demand from the boilers in mills using batch digesters, whereas mills with continuous digesters have a more uniform demand. Batch digesters are installed in groups of at least three and operate in sequence, with each digester preparing 6 to 20 tons of pulp per cook.

Within the digester, sodium hydroxide and sodium sulfide dissolve the ligneous substances that bind the cellulose fibers of the wood together. The cellulose fibers, which form the pulp, resist the action of the chemicals. In the cooking process, approximately one half of the wood substance is dissolved in the cooking liquor, and forms what is called black liquor. After the charge has been cooked, it is blown at full pressure to the blow tank where the cellulose fibers are deposited, then washed to remove spent cooking chemicals and dissolved residue.

The next major step is washing in which pulp fibers are separated from the black liquor. Most mills use countercurrent rotary vacuum washers in which the pulp is washed with progressively weaker black liquor and finally fresh water. After washing the pulp is further refined, and subsequently converted to paper. The weak liquor which was separated from the pulp goes on to further processing.

The kraft process is economically attractive because it is possible to recover and reuse the cooking chemicals, and to generate large quantities of steam and power from the dissolved carbonaceous matter in the black liquor. However, the black liquor leaving the washers contains far too much water to be burned. The next step removes most of this water.

RECOVERING THE SPENT CHEMICALS

Water removal from the weak black liquor is accomplished in large multiple-effect evaporators. Before black liquor can be fired into the recovery boiler, the concentration of the dissolved solids in the black liquor must be increased from an initial 16 to 18 percent to about 62 to 65 percent. This can be accomplished by either of two ways.

1. Multiple-effect evaporators can increase the concentration to about 50 percent utilizing low pressure steam. Then the liquor flows to a direct-contact evaporator. This type of evaporator brings the hot flue from the recovery boiler in direct contact with the black liquor to cause evaporation, thus the term *direct contact.*

2. Multiple-effect evaporators can also be followed by a concentrator. A concentrator is a special application of a multiple-effect evaporator. In this case, all the energy required for evaporation is furnished by low-pressure

steam. Overall mill energy utilization is highest with this system of evaporation.

The next step of the kraft process within the recovery unit involves five essential functions, in which

■ black liquor is prepared for firing
■ carbonaceous matter is burned out
■ sulfur compounds are converted to Na_2S
■ inorganic salts are smelted for removal
■ heat is efficiently utilized to produce steam.

The hot smelt produced in the recovery furnace flows in a continuous stream into the dissolving tank, where it is quenched and dissolved in weak wash to form "green liquor" which is a solution of sodium carbonate, Na_2CO_3, and sodium sulfide, Na_2S. The green liquor is pumped to a causticizing system in which slaked lime, $Ca(OH)_2$ is reacted with Na_2CO_3 to produce a solution of sodium hydroxide. The sodium sulfide in the solution remains unchanged. After this treatment, the liquor becomes "white liquor" and is returned

to be reused as cooking liquor in the digester.

The calcium carbonate sludge formed in the causticizing reaction is converted to calcium oxide in the lime kiln and is then hydrolized to calcium hydroxide for reuse in causticizing green liquor to white liquor.

This completes the kraft cycle. The chemicals needed for cooking are recovered and reused. Calcium oxide required for causticizing is reformed, and the dissolved wood substance is burned off to become a source of heat for steam and power generation.

PRODUCING POWER

In most integrated pulp and paper mills, the waste materials generated by the process furnish a large percentage of the total energy required to produce steam and power. The recovery boiler uses the heat energy from burning the carbonaceous matter in the black liquor, while the bark-fired boiler consumes other waste materials such as sawdust and planer shaving, as well as bark from the debarking

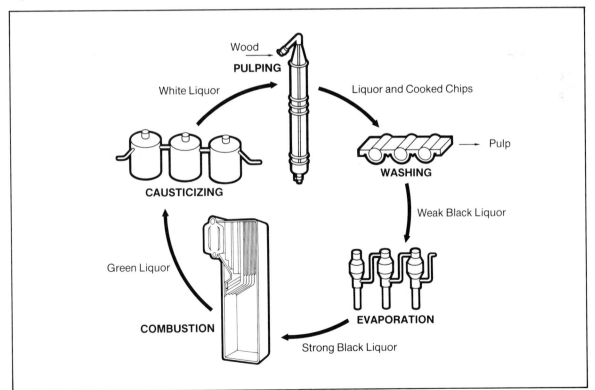

Fig. 32 **Pictorial diagram of the paper-making process**

drums. When more steam is required than is available from these waste streams, auxiliary fuels such as coal, oil or gas are also fired in the bark boiler.

The diagram of the paper making process shows where the major consumption of steam occurs. All high-pressure steam generated by the boilers is piped into turbines which drive the major auxiliaries, such as the paper machine, the boiler feedpumps, and the extraction turbines to generate power. In an ideal situation, it would be possible to generate all power required by means of back-pressure turbines without resorting to any condensing. In a typical pulp and paper mill, approximately 75 percent of the energy available in the fuel is converted to useful energy compared to a typical efficiency of only 35 percent in an electrical-generating station.

MILL CAPACITY AND ITS RELATION TO RECOVERY BOILER CAPACITY

The capacity of a mill is based on the tons of pulp that are produced in 24 hours. Thus, a 1000-ton mill is one which produces 1000 tons of pulp in one day. A mill of this size will also produce a certain amount of spent chemicals, that is, black liquor solids. On an average, 3000 pounds of black liquor solids will be produced for each ton of pulp produced. A 1000-ton mill will then produce about 3,000,000 lb of dry solids per day—the actual quantity can vary plus or minus 10 percent. Likewise, the heating value of the dry solids produced can vary from 5000 to 7000 Btu/lb from mill to mill.

Obviously, the thermal and process load which is imposed on the recovery boiler depends on the specific conditions in a particular mill, and cannot be related to a nominal mill requirement. Thus, recovery boiler capacity must be related to the following factors:

■ dry solids produced per day

■ percent solids concentration from multiple-effect evaporator

■ high heating value

■ elemental fuel analysis.

A typical elemental analysis of a black liquor derived from a combined hardwood-softwood cook is

Carbon	39.4%
Hydrogen	3.6
Sulfur	3.4
Sodium	21.2
Inert Mineral Oxides	1.0
Oxygen	31.4
Total	100.0
High Heating Value	6400 Btu/lb

Unfortunately, laboratory analysis and calorific value are related to the procedure for obtaining moisture content of the black liquor. The above values were derived using the standard as recommended by the Technical Association of the Pulp and Paper Industry.

FINAL FUEL PREPARATION

Before the strong black liquor leaving the multiple-effect evaporators can be introduced into the furnace for burning, the liquor must undergo several important changes.

■ The liquor must be concentrated to sufficient strength for firing.

■ Ash collected in the precipitator and the boiler hoppers must be returned to the incoming liquor stream.

■ Saltcake makeup must be introduced.

■ The liquor must be brought up to the proper pressure and temperature at the spray nozzles.

■ Liquor droplets of the proper size must be formed by the spray nozzles so that burning will take place on the furnace hearth.

When the multiple-effect evaporators are not designed to concentrate liquor to firing strength, the liquor must first be concentrated in a direct-contact evaporator in which hot flue gases in direct contact with the liquor evaporate excess water.

Unfortunately, the sulfur compounds in the liquor can chemically react with the carbon dioxide in the flue gas to form foul-smelling gaseous compounds which would then be discharged into the atmosphere. Reactions are

$$Na_2S + CO_2 + H_2O \rightarrow H_2S + Na_2CO_3$$

(1)

$$2CH_3SNa + CO_2 + H_2O \rightarrow 2CH_3SH + Na_2CO_3 \tag{2}$$

To avoid the generation of odorous gases such as H_2S and CH_3SH, the liquor is first passed through a black-liquor oxidizer in which air or oxygen is bubbled through the liquor (Fig. 33). Oxygen reacts with sodium-sulfur compounds to form sodium thiosulfate, a compound that does not readily react with the flue gas. Thus, the oxidizer chemically stabilizes the sulfur compounds in the liquor so that odorous emissions are greatly reduced.

After the liquor passes through the oxidizer, it is pumped to the precipitator area. Ash collected in the precipitator is mixed into the liquor stream in either of two ways. The ash can be allowed to fall directly into the liquor as occurs in a wet-bottom precipitator, or the ash can be collected dry and conveyed from the precipitator to a chemical ash mixing tank, where the ash is thoroughly mixed with the black liquor. Frequently, ash collected in the boiler hoppers is brought to this same tank to be mixed into the incoming liquor.

THE CASCADE EVAPORATOR

The liquor is then evaporated to a firing concentration of about 68 percent solids in a cascade evaporator by bringing hot flue gases into direct contact with strong black liquor as shown by Fig. 34. The evaporator consists of one or two wheels, that is, rotating tube sheets between which are many horizontal parallel tubes. Part of the tubes is submerged in liquor; the rest is in the gas stream. Those that are in the gas stream are completely coated with wet, dripping liquor. The slowly rotating cascade wheel causes the tubes to be alternately washed in the liquor bath, and exposed to the hot flue gases where water is evaporated. The tubes never dry out in the gas stream and are, therefore, good collectors of ash particles entrained in the gas stream.

Fig. 33 Chemical-recovery unit with oxidizer and cascade evaporator

Fig. 34 **Pattern of cascade-evaporator liquor flow**

Fig. 35 **Black-liquor flow diagram**

As the tubes rotate in the bath of black liquor, ash collected on the tubes is washed off. The swirling motion also agitates the liquor in the tank and thoroughly circulates it, thus preventing ash and solid material in the liquor from settling out or forming lumps that could cause plugging in the piping and spray nozzles. Fig. 34 shows how the liquor mixes and circulates in the tank of a cascade evaporator. Side channels provide for return circulation of the liquor as it is moved to one end of the tank by the rotation of the wheel. The agitation produced by the rotating wheel makes the cascade evaporator especially suitable for concentrating the more viscous liquors that are difficult to concentrate in multiple-effect evaporators.

Each wheel is driven by a constant-speed motor through a centrifugal clutch, gear reducer, and chain drive. As shown in Fig. 35, the liquor travels from the cascade evaporator to a flow box located next to the cascade tank. Within the flow box is a rotating cylindrical screen through which all the liquor must flow. The screen blocks the larger lumps which are deposited in the box where they dissolve.

From the flow box, the liquor moves into the salt cake mixing tank where pulverized sodium sulfate is added to compensate for the chemical losses in the mill. The black liquor is thoroughly mixed with a paddle type agitator. A horizontal screen within the tank prevents lumps of salt cake from flowing into the black liquor piping. Within the tank a primary black liquor heater raises the liquor temperature to about 210°F, thereby minimizing power required by the black liquor pump.

Following the salt cake mixing tank, the liquor flows to the heavy black liquor pump, and then onto a secondary black liquor heater where the temperature is raised to about 240°F. From here the liquor flows into the spray nozzles at the furnace.

Fig. 36 shows the liquor preparation system for recovery boilers that receive liquor at sufficiently high solids to permit direct firing. In this system the oxidizer and the direct-contact evaporator with its flow box are not required. In other respects, the liquor handling system is similar to the one shown in Fig. 33.

The final step in fuel preparation takes place at the black liquor spray nozzles which inject black liquor into the furnace through many spray nozzles located about 20 feet above the furnace hearth. Each spray nozzle is designed to produce a hollow cone of coarse droplets that will fall onto the furnace hearth. During the flight downward through the hot furnace gases, moisture evaporates from the liquor droplets which arrive at the glowing hot bed to complete the combustion and reduction reactions.

Fig. 37 shows black liquor spray assemblies or "guns". All the guns along one wall of the furnace are clamped to a common rocker shaft. In operation, the guns are slowly rocked up and down through an angle of about 30 degrees to distribute the liquor droplets over the burning bed. Smaller units have guns in only two walls; large units spray through all four walls.

Liquor temperature and pressure are very important in creating the proper size liquor droplets. By minimizing the pressure and holding the liquor temperature at an optimum value, the larger liquor particles best suited for proper furnace operation are created. A liquor pressure of about 15 psig and a liquor temperature of approximately 240°F generally give the most satisfactory operation. These values should be adjusted to suit the characteristics of individual liquors.

BURNING THE BLACK LIQUOR

The relatively great moisture content and size of the liquor droplets prevent the liquor from igniting at the liquor gun level. Instead, the liquor droplets fall onto a porous bed of burning char at the bottom of the furnace. During their flight downward, the droplets are flash dried; thus, the zone below the nozzles to the top of the bed is called the drying zone.

At the surface of the bed and in flight, the particles that are dried, are pyrolyzed, and partially burn. The quantity of air available for combustion in the lower furnace is deliberately limited to create a reducing atmosphere, which encourages the reactions:

Fig. 36 **Direct-fired chemical-recovery unit**

Fig. 37 **Black-liquor spray nozzles**

$$Na_2SO_4 + 2C \rightarrow Na_2S + 2CO_2 \text{ (in the bed)} \tag{3}$$

$$Na_2SO_4 + 4CO \rightarrow Na_2S + 4CO_2 \text{ (in flight)} \tag{4}$$

Because there is insufficient air to complete combustion, the lower furnace is called the reduction zone where sufficient heat is liberated to fuse the various inorganic salts that are formed in the bed. These fused chemicals flow to the smelt spouts and out of the furnace into the dissolving tank.

Air introduced in the lower furnace is called primary air which consists of about 65 percent of the total combustion air. The remainder of the air required to complete combustion is introduced at the oxidizing zone, which is located above the liquor nozzles. This air is known as secondary air. It completely burns any pyrolized gaseous compounds swept up-

ward from the bed. The furnace is a staged chemical reactor (Fig. 38) in which burning takes place in three zones: the drying zone, the reducing zone and the oxidizing zone.

Primary-air ports extend around all four walls of the furnace at a level of 3½ ft above the centerline of the floor tubes. On some furnaces, another level of primary-air ports is located at about 6 ft above the floor tubes.

Secondary air is introduced through four registers which discharge tangentially to an imaginary cylinder having its axis coincident with the main vertical axis of the furnace. This arrangement results in a cyclonic pattern of turbulent mixing which assures complete burnout of combustible and odorous gases in the oxidizing zone.

Both primary and secondary air are heated to about 300°F in steam-coil air heaters that use low-pressure steam from the mill 50 and 150 psig steam supply systems.

At certain times, oil or gas is fired through

Fig. 38 **Burning zones in a chemical-recovery-unit furnace**

starting burners in the lower furnace. At start-up, the heat from the starting burners dries and ignites the black liquor before a bed is developed. At shutdown, starting burners are used to burn down the bed. At low loads, and when the black liquor is likely to burn poorly, starting burners stabilize the combustion conditions. Four monitored starting burners provided for this purpose are located near the corners about five feet above the floor tubes.

Auxiliary fuel firing capability is also available for periods when there is no black liquor, or when there is a need for more steam than can be generated from black liquor at low firing rates. For this purpose, oil guns are located in the secondary air registers.

DESIGN BASIS FOR RECOVERY BOILERS

An analysis of the dry solids in black liquor shows a relatively high ash content compared to other fuels. About 45 percent is ash. Fortunately, most of this ash is captured in the bed and is not carried upward by the furnace gases into the superheater and boiler bank. Nevertheless, the ash loading in the flue gases is comparatively high, even higher than pulverized-coal-fired furnaces. Although ash loading is high, it is the nature of the ash itself that causes recovery boilers and superheaters to be so vulnerable to plugging if they are not designed or operated correctly.

PROBLEMS WITH PLUGGING

As a general rule, an ash that softens and fuses at a comparatively low temperature is likely to give trouble from slag deposits on boiler or superheater tubes. The rule certainly holds true for black liquor ash whose ash-softening temperature is typically about 1450°F. An even lower temperature is possible if the ash contains certain impurities such as sodium chloride or salts of potassium.

To avoid the problems of a highly slagging fuel, a pulverized-coal-boiler designer normally sizes the furnace large enough to cool the gases entering the superheater to below the ash-softening temperature. But this approach is impractical for recovery boilers as the furnace would simply be too tall. Instead, the designer must accept a slagging condition in the superheater, and design the superheater to be cleanable under that condition. This means the superheater tubes must be on wide transverse spacings to allow the furnace gases to pass through the superheater when the tubes are coated with slag. Wide spacing also helps the sootblowers penetrate into the superheater for better cleaning of the surface.

Another means of avoiding the problems of plugging is to use tangent-tube surface. When widely spaced superheater and screen assemblies are fabricated of tangent tubes, the surface is more easily cleaned because the de-

Fig. 39 **Typical recovery-unit furnace-wall corrosion**

posits cannot wrap around individual tubes. The situation is similar to the condition at the furnace walls, where the ash deposits build up until they fall off under their own weight. It is not necessary to maintain such wide spacing throughout the boiler and economizer. By proper design, the ash arriving at the boiler bank is well below the ash-fusion temperature. Less prone to slagging, ash deposits on the boiler tubes are easier to remove than are deposits on the superheater and screen tubes.

Even though the ash which deposits on boiler and economizer tubes arrives well below the ash-fusion temperature, it can be difficult to remove under certain conditions. To aid in the removal of ash, tubes absorbing heat are arranged vertically for experience has shown that vertical tubes are much easier to keep clean than horizontal tubes.

Ash collected in the boiler bank and economizer consists mainly of sodium sulfate. Under the influence of sulfur dioxide from the flue gas, some of the sodium sulfate is converted to sodium pyrosulfate. This compound becomes molten at a temperature of about 480 to 600°F and is capable of forming a very tenacious bond with the tube. It is, therefore, possible to have a slagging condition develop even in zones where the gas temperature is considerably below the ash-fusion temperature. Plugging

Fig. 40 **Cross section of recovery-unit furnace-wall deposits**

that is caused by this mechanism is controlled by judicious placement of sootblowers and by using operating techniques which minimize the production of sulfur dioxide.

Experience with particulate contained in the flue gases has also shown that ID-fan inlet vanes or inlet dampers are soon plugged and made inoperative, even when fans are located after the precipitator. Volume control is, therefore, always by variable speed devices.

CORROSION

Waterwall tube wastage in the lower furnace was rarely observed until about 1960 when operating pressures for new recovery boilers began to increase. At that time a pattern of waterwall wastage was observed in certain recovery furnaces operating above 900 psig. Wastage up to 0.01 in. per year took place in the liquor spray-gun area (See Fig. 39). It became clear that outer surface temperature of furnace tubes above about 600°F accelerates corrosion. Some form of lower-furnace waterwall protection is, therefore, necessary for operating pressures above 900 psig where saturation temperatures exceed 540°F.

Extensive field observations and laboratory tests conducted since 1961 have led to the conclusion that elemental sulfur is involved in the corrosion mechanism. These studies made clear that tubes in the affected areas are covered with a sheet of frozen "smelt" or wall deposit. Generally, a thin layer of irregularly spaced and porous material, probably dried black liquor, separates the wall deposit from the tube surface (Fig. 40). The space of about 1 mm may serve as a passageway for corrosive gases. On the outer surface of the frozen deposit, there is a pulsating flow of molten smelt. Depending on the ash-bed configuration, this molten outer layer may be in contact with the glowing ash bed and/or bathed in a gaseous stream of widely varying concentrations of primary air and combustion products.

The principal corrosion product is FeS, and laboratory and field studies have shown that the corrodent is nascent sulfur formed by the reaction of furnace gases with the frozen smelt on the tube surfaces.

$$Fe + S \rightarrow FeS$$

(5)

Several methods of waterwall protection have been developed to resist the corrosive attack.

■ Compound Tubing: A compound tube is a co-extruded tube consisting of a mild-steel inner layer and a stainless-steel outer layer. The outer corrosion-resistant layer of stainless steel has an average thickness of 0.065 inch. Bimetallic tubing has shown satisfactory service for over a 10 year period in Finland. Although there is no question as to its corrosion resistance, the cost of this tubing and the more complicated techniques required to fabricate the furnace panels make the expense of boilers with this tubing considerably higher than with conventional tubes.

■ C-E Multi-coated Metallizing: With this procedure, three layers of metal are applied by flame-spraying technique. First, grit or shot blasting prepares the surface of the completed furnace. Then an undercoat of 0.002 to 0.005 in. of nickel aluminide or nickel titanide is applied to establish a good bond to the tube surface. A middle layer of series 300 stainless steel is applied to a thickness of 0.007 to 0.009 inch. The outer layer is ultrafine aluminum to a thickness of 0.003 to 0.004 inch. A coat of silicate-aluminum sealer is sprayed or painted on to fill up the naturally occurring pores in the metalized outer coating.

While this protection method is much less costly than compound tubing, the coated section of the furnace walls must be inspected annually, and repairs made where necessary. Walls maintained in this manner should last for the life of the boiler.

An alternate metallizing procedure using a plasma instead of a flame is also available. In this case, a 0.005 inch layer of exothermic nickel-titanide is followed by 0.01 inches of chromium. Plasma assures unoxidized metal coatings and less porosity in the coating than flame spraying. Experience with plasma metal-

lizing of furnace is still limited, but this procedure is expected to require less maintenance than flame spray and will likely extend protection to two or three years.

■ Hard-Face Welding: Although the protective overlay has proven to be satisfactory in operation, it must be applied manually in the shop. Prebending of tubes and panels and other special handling is required to produce flat waterwall panels. Consequently, the cost of hard-face welded panels approaches the cost of panels fabricated of compound tubing.

■ Studs and Refractory: Chrome refractory or frozen smelt is retained by pin studs on the water-cooled tubes. Molten smelt is thus prevented from contacting the tube metal. Experience with studded tubing indicates that extensive repairs and replacement are required after five to seven years. Monitoring of wall thickness has also been extremely difficult.

SMELT-WATER EXPLOSIONS

When water contacts molten smelt, the elements exist for a potentially violent physical explosion. Unlike chemical explosions, physical explosions do not involve a reaction between two substances. Rather, a physical explosion is the result of a gas expanding very rapidly and can be powerful, destructive, and costly. Smelt-water explosions are more violent than typical nondetonative explosions in furnaces which involve conventional fuels such as coal, oil or gas in air. Whereas the latter develop much lower peak pressures and travel at the speed of sound, smelt-water explosions, like other physical explosions, produce higher pressures, perhaps by a factor of 10 or more, and travel at supersonic speeds. They are, by definition, shock wave phenomena.

A smelt-water explosion is the result of water changing suddenly to steam. The rapid change in state is the result of an extremely high heat-transfer rate that can exist between molten smelt and water. The seriousness of a smelt-water explosion is not related to the amount of smelt or water involved—a teaspoon of molten smelt in a cupful of water can produce a powerful explosion.

Weak black liquor can also produce an explosion when brought into contact with smelt. Concentrations above 58 percent, however, are considered safe to fire into the furnace. Many recovery boilers are equipped with solids meters which continuously monitor the black-liquor solids concentration. Should the solids concentration fall to an unsafe level, the liquor is automatically diverted from the furnace.

Many other special features in the design of a recovery boiler also serve to minimize the risk of a smelt-water explosion. For example:

■ the furnace structure has added strength to reduce the risk to operating personnel should an explosion occur

■ the furnace structure is planned so that an explosion will not damage the pressure parts, preventing boiler water from spilling onto the bed if tubes are ripped open

■ the upper-furnace framing system is designed to relieve excess furnace pressure in a safe location such as the upper furnace

■ if water is detected in the furnace an emergency system drains the boiler to 8 feet above the furnace floor to stop the leak while preventing overheating of the lower furnace tubes

■ furnace-bottom corrosion protection suits operating pressure and smelt corrosivity

■ if sources of water cannot be eliminated, safety interlocks or devices can be added to avoid dangerous situations.

REFERENCES

[1] William H. Pollock, "Coal-Fired Industrial Boilers for the 1980's," *Proceedings of the American Power Conference*, 41:835–841, 1979. Chicago: Illinois Institute of Technology, 1979.

[2] L. J. Cohan and J. H. Fernandes, "Potential Energy Conversion Aspects of Refuse," *ASME Paper no. 67-WA/PID-6*. New York: American Society of Mechanical Engineers, 1967.

[3] J. W. Regan, J. F. Mullen, and R. D. Nickerson, "Suspension Firing of Solid Waste Fuels," *Proceedings of the American Power Conference*, 31:599–608, 1969. Chicago: Illinois Institute of Technology, 1969.

[4] J. W. Regan, "Generating Steam From Prepared Refuse," *Proceedings of the Fourth National Incinerator Conference*, Cincinnati, May 17–20, 1970, pp. 216–223. New York: American Society of Mechanical Engineers, 1970.

[5] Joseph F. Mullen, "System for Pneumatically Transporting High-Moisture Fuels such as Bagasse and Bark and an Included Furnace for Drying and Burning Those Fuels in Suspension Under High Turbulence," *U.S. Patent no. 3,387,574*, assigned to Combustion Engineering, Inc., June 11, 1968.

[6] Gerald E. Dreifke, David L. Klumb and Jerrel D. Smith, "Solid Waste as a Utility Fuel," *Proceedings of the American Power Conference*, 35:1198–1206, 1973. Chicago: Illinois Institute of Technology, 1973.

[7] H. Eberhardt and W. Mayer, "Experiences with Refuse Incinerators in Europe: Prevention of Air and Water Pollution, Operation of Refuse Incineration Plants Combined with Steam Boilers, Design and Planning," *Proceedings of the 1968 National Incinerator Conference*, New York, May 5–8, 1968, pp. 73–86. New York: American Society of Mechanical Engineers, 1968.

[8] H. Hilsheimer, "Experience after 20,000 Operating Hours: The Mannheim Incinerator," *Proceedings of the 1970 National Incinerator Conference*, New York, May 17–20, 1970, pp. 93–106. New York: American Society of Mechanical Engineers, 1970.

[9] J. G. Singer and J. R. Mullen, "Closing the Refuse Power Cycle," *ASME Paper no. 73-PWR-18*. New York: American Society of Mechanical Engineers, 1973.

[10] A. P. Konopka, "Systems Evaluation of Refuse as a Low Sulfur Fuel: Part 3, Air Pollution Aspects," *ASME Paper no. 71-WA/Inc-1*. New York: American Society of Mechanical Engineers, 1971. (This information can also be found in NTIS publications PB-209 271 and PB-209 272, Springfield, VA: National Technical Information Service.)

R. E. Sommerlad, et al., "Systems Evaluation of Refuse as a Low Sulfur Fuel: Part 2, Steam Generator Aspects," *ASME Paper no. 71-WA/Inc-2*. New York: American Society of Mechanical Engineers, 1971. (This information can also be found in NTIS publications PS-209 271 and PB-209 272, Springfield, VA: National Technical Information Service.)

R. M. Roberts and E. M. Wilson, "Systems Evaluation of Refuse as a Low Sulfur Fuel: Part 1, The Value of Refuse Energy and the Cost of Its Recovery," *ASME Paper no. 71-WA/Inc-3*. New York: American Society of Mechanical Engineers, 1971. (This information can also be found in NTIS publications PB-209 271 and PB-209 272, Springfield, VA: National Technical Information Service.)

[11] Paul D. Miller and Horatio H. Krause, "Corrosion of Carbon and Stainless Steels in Flue Gases From Municipal Incinerators," *Proceedings of the 1972 National Incinerator Conference*, New York, June 4–7, 1972, pp. 300–309. New York: American Society of Mechanical Engineers, 1972.

[12] F. Nowak, "Considerations in the Construction of Large Refuse Incinerators," *Proceedings of the 1970 National Incinerator Conference*, New York, May 17–20, 1970, pp. 86–92. New York: American Society of Mechanical Engineers, 1970.

[13] Karl-Heinz Thoemen, "Contribution to the Control of Corrosion Problems on Incinerators with Water-Wall Steam Generators," *Proceedings of the 1972 National Incinerator Conference*, New York, June 4–7, 1972, pp.

310–318. New York: American Society of Mechanical Engineers, 1972.

[14] Pollock, W. H., "Supplementing Coal with Solid Waste Fuels," presented at the 1980 American Power Conference, Chicago, Illinois (Proceedings to be published in 1981). Published as Combustion Engineering publication TIS-6504, Windsor, CT: Combustion Engineering, Inc. 1980.

[15] Henry J. Blaskowski and Joseph G. Singer, "Gas Turbine Boiler Applications," *Combustion*, 28(11): 38–44, May 1957.

[16] William R. Norcross, William H. Pollock and John W. Regan, "High Capacity Shop-Assembled Boilers for Coal and Oil Firing," *Proceedings of the American Power Conference*, 38: 484–499, 1976. Chicago: Illinois Institute of Technology, 1976.

CHAPTER 9

Marine Boilers

The many limitations and unique requirements applicable to shipboard power plants make the marine boiler a very specialized form of steam generator. Customarily, marine boilers must meet the following overall conditions: high level of dependability, limited space, wide range of steam output capacities, ability to change load rapidly, good accessibility, and limited weight. In addition, because most ships are designed for specific trades, propulsion machinery for a certain ship must be selected to meet the operating conditions encountered in the trade that the vessel is intended to serve.

SERVICE REQUIREMENTS

Marine-boiler design properly starts with a review and study of the service requirements for the particular ship under consideration. Only after an economic evaluation of all potential propulsion plant cycles does the ship designer set the evaporation rate and the required steam pressure and temperature.

The plant heat balances, calculated at various steady steaming conditions, establish certain operating conditions which the boiler must meet. In this connection, it must be recognized that boiler performance is a parameter in the heat-balance calculations. For example,

the boiler efficiency can be set at a given value for any one evaporating rate, but heat-balance calculations at other evaporating rates must be based upon the corresponding boiler efficiencies as set by the performance characteristic of a particular boiler design.

Normal power is a specified characteristic of a given merchant ship and generally corresponds to 100 percent rating of the boiler. For naval vessels, 100 percent boiler rating corresponds to *full power.*

LOAD PATTERN AND BOILER DESIGN

Not only do the conditions set by the quantities which are readily defined by numerical values directly influence boiler design, but operating conditions which will be encountered in service also affect it. Although two ships might have the same shaft horsepower (shp) and the same evaporating rates for the boilers, one ship might be in a trade which calls for prolonged periods of steady steaming, and in contrast, the other ship might be in a service which requires the boilers to be changing load frequently. As examples, the former would be typical of a tanker, and the latter, a dredge or a ferry boat.

Analyses of boiler load variations during a series of voyages make it possible to graph the load pattern for the boilers in a particular trade.

In designing new ships, it is customary to plot these graphs with averages compiled over an extended period from data of ships that have been in the same trade that the new vessels will serve. Fig. 1 illustrates the boiler load pattern typical of a dry-cargo ship during a single round-trip voyage between the West Coast of the United States and the Orient.

Obviously, a dry-cargo boiler has a load pattern which differs from that of a tanker or a destroyer. Although the design of a ship and its machinery must take into consideration possible changes in service conditions, the prime objective is to get the optimum design for the trade in which the vessel will initially serve. Fortunately, most marine boilers have the inherent characteristic of being versatile to a degree. If later service conditions do bring about changes in the boiler load pattern, the boiler usually will be able to meet the new conditions within the limits determined by the other mechanical components of the propulsion plant.

Not only is the load pattern an important factor in deciding some of the principal characteristics of marine-boiler design, but it will also determine some of the detailed features which must be included. Consideration must also be given to various other service conditions, such as ship sailing schedule and quality of operating personnel. Some of the boiler design features which may be decided entirely, or in part, by service conditions are

- number of boilers per ship
- type of firing system
- furnace dimensions
- overall boiler dimensions
- extent of control systems
- size of steam drum
- type of steam generator
- relative amount of waterwall generating surface

SPACE LIMITATIONS AND BOILER DESIGN

Up to this point there has been no discussion of the extremely basic condition of space restriction which actually dictates the boiler design on many ships. To the boiler designer, it would be ideal if adequate space could be provided in the fireroom so that no limitations on size or shape had to be considered. Table I and Fig. 2 show the principal dimensions of one standard series of boiler designs. Although the ship owner and marine architect usually try to design the ship so that, as nearly as possible, space will be provided for the optimum boiler design, it is almost inevitable that space restrictions will be imposed. From the outset of the preliminary ship design to the time when the boilers are installed and accessibility has been satisfactorily proved, the boiler designer must constantly consider the space problem.

Frequently, the very purpose of the ship establishes limiting dimensions for the fireroom

Fig. 1 Boiler load pattern during voyage of dry-cargo ship

Table I. Principal Dimensions for Standard V2M8 Marine Boilers

Boiler Design	Capacity* 1000 lb/hr	Dimensions, Ft			
		A	B	C	D
V2M8-6	132	21	24.9	12.7	15
V2M8-7	154	21	24.6	16.3	15
V2M8-8	176	23.6	27.7	14.5	16.5
V2M8-9	198	23.5	27.3	15.9	16.5
V2M8-10	221	26.2	25.2	18.4	19
V2M8-11	243	26.5	26.5	19	19
V2M8-12	265	27.1	28.4	19.8	19
V2M8-13	287	26.2	25.2	23	19

*Varies with cycle conditions

space. For example, the train ferry must have as many continuous decks as possible. This feature immediately sets a limit upon the height allowed for the boiler space. For many ship types, the structural members of the ship hull present the most common reason for limiting the boiler dimensions.

SELECTION OF DESIGN

When the service conditions have been properly evaluated, the boiler designer determines the physical design characteristics which will best meet requirements. Ideally, the preliminary design should be completed in time for use by the ship designer in establishing the machinery arrangement and the layout of the main hull structurals passing through the fireroom. Space is generally the first item to be considered. If the optimum boiler design— the one which has the arrangement and physical characteristics most suitable for the service conditions and performance requirements— has any dimension that is definitely in excess of the space allowed, then a compromise has to be made. In designing the boiler furnace, the major factors to be considered are as follows:

- firing-equipment accessibility
- burner clearance to heating surfaces
- gas flow and flame travel
- circulation
- interrelationship of furnace dimensions with main generating-bank dimensions, and
- amount of waterwall surface

The burners must be located in positions that will be readily accessible from the firing aisle. The prescribed minimum burner clearances must be carefully maintained to avoid flame impingement on furnace-wall, floor, or screen generating tubes.

Selection of furnace dimensions must include provisions for the proper flow pattern of the combustion gases within the furnace and into the tube bank. It would be ideal if the gas flow could be controlled to the extent that the

mass flow rate and the gas temperature both would be uniform at all points where the gas enters the screen tubes. But achieving this theoretical condition is not generally possible. The boiler designer must, therefore, be guided by the results of past experience obtained during the testing and operating service of designs similar to the one under consideration.

In selecting the preliminary design for a marine boiler, detailed calculations on the circulation of the boiler circuits are usually unnecessary, if the design is reasonably similar to previous designs of the same general type for which complete circulation calculations have been performed. It is important to note that the maximum thermal circulation effect is obtained when the major portion of the heat absorbed is applied to the lower portion of a tube.

Most types of boilers have the arrangement and dimensions of their generating banks related to some degree to furnace dimensions. For example, in early designs of two-drum bent-tube boilers, limitations on the draft loss through the main bank would frequently set the main-bank dimensions, and the furnace height would be fixed accordingly. With some boiler designs, the furnace dimensions can be set at the optimum point, and the main-bank dimensions are essentially independent. This is made possible by having the distributing header located several feet away from the lower drum, as discussed later in this chapter in the section on

Fig. 2 **Principal dimensions applicable to Table I**

bent-tube boilers. In most instances, boilers are now designed with the maximum practical amount of waterwall heating surface.

DEVELOPMENT OF MARINE BOILERS

In tracing the history of the development and application of marine boilers, it is interesting that some of the basic requirements have always applied, although from time to time the emphasis has shifted from one requirement to another. At the outset, space and weight limitations were not considered to be as important as other factors, and yet at later stages the emphasis on those items brought about the development of new types of boilers. Generally, it has been the economic or military need for increased propulsion power that has instigated significant advances in boiler design.

The earliest types of marine boilers were relatively large pressure vessels, with furnaces located underneath them.[1] But it soon became apparent that such exterior furnaces were far from satisfactory, and they were then located inside the boiler shell. The boiler exterior had now developed into an approximate cube and, no matter how heavily stayed, its flat exterior placed very low limits on the steam pressure that could be carried and also left much to be desired from a maintenance and safety standpoint. The internal furnaces and tubes, however, were cylindrical and entirely satisfactory for the pressure demands of their time. By 1870, marine-boiler pressures had reached only 60 psig; by 1900 they had increased to about 300 psig.

SCOTCH MARINE BOILERS

To overcome the structural weaknesses and at the same time reduce cost of fabrication, the boiler shell was made cylindrical (replacing the earlier box construction) with provision to install one or more combustion chambers between the two flat sides of the shell. Known as the Scotch marine boiler, this boiler as finally developed met with wide and enthusiastic approval by marine engineers. Although minor changes have been made throughout the years, its design has remained much the same and its qualities of ruggedness, reliability, ease of maintenance, and ability to stand abuse made it—until recently—the most popular boiler in the marine field.

The boiler shown in Fig. 3 is coal-fired with a spreader stoker and has two furnaces. A close look at the illustration reveals two separate combustion chambers, each stayed to the other. Tubes used as flues for returning products of combustion from the combustion chambers to the smokebox covering the upper front of the boiler are also shown.

Even though the Scotch marine boiler proved to be popular and well-suited for shipboard installations, the fact that its pressure was limited to 300 psig retarded progress. There was a realization that advanced boiler designs with greater generating capacity, higher pressure, and increased efficiency were needed to meet the changing requirements brought about by the development of turbine propulsion machinery. Stiff commercial competition among merchant fleets as well as various naval powers made these developments most urgent. Marine engineers began to adapt various types of water-tube boilers to fit into the restricted space available for installations on shipboard.

Air to Windbox

Fig. 3 **Scotch marine boiler fired by spreader stoker**

Some adaptations proved highly advantageous with respect to heat transfer and weight, and offered a variety of designs suitable for pressures in excess of the maximum of firetube types. Thus, new possibilities were presented for the utilization of steam aboard ship.[2]

SECTIONAL-HEADER BOILERS

As an early water-tube boiler, the cross-drum type had generating tubes extending between a row of rear headers arranged vertically and connected to the drum, and a row of uptake headers at the front of the boiler. Vertical waterwall tubes were arranged at both sides of the furnace. At a later stage of development, the downtake headers in the steam drum were relocated to the front of the boiler and that basic arrangement is known today as the cross-drum sectional-header boiler.

The handhole plates in the headers of this type of boiler provide ready access and make it possible to turbine-clean the water sides of the main-bank generating tubes without the need for a person to enter the steam drum. Appreciably heavier than presently available boiler designs, the sectional-header boiler was used during World Wars I and II on many kinds of merchant ships. The design is ideally suited for mass production.

The C-E Type SM sectional header boiler as shown in Fig. 4 is designed for capacities up to about 150,000 lb of steam per hour and pressures up to 850 psig. Steel corner columns incorporated into the casing members form a boxlike structure which supports the boiler. An insulated casing encloses the entire unit. Where good accessibility is necessary, the casing panels are removable and are held in place by bolted batten bars. At other locations the casing panels are welded in place. Generally, the side and rear walls of the furnace have vertical waterwall tubes. Superheaters may be either interdeck or overdeck, depending on the steam temperature required.

Fig. 4 **C-E SM sectional header boiler, principal parts identified**

BENT-TUBE BOILERS

Just as the need for increased steaming capacities within fixed space and weight limitations spurred the development of the earlier water-tube-type boilers, so did the same need precipitate the advance to boiler designs of the bent-tube type.

The most compelling reasons for the development of higher capacity boilers came from the naval designers who, at about the end of the nineteenth century, were charged with developing the torpedo boats which were the forerunners of modern destroyer-type vessels.

The term *bent-tube boiler* covers a wide range of boiler designs characterized by the ability to raise steam pressure within a short period of time. This means smaller tube diameters, fewer headers, increased furnace ratings and wider application of watercooled furnaces. The boilers of this category also became known as multidrum type, express type, or by various other names corresponding to the designers of particular arrangements.

With advanced designs available for naval vessels, it was a quite logical step to utilize adaptations of those designs for high-powered passenger ships. Thus during the 1930's, the two-drum bent-tube design was developed for application to merchant ships with power plants ranging up to about 10,000 shp.

After World War II, ship operators and boiler designers became acutely aware that marine-boiler designs would have to be modified to avoid some of the difficulties that were being encountered with the prewar designs. During the war, with the emphasis upon standardization and multiple production, time was not available for the development of improved designs.

Another factor which prompted the development of new boiler designs stemmed from competitive and economic pressures compelling shipowners to look toward higher steam

Fig. 5 **C-E V2M Vertical Superheater Boiler with main parts called out**

pressures and temperatures, and also propulsion plants of greater power, as a means of achieving more profitable operation. It was also realized that ship boilers would have to be designed to burn efficiently whatever fuel oils would be available. Because of improved refining processes coupled with the natural motivations of profitable marketing, it was to be expected that the crude oil was to be processed to the fullest, and the resulting residual oil which normally goes to bunkers of ships would be progressively of lower quality. The prewar boilers were particularly vulnerable to fireside damage caused by slag deposits from burning such poor-quality fuels.

A comprehensive analysis of these problems led to the development of the C-E V2M vertical superheater boiler. Fig. 5 shows a typical arrangement of this design. By providing a separate drum or distributing header at the lower end of the screen tubes, it is possible to set the floor of the furnace independently of the location of lower drum and main bank. Not only does this allow greater latitude in establishing optimum furnace dimensions, but it also permits the superheater tubes to be parallel to the generating tubes. The access space within the

Fig. 6 **The V2M8 vertical superheater boiler design featuring the single-cased welded-wall furnace and the vertical in-line inverted U-loop superheater, fully drainable**

superheater contributes to ease of maintenance and inspection.

V2M8 AND V2M9 DESIGNS

Fig. 6 shows the V2M8 Vertical Superheater Boiler whose major design features are the single-cased welded-wall furnace and the vertical in-line inverted U-loop superheater, fully drainable. The boiler shown is top-fired with resulting improved gas distribution over the entire superheater furnace. Both the main-bank tubes and superheater elements are in-line for improved tube cleaning. Normally, sootblowing equipment includes retractable blowers in the superheater and rotary blowers in the main bank and economizer. Typical heat-recovery equipment consists of a small economizer followed by a regenerative air preheater or, in some cases, a regenerative air preheater only. The welded-wall construction provides a furnace with gas-tight integrity without the need for double casing or heavy refractory bricks behind the tubes. All that is required for insulation behind the walls is blanket insulation.

Some boilers of this type have been built with "double" or "twin" superheaters. With the double superheater, the elements are more widely spaced so that cleanliness is easier to maintain. Tube metal temperatures are also reduced, both because of the lower mass gas flow across the superheater and the location of the secondary superheater, which is furthest away from the furnace. The total surface, overall size, and weight of a double superheater are, however, much greater than that of the single superheater because of the reduced mass gas flow and consequent lower transfer rate.

To generate the much higher evaporations required by increasingly larger ships, the furnaces were required to be made very large. To keep the main bank at essentially the same vertical dimension as the V2M8 boilers, it was necessary to lengthen the furnace in a vertical dimension. The boiler then became a vertical two-drum dropped-furnace boiler. Because the lower part of the furnace (see Fig. 7) was unencumbered, it became clear that the boiler could be tangentially fired. The fuel nozzles are placed in each corner of the furnace, and fire at a target circle in the center of the furnace. This lengthens the fuel-particle residence time in the furnace, and allows for complete combustion and operation at very low excess air. Fig. 7 shows the boiler configuration; Fig. 8A, a diagram of tangential firing. Major design features include single-cased welded-wall construction, tangential firing, and vertical in-line double superheater, inverted U-loop, fully drainable. The boiler is supported at its midpoint, under the water drum and center headers.

In some of the larger designs of single-boiler ships, a nondrainable superheater has been used, because the boiler would be on the line from drydocking to drydocking.

Table II summarizes typical performance data for a regenerative air-heater boiler cycle.

The registers of a tangentially fired marine boiler are of a straight-throat type with primary- and secondary-air zones. The primary airflow is through the center compartment, where the oil gun and diffuser are also located. Secondary air is above and below the center compartment. See Fig. 8B. Under normal operation, the primary-air damper is fully open at all times the register is in operation, while the

secondary-air dampers are modulated to maintain a constant register draft loss. In this way, good combustion efficiency can be maintained over a wide boiler range.

Fig. 8C shows a typical draft-loss curve for tangential firing. The registers can be operated to cycle on and off for either a two- or four-register operation based on steam flow and drum pressure, or they can operate with four registers on whenever the vessel is under way. The oil guns are of the steam-atomizing type utilizing constant steam pressure at 150 psig with fuel pressure up to about 350 psig. Flame monitoring is accomplished by scanning along the axis of the flame and also scanning the flame across the furnace corner, with both scanners showing NO FLAME required to close the fuel-oil solenoid valve. Scanners will scan the individual flame up to about 30 percent boiler rating, after which they will scan the furnace as a whole. If the boiler rating is above 30 percent, the "fireball" in the furnace is large enough to ignite any incoming oil.

The fact that the registers are relatively distant from the superheater helps to keep the superheat elements clean for long periods of time, thus maintaining design outlet steam temperature.

On some of the later designs with nondrainable superheaters, where the retractable sootblowers must blow through a bank of eight or more superheater elements, additional retractable sootblowers have been installed in front of the superheater in the furnace. These were used because of the deep bank they had to blow through, as well as the fact that if superheaters

Fig. 7 **The C-E V2M9 vertical two-drum dropped-furnace boiler**

Table II. Typical Performance Data: Regenerative Air-Heater Boiler Cycle

Evaporation	220,000 lb/hr
Total steam temperature	955°F
Feedwater temperature	424°F
Superheater outlet pressure	865 psig
Excess air	3%
Efficiency	90.7%

Fig. 8 Diagram of tangential firing. Fuel nozzles, located in each corner of the furnace, fire at a target circle in the furnace center.

have a tendency to slag, it will be on the leading edge of the tubes closest to the furnace.

REHEAT DESIGNS

The major problem to be addressed by marine-boiler designers in considering the use of a reheat cycle is that, when the ship is stopped, there is no flow through the main steam turbine and, therefore, no steam flow through the boiler reheater. Consequently, the reheater must be protected by gas dampers or protection steam, or it must be placed in a low-temperature area in the gas stream, to avoid excessive tube-metal temperatures.

Fig. 9 shows a schematic of a reheat boiler system. This system does not require the isolation of the reheater by dampers or the steam cooling of the element when the reheat steam flow is secured. The system shown is for V2M9 reheat boiler with two drums and a dropped-bottom furnace. It has tangential firing on the superheater side while on the reheat side it has a reheater furnace with a register-type burner.

Referring to Fig. 9A, which shows conditions at 100-percent rating and normal operating conditions, it can be seen that approximately 17 percent of the total fuel fired is in the reheater furnace with the other 83 percent of the fuel being burned in the superheater furnace. The superheater side of the boiler is fired with 3-percent excess air using tangential firing, while the reheater side of the boiler is fired with 10-percent excess air; the resulting overall excess air for the boiler system is under 5 percent. During normal operation with approximately 83 percent of the total fuel fired in the superheater furnace, the gas temperature leaving the main bank is 950°F. These gases mix with the reheater-furnace gases and the net result is a temperature of approximately 1300°F entering the reheater. It should be noted that there is a small two-row screen below the reheater at the exit from the boiler which, in conjunction with the low gas temperature leaving the reheater furnace, essentially eliminates any radiant heat passing to the reheater.

Figs. 9B, 9C, and 9D show typical system conditions for overload with reheat, overload with the high-pressure feedwater heaters secured, and normal rating with the reheater burners secured, respectively.

During periods of maneuvering astern, the reheater burners and reheat steam flow are secured, Fig. 9C; the maximum gas temperature when all of the oil is being fired in the superheater furnace is no greater than 1030°F, which is well below the safe operating temperature of low-alloy steel tubing (2.25% chromium content, to ASTM T-22). It should be noted that, during this period, all of the gases pass over the superheater. A submerged coil desuperheater is required to control superheated steam temperature, which naturally tends to rise. The maximum degree of steam temperature control is calculated to be 170°F. (This is at a condition equivalent to the overload rating with the high-pressure feedwater heaters secured.) The reheater also has the built-in feature that, during "ahead" maneuvering or at any time before the ship is "full away" (with the reheater burners still secured), some degree of reheat will be imparted to the reheat steam because of the low-temperature gas passing over it. At approximately 100-percent design steam flow with all of the fuel being burned in the superheater furnace, the reheat steam temperature will be 780°F. The gas temperature entering the reheater under these operating conditions is 970°F.

The reheater is a counter-flow heat exchanger with steam inlet conditions of 350 psig and 630°F, and outlet conditions of 330 psig and 955°F. A small economizer and regenerative air heater are installed behind the reheater to produce 90.7-percent boiler efficiency. The high boiler efficiency is based on operation at low excess air. As the reheater is situated in a low gas-temperature zone, it can also tolerate substantial imbalance in steam distribution in the tubes without undue tube overheating.

The reheat boiler and reheater cross section are shown in Fig. 10; the major design features are welded-wall construction, tangentially fired superheater side, front-fired reheat side, and two-drum dropped-furnace design. Table III lists typical performance data for the boiler.

Sensing the reheater outlet temperature and firing the reheater furnace for set point govern reheat temperature. Firing the superheater furnace for set point regulates drum pressure or superheater outlet pressure. A submerged-coil desuperheater in the steam or water drum controls superheater temperature. Fig. 11 shows a V2M8 reheat boiler of a somewhat smaller capacity than the V2M9, but with the same system design concepts.

Fig. 9 **Schematic of a V2M9 reheat boiler system with a two-drum dropped furnace**

Table III. Performance Data Typical of Reheat Boiler and Reheater Cross Section

	Normal
Total evaporation	278,000 lb/hr
Desuperheated flow	26,500 lb/hr
Reheat flow	198,400 lb/hr
Superheated flow	251,500 lb/hr
Superheater steam temp.	955°F
Reheater steam temp.	955°F
Boiler efficiency	90.7%
Overall excess air	4.2%
Superheater furnace excess air	3%
Reheater furnace excess air	10%
Superheater furnace release rate	55,500 Btu/hr-ft³
Reheater furnace release rate	47,800 Btu/hr-ft³
Superheater outlet pressure	1486 psig
Reheater inlet pressure	350 psig
Reheater outlet pressure	330 psig

STOKER-FIRED DESIGNS

Fig. 12 shows a modern stoker-fired marine boiler designated as a V2M9S boiler. The boiler is a single-cased welded-wall design with single-cased uptakes; some areas around superheater headers, access doors, and windbox are double cased. Table IV compares typical performance data of a coal-fired design with an equivalent fuel-oil-fired design.

By comparing the furnace release rates, it can readily be appreciated that the coal furnace has about 3 times the volume of the oil furnace for the same power output. To minimize furnace and superheater problems, furnace temperature when burning coal is kept lower than the ash-fusion temperature. This temperature can be readily achieved with a totally watercooled furnace by limiting the grate release and furnace heat release. Overfire-air jets and cinder reinjection are located above the stoker grate, one line of cinder reinjection nozzles serving

Fig. 10 The V2M9 reheat boiler and reheater cross section with welded-wall construction, tangentially fired superheater side, front-fired reheat side, and two-drum dropped-furnace design

to reduce the carbon loss by about 4 percent. The cinder hopper is located between the two superheater sections. In addition to the stoker, a fuel-oil burner is incorporated in the upper furnace for in-port firing or take-home purposes. When the burner is in use, a layer of ash is retained on the grate to protect it from overheating. Tube spacings in both the superheater and main bank and the economizer fin spacings are increased over the fuel-oil-fired spacings to keep gas velocities low for minimum erosion.

WASTE-HEAT DESIGNS

Many vessels powered by medium- and slow-speed diesel engines recycle waste heat from exhaust gases to generate steam for tank heating, cargo heating and, in some cases, to drive a turbogenerator to supply the electrical load of the ship. There are various shapes and sizes of waste-heat designs; Fig. 13 shows a typical waste-heat boiler bank composed of horizontal finned tubes connected by return bends. All return bends are installed outside the gas passage with a gas-tight tube sheet separating them from the gas duct. This type of extended-surface heat exchanger is identical in basic construction to a marine-boiler economizer. The combination of large diameter tubes with welded helical fins for extended heat-transfer surface is simple, rugged, and compact. The boiler bank shown in Fig. 13 can be used in series with an auxiliary boiler, with water circulated through the waste-heat bank and returned to the steam drum of the auxiliary-boiler. Controls are then arranged to

automatically fire the auxiliary boiler so that drum pressure is maintained with varying loads. If the steam generation by waste-heat gas alone is too high, a steam dump to a condenser or gas bypass damper can be installed. If required, a waste-heat bank can also be arranged to run as an independent unit with its own steam drum and circulating-pump system.

The need for oxygen removal on low-pres-

Fig. 11 The V2M8 LTG reheat welded-wall main propulsion boiler

Table IV. Comparison of Performance Data Coal- and Oil-Fired Designs

	Coal	Oil
Furnace release rate, Btu/hr-cu ft	25,000	75,000
Grate release rate, Btu/hr-sq ft	700,000	. . .
Furnace absorption rate, Btu/hr-sq ft	37,000	70,000
Furnace outlet temp., °F	1900	2500

Fig. 12 A V2M9S stoker-fired marine boiler with a single-cased welded-wall design and single-cased uptakes

Fig. 13 A typical waste-heat boiler bank

sure auxiliary systems is just as great as in main propulsion systems. The direct-contact feedwater heater is a reliable and effective device for continuously maintaining feedwater at acceptable low levels of oxygen and should be installed. The advisability of using a deaerating feedwater heater has been recognized by not only boiler-water chemistry consultants, but also designers who have experienced problems with corrosion caused by poor water chemistry in waste-heat boiler systems.

CONTROLLED CIRCULATION® BOILERS

The marine boilers described to this point depend upon natural thermo-syphonic forces to maintain the circulation flow within the boiler. Such thermal or natural circulation results from the difference in hydraulic head between the saturated water in the downcomers and the relatively less dense mixture of steam and water in the steam-generating tubes. For the lower range of steam pressures, thermal-circulation forces are usually quite adequate. At higher pressures, providing a more positive means of maintaining the circulation becomes desirable and advantageous.

The Controlled Circulation Marine Boiler design is an ideal arrangement for shipboard steam plants in high-pressure ranges. Fig. 14 is a diagram of a typical arrangement illustrating the principle of operation for this boiler. With its features of positive circulation, compactness, light weight, suitability for high pressure and temperature, and adaptability to limited space conditions, the Controlled Circulation boiler can offer important advantages for advanced-design marine steam practice.

DESIGN PRINCIPLES FOR MARINE-BOILER FURNACES

A number of factors determine the configuration of a marine-boiler furnace. First of all, the type of boiler under consideration sets some of the furnace dimensions. As already discussed, fireroom space limitations, service requirements, and burner arrangement also influence the furnace layout. The furnace arrangement must also conform to criteria which are prerequisites for proper thermal and circulation performance. The amount of waterwall surface determines the furnace exit-gas temperature which, in turn, is most significant in the design of the superheater. Practical requirements must also be considered; for instance, the firing equipment must be located where it can be easily operated.

Two-drum bent-tube boilers are always fur-

nished with watercooled surfaces on the side and roof and, for the majority of designs, a rear waterwall is included; waterwalls may also be installed in the front wall.

SUPERHEATERS

Superheaters are essentially a series of tubular elements connected to headers. The saturated steam enters the inlet header from piping connected to the steam drum. In a single-pass superheater, the saturated steam flows from the saturated header through the superheater elements into the superheater outlet header. In the multipass superheater, the headers are diaphragmed to allow the steam to make as many passes as necessary to assure good steam distribution through all elements.

Marine superheater design requires a judicious balancing of economic and practical factors. There must be a sufficiently large temperature difference between the combustion gas passing over the superheater surface and the steam within the surface to result in a superheater of economic proportions. At the same time, there are practical limitations on superheater metal temperatures, and provision must be made to arrange superheater elements to resist slag accumulation. Screen tubes are

Fig. 14 **Diagrammatic arrangement of Controlled Circulation Marine Boiler**

located ahead of superheaters to obtain reasonable metal temperatures while at the same time allowing a certain amount of direct radiation to be absorbed by the superheater tubes. This results in a flatter steam-temperature curve at the superheater outlet.

Some boiler designs have the superheater behind the main generating bank. Such an arrangement requires a relatively greater amount of heating surface and an elaborate system for controlling superheater outlet temperature. An alternative arrangement incorporates a second furnace for controlling the steam temperature by varying the firing rate of the superheater furnace. Although such a boiler design permits a wide range of control, there are inherent complications in the operating procedures.

Most two-drum bent-tube boilers are designed with the superheater within the generating bank and with either horizontal or vertical superheaters. Positive means must be provided to keep superheaters clear of slag deposits. To permit convenient access for inspection, cleaning, and maintenance, modern designs include access spaces within the superheater banks.

The advantageous features of the vertical superheater, as shown earlier in Fig. 6, result in reduced maintenance and optimum service efficiency. Because the elements are arranged parallel to boiler tubes, clear lanes between generating and superheater tubes present the best arrangement for effective action of the

sootblowers. With the superheater tubes in a vertical position, it is difficult for slag to accumulate. Bulky supports are eliminated as it is possible to support each superheater tube from the superheater headers which are outside of the gas pass. Small slip spacers attaching superheater elements and adjacent generating tubes maintain the upper ends of the superheater elements in the correct lateral position.

DESUPERHEATERS

For most modern marine boilers, all of the steam generated by the boiler is passed through the superheater. Auxiliary steam requirements are met by desuperheating the required quantity of auxiliary steam. Because the superheater is located in a relatively high-temperature gas zone and overheating may occur if any substantial proportion of steam were taken directly from the steam drum to the auxiliary steam line, this arrangement is necessary to maintain a flow of steam through the superheater at all times. To provide low-temperature steam for auxiliaries and for other purposes, such as heating, Butterworthing (a special system for steam-cleaning cargo tanks), and evaporators, steam from the superheater outlet is passed through a desuperheater which absorbs some of the heat in the superheater steam.

Desuperheaters can be of the internal or the external type. The internal type contains tubular elements with necessary terminal connections to be installed within the boiler drum.

Fig. 15 **Internal-type desuperheater**

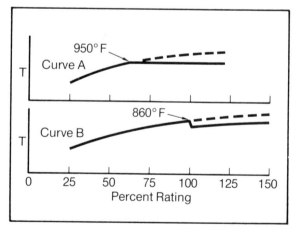

Fig. 16 **Superheater characteristic curves**

Fig. 15 shows a typical arrangement of an internal-type desuperheater as installed in a boiler drum. Note that the unit is arranged so that it may be passed through the drum manhole as a complete assembly. The external type includes a direct or indirect heat exchanger mounted in the steam line, with feedwater most generally used as the cooling medium.

STEAM-TEMPERATURE CONTROLS

For high-temperature applications, designing for a constant steam temperature over a relatively wide load range may be desirable, as indicated by the superheat characteristic Curve A in Fig. 16, or for nominal temperature applications to limit the steam temperature at infrequent overload ratings, as shown by Curve B. The dashed-line extensions of characteristic curves show expected temperatures without control. Fig. 17 shows a typical arrangement which will provide close control of steam temperature and, in so doing, protect the last passes of the superheater, turbine, and connecting steam piping. The steam temperature at the superheater outlet actuates an air-operated control valve. Below the set temperature, all steam passes through the orificed line, the control valve being closed. When the temperature tends to rise above the set temperature, the control valve opens to permit a portion of the steam to flow to the desuperheater and have its temperature reduced. The control valve has a hand jack for manual operation.

Fig. 17 Steam-temperature control arrangement for marine boiler

With the exception of manual operation of the automatic control valve, the same general arrangement is used to accomplish the limiting-type of temperature control, as shown in curve B of Fig. 16. At higher boiler ratings, when the temperature starts to exceed the predetermined maximum, the control valve is opened fully, accounting for the temperature drop just beyond normal rating and the continuing rise to maximum rating.

HEAT-RECOVERY EQUIPMENT FOR MARINE BOILERS

The general classification "heat-recovery equipment" covers heat exchangers which are located such that heat is absorbed from the combustion gases after the gases have passed through the superheater and steam-generating sections of the boiler. Tubular air heaters, Ljungstrom® regenerative-type air heaters, and economizers are the most common types for marine boilers.

ECONOMIZERS

The economizer is a series of horizontal tubular elements by means of which heat is recovered from combustion gas leaving the boiler and added to the incoming feedwater. The amount of heat absorbed in an economizer depends on the temperature difference between gas and water, the heat-transfer rate, and the amount of heating surface. It is the normal practice to use some form of extended surface on tubes to increase the heating surface per foot of tube length.

Economizers can be categorized as bare tube and extended surface types. The bare tube usually includes varying sizes which can be arranged to form hairpin or multiloop elements.

Because the coefficient of heat transfer is relatively low on the gas side of an economizer tube as compared to that on the waterside, it is desirable to have some form of extended heating surface on the outside of the tube so as to increase the overall rate of heat transfer. Many different configurations of extended surface are used, each with characteristics of a specific standard adopted by a particular boiler manufacturer. In turn, each type of extended-surface economizer has a heat-transfer rate that is peculiar to the shape and finish of the surface, the material employed, and the method of fabrication. Fig. 18 shows a widely used type of marine economizer extended surface.

Most marine economizers are designed for counterflow of gas and water, that is, water down through elements and gas up outside of elements. This is done to take advantage of the greater temperature difference between the gas and water. Under these conditions, the heat-transfer rate cannot be increased without incurring a substantial resistance to gas flow, and the use of extended surface to increase the heating surface per lineal foot is desirable. Whatever the arrangement of economizer, ample provision must be made to assure that the heating surface can be kept free of deposits. The coexistence of deposits and moisture can cause corrosion; accordingly, the spacing of the elements, the quantity and effectiveness of the sootblowers, and the design of the breeching above the economizers must all be carefully considered. Moisture can come from a number of sources:

1. Rain or spray down the stack

2. Leaks in economizers or other pressure parts

3. Condensation of moisture in gases because of the gas coming into contact with cold heat-transfer surfaces and cooling to below the acid dew-point temperature. Also, dependent on the sulfur content of the gas, this condensation forms a corrosive sulfuric-acid solution which attacks the metal surfaces.

Although a leak in an economizer pressure part cannot go long undetected, substantial corrosion-erosion damage can result quickly if a leak is allowed to persist. Therefore, it is advantageous to design economizers with the minimum of joints and handhole plates consistent with proper provision for replacing an element. Generally, the header tube joint is made up as a full welded joint or, as an alternate construction, the elements are welded to nipples in the headers.

Although the economizer is designed principally for steady steaming conditions, proper consideration must be given to the design of the elements so that steam will not be generated within the economizer during maneuvering. This means that there must be suitable water velocities and pressure drops to assure adequate circulation in each element. Under most conditions, there is sufficient differential between saturation and feedwater temperatures to prevent the generation of steam. But there may be some maneuvering conditions, such as the sequence from stop to full ahead, in which

Fig. 18 Close-up view of economizer spiral steel surface

Fig. 19 Regenerative air heater for marine service

steaming may become a problem. This is particularly true if the water level is high at the start of the maneuver and the boiler control system is of the single-element (water-level) type.

Usually, an economizer is installed at the boiler outlet adjacent to the steam drum with elements parallel to the drum. In most fireroom arrangements, sufficient space is available for a good economizer arrangement. However, to obtain the required economizer heat absorption, the economizer length, width, and number of tubes high may have to be varied to obtain the best arrangement for the space conditions available and to meet thermal performance conditions. In addition, the allowable gas-side pressure loss and water pressure drop must be considered.

Today, it is common practice to design marine economizers so that they can be bypassed if a leak occurs, thereby allowing the boiler to remain in service until the necessary repairs can be made. The economizer then must withstand entering gas temperatures without any feedwater flow through the economizer tubes. With the economizer bypassed, the loss in efficiency results in an increased fuel-firing rate, and increasing draft losses cause a higher fan load. Another important consideration is that there is generally an increase of total steam temperature because of the higher gas flow and increased furnace temperature.

AIR HEATERS

Using air heaters to improve the performance of steam-generating units began in marine practice prior to 1880. At that time, practically all the heaters were of the tubular type with various arrangements of vertical or horizontal banks of short or long tubes. In some, the gas passed through the tubes, while in others the tubes served as a passage for the air. Most marine tubular air heaters are of the horizontal type, preferable because of its simplicity and the ease of incorporating it into the boiler arrangement.

Most marine tubular air heaters are located immediately above the boiler gas exit where the unit can be fitted conveniently into the boiler design. For a two-pass heater, air both enters and exits at the rear side of the boiler, presenting an efficient arrangement for transporting air to the fuel burners.

REGENERATIVE AIR HEATERS

Regenerative air heaters for marine service are designed for horizontal or vertical flow of the air and stack gases. In this type of heat exchanger, the heating elements are contained in a slowly turning rotor of cellular construction. As the rotor turns, heat is absorbed continuously by the heating elements from the flue gas, while a like amount of heat is released simultaneously to the combustion air, as these fluids flow axially through the rotor. The rotor is enclosed in a gas-tight housing which is fitted at each end to make connections with the air and flue-gas ducts. Dampered integral air and flue-gas bypass ducts are incorporated in the four corners of the structure. Parallel air bypasses offer a way of controlling cold-end heating-element temperature during operation at reduced steaming rate. The flue-gas bypasses in parallel, together with the air bypasses, provide a means of limiting overall pressure loss at steaming rates above that corresponding to normal power. Fig. 19 shows a typical regenerative air heater for marine service.

A vertical-flow regenerative air heater can be located directly above the boiler outlet or in the area above the boiler, and connected with conventional ductwork. From the top of the air heater on the gas side, an uptake is led to the stack in the usual manner. Forced-draft fans may be located conventionally and connected to the air side of the heater by means of ductwork. Various arrangements can be utilized to suit the conditions (see Fig. 20).

STEAM AIR HEATERS

Both the boiler operating conditions and the efficiency required of a boiler unit affect the selection of the heat-recovery equipment to be incorporated in the design of a boiler. These are related to the specification of a suitable steam cycle for a marine installation. The best steam cycle for one installation may not be advantageous to another. Therefore, for certain installations, an air heater alone may be optimum. Where feedwater temperature and pressure conditions permit, an economizer or a combination of an economizer and a steam air heater is used to obtain the boiler efficiency required, with no gas-to-air heater.

One method to improve the steam-cycle efficiency is by means of the feedwater heating system, and here the steam air heater uses steam extracted from the feedwater heater or auxiliary exhaust. This reduces the flow of steam to the condenser and improves cycle efficiency. An alternative method is to extract low-pressure bleed steam from the main turbines.

In the condensing of the bleed steam or auxiliary exhaust, heat is transferred to the air used for combustion. Because the condensing steam-film coefficient of heat transfer is high, extended surface is used to advantage. Closely pitched tubes and fins can be utilized, as both the air and heating fluids are clean, eliminating entirely the necessity for cleaning.

In most steam-air-heater installations, bleed steam at 10 to 45 psig is used. Although a feedwater heater uses steam at relatively high pressure, the steam air heater uses auxiliary exhaust or low-pressure bleed steam. Utilizing the lower pressure bleed steam is a good method of improving cycle efficiency.

Another point to be considered is that the auxiliary exhaust can be used to advantage in a steam air heater while boilers are steaming in port, thereby improving low-load boiler operating conditions. Suitable air temperature for good combustion is readily maintained, whereas with a tubular or regenerative-type air heater, a bypass system around the heater is necessary to avoid low stack temperatures.

FLUID REGENERATIVE AIR HEATER

Fig. 21 shows an arrangement of a fluid regenerative air heater. This is an arrangement where the feed pump takes suction from the deaerating feedwater heater and discharges to the secondary economizer where the 285°F feedwater cools the stack gases to approximately 310°F. In this process, the water is heated to about 340°F. The feedwater is then routed to an air heater where it is cooled by the incoming combustion air to its original temperature of 285°F and, in this process, the combustion air is heated to approximately 310°F. The water then passes through the fourth and fifth stage heaters entering and leaving at temperatures of 285°F and 423°F respectively.

From the heaters, the water enters the primary economizer and then goes to the boiler. The primary and secondary economizer elements are all of spiral steel-fin construction which has been proven by many years of marine service.

For a 45,000 shp plant, in changing from a steam-air-heater/economizer cycle to a straight regenerative air-heater cycle, there is an overall plant efficiency increase of about 4 percent. Of this 4 percent increase in efficiency, about 1.5 percent is from the decrease in stack temperature, usually from 310°F to about 250°F; the other 2.5 percent is from the additional regenerative feedwater heating of the high-pressure heaters (less heat rejected to the condenser cooling water). From the standpoint of efficiency, the regenerative air preheater is the more attractive. Some shipowners, however, still prefer the economizer/steam-air-heater

Fig. 20 **Arrangement of regenerative air heaters aboard ship**

cycle because of longer life of economizer surface when compared to the cold end of an air preheater surface.

Under such a constraint, the use of a closed-loop fluid regenerative air preheater can be considered for the following reasons:

1. The plant efficiency will be increased by approximately 2.5 percent because of the use of high-pressure feedwater heaters;

2. The stack gas temperature will remain the same as is presently used in a steam-air-heater/economizer cycle; maintenance, therefore, will remain at the standards that are acceptable today;

3. Gas inerting systems can utilize the cool stack gas after the economizer because there is no air leakage in an economizer system;

4. Forced-draft fans can be selected smaller than in the equivalent regenerative air preheater plant because there is no air leakage in the economizer system.

FUEL BURNING

Oil burners for marine boilers must have features and operational characteristics consistent with the service requirements of the propulsion plant. First of all, a marine burner must be capable of properly burning the oil within a furnace of minimum dimensions. Likewise, the design of the furnace and the location of the burners must go hand in hand with the inherent characteristics of the particular type of burner selected for a given application. The burner must also be capable of producing efficient firing over a wide range of oil flow rates and be able to change load rapidly to meet the maneuvering requirements. For ships which maneuver for a substantial proportion of the operating time, it is essential that the boilers be fitted with burners capable of varying the firing rate over a wide range without the need of changing atomizer tips.

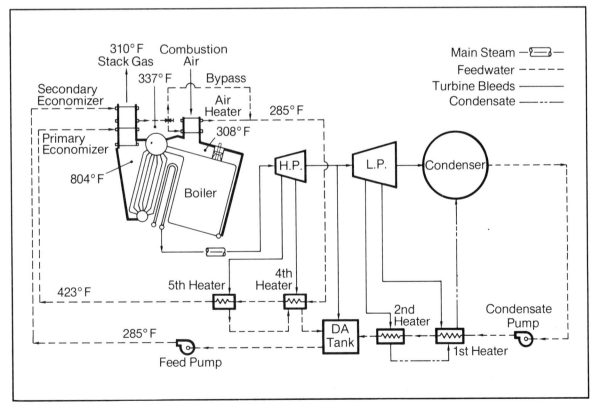

Fig. 21 **Component arrangement of a fluid regenerative air heater**

Before the fuel oil can be burned, the oil must be changed from a liquid to an atomized condition. Simultaneously, it must be mixed with an ample supply of air to permit combustion. A burner actually consists of two parts: the atomizer or burner barrel which serves to deliver a flow of atomized oil to the furnace (see Fig. 22), and the register which serves to supply a flow of air to the furnace. The burner barrel contains a sprayer plate, or swirl chamber, and an orifice tip which act together to produce the spray of fine oil particles.

The straight mechanical type of oil burner consists of a burner atomizer which converts the potential energy of the oil pressure into a flow of atomized oil particles. The register introduces and mixes the air with the oil spray produced by the atomizer. The oil flow is regulated by varying the supply pressure. On some installations this is accomplished manually; on others, it is automatically performed. Airflow is regulated by manual adjustment of the forced-draft fan output or by the automatic adjustment of the combustion control. This type of burner has a range or turndown ratio of between 1.5 and 3.0, depending on the pressure of the fuel-oil service system.

The return-flow type of burner functions with a constant-pressure oil supply, and the atomizer barrel contains a passage to permit a portion of the oil to return to the fuel-oil service pump suction. Regulating the control valve in the return line varies the firing rate. This type of burner achieves a much wider range than the straight mechanical burner.

The steam-atomizing-type burner uses a flow of steam which mixes in the atomizer tip with the oil flow. A portion of the energy in the steam serves to break up the oil particles, and better atomization results. This type burner offers a high turndown ratio and the advantage of being able to burn low-quality fuel efficiently.

COAL

Although the vast majority of shipboard boilers are fired by oil fuel, there remain some ship trades where economic conditions make it very desirable to burn coal. Modern coal-fired marine boilers use stokers. Although many types of stokers (including chain grate, underfeed, overfeed and spreader types) have been used for marine service, the spreader stoker has proven itself over a long period of operation to be best suited and most efficient in meeting the requirements. It is capable of burning a wide range of bituminous coals and has the ability to respond quickly to load changes. These features make spreader stokers attractive for vessels that will continuously serve in trades which have a readily available source of coal. Chapter 13 gives further descriptive material on the spreader stoker.

Fig. 22 The atomizer or burner barrel delivers a flow of atomized oil to the furnace

Fig. 23 Exterior view of marine boiler showing casing arrangement

BOILER CASINGS

The primary function of a boiler casing, Figs. 23 and 24, is to contain the products of combustion in such a way that the gases flow from the furnace through the steam-generating, superheater and heat-recovery tube banks, and out the breeching. Although both single and double-cased designs may be used, the function of containing the products of combustion takes place in that casing which is immediately exterior to the refractory and insulation wall.

Many modern boilers are built double cased. In this arrangement air pressure in the space between the inner and outer casings is greater than the pressure within the furnace. Accordingly, if there are any open joints in the inner casing, there will be an airflow into the furnace

instead of an outward flow of gas and soot. But this advantage should not be overexploited to the extent of disregarding the maintenance of a tight inner casing. If the flow of air through inner casing leaks is allowed to become substantial, boiler efficiency will be impaired and other detrimental effects will accrue.

DESIGN OF INNER CASING

The inner casing, or the only casing in a single-cased boiler, must be designed to accommodate the refractory and insulation. These materials must be arranged to protect the casing from exposure to gases and must insulate the casing from high temperatures. Structural members should preferably be located outside the inner casing. Whenever this is not possible, as may be the case for some supports of furnace insulation and refractory, alloy ma-

Fig. 24 **Details of boiler casing as fabricated in the assembly plant**

terial should be used if there is any possibility of exposure to high temperature.

The space between inner and outer casings of a double-cased boiler provides a convenient duct system by which the air for combustion can flow to the burners. Because there can be a wide choice of locations for the air inlet connection, the arrangement presents considerable flexibility to the design of the forced-draft system. Those sections of the air space not sustaining the main flow of combustion air are provided with a flow of cooling air which ultimately discharges into the windbox. Thus, all of the inner casing is pressurized. Because the airflow absorbs a large proportion of the heat given off by the inner casing, there is a reduction in boiler radiation losses.

In laying out the arrangement of casing, calculations must be made to determine that the air pressure-drop values are not excessive and that the velocities and airflow pattern in the windbox will be suitable for the even distribution of air to the registers. In determining the dimensions of the air space, allowance must be made for the restrictions imposed by downcomers, structural members and fittings such as sootblower sleeves.

METHODS OF SUPPORT

For most designs of bent-tube boilers, the weight of the pressure parts, and the included water, is carried by the water-drum saddles and waterwall header saddles. Economizers and tubular-type air heaters are generally supported by the boiler casing, although for some of the higher powered ships, it has been expedient to locate the heat-recovery unit apart from the boiler, where the ship structure provides support. Such an arrangement may be necessary to obtain a better layout of the breeching when there is a narrow fidley which limits the space directly above the boiler. The Ljungstrom air heater is usually located on a deck or platform above the boiler with the ship structure providing support. It is customary, however, for the boiler casing to support the steam air heater.

For some types of boilers, the casing structure must also support the pressure parts, and this requires that heavier structurals be included at the points of loading. The sectional-header-type boiler has column-type supports built into each corner of the casing, as described earlier.

The loadings from connecting piping, particularly main-steam piping, can produce excessive stresses in the boiler connections. According to accepted procedure, the boiler manufacturer specifies the maximum allowable forces and moments which can be taken by the connections, and the shipbuilder designs the piping to stay within the limits.

CONTROLS
AND INSTRUMENTATION

It is essential that the shipboard boiler plant have adequate instruments to enable the operating personnel to raise steam, maintain design conditions for steady steaming, secure the boiler units and to detect promptly malfunctions and failures. It is customary to have most boiler instruments situated on a gage board which also contains the combustion and feedwater controls. Duplicate instruments for principal variables are provided at the main throttle station gage board.

Shipboard boiler controls can properly be classified into two basic groups: controls of the type which regulate continuously and those of the type which act to perform a prescribed operation when a limiting condition has been exceeded.

Regulating-type controls include those for

- combustion
- boiler-water level
- fuel-oil temperature
- fuel-oil viscosity
- blowdown
- superheat temperature

Combustion controls of the pneumatic or electric types are widely used for merchant-type ships, while naval vessels use pneumatic controls exclusively. Different systems that are available offer varying degrees of automatic control. Generally, the combustion-control system maintains constant steam pressure by controlling the flow of air and oil to the boiler. The more advanced combustion controls transmit the air and oil loadings simultaneously but with a slight lag between air and oil, so that with an increasing boiler load, the air will lead the oil, and on a decrease in boiler load, the oil will lead the air. Such an arrangement makes it possible to minimize the emission of smoke during maneuvering.

In years past, many ships were manufactured with feedwater-regulator control systems operating solely as a function of drum water level. As boiler steam conditions and evaporation rates were advanced to meet the requirements of higher powered propulsion plants, it was found necessary to have a two-element control. In this type, impulses of drum water level and steam flow are combined to give a better response during maneuvering conditions. The two-element system is installed on many cargo ships and has been proven as a reliable system.

Some types of ships have three-element-type feedwater controls. In the three-element system, drum level, feedwater flow and steam flow are measured and transmitted to the regulating valve in the feed line. In this system the relative difference in flow between steam flow from the boiler and feedwater flow to the boiler is used as an impulse for a greater degree of control.

There are many controls which serve to operate or present a warning signal when a dangerous condition is approached. Controls of this type include

- high water-level alarm
- low water-level alarm
- low stack-temperature alarm, and
- fuel-oil shutoff for forced-draft fan failure

COMMON ATTRIBUTES OF MARINE AND STATIONARY DESIGN PRACTICE

The special considerations required for the design of marine boilers have been discussed in this chapter. Many relate to the differences in operating conditions between land and marine practice. For example, the output of a marine power plant is basically a function of the speed and the displacement of a ship, and there is no exact counterpart to this in industrial or utility power plants.

It is important to realize, however, that the same fundamentals apply to both marine and land power-plant practices. Where common problems have materialized, as in the need for developing improved firing methods, similar solutions have been found and applied in both areas. On the other hand, space and height limitations are of primary concern to the marine-boiler designer.

Marine boilers operate successfully at very much higher heat release rates and smaller box volumes than field-erected stationary boilers. This is partly accounted for by the nature of marine power-plant operation. For one thing, feedwater is of high quality because at sea evaporators furnish makeup. In addition, two or more boilers are generally installed, and although one will operate at rated capacity while the ship is at sea, at least one can be shut down for inspection and maintenance while in port. This is in marked contrast to the operating conditions in some types of industrial and utility power plants which have what amounts to an almost continuous base load. Under these conditions there are rarely periods of low-load demand, and boilers may be operated for sustained periods of a year or longer between shutdowns for inspection and maintenance.

REFERENCES

1. Robert F. Latham, *Naval Boilers*. Annapolis, Md.: U.S. Naval Institute, 1956.

2. Otto de Lorenzi, editor, *Combustion Engineering: A Reference Book on Fuel Burning and Steam Generation.* New York, Combustion Engineering Company, Inc., 1947.
   See the revised edition, 1966 edited by Glenn R. Fryling and published by Combustion Engineering, Inc.

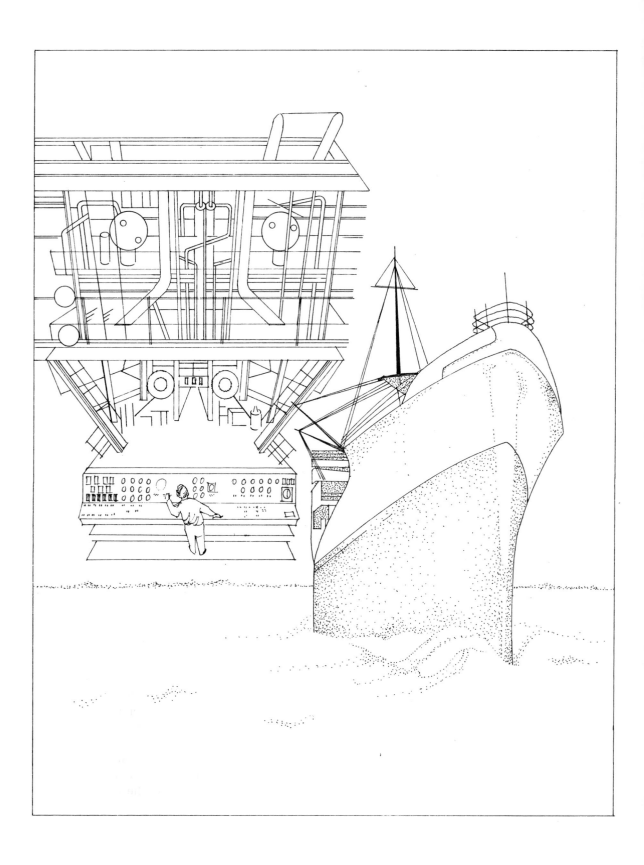

CHAPTER 10

Metallurgy and Materials

The aim of the designer of a large steam-generating unit is to use materials and fabricating methods in the most economical way to produce a unit that will perform properly for its planned useful life. Achieving these objectives requires a fundamental knowledge of material properties and behavior under a wide range of manufacturing and service conditions.

With only a few exceptions, steel is the material used in the construction of pressure parts and support members for boilers. Selection of the appropriate type of steel involves the following considerations:

■ the degree of difficulty or ease with which a particular material can be fabricated or welded

■ mechanical properties of the material such as strength (including tensile, yield, fatigue creep, and creep-rupture strengths), ductility, and toughness

■ compatibility with the expected service environment

■ effect of fabrication practices on mechanical and corrosion-resistance properties

■ possible degradation of properties caused by long-time service exposure.

Because these material-related considerations are so fundamental to both basic design and details of construction, there needs to be a close interaction between the designer and such material-performance disciplines as metallurgical, corrosion, welding, and materials engineering. All available materials data evolved through experience and research must be used in order to properly select materials and to specify construction details, fabrication procedures, destructive and nondestructive tests, and operating limits and controls necessary for satisfactory service.

This chapter presents some of the many considerations relating to the selection of materials and their operation in service, and describes typical field-service difficulties, all of which demonstrate the importance of a knowledge of metallurgy and materials to the boiler designer and operator.

SPECIFICATIONS AND CODES

The first boiler explosion took place around 1700 in a British mine in which a primitive steam-operated pump had been installed. Over the next 100 years, there was increased use of boilers in stationary installations, but it was the loss of life resulting from marine boiler explosions in the early 1800's that led to a pioneering American investigation by the Franklin Institute of Pennsylvania in 1830.

Many state laws subsequently were enacted to regulate boiler construction and operation, but not until the period 1911–1914 did the *ASME* Boiler Code develop.[1] Originating basically as a safety code to prevent boiler explosions, the *ASME* Code today promotes the acceptance of properly designed equipment on a national and international basis by assisting in the standardization of safety rules.

As formally adopted in 1915 and since administered by the ASME, the Code included many of the earlier regulations and resolved many of the conflicts in the rules. Since that time, a majority of the American states, as well as the Canadian provinces, have adopted boiler laws which make the *ASME* Boiler and Pressure Vessel Code the basis of their legal requirements. The rules of the *ASME* Code are kept up to date by continuing review of the Boiler and Pressure Vessel Committee, a group representing a balance of material suppliers, fabricators, users, insurers, and enforcement jurisdictions. This group sponsors regular revisions of the Code to keep up with technical advancements and responds to questions of interpretation of the rules.

In America, administration of code requirements is the responsibility of the individual state in which the boiler is to be installed, and the National Board of Boiler and Pressure Vessel Inspectors coordinates this effort.

Another technical group, the American Society for Testing and Materials (ASTM), incorporated in 1902, prepares and publishes specifications for purchase, testing, and examination of a variety of materials. This activity, which is directly related to the Society objective of promoting knowledge of engineering materials, is carried on through committees which include representatives of producers, fabricators and consumers.[2] Similarly, Committees of the American Welding Society write specifications for welding consumables.

Such specifications are widely used to procure and acceptance-test materials to meet defined levels of quality, thereby promoting both safety and economy. Groups such as the ASME Boiler and Pressure Vessel Committee also use these materials specifications, either as written or with modifications, to establish recognized grades of materials applying to their code rules for design, allowable stresses, fabrication methods, and inspection.

The American National Standards Institute (ANSI) publishes a variety of standards, many of which apply to boiler and pressure vessel construction or related uses. Standards such as ANSI B31.1 (Code for Pressure Piping), the ANSI B16.5 (Steel Pipe Flanges and Flanged Fittings) and ANSI B16.34 (Steel Valves) are frequently used. Several agencies of the United States government also publish codes and specifications for certain equipment used in their power plants and other facilities.

A basic limitation of all codes is that their rules must be expressed in sufficiently general terms to cover a wide range of applications. Because they only define reasonable minimum standards, there are sure to arise cases in which a power-plant designer must make further investigation and exercise additional effort. A great variety of supplementary information is available from publications of the various engineering societies and from technical bulletins of equipment suppliers.

MATERIALS OF CONSTRUCTION

Fossil boiler equipment in electric-generating service operates at high pressures and temperatures, generally between 2000 and 4000 psig, and 1005° and 1055°F, at the primary-steam outlet. The material grades listed in Table I are widely used in boilers designed in North America; there are extensive data and both shop and field experience with these ferritic and austenitic steels.

RAW MATERIAL FORMS

The product forms of steel available to the designer include plates and sheets, forgings, castings, seamless and welded tubing and piping, and rolled and extruded shapes. All are limited in size by the facilities and capabilities of the various material suppliers. Table I indicates several product forms with specifications covering the procurement from the *ASME*

B&PV Code, Section II, Materials, and from the ASTM specifications.

PLATES

Plates are used in the fabrication of boiler drums and plate-formed headers. The plates used to fabricate the shell and heads of these drums are as thick as 8 inches. Boiler drums are made of carbon-steel plate, usually either SA-515 Grade 70 or SA-299.

During the plate-rolling process in the producing steel mill, discontinuities and heterogeneities in the ingot are elongated in the direction of rolling. Because of this, plates may exhibit what is called directional or anisotropic properties and may be weaker when tensile tested *across* the thickness than when tested parallel or transverse to the direction of rolling. These directional discontinuities are generally not harmful except when they are large enough in size to affect heat transfer or are excessive in quantity so as to affect weldability. The customary practice for heavy plates used in boiler applications is to apply selective magnetic-particle and ultrasonic examinations to determine that the material is free of excessive discontinuities in areas where welding will be performed. See Chapter 18, "Steam Generator Manufacturing" for details on drum fabrication and testing.

TUBING

Steam is generated, superheated, and reheated in steel tubing, commonly between 1½ and 3 in. outside diameter. Large units may require as much as 300 miles of such tubing. The tubing is designed to last the life of the unit (up to 30 or more years) even though, in the case of superheated-steam tubing or power-plant piping, it is operated at a visibly "red-hot" temperature sometimes above 1100°F.

From the standpoint of geometrical shape and physical construction, there is no essential difference between pipe and tubing. Pipe sizes are generally designated by their nominal inside diameter for a particular type of service. Tubes, by contrast, are usually specified in terms of outside diameter and minimum wall thickness.

Pipe sizes and wall thickness are standardized with consideration of threading ends for joining together lengths with such fittings as flanges, nipples, valves, tees and the like. Such fittings are generally not installed with tubing. Where pressure-tight connections must be made, tubes are welded together, or their ends are expanded into tube sheets.

Selection of the material used depends upon the actual metal temperature to be sustained. The steam-generation tubes are primarily of carbon-steel material in recirculation-type subcritical-pressure units. In low-temperature regions the superheater and reheater tubing is also of carbon-steel analysis. As steam temperature increases to the outlet value, selection then progresses through carbon-molybdenum steel, then low chromium-molybdenum steel, intermediate chromium-molybdenum steel, and finally austenitic stainless steel, depending upon the design metal temperatures in the various areas. Austenitic stainless steel contains sufficient amounts of such alloying elements as nickel and chromium to retain austenite, a solid solution of carbon in gamma iron.

For many years, Grades TP 321 and TP 321H austenitic stainless steel had been used for high-temperature service. But changes in the *ASME* Boiler Code allowable stresses has favored Grades TP 304H and TP 347H, with these latter grades most widely used at present. Although Grade TP 316H is seldom used in the tubing portions of the superheater, it has been and will continue to be used when austenitic stainless piping and headers are required for steam temperatures of 1100°F and higher.

FORGINGS

Boiler drums and similar vessels may use forgings for reinforcing rings around openings and nozzles; some moderately sized high-pressure vessels are made entirely by forging. In most cases, the largest opening required for a boiler drum is an access opening of about 16 in. inside diameter which is reinforced by a forging welded to the drum head. Forgings are also used for fittings, valves and flanges.

CASTINGS

Castings have not been widely used as boiler pressure parts except in special applications such as valve or pump bodies, where the relative ease in forming thick-walled spherical and other special shapes has been an advantage. Techniques in casting steel have improved, supported by developments in nondestructive testing such as radiography and ultrasonic examination. Some parts and attachments in

boiler service are exposed to high temperatures approaching the local gas temperature. Heat-resistant alloys such as 25% Cr –12% Ni (AISI Grade TP 309) are required for such items. As is common in many industry publications, steel of this type will be referred to throughout this chapter without the percentage qualifier as 25 Cr –12 Ni. Many of these parts are cast, but forgings and plate have also been used.

Castings are also advantageous in such boiler

Table I. Materials Used in Boiler Construction

ALLOY	Product Form	ASME or ASTM Spec.	Grade	Minimum Tensile Strength ksi	Minimum Yield Strength	C	Mn	P	S	Si	Ni	Cr	Mo
Carbon Steel Low-Strength	Tubes	SA-192	...	(47)	(26)	0.06–0.18	0.27–0.63	0.048	0.058	0.25	...	...	...
	Tubes (ERW)	SA-178	A	...	...	0.06–0.18	0.27–0.63	0.050	0.060	...	...	...	...
	Tubes (ERW)	SA-226	...	(47)	(26)	0.06–0.18	0.27–0.68	0.050	0.060	...	...	...	...
Intermediate Strength	Tubes	SA-210	A-1	60	37	0.27	0.93	0.048	0.058	0.10 Min	...	...	...
	Tubes (ERW)	SA-178	C	60	37	0.35	0.30	0.050	0.060	...	...	...	...
	Pipe	SA-106	B	60	35	0.30	0.29–1.06	0.048	0.058	0.10 Min	...	...	...
	Castings (b)	SA-216	WCA	60	30	0.25	0.70	0.040	0.045	0.60	...	...	...
	Structural Shapes	A36	...	58	36	0.26	...	0.040	0.05	...			
High Strength	Pipe	SA-106	C	70	40	0.35	0.29–1.06	0.048	0.058	0.10 Min	...	...	...
	Plate	SA-299	...	75	40	0.30	0.86–1.55	0.035	0.040	0.13–0.33	...	...	...
	Plate	SA-515	70	70	38	0.35	0.90	0.035	0.04	0.13–0.33	...	...	...
	Forging	SA-105	...	70	36	0.35	0.60–1.05	0.040	0.050	0.35	...	...	...
	Casting (b)	SA-216	WCB	70	36	0.30	1.00	0.040	0.045	0.60	...	...	...
FERRITIC ALLOYS C–0.5 Mo	Tubes	SA-209	T1	55	30	0.10–0.20	0.30–0.80	0.045	0.045	0.10–0.50	...	...	0.44–0.65
1 Cr–0.5 Mo	Forging	SA-336	F12	70	40	0.10–0.20	0.30–0.80	0.040	0.040	0.10–0.60	...	0.80–1.10	0.45–0.65
	Tubes	SA-213	T12	60	30	0.15	0.30–0.61	0.045	0.045	0.50	...	0.80–1.25	0.44–0.65
	Pipe	SA-335	P12	60	30	0.15	0.30–0.61	0.045	0.045	0.50	...	0.80–1.25	0.44–0.65
	Plate	SA-387	12 Cl 2	65	40	0.17	0.36–0.69	0.035	0.040	0.13–0.32	...	0.74–1.21	0.40–0.65
	Forging	SA-182	F12	70	40	0.10–0.20	0.30–0.80	0.040	0.040	0.10–0.60	...	0.80–1.25	0.44–0.65
1.25 Cr–0.5 Mo	Tubes	SA-213	T11	60	30	0.15	0.30–0.60	0.030	0.030	0.50–1.00	...	1.00–1.50	0.44–0.65
	Pipe	SA-335	P11	60	30	0.15	0.30–0.60	0.030	0.030	0.50–1.00	...	1.00–1.50	0.44–0.65
	Plate	SA-387	11 Cl 2	75	45	0.17	0.36–0.69	0.035	0.040	0.44–0.86	...	0.94–1.56	0.40–0.70
	Forging	SA-182	F11	70	40	0.10–0.20	0.30–0.80	0.040	0.040	0.50–1.00	...	1.00–1.50	0.44–0.65
	Casting (b)	SA-217	WC6	70	40	0.20	0.50–0.80	0.040	0.045	0.60	...	1.00–1.50	0.45–0.65

components as stokers and pulverizers where parts can be made to desired shapes with little or no machining. Composition of the iron or low-alloy steel may be varied to match the severity of the specific temperature service. For example, bases for bowl mills are gray cast iron because of its excellent vibration-damping characteristics. In other parts of pulverizers, ductile-iron castings and steel castings are used. Where wear resistance is a major re-quirement, special alloy iron castings and forgings of hard, abrasion-resistant materials are available for liners, grinding rings, rolls and other parts.

STRUCTURAL MATERIALS

A considerable amount of steel in structural and sheet form is used for support and gas-enclosure purposes. The basis of selecting the appropriate steel involves design consid-

---

Table I. **Materials Used in Boiler Construction — *Continued***

ALLOY	Product Form	ASME or ASTM Spec.	Grade	Minimum Tensile Strength ksi	Minimum Yield Strength ksi	C	Mn	P	S	Si	Ni	Cr	Mo
2.25 Cr–1 Mo	Tubes	SA-213	T22	60	30	0.15	0.30–0.60	0.030	0.030	0.50	...	1.90–2.60	0.87–1.13
	Pipe	SA-335	P22	60	30	0.15	0.30–0.60	0.030	0.030	0.50	...	1.90–2.60	0.87–1.13
	Plate	SA-387	22 Cl 1	60 (c)	30 (c)	0.17	0.27–0.63	0.035	0.035	0.50	...	1.88–2.62	0.85–1.15
		SA-387	Cl 2	75 (d)	45 (d)								
	Forging	SA-182	F22	75	45	0.15	0.30–0.60	0.040	0.040	0.50	...	2.00–2.50	0.87–1.13
	Casting (b)	SA-217	WC9	70	40	0.18	0.40–0.70	0.040	0.045	0.60	...	2.00–2.75	0.90–1.20
5 Cr–0.5 Mo	Tubes	SA-213	T5	60	30	0.15	0.30–0.60	0.030	0.030	0.50	...	4.00–6.00	0.45–0.65
9 Cr–1 Mo	Tubes	SA-213	T9	60	30	0.15	0.30–0.60	0.030	0.030	0.25–1.00	...	8.00–10.00	0.90–1.10
AUSTENITIC STAINLESS ALLOYS 18 Cr–8 Ni	Tubes	SA-213	TP 304H	75	30	0.04–0.10	2.00	0.040	0.030	0.75	8.00–11.00	18.00–20.00	...
	Pipe	SA-376	TP 304H	75	30	0.04–0.10	2.00	0.040	0.030	0.75	8.00–11.00	18.00–20.00	...
	Plate	SA-240	304	75	30	0.08	2.00	0.045	0.035	1.00	8.00–10.50	18.00–20.00	...
		SA-240	304H	75	30	0.04–0.10	2.00	0.045	0.030	1.00	8.00–12.00	18.00–20.00	...
	Forging	SA-182	F304H	75	30	0.04–0.10	2.00	0.040	0.030	1.00	8.00–11.00	18.00–20.00	...
18 Cr–10 Ni–Ti	Tubes (e)	SA-213	TP 321H	75	30	0.04–0.10	2.00	0.040	0.030	0.75	9.00–13.00	17.00–20.00	...
18 Cr–10 Ni–Cb	Tubes (f)	SA-213	TP 347H	75	30	0.04–0.10	2.00	0.040	0.030	0.75	9.00–13.00	17.00–20.00	...
16 Cr–12 Ni–2 Mo	Tubes	SA-213	TP 316H	75	30	0.04–0.10	2.00	0.040	0.030	0.75	11.00–14.00	16.00–18.00	2.00–3.00
	Pipe	SA-376	TP 316H	75	30	0.04–0.10	2.00	0.040	0.030	0.75	11.00–14.00	16.00–18.00	2.00–3.00
	Forging	SA-182	F316H	75	30	0.04–0.10	2.00	0.040	0.030	1.00	10.00–14.00	16.00–18.00	
	Plate	SA-240	316H	75	30	0.04–0.10	2.00	0.045	0.030	1.00	10.00–14.00	16.00–18.00	2.00–3.00
	Structural										10.00–14.00	16.00–18.00	2.00–3.00
	Sheet	A167	316L	70	25	0.03	2.00	0.045	0.03	1.00			
25 Cr–12 Ni	Casting	SA-351	CH20	70	30	0.20	1.50	0.040	0.040	2.00	12.00–15.00	22.00–26.00	

(a) Single values shown are maximums.
(b) Residual elements not to exceed 1.00%.
(c) Annealed.
(d) Normalized.
(e) Titanium content not less than four times carbon content and not more than 0.60%.
(f) Cb + Ta not less than eight times the carbon content and not more than 1.00%.

erations similar to those used for pressure-containing service.

Generally, large utility boilers are suspended from large girders at the top of the unit to allow the unit to expand downward with an increase in temperature. Supporting extremely heavy loads, the girders operate at ambient temperatures which may be quite low, say −40°F. Therefore, they must be designed and fabricated to exhibit adequate toughness for resistance to brittle fracture. The precautions described in the later section on heat treatment are applicable to these structures as they are to the pressure vessels.

In some instances, as with flue-gas scrubber systems, compatibility with a corrosive service environment is of critical importance to the selection of the appropriate grade of steel.

WELD METALS

The metals used in welding drums, headers, tubing, ducts and other platework must be designed to exhibit properties compatible with the base metals. The composition of the weld filler metals and fluxes, when these are required, must be tailored to each different welding process used in the shop and field.

METALLURGICAL FUNDAMENTALS[3]

For purpose of classification, the science of metallurgy is generally divided into two fields:

process metallurgy, the science of obtaining metals from their ores, and physical metallurgy, the science concerned with the physical and mechanical characteristics of metal and alloys. These fields, in turn, are part of the basic sciences of chemistry and physics involving the study of the structures of atoms—their sizes and forces of attraction and the arrangements of these atoms in forming molecular structures, grain structures, and grain boundaries of multicrystalline materials.

PHASE DIAGRAMS

Some metals used for engineering purposes are commercially pure. This is true of copper for electrical wiring. Deliberately combining elements to form an alloy can enhance mechanical or physical properties. Some combinations result in a single-phase, solid-solution alloy. It is called single phase because the atoms are dissolved in the structure such that visual, microscopic and X-ray observations reveal a single crystal structure. Such a solid solution most readily forms when the two components are similar in atomic size and in electronic structure. The distribution of the atoms may be random (Fig. 1), ordered (Fig. 2), or interstitial (Fig. 3).

Element combinations may result, however, in a mixture of two or more phases. Fig. 4 shows a two-phase structure of sigma phase in Grade TP 321 austenitic material. Sigma phase is a hard and brittle intermetallic compound of var-

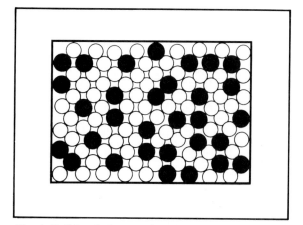

Fig. 1 Solid-solution random distribution of atoms

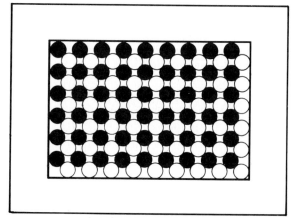

Fig. 2 Solid-solution ordered distribution of atoms

iable composition that adversely affects the room-temperature ductility of stainless steel.

Fig. 5 shows a two-phase structure of pearlite (alternate lamellae of cementite and ferrite) and ferrite (carbon steel SA-192 of Table I). Cementite is a compound of iron and carbon known as iron carbide of the approximate formula Fe_3C, characterized by an orthorhombic crystal structure; ferrite is a solid solution in which alpha iron is a solvent, characterized by a body-centered cubic crystal structure.

The phase relationships depend upon temperature. Fig. 6 shows a phase diagram for a simple system of lead and tin at equilibrium conditions. This diagram can be used as a map to determine the phases present at any particular temperature and composition. For example, at 50 percent tin and 212°F, the phase diagram indicates two solid phases. Alpha is a solid solution of lead with some dissolved tin; beta is almost pure tin with very little dissolved lead. At about 400°F, an alloy of 10 percent tin and 90 percent lead lies in an area which is entirely in the alpha phase. It is a solid solution of lead with some tin dissolved in it. At the same temperature, but for 30 percent tin and 70 percent lead, the phase diagram indicates a mixture of liquid and solid solution. If this latter composition were heated to a temperature of 575°F, it would become all liquid.

The phase fields in equilibrium diagrams, of course, depend on the particular alloy systems. When copper and nickel are mixed the phase diagram is as shown in Fig. 7. This phase diagram is comparatively simple, as only two phases are present. In the lower part of the diagram, all compositions form only one solid solution and therefore only one crystal structure.

Fig. 8 shows a portion of the phase diagram for the iron-carbon system. The phase relations for a ternary alloy become more complex as shown for an iron-carbon-chromium alloy in Fig. 9. Such phase relationships are used in regulating heat treatments in alloys.

T-T-T CURVES

The phase relations such as shown in Figs. 6, 8 and 9 are representative of equilibrium conditions obtained as a result of slow heating, slow

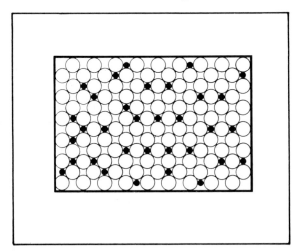

Fig. 3 Interstitial distribution of atoms in solid solution of carbon in iron (face-centered cubic structure)

Fig.4 Two-phase structure of sigma phase in austenite Grade TP 321 material at 500X. Ten-percent potassium hydroxide etch, one half second

cooling and long time at temperature. Time is required for change from one phase to another. Energy change is involved. Reaction rates are usually faster at higher temperatures except near the temperature of transformation from one phase to another where extra energy is required to nucleate a new phase.

Temperature-time-transformation curves (T-T-T) exemplify reaction rates for phase changes. The Fig. 10 T-T-T curve is for a steel of 0.8 percent carbon content shown in the Fig. 8 equilibrium diagram. It can be seen that rapidly cooling this steel to low temperature allows the gamma phase (austenitic material) to be present down to low temperature for a considerable time period before transformation occurs. The transformation product at this low temperature differs from what it would be if transformation occurred at a higher temperature, and is of higher hardness and strength with sufficiently high carbon content. This trans-

formation product is a hard material called martensite. Such a phenomenon is one of the basic methods of varying properties of steel by heat treatment. Each alloy subject to phase changes with temperature change exhibits a characteristic T-T-T curve.

GRAIN STRUCTURE

A grain is a single crystal usually without a regular external crystalline shape. In a solid, the presence of surrounding grains usually controls its shape. Within any particular grain, all of the atoms are arranged in one pattern, characterized by the unit cell. But at the grain boundary between two adjacent grains, there is a transition zone not directly aligned with either grain. Fig. 11 shows this transition zone.

When a metal is observed under a microscope, although the individual atoms can-

Fig. 6 Equilibrium diagram for a simple system of lead and tin

Fig. 5 Two-phase structure of pearlite and ferrite in low carbon steel at 500X. Two-percent nital etch

Fig. 7 Simple two-phase equilibrium diagram of nickel and copper

not be seen, the grain boundaries can be readily located if the metal has been smoothly polished to a mirrorlike surface and etched with an acid. The grain boundaries will be attacked differently from the body of the grain and become visible. Different phases will also become visible. The grain boundaries of the single-phase austenitic alloy (Fig. 12) shows fine and coarse-grained material (ASTM A-213-TP 321).

Thermal treatment can regulate the grain size. An increase in temperature causes increased thermal vibration of the atoms. This vibration facilitates transfer of atoms across the grain boundary from small to large grains. A subsequent decrease in temperature slows or stops the process, but does not reverse it. Grains may grow through mechanical working, by the use of heat treatment, through phase changes, or a combination of these methods. The only way to refine the grain size is to distort, break, or remove the grains which have grown and start new grains. The process depends upon the characteristics of the particular alloy involved. Grain growth will occur only above certain temperatures and depends upon time at temperature. This temperature may be quite low with some materials which have been critically cold-worked.

The ASTM has standardized a grain-size index in which the grain-size number, n, is obtained as follows.

$$N = 2^{n-1}$$

(1)

where N is the number of grains observed per square inch at a linear magnification of 100X. For most metals, the grain size ranges from number one to number eight, number one being a large grain and number eight a small grain.

Because the properties of metals vary greatly depending upon grain size, proper control must be exercised.

HARDENABILITY

As discussed previously in the section on T-T-T curves, plain carbon steel is hardened by quenching in water to cool the piece rapidly, thereby avoiding transformation at the fastest reaction rate temperature of 1000°F ("nose" of Fig. 10 T-T-T curve). This is possible if the thickness of material is light enough to cool completely at the required rate. But a heavy

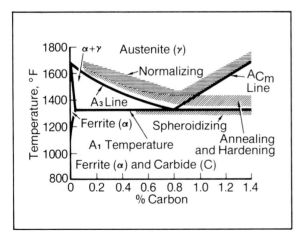

Fig. 8 A portion of the iron-carbon phase diagram showing temperature of importance to the heat treatment of carbon steel

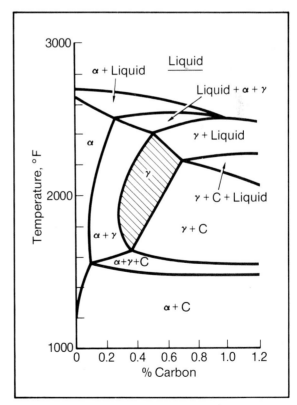

Fig. 9 Iron-chromium-carbon alloy phase diagram (15% chromium)

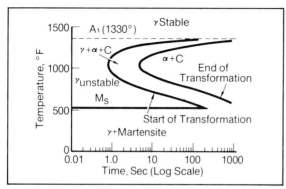

Fig. 10 Time-temperature-transformation (T-T-T) curves for steel in Fig. 8 with 0.8 percent of carbon (eutectoid)

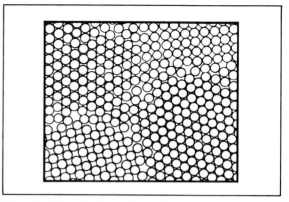

Fig. 11 Atomic transition at grain boundary between two grains

thickness piece cannot be cooled fast enough at the center of the thickness, and transformation will take place more rapidly and at a higher temperature at the center. This results in a softer transformation product.

Alloy additions to this steel retard the transformation rate (shift the curve of Fig. 10 to the right) and allow hardening to greater depths. This also permits less severe quenching and results in lower thermal stress with reduced possibility of cracking. Highly alloyed steels may be hardened by air cooling. Because steels hardened to high values are also brittle as hardened, a reduction of hardness is generally accomplished by reheating to an intermediate temperature. This markedly improves toughness. This process is called tempering.

HEAT TREATMENT

Table II[4] helps to understand some of the processes whereby metallic structure can be changed through heat treatment. Thermal treatment can markedly affect ductility and toughness of base metal, weld metal, and heat-affected zones; the type of treatment is selected with knowledge of the material property needs during fabrication and in service.

Thermal treatment is often required to soften zones which become cold-worked in local areas during the forming operations. Whether such treatment is necessary depends on the degree of cold work, the likelihood of subsequent strain aging, and the potential for controlling the degree of cold work developed during processing.

Though careful handling of large parts can sometimes prevent the development of heavily cold-worked surface areas, this is not usual. And heavily cold-worked zones can act as crack starters, causing brittle failures below the nil ductility temperature. On a finished part, such zones can also serve as nuclei for starting cracks at low temperatures under shock conditions. Heat treatment minimizes this effect.

During fabrication, welds may require thermal treatment to eliminate cracking. Heavy plates of carbon steel (more than 5 in. thick) and lighter plates of low-alloy steels have been known to crack if allowed to cool to room temperature after welding. Steels such as these may require heat treatment before cooling from preheat temperatures. This treatment, which may be at a relatively low temperature (600° to 1000°F) for a short time, eliminates cracking. Necessary for certain structures, it is generally termed an *interstage* thermal treatment. This is because it is applied to individual parts of an assembly or after partial welding of subassemblies.

When processing steels for high-temperature operation, it is important to tailor the thermal treatment so that the material will remain stable during the service life. Such custom treatment will avoid the development of serious defects, such as "eyebrow" or "chain-type" graphitization (of carbon and carbon-molyb-

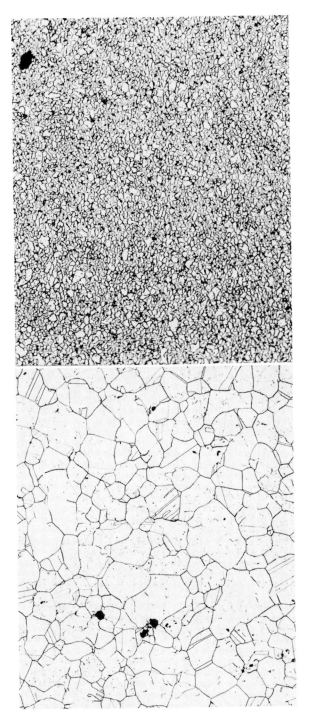

Fig. 12 Grain-size boundaries of single-phase austenitic alloy showing fine and coarse grained material (ASTM A-213-TP321). Grain-size number eight and smaller (top) and four to seven (bottom) at 100X. Sixty percent nitric acid etch

denum steels), strain-induced precipitation cracking (particularly possible with the stabilized austenitic steels), aging embrittlement, large grain size (which may cause excessively low ductility) and low stress-rupture strength or creep-rupture ductility.

Some steels are susceptible to very low ductility in a narrow range of elevated temperature. Such a condition, combined with the presence of stress, can produce sufficient strain to exhaust the ductility and result in cracking. This can occur with operation in the low-ductility temperature range, or in passing through the low-ductility temperature range during application of a postweld heat treatment. The latter is known as stress-relief cracking or reheat cracking. The characteristics of such susceptible materials must be known for proper handling.

With steels to be used at low temperature, thermal treatment may be advisable to ensure resistance to brittle fracture. Carbon steels improperly deoxidized are subject to loss of toughness and ductility by quench aging. If not corrected, this deficiency can result in failure during fabrication or operation. Small defects (such as cracks at arc strikes) can exhibit residual stresses as high as the yield point at the defect and may act as crack starters with additional loading. If thermally treated, such areas are generally relatively harmless. For some combinations of conditions, the use of careful nondestructive tests to prove freedom from macroscopic defects may allow the thermal treatment to be eliminated.

MECHANICAL PROPERTIES OF STEEL

Certain mechanical properties of steel affect its fabrication and service. Among these are tensile properties, hardness, toughness, fatigue strength, and high temperature characteristics.

TENSILE PROPERTIES

The standard tension test provides data on yield strength, tensile strength, and ductility. When metals are pulled (stressed) with a uni-

Table II. Heat-Treating Processes

Process	Example	Purpose	Procedure
Annealing	Cold-worked metals	To remove strain hardening[a] and increase ductility	Heat above recrystallization[b] temperature
Annealing	Steel	To soften	Heat into austenitic[c] range and slow cool
Normalizing	Steel	Homogenization and strain relief[a]	Heat into austentic range and air cool
Process annealing and stress-relieving	Steel	To soften and toughen	Heat close to, but below, the eutectoid[d] temperature
Spheroidizing	Steel	To soften and toughen	Heat for a sufficiently long time close to, but below, the eutectoid[d] temperature
Quenching	Steel	To harden	Quench from austenite to martensite[e]. (This is followed by tempering.)
Tempering	Quenched steel	To toughen	Heat briefly at low temperature
Austempering	Steel	To harden without developing brittle martensite	Quench from austenite to a low temperature below the nose[f] of the transformation curve, but above the martensite transformation temperature. Hold until transformation is complete.
Marquenching	Steel	To harden without quench cracking	Quench from austenite to a temperature below the nose of the transformation curve, but above the martensite transforming temperature. Hold until temperature has equalized. Cool slowly to martensite. (This is followed by tempering).
Solution treating	Stainless steel	To produce a single phase alloy	Heat above the solubility curve into a single phase area and quench to room temperature.
Age-hardening	Various ferrous and nonferrous alloys	To harden	Solution treat. Cool to provide supersaturation. Reheat to an intermediate temperature until the initial precipitation starts. Cool to surrounding temperatures.

[a] When a sufficient stress is applied to a metal such that the piece does not return to its original dimensions, the yield strength has been exceeded. Because most metals are weaker in shear than in pure tension, they yield by plastic shear or slip of one plane of atoms over another. This slip occurs most readily along planes containing the greatest number of atoms per unit of area. These parallel planes are more widely

separated than other planes. Plastic movement along these planes causes distortion of the planes because of restraint of surrounding metal and allows added amount of slip to occur less readily. This resultant increase in strength is called strain hardening.

[b] Because plastic deformation at low temperatures causes distorted crystal patterns, the tendency is for the atoms to return to a more perfect unrestrained condition. Heating to a higher temperature increases thermal vibration of the atoms which allows readjustment to take place. As such readjustment also results in decreased hardness, the temperature of marked softening is called the recrystallization temperature. Recrystallization temperature depends upon degree of plastic deformation (cold work), time at temperature, material, and material purity. Generally, it is between ⅓ and ½ of the melting temperature (degrees absolute). Plastic deformation at temperature below the recrystallization temperature is called cold working whereas above the recrystallization temperature is called hot working.

[c] A solid solution in which gamma iron is the solvent; characterized by a face-centered cubic crystal structure.

[d] See Fig. 8. Eutectoid temperature is 1330°F. Eutectoid carbon content is 0.8 percent.

[e] An unstable constituent is quenched steel, formed without diffusion and only during cooling below a certain temperature known as the M_s temperature (see Fig. 10). The structure is characterized by its acicular or needlelike appearance on the surface of a polished and etched specimen. Martensite is the hardest of the transformation products of austenite. Tetragonality of the crystal structure is observed when the carbon content is greater than about 0.5 percent.

[f] See Fig. 10. "Nose" of curve is at approximately 1000°F. The start of martensite transformation on cooling for this steel is approximately 500°F.

---

axial increasing load, the material stretches (strains). Diagrams such as Fig. 13 show the relationship between stress and strain for specific materials. With increasing load, the material strains elastically until it reaches the yield point. During this period of elastic behavior, there is no permanent deformation; strain is directly proportional to the stress. This relationship is described by Hooke's Law which states that stress equals strain multiplied by the modulus of elasticity (Young's Modulus) of the material.

Continuing to increase the loading beyond the yield point results in plastic strains and eventual breakage of the test specimen. Ductility is a measure of the amount of plastic deformation the steel will sustain before breaking. It is usually expressed as a percentage elongation or reduction in cross-sectional area of the test specimen. How much plastic strain a steel will exhibit is quite variable and is generally inversely related to the tensile strength of the material. High-strength steels typically will exhibit much less ductility than softer, lower-strength steels.

Because the true yield point is difficult to establish with any accuracy, most current tensile testing of steels involves the determination of yield strength rather than yield point. Yield strength, which can be easily established, is defined as the stress necessary to produce a specified value of plastic elongation, usually 0.1, 0.2, or 0.5 percent as measured over the gage length of the tensile specimen.

Most of the specifications covering the steels used in the construction of a boiler require room-temperature tensile testing with minimum values of tensile strength, yield strength and ductility specified. But for design purposes, the tensile and yield strength of each grade of steel used needs to be determined at temperatures up to the creep range of the grade. Various organizations including the producers and fabricators of steel perform such tests and the data from these tests are used by the *ASME* Boiler and Pressure Vessel Code to set maximum allowable stresses.

Some of the many product form specifications—most noticeably those for pipe and

Fig. 13 **Stress-strain curve for two steels with different strength and ductility.**

tube—require various deformation tests such as flattening, flaring, or bending. These additional tests of ductility provide evidence of the ability of the steel to withstand fabrication or installation operations such as bending, swaging and tube expansion.

HARDNESS

The hardness of a material is a measure of resistance to plastic deformation and is related to the tensile strength of the steel. It is also used as an indicator of the machinability and abrasion resistance of a steel. Usually, hardness is determined by Brinell, Rockwell, or Vickers tests in which a small ball or pyramid-shaped point is pressed into the surface of the metal with a specified force for a specified time. The size of the indentation is measured automatically or by microscope and is expressed as a hardness number. The smaller the indentation, the higher the hardness number.

The use of hardness testing is permitted in some material specifications to approximate tensile strength. ASTM Specification A-370 contains hardness-to-tensile-strength conversion charts for different groupings of steels. In some material specifications, particularly those in which the ductility of the steel is important to its workability, maximum hardness values are specified.

TOUGHNESS

Under most circumstances, steel can tolerate localized stresses above the yield point by plastically absorbing and redistributing these stresses. But under certain conditions, even steels having considerable ductility are subject to a brittle (cleavage) mode of failure when subjected to concentrated stresses at low temperatures. The property of toughness is the ability of a material to resist this failure.

Various impact tests evaluate the property of toughness. One of the more commonly used tests is the Charpy V-notch impact test. In this test, a swinging pendulum strikes a single blow to a notched horizontal specimen supported on both ends. The energy absorbed by the specimen is related to the height of rebound and is expressed as ft-lbs.

The mode of failure in the impact test changes from ductile (shear) to brittle (cleavage) as the temperature is lowered. The temperature range at which this occurs is called the transition range. Material within or below its transition temperature range may crack extensively if subjected to an impact load, or if construction details are such that localized yielding is prevented.

The transition temperature range depends upon the particular metal composition and melting practice as well as the subsequent working and heat treatment. For many types of carbon or low-alloy steels, the transition temperature may be as high as 70°F or above. The possibility of brittle fracture must be considered in the fabrication of materials (bending and forming in various manners), in testing the finished structure, and in any service involving operation below the transition temperature. Care in design, fabrication, inspection and, when necessary, field repair, is required to eliminate conditions which might promote brittle fracture.

Fig. 14 shows the impact strength versus temperature for a material having a high transition temperature. Also shown are the broken surfaces of the impact specimens in which the ductility variation with temperature of testing is obvious. The material tested at the lower temperature has broken in a cleavage fracture along crystallographic planes and shows a shiny-grain appearance which at one time led to the mistaken impression the material had crystallized. Actually, what appears in the figure is the progression from a brittle-cleavage fracture to a ductile-shear fracture as the temperature of testing is increased. Corrosion-resisting pressure vessels of this material may be successfully fabricated and used provided sufficient consideration is given to this property. The importance of the degree of stress-concentrating mechanical notch in this type material is shown in Fig. 15.

The examples given are for chromium-iron materials having a particularly high transition temperature. Steels used in boilers have transition temperatures considerably below that shown in the example. Metals to be stressed in operation at low temperatures are selected based upon these considerations and purchased to specified impact requirements.

Heat-treatable steels in the quenched and tempered condition may have considerably improved transition-temperature properties. High-nickel steels exhibit low transition temperatures. Austenitic stainless steels and metals such as copper and aluminum, in general, do not change abruptly in toughness as a function of temperature and may be used to temperatures as low as that liquefied air.

FATIGUE

The stress a material can withstand under repeated application and removal of load is less than that it can withstand under static conditions. The yield strength, which is a measure of static stress a material can sustain without appreciable permanent deformation, can be used as a guide in design only for material subjected to static loading. Dynamic, cyclic loading causes slip and cold-working in minute areas localized at grain boundaries and at stress-concentrating notches of various types.

As sufficient work-hardening develops, microscopic cracking develops and grows until complete fracture results. Fatigue strength is

the magnitude of a cyclic stress which a material can resist for a specified number of cycles before failure. But at sufficiently low stress levels, many materials can tolerate an almost infinite number of cycles. Fig. 16 shows the endurance limit for one material.

Areas of peak stress such as changes in section or stress-concentrating notches promote the localized concentration of cyclic strains. Fig. 17 shows the photoelastic distribution of stress in a welded waterwall tube panel when subjected to an in-plane tensile load. Fatigue evaluations of welded walls have included cyclic-loading testing of full-size panels under bending and in-plane loads. With such testing, endurance limits for the actual as-built component have been established.

Figs. 18 and 19 present an example of fatigue cracking. The cause of the crack was an unanticipated gas-flow-induced vibration of the superheater tube. Antivibration restraints have been applied to correct this type of problem.

HIGH-TEMPERATURE PROPERTIES

At temperatures exceeding about 650°F, most steels suffer a gradual decrease in tensile and yield strength. At still higher temperatures, the strain in a material is a function not

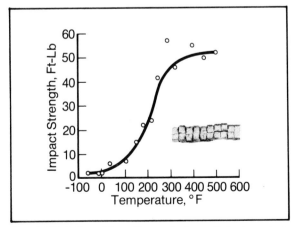

Fig. 14 Relationship of impact strength to temperature for a material having a high transition temperature. (16% Cr weld metal)

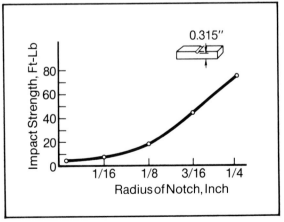

Fig. 15 Effect of radius of notch (shown by stress concentration) on impact values of 18 percent Cr weld metal

only of the applied stress but also of the time under stress at temperature. In this high-temperature range, the metal will deform (creep) continuously even at stresses much lower than the short-time yield strength. If held for sufficient time under these conditions, the material will rupture.

Because no way has been found to predict this behavior quantitatively from short-time tests, it is necessary to perform tests of creep and stress rupture at several stress levels, temperatures, and over time periods as long as possible. Such tests, and extrapolations as necessary, establish values of creep strength and stress-rupture strength. The creep strength of a metal at a certain temperature is the steady stress that produces a specified low rate of elongation. For long-time service, such as *ASME* Boiler Code applications, a creep rate of 0.01 percent in 1000 hours is used. The stress-rupture strength is the steady stress required at a particular temperature to cause rupture in a specified long period of time.

Fig. 20 illustrates how creep and rupture strengths for a 2¼ Cr-1 Mo steel are established from test data. Creep-rate data for 1000°, 1100° and 1200°F are plotted versus stress. The intersection of these data lines with that for 0.01 percent in 1,000 hours sets the respective creep strengths of 7,800 psi, 5,000 psi and 2,400 psi. The other curves show rupture life versus stress for the same three temperatures. Lines through these data are extrapolated to 100,000 hours to establish rupture strengths of 13,000 psi, 7,000 psi and 3,300 psi respectively.

Paragraph A-150 of Section I of the *ASME* Boiler and Pressure Code lists the following criteria for consideration by the Code Committee in establishing allowable stresses:

■ ¼ of the specified minimum tensile strength at room temperature

■ ¼ of the tensile strength at elevated temperatures

■ ⅔ of the specified minimum yield strength at room temperature

■ ⅔ of the yield strength at elevated temperatures.

Fig. 16 Endurance limit for a hot-worked bar stock

Fig. 17 Photoelastic pattern showing peak stress in welded waterwall tubes

Fig. 18 Fatigue crack in horizontal superheater tube at end of plate support members. Vibration in the length of tube to the right side of the spacer eventually caused the fatigue crack to initiate at the attachment and propagate circumferentially.

Fig. 19 **Through-the-wall nature of the Fig. 18 fatigue crack. Typical of fatigue, there is a single, tight transgranular crack.**

■ 100 percent of the stress to produce a creep rate of 0.01 percent in 1,000 hr

■ 67 percent of the average stress to produce rupture at the end of 100,000 hours, or 80 percent of the minimum stress for rupture at the end of 100,000 hours as determined from the extrapolated data, whichever is lower.

Fig. 21 applies these criteria to establish the allowable stress for a 2¼ Cr-1 Mo steel. For this material, item 1 controls up to 800°F. At 950°F and above, the creep strength and rupture strength, the fifth and sixth items, require a rather sharp decrease in the allowable stress.

The relative influence of the different criteria varies with materials as well as with temperature. Fig. 22 shows the effect of temperature on *ASME* Boiler Code allowable stresses for a number of alloys used for high-temperature service. The carbon steels begin to lose strength above 700°F, and by 850°F are down to about one-half their room-temperature values. The low-chromium ferritic alloys start to lose strength above 800°F and are down to half strength at about 1000°F. The austenitic stainless steels decline somewhat from room temperature to 1000°F because of reduction in yield strength; above 1000°F, creep and rupture strength cause a rapid decrease to half strength or less by 1200°F.

The high-temperature strength and ductility of steel may be strongly affected by grain size,

cold working, heat treatment and other variables. Material suppliers and equipment manufacturers must give careful consideration to these factors in their manufacturing and fabrication procedures.

CREEP AND FATIGUE INTERACTION

When metals are exposed to cyclic loadings while operating at temperatures within their creep range, creep effects can reduce fatigue life. Fig. 23 indicates how the fatigue behavior of a steel varies for different testing conditions at elevated temperature.[5] The introduction of

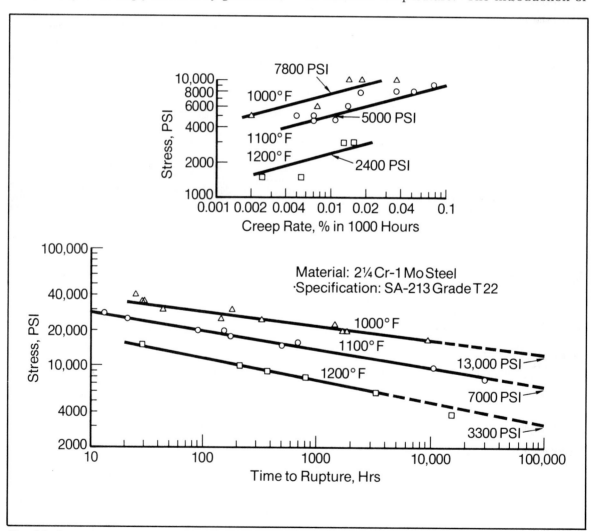

Fig. 20 **Creep rate (upper) and rupture strength (lower) for a 2¼ Cr-1 Mo steel**

periods of hold time at temperature, while under maximum strain, causes the slope of the curves to change considerably. The periods of hold time allow creep relaxation to occur to the detriment of fatigue life.

The problem of creep and fatigue interaction is complex both in the formulation of a realistic design basis consistent with proven past practice of successful cyclic operation within the creep range and in the obtaining of material-property data which can be used in design. Attention is being given to the subject worldwide. In the USA, organizations involved in cooperative research include the Pressure Vessel Research Committee, the Metal Properties Council and the ASME B&PV Committee.

DISSIMILAR WELDS

Fig. 24 is an example of cracking damage because of interaction between creep and fatigue.

Welds using Grade TP 309 austenitic stainless filler metal have been used to join ferritic tubes to austenitic stainless tubes. The austenitic steels have a coefficient of thermal expansion approximately 40 percent greater than the ferritic steels. This mismatch results in high shear strains at the interface between the austenitic filler metal and the ferritic tube. With cycling, these strains can cause intergranular cracking within the weaker ferritic material.

Field repairs of TP 309 dissimilar-metal welds are made by rewelding with nickel-base filler-metal welds. The nickel-base metals have a coefficient of thermal expansion similar to the ferritic steels, and the expansion mismatch strains imposed on the ferritic tube are significantly reduced. However, the nickel-base filler-metal welds, while giving better service performance than the TP 309 welds, are not totally free of interface cracking problems.

Fig. 21 Use of *ASME* Boiler Code criteria to establish allowable stress for a 2¼ Cr-1 Mo steel

Fig. 22 Effect of temperature on *ASME* Boiler Code allowable stresses for grades of steel tubing

There is some uncertainty as to whether the interface cracking associated with nickel-base filler metals is primarily a function of strain or metallurgical changes. Further research is required to provide an understanding of the factors that promote cracking, such as testing of full-size tubular specimens of various dissimilar metal welds under pressure and temperature cycling conditions (Fig. 25).

Fig. 26 shows another example of interaction cracking from creep and fatigue. Differences in thermal expansion of superheater terminal tubes which are welded to the outlet headers and seal welded at the furnace enclosure have caused circumferential cracking in the tubes at the toe of the tube-to-header weld. Strain cycling caused these cracks to initiate and propagate in a fatigue manner.

Note the similarities in appearance between this cracking and that described in the earlier discussion of fatigue and shown in Figs. 18 and 19. But there is a significant difference in the nature of these two cracks which occurred as a result of fatigue cycling. The vibration-induced crack is transgranular (across grains) which is typical of fatigue, but the cracking in the tube at the superheater outlet header is intergranular (along grain boundaries). Intergranular cracking is typical of that which occurs in longer-time creep or stress rupture, and low-cycle high-strain loading in the creep range will likely produce intergranular rather than transgranular cracking.

SERVICE EXPOSURE CONSIDERATIONS

Proper selection and usage of materials require knowledge of the expected service conditions and an understanding of how the material will behave under those conditions.

Dependent on its environment, material behavior can differ significantly. Austenitic stainless-steel tubes, for example, are widely used for steam service. In this service, essentially all of the common grades of austenitic stainless can be considered equally compatible with the service environment, and there is no concern about resistance to pitting or intergranular corrosive attack (see the subsection ''Sensitization'' later in this section). But in the aqueous environment of boiler flue-gas wet scrubbers, only grades of stainless steel containing molybdenum (Grades TP 316, TP 317 and so forth) can tolerate the corrosive environment without excessive pitting. (See Fig.

Fig. 23 **Effect of temperature and creep-relaxation hold time on number of cycles to failure. Material 2¼ Cr-1 Mo**

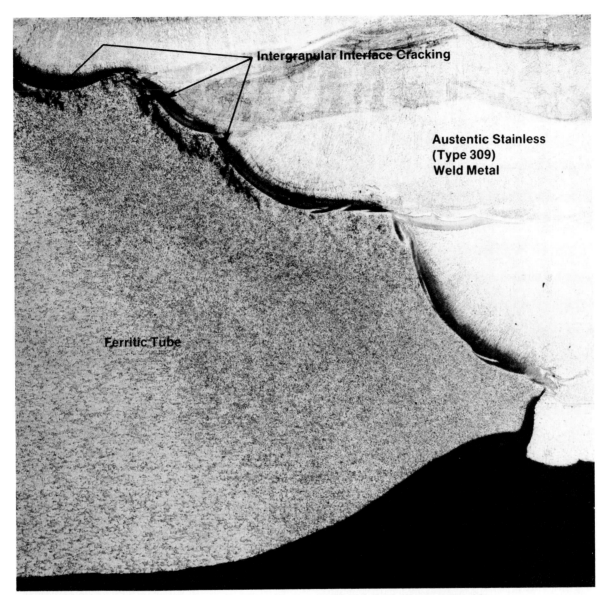

Fig. 24 **Typical interface cracking associated with Grade TP 309 dissimilar metal weld**

27.) Also, because of the potential for acidic aqueous conditions in the scrubber, grades of extra-low-carbon stainless (Grades TP 316L and TP 317L) are used to avoid the possibility of intergranular corrosive attack.

Although Grade TP 316L stainless is widely used in flue-gas wet scrubbers, austenitic stainless steels are not suitable for the heat-exchange surface which reheats the scrubbed gases to temperatures 25° to 40°F above the adiabatic saturation temperature. In this wet-to-dry service environment, austenitic stainless steels can and reportedly have experienced stress-corrosion cracking. (See "Stress-Corrosion Cracking," this chapter.) Because of this, C-E designers use carbon-steel tubes and fins for the reheaters in scrubber systems.

As the foregoing examples demonstrate, knowledge of the environment and its effect on the material is a key to the proper use of the material. The next section presents some of the service exposure conditions that affect the performance of boiler materials.

GRAPHITIZATION

At temperatures above 800°F, carbon steel is subject to graphitization; above 875°F, carbon-molybdenum steel is similarly affected. The carbon normally present in the steel in the form of carbides may transform over a long period of time to graphite. This transformation may take place preferentially along heat-affected zones of welds, or along stress lines, to form chain-type graphitization, an example of which is shown in Fig. 28.

Carbon-steel pipe and carbon-molybdenum pipe in long-time service, particularly when operated at temperatures well above 800°F and 875°F, respectively, have experienced numerous instances of chain-type graphitization resulting in failure or requiring repair or replacement.[6]

Because of these problems, C-E has for many years avoided the use of carbon molybdenum for piping components and has limited the use of carbon-steel pipe to 800°F. For higher temperature service, the use of steels containing one-half percent or more chromium eliminates the danger of graphitization.

Carbon-steel and carbon-molybdenum tubing has not shown a similar tendency to graphitize as has piping. The graphitization occasionally found in tubing is usually in the form of well-dispersed nodules (Fig. 28) which

Fig. 25 Thirty-two individual creep-rupture tubular specimens, each containing one or two dissimilar welds, before being inserted into furnace on the right. Specimens, which have been thermally aged, are exposed to internal pressures at temperatures somewhat higher than would be encountered in service and cycled, with a 3-day hold time at temperature, to simulate long-time service exposure.

do not weaken the steel. Carbon-steel and carbon-molybdenum tubing may, therefore, be used in applications when the temperatures reach 850°F and 900°F respectively.

RESISTANCE TO HIGH-TEMPERATURE OXIDATION AND CORROSION

Chromium is the most useful alloying element for imparting oxidation and corrosion resistance to steel. Fig. 29 shows the degree of oxidation scaling versus temperature for a number of steels with a range of chromium from 0 to 18 percent. Similarly, chromium additions improve resistance of a steel to molten-ash corrosion (see Chapter 3). Low levels of chromium, in the range of ½ to 2¼ percent, provide a useful improvement in high-temperature-corrosion resistance. Within this chromium range, high-temperature strength accompanies the trend of somewhat improved corrosion resistance.

For these reasons, there is widespread use of the family of low-chromium alloys, up to 2¼% Cr, for intermediate temperature-range appli-

Fig. 26 Intergranular creep and fatigue cracking at toe of tube-to-superheater outlet-header weld caused by repeated exposure to thermal expansion strains

Fig. 27 Difference in corrosion resistance between TP 304 (upper) and TP 316L (lower) in boiler flue-gas wet scrubber after identical exposure for two and one half years cations, where carbon steel and carbon molybdenum are not used because of their low high-temperature strength (see Fig. 22) and their tendencies to graphitize. The temperatures at which these alloy grades are used involve considerations of high-temperature strength and corrosion/oxidation resistance. For superheater and reheater tubes in the gas pass, alloy grades SA-213 T-11 (1¼% Cr) and T-22 (2¼% Cr) are limited by C-E to gas-side

surface temperatures of 1025°F and 1075°F, respectively. These temperatures, well below the point at which oxidation scaling is significant, were established based on reviews of external-wastage-rate data from units in service experiencing coal-ash corrosion. With these limits, excessive external corrosion metal loss is not expected even when coals with a corrosive tendency are burned.

Generally, the 2¼ Cr-1 Mo steel is the highest alloy used for pressure-part components outside of the gas pass because the metal has good strength and oxidation resistance at outlet steam temperatures between 1005°F and 1055°F. But because some gas-touched portions of the superheater and reheater are exposed to metal temperatures in excess of 1075°F, alloys with high-temperature strength and oxidation/corrosion resistance are needed. There has been some past use of tubing with 5 percent chromium, but these alloys did not provide a significant improvement in corrosion resistance and have lower high-temperature strength than the T-22 grade.

SA-213 T-9 (9 Cr-1 Mo) has been, and continues to be, used in some reheaters. The material has good oxidation/corrosion resistance

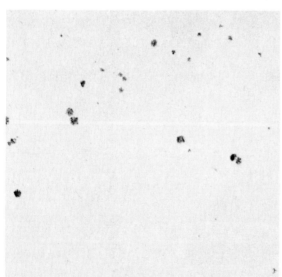

Fig. 28 **Examples of chain-type graphitization at 100X (upper) and random graphite nodules at 50X (lower). Unetched**

Fig. 29 **Amount of oxidation (scaling) of carbon, low-alloy, and stainless steels in 1000 hours in air at temperatures from 1100° to 1700°F**

and may be used to outside surface temperatures as high as 1175°F, but at these temperatures the high-temperature strength (ASME allowable mid-wall stresses) is quite low, less than that for the T-22 (2¼ Cr-1 Mo) grade.

Austenitic stainless steels (grades TP 304H and TP 347H) are used for most of the tubing operating at surface metal temperatures above 1075°F. Not only do these materials have excellent high-strength properties which are characteristic of austenite, but they also have excellent oxidation resistance because of their 18-percent (nominal composition) chromium content. But it is important to recognize that no tube alloy operating above 1000°F is immune to oil- or coal-ash corrosion. By virtue of their higher operating temperatures, the austenitic stainless steels will experience metal loss if there are molten ash deposits (see Chapter 3).

However, because molten coal-ash deposits do not exist at temperatures exceeding about 1300°F (see bell-shaped curve Fig. 11, Chapter 3, "Properties of Coal Ash"), materials for tube shields, spacer attachments, supports, baffles, and other nonpressure parts normally operating at temperatures above 1300°F can be used without excessive concern for corrosion. Experience has shown that oxidation behavior in normal boiler flue gas is similar to that in air. *Table III* shows the temperature levels at which oxidation scaling becomes significant for a number of alloy grades.

Currently, coal-ash corrosion is not as prevalent in boilers in the United States as it was in

the 1950's and 1960's. This, in part, relates to the fact that many of the coals being burned today are not particularly corrosive. Also, since the 1950's, most coal-fired utility units have been selected for 1005°F main steam temperature rather than 1055°F as was sometimes the case in the 1950's. However, the efficiency advantages of higher steam temperatures may make it desirable to return to 1050°F and higher steam cycles..In such cases, the ability to predict corrosiveness or to prevent it by coal-cleaning or additive techniques, as is discussed in Chapter 3, will be of importance to the selection, design and reliability of such units.

OXIDE SCALES AND EXFOLIATION

Oxides form on the outside surfaces of boiler components as a result of direct combination with oxygen in the air or in the flue gases. Oxidation also occurs in the internal wetted surfaces of the furnace walls and steam-touched surfaces of the superheater and reheater as a result of iron-water and iron-steam oxidation reactions.

Those oxide scales that form on boiler tube surfaces are thin and protective. In fact, the oxide that forms on wetted surfaces—magnetite—is critical to the compatibility of steel and boiler water. Because of the fundamental importance of magnetite, the half-joking description of a boiler as a thin layer of magnetite supported by steel has been quoted by many. Chapter 11, Water Technology, describes the boiler-water chemistry control necessary to maintain this protective layer.

Oxides forming on the steam sides of the superheater and reheater tubes inhibit oxidation by reducing the diffusion process. Oxidation rates decrease with time in a manner shown in Fig. 30. This formed-in-place oxide scale should not be confused with deposits (salt, debris or transported oxides deposit upon tube surfaces). Oxide scale that forms in-situ does not measurably affect heat transfer as deposits can. Fig. 31 shows a localized overheating blister caused by deposits. Under certain conditions, oxide scale that forms on the outside and inside surfaces of superheater and re-

Table III. Maximum Temperature Without Excessive Scaling*

Alloy Nominal Analysis	AISI Grade	Maximum Temp°F Without Excessive Scaling
17 Cr	430	1550
27 Cr	446	2000
18 Cr–8 Ni	304	1650
25 Cr–12 Ni	309	2000
25 Cr–20 Ni	310	2000

*ASTM, Data on Corrosion and Heat-Resistant Steels and Alloys—Wrought and Cast, ASTM, May, 1950.

heater tubes and pipes may break loose and exfoliate. Because of the conservative temperature limits on the usage of these steels adopted by manufacturers such as C-E, exfoliation does not present a problem of excessive metal loss which might lead to rupture of tubes or piping. However, the exfoliated oxide scale from the inside surfaces of ferritic tubes and pipes is a cause of solid particle erosion (SPE) damage in steam turbines. So the term *exfoliation*, as it is widely used in the steam-power-generation industry, is in connection with the concern for SPE caused by spalled steam-side oxides.

OXIDE SCALE ADHERENCE

In many instances, tubes removed from long-time service exhibit little or no exfoliation or poorly adhering scale. This is typical of most samples removed from superheaters. Conversely, ferritic reheater tubes frequently demonstrate severe exfoliation, or large areas of non-adhering scale. Figs: 32, 33, 34 and 35 show examples. Examinations of main and hot-reheat steam piping and final outlet headers indicate that these large diameter components tend to exfoliate significantly.

EFFECT OF TEMPERATURE AND SCALE THICKNESS

Although engineering intuition may suggest that exfoliation would tend to be more severe as temperatures and scale thickness increase, examinations of numerous ferritic tubes from service indicate that this is not the case. In fact, the exfoliation tendency seems to be greatest on the thinner scale. (Erosion damage to the turbines, of course, would be more severe with thicker scale. But precise knowledge as to the variables of importance to SPE, including the variable of steam temperature, is lacking.)

POSSIBLE CAUSES OF EXFOLIATION

Several explanations have been offered as possible causes of exfoliation. C-E investigators have postulated a thermal-quench explanation which appears to best fit the presently available facts. During start-up of reheat-type steam generators, there is no cooling steam

flow through the reheater. Gas temperatures are limited to 1000°F during start-up, and reheater tube temperatures will approach this limit. When steam is first admitted to the turbine and reheater, its temperature is significantly lower than that of the tubes, and the steam thermally quenches the scale. It appears that the quenching acts to separate the cylinder of internal scale from the tube and to promote separations along planes of weakness within the scale.

This thermal-quench explanation is consistent with the different exfoliation behavior of reheater and superheater tubes. It also fits well with the observation that thin scale tends to

Fig. 30 Oxidation metal loss versus time for 1¼ Cr-1 Mo steel in steam at 1100°F

Fig. 31 Internal deposits cause overheating, which often leads to blister-type failures; that is, the area of the superheater tube immediately under the deposit undergoes highly localized creep swelling and thinning.

Fig. 32 Severely exfoliated reheater tube (2¼ Cr-1 Mo) after 39,000 hours service. Maximum scale 9 mils

Fig. 33 Superheater tube (2¼ Cr-1 Mo) after 158,000 hours in service. Maximum scale 20 mils

Fig. 34 Tube cross section showing typical two-layer oxide structure adhering well to internal surface of superheater tube (tube base metal is the white portion) at 15X

Fig. 35 Tube cross section showing exfoliated oxides on reheater tube at 15X have a greater exfoliation tendency. Under equal thermal-quench conditions, the temperature differentials and separation strains between scale and base tube will be greatest with the thinner scale. During hot restarts, with boiler parts still at elevated temperatures, scale on non-gas-touched tubing and piping is exposed to thermal-quench transients similar to that described for gas-touched reheater tubes. Reports from Europe attribute the absence of turbine SPE damage there to the use of turbine bypasses, which allow the boiler to be fired with steam flow passing from the superheater outlet piping directly to and through the reheater to the condenser. In such units, cold- or hot-restart thermal transients which can act to weaken scale-to-tube adherence are avoided. These turbine bypasses may divert any exfoliated scale during start-up directly from the condenser. However, bypass valves and steam distributors in the condenser reportedly do not suffer any noticeable erosion damage, which further supports the view that these bypasses may *prevent* or minimize the exfoliation process.

SOLUTIONS TO EXFOLIATION

Industry has considered, and is exploring further, a range of possible solutions for avoiding or minimizing exfoliation and SPE damage. The following discussion is not intended to provide an all-inclusive listing of these various possibilities, but rather will review what can be done to the steam-touched surfaces in operating units and in units yet to be designed.

EXISTING UNITS

At present, chemical cleaning is the only option available for existing units. With proper care the steam-touched materials can be safely cleaned to remove all oxide scaling. But chemical cleaning, if not correctly performed, can be damaging to the materials, and a decision to chemically clean should only be made with a full understanding of the inherent risks and the precautions to be taken.

A decision of whether chemical cleaning

should be performed, and to what extent, involves cost/benefit considerations specific to the individual circumstances. In this connection, it should be noted that particles other than exfoliation scale, such as maintenance repair debris, may cause some SPE damage. So careful assessment of the damage and its likely source is also needed.

The Electric Power Research Institute has funded studies as to the efficacy and feasibility of applying a chromium-rich oxide coating to the inside of tubes following chemical cleaning. Such a chromate treatment process may negate the need for repeat cleanings or may increase the operating time between cleanings.

NEW UNITS

For units not yet designed, steps can be taken to avoid significant ferritic tube and pipe exfoliation. The exfoliation-prone ferritic portions of the superheater and reheater can be upgraded to austenitic stainless steel. There is no established temperature at which exfoliation is not considered a problem, but at 950°F and lower steam temperatures the scale is quite thin even after long-time service. The 1075°F outside-surface-temperature limit that C-E has imposed on the usage of T-22 (2¼% Cr) tubing to minimize external corrosion, also minimizes the quantity of exfoliated scale by reducing the amount of ferritic material.

Austenitic stainless materials can be applied to the inside surfaces of pipes and headers by weld-deposit cladding. C-E and others have extensive experience using these weld cladding techniques in the fabrication of nuclear and chemical-process vessels.

The same internal surfaces of ferritic tubes, pipes and headers which can be replaced or clad with stainless may alternatively be "chromized." This process involves the high-temperature (about 2000°F) diffusion of chromium into the inner surface of the steel. Both the amount and the depth of chromium diffusion are time and temperature controlled. In high-temperature service, a thin chromium-rich oxide scale forms on the surfaces to inhibit oxidation scaling.

OVERHEATING

The term *overheating* describes creep-rupture failure. This term can be misleading in the sense that it may convey the incorrect thought that temperature alone was somehow metallurgically damaging to the steel. Actually, overheating describes an exposure to temperatures too high for the operating stress. A T-22 tube, operating at a stress level of 5,000 psig, will give long life at a temperature of 1075°F, but the same tube would fail by overheating at 1000°F if operated at a stress of 15,000 psi.

Overheating failures can be categorized as either short-time or long-time. Fig. 36 shows examples of such failures.

SHORT-TIME OVERHEATING

Such failures result from exposure to temperatures significantly (hundreds of degrees F) above design and indicate a severe abnormality such as a loss of normal water or steam flow. Short-time tube failures exhibit considerable creep elongation which shows itself in large increases in diameter, particularly the inside diameter, and considerable reduction in wall thickness at the fracture surface. Fig. 37 shows a cross section through a waterwall tube which experienced short-time overheating. (A rupture typical of that shown in the lower photo-

graph of Fig. 36 had occurred in the tube a short distance away from this cross-sectional slice.) On the half of the tube exposed to the furnace, there is creep thinning caused by the combination of internal pressure and a temperature too high to resist the pressure forces. The egg-shaped inside of the tube is a typical condition associated with short-time overheating failures. These physical conditions of thinning and diametral growth provide the best and easiest means of assessing the degree of damage sustained. Under short-time conditions, tubes that have not experienced significant thinning or creep swelling have not been measurably damaged as a result of the overheating.

LONG-TIME OVERHEATING

Tubes which accumulate many hours of exposure to temperatures moderately above their long-time strength capability are also vulnerable to creep rupture. Creep elongation effects (swelling and wall thickness reduction) are

Fig. 37 Cross section of tube exposed to short-time overheating. Furnace side of tube at top has thinned and ovalized as a result of exposure to excessively high temperatures while the tube is under internal pressure.

Fig. 36 Stress-rupture failure of carbon steel tube caused by overheating over a long time period (top) and a stress rupture failure because of overheating for only a few minutes (bottom).

much less pronounced in long-time overheating failures. The upper photo in Fig. 36 shows a long-time overheating failure and the thick rupture edge typical of this failure mode. Long-time creep-rupture failures usually show evidence of considerable secondary cracking (intergranular) in addition to the main crack associated with rupture. Fig. 38 shows an example of such cracking.

MICROSTRUCTURE

When exposed to temperatures above 900°F, but less than the lower transformation temperature (the A_1 temperature of Fig. 8, which is 1330°F for carbon steel), carbon and low-alloy steels are subject to spheroidization. See Fig. 39. The carbides present in the annealed condition are not in their lowest free-energy state, and exposure to temperature results in the coalescence of these carbides into spheroidal form. This natural change is both time- and temperature-dependent, with less time required to spheroidize as temperatures increase. Because manufacturing heat treatments can cause spheroidization, and in view of its time-temperature dependence, spheroidization is not a good means by which to estimate the service exposure temperature of overheated tubes. But by comparing microstructures within the tube (for example, the sides exposed to and

Fig. 38 Macrostructure of a heavy wall carbon-molybdenum steel pipe which has failed because of stress rupture over a long period of time. 2X

away from the furnace) spheroidization can be useful as a indicator of differences in, and probable range of, exposure temperature.

When heated to higher temperatures, the ferrite in carbon and low-alloy steels transforms into austenite (see subsection "Phase Diagrams" in this chapter). The temperature at which austenite begins to form is called the lower critical temperature, and the upper critical temperature is that at which there is complete transformation to austenite (A_1 and A_3 temperatures of Fig. 8).

If a tube is heated above the lower critical temperature and then ruptures, the quenching effect of the escaping steam will result in the transformation of the austenite into martensite and other product forms. See Fig. 40. Because of this, exposure temperatures can be established with reasonable accuracy if the lower critical temperature has been exceeded.

STRESS-CORROSION CRACKING

Steels, as well as other metals, are subject to a form of cracking called stress-corrosion cracking. When under tensile strains, the austenitic stainless steels are susceptible to this type of cracking if exposed to aqueous solutions containing caustic or halides, particularly chlorides. See Fig. 41. Because the austenitic stainless steels are used most frequently in superheated-steam environments, there is little likelihood of exposure to damaging environments in service. But during the initial start-up of a plant, the increased potential for exposure of water contaminated with caustic or chloride requires that precautions be taken to avoid such contamination (see Chapter 20).

CAUSTIC EMBRITTLEMENT

Under certain exposures to high levels of sodium-hydroxide, ferritic boiler steels can experience a form of stress-corrosion cracking which has been given the specific name of caustic embrittlement. Leakage of caustic-treated boiler water through crevices such as rolled joints—which have residual stresses introduced during rolling—can concentrate caustic and result in cracking of the type shown

Fig. 39 **Photomicrographs showing an annealed structure at top and a spheroidized structure at bottom at 500X. Nital etch**

Fig. 40 **Microstructure resulting from overheating to between the lower and upper critical temperatures (1330° to 1600°F) for carbon steel tube material (top) and to above the upper critical temperature (bottom) both followed by rapid cooling because of rupture. 500X nital etch**

Fig. 41 **Very rapid failure of TP 316 austenitic steel through stress-corrosion cracking**

in Fig. 42. When boilers were of riveted construction and crevices were the rule, it was much more commonly found than in today's welded construction. Proper water treatment can prevent caustic embrittlement.

SENSITIZATION

Austenitic stainless steels, when exposed to elevated temperatures, may lose some of their corrosion-resistant properties at the boundaries between individual grains. (See subsection "Grain Structure," this chapter.) The chromium in the steel has a tendency to combine with the carbon and migrate into the grains, causing a depletion of chromium at the grain boundary. This condition is called sensitization. If sensitized steels are exposed to corrosive aqueous solutions such as acids, the grain boundaries can corrode preferentially resulting in intergranular attack (IGA).

In superheater and reheater service, sensitization which occurs naturally as a result of service exposure presents no problem. But in aqueous applications, such as wet flue-gas scrubbers, IGA is a possibility at heat-affected zones of welded joints, which can become sensitized by the heat of welding.

In these low-temperature applications, either extra-low-carbon grades of stainless such as TP 304L or TP 316L, or stabilized grades of stainless such as TP 321 or TP 347, can provide protection against sensitization and IGA. (The titanium and columbium added to TP 321 and TP 347 have a stronger affinity to combine with carbon than does chromium, and thus the term *stabilized*.) These grades of steel greatly reduce the tendency for grain-boundary depletion of chromium. As indicated earlier, boiler flue-gas wet scrubbers also require a grade of stainless steel that is more resistant to pitting attack; the extra-low-carbon Grade TP 316L is widely used in this application.

METALLURGICAL AND MATERIALS ENGINEERING TECHNOLOGY

Metallurgical and materials engineering capability and its close interaction with all phases of materials use are essential to the successful design, fabrication, and service behavior of a boiler and associated equipment. To attain this end, a laboratory works closely with manufacturing, quality control, engineering, construction and field services. A continuous process of feedback and information exchange between laboratory and functional departments assures that material-related needs and problems are being properly addressed.

Six basic and interrelated areas typify the activities of a metallurgical and materials laboratory. These include:

■ material properties and corrosion resistance investigations

■ welding and fabrication process development

Fig. 42 **Caustic embrittlement, a type of stress-corrosion cracking associated with crevices in which caustic can concentrate. It is generally an intergranular attack, although it can also proceed transgranularly.**

■ metals processing and alloy development
■ nondestructive examinations
■ metallographic and chemical analysis
■ metallurgical specifications development.

The following C-E Metallurgy and Materials Laboratory case study demonstrates how capabilities in these areas have helped to improve superheater and reheater materials.

A LABORATORY CASE STUDY

As was mentioned earlier, many units in the early 50's used Grade TP 321 stainless tubing in superheaters and reheaters. The materials were selected in accordance with the *ASME* Code, Section I, and were purchased in accordance with specifications prepared by ASTM and adopted by ASME. After relatively short service, an industry-wide phenomenon took place. These materials began to creep (swell) excessively and some tube ruptures occurred.

Metallurgical analysis showed that the tube materials exhibiting poor creep-resistance properties were fine-grained, and for a time this was thought to be the reason for the excessive creep. But it was subsequently established that higher solution annealing temperatures were needed to justify the *ASME* Code allowable stresses. The high-temperature H grades, with specified minimums on carbon and heat-

Fig. 43 **Top: An instrumented creep-testing machine with two-zone furnace heating is used to evaluate alloys for high-temperature service. Center: The computerized acquisition and process control system analyses creep and rupture data from testing machines shown above. Bottom: Diagram illustrating C-E's computer-controlled creep-and-rupture data acquistion system**

treating temperature, were added to the specifications. Grain size, which increases with temperature, was only an indicator of the solution annealing temperatures applied, and not necessarily the same indicator applicable to all H grade materials.

The H grade materials proved quite resistant to creep, but some TP 321H cold-worked bends ruptured in service—a problem not encountered with the finer grain steels. Metallurgical analysis and evaluation established the need to stress relieve cold-worked bends in H-grade tubing to avoid ruptures caused by reduced rupture ductility.

The TP 321 problem and its direct impact on utilities and their vendors forcefully pinpointed the danger of relying on materials property data developed by others which is of such critical importance to the behavior of the material in boiler service. This awareness led to the development of a computer-controlled creep-rupture data acquisition system (see Fig. 43) as well as other laboratory research activities in the areas of metal processing, material-property data acquisition and evaluation, metallurgical analysis, and nondestructive examination.

MATERIAL PROPERTIES AND CORROSION RESISTANCE

The importance of this activity to the design and performance of boiler materials has been discussed earlier in this chapter. Fig. 44 and 45 show some of the important test equipment available for materials evaluation.

WELDING AND FABRICATION PROCESS DEVELOPMENT

In 1930, welding became accepted as a means of fabricating boiler components. Before then, drums were either riveted or fully forged. Destructive testing of welded test vessels was instrumental in gaining *ASME* Boiler Code acceptance of welding. Combustion Engineering manufactured and tested the first welded boiler drum in 1930 (see Fig. 46). In recognition of that historic event, this vessel was designated an ASM Historical Landmark in 1977 and in May 1980 was designated an ASME National Historic Landmark.

Since the thirties, numerous welding processes have been continually under investigation. These include all the standard processes such as shielded metal arc, submerged arc, gas metal arc, gas tungsten arc, plasma and electroslag welding. Research has also involved special processes such as low-heat-input vertical-up welding for massive thicknesses and solid-phase welding for tubular parts.

With capabilities in chemical and metallographic analysis and in mechanical testing, a laboratory can accurately determine the effects of additives and trace elements in wire and flux combinations and provide optimum formulations in servicing standard or special welding applications. These formulations control the deposited metal to meet requirements during fabrication such as soundness, resistance to hot and cold cracking under various restraint conditions, and properties matching those of the base metals, including the properties of the base-metal zone heat-affected by the welding. The base metals and weld metals must also be matched to meet long-time service temperature conditions which could lead to such problems as aging embrittlement.

METALS PROCESSING AND ALLOY DEVELOPMENT

Facilities have to be available in such a laboratory to melt, cast and subsequently fabricate primary metal shapes from steels and alloys of any analysis. The scale-size or actual-size products can then be evaluated to study the effects that the alloying elements have on metallurgical structure, high-temperature mechanical properties, corrosion resistance and fabricability.

Coreless air induction furnaces are also used to produce experimental alloys. Alloys melted in these furnaces are cast into static molds (for conversion to plate, rod, strip or wire) or spinning molds. The latter are used to produce hollows to be formed into tube or pipe.

Vacuum induction equipment is also used for melting. Heats of materials produced by the air or vacuum induction melting processes can be electroslag remelted to obtain a directionally solidified product with reduced microsegregation and porosity.

NONDESTRUCTIVE EXAMINATIONS

Chapter 18 "Steam-Generator Manufacture" discusses the importance of nondestructive testing (NDT) to the boiler industry and describes the basic testing procedures: liquid penetrant, magnetic-particle, ultrasonic, eddy-current and radiographic techniques. Laboratory-developed procedures to implement proper application and interpretation of test results support operations in quality control, manufacturing and field service.

METALLOGRAPHIC AND CHEMICAL ANALYSIS

A variety of analytical means is used to establish the metallurgical and chemical characteristics of boiler steels before and after fabrication, and after service exposure.

Instruments used for such analysis include X-ray diffraction and dilatometer equipment as well as a variety of chemical analyzers using principles of optical emission, atomic absorption, and X-ray fluorescence. Optical microscopes are used, but for purposes of extreme magnification and identification of micro-

Fig. 44 **Tensile specimens in aqueous solutions are tested for corrosion resistance while under tensile load strain.**

Fig. 45. A 200,000 lb servo-controlled hydraulic test station determines fracture toughness of materials.

Fig. 46. The first welded boiler drum was manufactured and tested by Combustion Engineering at Chattanooga, Tennessee. In recognition of that historic event, this vessel has been designated an ASME National Historic Landmark.

constituents, electron microscopy equipment is necessary.

FAILURE ANALYSIS

Metallurgical analysis is fundamental to that process of establishing the cause and correction of in-service material-related problems called failure analysis. Failure analysis provides the basis for improvements in design or operation. It is important to a boiler manufacturer in identifying and preventing problems that are generic in nature. It is of equal importance in solving problems specific to individual boilers. We strongly encourage the determination of metallurgical cause of boiler materials problems because such information is often a prerequisite to the solution and to the prevention of such problems.

METALLURGICAL SPECIFICATIONS

The know-how obtained in development and in problem solving requires continuing incorporation into documents for implementation.

Purchase instructions developed by C-E cover metallurgical requirements for the base products (plates, forgings, castings, structurals, tubes, and pipe), beyond those specified in industry material specifications. Metallurgical and process specifications similarly cover detail requirements for inspection and testing, metallurgical design aspects, and fabrication operations and practices for specific components (metal cutting, forming, heat treating, welding and coating).

REFERENCES

[1] Arthur M. Greene, Jr., *History of the ASME Boiler Code.* New York: American Society of Mechanical Engineers, 1955.

[2] American Society for Testing and Materials, *ASTM Directory.* Philadelphia: American Society for Testing and Materials, 1979.

[3] Lawrence H. Van Vlack, *Elements of Materials Science: An Introductory Text for Engineering Students,* 3rd ed. Reading, MA Addison-Wesley Publishing Co., 1977.

[4] Lawrence H. Van Vlack, *Elements of Materials Science,* 2nd ed. Reading, MA: Addison-Wesley Publishing Co., 1964, Table 11–1, Common Heat Treating Processes, pp. 308–309.

[5] H. G. Edmunds and D. J. White, "Observations of the Effect of Creep Relaxation on High-Strain Fatigue," *Journal of Mechanical Engineering Science,* 8(3): 310–321, Sept. 1966.

[6] *Graphitization of Steel Piping,* presented at the annual meetings of the American Society of Mechanical Engineers, New York, NY, Nov. 29–Dec. 3, 1943; Nov. 27–Dec. 1, 1944; and Dec. 2–6, 1946; under the auspices of the joint ASTM-ASME Research Committee on the effects of temperature on the properties of metals. New York: American Society of Mechanical Engineers, 1944, 1945 and 1947, respectively. Issued as pamphlets and bound at the end of the *Transactions of the ASME,* Vols. 66, 1944; 67, 1945; and 69, 1947; respectively.

CHAPTER 11

Water Technology

Water is a basic engineering material used in the production of steam for power generation and process use. Effective treatment or conditioning of water has made possible the use of more efficient steam cycles in the subcritical and supercritical pressure ranges. Many industrial processes have special requirements for high quality water, free from objectionable contaminants.

These statements are indicative of the significant role of *water technology* as an interdisciplinary professional field which comprises elements of basic chemistry as well as chemical and mechanical engineering. This chapter will discuss specific boiler applications of water technology, but many of the same considerations hold for various types of process operations. In practically every instance, a careful review of sources of water and its conditioning is required to avoid economic losses because of slowdown in production, damage to equipment, and increased costs of operation.

The sources of water supply to an industrial site differ and can originate from a polluted river or stream, mountain runoff, wells or a lake. The composition of impurities in water varies over a wide range. Water may be polluted with sewage, chemical or organic wastes, bacteria, dissolved gases, suspended mineral matter and dissolved solids of both scaling and

nonscaling composition. If water were pure "H_2O" and nothing else, or were of a constant solids composition, the conditioning of water for industrial use would be uniform and simple. Because this is not the case, the conditioning of water contains elements of both a specialized science and an engineering art.

In using water for generation of steam for process or electric power, consideration must be given to water treatment for the prevention of corrosion, scaling, and contamination of steam. Such attention must involve the treatment of the raw water introduced into the cycle and, in many cases, the conditioning of the water present in the preboiler cycle and in the boiler itself. How much consideration is given to the contaminants present in water depends largely upon the end use of the water. From an operating standpoint, boiler pressure and boiler-water temperature are the chief factors limiting the water quality necessary to prevent scaling and corrosion.

An increase in temperature influences the formation of deposits and the corrosion of metals in contact with water. Treatment must be suited to the operating pressure because chemical reactions and corrosion processes increase in activity and become more critical as the cycle advances from the comparatively low levels in industrial power plants to the super-

Table I. Common Impurities Found in Water

Constituent	Chemical Formula	Difficulties Caused	Means of Treatment
Turbidity	None—expressed in analysis as units.	Imparts unsightly appearance to water. Deposits in waterlines, process equipment, etc. Interferes with most process uses.	Coagulation, settling and filtration.
Color	None—expressed in analysis as units.	May cause foaming in boilers. Hinders precipitation methods such as iron removal and softening. Can stain product in process use.	Coagulation and filtration. Chlorination. Adsorption by activated carbon.
Hardness	Calcium and magnesium salts expressed as $CaCO_3$.	Chief source of scale in heat exchange equipment, boilers, pipelines, etc. Forms curds with soap, interferes with dyeing, etc.	Softening. Demineralization. Internal boiler water treatment. Surface-active agents.
Alkalinity	Bicarbonate (HCO_3), carbonate (CO_3), and hydrate (OH), expressed as $CaCO_3$.	Foaming and carryover of solids with steam. Embrittlement of boiler steel. Bicarbonate and carbonate produce CO_3 in steam a source of corrosion in condensate lines.	Lime and lime-soda softening. Acid treatment. Hydrogen zeolite softening. Demineralization. Dealkalization by anion exchange.
Free Mineral Acid	H_2SO_4, HCl, etc. expressed as $CaCO_3$.	Corrosion.	Neutralization with alkalies.
Carbon Dioxide	CO_2	Corrosion in waterlines and particularly steam and condensate lines.	Aeration. Deaeration. Neutralization with alkalies.
pH	Hydrogen ion concentration defined as: $pH = \log \frac{1}{(H^+)}$	pH varies according to acidic or alkaline solids in water. Most natural waters have a ph of 6.0–8.0.	pH can be increased by alkalies and decreased by acids.
Sulfate	$(SO_4)^{--}$	Adds to solids content of water, but in itself, is not usually significant. Combines with calcium to form calcium sulfate scale.	Demineralization.
Chloride	Cl^-	Adds to solids content and increases corrosive character of water.	Demineralization.
Nitrate	$(NO_3)^-$	Adds to solids content, but is not usually significant industrially. Useful for control of boiler metal embrittlement.	Demineralization.
Silica	SiO_2	Scale in boilers and cooling water systems. Insoluble turbine blade deposits because of silica vaporization.	Hot process removal with magnesium salts. Adsorption by highly basic anion exchange resins, in conjunction with demineralization.

Table I. **Common Impurities Found in Water — *Continued***

Constituent	Chemical Formula	Difficulties Caused	Means of Treatment
Iron	Fe^{++} (ferrous) Fe^{+++} (ferric)	Discolors water on precipitation. Source of deposits in waterlines, boilers, etc. Interferes with dyeing, tanning, papermaking, etc.	Aeration. Coagulation and filtration. Lime softening. Cation exchange. Contact filtration. Surface-active agents for iron retention.
Manganese	Mn^{++}	Same as iron.	Same as iron.
Oxygen	O_2	Corrosion of waterlines, heat exchange equipment, boilers, return lines, etc.	Deaeration. Sodium sulfite. Corrosion inhibitors.
Hydrogen Sulfide	H_2S	Cause of "rotten egg" odor. Corrosion.	Aeration. Chlorination. Highly basic anion exchange.
Ammonia	NH_3	Corrosion of copper and zinc alloys by formation of complex soluble ion.	Cation exchange with hydrogen zeolite. Chlorination. Deaeration.
Dissolved Solids	None	"Dissolved Solids" is measure of total amount of dissolved matter, determined by evaporation. High concentrations of dissolved solids are objectionable because of process interference and as a cause of foaming in boilers.	Various softening process, such as lime softening and cation exchange by hydrogen zeolite, will reduce dissolved solids. Demineralization.
Suspended Solids	None	"Suspended Solids" is the measure of undissolved matter, determined gravimetrically. Suspended solids cause deposits in heat-exchange equipment, boilers, waterlines, etc.	Subsidence. Filtration, usually preceded by coagulation and settling.
Total Solids	None	"Total Solids" is the sum of dissolved and suspended solids, determined gravimetrically.	See "Dissolved Solids" and "Suspended Solids."

*Adapted from *Betz Handbook of Industrial Water Conditioning*, 7th Edition, 1976 Betz Laboratories, Inc., Philadelphia, Pa.

critical pressures in utility boilers.

As major causes of forced outages, internal corrosion and deposition cost electric utilities millions of dollars in repairs and lost availability. This is both unfortunate and unnecessary; the causes of corrosion are generally known and there are effective means of preventing or reducing damage from corrosion:

■Maintain recommended water treatment for both the boiler-water and feedwater systems.

■Control oxygen concentrations in the feedwater to minimize corrosion and formation of pre-boiler corrosion products, which end up as deposits on heat-transfer surfaces in the boiler.

■Comply with operating procedures during start-ups, shutdown, and outages to minimize corrosion and to avoid the entry of corrosion products into the boiler.

■Maintain boiler free from significant amounts of deposits by periodic chemical cleaning.

TECHNIQUES OF WATER TREATMENT

The extent of water conditioning or treatment depends both on the original supply source and the ultimate end use of the product. Table I lists common impurities found in water, sets forth some of the resulting problems, and indicates common treatment methods.

The techniques of water treatment cover a wide variety of raw-water preparation schemes. This art is covered in detail in established references.[1] Some of the basic chemical reactions involved in the treatment of raw water to produce suitable makeup for boilers will be discussed in a general manner.

Any evaluation of water conditioning must consider the impurities present in power-station raw-water makeup in relation to tendencies toward scaling, corrosion, and deposits. Raw water contains many contaminating elements including (a) mud, clay and silt; (b) oxygen, carbon dioxide and hydrogen sulfide; (c) sewage, bacteria and algae; (d) scale-forming compounds of calcium, magnesium and silica; (e) oil; (f) iron compounds; (g) organic wastes; (h) sulfuric, hydrochloric and other acids; (i) normally soluble compounds, such as sodium bicarbonate, sodium carbonate, sodium hydroxide and sodium chloride.

Table II gives typical analyses of water supplies of the U.S. The river water analyses are of filtered water, and for the most part represent yearly averages. River waters change considerably with the seasons, and the maximum and minimum concentrations may be 50 percent above and 50 percent below the average. Spring and well waters and waters from large lakes have a fairly constant composition.[2]

The usual unit for reporting dissolved and also suspended solids in feedwater and boiler water is *parts per million* (ppm). This is a rational unit which is easily understood and which avoids misunderstanding. In other words, one million pounds of water will contain so many pounds of solids. With high subcritical-pressure and supercritical-pressure boilers requiring very pure water, the term *parts per billion* (ppb) is now in use. One ppb equals 0.001 ppm.

RAW-WATER PROCESSES

Raw water contains various gaseous and solid impurities which must be reduced before the water can be supplied as makeup to a boiler. This is particularly true if the water is taken from a river which may be contaminated with mine washings, gases, organic and chemical wastes as well as silt and other minor impurities. To reduce these substances, the processes of aeration, settling, coagulation, and filtering are commonly used. A brief description of each method follows.

AERATION

This process (Fig. 1) removes such undesirable gases as carbon dioxide and hydrogen sulfide from water by admixing water and air to reduce the solubility of the objectionable gas in water. The removal of gas follows Henry's Law which indicates that the solubility of a gas in water is directly proportional to its partial pressure in the surrounding atmosphere. The partial pressure of a gas such as carbon dioxide is low in a normal atmosphere. Establishing an equilibrium between water and air by aeration results in saturation of the water with oxygen and nitrogen and results in the practical elimination of such gases as carbon dioxide and hydrogen sulfide. Increasing the temperature, the aeration time and the surface area of water improves the removal of gases.

COAGULATION

Adding chemical coagulating materials reduces surface-water contamination in the form of coarse suspended solids, silt, turbidity, color and colloids. The chemicals form a floc which assists in agglomerating impurities. Settlement of the particles permits a clear effluent from the coagulating chamber. Fig. 2 illustrates a typical clarifier. Removal of colloids requires a careful analysis of the impurities to establish the nature of their electrical charge, one of the principal factors contributing to their remaining in the suspended state. Some chemicals used for coagulation are filter alum, sodium aluminate, copperas, ferrisul, activated silica, and various proprietary organic compounds.

Temperature, pH, and mixing affect the efficiency of coagulation. Some of the reactions involved are

Filter alum (formation of aluminum hydroxide)

$$Al_2(SO_4)_3 + 3Ca(HCO_3)_2 \rightarrow$$
$$3CaSO_4 + 2Al(OH)_3 + 6CO_2$$

Sodium aluminate

$$6NaAlO_2 + Al_2(SO_4)_3 \cdot 18H_2O \rightarrow$$
$$8Al(OH)_3 + 3Na_2SO_4 + 6H_2O$$

Copperas (formation of ferrous hydroxide)

$$FeSO_4 + Ca(HCO_3)_2 \rightarrow$$
$$CaSO_4 + Fe(HCO_3)_2$$

$$Fe(HCO_3)_2 + 2Ca(OH)_2 \rightarrow$$
$$Fe(OH)_2 + 2CaCO_3 + 2H_2O$$

Ferrisul

$$Fe_2(SO_4)_3 + 3Ca(HCO_3)_2 \rightleftharpoons$$
$$2Fe(OH)_3 + 3CaSO_4 + 6CO_2$$

FILTRATION

Filters separate coarse suspended matter from raw water, or remove floc or sludge com-

---

Table II. Analyses of Typical Surface and Ground Waters in the United States

Analysis Number[a]	1	2	3	4	5	6	7	8	9	10	11	12	13
Silica (SiO_2)	2.5	0.4	2.3	8.2	13	8.0	8.4	9.6	16	23	34	12	39
Iron (Fe)	0.03	0.05	.09	.12	0.04		0.15	0.04	0.0			2.1	.09
Calcium (Ca)	5.3	27	32	1.7	72	79	40	3.4	7.2	70	26	72	7.2
Magnesium (Mg)	1.7	7	10	0.4	6.4	28	16	1.5	2.5	24	10	33	4.2
Sodium (Na)	1.4	3[b]	3.5	1.9	41	99	94	5.6	147	12[b]	138	358[b]	7.5
Potassium (K)	0.6		1.0	0.7	4.7	4			0.4		1.6		
Carbonate (CO_3)	0	1	0	0	0	4	0	0	0		0		
Bicarbonate (HCO_3)	10	99	138	3	174	137	46	21	328	179	170	293	50
Sulfate (SO_4)	11	13	17	4.4	138	290	298	3.3	2.6	135	70	560	0.8
Chloride (Cl)	2.6	7	6.5	2.6	9.5	79	14	3.6	51	8	139	195	6.8
Fluoride (F)	0.1		0.1	0.6	0.4	0.4	0.1	0.2	0.8			2.5	0.0
Nitrate (NO_3)	0.3	0.2		0.2	4.0	0.2	3.6	0.7	0.0		0.0	1.1	0.0
Dissolved solids	34	130	171	23	386	661	554	42	392	392	503	1380	90[c]
Total hardness as $CaCO_3$	20	98	121	6	206	315	166	15	28	276	106	316	35
Noncarbonate hardness	6	16	8	3	64	197	128	0	0	126	0	76	0
Specific conductance (micromhos at 25 C)	53.4		263	29.5	575	1040	822	55.5	651		867		
Color	1		3	15	5		6	4	10			0	2.5
pH	6.9	8.1	8.2	5.8	7.7	8.4	7.6	7.0	8.0	7.6	7.9		7.5

[a] Analyses numbers are identified as follows:

1 = New York City, NY, Catskill supply (reservoir—finished).
2 = Detroit, MI, Detroit River (raw).
3 = Chicago, IL, Lake Michigan (raw).
4 = Fitchburg, MA, Pond (finished).
5 = Omaha, NE, Missouri River (raw).
6 = Los Angeles, CA, Colorado River (raw).
7 = Pittsburgh, PA, Monongahela River (finished).
8 = Macon, GA, Ocmulgee River (raw).
9 = Houston, TX, Well 1932 ft deep.
10 = Jacksonville, FL, Well 1064 ft deep.
11 = El Paso, TX, Well 703 ft deep.
12 = Galesburg, IL, Well 2450 ft deep.
13 = Bremerton, WA, Anderson Creek.

[b] Computed by difference in epm and reported as sodium.
[c] Sum of determined constituents.

Values are in parts per million where this unit is appropriate.

Fig. 1 **Forced-draft aerator**

ponents from coagulation or process softening systems. Generally, gravity and pressure-type filters as shown in Figs. 3 and 4 are used for this purpose. Beds of graded gravel or coarse anthracite are the common materials used in the filter bed. Diatomaceous earth and special precoat filters are generally used to remove oil and reduce color in feedwater makeup.

CHEMICAL SOFTENING PROCESSES

Nonscaling feedwater can be obtained with proper pretreatment of raw water. Various chemical combinations can remove hardness, silica and silt from makeup water. Economics and operating pressure dictate the technique selected for the application.

LIME-SODA SOFTENING

To soften water by this process, lime (calcium hydroxide) is added to precipitate the calcium bicarbonate as calcium carbonate and magnesium salts as magnesium hydroxide. Soda ash (sodium carbonate) is added to react with calcium chloride and calcium sulfate to form calcium carbonate. The general reactions are as follows:

Fig. 2 **Solids-contact clarifier**

Fig. 3   Gravity filter

$$Ca(HCO_3)_2 + Ca(OH)_2 \rightarrow 2CaCO_3\downarrow + 2H_2O$$

$$CaSO_4 + Na_2CO_3 \rightarrow CaCO_3\downarrow + Na_2SO_4$$

$$Mg(HCO_3)_2 + 2Ca(OH)_2 \rightarrow$$
$$Mg(OH)_2\downarrow + 2CaCO_3\downarrow + 2H_2O$$

$$MgSO_4 + Ca(OH)_2 \rightarrow Mg(OH)_2\downarrow + CaSO_4$$

Because of the increase in reaction rate and the decrease in solubility of calcium carbonate, this process is more efficient at hot temperatures. The hardness in the effluent of a cold lime-soda process depends upon the excess of soda ash and is generally above 33 ppm. Alkalinity reduction depends on the removal of magnesium and calcium bicarbonates. In the hot lime-soda process, the hardness residual in the effluent ranges from 17–25 ppm.

Fig. 4   Vertical-type pressure sand filter

HOT-PROCESS PHOSPHATE SOFTENING

In this process, phosphate chemically precipitates calcium and magnesium salts. The calcium hardness is precipitated in the form of tricalcium phosphate and the magnesium as magnesium hydroxide. Chemical reactions are completed at a temperature of 212°F or above. The reactions can be controlled to reduce the hardness to nearly zero.

Normal low hardness, below 60 ppm, can be eliminated in a single stage. Generally, high hardness water is handled in a two-stage softener arrangement. The hot-process phosphate softener is particularly suited for turbid waters, which are low in hardness and alkalinity. Softening, turbidity control, deaeration and silica reduction can be combined in a single unit. Fig. 5 shows a typical hot-process settling tank. Usually, surface-acting organic agents are added to stabilize the precipitates formed in the softener. Anthracite coal filters are best for removal of turbidity from the effluent. Some of

Fig. 5 **Hot-process phosphate softening**

the chemical reactions in the softener to reduce calcium and magnesium hardness are

$$3Ca(HCO_3)_2 + 6NaOH \rightarrow$$
$$3CaCO_3\downarrow + 3Na_2CO_3 + 6H_2O$$

$$3CaCO_3 + 2Na_3PO_4 \rightarrow$$
$$Ca_3(PO_4)_2\downarrow + 3Na_2CO_3$$

$$Mg(HCO_3) + 4NaOH \rightarrow$$
$$Mg(OH)_2\downarrow + 2Na_2CO_3 + 2H_2O$$

Addition of magnesium sulfate, magnesium

hydroxide, dolomitic lime and magnesium oxide aids in the reduction of silica. Removal of silica from solution is accomplished by adsorption by the presence of magnesium hydroxide formed in the softener.

ZEOLITE SOFTENING

The name *zeolite* refers to a group of water-softening chemicals capable of exchanging ions with which they come in contact. These materials may be natural compounds (green

Fig. 6 **Sodium zeolite softener**

sand) or synthetic compounds such as sulfonated coal, phenolic and polystyrene resins. Hard water is passed downward through a bed of sodium-regenerated zeolite contained in a steel pressure vessel. See Fig. 6. As the water passes through the ion–exchange material, the calcium and magnesium ions are exchanged for sodium in the zeolite (Z).

The reactions are

$$Ca(HCO_3)_2 + Na_2Z \rightarrow CaZ\downarrow + 2NaHCO_3$$
$$Mg(HCO_3)_2 + Na_2Z \rightarrow MgZ\downarrow + 2NaHCO_3$$

Regeneration of the zeolite bed is accomplished by passing a salt solution through the softener.

$$CaZ + 2NaCl \rightarrow CaCl_2 + Na_2Z$$

The calcium chloride is passed to waste and the zeolite bed is ready for further softening.

Salt (sodium chloride) or acid can regenerate synthetic zeolites. Acid- and salt-regenerated zeolites can be used in combination to reduce alkalinity in waters having a high bicarbonate hardness. The reaction in the hydrogen zeolite may be written as follows:

$$Ca(HCO_3)_2 + H_2Z \rightarrow CaZ\downarrow + 2H_2CO_3$$
$$Mg(HCO_3)_2 + H_2Z \rightarrow MgZ\downarrow + 2H_2CO_3$$

The mixed effluent from the hydrogen and sodium zeolites is deaerated to remove the carbon dioxide. Generally, the exhausted acid zeolite is regenerated with sulfuric acid.

Zeolite softening of makeup is the most common way to prepare water for use in industrial boilers. It is simple to operate and control. While sodium zeolite softening is very attractive, it must be applied with understanding of its limitations. Turbid waters are unsuited; total solids are not reduced and with high bicarbonate water, high quantities of carbon dioxide can be expected in the steam. Silica is not reduced by zeolite softening.

Although using hydrogen zeolite reduces solids, the equipment operator must recognize a number of disadvantages: As in the sodium zeolite, turbidity must be low. The cost of the chemicals, acid and salt, may be considerable. Handling of acids introduces a hazard to operators, and corrosion resistant pipe must be used to transport the water to the degasifier.

Synthetic zeolites are used with other water-softening equipment in preparation of makeup water. The hot-lime zeolite softener is a widely used technique in preparing water for intermediate-pressure industrial boilers.

Using chemicals at temperatures about 250°F facilitates reduction of hardness, alkalinity, and silica. The hot-lime softening reduces the carbonate and magnesium hardness as well as the total solids in the raw water. If the magnesium content in the raw water is below the level to reduce silica, activated magnesium oxide or dolomitic lime is added for reaction.

Use of the hot-lime zeolite produces a water of 0–2 ppm hardness, 20–30 ppm alkalinity and 0.5–1.0 ppm of silica.

DEMINERALIZATION

In demineralization, ion exchange removes ionized mineral salts. Cations as calcium, magnesium, and sodium are removed in the hydrogen cation exchanger and anions as bicarbonates, sulfates, chloride, and soluble silica are removed in the anion exchanger.

Synthetic cation and anion exchange resins are used in demineralization of water. Sulfonic, carboxylic, and phenolic hydroxyl compounds are used for cation exchange; amino or quartenary nitrogen, for anion exchange. The cation exchanger is regenerated with acid while the anion exchange material is regenerated with caustic. If the cation resin is designated as Z and the anion material as R, the simple reactions in a two-stage demineralizer may be expressed as:

$$\text{Cation: } H_2Z + CaSO_4 \rightarrow CaZ + H_2SO_4$$
$$\text{Anion: } H_2SO_4 + 2R \cdot OH \rightarrow R \cdot SO_4 + H_2O$$

Demineralization can yield a pure water, equal or superior to the best evaporated vapor. The anion and cation resins can be arranged in various combinations to produce the best water most economically. Two-, three- or four-bed units or a single mixed-bed demineralizer can be used to accomplish the required result. Fig. 7 illustrates possible combinations of these systems to produce a specific water quality. As strong base exchangers are temperature sensitive, they should not be used above 120°F. Cation exchange resins can tolerate temperatures of 250°F.

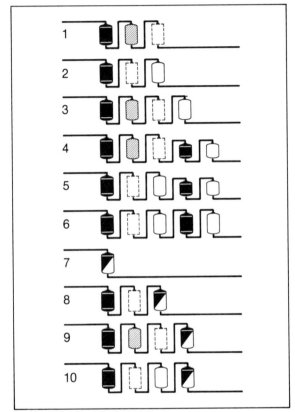

Fig. 7 Ten major demineralizer systems: black, strong-acid cation exchanger; white, strong-base anion exchanger; shaded, weak-base anion exchanger; half black and half white, mixed-bed; broken rectangle, decarbonator or vacuum deaerator. (1) Two-bed with weak-base; (2) two-bed with strong-base; (3) three-bed; (4) four-bed, primary with weak-base; (5) four-bed, primary with strong-base; (6) parallel two-beds, as in system 2, or four-bed as in system 5 (except for size of secondary unit); (7) mixed-bed; (8) cation bed, decarbonator, and mixed-bed; (9) two-bed, as in system 1, and mixed-bed; (10) two-bed, as in system 2, and mixed-bed. The secondary units in systems 4 and 5, which are used only for polishing, may be smaller than the primary, as indicated.

Use of finely sized resins in demineralizers requires a water source low in turbidity and organic matter. Clarification, filtration and chlorination are generally required to reduce organic matter to a low level. Failure to reduce the organic level in the water results in a marked reduction in capacity of the exchangers because of fouling of the resins.

The advance of demineralization to provide a high-purity makeup water may be partly attributed to the development of highly basic anion exchange resins which allow the removal of soluble silica from raw water. Mixed-bed demineralizers, in which the cation and anion resins are intimately interspersed, see Figs. 8 and 9, have successfully provided a high-quality makeup water as well as for polishing purposes in cleaning up impurities in condensates of utility units. Fig. 10 is a schematic of a complete makeup water system for a utility power plant.

WATER TECHNOLOGY FOR BOILERS

In the field of high-pressure boilers, there can be no compromise in water treatment. The

Fig. 8 Mixed-bed demineralizer. It houses mixture of cation and anion exchange resins. Air for mixing enters through bottom distributor.

most efficient combination of techniques must be utilized to assure a delivery of pure water, nearly free of soluble and insoluble solids, to the boiler feedwater system. Evaporation or demineralization of makeup must be used to assure the reduction of solids such as silica in the water supply to the boiler. Normally, silica vaporization is the principal control item for

Fig. 9 Regeneration of mixed-bed, from initial backwash to end of rinse and return to service, takes from 2 to 3 hours

solids content in the boiler water. The makeup to high-pressure utility boilers is generally less than 3 to 5 percent of the feedwater supply. For this application, the more costly methods for solids removal can be economically justified because operation with low blowdown of water from the boiler can be assured. Also, the steam purity is of a magnitude which results in less deposition of solids in the turbine, thus assuring sustained high efficiency. Analogously, stringent requirements for water purity are necessary in high-pressure industrial boilers where makeup requirements are high, ranging from 30 to 100 percent of the feedwater supply.

At steam pressures below 600 psig, there is a greater latitude in the selection of methods for the preparation of boiler makeup. Turbine problems relating to vaporized solids are minor, and the requirements for feedwater are primarily concerned with the prevention of scale and sludge formation in the boilers. Most industrial boilers operate with high makeup, and the raw water to these units is treated to remove hardness, insoluble residues like silt, excess silica and alkalinity.

The capital and operating costs for the treatment of water to these boilers are substantially less than for higher pressure industrial and utility units. Higher solids and turbidities are tol-

Fig. 10 **Demineralizer and pretreatment flow diagram**

erated in the boiler water of such low pressure units. Under these conditions, the problems of steam contamination and deposits increase. The addition of foam depressers and dispersing chemical substances as well as the use of higher quantities of boiler-water blowdown are often necessary to permit sustained operation. To prevent tube ruptures during operation, deposits must be cleaned from boiler-water surfaces at periodic intervals.

The greatest incidence of problems in steam-generating equipment is related to (a) scale or deposits, (b) corrosion and (c) carryover of solids with the steam to the superheater.

SCALE AND DEPOSITS

Chief contributors to the formation of a heat deterrent scale or deposit are (1) contaminating elements present in the makeup water, (2) corrosion products formed outside the boiler and introduced into the unit with the feedwater, (3) contaminants from process equipment introduced into condensate returned to the boiler and (4) solids present in condenser leakage.

In the process of evaporation of water to steam, scale and sludge deposits form on heated surfaces of a boiler tube. The chemical substances in water concentrate in a film at the evaporation surface. Soluble constituents are readily redissolved by the water displacing the bubble of steam at the point of evaporation. Insoluble substances tend to form on the metal surface, gradually raising the metal temperature until creep and failure occur. Most scale-forming substances have a decreasing solubility in water with an increase in temperature. The higher the temperature, the more rapidly a heat-deterrent scale will form on the metal surface. The operating temperature, the rate of heat release at the evaporation surface, and the nature of the chemical substance influence scale formation.

Substances such as calcium bicarbonate decompose in the boiler water to form calcium carbonate, carbon dioxide and water as follows:

$$Ca(HCO_3)_2 \rightarrow CaCO_3 + CO_2 + H_2O$$

Calcium carbonate has a limited solubility and will agglomerate at the heated surface to form a

scale. At lower pressures and steaming rates, this reaction can be tolerated with the bulk of the deposit removed by blowdown.

Calcium sulfate (permanent hardness) is more soluble than calcium carbonate and will deposit as a heat deterrent scale in place on the tube. At lower pressures, and during the early history of steam generation, soda ash was added to control calcium sulfate scaling.

$$CaSO_4 + Na_2CO_3 \rightarrow CaCO_3 + Na_2SO_4$$

The presence of alumina, iron and copper oxides, and silica with calcium and magnesium compounds in raw water aggravates the scale problem in low- and medium-pressure boilers where a limited amount of external softening is used in preparing boiler feedwater. In these cases, chemical reactions in boilers at heated surfaces lead to the formation of undesirable scale as calcium silicate $(CaSiO_3)$, quartz (SiO_2), analcite $(Na_2O \cdot Al_2O_3 \cdot 4SiO_2 \cdot 2H_2O)$, acmite $(Na_2O \cdot Fe_2O_3 \cdot 4SiO_2)$ and magnesium silicate $(MgSiO_3)$. Formation of these compounds on heated surfaces occurs in evaporation of boiler water because of limited solubility or by interaction with other chemical components present at the point of steam formation. These substances have a low thermal conductivity, and a paper-thin scale layer will overheat the boiler tube metal.

USE OF PHOSPHATES
FOR INTERNAL TREATMENT

The work of R. E. Hall and associates led to the use of phosphates for converting calcium and magnesium salts to their respective phosphates, compounds which are readily dispersed and removed by blowdown. Trisodium phosphate, disodium hydrogen phosphate and sodium metaphosphate or sodium pyrophosphate are used to alkalize the water. Some of the reactions[3] are

$$2Na_3PO_4 + 3CaSO_4 \rightarrow Ca_3(PO_4)_2 + 3Na_2SO_4$$
$$3MgCO_3 + 2Na_3PO_4 \rightarrow Mg_3(PO_4)_2 + 3Na_2CO_3$$
$$Mg(HCO_3)_2 + 4NaOH \rightarrow$$
$$Mg(OH)_2 + 2Na_2CO_3 + H_2O$$
$$MgCl_2 + 2NaOH + SiO_2 \rightarrow$$
$$MgSiO_3 + 2NaCl + H_2O$$

The preferred form of magnesium salts in boiler water is magnesium hydroxide. Introducing magnesium generally reduces silica in industrial boiler water. Calcium phosphate is preferred in the apatite form which is developed in a high alkalinity water. This reaction may be written as:

$$10CaCO_3 + 6Na_3PO_4 + 2NaOH \rightarrow$$
$$3Ca_3(PO)_4)_2 \cdot Ca(OH)_2 + 10Na_2CO_3$$

The extent of internal treatment varies with the quality of makeup water. Deposit formation is minor where the hardness is below two ppm in the feedwater. Best results are obtained when the calcium and magnesium salts are zero. The latter condition is mandatory at higher boiler pressures. The quantity of silica and hardness which can be tolerated in boilers depends largely on the pressure, rate of steam generation and the operating factors involved. Where efficiency and economy at high ratings receive prime consideration, better quality water is required.

Increasing the schedule of internal treatment results in a boiler water with a high solids content. To operate low pressure boilers in this manner, it is generally necessary to add organic substances such as polyacrylates to condition sludge in the water. Increasing the solids content in the boiler water in the presence of organic impurities, oil, or process contaminants leads to the formation of foam. In this condition, antifoam chemicals must be added to prevent contamination of steam by carryover.

SIGNIFICANCE OF IRON-WATER REACTION

A number of influences characterize the reaction of boiler steel and water: the chemical constituents present in solution, the quantity of dissolved gases, the structural characteristics of the steel, and the rate of heat input to the boiler metal. Although the reaction is understood in general there is insufficient information to explain the mechanism in exact detail. Many theories have been forwarded to clarify this problem. But despite lack of fundamental data, experience and experimental evidence have permitted the development of controls which satisfactorily contain the corrosive activity. This section will deal with existing techniques developed to understand and control reactions in boilers.

The fundamental reaction of iron and water is to produce iron hydroxide and hydrogen as follows:

$$Fe + 2H_2O \rightarrow Fe(OH)_2 + H_2$$

It is an established fact that the end product of reaction in boilers is magnetic oxide of iron. (Fe_3O_4). The control of corrosion, therefore, is based on the knowledge of the rate-controlling step in the overall reaction. Schikorr established a mechanism which accounted for the production of magnetic oxide of iron. In simplest form, the reactions would be

$$Fe + 2H_2O \rightarrow Fe(OH)_2 + H_2$$
$$3Fe(OH)_2 \rightarrow Fe_3O_4 + 2H_2O + H_2$$

From a consideration of physical chemical relationships, it can be shown that the formation of iron hydroxide is the rate-controlling step in the Schikorr hypothesis. Therefore, the rate of the overall reaction is based on the solubility and stability of this product.

The initial reaction above is pH- or alkalinity-controlled since, by the laws of chemical equilibrium, addition of alkalinity would reverse the reaction to the left. Corey and Finnegan found that iron placed in contact with deaerated and chemically pure water will produce an equilibrium pH of approximately 8.3. Increasing the alkalinity reduces the solubility of the iron corrosion product and inhibits reactivity. The control of this reaction has been well established in the protection of metal surfaces existing ahead of the boiler.[4]

The reaction of water and steel is spontaneous and rapid at high boiler temperatures. The only reason that boiler steel can survive normal operating conditions is that the corrosion end product, magnetite (Fe_3O_4), forms a protective barrier on the metal surface to stifle further corrosion. In the simplest analysis, the function of alkalinity control is to maintain an environment in which the oxide film is stable and protective. The objective of water treatment in boilers is to protect this film against the aggressive action of impurities introduced into the boiler with the feedwater.

The work of Berl and Van Taack (Fig. 11)[5] has been used to relate corrosion of steel over a range of pH values. In interpreting the results of Fig. 11, it may be concluded that the protective oxide is solubilized at pH values below 5.0 and above 13.0. Minimum corrosion is indicated at pH values of 9.0 to 11.0, although corrosion is low over a wide band of pH values. These data are valid, but they were obtained in autoclave tests where boiling, and thus concentration of the alkalinity, did not occur. Unfortunately, corrosion occurs by concentration at the local tube wall and not by concentrations existing in the bulk boiler water. This attack takes place *beneath* deposits where boilerwater salts, as caustic, can concentrate and react with the protective oxide film.

COORDINATED PHOSPHATE CONTROL

Boiler-water pH can be established without caustic soda. With the use of sodium phosphate, a suitable alkalinity in boiler water can be achieved without the negative reaction associated with caustic soda. Whirl and Purcell[6]

developed the pH-control method termed the *coordinated phosphate pH control*. This method is illustrated by the relationship of pH and the phosphate concentration in boiler water shown in Fig. 12. Values noted on the curve represent pH values obtained by dissolving stoichiometrically pure trisodium phosphate (Na_3PO_4). Conditions below the curve represent solutions of trisodium phosphate and disodium hydrogen phosphate (Na_2HPO_4). The area above the curve, which represents solutions of trisodium phosphate and caustic, is to be avoided.

In the coordinated phosphate pH control, specifications can be maintained by adding sodium hydroxide together with disodium phosphate (Na_2HPO_4), sodium metaphosphate ($NaPO_3$) or phosphoric acid (H_3PO_4). Normally, combinations of trisodium phosphate and disodium phosphate are preferred because difficulties from erroneous chemical feed are less serious.

Alkalinity control is attained by the addition of phosphate ions to water to produce a captive quantity of hydroxide (OH) by the reversed hydrolysis reaction as follows:

$$PO_4 = + H_2O \rightleftharpoons OH- + HPO_4 =$$

This reaction is complete at pH levels below 11.0. The hydrolysis reaction of dibasic phosphate also proceeds in water as follows:

$$HPO_4 = + H_2O \rightleftharpoons OH- + H_2PO_4-$$

Fig. 11 **Relative corrosion rate of carbon steel versus pH**

Fig. 12 Coordinated phosphate pH Control

The latter reaction is complete at low pH levels (5 to 7) but is less than 0.1 percent at a pH level of 10. Thus, dibasic phosphate neither hydrolyzes nor dissociates in the normal boiler-water pH range. Additions of disodium phosphate have little effect on pH in the range 10 to 11.0.

Monobasic phosphate dissociates to the dibasic form, and the addition of one mol of monosodium phosphate (NaH_2PO_4) is capable of neutralizing one mol of sodium hydroxide. As one mol will increase boiler-water pH equivalent to the addition of one mol of sodium hydroxide, trisodium phosphate assures pH control. Adding monosodium phosphate can reduce excess caustic.

ROLE OF OXYGEN

The presence of oxygen accelerates the combining of iron and water. Oxygen can react with iron hydroxide to form a hydrated ferric oxide or magnetite. Generally localized, this reaction forms a pit in the metal. Severe attack can occur if the pit becomes progressively anodic in operation. Oxygen reacts with hydrogen at the cathodic surface and depolarizes the surface locally. This permits more iron to dissolve, gradually creating a pit.

The most severe corrosion action occurs when a deposit covers a small area. The creation of a differential aeration cell about the deposit can lead to a severe local action. The metal beneath the deposit is lower in oxygen than areas surrounding it, becomes anodic and

Fig. 13 Copper bonded with EDTA

is attacked. Pitting is most prevalent in stressed sections of boiler tubing, such as at welds and cold-worked sections, and at surface discontinuities in the metal.

Power plants employing tight cycles to prevent oxygen infiltration and condenser leakage are generally free from corrosion problems. On the other hand, many cycles are vulnerable to oxygen leakage into the feedwater as a result of design or operation. Oxygen enters the system undetected during periods of operation which are poorly monitored.

Efficient operation of boilers requires the exclusion of oxygen from the feedwater. The normal guaranteed value of oxygen leaving the deaerating heater or a deaerating condenser is less than 0.005 ppm. To achieve low residual, it is necessary to exclude air leakage into the condenser, to judiciously control the addition of undeaerated water to the condensate or feedwater, to prevent the addition of aerated heater drips into the condensate, and to assure the exclusion of air into the feedwater cycle during short outages of the boiler.[7]

One major problem in curtailing corrosion from oxygen is the exclusion of air upon boiler start-up. Normally, pressure in a deaerator is not attained until steam is admitted to the turbine and bleed steam is available for heating. It is possible to introduce more oxygen into the boiler at this time than in several months of normal operation. Admitting auxiliary steam to a deaerator to pressurize the unit to 3–5 psig can prevent much of this problem. In this condition, air is excluded and the feedwater delivered to the boiler is low in oxygen during start-up operation.

REMOVAL OF RESIDUAL OXYGEN

Chemical agents added to the feedwater or boiler water generally remove small residual quantities of oxygen. Hydrazine (N_2H_4) and sodium sulfite (Na_2SO_3) are commonly used. Sulfite reacts with oxygen to form a soluble sodium sulfate as follows:

$$Na_2SO_3 + \tfrac{1}{2}O_2 \rightarrow Na_2SO_4$$

Thus, the principal emphasis should be placed on the removal of oxygen by mechanical deaeration as well as minimizing the ingress of oxygen into the system.

USE OF CHELANTS FOR INTERNAL CONTROL

Chelants are weak organic acids with the capability of complexing or binding many cations (calcium and magnesium hardness as well as heavy metals) into a soluble organic ring structure as illustrated in Fig. 13. Chelants are in the neutralized sodium-salt form. They hydrolyze in boiler water to an organic anion. Full hydrolysis depends on a relatively high pH level. The anionic chelant has reactive sites that attract coordination sites on cations. These coordination sites are areas on the ion that are receptive to chemical bonding. In this manner, cations (hardness salts) entering the boiler as contamination from the condensate system, combine with the chelant to form a stable chelate. Deposition of hardness on boiler internal surfaces may therefore be prevented.

Although many substances have chelating properties, *EDTA* (Ethylene Diamine Tetracetic Acid) is the most suitable for boiler feedwater treatment. As with any internal chemical treatment, however, the application and limitations must be clearly understood. Currently, chelants are limited to boiler pressures of less than 1000 psig because of their thermal decomposition at saturation temperatures corresponding to higher pressures. In addition, overfeeding of chelants can lead to corrosion of boiler tubes as chelation of the protective magnetite (Fe_3O_4) film can occur. For a more detailed discussion, see reference 1.

CORROSION DAMAGE IN POWER PLANTS

The major purpose of feedwater and boiler-water treatment is to avoid corrosion and associated tube failures. Most materials that form boiler deposits originate in the preboiler system. Adherence to recommended operating procedures during start-up, normal operation,

shutdown, and outages of a power plant is vital to minimize corrosion and to avoid the entry of corrosion products into the steam generator. Corrosion damage may be in the form of a general attack of the metal surface, pitting, or localized attack of the metal surface beneath internal deposits.

GENERAL SURFACE ATTACK

One type of corrosion is oxygen attack of ferritic materials of construction. Such corrosion may take place throughout the preboiler/boiler cycle. Corrosion from oxygen can occur during any period of the power-plant lifetime, from erection to operation, as well as standby conditions.

Another type of general overall corrosion is caused by acid or alkaline contamination of the boiler water in the presence of deposited products, and occurs during system operation. Improper condensate and feedwater pH levels also cause this type of general attack within the preboiler system.

PITTING AND LOCALIZED ATTACK

Pitting of various types can affect the internal surfaces of all tubes and components. Pitting is electrochemical in nature, with the pitted area anodic to the surrounding nonpitted metal surface. If conditions favorable to pitting exist —such as excessive dissolved oxygen in the boiler water/feedwater or an acidic chemical environment—one of several normally innocuous factors can cause severe local attack. Crevices, such as those formed by deposits or minor variations in metallurgical structure, may act to promote localized corrosion. Normal, but higher-than-average, peak stress also can contribute to preferential pitting.

There has been the increased trend in fossil systems toward peaking, variable-pressure, low-load, and two-shifting operations, with frequent shutdowns—all which have contributed to increased numbers of failures associated with peculiar corrosion patterns related to frequent introduction of oxygen during outage and start-up periods. A look at several instances of pitting attack will provide a better

Fig. 14 Pitting on internal surface of waterwall tube (mag 3/4X)

Fig. 15 Sectional view of one pit shown in Fig. 14 (mag 3-1/2X)

Fig. 16 Cracklike corrosion penetrations on internal surface of waterwall tube

Fig. 17 Sectional view across cracklike penetration shown in Fig. 16

Fig. 18 General pitting attack from inside surface of waterwall tube. Pitting affected entire tube circumference but was more severe under external web (mag 8X).

appreciation for the need in developing protection when the corrosion potential is high.

EXAMPLES OF PITTING CORROSION

Figs. 14 through 23 show a variety of corrosive attack attributable to pitting. Generally, the term *pitting* denotes localized crater-like attack of a type shown in Figs. 14 and 15. But there are failures in which individual pits join, producing crack-like penetrations of the type indicated in Fig. 16. In the absence of a corrosion or metallurgical term describing this type of corrosion penetration, the condition has been included under the broad category of pitting attack.

The orientation and location of the crack-like indications shown in Fig. 17 can best be explained by pitting preferential to an area of somewhat higher strain than the surrounding metal. Differences in strain promote the formation of anode-cathode cells and the resulting corrosion at the anode is oriented perpendicular to the direction of maximum residual or applied strain.

The pitting attack shown in Figs. 18 and 19 affected the entire tube circumference, but was deepest under the welded web. In this instance, differences in metallurgical structure may also have been a factor in promoting the electrochemical cell.

This type of pitting attack has also been found in some lower waterwall drums. Fig. 20 shows an example of that attack.

The overall character of these cracklike indications are not typical of corrosion fatigue cracking. The bottom of the penetrations show no evidence of cracking and the shape of the void indicates they were formed as a result of corrosion. When tubes exhibiting internal surface cracklike indications (Fig. 21) have been reverse flattened and bent to force fracture along these linear indications, the penetrations show themselves to be a series of aligned corrosion pits (Fig. 22). The evidence strongly suggests that a pitting mechanism can initiate and propagate cracklike penetrations. In some instances the penetrations appear to be a series of pits atop one another, giving the impression of separate time periods when pitting attack has resumed at the bottom of the penetrations as shown in Fig. 23.

CORROSION IN THE FEEDWATER CYCLE

Eliminating corrosion in the feedwater heaters and piping aids materially in decreasing the problem of deposition of oxides on heat-transfer surfaces of boilers. This is accomplished by reducing the level of dissolved gases, as oxygen and carbon dioxide, in feedwater and by adjusting the pH of the water.

Fig. 19 Pitting attack similar to Fig. 18 with deep, clearly corrosion-related, localized, cracklike penetration under external web (mag 8X)

Fig. 20 Cracklike corrosion penetration at inside surface of lower waterwall drum at toe of nozzle weld

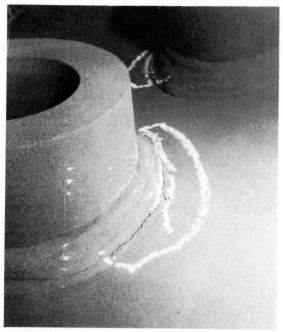

Fig. 22 Sectional through-the-wall view of Fig. 21 tube after flattening and bending to promote fracture along a penetration. Inside diameter (ID) surface is at bottom, and darker craters from the ID surface are pits. (The remaining wall portion is sound metal which fractured as a result of the flattening and reverse bending.) The cracklike penetrations result from aligned pits.

Fig. 21 Internal surface of tube with longitudinally oriented, cracklike indications (mag 3X)

Fig. 23 Crack-like corrosion penetrations halfway through tube wall, strongly suggesting that propagation results from separate time periods of pitting at the root of the penetration

Formerly this was done by adding compounds such as caustic to the feedwater or by adding a part of the boiler blowdown to the condensate.

Feedwater used to control the temperature of superheated or reheated steam cannot have solid chemicals, such as caustic or phosphate, added to it. To assure protection to preboiler equipment, volatile alkaline chemicals have been developed to raise the pH of the water without forming solid residues in the boiler. The selection of chemical is based on its temperature stability in the superheater and reheater.

Controlled quantities of ammonia (NH_3), morpholine (C_4H_9NO) or cyclohexylamine ($C_6H_{11}NH_2$) will elevate the pH of the feedwater. These compounds volatilize with the steam from boiler water and react with gases like carbon dioxide to neutralize the acidity of the condensate. Classed as neutralizing amines, they are commonly used to protect metallic surfaces from corrosion in the equipment ahead of the boiler.

Amines such as morpholine and cyclohexylamine are preferred to ammonia for pH control in situations where excessive decomposition of these chemicals does not occur in the boiler. If present in high concentrations, ammonia will attack the copper alloys in feedwater heaters. A copper ammonium complex is formed when the pH of the condensate is above 9.7. Also, the copper activity with ammonia is accelerated in the presence of oxygen. Typical reactions of copper and excessive ammonia are as follows.

$$2Cu + 4NH_3 + 2H_2O \rightarrow$$
$$2Cu(NH_3)_2{}^{++} + H_2 + 2OH -$$
$$Cu + 4NH_3 + 2H_2O \rightarrow$$
$$Cu(NH_3)_4{}^{++} + H_2 + 2OH -$$

Amines do not exhibit similar reaction tendencies. It has also been established that ammonia, in controlled quantities of 0.2 to 0.3 ppm in a condensate low in carbon dioxide, will assure a protective pH in the cycle (9.0) and will not attack copper surfaces.

This chemical action increases the concentration of solids in boiler water. Hydrazine reacts with oxygen to form nitrogen and water.

$$N_2H_4 + O_2 \rightarrow N_2 + 2H_2O$$

Temperature affects the reactivity and stability of sulfite and hydrazine. The reaction of sulfite with oxygen proceeds at room temperature. Generally, cobalt catalyst is added to speed up the reaction at lower temperatures. Sulfite decomposition increases with temperature and local concentration in boiler water. Sodium sulfite decomposes in boiler water as follows:

$$Na_2SO_3 + 2H_2O \rightarrow 2NaOH + H_2SO_3$$
$$H_2SO_3 \rightarrow H_2O + SO_2$$

Sulfur dioxide (SO_2) is an acidic anhydride which increases corrosion of metals when it is dissolved in condensate films formed on wetted surfaces of a turbine or condenser.

Concentration of sulfite must be controlled to minimize decomposition at elevated pressures. Recommended limits are shown in Table III. Above 2100 psig, sulfite decomposition is accelerated. For this reason, sulfite should not be used for reducing oxygen in very high pressure boilers.

Sodium sulfite is an effective reducing agent on boiler water. Besides its reaction with oxygen, the chemical reduces oxides of iron and copper as follows:

$$2CuO + Na_2SO_3 \rightarrow Cu_2O + Na_2SO_4$$
$$3Fe_2O_3 + Na_2SO_3 \rightarrow 2Fe_3O_4 + Na_2SO_4$$

Its consumption in boiler water is a measure of oxygen and oxidized substances added with the feedwater into a boiler. The reduction of cupric oxide begins at about 280°F and is complete at about 400°F. Reduction of ferric oxide begins at about 440°F and is complete at 540°F.

Hydrazine reacts with oxygen very slowly at temperatures below 350°F. Above 450°F, hydrazine is decomposed rapidly to nitrogen, hydrogen and ammonia. The principal benefit of

Table III. Limits

Boiler Pressure, psig	Concentration, ppm
Below 600	20–40
600–900	5–10

hydrazine is its ability to reduce the oxidized forms of copper and iron. In this state the general corrosion of the metal surfaces is reduced in the preboiler cycle. Copper oxide is reduced with hydrazine at temperatures as low as 150°F. Iron oxide (Fe_2O_3) can be reduced at a temperature of 250°F.

Normally, hydrazine is added to the cycle at the outlet of the condensate pump at a rate to assure a residual of 10–20 ppb (parts per billion) at the inlet of the economizer.

Some of the reactions of hydrazine in the feedwater cycle and boiler are

Decomposition
$$3N_2H_4 \rightarrow N_2 + 4NH_3$$
$$2N_2H_4 \rightarrow N_2 + H_2 + 2NH_3$$

Reduction
$$6Fe_2O_3 + N_2H_4 \rightarrow 4Fe_3O_4 + N_2 + 2H_2O$$
$$2CuO + N_2H_4 \rightarrow Cu_2O + N_2 + 2H_2O$$

Reducing agents aid in curbing corrosion but will not prevent metal attack when oxygen is present in the boiler feedwater. At higher temperatures, the action of oxygen with steel exceeds that of the reducing agents.

Table IV lists the stability characteristics of volatile amines. Both morpholine and cyclo hexylamine have temperature stability limits. Ammonia, hydrogen and carbon decomposition products are formed in the dissociation of these amines at high temperatures. Ammonia is stable and has been used at steam temperatures as high as 1200°F. As a result, ammonia is the recommended compound for use in controlling pH of condensate in high-pressure, high-temperature boiler systems. The other amines are not recommended with metal temperatures in the boiler higher than the 1000°F level.

Another method used to protect feedwater heaters and piping is the addition of filming amines. Their function is to form an impervious nonwettable film that acts as a barrier to reaction between the metal and water. Octadecylamine ($C_{18}H_{37}NH_2$) is the most commonly used filming amine. These compounds have practical value in industrial plants where the area of surfaces to be protected are large and the makeup is high. Best results are obtained when the pH level of the water is below 8.0.

Control of iron and copper corrosion in the feedwater system should be regulated to assure less than 10 ppb of these compounds in the feedwater. This is obtained in systems using neutralizing amines at a pH level of 8.8 to 9.2 and where the oxygen content is low.

Minimum corrosion of metals in feedwater heaters and piping occurs when a protective pH is maintained and the content of dissolved gases such as oxygen, carbon dioxide, sulfur dioxide and hydrogen sulfide is at a minimum. The chemical control for pH by ammonia or neutralizing amines must be established to ascertain that the rise in alkalinity is from the chemical itself. As noted in the laboratory studies of Corey and Finnegan previously cited, pure condensate (neutral pH) will dissolve iron and copper so as to elevate the pH of

Table IV. Stability of Volatile Water-Treating Materials

Chemical	Formula	Pressure psig	Temp °F	Percent Decomposed
Ammonia	NH_3	4270	1202	0
Cyclohexy-lamine	$C_6H_{11}NH_2$	4270	1202	88
Morpholine	$O(C_2H_4)_2NH$	4270	1202	100
Hydrazine	N_2H_4	4270	1202	100

Fig. 24 Ductile gouging

the feedwater to a value approaching 8.5 at the inlet to the economizer. In this case then, the pH rise is at the expense of metals, and the boiler feedwater will contain excessive quantities of corrosion products.

Oxygen will increase the overall corrosion problem in the feedwater system. Ferric hydroxide $(Fe[OH]_3)$ is highly insoluble and precipitates readily on heated surfaces. Changes in flow characteristics dislodge the oxides and they are eventually introduced into the boiler. In most cases, feedwater analysis will not disclose the presence of corrosion where oxygen is high. The reaction in forming the insoluble residue is

$$Fe + 2H_2O \rightarrow Fe(OH)_2 + H_2$$
$$4Fe(OH)_2 + O_2 + 2H_2O \rightarrow 4Fe(OH)_3$$

While a pH value of about 9.0 will reduce the solution of copper, the principal influence in the attack of copper is the presence of oxygen. In the reactions

$$2Cu + 2H_2O \rightarrow 2Cu^+ + H_2 + 2e^-$$
$$Cu + 2H_2O \rightarrow Cu^{++} + H_2 + 2OH$$

it is apparent that presence of oxygen reduces the hydrogen overvoltage of the copper and accelerates corrosion.[8]

CORROSION DAMAGE IN BOILERS

Deviations from recommended chemistry limits which result in depressed or elevated pH values promote failures of boiler tubing. Although there are many variations, the majority of failures can be classified into one of the following two categories:

■ Ductile gouging—Normally, irregular wastage of the tube metal beneath a porous deposit characterizes this type damage. The damage progresses to failure when the tube wall thins to a point where stress rupture occurs locally. In this process, the microstructure of the metal does not change and the tubing retains its ductility. Fig. 24 illustrates ductile gouging.

■ Hydrogen damage—This type corrosion damage usually occurs beneath a relatively dense deposit. Although some wastage occurs, the tube normally fails by thick-edge fracture before the wall thickness is reduced to the point where stress rupture would occur. Hydrogen, produced in the corrosion reaction, diffuses through the underlying metal, causing decarburization and intergranular microfissuring of the structure. Brittle fracture occurs along the partially separated boundaries, and in many cases, an entire section is blown out of an affected tube. Examples of these failures are shown in Figs. 25 and 26.

Fig. 25 **Thick-edge waterwall tube failure caused by hydrogen damage**

Fig. 26 **Another typical waterwall failure from hydrogen damage**

Internal metal oxide deposits which permit boiler-water solids to concentrate during the process of steam generation accelerate both types of attack. When the boiler water contains highly soluble alkaline treatment chemicals such as sodium hydroxide or potassium salts, ductile attack is more probable. Hydrogen damage, on the other hand, is more likely to occur when a low pH boiler-water environment results from condenser leakage or some other type of system contamination.[9]

According to an ASME/EEI-sponsored laboratory research program[10], clean tubes are not susceptible to corrosion even under high heat-transfer conditions unless unusually high concentrations of acid or alkali are present. In addition, fouled tubes do not appear to be susceptible to corrosion when contaminants are present if proper boiler-water treatment is maintained. These observations can be explained by the "concentrating film" theory.

The Berl and Van Taack curve (Fig. 11) illustrates the relative corrosion of carbon steel under various acid and alkaline conditions. Bulk boiler-water concentrations are always well within the range of low corrosion rates. But, as heat is transferred through the boiler tube wall to a water-steam mixture, a temperature gradient is established, and the internal tube metal temperature must reach a value slightly higher than the bulk fluid temperature. As boiler water is converted to steam, the dissolved solids concentrate in a residual film as shown in Fig. 27. The solids concentration in this film increases until the boiling point of the solution is elevated to the temperature at the wall.

It is improbable that such high concentrations can be reached in a clean tube under normal boiling conditions. Theoretically, the bulk of the film-temperature drop is experienced within a laminar film of about 0.001-in. thickness. Free diffusion of ions into the turbulent fluid would prevent the establishment of a concentration gradient. Only when porous internal deposits are formed in areas of heat absorption is it possible to produce very high concentrations. The deposit itself acts as a dif-

fusion barrier and in so doing increases the probability of high local concentrations being reached.

Because porous deposits may exist, boiler-water chemicals should be of a type that will not become highly corrosive when concentrated. Experience indicates that caustic soda and potassium salts are particularly objectionable. Alkalinity can be produced with sodium phosphate (coordinated phosphate treatment) without the risk of extremely high pH values being present upon concentration. Alkalinity control of boiler water may also be achieved by adding a volatile amine such as ammonia and is required for once-through units.

Condenser cooling waters represent a potential source of contamination of the boiler water. Depending on the chemical constituents dissolved in the cooling water, highly acid or alkaline materials may be formed in the boiler environment as a result of condenser leakage.

Because of its poor buffering capability, volatile treatment provides little protection against

Fig. 27 Illustration of "concentrating film" theory. Film temperature gradient of 15° is developed because of heat transfer. Soluble solids in boiler water are concentrated in the surface film during steam generation to produce "nonboiling equilibrium." Although the caustic concentration in the boiler water is only 100 ppm, the concentration in the surface film must equal 220,000 ppm to elevate the boiling point 15°.

acid attack of boiler tubing. With a stronger alkaline additive, coordinated phosphate treatment results in a more highly buffered boiler water, one in which acid-producing reactions from salt inleakage are better suppressed. Optimum treatment programs based on this method are discussed in the following section.

TUBE FAILURES CAUSED BY OVERHEATING

While the preceding discussion focused on the role played by internal deposits in the cor-

rosion of boiler tubes, it should be emphasized that deposits also promote the majority of tube failures caused by overheating.

Fig. 28 illustrates the temperature conditions existing in a typical furnace-wall tube. The heat flux of 100,000 Btu/ft²·hr is established by the furnace flame-temperature spectrum and the bulk fluid temperature of 640°F is fixed by boiler pressure. The temperature profile is then established by the ΔT required to drive the 100,000 flux through each segment of resistance. With nucleate boiling on a clean tube, the ΔT across the fluid film is quite small (10°F) and the overall temperature differential (90°F)

Fig. 28 **Furnace wall tube—nucleate boiling**

Fig. 30 **Furnace wall tube—film boiling**

Fig. 29 **Furnace wall tube—nucleate boiling with deposit**

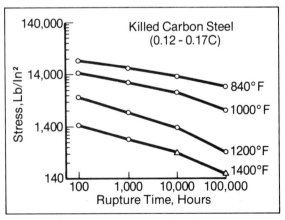

Fig. 31 **Stress and temperature versus time-to-rupture**

results from the resistance of the tube metal.

Fig. 29 shows what happens to the tube-temperature profile if an internal deposit exists. Approximately 60°F is required to drive the 100,000 heat flux through the deposit, so both the inside and outside metal temperatures must rise correspondingly.

Fig. 30 illustrates the temperature profile under a film-boiling condition. The reduced-film coefficient increases the ΔT across the film to 310°F and the metal temperatures rise correspondingly. It should be noted that the flux is constant at 100,000 Btu/ft² · hr for all cases.

STRESS RUPTURE

The strength of carbon steel tubing is nearly constant to about 840°F, at which point it begins to lose strength rapidly. If tube metal temperature is gradually increased beyond this temperature, it will plastically deform (creep) and then rupture. The approximate time-to-rupture is a function of the hoop-stress and the temperature (Fig. 31). The hoop stress (S) equals the product of the internal pressure (P) times the tube radius (r) divided by the wall thickness (x).

$$S = \frac{P\,r}{x}$$

(1)

Simple visual examination of a failed section reveals a great deal about the tube-temperature history. In deposit-caused overheating, local tube temperatures rise gradually so that specific points begin to creep before others (blistering). Deposits tend to form nonuniformly, and even a 20°F difference in temperature can have a pronounced effect on localized creep. Blistering is almost always caused by internal deposition, and conversely, overheating because of deposits will almost always be evidenced by blisters.

When an upset of boiling conditions, such as departure from nucleate boiling (DNB) elevates tube temperature, a temperature excursion will occur. Metal temperature will jump quickly

from the normal condition to a higher value consistent with the upset.

If the temperature excursion is great, the tube may fail very quickly. For instance, if a tube is completely blocked during operation, the tube temperature will rise immediately to the failure-point temperature. The rapid plastic deformation of these very short-term ruptures produces very thin-edged fractures. In the case of major flow interruptions, the tube bulges over an extended length and fails like a balloon bursting.

If a DNB excursion places the tube-metal temperature in the range of 840 to 1020°F, the tube will take a longer time to fail. During this period, intergranular oxidation of the metal will occur and will weaken the structure. Long-term failures, therefore, tend to be thick-edged. The higher the temperature and stress conditions are above the creep limit, the shorter the time to failure and the thinner the metal edge at the fracture. Fig. 32 presents examples of a short, an intermediate, and a long-term failure.

Metallographic analysis is an important tool for analyzing tube-temperature history. The normal pearlitic microstructure of carbon steel boiler tubing can be seen in Fig. 33. The light areas are iron, and the dark areas are pearlite consisting of alternate layers of iron and iron carbide. The normal operating temperature of a boiler tube will not alter this structure. If the temperature of steel is maintained in the range of 930 to 1340°F for an extended period of time, carbon migrates from the pearlite to form spheres of carbon. This process, known as spheroidization, progresses slowly at 930°F and rapidly at temperatures near the lower critical range (1340°F). Fig. 34 shows carbon steel with various degrees of spheroidization.

If the tube is heated to a temperature greater than 1340°F and is then allowed to cool slowly to below 930°F, the normal pearlitic structure will be re-established. But, if the tube is heated above 1340°F and is cooled very rapidly, a martensitic structure (Fig. 35) will be produced. This type of microstructure is likely to be found in very short-term overheating failures in

11–26

which the water escaping through the rupture suddenly quenches the overheated tube metal.

RESEARCH STUDY ON INTERNAL CORROSION

The previously referenced *ASME/EEI-* sponsored laboratory research program on internal corrosion was instrumental in bringing an understanding to the various corrosion mechanisms discussed in the previous sections. The following recap of the more important conclusions includes our interpretation of their practical significance:

1. When heat-transfer surfaces are free of deposits, corrosion is unlikely to occur over a wide range of heat-transfer and boiling conditions regardless of the method of water treatment employed.

2. Corrosion will not occur with volatile treatment of pure boiler water (less than two ppm solids) even when heat-transfer surfaces are fouled and/or conditions of DNB exist.

3. Corrosion will not occur when coordinated phosphate treatment is employed even when heat-transfer surfaces are fouled and/or conditions of DNB exist.

4. Under the conditions of item 3, chemical hideout of sodium phosphate will occur if heat-transfer surfaces are fouled and/or DNB conditions exist.

5. There appears, however, to be no relationship between hideout and corrosion of tube metal.

Fig. 32   Physical appearance of overheating failures

**Fig. 33   Photomicrograph—
normal pearlitic structure of carbon steel**

Fig. 34   Spheroidization: left, mild; right, extensive

Fig. 35 **Martensitic structure**

6. Caustic soda concentrations ranging from 10–20 ppm in the boiler water (with a pH of from 10.5 to 10.8) can cause serious corrosion if internal surfaces are fouled with deposits. Corrosion is rapid even under nucleate boiling conditions, and complete penetration of a 5-mm tube wall can occur in several days.

7. With certain types of condenser cooling water, a condenser leak will cause a pH reduction in the boiling water. With fouled surface conditions, hydrogen embrittlement may then occur. The rate of attack is rapid and of the same order of magnitude described in item 6.

8. The analysis of cooled samples can be very deceptive in interpreting behavior in high-temperature boiler-water environment a sample which is alkaline at room temperature may be acidic at high temperatures, and vice-versa. Understanding the behavior of each specific contaminant which can be introduced by way of condenser leakage is essential.

9. The rate of deposition of preboiler corrosion products increases with increasing heat-flux. Deposition is substantially greater on the hot side of the tube where boiling occurs.

The research program did not conclude that corrosion was the fault of either the operator or the designer. It demonstrated that both chemical and mechanical factors are involved and that they are largely interdependent. A change in one variable will affect the manner in which other variables influence corrosion. Normally, several factors must be simultaneously out-of-line to produce corrosion. As a result, corrosion is a fairly low probability event despite the fairly large number of potentially adverse physical and chemical conditions which temporarily exist.

UTILITY BOILER-WATER AND FEEDWATER TREATMENT IN THE PREVENTION OF CYCLE CORROSION

If extensive corrosion during outage conditions is to be avoided, proper wet lay-up methods are essential. Because large utility boilers cannot be successfully dried to produce an internal atmosphere free of moisture, wet lay-up procedures are recommended even for long outage periods.[11]

PROTECTION DURING OUTAGE CONDITIONS

For any outage longer than four days, the preboiler/boiler cycle should be filled, to the greatest extent possible, with a solution inhibited to prevent corrosion, and pressurized with nitrogen to prevent air inleakage. Excellent results have been obtained with condensate containing appropriate amounts of hydrazine and ammonia for lay-up periods of several years. As both materials are volatile, there is no objection to their use even in nondrainable superheater and reheater sections of the boiler. Where freezing is a problem, it is sometimes necessary to drain portions of the steam generator. This should be accomplished under a positive nitrogen pressure. Nitrogen blanketing is recommended even when the boiler can be maintained full of inhibited condensate.

The success or failure of standby protection also depends upon the proper design and selec-

Table V. Recommended Lay-Up Procedures C-E Drum-Type Utility Units

Type of Shutdown	Procedure	Notes
Preoperational Period Post Hydro (See Note 1)	With the economizer, waterwalls, superheater, and reheater filled to overflowing pressurize the unit with nitrogen to 5 psig pressure (See Notes 4 & 6).	1. All nondrainable sections to be hydrostatically tested should be filled with demineralized or condensate quality water containing 10 ppm of ammonia and 200 ppm of hydrazine. This should produce a solution pH of approximately 10.0. The superheater should be filled first, to overflow into the boiler drum. Then the economizer and waterwalls can be filled through normal fill connections (See Note 2) with demineralized or condensate quality water, or if not available, any source of clean, filtered water may be used. This water should also contain 10 ppm of ammonia and 200 ppm of hydrazine.
Preoperational Period Post Chemical Cleaning	1. Introduce demineralized or condensate quality water containing 10 ppm of ammonia and 200 ppm of hydrazine into the superheater, reheater, feedwater heaters, (tube side) and associated piping, economizer and waterwalls (Refer to Notes 3 & 4). 2. Nitrogen cap the superheater, feedwater heaters (shell side) and drum. Maintain 5 psig nitrogen pressure (See Notes 5 & 6).	2. Hydrazine and ammonia should be added in a manner that results in a uniform concentration throughout. They may be added to the system in several ways, as for example: a. By pumping concentrated solutions through the chemical feed equipment and blend filling to achieve the desired concentrations.
Short Outage— 4 Days or Less	1. Maintain the same hydrazine and ammonia concentrations as those present during normal operation. 2. Establish and maintain a 5 psig nitrogen cap on the superheater and the steam drum (See Notes 5 & 6). 3. Nitrogen cap the shell side of the feedwater heaters.	b. If condenser leakage is not a cause for shutdown, concentrated solutions can be introduced directly into the hotwell where they can be mixed to achieve the desired concentrations. If condensate demineralizers are used, they must be bypassed during this operation. It is important to have the fluid temperature in the cycle below 400°F before addition of hydrazine. If this temperature is exceeded, the hydrazine will decompose.
Short Outage— 4 Days or Less, Unit Partially Drained for Repairs	1. Drain and open only those sections requiring repairs. 2. Isolate remainder of unit under 5 psig nitrogen pressure where possible (See Notes 5 & 6). 3. Maintain the same hydrazine and ammonia concentrations for water remaining in the cycle as those present during normal operation. 4. Nitrogen cap the shell side of the feedwater heaters.	3. The tube side of copper alloy feedwater heaters should be filled with demineralized water containing 0.5 ppm of ammonia and 50 ppm of hydrazine. 4. If freezing is a problem, the water in drainable circuits can be displaced with nitrogen and the unit laid up under 5 psig nitrogen pressure. Auxiliary heat may be applied to keep the nondrainable sections from freezing.
Long Outage— Longer than 4 Days	1. Fill the superheater and reheater with demineralized or condensate quality water containing 10 ppm of ammonia and 200 ppm of hydrazine. The pH of the solution should be approximately 10.0. Add the fill water to the outlet of the nondrainable sections (See Note 4). 2. Increase the hydrazine and ammonia concentration in the waterwalls, economizer and feedwater heaters (tube side) and associated piping to 200 ppm and 10 ppm respectively (See Notes 2, 3, and 4).	5. If the reheater can be isolated, it should also be capped with 5 psig nitrogen. When the outage is expected to extend beyond 2 months, provisions should be made to isolate and nitrogen cap the reheater, if this was not done previously.

Table V. Recommended Lay-Up Procedures C-E Drum-Type Utility Units

Type of Shutdown	Procedure	Notes
	3. Establish and maintain a 5 psig nitrogen cap on superheater and drum (Notes 5 & 6). **4.** Nitrogen cap the shell side of the feedwater heaters.	**6.** Nitrogen cap should be applied through the drum vent and superheater outlet header drain/vent, as the unit is cooled, when pressure drops to 5 psig. Admission of air through atmospheric vents should be avoided.
Long Outage— Longer than 4 Days, Unit Partially Drained for Repairs	**1.** Drain and open only those sections requiring repairs. **2.** Fill the superheater and reheater (if not requiring draining for repairs) with demineralized or condensate quality water containing 10 ppm of ammonia and 200 ppm of hydrazine. The pH of the solution should be approximately 10.0. Add the fill water to the outlet of nondrainable sections (Note 4). **3.** Increase the hydrazine and ammonia concentrations in the tube side of the feedwater heaters and the undrained circuits of the economizer and waterwalls to 200 ppm and 10 ppm respectively (See Notes 2, 3 & 4). **4.** Establish and maintain a 5 psig nitrogen cap on the undrained sections of the unit, where possible (See Notes 5 & 6). **5.** Nitrogen cap the shell side of the feedwater heaters. **6.** After completion of the repairs fill the drained sections with demineralized or condensate quality water containing 10 ppm of ammonia and 200 ppm of hydrazine. Cap with nitrogen (See Notes 2, 3, 4, & 5).	

Table VI. Recommended Lay-Up Procedures C-E Combined Circulation Units

Post Chemical Cleaning Preoperational Period	**1.** Introduce demineralized or condensate quality water containing 10 ppm of ammonia and 200 ppm of hydrazine into the feedwater heaters (tube side), economizer, furnace walls, superheater and reheater (Refer to Notes 2 & 3). **2.** Nitrogen blanket the shell side of the feedwater heaters, superheat, and furnace wall sections. Maintain 5 psig nitrogen pressure (Refer to Note 4).	**1.** Hydrazine and ammonia should be added in a manner that results in a uniform concentration throughout. They may be added to the system in several ways as for example: a. By pumping concentrated solutions through the chemical feed equipment and blend filling to achieve the desired concentrations. b. If condenser leakage is not a cause for shutdown, concentrated solutions can be introduced directly into the hotwell where they can be mixed to achieve the desired concentrations. The condensate polishing system must be bypassed.
Short Outage 4 Days or Less	**1.** Maintain the same hydrazine and ammonia concentrations as those present during normal operation. **2.** Establish and maintain a 5 psig nitrogen cap on the superheater and furnace wall sections (Refer to Note 4). **3.** Nitrogen blanket the shell side of the feedwater heaters.	During hydrazine and ammonia introduction, circulation should be maintained through BE and WD valves to insure

Table VI. Recommended Lay-Up Procedures C-E Combined Circulation Units

Type of Shutdown	Procedure	Notes
Short Outage 4 Days or Less, Unit Partially Drained for Repairs	1. Drain and open only sections requiring repairs. 2. Isolate remainder of unit under 5 psig nitrogen pressure where possible (Note 4). 3. Maintain the same hydrazine and ammonia concentration for water remaining in the cycle as during normal operation. 4. Nitrogen blanket the shell side of the feedwater heaters.	adequate mixing in the system. If the superheat section is to be laid up wet, circulation should be maintained through the BE, SA and SD valves. Furnace wall outlet pressure should not exceed 1000 psig while maintaining circulation during introduction of hydrazine and ammonia. It is important to have the fluid temperature in the cycle below 400°F before the addition of the hydrazine. If this temperature is exceeded, the hydrazine will decompose.
Long Outage Greater than 4 Days	1. Fill the superheater and reheater with demineralized or condensate quality water containing 10 ppm of ammonia and 200 ppm of hydrazine. The pH of the solution should be approximately 10.0. Add the fill water to the outlet of nondrainable sections (Note 3). 2. Increase the hydrazine and ammonia concentrations in the economizer, furnace walls, and feedwater heaters (tube side) and associated piping to 200 ppm and 10 ppm respectively (Refer to Notes 1 & 3). 3. Establish and maintain a 5 psig nitrogen cap on the furnace wall and superheat sections (Refer to Note 4). 4. Nitrogen cap the shell side of the feedwater heaters.	2. All sections to be hydrostatically tested should be filled with demineralized or condensate quality water containing 10 ppm of ammonia and 200 ppm of hydrazine. This should produce a solution pH of approximately 10.0. 3. If freezing is a problem, the water in the drainable circuits can be displaced with nitrogen and the unit laid up under 5 psig nitrogen. Auxiliary heat may be applied to keep the nondrainable sections from freezing. 4. If the reheat section can be isolated, it should also be capped with 5 psig nitrogen. When the outage is extended to 2 months or longer, provisions should be made to isolate and nitrogen cap the reheat sections, if this was not done previously.
Long Outage Greater than 4 Days, Unit Partially Drained for Repairs	1. Drain and open only those sections requiring repairs. 2. Fill the superheater and reheater (if draining for repairs is not required) with demineralized or condensate quality water containing to 10 ppm of ammonia and 200 ppm of hydrazine. The pH of the solution should be approximately 10.0. Add the fill water to the outlet of nondrainable sections (Note 3). 3. Increase the hydrazine and ammonia concentrations in the tube side of the feedwater heaters and the undrained circuits of the economizer and furnace walls to 200 ppm and 10 ppm respectively. (Notes 1 & 3). 4. Establish and maintain a 5 psig nitrogen cap on the undrained section of the unit, where possible (Refer to Note 4). 5. Nitrogen cap the shell side of the feedwater heaters. 6. After repairs, fill drained sections with demineralized or condensate quality water containing 10 ppm of ammonia and 200 ppm of hydrazine. Cap with nitrogen (Notes 1 & 3).	

tion of chemical-feed equipment and the ability to provide an inert gas blanket.[12] Utilities with operating units that are predominantly base-loaded may get along with simple, inexpensive manual systems for introduction of lay-up additives and nitrogen. Systems having load characteristics that result in frequent boiler shutdowns require more elaborate, foolproof, wet lay-up protection systems if problems are to be avoided. Tables V and VI detail recommended procedures to be utilized on all high-pressure utility units.

MINIMIZING CORROSION DURING START-UP OPERATION

During the start-up of a high-pressure boiler, deaeration and pH adjustment must be provided to assure that low feedwater-corrosion-product levels are achieved. Plant start-ups without deaeration will promote continued corrosion of feedwater-system materials of construction.[13,14,15] This will result in significant quantities of corrosion products being carried into, and depositing within, the steam generator. The supply of undeaerated feedwater will also increase corrosion of steel components within the steam generator. Deaeration of condensate during start-up operations can be obtained by use of deaerating condensers or by external deaerating heaters. Since deaeration should be accomplished early in the start-up sequence, auxiliary steam must be available for turbine-seal and deaeration requirements.

CYCLING UNITS

An adequate source of auxiliary steam should be available to the deaerating heater while the unit is starting up. If this is unavailable, pegging-steam directly from the drum should be provided until turbine extraction steam is available. As an alternative, a blowdown flash tank designed for 5 percent of the maximum steaming rate of the boiler can also be used. In units without a deaerating heater, deaeration is achieved solely by the condenser. For the condenser to effectively deaerate cold feedwater, a significant vacuum must be maintained. A reasonable approach is to recycle and deaerate the condensate in the system prior to start-up, with the necessary degree of condenser vacuum and fluid temperature.[14,16,17] (See Fig. 36.) This requires connection of a recycle line from the discharge of the feedwater heaters back to the deaerating section of the condenser to prevent the air-rich condensate in the condenser from being introduced into the boiler. The turbine must be sealed and a condenser vacuum established prior to recycle.

Including a preboiler recycle line has an additional benefit when part-flow condensate demineralization is employed in the cycle. Demineralization permits filtration of corrosion products from the recycling feedwater, and will further permit cleanup of the drains from the shell sides of the feedwater heaters during start-up. Characteristically, these heater drains contain the highest levels of crud in the system. A condensate demineralizer system designed for about 25 percent of full-load condensate flow provides all of the benefits described.[13]

Tables VII and VIII list the recommended feedwater control limits for start-up operation of drum-type cycling units.

HIGH-PRESSURE DRUM-TYPE UNITS

Although base-loaded utility drum-type units suffer from corrosion more during operation than during start-up, attention must still be directed toward procedures to prevent excessive corrosion during start-up periods. It

Fig. 36 Solubility of oxygen in water from air saturated with water vapor

has not been found necessary to install special preboiler recirculation lines or condensate demineralization equipment on base-loaded high-pressure drum-type units. Normal start-up sequence which includes the initiation of light steaming rates early in the start-up operation, coupled with boiler drum blowdown, have been found effective in reducing the impact of standby corrosion-product deposition. As already noted, conversion of the base-loaded drum-type unit to peaking or cycling

operation can bring with it a multitude of new problems.

SUPERCRITICAL—FEEDWATER

Start-up specifications are important in supercritical cycles, and neglect in this area may result in considerable deposit-caused difficulties. Combustion Engineering has placed primary emphasis on the development of start-up/cleanup procedures which assure steam-generator cleanliness over long periods of time. A sub-loop cleanup philosophy is

Table VII. Initial Start-Up and Restarts After Long Outages*, Cycling Drum-Type Boiler

Phase	Flow Path	Operations	Control Limits	Expected Cleanup Time
Preboiler Cleanup	1	Flush to waste at approx. 25% MCR	3 ppm (max.) suspended solids, measured at HP heater outlet	8 Hours
	2	Pressurize deaerator to 10–15 psig with auxiliary steam, establish condenser vacuum, and place demineralizer in service. Using condensate or a fuel pump and preboiler recirculating valve, clean up cycle maintaining 25% MCR deaerated flow. Blowdown deaerator storage tank as necessary to prevent recontamination of system.	Total suspended solids 250 (max.) Oxygen 10 Hydrazine 20 pH Copper-alloy system 8.8–9.2 Copper-free system 9.2–9.4 (All concentrations in ppb, measured at HP heater outlet; oxygen measured at deaerator outlet.)	Time dependent on run-in of equipment
System in Service		Close preboiler recirculating valve, place boiler feed pump in service and fire unit for turbine warmup roll, and synchronization. Proceed to normal feedwater control limits. Cascade heater drains to condenser for polishing until unit load exceeds 25%.	Normal Feedwater Limits Total solids 50 (max.) Total iron 10 Total silica 20 Copper 10 Oxygen 5 Hydrazine 10–20 pH Copper-alloy system 8.8–9.2 Copper-free system 9.2–9.4 (All concentrations in ppb, measured at HP heater outlet; oxygen measured at deaerator outlet.)	Normal limits should be obtained before exceeding one-third unit load.

Note: Suspended solids concentration measured by Millipore® filters with appropriate color comparator charts.

*Duration of outage longer than 4 days

utilized in which the crud level in the preboiler system is reduced to a low value before passing feedwater to the steam generator. This procedure assures the delivery to the boiler of feedwater which is low in iron, silica, copper, and oxygen.

Keeping oxygen values below 10 ppb enhances effective and rapid contaminant reduction within the preboiler cycle. Hydrated iron oxide, exposed to high-oxygen values, precipitates readily and delays cleanup time. Conversion of this material by deaeration to black magnetite is essential for fast cleanup because condensate purification equipment readily

removes magnetite. Additionally, the low-oxygen environment prevents further oxide generation.

When performed at a sufficiently high velocity, preboiler recirculation completely removes contaminants prior to furnace-wall cleanup. Based on experience, a velocity of 2 feet per second is recommended for this purpose and is obtained at approximately 25 percent maximum continuous rating (MCR) with currently designed feedwater heaters. When employing the recommended cleanup program, contaminant reduction to specified feedwater quality limits takes less than eight hours on start-up

Table VIII. Cold Restarts After Short Outages*, Cycling Drum-Type Boiler

Phase	Flow Path	Operations	Control Limits	Expected Cleanup Time
Preboiler Cleanup	2	Pressurize deaerator to 10–15 psig with auxiliary steam, establish condenser vacuum, and place demineralizer in service.		4 hours if C-E recommended lay-up procedure has been employed.
			Total suspended solids 250 (max.) Oxygen 10 Hydrazine 20	
		Using condensate or feed pump and preboiler recirculating valve, clean up cycle maintaining 25% MCR deaerated flow.	pH Copper-alloy system 8.8–9.2 Copper-free system 9.2–9.4	Does not represent a delay; this cleanup may be completed before boiler is available.
		Blow down deaerator storage tank as necessary to prevent recontamination of system.	(All concentrations in ppb, measured at HP heater outlet; oxygen measured at deaerator outlet.)	
System in Service		Place boiler feed pump in service.	Normal Feedwater Limits	
		Fire unit for turbine warmup, roll, and synchronization.	Total solids 50 (max.) Total iron 10 Total silica 20 Copper 10 Oxygen 5 Hydrazine 10–20	Normal limits should be obtained before exceeding one-third unit load.
		Proceed to normal feedwater control limits.	pH Copper-alloy system 8.8–9.2 Copper-free system 9.2–9.4	
		Cascade heater drains to condenser for polishing until load exceeds 25%.	(All concentrations in ppb, measured at HP heater outlet; oxygen measured at deaerator outlet.)	

Notes: 1. No cleanup is required if feedwater quality meets recommended limits.

2. Suspended solids concentration measured by Millipore® filters with appropriate color comparator charts.

*Duration of outage maximum 4 days.

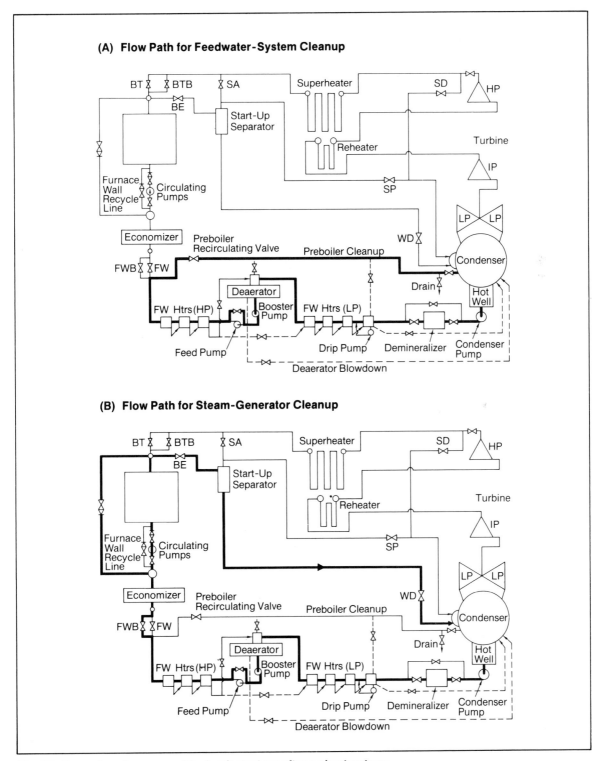

Fig. 37 **Procedure for supercritical unit start-up after a short outage**

Table IX. Recommended Start-Up/Cleanup Procedure, C-E Combined Circulation® Units (with Deaerating Heater)

Cold Restarts After Short Outages

Phase	Flow Path	Operations	Control Limits		Expected Cleanup Time
Feedwater System Cleanup	1	Pressurize deaerator to 10–15 psig with auxiliary steam, establish condenser vacuum, and place demineralizer in service.	Total Solids Total Iron Total Silica Copper Oxygen Hydrazine pH	250 (max.) 50 30 20 10 20 9.2–9.4	4 hours if C-E recommended lay-up procedure has been employed. Does not represent a delay; this cleanup may be completed before boiler is available.
		Utilizing condensate or booster pump and preboiler recirculating valve, clean up cycle maintaining 25% MCR deaerated flow. Blow down deaerator storage tank as necessary to prevent recontamination of system.	(All concentrations in ppb, available.)		

Transition Period: When control limits are met at HP heater outlet, close preboiler recirculating valve and establish BE and WD through-flow, using condensate or booster pump. To prevent excessive pressure drop across BE valve, furnace wall outlet pressure should not exceed 1000 psig during cold water operation.

Phase	Flow Path	Operations	Control Limits		Expected Cleanup Time
Steam Generator Cleanup	2	Continue BE and WD through-flow until cleanup is complete. Furnace-wall circulating pump on during this phase.	Total Solids Total Iron Total Silica Copper	750 (max.) 500 30 20	Less than 1 hour if C-E recommended lay-up procedure has been employed.
		Blow down deaerator storage tank as necessary to prevent contamination of system. When control limits are met, proceed to next step.	(All concentrations in ppb, measured at furnace-wall outlet.)		
System in Service		Place boiler feed pump in service	Normal Feedwater Limits		
		Fire unit for turbine warmup, roll, and synchronization. Proceed to normal feedwater exceeding limits. Cascade heater drains to condenser for polishing until load exceeds 25%.	Total Solids Total Iron Total Silica Copper Oxygen Hydrazine pH	50 (max.) 10 20 2 5 10 9.2–9.4	Normal limits should be obtained before exceeding one-third unit load.
			(All concentrations in ppb, measured at HP heater outlet; oxygen measured at deaerator outlet.)		

following long outages. Preboiler cleanup following short outages (up to four days) can be accomplished in three to four hours. No preboiler cleanup is required for a hot restart if the quality of the condensate meets the established standards of purity.

SUPERCRITICAL—STEAM GENERATOR

Cleanup of the furnace-wall system in a Combined Circulation supercritical unit is performed reliably and quickly because the boiler recirculation pumps provide effective scrubbing velocity. Particulate contamination is maintained in suspension and is easily removed through the start-up/separator system. This blowdown flow through the start-up system rapidly reduces furnace-wall contamination. Experience shows that the boiler furnace walls can be cleaned effectively if supplied with a deaerated feedwater at about 250°F.

Furnace-wall cleanup after long outages will normally take less than three hours. Cleanup operations after outages up to four days will not require a furnace-wall cleanup step if appropriate wet lay-up procedures have been employed. The unit should be capable of being fired as soon as any necessary preboiler recirculation is completed. A delay in start-up will occur only when the condensate is badly contaminated; under these conditions, such a delay can always be justified.

A discussion of the complete procedures and feedwater control limits recommended for start-up and normal operation of Combined Circulation units is beyond the scope of this chapter. For illustrative purposes, however, Table IX and Fig. 37 detail the procedure employed for start-ups after short outages. Start-up cleanup operations after long–duration outages require more time and additional flow paths and steps. The effectiveness of this cleanup philosophy has assured that operational chemical cleanings have not been required more often than every three to four years.[18,19]

PREVENTIVE CHEMISTRY DURING OPERATION, DRUM-TYPE UNITS

Two basic types of boiler-water treatment can be successfully utilized in high-pressure drum-type boilers: coordinated phosphate and volatile-based treatment. Volatile treatment does not require the direct addition of any treatment chemicals to the boiler. The ammonia used for feedwater pH adjustment controls boiler-water pH. Fig. 38 illustrates a low-level coordinated phosphate curve for use in high-pressure boilers. Operation with pH and phosphate values which are below the curve establishes that no free hydroxide exists within the boiler water. The recommended operating chemistry shown in Table X is reflective of this fact. Because free hydroxide does not exist under these specified conditions, ductile tube failures from caustic attack, as discussed previously, will not occur.[20]

Table X illustrates a philosophy of boiler operation with respect to level of contamination entering the cycle. The recommendations and guidelines presented in this table, coupled with recommended feedwater quality, represent the chemistry specifications which will result in long-term steam-generator integrity and cleanliness. It should be noted that coordinated phosphate boiler-water treatment must be employed during periods of condenser leakage. Volatile treatment does not have enough buffering ability to maintain pH control under these conditions.

Certain deviations from normal chemistry specifications may occur on occasion during plant life, with little or no effect on component integrity. These deviations are designated as abnormal conditions in Table X. Other possible deviations may result in extensive corrosion problems. The serious nature of such deviations requires immediate action, and this is noted where applicable.

FEEDWATER CONTROL

The steam generator acts as a concentrating device during operation. Soluble feedwater impurities which enter the boiler become concentrated in the boiler water because the steam leaving the drum carries off negligible quantities of solids. The recommended feedwater impurity limits given in Table XI cover a number of constituents. The total solids limit is specified to minimize boiler fouling. The silica concentration limit in normal operation is sufficiently low to assure that silica carryover to the turbine by the vapor or steam solubility phenomena does not occur. The oxygen and pH specifications should limit the pickup of iron and copper from the preboiler equipment to those feedwater levels necessary for long-term steam-generator cleanliness.

As long as feedwater total solids (TS) concentration is less than 0.5 ppm, boiler/turbine cycle operation is considered normal. Coupled with this is the requirement that pH value, oxygen level, and copper/iron levels are within the values shown on Table XI. There are no operational limitations, and the boiler-water control is normal.

Operation with feedwater TS concentration between 0.5 and 2.0 ppm should be limited, and condenser repairs should be scheduled as soon as practical. Values of feedwater solids concentration above 2.0 ppm TS are considered emergency levels. Unit load should be immediately reduced, the damaged condenser section isolated, and necessary repair work scheduled. The boiler-turbine cycle should be shut down if feedwater concentration cannot be reduced within eight hours to values below 2.0 ppm.

Fig. 38 **Coordinated phosphate treatment curve**

PREVENTIVE CHEMISTRY IN OPERATION OF SUPERCRITICAL UNITS

Because a supercritical unit requires the ultimate in feedwater quality, a condensate demineralizer must be included in the preboiler cycle to prevent condenser leakage salts from entering the feedwater. The normal feedwater limits for supercritical units are presented in Table XI.

Utility operators who have followed recommended start-up cleanup procedures, as well as recommended lay-up procedures, have maintained a high degree of cycle cleanliness. Virtually all Combined Circulation units are experiencing operational chemical-cleaning frequencies of from three to four years.

The successful operation of a supercritical unit with respect to water technology is coupled to the proper operation of the in-line condensate demineralizer system. Table XII summarizes information on the operation of a supercritical unit during condenser leakage. The methods of limiting operation and controlling the condensate demineralizer presented in this table, if properly implemented, will assure steam generator and turbine cleanliness.

ANALYTICAL METHODS

The implementation of control methods to minimize corrosion-product release, as well as the detection of contaminant inleakage, requires a continuous analytical program. All automatic analytical instrumentation should be maintained operational and calibrated.

If chemical auto-analyzers are not operational, greater emphasis must be placed on laboratory analyses. Membrane-filter testing may provide an adequate indication of water quality with respect to corrosion products. But primary reliance must be placed on laboratory analytical methods for contaminant and corrosion-product-level determinations. The findings of chemical analyses should determine whether, for example, cleanup circulation should continue on a supercritical unit, or whether silica values are low enough in a drum-type unit to allow a pressure increase.

Table X. Criteria for Operation of High-Pressure Drum-Type Boilers

Hotwell Conditions	Operational Limitations	Basic Boiler-Water Control		Boiler-Water Control
		Phosphate–pH	Volatile	
Total Solids <0.05 ppm (Recommended)	None	TS <50 ppm pH 9.4–9.7 PO₄ 5–10	TS <2 ppm pH 8.5–9.0	Normal
Total Solids <0.5 ppm (Acceptable)	Volatile treatment of boiler water not suitable.	TS <50 ppm pH 9.4–9.7 PO₄ 5–10		If on volatile treatment, change to coordinated phosphate-pH Control.
Total Solids 0.5 to 2.0 ppm (Abnormal)	Limited operation. Schedule inspection and repair of condenser as soon as system load requirements permit.	TS <100 ppm pH 9.5–10.5 PO₄ 5–20 ppm		Immediately start chemical injection pumps to maintain excess phosphate and pH conditions. Do not continue to operate unit if pH cannot be maintained above 8.0 or the total solids below 100 ppm. Increase blowdown to limit total dissolved solids concentration. Avoid unnecessary use of desuperheating spray water by (1) permitting reheat temperature to fall, or (2) reducing load.
Total Solids >2.0 ppm (Excessive)	Emergency operation. 1. Immediately reduce load as necessary to permit isolation of damaged condenser. 2. Prepare for orderly shutdown of the unit if hotwell concentration cannot be quickly reduced below 2.0 ppm.	TS <100 ppm pH 9.5–10.5 PO₄ 5–20 ppm		See above. Prepare to establish chemical conditions for wet lay-up of boiler unit and auxiliary equipment during condenser repair.

On any high-pressure utility boiler/turbine cycle, the condenser leak detection system is particularly important. Leakage instrumentation should be installed such that, if the condenser has segmented compartments, each compartment can be analyzed for leakage individually. Cation conductivity offers good sensitivity for detecting condenser leaks. Many plants are also being equipped with sodium analyzers for maximum sensitivity.

Table XIII gives a recommended frequency of analysis for high-pressure utility steam generators if continuous analyzers are not available.

INDUSTRIAL BOILER-WATER TREATMENT

Internal chemical treatment systems are primarily designed to prevent scale formations resulting from residual amounts of calcium and magnesium hardness in the feedwater. External treatment and control must provide a feed-water low in hardness, alkalinity, silica, metal oxides, and oxygen. Because of their extreme solubility, sodium salts are of concern only to the extent of their contribution to the total dissolved solids concentration. However, boiler-tube scale consisting of calcium and magnesium components is not uncommon in units operating below 900 psig. These scales often are the direct result of loss of chemical

control, permitting dense calcium precipitates such as calcium sulfate or calcium silicate to form. They may also be a more subtle result of porous-hardness sludge or metal oxides which permit boiler water to penetrate to the tube surface precipitating complex silicate scales.

Formation of scale, below 900 psig, is generally more of a concern with respect to causing overheating failures than promoting corrosion attack. Two basic systems are now available for prevention of internal hardness scales: the conventional phosphate-hydroxide methods and the more recently adopted substitute systems involving chelating agents. Both are proven systems, but the success of either depends on the diligence with which they are applied.

PHOSPHATE-HYDROXIDE METHOD

The phosphate-hydroxide methods can be segregated into one that maintains an excess of hydroxide alkalinity and one that involves no excess or "free" hydroxide content. The former has a long history of use and is still the most prevalent system for low-pressure operation. Table XIV presents typical control limits.

The intent of phosphate control systems is to provide conditions conducive to the precipitation of calcium as a calcium hydroxyapatite,

Table XI. Recommended Feedwater Limits, High-Pressure Drum-Type Units

Total solids	50 ppb max.
Total iron	10 ppb max.
Total copper	10 ppb max.
Total silica	20 ppb max.
Oxygen	5 ppb max.
Hydrazine	10–20 ppb max. residual
pH	8.8–9.2 (copper-alloy system)
	9.2–9.4 (copper-free system)

All measurements made at high-pressure heater outlet or economizer inlet.

Oxygen can be measured at deaerater outlet if cycle is equipped with deaerating heater.

Table XII. Criteria for Operation of Supercritical Unit During Condenser Leakage

Concentration	Hotwell Salt Description	Leakage Operational Limitations	Demineralizer Control
<0.5 ppm	Normal	None.	Normal
0.5–2.0 ppm	Abnormal	Limited operation. Schedule in spection and repair of condenser as soon as system load requirements permit.	Control demineralizer sequence to assure that tanks will not exhaust simultaneously. If ammonia cycle is employed, override ammonia step.
<2.0 ppm	Excessive	Emergency operation. Prepare for orderly shutdown of the unit. Immediately reduce load as necessary to permit isolation of damaged condenser section. Initiate shutdown if hotwell concentration cannot be quickly reduced below 2.0 ppm.	Place all available tanks in service immediately. If reduced load operation is assumed, transfer resin which is most exhausted and bring in spare charge. Override ammonia regeneration step.

Table XIII. Recommended Frequency of Analysis for High-Pressure Utility Units

Should condenser leak-detection equipment be out of service, manual conductivity readings should be taken at the condensate pump discharge three times daily.

Supercritical-Type Feedwater at Economizer Inlet	Drum-Type Feedwater at Economizer Inlet
pH, per shift	Same as supercritical units
O_2, per shift	
Silica, twice weekly	**Boiler water**
Copper, twice weekly	pH, per shift
Total iron, twice weekly	PO_4, per shift
	Total solids, per shift
	Silica, twice weekly

$3Ca_3(PO_4)_2 \cdot Ca(OH)_2$ and magnesium as serpentine, $3MgO \cdot 2SiO_2 \cdot 2H_2O$.

In contrast to low-pressure operation, boiler tube failures in units above 900 psig can be caused by corrosion. Accordingly, the coordinated phosphate pH system is used to control boiler-water chemistry as with utility high-pressure boilers. Table XV lists typical control limits for indicated units operating above 900 psig. The criteria in this table for the quality of the condensate returned to the feedwater system (hotwell conditioners) are primarily for those units where feedwater is used as a de-superheating spray water.

CHELATION

Chelating agents have received wide acceptance as a substitute system for the conventional phosphate-hydroxide treatment methods. The most common is the sodium salt of ethylenediaminetetraacetic acid (EDTA). As briefly explained in a previous section, these organic agents act with the residual calcium

and magnesium in the feedwater to form soluble complexes. Ideally, this should result in boiler surface conditions which are completely free of any hardness deposits. The soluble hardness complexes will be removed through the continuous blowdown line. With conventional phosphate treatment, it is difficult to maintain all of the hardness end products in suspension. As a result, some accumulations normally are found in drums and headers.

Most experience with this treatment method has been limited to operating pressures of 900 psig and below, but some use on 1250- and 1350-psig units has been reported. Economically, justification for its use is limited to feedwaters of low hardness concentrations (1 to 2 ppm). Such evaluation usually considers the savings realized by the elimination or reduced frequency of chemical cleaning.

Chemical additions are made in a continuous mode, with the amount based on the concentration of hardness salts in the feedwater. The chelants must be injected after the boiler feed-

Table XIV. Typical Phosphate Control Limits

	450–600	600–900
Pressure (psig)	450–600	600–900
Hydroxide Alkalinity as OH (ppm)	50–100	25–50
Phosphate as PO_4	20–40	5–10
Sodium Sulfite as NA_2SO_3	20–40	5–10
Silica	50 (max.)	10 (max. @ 900 psig)

water pump to prevent corrosion of the pump components. Earlier attempts to utilize the chemical-feed line to the boiler drum also resulted in severe corrosion of this line. High-oxygen concentrations in the feedwater drastically increase the corrosivity of the chelants. Thus, it is imperative that good deaeration of the feedwater be maintained.

A chelant program can be effective in preventing deposits or damaging boiler tubes depending primarily on the knowledge and experience of the user. Of course, before initiating such a program on any boiler, guidelines, control limits, and analytical procedures must be established with the cooperation of the chelant supplier or water-treatment consultant.

CARRYOVER AND STEAM SAMPLING

The mechanical aspects of steam and water separation are covered in Chapter 5, in which

drum-internal design for utility and industrial boilers is described. This section deals with the phenomenon of carryover, methods of steam sampling, and techniques of steam-purity determination. Once again, these subjects cannot be understood solely by rigorous theoretical analysis. Knowledge of laboratory testing procedures and ability to interpret field operating experience are required. Despite intensive research efforts, there is incomplete understanding and much empiricism remains in the techniques for correcting problems resulting from incomplete separation of steam and water in boiler equipment.

CLASSIFICATION OF CARRYOVER

Carryover of boiler water in steam leaving the drum provides a path for introducing solid materials into the steam. Modern separator designs can mechanically reduce the moisture content of the steam to 0.2 percent or less. But in addition to mechanical carryover of

Table XV. Criteria for Maintaining Boiler-Water Concentrations, Drum-Type Boilers

Hotwell Conditions	Operational Limits	Control Values		Boiler-Water Control
Total Solids <1 ppm (Normal)	None	TS pH PO$_4$	<100 ppm 9.8–10.2 15–25 ppm	Normal
Total Solids 1 to 4 ppm (Abnormal)	Limited Operation 1. Schedule inspection and repair of condenser as soon as system load requirements permit.	TS pH PO$_4$	<200 ppm 9.8–10.5 15–50 ppm	Immediately start chemical injection pumps to maintain excess phosphate and pH conditions. Do not continue to operate unit if pH cannot be maintained above 8.0 or the total solids below 200 ppm. Increase blowdown to limit total dissolved solids concentration. Avoid unnecessary use of desuperheating spray water.
Total Solids >4 ppm	Emergency Operation 1. Immediately reduce load as necessary to permit isolation of damaged condenser section. 2. Prepare for orderly shutdown of the unit if hotwell concentration cannot be quickly reduced below 4 ppm.	TS pH PO$_4$	<200 ppm 9.8–10.5 15–50 ppm	See above. Prepare to establish chemical conditions for wet lay-up of boiler unit and auxiliary equipment during condenser repair.

boiler water, another mechanism exists that results in the contamination of steam with solid materials.

As operating pressures increase, the steam phase exhibits greater solvent capabilities for the salts that may be present in the water phase. These salts will be partitioned in an equilibrium between the steam and water, a phenomenon known as vaporous carryover. Vaporous carryover will contribute an additional quantity of boiler water solids directly to the steam, independent of the efficiency of steam-water separation components.

Silica was the first material found to exhibit significant vaporous carryover. Silica fouling of turbines was common until it was recognized that successful control of the amount of silica in the steam could only be accomplished by controlling the amount of silica in the boiler water. A similar solution will be required for other solids when operating at high pressures.

Vaporous carryover contributes a significant proportion of total solids in the steam as drum operating pressures increase above 2600 psig. Table XVI shows findings of a laboratory study on vaporous carryover.[21] For various salts, the table lists percent vaporous carryover, which is the ratio of the salt concentration in the steam and boiler water. In each case, sodium was measured and then converted to the appropriate salt concentration.

When calculating total solids in the steam, vaporous carryover is assigned a value of 0.1 percent at drum operating pressures above 2600 psig.

Mechanical carryover may be classified under four headings: priming, spray, leakage, and foam carryover. Each results in troublesome deposits in the superheater or on the turbine blades.

Priming is the development of excessive moisture in the steam because of spouting or surging of boiler water into the steam outlet. This is a rare, easily identified type of carryover. It is usually promoted by the maintenance of too high a water level in the drum, spouting of a submerged riser or sudden swelling of the water in the boiler on a drop in pressure, or sudden increase in rating. Priming is rarely, if ever, associated with boiler-water concentration.

Spray carryover, mist or fog are degrees of atomization of the boiler water. Mist is carried from the drum by the steam as dust is carried by air currents. This carryover is present to a degree in all boilers, and it is the function of drum internals to separate and filter out such spray before the steam leaves the drum. Development of spray carryover indicates failure of the drum internals because of exceeding the velocity limitations of the purification equipment. It is characterized by initial development below the full rating of the boiler and it continues to increase with boiler load. Spray carryover is not sensitive to boiler-water concentration below the foaming range. Improved drum internals are capable of reducing the steam-borne mist to a value as low as a few parts per billion of solids.

Leakage is a general term applied to bypassing of impure steam or boiler water through the drum internals. Normally localized, this form of carryover is directly related to poor design or installation of drum internals. At times, the local contamination may not be sufficient to be

Table XVI. Summary of Laboratory Results

| Pressure (psig) | 2600 | | 2800 | | 3000 | |
Concentration (ppm)	15	500	15	500	15	500
Sodium Sulfate	.02%	.03%	.04%	.07%	.28%	.48%
Disodium Phosphate	.01%	.07%	.03%	.18%	.41%	.74%
Trisodium Phosphate	.02%	.11%	.04%	.30%	.35%	1.3 %
Sodium Chloride	.04%	.18%	.09%	.36%	.39%	1.2 %
Sodium Hydroxide	.02%	.31%	.08%	.69%	.55%	2.2 %

reflected in steam-purity measurements of total steam flow. A careful inspection of drum internals will usually reveal this source of carryover. Where the leakage is sufficient to register impurity tests of steam, it will be found that the impurity increases slowly with rating and is relatively insensitive to changes in water level and boiler-water concentration.

Foam carryover is the development of excessive moisture in the steam from carryover of foam from the drum. It is the most common form of carryover in low-pressure units, in which the boiler water may contain high concentrations of dissolved solids, and is the most troublesome and most erratic type.

Foam forms in the steam-generating sections of the boiler when the water-films around the generated steam bubbles are stabilized by the impurities in boiler water. Boiler circulation carries this foam up to the boiler drum where it tends to accumulate at the water level. The foam produced may entirely fill the steam space of the boiler drum or it may be of a relatively minor depth. Although foaming in boilers has been recognized for many years, its causes are not clearly defined and are worthy of further investigation.

The bulk water in the circulating mixture entering the drum is readily separated, but the wet emulsion of very small foam bubbles collects at the water level to a depth largely dependent on the rate of drainage of excess water out of the foamy mass. A considerable amount of moisture is trapped in the foam. When foam carryover occurs, it is frequently sudden and excessive, and the steam sample registers a solids content characteristic of boiler water.

IDENTIFICATION OF CARRYOVER

A systematic field investigation can identify carryover. A variety of factors which may be classified as mechanical, water or operating conditions affects the sources of carryover and the carryover itself to different degrees. As noted previously, foaming in the boiler is the most common type of carryover and is most troublesome and erratic. Special test methods have been devised to demonstrate the presence of foam blankets and for obtaining boiler performance without danger of serious carryover to the superheater and turbine.[22]

Steam flow, water level and boiler-water concentration are the three major factors that can create carryover. By varying these three factors, one at a time, test results can usually be interpreted to determine the specific source of a carryover condition.

Steam flow establishes the velocity distribution in the boiler drum. Excessive steam flow can increase steam velocity to a point that entrained moisture can overload the dryer.

High water can create spouting and excessive carryover. This can occur at low steaming rates and boiler-water concentrations.

Foaming is a characteristic of boiler-water concentration. With water level and steaming rate at recommended values, any carryover which can be precipitated or eliminated by a change in boiler-water concentration can be attributed to foaming.

Fig. 39 illustrates the development of foaming in a drum. The plot indicates purity values of steam samples taken ahead of the steam dryer and at the outlet of the boiler drum for a constant level of water in the drum and a typical steam load. The principal change is in the boiler-water concentration.

At a boiler-water concentration of about 550 ppm, the sample ahead of the dryer was about 5 mmhos (1 mmho is approximately 0.5 ppm of solids) and the sample at the boiler outlet was about 7 mmhos. Increasing the boiler-water concentration to about 1800 to 2000 ppm did not alter the purity of the steam leaving the boiler drum. But the sample ahead of the steam dryer increased gradually to a value of about 40 mmhos. Thus, with an established steam flow, and a similar water level, there was a marked increase in solids content of the steam entering the dryer. This is indicative of the presence of a mildly foamy condition in the boiler drum as the only change was in the concentration of boiler-water solids.

Increase of boiler-water solids to about 2800 to 3000 ppm in the boiler water, at the same steam load and water level as in the prior two tests, produced severe foaming in the boiler. The space between the water level and the dryer was practically filled with a foam blanket on the water. This is evident in the high solids content of the sample entering the dryer. Severe foam carryover occurred when the water level in the drum was at or above drum center. This was not a factor in the prior tests. Thus, a small change in water level was sufficient to push the foam blanket into the drum internals creating a severe case of foam carryover.

CAUSES OF FOAMING

Foaming is basically a result of chemical conditions, and boiler-water concentration and composition are important factors involved. High total solids and high suspended solids aggravate the formation of foam. High caustic alkalinity, oil, organic contamination and excess phosphate also increase the foaming tendency in boiler water. While the general effect of a component upon foaming may be anticipated, it is impossible to predict whether foam formation will occur by a cursory examination of boiler water. Extreme cases are on record where excessive foamover occurred with less than 650 ppm in one boiler and, in another case, no carryover troubles developed with concentrations as high as 15,000 ppm. Although these inconsistencies exist, it is necessary to maintain a lower value of foam-producing chemicals in boiler water or add foam dispersing chemicals to the water.

Organic antifoam agents have been developed to dispel certain foams at higher steam pressures. Ordinary tannin and starch compounds are only effective at low pressures. Lignin sulfonates, alkaline polyamides, polymerized esters and alcohols have been effective foam dispersing agents. The function of an efficient antifoam agent is to reduce the number of

Fig. 39 **Development of foaming in a boiler drum**

small bubbles and to confine steam-bubble formation to a small number of large bubbles which will exhibit the tendency to coalesce and grow larger. Under these conditions, the bubbles are unstable and tend to break easily. Antifoam agents are not equally effective with all boiler waters. It is necessary to select an antifoam compatible with the chemical characteristics of the boiler water, and trial of several compounds may be necessary before the foam can be neutralized satisfactorily.

Foam will fill the free surface area of a separating device increasing local velocities and promoting a serious carryover of boiler water. Foam carryover may be stopped by a quick reduction in boiler-water concentration or lowering the drum level. Centrifugal devices have shown a greater ability to handle foamy waters than simple internals. The basic function of a centrifugal device is to dehydrate the foamy emulsion. The dehydrated-foam bubbles can be easily broken up by screens or other simple devices. Foam in this type of separator will decrease the water-separating efficiency of the device.

In general, foam carryover from a boiler can be avoided by keeping boiler-water concentrations within the range suggested by the American Boiler Manufacturers Association (ABMA). These specifications, of course, cannot be a guarantee against foaming which, as indicated previously, is primarily a chemical problem.

Concentration limits as a function of pressure are shown in Table XVII.

In both utility and industrial plants, adherence to the ABMA specifications has produced satisfactory operation because of marked improvements in water technology and boiler design. Normally, the steam-purity-specification limit for low-pressure boilers is less than 0.5 percent moisture in the steam. With the use of superheaters and higher pressures, the boilers must deliver a steam product containing less than 1.0 ppm of solids entrained in the steam. Steam purity of high-pressure boilers has been markedly improved and values of less than 0.01 ppm of impurity are achieved.

STEAM SAMPLING METHODS

Steam samples for measuring purity are usually taken ahead of the superheater. These are condensed and cooled. Collecting a true sample that is representative of a large mass of material always presents a difficult problem. The sample size, particle-size distribution and density relationship are some factors which must be considered where there is a question of lack of homogeneity. In a homogeneous sample of fine particle size, sampling is a relatively easy operation.[22]

In sampling steam, the impurities may be solid, liquid, and gaseous. The solid may be in the form of a finely divided sludge particle. Liquid impurity may be in the form of fog or mist in minute droplets, possibly having a solid particle as a nucleus. More adversely, it may be in a form of a surface film on a pipe wall. Moisture itself is not involved in the concept of steam purity except that it may carry solids in solution or suspension.

Sampling impurities in steam is analogous to the difficulty of locating a needle in a haystack. At a sampling rate of 100 pounds per hour, the impurity content of 1 ppm is represented by the withdrawal of 0.7 grains of solid per hour. Steam lines contain bends, elbows, valves and other fittings which can disturb the flow and segregate the impurities.

B. J. Cross has outlined the assumptions reached in the design of the steam sampling nozzle described in *ASTM Standards* D 1066. The velocity front must be reasonably flat, and the density difference of steam and mist or fog carried along with it must be in the same order of magnitude as that of water and steam at the pressure and temperature of the steam in the line. Basic prerequisites for use of the ASTM nozzle design are that the velocity of the steam entering the ports is the same as the line velocity of the steam and that each port of the sampling nozzle shall represent an equal area of the sampling section.[23]

Turns and other irregularities of the steam line influence distribution of solid and liquid impurities. The sample point should be as remote as possible from a source of distur-

Table XVII. Recommended Boiler Water Limits and Associated Steam Purity

Drum Pressure psig	Range of Total Dissolved Solids[1] in Boiler Water ppm	Drum-Type Boilers Range of Total Alkalinity[2] in Boiler Water ppm	Suspended Solids in Boiler Water ppm (Maximum)	Range of Total Dissolved Solids[2] in Steam ppm
0–300	700–3500	140–700	15	0.2–1.0
301–450	600–3000	120–600	10	0.2–1.0
451–600	500–2500	100–500	8	0.2–1.0
601–750	400–2000	80–400	6	0.2–1.0
751–900	300–1500	60–300	4	0.2–1.0
901–1000	250–1250	50–250	2	0.2–1.0
1001–1800	100	Note (3)	1	0.10
1801–2350	50		N/A	0.10
2351–2600	25		N/A	0.05
2601–2900	15		N/A	0.05
		Once-Through Boilers		
1400 and Above	0.05	N/A	N/A	0.05

Notes: 1. Actual values within the range reflect the TDS in the feedwater. Higher values are for high solids; lower values are for low solids in the feedwater.
2. Actual values within the range are directly proportional to the actual value of TDS of boiler water. Higher values are for the high solids; lower values are for low solids in the boiler water.
3. Dictated by boiler water treatment.
4. These values are exclusive of silica.

bance. It should also be located where there is a run of at least ten diameters of straight piping. The preferred location with respect to position, in order of decreasing preference, is

(a) vertical pipe, downward flow

(b) vertical pipe, upward flow

(c) horizontal pipe, vertical insertion

(d) horizontal pipe, horizontal insertion

DETERMINATION OF STEAM PURITY

Steam purity is normally determined by measuring either the electrical conductivity or sodium content of the condensed steam sample.

Measuring electrical conductivity is widely used to monitor steam purity in industrial low-pressure boilers. This method is described in *ASTM Standards* D 1125. Tests for Electrical Conductivity and Resistivity of Water.

Gases dissolved in a condensed sample affect conductance and indicate an erroneous level of solid impurity. These gases may be removed by degasification. Methods suggested for establishing the content of solids impurity in steam are described in *ASTM Standards* D 2186, Deposit-Forming Impurities in Steam, which provides four alternative techniques. The referee method for establishing the total solids in the steam is by evaporation, as specified in *ASTM Standards* D 1888, Tests For Particulate and Dissolved Matter in Water.

Determination of solids in steam by conductance is not sensitive to impurities in the parts per billion range, which is the range required for determination of steam purity in high-pressure utility boilers. Analysis of the steam sample to detemine the sodium content in the impurity, by flame spectrophotometric technique, is the most accurate method developed to establish solids content. This technique is described in *ASTM standards* D 1428, Tests for Sodium and Potassium in Water and Water-Formed Deposits by Flame Photometry.

REFERENCES

[1] Eskel Nordell, *Water Treatment for Industrial And Other Uses*, second edition. New York: Reinhold Publishing Corp., 1961.

Sheppard T. Powell, *Water Conditioning For Industry*, first edition. New York: McGraw-Hill Publishing Co., 1954.

Betz Laboratories, Inc., *Betz Handbook of Industrial Water Conditioning*, seventh edition. Trevose, Pa.: Betz, 1976.

P. Hamer, et al., eds., *Industrial Water Treatment Practice*. London: Butterworths, 1961.

Frank N. Kemmer and John McCallion, general editors, *The NALCO Water Handbook*. New York: McGraw-Hill Book Company, 1979.

[2] E. W. Lohr and S. K. Love, *The Industrial Utility of Public Water Supplies in the United States, 1952: Parts I and II*, Geological Survey Water Supply Papers 1299 and 1300, respectively. Washington: U.S. Government Printing Office, 1954.

[3] R. E. Hall, et al., "Phosphate in Boiler Water Conditioning," *Journal of the American Water Works Association*, 21(1): 79–100, January 1929.

[4] Richard C. Corey and Thomas J. Finnegan, "The pH, Dissolved Iron Concentration and Solid Product Resulting from the Reaction Between Iron and Pure Water at Room Temperature," *Proceedings of the American Society for Testing and Materials*, Preprint no. 101, 1939.

[5] E. Berl and F. van Taack, "Über die Einwirkung von Laugen und Salzen auf flusseisen unter Hochdruckbedingungen und über die Schutzwirkung von Natruimsulfat gegen den Angriff von Aetznatron und von Chlormagnesium," (The Action of Caustic and Salts on Steel under Conditions of High Pressure and the Protective Effect of Sodium Sulfate against the Attack of Sodium Hydroxide and Magnesium Chloride), *Forschungsarbeiten*, no. 330. Berlin: VDI, 1930.

[6] S. F. Whirl and T. E. Purcell, "Protection Against Caustic Embrittlement by Coordinated Phosphate-pH Control," *Proceedings of the Third Annual Water Conference*, Pittsburgh, November 9–10, 1942, pp. 45–60. Pittsburgh: Engineers' Society of Western Pennsylvania, 1942.

[7] H. A. Grabowski, et al., "Problems in Deaeration of Boiler Feedwater," *Combustion*, 25(9): 43–48, March 1955.

[8] Samuel Glasstone, "Overvoltage and Its Significance in Corrosion," *Corrosion and Material Protection*, 3(6): 15–18, June–July 1946.

[9] H. A. Klein and H. A. Grabowski, "Corrosion and Hydrogen Damage in High Pressure Boilers", Presented at the Second Annual Educational Forum on Corrosion, National Association of Corrosion Engineers, Drexel Institute of Technology, Philadelphia, September 15–17, 1964. Combustion Engineering publication TIS-2652.

[10] P. Goldstein and C. L. Burton, "Research Study on Internal Corrosion of High-Pressure Boilers," *Transactions of the ASME. Journal of Engineering for Power*, 91, Series A: 75–101, April 1969; also in *ASME Paper No. 68-PWR-7*. New York: American Society of Mechanical Engineers, 1968.

[11] J. A. Armantano and V. P. Murphy, "Standby Protection of High Pressure Boilers," *Proceedings of the 25th International Water Conference*, Pittsburgh, September 28–30, 1964, pp. 111–124. Pittsburgh: Engineers' Society of Western Pennsylvania, 1964.

[12] L. H. Vaughn and C. V. Runyan, "Corrosion Protection of Boilers and Associated Equipment During Idle Periods," *Proceedings of the American Power Conference*, 33: 721–729, 1971. Chicago: Illinois Institute of Technology, 1971.

[13] B. T. Hagewood, et al., "The Control of Internal Corrosion in High-Pressure Peaking Units," *Proceedings of the American Power Conference*, 30: 939–948, 1968. Chicago: Illinois Institute of Technology, 1968.

[14] H. A. Grabowski, et al., "Problems in Deaeration of Boiler Feedwater," *Combustion*, 25(9): 43–48, March 1955.

[15] A. F. Kelly, et al., "Modify Base-Load Turbines for Peaking Service," *Power*, 115(4): 62–63, April 1971.

[16] F. N. Speller, "Control of Corrosion by Deactivation of Water," *Franklin Institute Journal*, 193(4): 515–542, April 1922.

[17] F. Gabrielli and W. R. Sylvester, "Water Treatment Practices for Cyclic Operation of Utility Boilers," *Proceedings of the International Water Conference*, Pittsburgh, October 31–November 2, 1978, pp. 193–208. Pittsburgh: Engineers' Society of Western Pennsylvania, 1979; also in Combustion Engineering publication TIS-5859.

[18] J. J. Kurpen and D. L. Dixson, "Operating Experience in Cycle Cleanup for Supercritical Pressure Units," *Proceedings of the American Power Conference*, 30: 883–896, 1968. Chicago: Illinois Institute of Technology, 1968.

[19] K. L. Atwood and G. L. Hale, "A Method For Determining Need for Chemical Cleaning of High-Pressure Boilers," *Proceedings of the American Power Conference*, 33: 710–720, 1971. Chicago: Illinois Institute of Technology, 1971.

[20] H. A. Klein, "Use of Coordinated Phosphate Treatment to Prevent Caustic Corrosion in High Pressure Boilers," *Combustion*, 34(4): 45–52, October 1962.

[21] S. L. Goodstine, "Vaporous Carryover of Sodium Salts in High Pressure Steam." proceedings of the *American Power Conference*, 36: 784–789. Chicago: Illinois Institute of Technology, 1974; also in Combustion Engineering publication TIS-3973.

[22] P. B. Place, "Carryover Problems and Identification of Carryover Types," *Combustion*, 18(9): 29–34, March 1947.

P. B. Place, "Investigation of Carryover Problems and Identification of Types," *Proceedings of the Seventh Annual Water Conference*, Pittsburgh, January 6–8, 1947, pp.

43–62. Pittsburgh: Engineers' Society of Western Pennsylvania, 1947.

P. B. Place, "Steam Purity Determination. Part I. Evaluation of Test Results," *Combustion*, 25(10): 62–65, April 1954.

P. B. Place, "Steam Purity Determination. Part II. Methods of Sampling and Testing," *Combustion*, 25 (11): 41–44, May 1954.

P. B. Place, "Steam Purity Determination. Part III. Interpretation of Test Results," *Combustion*, 25 (12): 43–46, June 1954.

[23] B. J. Cross, "The Sampling of Steam for the Determination of Purity," *Proceedings of the Eleventh Annual Water Conference*, Pittsburgh, October 16–18, 1950, pp. 71–82. Pittsburgh: Engineers' Society of Western Pennsylvania, 1950.

"Standard Method of Sampling Steam," ASTM Standards D1066. *Annual Book of ASTM Standards*, Part 31: Water. Philadelphia: American Society for Testing and Materials, latest edition.

BIBLIOGRAPHY

Atwood, K. L., "Solvent Selection for preoperational and Operational Cleaning of Utility Boilers," *Combustion*, 42 (3): 16–21, September 1970.

Atwood, K. L. and J. A. Martucci, "The Application of Hydrochloric Acid and Ammonium Bromate for Scale Removal in Utility Boilers," *Proceedings of the 28th International Water Conference*, Pittsburgh, December 11–13, 1967, pp. 167–179. Pittsburgh; Engineers' Society of Western Pennsylvania, 1967.

Brown, R. D. and D. A. Harris, "Large Coal-Fired Cycling Unit," paper presented at the ASME-IEEE-ASCE Joint Power Generation Conference, Portland, OR, September 28–October 2, 1975. Combustion Engineering publication TIS-4558.

Chojnowski, B. and R. D. B. Whitcutt, "Corrosion Failure: One Cause and a Cure in an Operational Boiler," *Combustion*, 48 (5): 28–33, November 1976.

Clayton, W. H., et al., "Design for Peaking/Cycling," paper presented at the Joint Power Generation Conference, Pittsburgh, September 27–30, 1970; also in *ASME Paper No. 70-PWR-9*. New York: American Society for Mechanical Engineers, 1970. Also in Combustion Engineering Publication TIS-2927.

Gabrielli, Frank, et al., "Contamination Prevention of Superheaters and Reheaters During Initial Startup and Operation," *Proceedings of the American Power Conference*, 38: 296–310, 1976. Chicago: Illinois Institute of Technology 1976.

Gabrielli, F., et al., "Prevent Corrosion and Deposition Problems in High-Pressure Boilers," *Power*, 122 (7): 85–92, July 1978. Included in Combustion Engineering Reprint TIS-5271, pp. 37–43.

Goodstine, S. L. and J. J. Kurpen, "Corrosion and Corrosion Product Control in the Utility Boiler-Turbine Cycle," *Combustion*, 44 (11): 6–18, May 1973.

Greene, N. D. and M. G. Fontana, "A Critical Analysis of Pitting Corrosion," *Corrosion*, 15 (1): 41–47, January 1959.

Kennedy, C. M., et al, "Experience with High Rate Ammoniated Mixed Beds for Condensate Polishing of CIPSCO Coffeen Station." *Combustion*, 39 (9): 19–30 March 1968.

Klein, H. A., "Corrosion of Fossil Fueled Steam Generators." *Combustion* 44 (7): 5–20, January 1973.

Klein, H. A., "A Field Survey of Internation Corrosion in High Pressure Utility Boilers," *Proceedings of the American Power Conference*, 33: 702–709, 1971. Chicago: Illinois Institute of Technology, 1971.

Klein, H. A. and K. L. Atwood, "Chemical Cleaning of Utility Boilers." *Proceedings of the American Power Conference*, 26: 762–778, 1964. Chicago: Illinois Institute of Technology, 1964.

Klein, H. A. and P. Goldstein, "The Effects of Water Quality on the Performance of Modern Power Plants." Presented at the 24th Annual Conference of the National Association of Corrosion Engineers, Cleveland, Ohio, March 18–22, 1968, Paper No. 12; also in Combustion Engineering publication TIS-2891.

Kurpen, J. J., "Externally Regenerated Condensate Demineralization Systems for Once-Through Steam Generators." Presented at the Liberty Bell Corrosion Course, Philadelphia, PA., Sept. 16–18, 1969. Sponsored by Natl. Assn. of Corrosion Engineers and Drexel Institute of Technology; also in Combustion Engineering publication TIS-3071.

Levendusky, J. A. and L. Olejar, "Condensate Purification Applications of the Power Process in High-Pressure Utility Plant Cycles." *Proceedings of the American Power Conference*, 29, 840–856, 1967. Chicago: Illinois Institute of Technology, 1967.

Rivers, H. M., "Concentrating Films: Their Role in Boiler Scale and Corrosion Problems." *Proceedings of the Twelfth Annual Water Conference*, Pittsburgh, Oct. 22–24, 1951, pp. 131–145 Pittsburgh: Engineers' Society of Western Pennsylvania, 1951.

Stocky, D. G. and K. L. Atwood, "Non-destructive Testing for Location of Corrosion Damage in High Pressure Boilers.[11] Presented at the Meeting of the Southeastern Electric, Exchange, New Orleans, April 29–30, 1971; also in Combustion Engineering publication TIS-3246.

Ulmer, R. C. and H. A. Klein, "Impurities in Steam from High Pressure Boilers." *Proceedings of the ASTM*, 61: 1396–1411, 1961.

Wages, C. W. and C. W. Smith, "Operating Experience of a Deep-bed Condensate Polishing System." *Proceedings: 38th International Water Conference*, Pittsburgh, PA, Nov. 1–3, 1977, pp. 111–121. Pittsburgh, Engineers' Society of Western Pennsylvania, 1978.

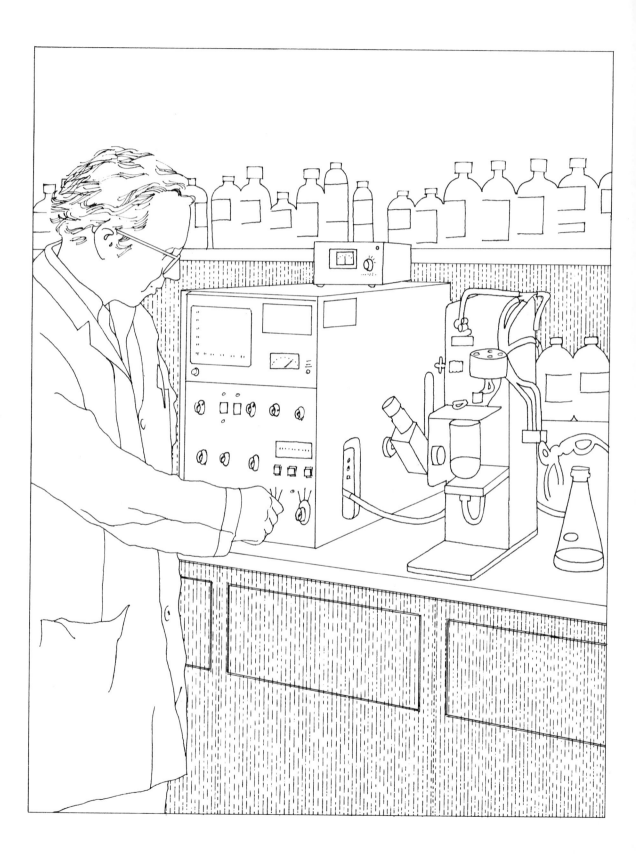

CHAPTER 12

Pulverizers and Pulverized-Coal Systems

The main reason why pulverized-coal firing is favored over other methods of burning coal is because pulverized coal burns like gas and, therefore, fires are easily lighted and controlled. Almost any kind of coal can be reduced to powder and burned like gas.

"A change of coal upsets the operation of a pulverized-coal plant to a much smaller degree than it does a stoker-fired plant. Pulverized-coal furnaces can be readily adapted to burn other fuels that burn like gas, and in that respect are capable of burning almost any fuel which is used for making steam."[1] Henry Kreisinger, former Director of Research at Combustion Engineering, made this statement at a 1937 meeting of the American Society of Mechanical Engineers in Windsor, Canada.

Today, over 40 years later, pulverized-coal burning has so dominated the utility market that power generation by stoker firing is no longer a consideration. A major reason for the success of pulverized-coal burning is the ability to adapt operating conditions to all coal ranks from anthracite to lignite. While certain considerations must be made to accommodate fuels with such a wide range of properties, the years of experience since Kreisinger's statement have simply served to prove the versatility and advantages of pulverized-coal firing.

HISTORICAL PERSPECTIVE

One of the most significant engineering achievements of the twentieth century is the commercial perfection of methods for firing coal in pulverized form. In fact, the development is one of the cornerstones making possible the extremely large, modern, steam-generating unit with its high thermal efficiency, reliability, and safety.

Worldwide, practically every coal mined is being burned with complete success in pulverized form. Similarly, many other types of low-grade, waste, and byproduct solid fuels may also be fired economically and efficiently in this manner. As pulverized-fuel firing has contributed to the reduction of labor costs in steam power plants, it has also increased operational flexibility and practicable usage of an extremely wide range of fuels.

Over the years, the concept of pulverized-coal firing has attracted the attention of some of the finest engineering minds. Familiar with early nineteenth century French experiments, Sadi Carnot provided a critical thermodynamic analysis of the pyréolophore, an engine fired by powdered coal, in his 1824 engineering classic, *Reflections on the Motive Power of Fire.*[2]

During the 1890's Rudolf Diesel conducted

his first experiments on the internal combustion engine bearing his name with pulverized coal as the primary fuel. At this time pulverized-coal firing was achieving its first real commercial success in the cement industry.[3] In the early 1900's, Thomas A. Edison made improvements in the firing of pulverized coal in cement kilns, greatly increasing their efficiency and output.[4]

In all fairness, however, recognition must be given also to hundreds of engineers of lesser renown who have made equal or greater technical contributions. Since the first information attributed to the Niepce brothers was published in France in the early 1800's, there have been many examples of engineers whose visions of future developments in pulverized-coal technology have far outreached the materials and technical understanding of their time.

Largely developed as an empirical art, pulverized-coal firing progress has been marked by the efforts of devoted engineers whose success may be attributed to persistence despite many discouraging obstacles. Generally, theoretical understanding has followed rather than preceded practical accomplishment in the field of pulverized-coal firing.

INCENTIVES FOR DEVELOPING PULVERIZING TECHNIQUES

Some elements of engineering reasoning which have stimulated invention and improvement of devices to burn coal in pulverized form include the following: (1) Coal is widely available for combustion purposes. (2) Burning gas appears to be a simpler process than consumption of large pieces of coal. (3) If coal can be finely divided and burned like a gas, it becomes an even more attractive fuel, promising greater boiler efficiency and simplicity of combustion.

In the U.S., the rapid increase in oil prices in the 1890's was the principal incentive for developing the use of pulverized coal for firing cement kilns—the first industrial application to achieve outstanding commercial success. E. H. Hurry and H. J. Seaman of the Atlas Portland Cement Company began a series of experiments relating to the use of pulverized coal in 1894, and in the following year it was successfully applied to a rotary cement kiln. Since that time, pulverized coal has been the dominant fuel in the cement industry.

By the time of World War I, powdered coal—the term then generally used for what is now designated as pulverized coal—had gained sufficient acceptance for the ASME to sponsor a symposium bringing together the accumulated experience in the several fields of application. Reading the record of this symposium will give a clear understanding of the empirical nature of the wide variety of equipment available for various types of pulverized-coal firing.[5]

PIONEERING UTILITY INSTALLATIONS

By the end of the war, pulverized coal still had not achieved its full potential despite an increasing number of applications which spread from the cement to the metallurgical industry, to the steam locomotive and to several stationary boilers. Although all of the elements for outstanding success appeared to be present, someone was needed to integrate the many ideas and to provide a new thrust for pulverized-coal firing in the central-station industry. No one can lay more claim for initiating this impetus than John Anderson, then chief engineer of power plants of what is now Wisconsin Electric Power Company. He effectively enlisted the support and active participation of exceptionally able engineers from his own organization, the public-utility industry, equipment suppliers, and the U.S. Bureau of Mines. Anderson's pioneering efforts resulted in pulverized-coal installations in the existing Oneida Street Station and the bold new concept of Lakeside.[6]

Although American research in this field stems from the establishment of the U.S. Bureau of Mines in 1910 with its extensive program of boiler and equipment testing,[7] there was also earlier work in this country and abroad on the inflammability of dust clouds causing explosions in coal mines. Empirical progress in the art of pulverized-coal firing linked these two areas of research, and brought forth a series of reports and investigations ranging from power-plant tests to studies of particle flow and the thermodynamics of combustion.

Two outstanding test reports stand as engineering classics. Based on experimental work at the Oneida Street and Lakeside Stations, these reports contain important basic information on pulverized-coal firing and establish a pattern for subsequent research, including many of the activities of the ASME Furnace Performance Factors Committee.[8]

Studies on velocities and characteristics of pulverized-coal particles were reported by E. Audibert[9] and John Blizard,[10] who a few years earlier had published a comprehensive study of the state of the pulverized-coal art.[11] Research linking studies of inflammability of coal-mine dust to desired combustion properties appears in an article by Henri Verdinne.[12] W. Nusselt published results of research on coal-particle ignition times in 1924,[13] and P. Rosin reported on studies of heat liberation based on thermodynamic data in 1925.[14] The first of a series of papers on boiler heat-transfer studies at Yale University by W. J. Wohlenberg and his colleagues was also published by ASME in 1925.[15]

Despite the extensive theoretical studies that were made in the 1920's, much of the progress was achieved on an empirical basis of trial and error with boiler installations of ever-increasing size. This was particularly true in the development of pulverizers, where the theory of the underlying principles had not advanced very rapidly. Even today, the laws for crushing materials are subject to much dispute.

Rittinger's law of crushing dates back to a book published in Germany in 1867. It states that the work required to produce material of a given size from a larger size is proportional to the new surface produced. This expression finds more general acceptance than Kick's law, which was first published in 1885 and which states that the energy required to effect crushing or pulverizing is proportional to the volume reduction of the particle. While Rittinger's law is a closer approximation, neither of these laws can be used for comparing efficiencies of

coal pulverizers which are different.

The energy that is required to effect pulverization is dissipated in a number of ways. It cannot be accounted for in the specific manner which is applicable to a boiler or power-plant heat balance. For this reason, both pulverizer design and application have retained many of the elements of an engineering art.

PULVERIZING PROPERTIES OF COAL

To predict pulverizer performance on a specific coal with some degree of accuracy, the ease with which the coal can be pulverized must be known.

GRINDABILITY

A grindability index has been developed to measure the ease of pulverization. Unlike moisture, ash, or heating value, this index is not an inherent property of coal. Rather, it represents the relative ease of grinding coal when tested in a particular type of apparatus. The consistency of grindability test results permits the pulverizer manufacturer to apply the findings to a particular size and, to a lesser degree, type of pulverizer.

Grindability should not be confused with the hardness of coal. (See also Tables IV and V and related text.) The same coal may have a range of grindabilities depending on other constituents in the coal. Fig. 1 gives typical curves for North Dakota lignites and shows the variation in Hardgrove grindability as the moisture content changes. Typically, anthracites and some lignites have at least one point where their grindabilities are very close. Anthracite, however, is a very hard coal whereas lignite is soft, yet both are difficult to grind.

Pulverizing a small air-dried sample of properly sized coal in a miniature mill determines its grindability. Results may then be converted into a grindability-index factor which, with appropriate correction curves, can be used to interpret mill capacity.

The Hardgrove method was developed to measure the quantity of new material that will pass a 200-mesh sieve. The apparatus for this method, shown in Fig. 2, is extremely simple. A 50-gram sample of air-dried coal, sized to less than 16 and greater than 30 mesh, is placed in the mortar of the test machine along with eight 1-in.-diameter steel balls. A weighted upper race is placed on the ball and coal charge, and is turned 60 revolutions. The sample then is removed and screened.

The quantity passing the 200-mesh sieve is used in the preparation of a calibration chart, from which the grindability of the coal sample is determined in accordance with *ASTM Standards* D 409, Grindability of Coal by the Hardgrove-Machine Method. Four coal samples, obtained from ASTM, standardized especially for this purpose and representing grindability indices of 40, 60, 80, and 100, are used for calibration of each grindability machine and associated apparatus, before the equipment is used to test coals.

Frequently, too much emphasis is placed on grindability while other factors affecting mill capacity, such as moisture, are almost entirely overlooked. Pulverizer capacity is proportional to the grindability index of the coal, but corrections must also be made for fineness of product and moisture of the raw feed.

MOISTURE

Usually a reference to moisture in coal pertains to the total moisture content. This is comprised of what is commonly termed *equilibrium* moisture and *surface* or *free* moisture. Equilibrium moisture varies with coal type or rank and mine location, and would be more accurately called "bed" or "seam" moisture. In reality, surface moisture is the difference between total moisture and bed moisture.

Surface moisture adversely affects both pulverizer performance and the combustion process. The surface moisture produces agglomeration of the fines in the pulverizing zone, and reduces pulverizer drying capacity because of the inability to remove the fines efficiently and as quickly as they are produced. Agglomeration of fines has the same effect as coarse coal during the combustion process, because the surface available for the chemical reaction is reduced. Since in-mill drying is the accepted method of preparing coal for pulverized-fuel burning, sufficient hot air at adequate temperature is necessary in the mill-

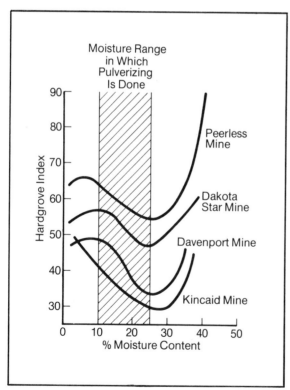

Fig. 1 Variation of grindability index with moisture content, North Dakota lignites (average of standard and corrected values)

Fig. 2 Hardgrove grindability machine

ing system. Curves such as those shown in Figs. 3 and 4 indicate the air temperature required to dry coal of varied total moistures and coal-air mixtures.

The achieving of rated pulverizer capacity depends upon having sufficient heated air available to dry the coal. If there is a deficiency of hot air, the mill output will be limited to the "drying capacity" and not the "grinding capacity." Thus, it may be possible to obtain more capacity with a relatively dry coal of lower grindability than with a high-moisture coal of higher grindability.

RELATION OF PULVERIZER CAPACITY TO GRINDABILITY

As stated previously, mill capacity is not directly proportional to grindability. Thus, if the actual capacity of a pulverizer with 50 grindability is 10,000 lb per hr, then with 100 grindability it will be about 17,000 lb per hr, and not 20,000 lb per hr. This is because of the differences between a commercial pulverizer and a grindability test machine which, with no provision for continuous removal of fines, is of the batch type rather than the continuous type. The crushing pressure of the test equipment is also considerably less. As a result, some of its energy is dissipated in deforming the coal particles without breaking them.

Although the test equipment does not indicate a direct proportion of capability between hard and soft materials, the value of these tests is not reduced. Correction factors developed by pulverizer manufacturers on commercial equipment provide for overcoming these discrepancies. Fig. 5 gives correction curves for variations in fineness, grindability, and moisture. As a rule of thumb, for every point the grindability index of a particular coal changes, there will be a corresponding change of $1\frac{1}{3}$ percent in pulverizer capacity. Similarly, for every percentage point of change in fineness from the basic design point of a pulverizer,

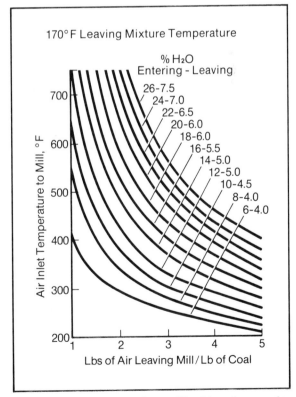

Fig. 3 **Temperature of air to mill, eastern coals**

Fig. 4 **Temperature of air to mill, midwestern coals**

there will be a corresponding change of 1½ percent in capacity.

VARIATION OF LIGNITE GRINDABILITY WITH MOISTURE

The Bureau of Mines at Grand Forks, North Dakota, and others have reported the grindability of lignites at various moistures, and the results show a wide variation, as in Fig. 1. Some feel that such curves are of little value because it seems impossible to select the proper index from them; others feel that they do have significance. With the increased use of lignites, solution of this problem is important.

In setting up the present ASTM code for grindability, the test specifies use of an air-dried sample. In the C-E bowl mill, *all* of the surface moisture and some of the equilibrium moisture are evaporated during pulverization with a hot-air sweep. The moisture content of the pulverized product leaving the mill is con-

ceived to be the moisture level that exists in the grinding zone. Thus grindability vs. moisture indices above the equilibrium level are of little interest. Hardgrove indices therefore have meaning to the pulverizer designer only below the equilibrium-moisture level and in the general range of moisture contents between 10 and 25 percent.

The actual choice of the grindability index for pulverizer design capacity requires consideration of total moisture, equilibrium (bed) moisture, and the selected hot-air temperature.

RELATIONSHIP OF COAL RANK TO REQUIRED FINENESS

Successful pulverized-coal firing depends on recognizing differences in coals and on making whatever modifications are necessary to provide the optimum conditions for efficient combustion. Experience over the years has established that a relationship exists between

Fig. 5 **Mill correction factors for grindability, fineness, coal type, and moisture— bituminous coals with preheated air**

rank of bituminous coals and degree of fineness required for successful operation.

To insure complete combustion within the furnace confines for minimal carbon loss, high-rank coals must be pulverized to a finer size than coals of lower rank. Although in part dependent on the type of firing system used, the approximate limits within the following ranges have been established through operating experience.

Coal Rank	Passing 200 Mesh (74 μ) Wt %	Retained on 50 Mesh (297 μ) Wt %
Subbituminous C coal and Lignite	60–70	2.0
High-Vol. Bit. C, Subbituminous A and B	65–72	2.0
Low and Medium-Vol. Bituminous, High-Vol. Bit. A and B	70–75	2.0

When firing certain coals in the low-volatile group in small pulverized-coal furnaces, the fineness percentage may be increased to as high as 80 percent to insure adequate burnout of the carbon content.

SPECIFICATIONS FOR CLASSIFYING COALS

Table I lists the specifications as set by ASTM for classifying coal by rank. Rank classifications are based on varying combinations of volatile-matter content, heating value, and agglomerating properties.

After the predrying step is accomplished in the pulverizing operation, the low-rank subbituminous coals and lignites manifest a higher degree of reactivity than do the higher rank bituminous coals. Recent investigations confirm that this increased reactivity results primarily from the lack of agglomerating properties and increased O_2 content.[16] Data from these investigations are summarized in Table II, Coal Properties.

A comparison of flammability indices with volatile matter and heating value suggests that factors other than these have a great influence on ignition temperature and particle burnout. Because lower flammability temperatures are experienced primarily with lignitic and subbituminous coals, it is reasonable to ask what property is common to lower rank coals. Exclusive of heating value, the most obvious difference between the two groups is that property known as "agglomerating character"—subbituminous coals and lignites do not agglomerate. As applied to coals, agglomeration is the property of particles fusing into a cokelike mass or bonding together into a firm cake when the particles are heated to temperatures of 1000°F or above.

While the determinations of both volatile matter and heating value are well defined, tests for establishing the agglomerating character of coals are less commonly known. *ASTM Standards* D 388, Specifications for Classification of Coals by Rank, describes agglomerating character as: "The test carried out by the examination of the residue in the platinum crucible incidental to the volatile-matter determination. Coals which in the volatile-matter determination produce either an agglomerate button that will support a 500-g weight without pulverizing, or a button showing swelling of cell structure, shall be considered agglomerating from the standpoint of classification."

Since the agglomerating property of coals is the result of particles transforming into a plastic or semiliquid state when heated, it reflects a change in the surface area of the particle. This surface change is manifested by a transformation of the particle from an angular, irregular shape into a spherical or sphere-like particle. Also, the surface character of the particle changes from a porous, irregular, absorptive surface to a glasslike nonporous surface. Thus, with the application of heat, agglomerating coals tend to develop a nonporous surface while that of nonagglomerating coals becomes even more porous with pyrolysis. This explanation indicates why agglomerating coals require a correspondingly finer particle size to maintain an equivalent surface area for efficient, rapid ignition and burnout.

Table I. Classification of Coals by Rank[a]

Class and Group	Fixed Carbon Limits, % (Dry, Mineral-Matter-Free Basis)		Volatile Matter Limits, % (Dry, Mineral-Matter-Free Basis)		Calorific Value Limits, Btu/lb (Moist,[b] Mineral-Matter-Free Basis)		Agglomerating Character
	Equal or Greater Than	Less Than	Equal or Greater Than	Less Than	Equal or Greater Than	Less Than	
I. Anthracitic							
1. Meta-anthracite	98	...	...	2	...	...	
2. Anthracite	92	98	2	8	...	...	nonagglomerating
3. Semianthracite[c]	86	92	8	14	...	...	
II. Bituminous							
1. Low-volatile bituminous coal	78	86	14	22	...	...	
2. Medium volatile bituminous coal	69	78	22	31	...	...	
3. High-volatile A bituminous coal	...	69	31	...	14,000[d]	...	commonly agglomerating[e]
4. High-volatile B bituminous coal	...	...	...	...	13,000[d]	14,000	
5. High-volatile C bituminous coal	...	...	...	...	11,500	13,000	
					10,500	11,500	agglomerating
III. Subbituminous							
1. Subbituminous A coal	...	...	...	...	10,500	11,500	
2. Subbituminous B coal	...	...	...	...	9,500	10,500	
3. Subbituminous C coal	...	...	...	...	8,300	9,500	nonagglomerating
IV. Lignitic							
1. Lignite A	...	...	...	...	6,300	8,300	
2. Lignite B	...	...	...	...	...	6,300	

[a] This classification does not include a few coals, principally nonbanded varieties, which have unusual physical and chemical properties and which come within the limits of fixed carbon or calorific value of the high-volatile bituminous and subbituminous ranks. All of these coals either contain less than 48% dry, mineral-matter-free fixed carbon or have more than 15,500 moist, mineral-matter-free British thermal units per pound.

[b] Moist refers to coal containing its natural inherent moisture but not including visible water on the surface of the coal.

[c] If agglomerating, classify in low-volatile group of the bituminous class.

[d] Coals having 69% or more fixed carbon on the dry, mineral-matter-free basis shall be classified according to fixed carbon, regardless of calorific value.

[e] It is recognized that there may be nonagglomerating varieties in these groups of the bituminous class, and there are notable exceptions in high-volatile C bituminous group.

Reprinted from *ASTM Standards* D 388, Classification of Coals by Rank.

In addition to the correlation of agglomerating properties with coal reactivity, an equally strong correlation exists between the ultimate-analysis oxygen level of coals and their response to reactivity as reflected in the flammability temperatures. Data in Table II show ranges in oxygen from 4.8 to 14.8 percent for agglomerating coals, moisture- and ash-free (MAF), and from 18.7 to 26.6 percent MAF for the lower rank coals that are nonagglomerating. Seemingly, the higher the inherent or organically bound oxygen content of the coal, the more reactive the coal. These data do not conflict with the observed correlation with agglomerating character. In fact, deliberately varying degrees of oxidation temper or destroy the agglomerating properties of caking coals. Apparently, the breaking point between agglomerating and nonagglomerating coals is a 14–15 percent oxygen level, MAF.[17]

STANDARDS FOR MEASURING FINENESS

When burning solid fuels in suspension, it is essential that the fuel-air mixture contain an appreciable quantity of extremely fine particles to insure rapid ignition. Conversely, to obtain maximum combustion efficiency, a minimum amount of coarse particles in this same fuel-air mixture is desirable. The former condition is usually expressed as percentage through a 200-mesh screen (74 microns), while the latter is designated as percentage retained on a 50-mesh screen (297 microns).

The number of openings per linear inch designates the mesh of a screen. Thus, a 200-mesh screen has 200 openings to the inch or 40,000 per square inch. The diameter of the wire used in making the screen governs the size of the openings. The U.S. Standard and W. S. Tyler are the most common screen sieves. The mesh and opening of these and other international screens are shown in Table III and Fig. 6.

CLASSIFICATION AND SIZE CONSIST

In some reactions, such as setting of cement, surface area is of extreme importance. In the combustion of pulverized coal, however, while it is important to have a proper percentage of

Table II. Coal Properties

	Bituminous					Subbituminous			Lignite
	Low Volatile	Medium Volatile	High Volatile			A	B	C	A
			A	B	C				
Agglomerating character	Agg.	Agg.	Agg.	Agg.	*	Non Agg.	Non Agg.	Non Agg.	Non Agg.
Proximate, %									
Moisture (seam)	2.0	2.0	4.0	7.0	10.0	14.0	19.0	25.0	40.0
Volatile matter, VM	21.1	32.3	38.4	33.8	35.9	35.3	34.5	25.8	25.9
Fixed carbon, FC	68.6	55.8	51.5	47.3	43.3	41.2	37.5	40.9	27.4
Ash	8.3	9.9	6.1	11.9	10.8	9.5	9.0	8.3	6.7
HHV, Btu/lb, As-fired	13,150	13,210	13,410	11,610	10,590	9,840	8,560	7,500	5,940
Flammability index, F	1,010	1,030	950	1,030	990	970	970	990	890
Ultimate (MAF), %									
Hydrogen	5.0	5.5	5.6	4.6	5.5	5.4	5.1	5.6	4.3
Carbon	88.5	84.1	82.5	81.0	74.3	74.2	69.8	66.4	67.0
Sulfur	0.4	1.1	2.5	0.9	4.0	0.5	0.8	0.6	0.9
Nitrogen	1.3	1.7	1.5	1.3	1.4	1.2	1.1	1.3	1.2
Oxygen	4.8	7.6	7.9	12.2	14.8	18.7	23.2	26.1	26.6

* Agglomerating but noncaking

fine particles having a large surface area, it is equally necessary to eliminate the oversize on the coarser screen. Despite the percentage less than 200 mesh (−200 mesh), as little as 3 to 5 percent greater than 50 mesh (+50 mesh) may produce furnace slagging and increased combustible loss, even though combustion conditions are excellent for the finer coal. The small amount of oversize represents very little additional surface if it is pulverized to all −50 mesh and all +200 mesh.

As an illustration, assume a typical screen analysis of a high-volatile bituminous coal sample, pulverized to 80 percent −200 mesh:

- 99.5% −50 mesh
- 96.5% −100 mesh
- 80.0% −200 mesh

This represents a surface area of approximately 1500 sq cm per gram, with over 97 percent of the surface in the −200 mesh portion.

By overgrinding and poor classification it would be possible, on a commercial-sized mill, to have a sample of the following analysis:

- 95% −50 mesh
- 90% −100 mesh
- 80% −200 mesh

Table III. Comparison of Sieve Openings

Mesh	Inches	mm
U.S. Standard Sieve		
20	0.0331	0.84
30	0.0234	0.595
40	0.0165	0.420
50 *	0.0117	0.297
60	0.0098	0.250
100 *	0.0059	0.149
140	0.0041	0.105
200 *	0.0029	0.074
325	0.0017	0.044
400	0.0015	0.037

Mesh	Inches	mm
W. S. Tyler Sieve		
20	0.0328	0.833
28	0.0232	0.589
35	0.0164	0.417
48 *	0.0116	0.295
60	0.0097	0.246
100 *	0.0058	0.147
150	0.0041	0.104
200 *	0.0029	0.074
325	0.0017	0.043
400	0.0015	0.037

*Commonly used screens in pulverized-coal practice for combustion purposes.

Fig. 6 International screen opening comparisons

This is not a satisfactory grind, because of the high percentage retained on the 50 mesh, even though the surface area is still 1500 sq cm/g.

In the pulverizing process, then, classification plays a major role in matching the particle size to the reactivity of the fuel. Both fine and coarse particles must be controlled within limits by the use of mechanical classification techniques. Careful attention, therefore, must be paid to both the design and the operation of the classification system.

SAMPLING PULVERIZED COAL

It is apparent that product fineness has a considerable bearing on pulverizer performance. Fineness samples should, therefore, be analyzed periodically. In a storage system, this sample may be taken directly from the mill cyclone discharge.

On a direct-fired system, obtaining the sample is more difficult because it must be taken from a flowing coal-air stream. A sampling device, consisting of a small cyclone collector, sample jar, and sampling nozzle with connecting hose, may be utilized. See Fig. 7.

The sample is obtained by traversing the pipe across its diameter, from two points in the same plane and at 90° to each other. The entire pipe diameter must be traversed, and the rate of

Fig. 7 **Powdered-coal sampling device and aspirating fittings**

movement must be uniform. Samples must be taken in both directions for the same period.

Currently, the industry has further refined these sampling techniques for greater accuracy. In this refinement, the pipe traverse with the coal-sampling device is timed to obtain an isokinetic coal sample. The method uses the proportion of coal-pipe area to the sample-probe-opening area in conjunction with the pulverized-fuel loading in the individual transport pipe. Because pulverized fuel in a transport pipe is not a homogeneous mixture, another sample taken at the same time at a different location in the same pipe may yield different results.

With collection completed, the pulverized-coal samples from each mill are thoroughly mixed. Fifty grams of the sample is placed in the top sieve of a nested stack of 50-mesh, 100-mesh and 200-mesh sieves. The nest is then shaken either by hand or by a mechanical shaking device until the procedure has separated the coal particles by size. The results of the percentages of coal passing through the individual screens, plot as a straight line on a typical sieve distribution chart. (See Fig. 8.) *ASTM Standards* D 197, Sampling and Fineness Test of Pulverized Coal and *ASME PTC 4.2*, Coal Pulverizers, give additional information on recommended sampling techniques.

CLOSED-CIRCUIT GRINDING

When a large piece of coal is reduced to a number of smaller ones by any method, a larger number of finer particles will be produced simultaneously. Therefore, it is not possible for a pulverizer to produce a product that will pass a 50-mesh screen without also obtaining a large percentage of material finer than 200 mesh. Thus, if a quantity of coal at one stage of pulverization contains 50-percent material that will pass through a 50-mesh sieve, and if this −50-mesh material is removed from the grinding zone, it will contain a smaller percentage of −200-mesh material than if it had been permitted to remain in the grinding zone until the total quantity had been reduced to pass a 50-mesh sieve.

As already noted, an abundance of fine particles is necessary to insure prompt ignition of coal in suspension burning. Substantial energy consumption is required in the production of this fine material. However, when grinding finer than necessary, power is wasted and the pulverizing equipment must be larger than actually required. Removal of the fines from the pulverizing zone as rapidly as they are produced and return of the oversize for regrinding eliminates unnecessary production of fines and reduces energy requirements. Better product sizing and increased capacity result from the removal of the fines, a process called closed-circuit grinding. The pulverizing system component which accomplishes this size control is known as the classifier.

ABRASION

Pulverizing results in an eventual loss of grinding-element material. Balls, rolls, rings, races, and liners gradually erode and wear out as a result of abrasion and metal displacement in the grinding process. Thus, the power for grinding and the maintenance of the grinding elements make up the major costs of the pulverizing operation.

In itself, "pure coal" is relatively nonabrasive; however, such foreign materials as slate, sand, and pyrites, commonly found in coal as mined, are quite abrasive. These are the undesirable constituents that produce rapid and sometimes excessive wear in pulverizing apparatus. The economics of coal cleaning to remove such abrasive foreign materials depends on many variables and must be determined for each individual application.

The resistance of a smooth plane surface to abrasion is called its hardness. It is commonly recorded in terms of 10 minerals according to Mohs' scale of hardness, Table IV. There is no quantitative relation between these, the diamond being much greater in hardness above sapphire than sapphire is above talc. Hardness of selected common materials is shown in Table V; the relatively low hardness of pure coal is compared to the abrasive impurities usually found in the commercial product.

COAL PREPARATION

Coal should be prepared properly for its safe, economical, and efficient use in a pulverizing system. Controllable continuity of flow to the pulverizer must be maintained. Organic foreign materials such as wood, cloth, or straw should be removed. Such materials may collect in the milling system and become a fire hazard, or they may impair material or airflow patterns in the mill. Although many mills are designed to reject, or are not adversely affected by, small inorganic or metallic materials, a magnetic separator should be installed in the raw-coal conveyor system to remove larger metallic objects. If this is not done, these objects may damage the pulverizer coal feeder or obstruct the coal flow.

The raw coal should be crushed to a size that will promote a uniform flow rate to the mill by the feeder. Favorable size consist will minimize segregation of coarse and fine fractions in the bunker, and result in a more uniform rate of feed to various pulverizers being supplied from a given bunker. When mixed with relatively dry lump coal, fine coal with high surface moisture accentuates the segregation problem in bunkers. Crushing by size-reduction of the

Fig. 8 Typical fineness sample results

dry lumps exposes additional dry surfaces for the adsorption of moisture from the wet fines, thereby producing a more uniform size and moisture distribution in the raw-coal mass.

Most commonly, direct-firing of pulverized coal is the method used for steam generation. In this application, an uninterrupted and uniformly controllable supply of pulverized coal to the furnace is an essential requisite. A steady and continuous flow of raw coal to the pulverizer will insure this.

An ideal feed is one that is closely sized and double-screened (¾ in. x ¼ in.). Coal of this size will permit excess water to drain off; it will flow freely from bunkers and can be fed uniformly. However, such favorable sizing can be obtained only at a considerable price premium and this usually precludes its use. In most cases, power plants will receive coals classified as run-of-mine or screenings with lumps; therefore, crushing equipment must be installed to provide uniform raw-feed sizing. Generally coal-feed sizing up to 1½ in., as sieved through a round screen, is permissible with large pulverizers.

COAL CRUSHERS

Although there are numerous types of crushers commercially available, the type generally used for smaller capacities is the swing-hammer type. This crusher has proved satisfactory for overall use and has demonstrated reliability and economy. The swing-hammer crusher consists of a casing enclosing a rotor to which are attached pivoted hammers or rings. Coal is fed through a suitable opening in the top of the casing and crushing is effected by impact of the revolving hammers or rings directly on, or by throwing the coal against, the liners or spaced grate bars in the bottom of the casing. The degree of size reduction depends on hammer type, speed, wear, and bar spacing. The latter is usually somewhat greater than the desired coal size. These crushers produce a uniform coal sizing and break up pieces of wood and foreign material with the exception of metallic objects. Foreign material that is too hard to crush is caught in pockets.

Roll crushers have been used but are not entirely satisfactory because of their inability to deliver a uniformly sized product. Probably the most satisfactory crusher for large capacities is the Bradford breaker. This design, Fig. 9, consists of a large-diameter, slowly revolving (approximately 20 rpm) cylinder of perforated steel plates, the size of the perforations determining the final coal sizing. In diameter, these openings are usually 1¼ in. to 1½ in. The breaking action on the coal is accomplished as follows: the coal is fed in at one end of the cylinder and carried upward on projecting vanes or shelves. As the cylinder rotates, the coal cascades off these shelves and breaks as it strikes the perforated plate. As the coal drops a relatively short distance, coal crushing occurs with the production of very few fines. Coal broken to the screen size passes through the perforations to a hopper below. Rocks, wood, slate, tramp iron, and other foreign material are rejected. This breaker produces a relatively uniform product and uses very little power.

Table V. Common Materials and Their Mohs' Hardness

Coal	0.5–2.5
Slate	0.50–6.0
Mica	2.0–6.0
Pyrite	6.0–6.5
Granite	6.5
Marble	3.0
Soapstone	1.0–4.0
Kaolin clay	2.0–2.5
Iron ore	0.50–6.5
Carborundum	9.5

Table IV. Mohs' Scale of Hardness

1—Talc	6—Feldspar
2—Gypsum	7—Quartz
3—Calcspar	8—Topaz
4—Fluorspar	9—Sapphire
5—Apatite	10—Diamond

Fig. 9 **Bradford breaker**

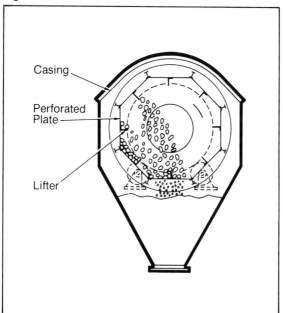

COAL FEEDERS

A coal feeder is a device that supplies the pulverizer with an uninterrupted flow of raw coal to meet system requirements. This is especially important in a direct-fired system. There are several types, including the belt feeder and the overshot roll feeder.

THE BELT FEEDER

The belt feeder uses an endless belt running on two separated rollers receiving coal from above at one end and discharging it at the other. Varying the speed of the driving roll controls the feed rate. A leveling plate fixes the depth of the coal bed on the belt.

The belt feeder can be used in either a volumetric or gravimetric type of application (see Fig. 10). The gravimetric type has gained wide popularity in the industry for accurately measuring the quantity of coal delivered to each

Fig. 10 **Schematic of belt-type gravimetric coal feeder.**

individual pulverizer. Generally, they are applied to steam generators having combustion-control systems requiring individual coal metering to the fuel burners.

There are two accepted methods of continuously weighing the coal on the feeder belt. One method uses a series of levers and balance weights; the other, a solid-state load cell across a weigh span on the belt. Both are very accurate mechanisms and both are well accepted by utilities. This same belt feeder design can also be used for volumetric measurement.

THE OVERSHOT FEEDER

The overshot roll feeder, Fig. 11, has a multi-bladed rotor which turns about a fixed, hollow, cylindrical core. This core has an opening to the feeder discharge and is provided with heated air to minimize wet-coal accumulation on surfaces and to aid in coal drying. A hinged, spring-loaded leveling gate mounted over the rotor limits the discharge from the rotor pockets. This gate permits the passage of oversize foreign material.

Feeders of this type may be separately mounted, or they may be integrally attached to the side of a pulverizer.

The roll feeder and the belt feeder, by virtue of their design, may be considered highly efficient volumetric feeding devices.

METHODS OF PULVERIZING AND CONVEYING COAL

Early coal-pulverizing installations received undried coal and utilized ambient air in the mill system. Because no heat was added to the system, the coal feed was limited to that of very low moisture content; therefore, maximum pulverizer capabilities were not realized. Subsequently, external coal dryers were added to the system. Because of the lack of cleanliness, high initial cost, fire hazard, and space requirements, these dryers were replaced with the now universally accepted mill drying.

Three methods of supplying and firing pulverized coal have been developed: the storage or bin-and-feeder system, the direct-fired system, and the semidirect system. These methods differ on the basis of their drying, feeding, and transport characteristics.

THE STORAGE SYSTEM

In a storage system, Fig. 12, coal is pulverized and conveyed by air or gas to a suitable collector where the carrying medium is separated from the coal which is then transferred to a storage bin. The hot air or flue gas introduced into the mill inlet provides for system drying requirements and is vented to rid the system of

Fig. 11 Overshot roll feeder

Fig. 12 Storage system

Fig. 13 Direct-fired system

moisture evaporated from the fuel. From the storage bin, the pulverized coal is fed to the furnace as required.

THE DIRECT-FIRED SYSTEM

In a direct-fired system, Fig. 13, coal is pulverized and transported with air, or air slightly diluted with gas, directly to the furnace where the fuel is consumed. Hot air or diluted furnace gas supplied to the pulverizer furnishes the heat for drying the coal and transporting the pulverized fuel to the furnace. Known as primary air, this air is a portion of the combustion air. As a reduction in oxygen concentration in this primary-air stream affects rapidity and stability of ignition, it is necessary, when using hot gas, to draw it from a point of low CO_2 concentration and high temperature. This prevents use of flue gas for drying in direct-firing.

Fig. 14 illustrates a schematic arrangement of the primary-air system for a pulverizer using a Ljungstrom® trisector air heater. As the name implies, this air heater has three sections: flue gas, primary air (the air that dries and conveys the coal to the furnace) and secondary air (the balance of the air that goes to the furnace). The primary-air section is located between the openings for the secondary air and the flue gas (Fig. 15). With this design, a higher primary-air temperature can be obtained. If there is a large variation in primary airflow, there is relatively little effect on heat recovery, because heat not recovered in the primary section will be picked up subsequently in the secondary section.

THE SEMIDIRECT SYSTEM

In a semidirect system, Fig. 16, a cyclone collector located between the pulverizer and furnace separates the conveying medium from the coal. The coal is fed directly from the cyclone to the furnace in a primary-air stream which is independent of the milling system. The drying medium, therefore, can be the same as in a storage or bin system.

SOURCE OF HEATED AIR

The best source of hot air for mill drying is either a regenerative or recuperative air heater using combustion gas as the source of heat. Those used in connection with large boiler installations usually provide sufficiently high temperature for almost any fuel moisture condition. On small installations, where the moisture in the coal is not high, steam air heaters may dry the coal. For higher moisture conditions a furnace-gas supplement may be necessary. Direct-fired air heaters, properly interlocked and protected, may also be used to supplement air-heating requirements.

All the moisture contained in coal must be evaporated before ignition can take place. For rapid ignition, therefore, surface moisture must be removed before the fuel is injected into the furnace. This same drying process facilitates pulverization. The type of fuel and its surface moisture govern mill-drying requirements.

The drying capability of a given pulverizer design depends on the extent of circulating load within the mill, the ability to rapidly mix the dry classifier returns with incoming raw, wet, coal feed, and the air weight and air temperature which the design will tolerate. Some pulverizers are designed to operate satisfactorily with inlet air temperatures up to 825°F, while others are capable of using air at a maximum of 600°F.

High-rank bituminous coals have a relatively dense structure and appear dry only when containing less than 2 or 3 percent total moisture. The inherent moisture of these fuels varies from 1 to 2 percent. Extremely low-rank fuels, such as lignite, are of a relatively porous or cellular structure and contain inherent moisture

Fig. 14 Primary-air system of balanced-draft furnace. Air pressures shown are illustrative only.

of from 15 to 35 percent. These same fuels with 3 percent surface moisture (18 to 38 percent total moisture) still appear dry. For both the pulverizing and ignition processes, it is necessary to reduce the total moisture contained in the fuel to the inherent moisture level.

If a particular pulverizer design requires low airflow for fineness maintenance, wet coal cannot be utilized without a considerable reduction in mill capacity. The design should permit high-temperature incoming air in sufficient volume to maintain a condition of relative humidity below saturation at the mill output temperature. A pulverizer designed for a larger volume of low-temperature inlet air for normal moisture fuel will require the admission of large quantities of cold tempering air when grinding dry coals.

The type of fuel and the kind of system being used will determine the mill outlet temperature. As Table VI indicates, outlet temperatures for storage-systems mills are lower than for direct or semidirect firing, because most coals will not store safely at the temperatures used in direct firing. Storage-bin fires caused by spontaneous combustion of the fuel may result from

Fig. 15 Ljungstrom® trisector air heater

Table VI. **Allowable Mill Outlet Temperatures, °F**

System	Storage	Direct	Semidirect
High-rank, high-volatile bituminous	130 *	170	170
Low-rank, high-volatile bituminous	130 *	160	160
High-rank, low-volatile bituminous	135 *	180	180
Lignite	110	110–140	120–140
Anthracite	200	. . .	. . .
Petroleum coke (delayed)	135	180–200	180–200
Petroleum coke (fluid)	200	200	200

* 160°F permissible with inert atmosphere blanketing of storage bin and low oxygen concentration conveying medium.

inadequate mill outlet temperature control. These may be inhibited by maintaining an oxygen-deficient atmosphere, such as flue-gas inerting, over the bin coal level. Oxygen limits for various fuels are shown in NFPA 69, "Explosion Prevention Systems."

Mill capacity is based on coal input, and output on a given coal on a dry basis will decrease with increasing moisture content. Thus in selecting a mill size, if too much reduction of capacity is experienced with high-moisture fuels, the mill can be too large under normal conditions of moisture or too small under excessive moisture conditions.

PULVERIZING AIR SYSTEMS

All coal-pulverizing systems utilize air or gas for drying, classification and transport purposes. Two methods are utilized for supplying the air requirements and overcoming system resistance. In a direct-firing system, one method utilizes a fan behind the pulverizer, while the other has a fan ahead of it. The former is a suction system and the fan handles coal-dust laden air, while the latter is a pressure system and the fan handles relatively clean air.

In a suction system the exhauster accounts for approximately 40 percent of the total power requirements (mill plus fan), while in a pressure system the blower is approximately 50 percent of the total.

With direct firing, the exhauster or blower volume requirement will depend upon the pulverizer size, and is usually fixed by the base capacity of that pulverizer. The pressure or total head requirement is a function of the pulverizer and classifier resistance and the fuel distributing system and burner resistances. These resistances are in turn affected by the system design, the required fuel-line velocities and density of the mixture being conveyed.

In a storage system, the fan is located behind the dust collector and handles only a very small quantity of extremely fine (−200 mesh) dust at a relatively constant temperature (approximately 130°F). These fans are, therefore, designed for high efficiencies and need not be designed for a head higher than their operating temperature requires.

INDIRECT COAL-STORAGE PULVERIZING SYSTEMS

Initial attempts at utilizing pulverized coal as a utility fuel led to the development of the

Fig. 16 **Semidirect system**

indirect-fired system. In this system, a cyclone collector separates the coal from the air used in the pulverizer for drying, classifying, and conveying. The pulverized coal is conveyed either mechanically or pneumatically to storage hoppers or bunkers. Mechanical, controllable feeders at the bunker outlets deliver the required quantity of coal to the fuel lines. At or near these feeders, the coal is reentrained in air called "primary air" in proper proportions for transport to the burners.

In some installations, the primary air is taken from the room or a preheated air duct, or both. In other cases, the vented air from the pulverizer system is used for all or part of the primary-air source.

PRIMARY AIR

On installations of the first kind, the *only* air used is that needed to carry the coal to the furnace and to provide the required velocity of coal-air mixture at the burners. The quantity depends, therefore, on the type of firing system, the type of piping system used (whether fuel lines are sloping, horizontal or vertical), and the burner and furnace arrangement.

Temperature Specifications

Pulverized-coal feeder and fuel-piping arrangements determine the primary-air temperature. This may be as high as 600°F. Because any tempering air admitted to the system reduces the quantity of air passing through the air heater, which reduces the overall unit efficiency, a minimum amount of tempering air should be used in the primary-air system.

When full preheat cannot be used, tempering is usually carried out at the suction side of the fan by dampering the preheated air and placing an adjustable cold-air opening between this damper and the fan inlet. If equipment arrangement permits, a dampered cold-air attachment from the forced-draft fan may be made at this location. The temperature of the air handled by the fan with such an arrangement should be the maximum usable with the particular feeder and piping arrangement.

If vented air is to be used when available, the temperature will depend on that of the vent, the position of the vent in the return air line, and on whether preheated or cold air is added to the primary air at the fan inlet. The vented air will usually have a 70 to 90 percent relative humidity, a temperature of 110 to 160°F and will contain coal fines vented from the collectors.

VENTED-AIR

To pulverize and classify coal economically and properly, it either must be dry when delivered to the pulverizer or must be dried during the pulverizing operation. This drying is accomplished by supplying hot air or flue gas to the pulverizing system.

In a storage system, either all or a portion of the drying medium is discharged from the system by venting. This removes the moisture which has been evaporated from the fuel. Aside from the adverse effects resulting from lack of drying in the pulverizer, a storage system requires the removal of moisture to eliminate or minimize difficulties in handling, storing and feeding of the pulverized fuel. The drying medium supplies a major portion of the heat to evaporate the fuel moisture and, in so doing, approaches saturation. Some of this almost-saturated mixture, approximately equal to the weight of hot drying medium supplied, must be removed or vented from the system. The amount vented will depend on the pulverizer output, the moisture removed from the fuel, the initial temperature of the drying medium, the temperature of the vented material and the efficiency of the drying system. This latter may be measured in terms of relative humidity.

The vented mixture may be disposed of in either of two ways: by venting to the atmosphere directly or through the boiler stack, or by using it as part of the air supply to the furnace. In the first case, since the vent contains some extremely fine coal (up to 2 percent of the amount being pulverized), economically it cannot be vented directly without collecting the coal dust in cyclone concentrators, bag filters, air washers or a combination of these. In the second case, the air need not be cleaned. In any case, there is sufficient resistance in the venting system to require a separate fan (unless the primary-air fan is designed for the additional pressure requirements).

Vent fans handle air that is dusty and relatively close to saturation. Vented-air piping must be designed for high velocities as the quantities vented will vary with the moisture in the fuel, and all pockets or horizontal runs, where coal can collect and perhaps become ignited, should be avoided. A minimum slope of 60 deg for these lines is desirable.

The vent fan must handle a quantity equal to the weight of hot air supplied for mill drying, plus the mill leakage and the moisture removed from the fuel.

DIRECT-FIRING ARRANGEMENTS

Most direct-fired pulverized-coal systems are for furnaces operated under suction (balanced-draft). Fig. 17 shows an arrangement of equipment for a suction-type mill when applied to a furnace of this design; Fig. 14 shows a pressure-type mill for a similar furnace.

With a suction mill, the coal feeder discharges against a negative pressure, whereas in the pressurized mill, the feeder discharges against a positive pressure of 18 to 21 in. WG. No coal feeder can act as a seal; thus, the head of coal above the feeder inlet must be utilized to prevent backflow of the primary air. As a rule of thumb, the height of the coal column above the

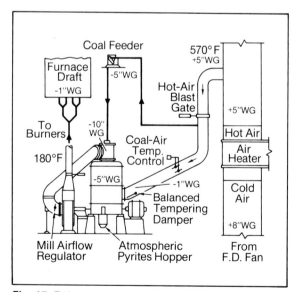

***Fig. 17* Balanced-draft furnace with suction mill. Air pressures shown are illustrative only.**

feeder should equal 1 ft for every 3 in. of primary-air mill-inlet pressure. If the primary-air-fan inlet pressure is 30 in., then the coal-column height will be 10 ft.

There are three basic air conveyance systems used by C-E for direct firing: (1) the suction system in which an exhauster induces airflow through the pulverizer and discharges the coal-air mixture under pressure to the furnace; (2) the pressurized-exhauster system in which the pulverizer is pressurized by the forced-draft fan with both hot and ambient air and discharges the coal-air mixture through an exhauster, acting as a booster fan, to the furnace (this system is used only in conjunction with pressurized furnaces); and (3) the cold primary-air system in which a primary-air fan forces air through an air heater, ductwork, and pulverizer and then forces the coal-air mixture to the furnace.

SUCTION SYSTEM

The suction system has a number of advantages. It is quite easy to keep the area around the pulverizer clean. It is easy to control the airflow through the pulverizer by dampering the constant-temperature coal-air mixture with a positioning device. Control of the coal-air mixture temperature is by a single hot-air damper and a barometric damper through which a flow of room air is induced by the suction in the pulverizer. With this control, the fan is designed for a constant, low-temperature mixture and has a low power consumption, even though such material handling fans have a relatively low efficiency of 55 to 60 percent.

The main disadvantage of the suction system is the maintenance required on the exhauster. On the other hand, by using proper design techniques and wear-resistant materials, the maintenance on an exhauster can be minimized. Exhauster maintenance costs are more than offset by the power and capital savings of the system; this justifies the continued use of the suction system on smaller units.

PRESSURIZED-EXHAUSTER SYSTEM

To obtain sufficient pressure for firing a pressurized furnace, the pressurized exhauster system was developed; there are a number of these systems in operation. This system retains the advantages of the suction system in the design of the fan for constant, low-temperature mixture and the relative ease of airflow control. Two dampers, one in the hot-air duct to the mill and one in the cold-air duct to the mill, control the amount of pulverizer airflow. This flow varies with, but is not proportional to, the amount of fuel being fed to the pulverizer. Biasing the hot- and cold-air dampers controls the temperature of the mixture leaving the pulverizer.

One advantage of the pressurized exhauster system is that the low pressures in the pulverizers do not present as severe a problem of sealing the head of coal over the raw-fuel feeder as with pulverizers under direct blower pressure. The disadvantage of the system, as with the suction system, is exhauster maintenance.

COLD PRIMARY-AIR SYSTEM

In this system the primary-air fan handles only ambient air. The fan is located ahead of the air preheater, with a separate primary-air system through the air heater. Although not as simple as the other two systems, its chief advantage is in fan power and maintenance. As the fans handle cold air, they can be smaller, run at higher speeds, and use highly efficient airfoil blade shapes. Inlet vanes can control airflow and further add to fan efficiency.

Some other advantages of this system are that, with high-efficiency fans handling ambient air, design for higher pressure differentials is possible and larger mills with longer fuel-pipe runs are practical. Thus, mills may be located farther from the boiler. Because individual fans for each pulverizer are not necessary, the space requirements for the pulverizer bays can be reduced. Morever, experience has proven that metering airflow on the inlet-air side of the pulverizer is most desirable. With the higher fan head available, the airflow can be quite easily measured by installing a venturi or other metering means.

Even with fewer pulverizer fans, controlling airflow to the various pulverizers is still relatively simple. The total primary air required is

a function of the number of pulverizers in operation. This permits the use of a simple control for the airflow requirements. Because of possible variations of load and coal moisture content between pulverizers, it is necessary to control not only the total airflow but the temperature of the air to individual pulverizers. This is accomplished with a system similar to that outlined under the pressurized exhauster system, which uses a hot primary-air duct and a cold primary-air duct with a damper in each for each mill. The airflow requirement for a pulverizer is met by operating both dampers, while controlling temperature by properly proportioning the flow between the hot- and cold-air ducts.

When very wet coals are pulverized in the suction systems described, the exhauster supplies less air at the very time maximum airflow is required for maximum drying. In the suction and pressurized systems with the exhauster located between the pulverizer and the furnace, the high evaporated-water vapor content in the coal-air mixture will reduce the exhauster air-handling capacity. In the pressurized exhauster system only, this can be partially overcome if the forced-draft-fan head capability is adequate. These disadvantages can be corrected by over-designing the fans, but this produces inefficiencies when the unit is operating with normal moisture coal. Conversely, the cold primary-air system may produce a higher capacity at any time it is needed.

The cold primary-air system offers numerous advantages. As compared with the other systems, the total savings with this system, from elimination of exhauster maintenance and reduction in fan power, may be 35 to 40 percent of the cost per unit of coal pulverized. This operating saving is partially offset by the capital charges for additional ductwork, dampers, and controls. With larger units and pulverizers, the use of the cold primary-air system becomes economically favorable.

AIR HEATING FOR THE COLD PRIMARY-AIR SYSTEM

By definition, the cold primary-air system requires independent primary-air heating accomplished in the past by several different methods. Several systems have been installed using a separate primary tubular air heater with Ljungstrom air heaters for secondary air, while some have been installed using separate primary Ljungstrom air heaters. These systems are expensive and become rather complicated in ductwork design. With the cold primary-air system, the trisection Ljungstrom air heater shown schematically in Fig. 15 is now being used as a basic design. As the name implies, the flow channels of this air heater have been divided into three sections, with the primary-air section being located between the secondary-air and flue-gas sections. With this arrangement, primary-air temperatures higher than that of the secondary air can be obtained. Further, the efficiency of heat recovery is not significantly affected by variations in pulverizer hot-air requirements, because the secondary air recovers the heat which is not recovered by the primary air sections.

PRINCIPAL TYPES OF PULVERIZERS

To effect the particle size reduction needed for proper combustion in pulverized-coal firing, machines known as pulverizers or mills are used to grind or comminute the fuel. Grinding mills use either one, two, or all three of the basic principles of particle size reduction, namely, impact, attrition, and crushing. With respect to speed, these machines may be classified as low, medium and high. The four most commonly used pulverizers are the ball tube, the ring-roll or ball-race, the impact or hammer mill, and the attrition type; their speed characteristics are shown in Table VII.

BALL-TUBE MILLS

A ball-tube mill (Fig. 18) is basically a hollow horizontal cylinder, rotated on its axis,

Fig. 18 Arrangement of ball-tube mill

whose length is slightly less to somewhat greater than its diameter. Heavy cast, wear-resistant liners fit the inside of the cylindrical shell which is filled to a little less than half with forged steel or cast alloy balls varying from 1 to 4 in. in diameter. Rotating slowly, 18 to 35 rpm (about 20 rpm for an 8 ft diameter mill) the balls are carried about two thirds of the way up the periphery and then continually cascaded towards the center of the cylinder.

Coal is fed into the cylinder through hollow trunnions and intermingles with the ball charge. Pulverization which is accomplished through continual cascading of the mixtures results from (a) impact of the falling balls on the coal, (b) attrition as particles slide over each other as well as over the liners and (c) crushing as balls roll over each other and over the liners with coal particles between them. Larger pieces of coal are broken by impact and the fine· grinding is done by attrition and crushing as the balls roll and slide within the charge.

Hot airflow is passed through the mill to dry the coal and remove the fines from the pulverizing zone. In most designs used for firing boilers or industrial furnaces, an external classifier regulates the size or degree of fineness of the finished product. The oversize or rejects from the classifier, sometimes called tailings, already dried in the pulverizing and classifying process, are returned to the grinding zone with the raw coal. This type pulverizer is particularly susceptible to reductions in capacity from surface moisture of the coal. Reducing the average moisture content of the mixture is very important in maintaining a continuous flow of coal through the feed end. The recirculation of dried tailings, then, reduces the tendency for wet coal to plug the feed end.

Table VII. Pulverizer Types

Speed:	Low	Medium	High
Type:	Ball-Tube Mill	Ring-Roll or Ball-Race Mill	Impact or Hammer Mill Attrition Mill

During operation, the relatively large quantity of pulverized coal in the grinding zone of a ball-tube mill acts as a storage reservoir from which sudden increases in fuel demand are supplied. The power consumption of ball-tube mills, kW per unit of coal pulverized, is very high, particularly at partial loads. Relatively large physically per unit of capacity, they require considerable floor space. Because of their size and weight, the initial capital cost is quite high. The presence of a high circulating load within the mill results in an overproduction of fines within the mill charge. Using an adequate external classifier permits the removal of the fine product from the grinding zone and reduces the production of extreme fines. The comparatively poor mixing of heated air with the partially pulverized material reduces the drying efficiency of this type of mill. High-moisture coals produce a large reduction in mill capacity.

Ball-tube mills are not well suited to intermittent operation as the large amount of heat stored in the coal and ball charge may produce overheating and fires when the mill is idle. The mass of this mill type makes it necessary to use high-power, high-starting-torque motors. In addition, these mills are very noisy. Most installations require that insulated "dog houses" be erected over each mill for noise attenuation.

Maintenance in the grinding zone of ball-tube mills is relatively easy to perform. Periodically, a ball charge is added to the mill to make up for metal lost in the grinding process. It may take years to wear out the cast liners, but considerable downtime is necessary for their replacement. Over the long run, maintenance costs per unit of coal ground are about the same as for ring-roll type pulverizers.

IMPACT MILLS

An impact mill consists primarily of a series of hinged or fixed hammers revolving in an enclosed chamber lined with cast wear-resistant plates. Grinding results from a combination of hammer impact on the larger particles and attrition of the smaller particles on each other and across the grinding surfaces. An air system with the fan mounted either internally or externally on the main shaft induces a flow through the mill. An internal or external type of classifier may be used. (See Figs. 24 and 25)

This class of mill is simple and compact, low in cost and may be built in very small sizes. Its ability to handle high inlet-air temperatures, plus the return of dried classified rejects to the incoming raw feed, makes it an excellent dryer.

However, the high-speed design results in high maintenance and high power consumption when grinding fine. Progressive wear on the grinding elements produces a rapid drop-off in product fineness, and it is difficult if not impossible to maintain fineness over the life of the wearing parts. Using an external classifier permits maintenance of fineness, but only at the expense of a considerable reduction in capacity as parts wear. The maximum capacity for which such mills can be built is lower than most other types.

ATTRITION MILLS

No true attrition mill is used for coal pulverizing because of the high rate of wear on parts. A high-speed mill which uses considerable attrition grinding along with impact grinding is, however, used for direct firing of pulverized coal. In this mill, the grinding elements consist of pegs and lugs mounted on a disc rotating in a chamber; the periphery of the chamber is lined with wear-resistant plates and its walls contain fixed rows of lugs within which the rotating lugs mesh. The fan rotor is mounted on the pulverizer shaft. Instead of an external classifier, a simple shaft-mounted rejector type is used. This design utilizes wear-resistant alloy lug and peg facings and casing linings to reduce the wear effect on fineness and extend the periods between parts replacement. This mill type exhibits all the characteristics of the impact mills.

RING-ROLL AND BALL-RACE MILLS

Ring-roll and ball-race mills comprise the largest number of pulverizers used for coal grinding. They are of medium speed and utilize primarily crushing and attrition of particle plus a very small amount of impact to obtain size reduction of the coal. The grinding action takes place between two surfaces, one rolling over the other. The rolling element may be either a ball or a roll, while the member over which it rolls may be either a race or a ring. The ball diameter is generally from 20 to 35 percent of the race diameter, which can be as large as 100″ diameter. If the element is a roll, its diameter may be from 25 to 50 percent of the ring diameter, which can be as much as 110″. Its face width, depending upon mill size, will vary from 15 to 20 percent of ring diameter.

When the rolling elements are balls, Fig. 19, they are confined between races. In the majority of designs, the lower race is the driven rotary member, while the upper race is stationary. Some designs also utilize a rotating upper race. The required grinding pressure is obtained by forcing the races together with either heavy springs or pneumatic or hydraulic cylinders. Some additional grinding pressure is obtained from centrifugal force of the rotating balls.

There are two general classes of mill that use rollers as the rolling elements. In one, Fig. 20, the roller assemblies are driven and the ring is stationary, while in another, Fig. 21, the roller assembly is fixed and the ring rotates.

Perhaps the most frequently used application of the first class is the C-E Raymond® roller mill, used in storage systems. Grinding pressure is obtained from centrifugal force resulting from rotation of these rolling elements.

Fig. 19 Diagram of ball-race mill

The other classification of ring-roll mills, namely those in which the ring rotates, constitutes the largest number of mills used for grinding coal; they are manufactured by the major boiler companies. The C-E bowl mill is of this latter type. The vertical driving shaft of these mills operate between 20–150 rpm, with larger mills running at the slower speeds.

Generally, such mills are equipped with self-contained or integral classifiers to regulate the fineness of the finished product. In some cases, this device may be external to the mill itself and is then termed an *instream classifier*.

Exhausters or primary-air fans create a flow of heated air through the mills. This heated air dries the coal, removes it from the grinding zone, carries it through the classifying zone, and conveys it to its point of use, whether this is a direct-fired furnace or the dust collector of a storage system.

When this type of mill is provided with sufficient air at a temperature to produce a satisfactory mill outlet temperature, it can handle very wet coals with only a small reduction in capacity. The high ratio of circulating load (classifier rejects returning to the grinding zone for further size reduction) to output, with the resulting rapid reduction of average moisture content, facilitates the grinding process. These mills require less power than any others.

Physically, these mills are compact and occupy a relatively small amount of floor space per unit of capacity. Some designs of ring-roll mills are extremely quiet in operation. Fineness of the product is relatively uniform throughout the life of the grinding elements.

Several references have been made to the ability of the various types of pulverizing equipment to grind different coals economically and efficiently. This capability is a reflection of the grinding pressures available, the method of application of this force, speed of moving elements, abrasion, and power and size limitations of the particular units. A list of materials capable of being commercially pulverized by the mill types described could be extended indefinitely; therefore, the scope of Table VIII covers combustible materials of primary concern in this book.

C-E PULVERIZER DESIGN

In the following sections, C-E pulverizers corresponding to the generic types are described. Their detailed design, construction and operational features, and fields of application are given.

Fig. 21 Diagram of bowl-type ring-roll mill journal assembly, spring-loaded

Fig. 20 **Diagram of roller-type ring-roll mill journal assembly**

C-E RAYMOND ROLLER MILL

The period between 1895, when the first pulverizers were installed in a Pennsylvania cement plant, and 1919, when a successful boiler installation was made at Oneida Street Station in Milwaukee, was a testing time for this type of equipment. Early during this period the C-E Raymond roller mill, Fig. 22, was developed to pulverize coal for storage systems serving metallurgical furnaces and cement kilns. By 1919, several hundred of these mills were be-

ing operated successfully. When, after World War I, pulverized coal gained a foothold in the central-station industry, this machine was a fully developed and standardized pulverizer specified for many pioneering installations.

The early mills were built for a maximum capacity of 6 tons per hour of 55 grindability coal when grinding to a fineness of 65 percent −200 mesh. By 1930, the maximum capability of this mill design had been increased to 25 tons per hour. Nearly all used external dryers to predry

Fig. 22 **Cutaway view, C-E Raymond roller mill**

the coal before use in the pulverizer. The economic disadvantages of these dryers helped to bring about internal mill drying, now the accepted practice. However, the original feature of air-separation and classification inherent in the roller mill has become the accepted standard of ring-roll pulverizer design.

A typical grinding and drying system incorporating a roller mill is shown in Fig. 23.

C-E RAYMOND IMPACT MILLS

The increase in possibilities for direct pulverized-coal firing resulted in the development in 1923 of a series of C-E Raymond impact mills with two basic designs: one for the smaller capacities, Fig. 24, in which the grinding elements, classifying means, and fan were all mounted on a common shaft rotating at 1800 rpm. The other design, Fig. 25, was for larger outputs and utilized an integral fan but external classifier. Both designs were provided with a mill-housing clearance space or tramp-iron pocket for accumulation and periodic removal of foreign material. The whizzer or rejector blades for fineness control were first used on these mills. These mills are excellent drying pulverizers because high-temperature air can be utilized and there is very violent turbulence of the mixture passing through the pulverizer. They are best suited to soft, relatively nonabra-

Table VIII. Types of Pulverizers for Various Materials

Type of Material	Ball-Tube	Impact and Attrition	Ball Race	Ring Roll
Low-volatile anthracite	X	...	...	...
High-volatile anthracite	X	...	X	X
Coke breeze	X	...	...	...
Petroleum coke (fluid)	X	...	X	X
Petroleum coke (delayed)	X	X	X	X
Graphite	X	...	X	X
Low-volatile bituminous coal	X	X	X	X
Med-volatile bituminous coal	X	X	X	X
High-volatile A bituminous coal	X	X	X	X
High-volatile B bituminous coal	X	X	X	X
High-volatile C bituminous coal	X	...	X	X
Subbituminous A coal	X	...	X	X
Subbituminous B coal	X	...	X	X
Subbituminous C coal	...	...	X	X
Lignite	...	...	X	X
Lignite and coal char	X	...	X	X
Brown coal	...	X	...	...
Furfural residue	...	X	...	X
Sulfur	...	X	...	X
Gypsum	...	X	X	X
Phosphate rock	X	...	X	X
Limestone	X	...	...	X
Rice hulls	...	X	...	...
Grains	...	X	...	...
Ores—hard	X	...	...	...
Ores—soft	X	...	X	X

Fig. 23. **Equipment for a complete grinding and drying system**

sive coals and for use on small boilers and furnaces. Life of grinding elements is short; maintenance and mill power are quite high.

C-E BOWL MILLS

The inability to use the roller mill for direct firing, and the limitations of the impact mill for this purpose were responsible for the development in the mid-1930's of the C-E Raymond bowl mill. The bowl mill is a medium-speed, ring-roll mill, with no metal-to-metal contact between grinding elements. The integral classifier with fineness adjustments made externally has given consistently satisfactory results. Increases in capacity have been made in planned steps averaging only approximately 25 percent for each extrapolation.

Two designs of this ring-roll mill are available. One, shown in Fig. 26, is operated under suction and is used for firing balanced-draft furnaces. The second, Fig. 27, is much more versatile for, when fitted with an exhauster, it can be used as either a suction or pressurized mill in conjunction with either a balanced-draft or pressurized furnace. If fitted with a

Fig. 24 **C-E Raymond impact mill**

primary-air fan, it can feed either a suction or pressurized furnace.

The C-E bowl mill consists essentially of a replaceable grinding ring carried by a rotating bowl. Fixed-position roller journal assemblies are mounted so that the roll face is approximately parallel to and in close proximity with the inside surface of the grinding ring. Stops are provided to prevent metal-to-metal contact between these two surfaces. Pressure for grinding is applied through externally adjustable compression springs or hydraulic cylinders. An integral multivaned classifier, connected to the mill outlet, is located above the grinding chamber. Classifier vanes are externally adjustable.

PULVERIZER DESIGN REQUIREMENTS

All coal-pulverizing equipment containing dust-laden air is built in accordance with the Standards of the National Fire Protection Association, NFPA 85F. This states that such equipment is to be designed to withstand an internal pressure of 50 psig for containment of a possible internal explosion. If the parts are made of steel or other ductile material, the allowable stress is not to exceed ¼ the ultimate or

Fig. 25 **C-E Raymond impact mill with external classifier and exhauster integrally mounted**

⅝ the yield strength of the material for sections in tension; the lesser of the yield strength or ½ the ultimate strength of the material for sections subject to bending. If made of cast iron or other nonductile material, the allowable stress is not to exceed ¼ the ultimate material strength for all parts.

The bowl-mill base and gear housing are made of gray-iron castings. The millsides, separator body, and separator top are fabricated of heavy steel plate with all seams and joints welded. The millside flanges and those of the mating separator body and top are constructed of heavy steel bars rolled to suit and welded to the cylindrical walls. The journal-opening frames are plate steel, and the journal covers, cast ductile iron. Ductile iron is also used for the bowl, bowl hub and gear hub.

Lower side liners, to protect the millside, are made of steel plate. Thermal insulation is installed around the millside for personnel protection. The mill-bottom insulation covers are fabricated of abrasion-resisting steel plate. Upper-side liners are steel plate to which air direction vanes are welded.

The separator-body liners, classifier-cone extension liners, journal-opening frame liners and journal head liners are made of Comballoy™ castings. This material has a high nickel content and has excellent abrasion resistance. The grinding-ring segments are cast of this same material. The grinding rolls are produced by a centrifugally chill-cast method with a gray-iron core and a hard alloy outer shell.

MILL BASE ALIGNMENT

The base casting has two machined support feet resting on sole plates. Because the worm drive shaft, Fig. 26, is offset from the mill centerline, it is desirable to keep the shaft centerline fixed rather than the mill centerline, letting the mill centerline move horizontally as the mill warms up to operating temperature. To accomplish this, one of the sole plates is dowelled to the base with a large-diameter pin pressed into both members on the shaft centerline. The opposite sole plate is provided with a slot on the shaft centerline which runs parallel to the shaft. The large dowel pin pressed into the base casting slides in the slot as the base expands. The mill worm shaft remains in preset alignment with the motor regardless of temperature. The sole plates have a series of large-diameter holes into which the grout is forced during setup, thereby keying or locking the sole plates to the mill foundation at the time the pulverizer is being installed.

The trunnion-shaft bushings of the roller journal in bowl mills, when made of metal, present a lubrication problem because the angular shaft movement is only a few degrees, is oscillating in nature, and has its pressure concentrated in a small area. These factors make it difficult to establish a lubricating film to protect the bushing.

Fig. 26 C-E bowl mill, deep bowl (RB) type

It is known that either natural or synthetic rubber is capable of absorbing energy and producing a flexible bushing when subjected to radial pressure by confinement between metal sleeves. Such bushings can accommodate oscillating motion without wear or lubrication. They can also absorb limited amounts of vibration. As a consequence, these so-called torsion bushings have been adopted for trunnion shafts. The rubber is bonded to metal inner and outer sleeves, and is compounded to suit conditions of load and movement. The metal inner sleeve is pressed onto the shaft and the outer one is clamped in a housing.

DESIGN AND SELECTION OF BEARINGS

In designing a pulverizer, the proper selec-

Fig. 27 C-E bowl mill, shallow bowl (RP, RPS, and RS) type

tion of bearings is important. There is a choice between journal type or sleeve bearings and the so-called antifriction bearings which include ball, tapered roller, cylindrical roller and spherical roller bearings. In certain cases rubber torsion bushings can be utilized.

Specific application often dictates which type to use. Usually, an antifriction bearing is chosen if loads are severe and space is limited. If close alignment of surfaces is a necessity, or if unbalanced loads at high speeds are present, then sleeve bearings with their inherent clearances are seldom used.

In ball bearings, the stress is very high because the contact area between balls and races is very small. In roller bearings, the stress is somewhat lower because of line contact. Consequently, a roller bearing having the same inside diameter, outside diameter, and width as a ball bearing can carry a much greater load. However, the ball bearing can be operated at a higher speed with less heating and can tolerate more misalignment than can a roller bearing.

The life of a bearing of any type varies as a power function of the load. No bearing will give unlimited life because there are many unpredictable factors, such as environment (exposure to foreign material and moisture), lubrication, operating temperature, shaft and housing fits and other conditions. In addition to these factors, fatigue of the bearing material from repeated stresses under rotation is ultimately unavoidable. How many revolutions a bearing can make before fatigue occurs is a function of bearing load and is a measure of a number of hours at a certain speed. Individual bearings of similar dimensions, operating under identical conditions, may have different lives. It is for this reason that a *nominal design* or a *rating life* is used as a basis for bearing selection. It is referred to as the B-10 life.

To insure trouble-free operation for machinery in continuous service, such as the components of a pulverizer or an exhauster, a suitable B-10 life is established.

The C-E bowl mill uses antifriction bearings on its vertical and horizontal shafts, as well as on the roller journal assemblies.

OPERATION OF THE C-E PULVERIZER

In operation, raw coal is fed into the center of the revolving bowl. Centrifugal action imparted to the coal by bowl rotation forces the coal to the grinding ring face where it is crushed by the rotating rolls. The partially pulverized coal passes over the edge of the bowl, is picked up by the hot-air stream, and is flash-dried. A single pass of coal between rolls and ring provides partial pulverization so that the product contains between 15 and 25 percent −200 mesh material, depending on physical conditions of the grinding elements and characteristics of coal. The separator-body liner assembly immediately above the bowl rejects the larger particles back into the grinding zone. Pyrites and tramp iron, because of their weight and the low air-stream mass velocity around the bowl, fall to the mill bottom where pivoted scrapers carry them to a reject spout. The rising air current around the bowl carries the intermediate and fine fractions of coal up into the classifier inlet vanes, where a spinning action is imparted.

ADJUSTABLE BOWL-MILL CLASSIFIER

About 75 to 85 percent of the classifier input, at the pulverizer outlet temperature, is returned to the grinding chamber for regrinding. This recirculation and mixing produces rapid predrying of the incoming raw coal, and enables the bowl mill to handle high-moisture coals without impairment of pulverizer capacity or classification. The setting of the adjustable vanes determines the degree of spin and thus the fineness of the material passing from the classifier to the connecting fuel lines and on to the furnace.

Pulverizer outlet fineness is proportional to the fineness of the material entering the classifier. Thus, high-grindability coal or high spring pressure on the rolls produces more fines, resulting in higher fineness leaving the classifier. Badly worn grinding elements or inadequate drying increases the oversize material, resulting in lower fineness. Finally, the velocity of air flowing through the mill can greatly influence product fineness.

The foregoing indicates the definite need for an externally adjustable, high-efficiency classifier. The bowl-mill classifier permits fineness changes of 15 to 25 percent on the −200 mesh product; i.e., from 55 to 60 percent −200 mesh to 75 or 80 percent −200 mesh. It is possible to make this adjustment while the mill is operating. Fineness effect on mill capacity is shown by the correction curves in Fig. 5.

ROLL PRESSURE ADJUSTMENT

Grinding-roll springs are pre-compressed to supply initial loading of the rolls. As the load in the bowl changes, the rolls move away or towards the ring, automatically increasing or decreasing spring pressure, in quick response to input variations.

Some large mills, Fig. 28, have a hydraulically loaded journal system which includes

Fig. 28 **C-E 110-inch bowl mill**

hydraulic cylinders, accumulators, a control unit, and a power unit. The control unit regulates journal pressure in proportion to pulverizer loading. The power unit then pressurizes the system by supplying all three journals with the same pressure thereby equally loading the bowl. Acting as shock absorbers in the system, the accumulators minimize the effects of large tramp iron on the mill.

DRIVE ARRANGEMENT AND LUBRICATION

With the exception of the 110″ series, all C-E bowl mills use a direct drive through an integral worm-gear unit, Fig. 26. The 110″ series has a triple-reduction, removable gearbox arrangement, Fig. 28. Very quiet in operation, the worm drive is designed for a large, single reduction. In addition, it permits the use of a single drive shaft for both the mill and exhauster on exhauster systems. This results in a compact installation with savings in electrical and space requirements.

Two basic lubrication systems are used on bowl-mill gearboxes. On smaller pulverizers, a shaft-driven integral pump submerged in the gearbox oil sump is utilized. The drive is completely bath- or integral-force-feed lubricated. On larger pulverizers, an externally operated oil-pump and motor assembly circulates oil to the bearings and gearing where necessary. The roller assemblies and exhauster bearings are bath-lubricated.

SAFETY AND CONTROLS

The production and handling of pulverized fuels can be hazardous. Because fine particles in suspension or deposition are readily volatilized and become combustible, under certain conditions explosions may take place. Notwithstanding these dangers, the industry

Table IX. C-E Bowl-Mill Sizes

Bowl-Mill Type	RB	RP, RPS+RS
Furnace firing	Suction	Pressure or Suction
Bowl diameter, in.	31–75	42–110
Capacity, lb/hr	3,550–59,000	12,000–200,000

has achieved a remarkable safety record since the inception of pulverized-coal firing. To protect property and life, all pulverizing equipment and related auxiliaries, including strength of equipment, valving and inerting, are designed in accordance with NFPA 85F mentioned previously.

Various controls and safety devices are utilized for the correct and proper operation of the equipment. Pulverizer output is controlled by regulation of feed rate in response to load signal. Airflow and air temperature are proportioned to feed rate by automatic control. Also included are permissive interlocks for the proper sequential operation of equipment, flow alarms to indicate cessation of coal flow to and from feeders, and load-limiting devices to prevent overfeeding the mills. Anticipating actions and more responsive feedback may often be included with the above in pulverizer control systems. Control systems and instrumentation are covered in detail in Chapter 14.

BOWL-MILL CAPACITIES

Bowl mills are available in a wide range of sizes. Table IX shows application and capacity ranges. Capacities are based on the use of 55 grindability coal pulverized to 70 percent through 200 mesh having a moisture content of 12 percent on low-rank bituminous coals or 8 percent on high-rank bituminous coals. See reference 18 for additional information.

REFERENCES

[1] Henry Kreisinger, "Combustion of Pulverized Coal," *Transactions of the ASME*, 60 (Paper no. FSP-60-8): 289–296, 1938.

[2] Nicolas Leonard Sadi Carnot, E. Clayperon, and R. Clausius, *Reflections on the Motive Power of Fire; and other Papers on the Second Law of Thermodynamics;* edited with an introduction by E. Mendoza. New York: Dover Pubs., 1962.

[3] Rudolf Diesel, *Theory and Construction of a Rational Heat Motor*, trans. by Bryan Donkin. London: Spon, 1894.

Friedrich Klemm, *A History of Western Technology.* Cambridge, Mass.: MIT Press, 1964, pp. 342–347.

[4] C. F. Herington, *Powdered Coal as a Fuel.* New York: Van Nostrand, 1918, pp. 68–72.

Frank Lewis Dyer and Thomas Commerford Martin, *Edison—His Life and Inventions*, with collaboration of William Henry Meadowcraft. New York: Harper and Bros., 1929, Vol. II, pp. 953–957.

[5] "Symposium on Powdered Fuel," Spring Meeting, American Society of Mechanical Engineers, St. Paul-Minneapolis, *Transactions of the ASME*, 36: 85–169, 1914.

R. C. Carpenter, "Pulverized Coal Burning in the Cement Industry," *Transactions of the ASME*, 36: 85–107, 1914.

William Dalton and W. S. Quigley, "An Installation for Powdered Coal Fuel in Industrial Furnaces," *Transactions of the ASME*, 36: 109–121, 1914.

F. R. Low, "Pulverized Coal for Steam Making," *Transactions of the ASME*, 36: 123–136, 1914.

"Topical Discussion on Powdered Fuel," *Transactions of the ASME*, 36: 137–169, 1914.

[6] John Anderson, "Pulverized Coal Under Central-Station Boilers," *Power*, 51(9): 336–339, March 2, 1920.

Paul W. Thompson, "Pulverized Fuel at Oneida Street Plant," *Power*, 51(9): 339–340, March 2, 1920.

"Four-Day Test on Five Oneida Street Boilers Burning Pulverized Coal," *Power*, 51(9): 354–357, March 2, 1920.

"Pulverized Coal at Milwaukee," *Power*, 51(9): 341–342, March 2, 1920.

"The New Lakeside Pulverized-Coal Plant, Milwaukee," *Power*, 52(10): 358–360, September 7, 1920.

"Largest Station Using Pulverized Coal," *Power*, 55(16): 604–610, April 18, 1922.

Henry Kreisinger and John Blizard, "Milwaukee's Contribution to Pulverized Coal Development," *Mechanical Engineering*, 61: 723–726 and 737, October, 1940.

F. L. Dornbrook, "Developments in Burning Pulverized Coal—Thirty Year Review of Experience in Milwaukee Plants," *Mechanical Engineering*, 70: 967–974, December, 1948.

[7] Henry Kreisinger, F. K. Ovitz, and C. E. Augustine, "Combustion in the Fuel Bed of Hand-Fired Furnaces," *U. S. Bureau of Mines Technical Paper 137*. Washington: U. S. Bureau of Mines, 1916.

Walter T. Ray and Henry Kreisinger, "The Flow of Heat Through Furnace Walls," *U. S. Bureau of Mines Bulletin 8*. Washington: U. S. Bureau of Mines, 1911.

Henry Kreisinger and Walter T. Ray, "The Transmission of Heat into Steam Boilers," *U. S. Bureau of Mines Bulletin 18*. Washington: U. S. Bureau of Mines, 1912.

Henry Kreisinger and J. F. Borkley, "Heat Transmission Through Boiler Tubes," *U. S. Bureau of Mines Technical Paper 114*. Washington: U. S. Bureau of Mines, 1915.

[8] Henry Kreisinger, John Blizard, C. E. Augustine, and B. J. Cross, "An Investigation of Powdered Coal as Fuel for Power-Plant Boilers—Tests at Oneida Street Power Station, Milwaukee, Wisconsin," *U. S. Bureau of Mines Bulletin 223*. Washington: U. S. Bureau of Mines, 1923.

Henry Kreisinger, John Blizard, C. E. Augustine, and B. J. Cross, "Tests of a Large Boiler Fired with Powdered Coal at the Lakeside Station, Milwaukee," *U. S. Bureau of Mines Bulletin 237*. Washington: U. S. Bureau of Mines, 1925.

[9] E. Audibert, "Etude de l'Entrainment du Poussier de Houille par l'Air," *Annales de Mines*, 1(3): 153–191, March, 1922.

[10] John Blizard, "The Terminal Velocity of Particles of Powdered Coal Falling in Air or Other Viscous Fluid," *Journal of the Franklin Institute*, 197(2): 199–208, February, 1924.

[11] John Blizard, "Transportation and Combustion of Powdered Coal," *U. S. Bureau of Mines Bulletin 217*. Washington: Government Printing Office, 1923.

[12] Henri Verdinne, "The Technique of Powdered Fuel Firing," *Fuel in Science and Practice*, 2: 146–151, 1923.

[13] W. Nusselt, "Der Verbrennungsvorgang in der Kohlenstaubfeuerung (The Combustion Process In Pulverized Coal Furnaces)," *VDI Zeitschrift*, 68(6): 124–128, February 9, 1924.

[14] P. Rosin, "Die Thermodynamischen uncl Wirtschafthichen Grundlagen der Kohlenstaubfeuerung (Thermodynamic and Economic Bases of Pulverized Coal Firing)," *Braunkohle*, 24(11): 241–259, June 13, 1925.

[15] Walter J. Wohlenberg and Donald G. Morrow, "Radiation in the Pulverized-Fuel Furnace," *Transactions of the ASME*, 47: 127–176, 1925.

[16] R. P. Hensel, "Coal Combustion," presented at the Engineering Foundation Conference on Coal Preparation for Coal Conversion, 1st, Franklin Pierce College, Rindge, N.H., 1975. Paper updated in 1978. Combustion Engineering, Inc., publication TIS-4599.

[17] R. P. Hensel, "The Effects of Agglomerating Characteristics of Coals on Combustion in Pulverized Fuel Boilers," *Symposium on Coal Agglomeration and Conversion*, Morgantown, W.V., 1975. Sponsored by the West Virginia Geological and Economic Survey in Cooperation With the Coal Research Bureau. Combustion Engineering, Inc., publication TIS-4353.

V. F. Parry, "Production, Classification and Utilization of Western United States Coals," Economic Geology, 45(6): 515–532, September–October, 1950.

[18] A. Bogot and T. B. Hamilton, "Maximizing Pulverizer Capabilities with Low Btu Western Coals," American Power Conference, Chicago, Illinois, 1974. Combustion Engineering, Inc., publication TIS-4008.

CHAPTER 13

Fuel-Burning Systems

In the process of steam generation, fuel-burning systems provide controlled, efficient conversion of the chemical energy of fuel into heat energy which, in turn, is transferred to the heat-absorbing surfaces of the steam generator. To do this, fuel-burning systems introduce the fuel and air for combustion, mix these reactants, ignite the combustible mixture and distribute the flame envelope and the products of combustion.

An ideal fuel-burning system fulfilling these functions would have the following characteristics:

■ no excess oxygen or unburned combustibles in the end products of combustion

■ a low rate of auxiliary ignition-energy input to initiate the combustion reaction

■ an economic reaction rate between fuel and oxygen compatible with acceptable nitrogen- and sulfur-oxide formation

■ an effective method of handling and disposing of the solid impurities introduced with the fuel

■ uniform distribution of the product weight and temperature in relation to the parallel circuits of heat-absorbing surface

■ a wide and stable firing range

■ fast response to changes in firing rate

■ high equipment availability with low maintenance

In actual practice, some of these characteristics must be compromised to achieve a reasonable balance between combustion efficiency and cost. For example, firing a fuel with the stoichiometric air quantity (no excess above the theorectical amount) would require an infinite residence time at temperatures above the ignition point at which complete burnout of the combustibles takes place. Thus, every firing system requires a quantity of air in excess of stoichiometry to attain an acceptable level of unburned carbon in the products of combustion leaving the furnace. This amount of excess air is an indicator of the burning efficiency of the firing system. Similarly, if firing devices are used to control the formation of oxides of nitrogen, there is a reduction in the response time of the firing system to load variations.

THE COMBUSTION REACTION

The rate and degree of completion of a chemical reaction, such as in the combustion process, are greatly influenced by temperature, concentration, preparation and distribution of the reactants, by catalysts, and by mechanical turbulence. All of these factors have one effect in common: to increase contacts between molecules of the reactants.

Higher temperature, for instance, increases the velocity of molecular movement permitting harder and more frequent contact between molecules. A temperature rise of 200°F at some stages can greatly increase the rate of reaction.

At a given pressure, three factors limit the temperature that can be attained to provide the greatest intermolecular contact. These are the heat absorbed by the combustion chamber enclosure, the heat absorbed by the reactants in bringing them to ignition temperature, and that absorbed by the nitrogen in the air used as a source of oxygen.

The concentration and distribution of the reactants in a given volume are directly related to the opportunity for contact between interacting molecules. In an atmosphere containing 21-percent oxygen (the amount present in air), this rate is much less than it would be with 90-percent oxygen. As the reaction nears completion, the distribution and concentration of reactants assume even greater importance. Because of the dilution of reactants by the inert products of combustion, the relative distribution—and opportunity for contact—approaches zero.

Preparation of the reactants and mechanical turbulence greatly influence the reaction rate. These are the primary factors available to the fuel-burning system designer attempting to provide a desirable reaction rate.

The beneficial effect of mechanical turbulence on the combustion reaction becomes apparent when it is realized that agitation permits greater opportunity for molecular contact. Agitation improves both the relative distribution and the energy imparted. Agitation assumes greater significance if achieved later in the combustion process when the relative concentration of the reactants is approaching zero.

PRACTICAL FUEL-FIRING SYSTEM DESIGN

In the practical application of a burner and fuel-burning system to a boiler, all fundamental factors influencing rate and completeness of combustion must be considered with the degree of heat-transfer efficiency.

There are two methods of producing a total flow pattern in a combustion chamber to provide successful molecular contacts of reactants through mechanical turbulence. One is to divide and distribute fuel and air into many similar streams and to treat each stream independently of all others. This provides multiple flame envelopes. In contrast, the second process provides interaction between all streams of air and fuel introduced into the combustion chamber to produce a single flame envelope.

The first concept requires that the total fuel and air supplied to a common combustion chamber be accurately subdivided. It also limits the opportunity for sustained mechanical mixing or turbulence—particularly in the early stages of combustion. The necessity of obtaining and sustaining good distribution of fuel and air is a design as well as an operating problem. There must be sufficient opportunity for contact of fuel and oxygen molecules as well as uniform distribution of product temperature and mass in relation to the combustion chamber. On the other hand, the single-flame-envelope technique provides interaction between all streams of fuel and air introduced into a common chamber. It allows more time for contact between all fuel and air molecules, and mechanical turbulence is sustained throughout the chamber. This avoids stringent fuel and air distribution accuracy requirements.

Firing systems representative of these two concepts are horizontally fired systems (characterized by individual flames) and tangentially fired systems (which have a single flame envelope). There are other types and combinations; one such is the vertically fired system, which uses characteristics of both previously described systems.

HORIZONTALLY FIRED SYSTEMS

In horizontally fired systems the fuel is mixed with combustion air in individual burner registers (Fig. 1). In this design, the coal and primary air are introduced tangentially to

Fig. 1 **Burner for horizontal firing of coal**

the coal nozzle, thus imparting strong rotation within the nozzle. Adjustable inlet vanes impart a rotation to the preheated secondary air from the windbox. The degree of air swirl, coupled with the flow-shaping contour of the burner throat, establishes a recirculation pattern extending several throat diameters into the furnace. Once the coal is ignited, the hot products of combustion are directed back toward the nozzle to provide the ignition energy necessary for stable combustion.

The burners are located in rows, either on the front wall only (Fig. 2) or on both front and rear walls. The latter is called "opposed firing."

Because the major portion of the combustion process must take place within the recirculation zone, it is imperative that the air/fuel ratio to each burner is within close tolerances. The rate of combustion drops off rapidly as the reactants leave the recirculation zone and interaction between flames occurs only after that

Fig. 2 **Flow pattern of horizontal (wall) firing**

point. The degree of interaction depends on burner and furnace configurations.

TANGENTIALLY FIRED SYSTEMS

The tangentially fired system is based on the concept of a single flame envelope (Fig. 3). Both fuel and combustion air are projected from the corners of the furnace along a line tangent to a small circle, lying in a horizontal plane, at the center of the furnace. Intensive mixing occurs where these streams meet. A rotative motion, similar to that of a cyclone, is imparted to the flame body, which spreads out and fills the furnace area.

When a tangentially fired system projects a stream of pulverized coal and air into a furnace, the turbulence and mixing that takes place along its path is low compared to horizontally fired systems. This occurs because the turbulent zone does not continue for any great distance as the expanding gas soon forces a streamline flow. The significance of this factor on the production of oxides of nitrogen is discussed later in this chapter. However, as one stream impinges on another in the center of the furnace, during the intermediate stages of combustion, it creates a high degree of turbulence for effective mixing.

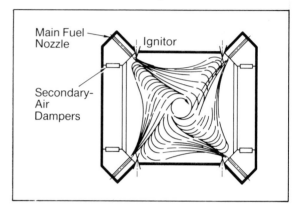

Fig. 3. **Tangential firing pattern**

Fig. 4 **Arrangement of corner windbox for tangential firing of coal**

13–4

Fig. 5 **Selective furnace utilization and steam temperature control are accomplished by tilting nozzles in a tangentially fired system**

The fuel and air are admitted from the furnace corners in vertical layers (Fig. 4). Dampers control the air to each compartment, making it possible to vary the distribution of air over the height of the windbox. It is also possible to vary the velocities of the air streams, change the mixing rate of fuel and air, and control the distance from the nozzle at which the coal ignites.

The vertical arrangement of nozzles provides great flexibility for multiple-fuel firing. It is possible to provide for full-load capability with gas or oil by locating the additional nozzles for these fuels in the secondary-air compartments adjacent to the coal nozzles. In addition, separate nozzles for injecting municipal refuse are frequently provided in both utility and industrial boilers. Refuse-burning systems are described in Chapter 9.

As illustrated in Fig. 5, fuel and air nozzles tilt in unison to raise and lower the flame in the furnace to control furnace heat absorption and thus heat absorption in the superheater and reheater sections. In addition to controlling the furnace exit-gas temperature for variations in load, the tilts on coal-fired units automatically compensate for the effects of ash deposits on furnace-wall heat absorption.

As wall blowers clean ash deposits from the furnace walls, the furnace exit gas temperature tends to decrease due to the increase in overall furnace absorption. The windbox nozzles are then automatically tilted upward at a controlled rate, and combustion is completed higher in the furnace. This effectively reduces the absorption in the lower part of the furnace, and increases the furnace exit-gas heat content to maintain steam at design temperatures.

Conversely, as furnace walls again gradually are covered with ash deposits and furnace heat absorption decreases due to the insulating effects of the ash, the tilts are gradually depressed and combustion is completed lower in the furnace. This exposes the hot gases to a greater proportion of furnace wall surface and effectively controls furnace exit-gas temperature and steam temperature until ash is again removed from the furnace walls.

VERTICALLY FIRED SYSTEMS

Vertically fired systems are used today only to fire solid fuels that are difficult to ignite, such as coals with moisture-and-ash-free volatile matter less than 13 percent. They require less supplementary fuel than the horizontal or tangentially fired systems, but have more complex firing equipment and therefore more complex operating characteristics.

The firing concept and the arrangement of the burners in the arches are shown in Figs. 6 and 7. Pulverized coal is discharged through the nozzles. A portion of the heated combustion air is introduced around the fuel nozzles and through adjacent auxiliary ports. High-pressure jets are used to avoid short-circuiting the fuel/air streams to the furnace discharge. Tertiary air ports are located in a row along the front and rear walls of the lower furnace.

The firing system produces a long, looping flame in the lower furnace, with the hot gases discharging up the center. A portion of the total combustion air is withheld from the fuel stream until it projects well down into the furnace. This arrangement has the advantage of heating the fuel stream separately from a significant portion of its combustion air to provide good ignition stability. The delayed introduction of the tertiary air provides needed turbulence at a point in the flame where partial dilution from the products of combustion has occurred. The furnace flow pattern passes the hot product gases immediately in front of the fuel nozzles to provide a ready source of inherent ignition energy which raises the primary fuel stream to ignition temperature. The flow pattern also ensures that the largest entrained solid fuel particles, with the lowest surface-area-to-weight ratio, have the longest residence time in the combustion chamber.

FIRING SYSTEMS THAT MINIMIZE NITROGEN-OXIDE FORMATION

Prior to 1970, some steam-generator firing systems produced great turbulence to achieve rapid mixing of the reactants and high energy release during the early stages of combustion. Surveys of these systems showed high levels of NO_x formation. With the advent of Environmental Protection Agency (EPA) restrictions in 1971, firing concepts underwent a change.

Firing systems developed in the 1970's to minimize NO_x formation are designed so that the fuel-bound nitrogen conversion is con-

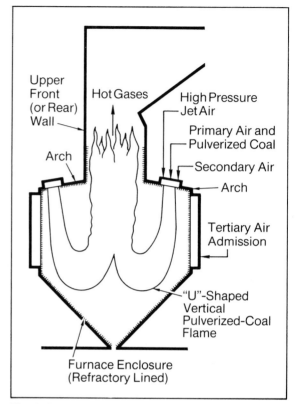

Fig. 6 **Flow pattern of vertical firing**

trolled by driving the major fraction of the fuel nitrogen compounds into the gas phase under overall fuel-rich conditions. In this atmosphere of oxygen deficiency, there occurs a maximum rate of decay of the evolved intermediate nitrogen compounds to molecular nitrogen. Following the admission of the remaining air, the slow burning rate reduces the peak flame temperature, to curtail the thermal NO_x production in the latter stages of combustion.

A comprehensive discussion of the mechanisms of nitrogen oxidation are included in Chapter 4 and the Bibliography on nitrogen-oxide control at the end of this chapter.

TANGENTIALLY FIRED LOW-NO_x SYSTEM

Early studies of NO_x emissions from all types of steam generators indicated that those from tangentially fired units were about half the values of those from horizontally fired systems.

This is due to the relatively low rate of mix-

Fig. 7 **Burner arrangement on the front arch of the furnace shown in Fig. 6**

Fig. 8 **Tangential-firing windbox with overfire air (OFA) ports and high energy arc ignitors**

ing between the parallel streams of coal and secondary air emitted from the corner windboxes. Thus, ignition and partial devolatilization occur within an air-deficient primary combustion zone that exists from the fuel nozzle to a point within the furnace at which the stream is absorbed into the rotating mass of gases termed the fireball.

The fireball itself is rich with oxygen because it contains all the air required for complete combustion of the fuel. Because a portion of the devolatilization occurs after the coal stream enters the fireball, the potential for fuel nitrogen is limited.

Two significant modifications have been made to the design and operation of the tangential windbox to extend the oxygen-deficient combustion zone.

The first modification added air compartments within the windbox above the uppermost coal nozzle, as shown in Fig. 8. Termed overfire air (OFA) ports, these compartments divert approximately 20 percent of the total combustion air to a burning zone above the windboxes. As a result, the fireball to the windboxes is at or near stoichiometric air conditions.

The second modification was an operating procedure which moved the ignition point closer to the nozzle. This change extended the duration of the primary combustion zone so that a greater portion of the devolatilization took place before entering the fireball. The ig-

Fig. 9 **Effect of overfire air on NO$_x$ production**

Fig. 9 shows the effect on NO$_x$ production of varying quantities of overfire air. Note the effect of total excess air on NO$_x$ levels. This is due primarily to the reduction in available oxygen within the fireball adjacent to the windboxes. With a constant windbox-to-furnace differential, reducing total excess air increases the proportion of overfire air at any given OFA damper position. This decreases the available oxygen below the OFA ports in even greater proportion to the change in total excess air.

nition point is controlled by varying the quantity and velocity of the air through the annulus of the fuel compartment by changing the position of the damper.

HORIZONTALLY FIRED LOW NO$_x$ SYSTEMS

A unique design developed for the Environmental Protection Agency (EPA) is the distrib-

Fig. 10 **Distributed mixing burner (DMB)**

Coal and Primary Air

Very Fuel Rich Zone (Average Stoichiometry 40%)

Progressive Air Addition Zone (Overall Stoichiometry 70%)

Final Air Addition Zone for Burnout (Overall Stoichiometry 120%)

Fig. 11 **Distributed mixing burner (DMB) concept**

uted mixing burner (DMB) shown in Fig. 10. The schematic (Fig. 11) illustrates how the design sequentially stages the fuel/air mixing in a distributed fashion. Conceptually, this is accomplished by dividing the total input to the furnace into three zones. In the first zone (primary air and coal plus a portion of the secondary air), the stoichiometry is maintained at a very rich condition during the start of the devolatilization process. Supplemental secondary air, termed *outer secondary air*, is then added to the rich products to establish conditions that maximize the decay of the volatilized fuel-nitrogen compounds. The tertiary air provides the oxygen necessary for complete combustion and provides a complete oxidizing zone around the rich primary zone. This oxidizing zone serves two purposes: it prevents corrosion due to a reducing atmosphere in the furnace and it limits the interactions between adjacent burners.

IGNITION SYSTEMS

The function of a fuel-burning system is to supply an uninterrupted flammable furnace input and to ignite that input continuously as fast as it is introduced and immediately upon its appearance in the furnace. Thus, no explosive mixture can accumulate in the furnace,

because the furnace input is effectively consumed and rendered inert. Ignition takes place when the flammable furnace input is heated above the ignition temperature.

Supplying correct ignition energy for the furnace input is a substantial task. Many factors establish the combinations of ignition energy quantity, quality and location that provide a satisfactory furnace input ignition rate at any instant. Unfortunately, these factors change rapidly and what constitutes sufficient ignition energy at one instant may be insufficient the next. From the rate-igniting standpoint there is never excess ignition energy. The more stable a fire, the more likely that the ignition energy substantially exceeds the minimum necessary to maintain ignition.

SUPPLY OF IGNITION ENERGY

As a safety factor, however, ignition energy for lightoff is not always supplied in great excess. Ignition energy usually is supplied in the form of heat, large amounts of which may not always be desired, particularly at low loads. In addition, ignition fuel can be expensive and may be difficult to obtain. Most stations use more costly fuel for auxiliary ignition than is used for main burner firing. If a large amount of premium light-off fuel is consumed, the cost can be substantial.

Igniting the input in prescribed steps also avoids undesirable furnace pressurizing during lightoff. A proportionately large increase in furnace input can be smoothly, adequately and continuously ignited, but the sudden increase in average furnace temperature tends to produce a quick increase in specific volume of the reactants which occurs because furnaces ordinarily cannot vent the excess material fast enough. The specific volume must not increase to the point that the furnace pressure increases.

Fig. 12 shows two methods of achieving a step-ignition for tangential firing. In the case on the left, the lowest elevation of ignitors are fired first and, after a suitable time, the elevation of oil warm-up guns are ignited. As furnace temperature stabilizes, the main coal nozzles adjacent to the oil guns are brought into operation. Thereafter, additional ignitors can be used to light off elevations of main coal nozzles directly.

In the alternative on the right in Fig. 12,

IGNITOR FUNCTIONAL DEFINITIONS

To fully understand the hardware, it may be necessary to review definitions contained in NFPA 85E "Explosion Prevention-Multiple Burner Boiler-Furnaces, Pulverized Coal-Fired, 1974."

Ignitor Types:

Class 1 (Continuous Ignitor)
"An ignitor applied to ignite the input through the burner and to support ignition under any burner light-off or operating conditions. Its location and capacity are such that it will provide sufficient ignition energy generally in excess of 10% of full load burner input, at its associated burner to raise any credible combination of burner inputs of both fuel and air above the minimum ignition temperature."

Class 2 (Intermittent Ignitor)
"An ignitor applied to ignite the fuel input through the burner under prescribed light-off conditions. It is also used to support ignition under the low load or certain adverse operating conditions. The range of capacity of such ignitors is generally 4% to 10% of the full load burner fuel input. It shall not be used to ignite main fuel under uncontrolled or abnormal conditions. The burner shall be operated under controlled conditions to limit the potential for abnormal operation, as well as to limit the charge of fuel to the furnace in the event that ignition does not occur during light-off. Class 2 ignitors may be operated as Class 3 ignitors."

Class 3 (Interrupted Ignitor)
"A small ignitor applied particularly to gas and oil burners* to ignite fuel input to the burner under prescribed light-off conditions. The capacity of such ignitors generally does not exceed 4% of full load burner fuel input. As a part of the burner light-off procedure, the ignitor is turned off before the time trial for ignition of the main burner has expired. This is to insure that the main flame is self supporting, is stable and is not dependent upon ignition support from the ignitor. The use of such ignitors to support ignition or to extend the burner control range shall be prohibited. This class of ignitor is dangerous for light-off or sustaining ignition of main coal burner."

*It is dangerous to use Class 3 ignitors with pulverized-coal main fuel. It is strongly recommended that only Class 1 & 2 Ignitors be used. Existing units with Class 3 Ignitors should be up-graded to at least Class 2.

Fig. 12 **Alternative step-ignition processes for tangential firing**

ignitors can be used to light off successive elevations of warm-up oil and these, in turn, will ignite adjacent main coal elevations.

Experience indicates that firing by these step-input methods will minimize furnace pressurization and unnecessary over-pressure trips.

IGNITION SYSTEMS FOR TANGENTIAL FIRING

Ignition systems available for tangentially fired systems include:

- spark ignition of distillate oils and high calorific value gases
- spark ignition of residual oils

Fig. 13 **Outside of tangential windbox showing coal-transport piping and ignitor assemblies**

Fig. 14 **Ionic Flame Monitoring side ignitor**

■ spark ignition of pulverized coal

Available ignitors can use a variety of fuels including natural gas, all grades of fuel oil, and most coals. The application of various ignitors (Fig. 13) is largely a function of ignitor fuel availability and economics.

IFM IGNITOR

The Ionic Flame Monitoring (IFM) side ignitor can spark-ignite high Btu gases or distillate oils. The IFM design (Fig. 14) follows the traditional C-E philosophy of providing an ignitor with both qualitative and quantitative indications of flame. The system incorporates the principle of flame ionization, which is present in all turbulent hydrocarbon flames, to detect the presence of combustion. In the burning process, energy is liberated by the combination of two or more reactants to form a product with a low energy level. During this burning process, many ions (charged particles) are liberated as electrons and charged nuclei. When a DC potential is placed across the flame, a varying current is generated due to the variable resistance the flame presents to the rod.

The system operates by imposing a DC potential on the rod that is in contact with the flame. The DC voltage level is modulated plus or minus around the imposed level by the flame and the imposed signal is then filtered out. The variance is amplified, changed to a pulse-shape and used to drive a flame indication relay.

The circuit is designed to be fail safe. If there is a component failure, a short circuit in the flame rod or lead wire, or a direct AC interference, a "no flame" indication will occur.

The common application of the ignitor is compatible with NFPA Class 2 classification. It is nominally sized for 4 percent of the heat input of the adjacent coal nozzle, and is used for initial light off and low-load stabilization. The ignitor can also be used to light off an oil-fired warm-up gun which then ignites the adjacent coal nozzle.

An alternate approach would be to use the IFM as only a Class 3 ignitor for a timed ignition of a warm-up oil gun. In this case a discriminating scanner is required to detect the firing of the oil gun. Because the side ignitor could be shut off immediately after oil gun ignition, less ignition fuel would be consumed. Such a system could use bottled gas as an ignitor fuel and lower cost residual oils in the oil gun.

HEA IGNITOR

The High Energy Arc (HEA) ignitor was developed to offset the decreasing availability and rising cost of ignition fuels such as natural gas and No. 2 fuel oil. The HEA ignitor effectively eliminates dependency on these fuels by igniting a No. 6 oil warm-up gun which, in turn, ignites the main coal nozzles (Fig. 8). The HEA ignitor is used with a discriminating scanner, which verifies the operation of the warm-up gun. The warm-up gun is designed for a proven oil flow of about 10 percent of an adjacent coal nozzle, with the discriminating scanner proving the presence of a flame. The combination of an HEA ignitor and a No. 6 oil-fired warm-up gun satisfies the NFPA definition of a Class 1 or Class 2 ignitor. The HEA ignitor alone would be a Class 3 ignitor.

Fig. 15 **High Energy Arc ignitor**

The HEA Ignition System consists of

■ a high energy arc ignitor

■ a warm-up oil compartment capable of producing a stable flame at all loads

■ a flame detecting system sensitive only to its associated oil gun

■ a control system to coordinate all the components and provide for unit safety

The high energy arc ignitor can ignite warm-up fuel oils ranging from No. 2 to No. 6 and crude oils. The ignitor is a self-contained electrical discharge device which produces a high-intensity spark. Use of a high-resistance transformer, to produce a full wave charging circuit and to control spark rate, enables the sealed power supply to store maximum energy and to deliver a greater percentage of this energy through insulated cables to the ignitor tip. A high spark energy also eliminates coking of the ignitor tip. The High Energy Arc ignitor consists of four basic components: the exciter, flexible cable, spark tube and guide pipe, and retractor assembly (Fig. 15).

A key to the successful application of spark-ignition is the presence of a strong recirculation pattern in the primary combustion zone (Fig. 16). The recirculation provides the energy required to vaporize and heat the oil to its ignition point, thus maintaining stable ignition after the spark has been deactivated.

The discriminating scanners are ultraviolet (UV) scanners with a reduced sensitivity, which permits each scanner to see only the flame from the associated warm-up oil gun and not the flame of the warm-up oil guns in adjacent or opposite corners.

DIRECT IGNITION OF PULVERIZED COAL (DIPC)

Steam generators designed for pulverized-coal firing require supplemental oil or gas for start-up and low-load stabilization. The cost and availability of these fuels are major concerns to many electric utilities.

The issue is compounded by the changing role of coal-fired units from the traditional base-load mode to cycling or two-shifting

Fig. 16 **Flame pocket is created on ignitor tip**

(A) Flame Pocket is Created on Ignitor Tip

(B) Flame Pocket Becomes Entrained in Recirculation Zone and Expands Towards Oil-Gun Tip

(C) Flame Pocket Reaches Oil-Gun Tip and Stabilizes

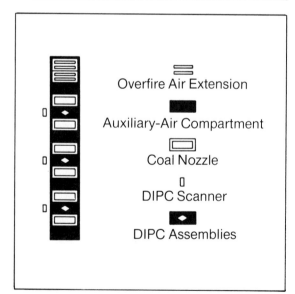

Fig. 17 **Direct Ignition of Pulverized Coal (DIPC) windbox**

modes. In the past, a utility's generating system consisted typically of base-loaded coal-fired units, cycling oil-fired boilers, and peaking gas turbines. In recent years nuclear units have been absorbing the base-load capacity and oil-fired units are being replaced with coal-fired units. This means that coal-fired units, in some cases, are responding to cycling or peaking loads, which places heavy demands on supplemental oil and gas systems to support these operating modes.

C-E has developed a method of using coal, rather than oil or gas, for unit start-up and low-load stabilization. The system, called Direct Ignition of Pulverized Coal (DIPC), uses an ultra high-energy electric arc (UHEA) to ignite a stream of coal in a dense phase transporting media. The DIPC firing assemblies replace oil or gas equipment in the auxiliary air compartments in a tangential windbox (Fig. 17).

SYSTEM DESCRIPTION

A critical component to the DIPC system is the firing assembly (Fig. 18). The coal/primary air stream is dispersed within the quarl assembly by means of a cone diffuser that performs two functions: it promotes rapid mixing of fuel with secondary air and it creates a reverse flow pattern in the downstream eddies. The two key conditions for spark-ignition of pulverized coal are a semidense coal/air mixture and a strong recirculation pattern at the point of ignition. Both are needed to propagate the energy provided by a spark pulse.

Coal Preparation System

A pulverized-coal storage system (Fig. 19) provides the fuel for preheating a cold furnace in the orderly step-ignition process described earlier. The system also vents the moisture driven from the coal in the pulverizing process and provides the semidense coal/air mixture required by the firing assembly.

Flue gas is used in the pulverizing system to maintain an inert atmosphere, as recommended by NFPA. A baghouse filter removes the fines from the cyclone effluent and returns them to the pulverized-coal storage bin. Finally, high-pressure clean air is used to transport the metered coal to the firing assemblies.

This DIPC ignition system has the following capabilities:

■ completely eliminates the need for oil during ignition and warm-up phases of a cold or hot start

■ provides stability of main coal fires at low loads and extends turndown on coal to an infinite range

■ provides the function of a spare pulverizer during pulverizer maintenance

■ can restore a portion of lost load resulting from degradation of coal quality

SUPPLEMENTARY INFORMATION ON IGNITION SYSTEMS

Appendix B provides valuable supplementary reading on furnace and ignition-system

Fig. 18 Direct Ignition of Pulverized Coal (DIPC) firing assembly

Fig. 19 Direct ignition of pulverized coal (DIPC) system

analysis. Qualitative criteria on combustion as well as pulverized coal, oil, and gas ignition include the Rosin combustion-intensity equation, the Semenov thermal-explosion jump, and the Vulis-Essenhigh approach.

STOKERS

Stokers are mechanical devices that burn solid fuels in a bed at the bottom of a furnace. They convert chemical energy in the fuel to thermal energy which is absorbed by boiler surfaces to generate steam or produce high-temperature water. Stokers are designed to permit continuous or intermittent fuel feed, fuel ignition, adequate supply of required air for combustion, free passage for the resulting gaseous products, and disposal of noncombustible materials.

Stokers are classified according to the direction from which the fuel reaches the fuel bed. In an underfeed stoker the fuel and air travel in the same relative direction—both entering the active burning zone from beneath the bed. Underfeed stokers are built in single-retort and multiple-retort designs.

Boilers with underfeed stokers of the single-retort design have been built in capacities from 5,000 to 50,000 lb of steam/hour on a maximum-continuous basis. Multiple-retort stokers have been built for boilers ranging from 40,000 to 300,000 lb of steam/hour.

Overfeed stokers have the fuel entering the active combustion zone from above, in opposition to the primary airflow. Included in the overfeed group are spreader stokers and mass-burning stokers. The spreader-type overfeed stoker delivers fuel so that a portion burns in suspension while the remainder burns on either a stationary or moving grate. Mass-burning or crossfeed stokers are more commonly referred to as either traveling-grate or vibrating-grate.

The traveling-grate stoker can be used to burn most solid fuels. With the single exception of caking bituminous coals, a travel-grate stoker can burn every type of fuel that is mined.

In addition, such waste and byproduct fuels as coke breeze, anthracite dredged from river bottoms, and municipal refuse are burned effectively. The traveling-grate stoker also may be used as a part of chemical process operations to produce coke and carbon dioxide.

Overfeed traveling-grate stokers are used in sizes from about 10,000 to 300,000 lb of steam/hour. A similar upper limit of steam applies to the size of spreader stokers.

Stokers are proportioned on the basis of grate heat-release rates which may range from 200,000 Btu/hr-sq ft for small single-retort stokers to 1,000,000 Btu/hr. sq ft or more for large spreader stokers where part of the fuel is burned in suspension.

This area of projected grate surface determines the furnace cross section. Furnace volumes are proportioned on the basis of heat-release rates which may range from 15,000 to 50,000 Btu/hr-cu ft, depending upon installation size, type of stoker, probable load factor, heat absorbing area and the like.

HISTORICAL DEVELOPMENT OF STOKER FIRING

Historically, the greatest impetus for the development of stokers came from two sources: objections to smoke emission resulting from hand firing and imperfect combustion and limitations on steam output of boilers inherent in manual stoking.

James Watt made the first documented attempt to fire coal by means of a mechanical stoker. In 1785 his patent described a device combining a coal hopper, a grate for fuel burning and provision for refuse disposal.

Most of the principles of both underfeed and overfeed mechanical stoking were understood and applied before 1860. Stoker improvements have made it possible to burn almost every conceivable solid fuel. Plants using stokers range from small industrial installations to moderate-sized electric-generating stations.

The developments subsequent to Watt's efforts are detailed well in Chapters 3, 4, 5, and 6 of the First Edition of *Combustion Engineering*.[1] Included are comprehensive descriptions of single- and multiple-retort stokers, chain-grate and traveling-grate stokers, and dump-grate spreader stokers. This text is limited to continuous-ash-discharge spreader stokers.

Although the relative importance of stokers as a means of firing coal has decreased, particularly in power-generating stations where the boiler and turbine-generator size has far exceeded the output capabilities of stokers, they remain an important type of commercial firing equipment for industrial power plants. Such plants burn a wide variety of waste, refuse, and byproduct fuels. To a limited extent stokers are applied to coal carbonization, briquetting, and ore-beneficiation operations.

SPREADER STOKERS FOR COAL FIRING

Spreader stokers use the combined principles of pulverized-coal and stoker firing in that fines are burned in suspension and the larger

Fig. 20 **Spreader stoker feeder/distributors**

particles are burned on the grate. Feeding and distributing mechanisms continually project coal into the furnace above an ignited fuel bed. This method of introducing fuel causes greater particulate loadings in the flue gas than the earlier described stoker designs in which the fuel quiescently enters the burning zone. With the spreader method of firing, the chemical characteristics of the coal have little effect on the fuel bed. Strongly caking coals show little tendency to mat and burn with the same ease as the free-burning variety. Flash drying the incoming fuel, rapidly releasing the volatiles and burning the fuel in suspension are factors that make this method of firing so applicable. Practically all types of coal have been successfully burned on spreader stokers, as have a wide variety of cellulose fuels, including bagasse, wood chips, bark, hogged wood, sawdust, shavings, coffee grounds and furfural residue.

Firing coal with a spreader stoker is accomplished by using one or more mechanical firing devices mounted on a front plate. These include a hopper, a feeder that regulates the flow of coal in proportion to the load, and a distributor rotor that spreads the coal into the furnace and distributes it on the grate. It is common practice to integrate the feeder and distributor into a single unit called a coal spreader (Fig. 20).

The fuel bed is a thin level fire on top of a uniform layer of ash. It is nonagitated and intensely active. Under proper operating conditions, there is never more than a few minutes supply of coal on the grate. This thin active fuel bed lays on a cooled, nonagitated ash bed and despite very low fusion temperatures the ash forms few clinkers. Also, this protective layer of ash, together with uniform airflow to the grate, keeps the grate castings relatively cool.

COAL-SPREADER DESIGN

The design of the coal spreader, major parts of which are identified in Fig. 21, is of utmost importance, for upon it depends the uniformity with which fuel is supplied to the furnace. When the coal is fine and dry, the feeder may feed too rapidly; when it is wet, the particles

Fig. 21 **Feeder-distributor for firing of coal on a spreader stoker**

may cohere, or may stick to the feeder causing an erratic supply of fuel to the distributor. For all conditions, including these governing extremes, the rotary feeder provides a positive control of the fuel feed rate. The feeding unit permits positive regulation of the fuel supply over a wide range by either manual or automatic control.

The coal is measured out of the feeder at a rate necessary to carry the boiler load. It then falls in a practically continuous stream into the path of the revolving distributor blades. These blades are usually mounted in rows parallel to the axis of the distributor rotor. The crisscrossing of fuel streams from a single distributor, or from a combination of distributors, results in a consistently uniform distribution of fuel on the grate, which may be of the dumping or continuous-discharge type.

CONTINUOUS-DISCHARGE GRATE

The design of the continuous-ash-discharge spreader stoker (Fig. 22) incorporates coal spreaders and/or cellulose distributors with the continuously moving fuel-supporting surface of a traveling-grate stoker. Unlike the traveling-grate stoker, the grate of the continuous-ash-discharge spreader stoker travels toward the coal spreaders or cellulose distri-

butors and discharges the ash into a pit located at the stoker front. The return grate carries siftings which fall through the active grate to the siftings hopper. The grate speed is regulated to maintain a uniformly thick ash bed of about 2 in. at the discharge end at all ratings.

Grate drives are either hydraulic (Fig. 23), or triple-reduction worm gear (Fig. 24) and, depending on grate size, provide between 200,000 to 550,000 in.-lb torque to the drive shaft, which rotates from 0.006 to 0.06 rpm. Thus, the continuous-ash-discharge grate has an operating speed range from 2 to 20 feet/hour.

The moving-grate surface is sectionalized. Each section is of the bar-and-key construction (Figs. 25 and 26) and has independent idler shafts. The grate bars are mild-steel fabricated I beams, while the grate keys are the ductile-iron type having a maximum working temperature of 1600°F. Constant load springs provide proper grate tensioning semi-automatically. Thermocouples in the stationary castings between the moving-grate sections monitor temperatures and signal overheat conditions that require corrective action.

Current boiler designs that include high-temperature combustion air preclude the application of conventional grease-lubricated stoker main and idler shaft bearings. Whenever

***Fig. 22* Spreader stoker, continuous ash discharge grate**

undergrate air temperatures exceed 400°F, self-lubricating bearings with a solid lubricant such as molybdenum disulfide or graphite are used exclusively.

The combustion-air chamber is located below the fuel-supporting surface; the air passes through the keys. Undergrate air is proportioned front to back by adjusting manual damper assemblies at the entrance to the undergrate compartments. Sealing between compartments is maintained by drag seals and, for cellulose units, an undergrate sand seal. Thus, uniform air pressure is maintained under compartmented areas without air leakage.

Flexibility of Operation

One of the outstanding characteristics of spreader-stoker firing is the ability to handle rapid load swings with little or no change in steam temperature and pressure. Turndown or load range generally extends from 25 percent of full load to maximum capacity. It is not unusual for a spreader-stoker installation to go from 25 percent to 100 percent of rated capacity in less than one minute. Also, if fuel is shut off the fire goes out almost immediately.

Overfire Air

In stoker-fired furnaces in which bituminous coals are burned, overfire air is quite com-

monly used to improve combustion efficiency by turbulent mixing of air with the unburned gases. Air and fuel-bearing gas mixing results from proper pressure and volume of the air.

The quantity of overfire air should be between 5 and 20 percent of the total quantity of air needed for fuel combustion. The amount of overfire air will be a function of the coal rank and the amount of excess air in the furnace. Relatively small jets of air at pressures up to 25 or 30" WG are used in most installations for improving combustion in the furnace, and for reducing visible emissions and cinder carryover. Extreme care is required in using these pressures, as penetration is a function of static pressure and volume of air per nozzle.[2]

FUEL SPECIFICATIONS FOR SPREADER-STOKER FIRING

Spreader stokers were developed to burn the lower grades of coal, but they are capable of handling all ranks from semianthracite to lignite as well as numerous waste and byproduct fuels. As might be expected, spreader-stoker performance is best when fuel quality and sizing are good. The thin, quick-burning fuel bed requires a relatively small size fuel. Because 25 to 50 percent of the fuel is burned in suspension, the size consistency of coal for spreader

Fig. 23 Hydraulic grate drive

Fig. 24 C-E Lloyd gear case

stokers has a direct bearing on boiler efficiency and on the tendency of the installation to emit particulates. Coal with a large percentage of fines will have high particulate emissions and high carbon loss. If the coal is coarse, with only a small percentage of fines, boiler response to load variations will be affected because fuel ignition depends on the fines. In general the spreader-stoker coal consistency should be such that 95 percent of the coal delivered to the coal spreader will pass through a ¾ in. round-hole screen with not more than 50 percent passing through a ¼ in. round-hole screen. Top-size should not exceed 1¼ in.

Using a carbon reinjection system (Fig. 27) can improve boiler efficiency. The reinjection system reclaims carbon separated from the flyash by using vibrating or rotating screens. Once the carbon has been separated from the flyash, carbon recovery nozzles reinject it into the high temperature zone of the furnace, just above the fuel bed.

The proper design of a carbon-reinjection system requires that the boiler designer know the percentage of combustibles remaining in various screen-sizes of the coal residue to be reinjected. The combustion potential of this material also is important. This knowledge can only be obtained from test data gathered from operating units. It is possible that the reinjected carbon particles will exhibit properties quite different from the main coal supply. In some instances, data will indicate that a reinjection system would not be appropriate.

SPREADER STOKERS
FOR CELLULOSE FUEL FIRING

Spreader-stoker firing systems have been applied to a number of boilers burning a variety of waste products such as bark, refuse, bagasse, and furfural residue.

In general, cellulose fuel has a higher moisture and volatile content than coal, and the combustion process involves three phases: drying, distillation of volatiles, and burning of fixed carbon. These take place in rapid succession. To get complete combustion of the volatile gases formed, approximately 30 to 50 percent of the air supply is furnished as tangential overfire air. This system has effectively increased burn-out and reduced particulate carryover.

The source of tangential overfire air is a hot-air duct which is controlled at a constant pressure of about 8″ WG, depending on furnace size and penetration required. The center lines of the overfire-air nozzles are tangent to a firing circle in the center of the furnace. All nozzles are oriented in the same direction to establish the same rotation as that of the tangential windboxes located above the overfire-air zone. This continuity of rotation throughout the

Fig. 25. **Bar-and-key grate construction**

Fig. 26 **Bar-and-key grate assembly**

Fig. 27 **Carbon reinjection system—cellulose firing**

over the grate. The fuel enters the furnace in a thick, uniform, and widely dispersed stream. Most is burned in suspension with the remainder consumed after falling to the grate. As with coal-fired spreader stokers, the grate surface may be of the dumping or continuous-ash-discharge type. A carbon-recovery system with sand-separation screens and steam injection (Fig. 27) is often incorporated to increase the efficiency of the boiler.

FIRING CELLULOSE FUELS IN SUSPENSION

High-pressure pneumatic transport in the paper industry has for many years been routinely applied to conveying applications up to one-half mile.

To apply this firing system requires that most of the solid-waste-fuel burning occur in suspension. Therefore, material such as diffuser bagasse, shredded industrial paper waste, and shredded municipal refuse, which tends to remain in suspension can be burned as a total fuel. The more dense materials such as bark, which tends not to remain in suspension, have to be reduced to a proper particle size. The size depends upon the percentage of the total heat input provided by the cellulose fuel and on whether the unit has a dump grate.

The solid-waste fuel is metered to four high-pressure pneumatic transport systems which convey it to tilting nozzles located in compartments of the corner windboxes. The light particles are flash dried and burned in suspension. Larger dense particles are partially dried and partially burned in a turbulent overfire-air zone in the lower furnace before falling to a small dump grate in the lower furnace. Burning on the grate adds heat to the lower furnace which increases the suspension drying and burning of incoming fuel (Fig. 31).

The cellulose fuel nozzle (Fig. 32) is part of the windbox assembly. The bucket at the end of the nozzle can be tilted ±30° along with an adjacent auxiliary air and supplemental fuel nozzle. The nozzle deflectors are located so that the waste fuel will be dispersed for proper mixing with windbox and overfire air. Tangential overfire air is distributed at various levels

lower furnace assures a strong vortex which promotes burn-out and reduces particulate carryover into the exiting gases.

Spreader stoker use predominates in bagasse burning, although a special type of feeder and distributor is required to successfully burn this bulky and fibrous fuel. Drum-type feeders, (Fig. 28) are attached to the bottom of a bunker from which they feed bagasse to the distributor unit at the bottom of an inclined chute. The drum-type feeder operates on a controlled volumetric basis, and the bagasse feed rate is proportioned to the demand from a master controller. An individual feeder serves each distributor directing fuel to the burners.

Distributors for cellulose fuels may be either mechanical or pneumatic. A mechanical distributor (Fig. 29) is essentially a rotating drum with blades placed at an angle to maintain uniform fuel distribution over the grate surface. The speed of the rotating drum is adjusted for fuel conditions and the throw required to properly cover the grate.

With the pneumatic distributor (Fig. 30) air jets project and distribute the fuel uniformly

Fig. 28 **Drum-type rotary bagasse feeder**

throughout the lower furnace including the hopper part of the boiler.

The dump grates (Fig. 33) are suspended in the hopper throat formed by the pressure parts. The shafts and bearings are located under the pressure parts where they are protected from the radiant heat of the furnace.

Grate castings are provided with nonplugging reverse tapered holes. Pneumatic cylinder assemblies actuate the grates. This simple design has had a record of extremely low maintenance and high availability.

The grate-burning system burns solid-waste fuel which was not burned in suspension. The introduction of fuel through corner windboxes increases suspension burning of fine particles but tends to concentrate large particles at the ends of the grate. Small boost fans supply air to nozzles at the end of the grate.

Overgrate air is introduced along the length of the grate by removing fins between the tubes in the throat area. Undergrate air is introduced into the ash hopper. This air must be metered because the resistance of the bed increases as the ash accumulates.

MORE ON FUEL FIRING

Other aspects of preparing, transporting, firing and burning fuel in steam-generator fur-

Fig. 29 **Mechanical distributor**

Fig. 30 **Pneumatic distributor**

Fig. 31 **Pneumatic firing system**

1. **Pneumatic Transport System.** Each of four systems include a positive displacement blower, silencers, air lock, and conveying lines.
   The solid-waste fuel is metered to this system for direct transport to the windbox nozzle.

2. **Windbox Nozzle.** Adjustable nozzles are incorporated in the tilting tangential windboxes. The arrangement permits optimization of firing conditions for the best burn out of the solid-waste fuel.

3. **Tangential Overfire Air.** Multiple elevations of tangential overfire air sustain the suspension burning of the waste fuel.

4. **Dump Grate.** This feature allows burn out of the relatively small percentage of solid-waste fuel which does not burn in suspension.

5. **Grate Air System.** Undergrate air provides most of the air for burning fuel which falls to the grate. Overgrate air is introduced from both ends of the grate to aid in distributing concentrations of fuel on the grate surface.

naces are covered in complementary chapters.

The processes of combustion and the formation of nitrogen oxides are further described in Chapter 4. Chapters 7 and 8 cover the integration of the firing system and furnace utility and industrial boilers designs and configurations. Firing equipment exclusively oriented to shipboard service is included in Chapter 9, Marine Boilers.

Chapter 12, Pulverizers and Pulverizing Systems focuses primarily on how coal is sized and transported to furnaces.

Chapter 14, Control Systems deals at length with safety and flame-detection systems so important to modern burning equipment.

Fig. 32 **Tangential burner assembly**

Fig. 33 **Dump grates at furnace bottom, closed position**

REFERENCES

[1] Glenn R. Fryling, ed., *Combustion Engineering a Reference Book on Fuel Burning and Steam Generation*, revised edition, New York: Combustion Engineering, Inc., 1966.

[2] R. B. Engdahl, *Combustion* Vol. 15, March, 1944 pp. 47–51. R. B. Engdahl and W. C. Holton *ASME Transactions* Vol. 65, 1943 pp. 73–86. W. Gumz, *Combustion* Vol. 22, April 1951, pp. 39–47.

BIBLIOGRAPHY

Bagwell, F. A., et. al., "Utility Boiler Operating Modes for Reduced Nitric Oxide Emissions," *Air Pollution Control Association Journal*, 21(11): 702–708, November 1971.

Bartok, William; A. R. Crawford; and G. J. Piegari, "Systematic Investigation of Nitrogen Oxide Emissions and Combustion Control Methods for Power Plant Boilers," R. W. Coughlin, A. F. Sarofin, and N. J. Weinstein, (eds.), *Air Pollution and Its Control*, AICHe Symposium Series, No. 126, Vol. 68, 1972, pp. 66–74. New York: American Institute of Chemical Engineers, 1972.

Bartok, William, et. al., *Systems Study of Nitrogen Oxide Control Methods for Stationary Sources. Volume II. Final Report.* June 20, 1968–November 20, 1969. Report No. PB-192 789 (GR-2-Nos-69). Springfield, VA: National Technical Information Service, 1969.

Blakeslee, C. E. "Reduction of NO_x Emissions by Combustion Modifications to a Gas-Fired 250-MW Tangential-Fired Boiler," *Proceedings of the 2nd Conference on Natural Gas Research and Technology*, Atlanta, June 5–7, 1972, Session VI, Paper 3. Chicago: Institute of Gas Technology, 1972.

Bueters, K. A., "Combustion Products Emissivity by F_e Operator," *Combustion*, 45(9): 12–18, March 1974.

Bueters, K. A., et. al., "NO_x Emissions from Tangentially Fired Utility Boilers—A Two Part Paper," Part I, "Theory," by K. A. Bueters and W. W. Habelt; Part II, "Practice," by C. E. Blakeslee and H. E. Burbach, presented at the 66th Annual AICHe Meeting, Philadelphia, November 11–15, 1973.

Bueters, K. A., J. G. Cogoli, and W. W. Habelt, "Performance Prediction of Tangentially Fired Utility Furnaces by Computer Model," presented at the 15th International Symposium on Combustion, Tokyo, August 25–31, 1974; published as Combustion Engineering publication TIS-3865, Windsor, CT: Combustion Engineering, Inc., 1974.

Fenimore, C. P., "Formation of Nitric Oxide from Fuel Nitrogen in Ethylene Flames," *Combustion and Flame*, 19(2): 289–296, October 1972.

Frey, D. J. and M. S. McCartney, "The Formation, Measurement, and control of Nitrogen Oxides in Existing Fossil Fuel Fired Steam Generators," presented at the 28th Engineering Conference, TAPPI, Boston, October 9–11, 1973; published as Combustion Engineering publication TIS-3598, Windsor, CT: Combustion Engineering, Inc., 1973.

Glamuzina, Robert W. and Michael S. McCartney, "Controlling NO_x and Particulate Emissions from Industrial Steam Generators," presented at the 31st annual Petroleum Mechanical Engineering Conference, Mexico City, September 19–23, 1976; published as Combustion Engineering publication TIS-4807, Windsor, CT: Combustion Engineering, Inc., 1976.

Habelt, W. W., "The Influence of the Coal Oxygen to Coal Nitrogen Ratio on NO_x Formation," presented at the 70th annual AICHe meeting, New York, November 13–17, 1977; published as Combustion Engineering publication TIS-5140, Windsor, CT: Combustion Engineering, Inc., 1977.

Habelt, W. W. and B. M. Howell, "Control of NO_x Formation in Tangentially Coal-Fired Steam Generators," presented at the Electric Power Research Institute NO_x Control Technology Seminar, San Francisco, February 5–6, 1976; published as Combustion Engineering publication TIS-4769, Windsor, CT: Combustion Engineering, Inc., 1976.

Habelt, W. W. and A. P. Selker, "Operating Procedures and Prediction for NO_x Control in Steam Power Plants," presented at the Central States Section of the Combustion Institute Spring Technical Meeting, Madison, Wisconsin, March 26–27, 1974; published as Combustion Engineering publication TIS-4001, Windsor, CT: Combustion Engineering, Inc., 1974.

Habelt, W. W. and A. P. Selker, "The Role of Tangential Firing and Fuel Properties in Attaining Low NO_x Operation for Coal-Fired Steam Generation," presented at the 71st Annual Meeting of the Air Pollution Control Association, Houston, June 25–29, 1978; published as Combustion Engineering publication TIS-5623, Windsor, CT: Combustion Engineering, Inc., 1978.

Heap, M. P., et. al., "Burner Design Principles for Minimum NO_x Emissions," *Proceedings, Coal Combustion Seminar*, Research Triangle Park, NC, June 19–20, 1973. Report No. PB-224 210 (EPA 650/2-73-021). Springfield, VA: National Technical Information Service, 1973.

Heap, M. P., et. al., *Burner Criteria for NO_x Control Volume I. Influence of Burner Variables on NO_x in Pulverized Coal Flames. Final Phase Report*, June 1971–June 1974. Report No. PB-259 911 (EPA/600/2-76/061a). Springfield, VA: National Technical Information Service, 1976.

Marshall, J. J. and A. P. Selker, "The Role of Tangential Firing and Fuel Properties in Attaining Low NO_x Operation for Coal-Fired Steam Generation," presented at the EPRI NO_x Control Technology Seminar, Denver, November 8–9, 1978; published as Combustion Engineering publication TIS-5623A, Windsor, CT: Combustion Engineering, Inc., 1978.

Pershing, D. W. and J. O. L. Wendt, "Pulverized Coal Combustion: The Influence of Flame Temperature and Coal Composition on Thermal and Fuel NO_x," *Sixteenth Symposium (International) on Combustion*, Massachusetts Institute of Technology, Cambridge, MA, August 15–20, 1976, pp. 389–399. Pittsburgh: The Combustion Institute, 1976.

Selker, A. P., "Overfire Air as a NO_x Control Technique for Tangential Coal-Fired Boilers," presented at the Environmental Protection Agency Symposium on Stationary Source Combustion, Atlanta, September 24–26, 1975; published as Combustion Engineering publication TIS-4707, Windsor, CT: Combustion Engineering, Inc., 1975.

Selker, A. P., *Program for Reduction of NO$_x$ from Tangential Coal-Fired Boilers. Phase II.* Final Report. July 1973–March 1975. Report No. PB-245 162 (EPA 650/2-73-005-a). Springfield, VA: National Technical Information Service, 1975.

Selker, A. P. and R. L. Burrington, "Overfire Air Technology for Tangentially Fired Utility Steam Generators Burning Western U. S. Coal," presented at the 2nd symposium on Stationary Source Combustion, New Orleans, August 29–September 1, 1977; published as Combustion Engineering publication TIS-5242, Windsor, CT: Combustion Engineering, Inc., 1977.

Zel 'Dovich, Ya. B., P. Ya. Sadovnikov, and D. A. Frank Kamenetskii, *Oxidation of Nitrogen in Combustion.* Translated by M. Shelef. Moscow-Leningrad: Academy of Sciences of the USSR, 1947.

CHAPTER 14

Control Systems

A power plant may be thought of as an electricity factory. In that context, modern power plants are among the most highly automated, and centrally controlled and monitored production facilities in the world.

As power plants began to grow in size and complexity many years ago, it became apparent that local monitoring and regulation of the plant systems in a timely manner had become impossible. Thus, instrumentation and controls in power plants came into being to provide the ability to operate the major plant systems from a central location (Fig. 1). Meters, gages, and lights displayed equipment status to the operator, while recorders made a permanent record of plant performance. Remotely operated air cylinders and electric motors gave the plant operators the capability of responding quickly and efficiently to changing plant requirements.

Since the early days of remote operation, the generation of electricity has become a very complicated business. Spiraling energy costs demand that as much electricity as possible be extracted from the fossil fuel consumed. Higher availability of equipment is needed to stem rising operating and maintenance costs. Protection of both personnel and equipment must be achieved and unscheduled shutdowns kept to a minimum.

While obviously instruments and controls cannot of themselves satisfy such concerns, the problems have resulted in a substantially increased requirement for sophisticated instrumentation and automatic control systems.

This chapter deals primarily with the major control systems associated with fossil-fuel-fired utility steam generators. Control systems for steam generators in industrial applications are also discussed, but in less detail.

INTERLOCKS AND SAFETY SYSTEMS

The concept of a centralized control room was a big step forward in power-plant control. Nevertheless, as first conceived and executed, remote-manual systems relied entirely upon operator judgment and response.

The multiplicity of operating steps required for safely and properly admitting fuel to a furnace (or removing incompletely burned fuel from a furnace) leaves considerable latitude for operator error, if left to his or her judgment. Adequacy of ignition-energy levels is another area that should not be left to operator discretion. Considering that a major furnace explosion can result from the ignition of unburned fuel accumulated in only one to two seconds,

Fig. 1 Instrumentation and controls permit operation of major power-plant systems from a central location. Control-room meters, gages, and lights display equipment status to the operator, while recorders permanently record plant performance.

it is apparent that human reaction time is inadequate, to say nothing of the need for an instantaneous decision-making capability.

The recognition of these limitations to a complete operator-dependent mode of operation led to the development of automatic protection systems, designed to minimize the risk of furnace explosions.

FURNACE EXPLOSIONS

Furnace explosions are rare and unlikely. When compared with the total number of unit operating hours, the hours lost because of explosions are minimal. This desirable situation exists because (a) furnaces are supplied with an explosive accumulation only during a minute percentage of their operating lives and (b) just a small part of those explosive charges receive sufficient ignition energy to actually cause an explosion.

In suspension burning, the primary control of the combustion process is the admission rate of fuel and air to a furnace, independently of each other. The dynamic response of the combustion reaction, however, depends on the diffusion of the fuel and air to a flammable limit, and the elevation of this diffused mixture to its kindling temperature. The aerodynamic diffusion of fuel and air results from both the rate and method of admission. This admission flow pattern produces diffusion mechanically by interscrubbing of the fuel and air masses. Molecular diffusion is also present as a result of the elevated temperature level at which the combustion process takes place.

Furnace explosions result from a rapid rate of volume increase of the gaseous combustion products when too great a quantity of fuel and air reacts almost simultaneously in an enclosure with a limited volume and strength. Avoiding furnace pressures in excess of furnace enclosure design pressure is, therefore, necessary to prevent furnace rupture.

The basis for any furnace explosion-prevention system must be to limit the quantity of flammable fuel-and-air mixture that can exist in the furnace at any given instant. The rate of maximum pressure rise possible during the reaction is a function also of the available oxygen per unit volume of reactants. The effect of any oxygen-density diluent (nitrogen, increased temperature, decreased pressure, excess fuel, inert gases) reduces the possible explosion pressure.

Furnace-explosion prevention should be aimed at limiting the quantity of diffused flammable fuel-air mixture that can be accumulated in a furnace in proportion to the total volume and the mechanical strength of the furnace.

While fuel and air are being admitted to a furnace, there are only three possible methods of preventing excessive flammable diffused accumulations.

1. Igniting all flammable mixtures as they are formed, prior to their excessive accumulation.

2. Diffusing all flammable mixtures with sufficient additional air, prior to ignition, to a point beyond the diffused flammable-mixture ratio; and accomplishing this with sufficient degree of diffusion before a critical percentage of the furnace volume is occupied by the flammable mixture.

3. Supplying an inert gas to diffuse simultaneously with the fuel and air, thereby diluting the oxygen content of the mixture below the flammable limit.

Implementation of these preventative methods requires operator action beyond the response, memory, and judgment capabilities of the normal operator controlling a plant in the manual mode. A fireside safeguard system must supervise the flow and processing of fuel, air, ignition energy and the products of combustion. Satisfactory boiler operation requires that these four ingredients be properly prepared, ratioed, directed and sequenced so that the furnace cannot contain an explosive mixture. At the same time, the combustion process must be supervised to check the results. Combustion must be kept efficient or the unconverted chemical energy may accumulate and subsequently become explosive.

The following factors influence the effective composition change of an explosive charge:

1. the facility for mixing,

2. the inert material in the fuel,

3. the fuel-air ratio (a near-stoichiometric ratio develops the highest explosion pressure), and

4. the kind of fuel.

A furnace explosion requires both sufficient explosive accumulation within the furnace and sufficient energy for ignition. The ignition requirements for an explosive charge are minute, making it impossible to protect against *all* possible sources of ignition, such as static electricity discharges, hot slag, and hot furnace surfaces. Therefore, the practical means of avoiding a furnace explosion is the prevention of an explosive accumulation.

The factors determining the magnitude of a furnace explosion—mass, change in composition, and reaction time—are related in the *explosion factor*.

$$\text{Explosion Factor} = \frac{\text{Mass}}{\text{Furnace Volume}}$$
$$\times \frac{\text{Composition Change}}{\text{Elapsed Time}}$$

$$(1)$$

Each furnace has a limiting explosion factor. If the conditions create an explosion factor exceeding this limit, a catastrophic explosion can result. Any lesser reaction will produce a furnace "puff" (a nondestructive explosion) or temporary upset.

To protect a furnace from an explosion, a safety system must insure a minimum reactive mass accumulation with a minimum available composition change and with a maximum reaction time required. Only composition control of the furnace atmosphere offers complete coverage in minimizing the explosion factor. After firing has begun, furnaces always contain sufficient mass to have an explosion and control of the time factor is impossible. Therefore, the composition change must be controlled to prevent furnace explosions with any assurance.

The mechanics of furnace explosions, although defining the actual process, do not describe the furnace operations which provide the explosive accumulations. Ideal furnace operation continuously converts reactive furnace inputs into unreactive products as fast as the inputs enter the furnace—this precludes furnace explosions. However, in practical furnace firing, unfavorable operations that create explosive situations are difficult to avoid completely.

Several correctly timed events precede a damaging furnace explosion. The furnace explosion event itself is the rapid change in composition of the furnace atmosphere (not the furnace inputs). The change in furnace composition is not spontaneous, and a suitable ig-

nition source, which can be substantially less than that required for continuous furnace-input ignition, must be supplied *after* the furnace explosive composition is attained.

The potentially reactive furnace accumulation must be formed from an earlier buildup process which introduces reactive inputs not converted by oxidation to nonreactive or inert products. This buildup process must continue long enough to create a damaging accumulation. The accumulation composition, which must be within the limits of flammability for that particular fuel, is formed in one or more basic ways.

■ A flammable input into any furnace atmosphere (loss of ignition)

■ A fuel-rich input into an air-rich atmosphere (fuel interruption)

■ An air-rich input into a fuel-rich atmosphere (air interruption)

Furnace firing systems are designed to start up air-rich by introducing fuel into an air-filled furnace. Main fuel is introduced after the integral auxiliary ignition system has satisfied permissive main-fuel interlocks that it can provide more ignition energy than the main fuel requires to be ignited or to remain ignited. Additional air is introduced around the primary-air/fuel mixture to take it beyond flammable limits, if it has not been ignited and reacted to inert combustion products; this is done to avoid a critical portion of the total furnace volume being occupied by a flammable mixture.

FLAME DETECTORS

In the prevention of furnace explosions, the detection of the absence of flame while fuel is being admitted is the only proper criterion for any control action initiated by a flame-monitoring system.

Flame-monitoring hardware must be reliable, must be sensitive to discern the minimum flame envelope, and must have fail-safe characteristics to avoid unnecessary trips. Reaction time of the flame-detecting device must be an absolute minimum to prevent the accumulation of diffused flammable reactants in the furnace, following a loss of flame, before the furnace protection system can initiate corrective action to prevent a furnace explosion.

The burning process exhibits many characteristics which can be sensed as indicators of existing flame. Heat sensors, for example, in the form of thermocouples and bimetallic strips have been used successfully for many years in small space-heating systems, though the application of these devices to larger installations has generally not been practical.

Another characteristic of the burning process used for flame detection is the electrical-conduction capabilities of the ionized gases of a flame. An electrical-conduction path is established by a flame rod which extends into the flame envelope; the ionized gases themselves and the boiler tubes serve as the ground return of the system. This flame-rod concept is also in use today on smaller burners fueled by oil or gas but the erosive nature of pulverized coal makes this type of flame detection impractical for that fuel.

Especially in large burner/furnace installations, the most practical characteristic to sense for proof of flame has proven to be the light emitted by the burning process. The light emission covers a very broad spectrum and it is a continuous, rather than a line, spectrum. The shape of the emission versus wavelength plot for fossil-furnace flames generally resembles the black-body curve, with peak emissions being noted which are characteristic of the fuel being fired.

The light emitted by these furnace flames is further characterized by a fluctuating intensity which depends on the area of the flame being viewed, as well as physical conditions at the fuel nozzle. Fuel/air ratio, fuel velocity, air velocity, and the location and effectiveness of turbulence-producing diffusers all influence the frequency of the pulsating intensity.

ULTRAVIOLET DETECTION

In the early 1960's, the use of ultraviolet (UV) detectors for proof of fossil flames became practical when the Geiger/Mueller-tube principle

Fig. 2 **An ultraviolet detecting tube. The interior tube atmosphere is helium at low pressure and the electrodes are extremely pure tungsten. Because the special glass envelope has a low attenuation, quartz is unnecessary.**

was applied to flame detection. Using the UV detector had a distinct advantage over previous light sensors with cadmium-sulfide or lead-sulfide cells which were responsive to very broad bands of light and had peak responses in the infrared (IR) range. The infrared was certainly a characteristic of the flame, but it was also emitted by hot refractory, hot metal, and hot gases, any of which could cause the IR detector to falsely indicate flame present. Contrarily, the UV radiation which is abundant in fossil flames is not emitted in significant quantities from hot bodies at the temperatures encountered in boiler furnaces.

Fig. 2 shows the ultraviolet detecting tube. As the special glass envelope has a low attenuation of UV, the use of quartz is not necessary. The interior tube atmosphere is helium at low pressure and the electrodes are extremely pure tungsten.

The UV tube works under the photoelectric-emission principle whereby the tungsten electrode will emit an electron when struck by a photon with energy (E_{ph}) in excess of the photoelectric work function (E_w) of tungsten.

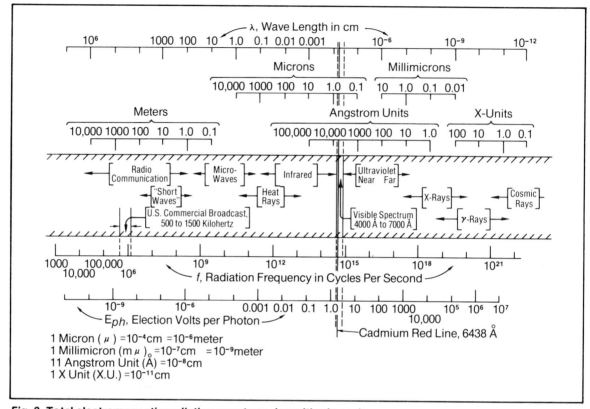

Fig. 3 Total electromagnetic radiation spectrum, logarithmic scales

The energy in electron volts of a photon of light is

$$E_{ph}q_e = hf$$

where, q_e = charge on electron
  h = Planck's constant
  f = frequency of photon

(2A)

By combining the constants we get

$$E_{ph} = \frac{12,400}{\lambda \text{ (in Ångstroms)}}$$

(2B)

The work function of tungsten is approximately 4.5 volts so it will emit electrons whenever struck by light with energy higher than that value. Visible light has an E_{ph} of 1.7 to 3.0 volts. Refer to Fig. 3 for the total electromagnetic radiation spectrum.

Because each photon of light results in only one electron being freed from the electrode, amplifying the electron flow to a detectable level is necessary. The helium gas in the UV tube performs this function. A large voltage difference accelerates photoelectric electrons to the opposite electrode; these electrons collide with molecules of helium, freeing additional electrons that collide with more molecules of helium, setting off a chain reaction. This process is called a Townsend avalanche, and the very large current flow it generates is readily sensed with electronic circuits.

Solid-state light sensors which transfer the light energy (E_{ph}) of the flame to a semiconductor device, such as a diode or transistor, have been available for some time. Here, the light energy raises an electron of the semiconductor to the conduction band rather than emitting an electron from an electrode as in the UV tube. Because the electrical potential barrier of the semiconductor is easily varied, a solid-state light detector can be devised which responds to any desirable portion of the light spectrum.

Although a solid-state detector designed for ultraviolet light might be used in a fashion similar to the UV tube, the solid-state device is very temperature sensitive, so it cannot be placed in the furnace in the same manner as a UV tube. To avoid this temperature problem, fiber-optic bundles transmit the light from the hot furnace region to a remote, cool location. This transmission distance is generally not more than 6 ft. The fiber-optic bundles commercially available exhibit a very high attenuation of ultraviolet light, but are much better in the visible region. This characteristic leads to the selection of the visible spectrum for solid-state flame detectors.

As mentioned earlier, infrared and visible detectors may falsely sense hot material or gases as indicative of flame. Flame detectors for operation in this spectral region also are designed to recognize the fluctuating intensity of the flame emissions. The frequency of the fluctuations is generally accepted as being between 2 and 600 cycles per sec. The higher frequencies are evident at the base of the flame or the ignition point; lower frequencies originate at the more distant areas or from the "fireball," where fuel streams from many admission nozzles combine and burn in large tangentially fired furnaces.

Modern flame detector designs generally require that multiple characteristics of a flame be sensed before the presence of a flame is acknowledged. Detector designs also include self-checking features to assure that sensor failures do not result in false information. This emphasis on assuring the validity of the "flame" or "no-flame" output of the detector is a vital step in the prevention of furnace explosions.

Fig. 4 is a photograph of a UV tube equipped with a magnetic shutter which closes at regular intervals to block the tube's view of the furnace. Its electronic arrangement is shown in Fig. 5.

As some of the basics of furnace explosion prevention have been discussed, protection systems can now be described in more detail.

Fig. 4 The UV tube at left is equipped with a magnetic shutter which closes at regular intervals to block the tube view of the furnace.

Fig. 5 The electronic circuitry verifies that the tube indicates "no-flame" when the shutter is closed.

FURNACE SAFEGUARD SUPERVISORY SYSTEM

One of the control systems furnished on almost all modern fossil-fuel-fired steam generators is a protective system which may be called burner control, burner management, fuel-firing safety, or, when supplied by Combustion Engineering, an FSSS® furnace safeguard supervisory system. The main function of this system is to prevent the formation of an explosive mixture of fuel and air in any portion of the steam generator during any phase of operation, including start-up and shutdown.

Preventing damage to the steam generator and/or the firing-system components requires simultaneous, continuous monitoring of a substantial number of parameters and, at times, instantaneous reaction to a hazardous situation. This task can be performed adequately only by a dedicated protective system such as a furnace safeguard supervisory system.

ITS ROLE IN THE STEAM-GENERATING PROCESS

Experience has shown that the furnace safeguard supervisory system cannot be treated as an auxiliary function of the steam-generator process (e.g. combustion, feedwater, and steam temperature) control systems. Rather, the furnace safeguard supervisory system is a separate and distinct system, more closely allied to the firing-system digital actions than to the process controls.

The most important design criterion of a fuel-firing protective system is that it be tailored specifically to the requirements and operating characteristics of the firing system.

SYSTEM ORGANIZATION

The components of the FSSS system can best be divided, for discussion purposes, into four sections (Figs. 6 and 7): (1) the operator's panel, (2) driven devices, (3) sensing elements, and (4) the logic system.

The operator's panel contains all the command devices (switches and/or push buttons)

Fig. 6 Typical air and fuel nozzle arrangements within a windbox

required to manipulate the firing-system equipment and all the feedback devices (status lights) required to monitor the status of this equipment.

The driven devices are primarily those by which fuel and air are admitted to the steam generator. Typical examples are valve operators (oil and gas firing), feeder and pulverizer motor starters (pulverized-coal firing), air-damper drives, and fan-motor starters.

Sensing devices include not only position information on the driven devices, but also such items as fuel pressures, temperatures and flow, and the presence of flame.

The heart of the furnace safeguard supervisory system is the logic system. All operator-initiated commands are routed to the logic system, and the status of all sensing elements is monitored continuously by the logic system. Operator commands are passed on to the driven devices only if its logic verifies that the proper safety permissives have been satisfied. On the other hand, the logic will shut down equipment automatically whenever continued operation would jeopardize the safety of this equipment or the steam generator.

A list of the typical conditions that would cause an emergency shutdown (trip) of a recirculation-type supercritical steam generator is as follows:

■ loss of all forced-draft fans
■ loss of all induced-draft fans
■ loss of all primary-air fans
■ turbine trip
■ inadequate waterwall circulation
■ high furnace-gas-side pressure
■ high superheater-outlet pressure
■ high waterwall-outlet pressure
■ high waterwall-outlet temperature
■ flame failure
■ loss of logic power to FSSS system

■ low airflow
■ operator's emergency trip push buttons depressed

DEGREES OF AUTOMATION

The FSSS arrangement discussed so far is commonly called a remote-manual system. With this type of system, the operator initiates the start-up and shutdown of each individual piece of equipment from a remote operating panel. The system logic insures that the operator commands are performed in the correct sequence and intervenes only when required to prevent a hazardous condition.

Higher levels of automation commonly specified are "automatic" and "automatic with load programming." An automatic system allows an operator to place in service or remove from service a related group of firing equipment (a subloop) in the proper sequence by initiating a single command. A typical example of a subloop would be the feeder, air dampers, and

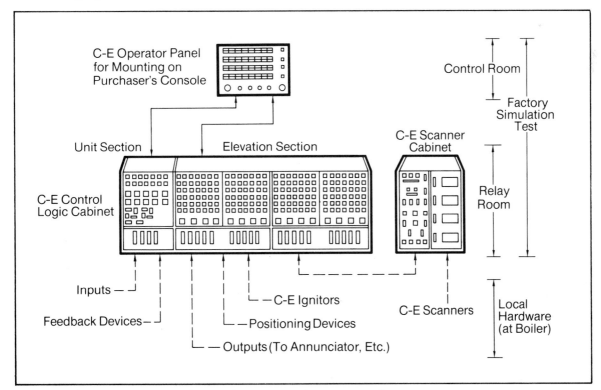

Fig. 7 **FSSS (furnace safeguard supervisory system) arrangement**

other equipment associated with a single coal pulverizer.

In the automatic mode of operation, a single operator command to start a pulverizer would initiate the following appropriately timed sequence of events (provided all of the required permissive conditions are established):

■ associated ignition system placed in service

■ pulverizer motor started

■ hot-air gate opened

■ pulverizer airflow and temperature controls released for automatic operation

■ feeder started

■ feeder speed control released for automatic operation

■ associated windbox dampers released for automatic operation

As the required load on the steam generator is varied over a wide range, firing system subloops are placed in, or removed from, service to maintain the most stable flame conditions and make the most efficient use of the firing-system components. With the inclusion of the load-programming feature, the FSSS system will take care of the above function automatically as steam-generator load demand changes.

BASIC SAFETY FUNCTIONS

Although the furnace safeguard supervisory system does not regulate the fuel and airflow quantities and does not, in most cases, initiate the start-up or normal shutdown of firing-system components, it does exercise authority over both the operator and the process controls through its safety interlocking features.

If, for example, the combustion control should drop the airflow below the minimum value (typically 30 percent) permitted during start-up, the system would trip the fuel automatically. Similarly, it will not permit the operator to start equipment out of prescribed safe sequences and will shut down equipment if prescribed operating practices are not followed. Removing ignitors too early, for example, would result in the shutdown of the associated main fuel.

The specific safety interlocking included in the furnace safeguard supervisory system depends on the physical characteristics of the firing system and type of fuel or fuels being fired. All safety systems of this type, however, are concerned with the following functions:

■ a prefiring purge of the furnace

■ establishment of the appropriate permissives for firing the ignition fuel (i.e., purge complete, fuel pressure within limits)

■ establishment of the appropriate permissives, including ignition permissives, for the main (load-carrying) fuel

■ continuous monitoring of firing conditions and other key operating parameters

■ emergency shutdown of portions or all of the firing equipment when required

■ a postfiring purge of the steam generator

The purpose of the prefiring purge is to be sure that any unburned fuel that may have accumulated in the furnace is completely removed prior to initiating firing. To do this, an airflow is passed through the steam generator at a minimum rating (usually 30 percent of that required for rated steam-generator capacity) for 5 minutes. At the same time, windbox dampers (Fig. 6) are maintained in a particular configuration, the fuel-admission devices are proven closed (or off), and the flame-monitoring devices indicate "no-flame." This combination of conditions will provide the proper velocities and number of air changes through the furnace and convection pass to assure the removal of any fuel accumulations. These purge-permissive requirements also provide a check on the proper operation of the air damper, fuel admission, and flame-monitoring sensing devices just prior to firing.

Upon completion of the purge, the steam generator is ready to be fired. The 30-percent minimum airflow requirement is maintained until the steam generator reaches 30-percent load in order to assure an air-rich furnace mixture during the entire start-up phase.

Initial firing is accomplished with a group of ignitors that have the capability of lighting the

Fig. 8 **Tangential-firing pattern at low-firing rates**

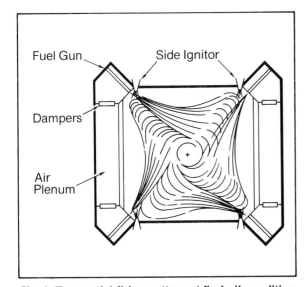

Fig. 9 **Tangential-firing pattern at fireball condition**

ignition fuel with an electric spark. A flame detector must be provided with each ignitor to determine the presence or absence of a stable flame. In the case of the C-E ignitor, the flame detector is an integral part of the ignitor, and a fuel-flow measurement is included to insure the proper quantity of ignition energy.

Depending on the choice of load-carrying fuel and the firing-system arrangement, the load-carrying fuel may obtain its ignition

energy directly from the ignitors or an elevation of ignition fuel guns may be used as an intermediate step. On coal-fired units, for example, ignition fuel is normally kept in service until two adjacent coal elevations are being fired at 50 percent of their rated capability, thereby assuring sufficient ignition energy to maintain stable firing conditons during the steam-generator start-up phase of operation.

FLAME MONITORING

The C-E tangential-firing configuration (Fig. 8) operates during start-up with a separate, independent flame emanating from each operating fuel-admission point (nozzle). Each flame is monitored independently by the use of continuous, self-flame-proving ignitors.

As soon as any elevation is fired at a rate exceeding 30 percent of its maximum continuous rating, the characteristics of this firing configuration change dramatically (Fig. 9). The thorough mixing of fuel and air produced by the rotating fireball (vortex) permits ignition energy produced at one location in the furnace to support the combustion of fuel admitted at other locations. The furnace, in effect, becomes a single burner. Under these firing conditions, multiple flame detectors monitor the furnace on a statistical basis. No individual fuel nozzles are shut down because of an adjacent flame detector indicating "no-flame." But should insufficient flame detectors confirm the presence of flame, the entire firing system is shut down.

The transition from start-up firing characteristics to fireball conditions is a gradual transformation as elevation loading is increased. The selection of the 30 percent elevation-loading condition as the point where the logic is transferred to fireball monitoring is based on field experience and assures a completely adequate margin of safety between the two firing conditions.

During the fireball phase of operation, sufficient ignitors in service at specified locations constitute proof of stable firing conditions. To eliminate the need to keep ignition fuel in service, however, optical flame detectors are used as the normal means of monitoring the fireball.

Front-fired (horizontal-burner) systems exhibit, at all firing rates, the individual burner characteristics which the tangential configuration exhibits at low firing rates; that is, the flame produced at one firing location does not provide ignition energy for fuel admitted at the other locations. The flame-monitoring system for such burners must be designed accordingly. Attempts to use front-fired flame monitoring techniques on tangential-firing configurations and vice versa have met with little success.

LOGIC ACCOMPLISHMENT

The logic portion of the furnace safeguard supervisory system may be implemented with electromagnetic relays, solid-state electronics, or, most recently, computer-based programmable controllers. All these implementations must be able to tolerate the dust, temperature variations, and electrical noise encountered in a power plant.

The normal method of powering the FSSS logic is to provide redundant AC sources to a transfer switch with the output of the transfer switch going to the system. To prevent a steam-generator shutdown during operation of the transfer switch, the AC-powered field devices are of the "energize-to-trip" type; that is, they require the presence of power to close. DC power from the plant battery system is also provided to the FSSS system to assure the capability of shutting off the fuel input in the event of a loss of both AC sources.

Relays have been the traditional building blocks of furnace safeguard supervisory system logic and are still widely used today. Relay systems are rugged, easy to understand and maintain, and operate directly from the voltage levels required for the driven devices and sensing elements.

Solid-state logic has been applied to system design for many years, but did not assume a dominant position until more recently. For a long period, the utility industry judged the traditional advantages of solid-state logic (less power drain, less space required, greater speed, and no moving parts to wear out) to be less important than the disadvantages (higher susceptibility to electrical noise and temperature variations, more complexity, and higher cost).

Fig. 10 shows a typical solid-state FSSS system logic cabinet. The built-in simulator provides maintenance personnel with a fast, convenient method to check the operation of the system logic without disturbing field wiring or, inadvertently, operating equipment.

Solid-state logic then evolved such that the electrical noise and environmental problems were mastered. The widespread use of solid-state in process controls has resulted in the ability of plant maintenance people to handle solid-state problem-solving easily. The plug-in solid-state modules provide an on-line repair capability not available to relay systems.

The additional expense of a solid-state system results primarily from the need to convert all incoming signals from the sensing-device voltage level to the logic voltage level and back from logic level to the voltage level required by the driven devices. (Logic devices cannot provide either the voltage or the current level required by the field devices.) As systems become more automated, however, the ratio of logic functions (inexpensive) to inputs and outputs (expensive) innreases and the differential expense vs. relay logic decreases.

PROGRAMMABLE CONTROLLERS

Another technique for implementing furnace safeguard supervisory system logic is the use of programmable controllers. (Fig. 11)

These are minicomputers which have a built-in compiler (translator) that makes it possible to program the system directly from logic diagrams. They are also configured to be strong in logic capability and can be packaged ruggedly enough for the power-plant environment.

In a programmable-controller-based system, each controller is considered a component which may undergo some small amount of downtime. A basic design criterion of such a system is that failure of a single controller, with all of its logic capability, shall neither jeopardize the safety of the steam generator nor require the steam generator to be shut down.

This design criterion is satisfied by con-

Fig. 10 Logic cabinet of FSSS system includes a built-in simulator.
The system currently provides protection and automation for an 850-MW unit .

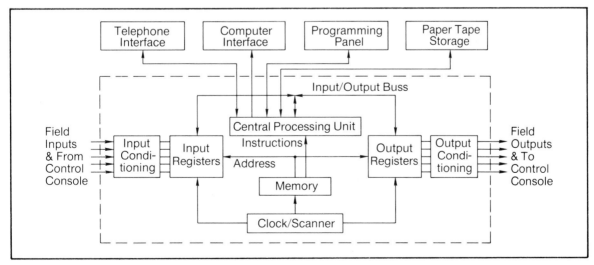

Fig. 11 Typical logic-processor architecture

structing a furnace safeguard supervisory system of multiple small programmable controllers arranged to provide safety redundancy (Fig. 11). By limiting redundancy to those portions of the system logic that are directly concerned with safety, rather than operator convenience, the expense of total redundancy can be avoided.

Fig. 12, C-E Distributed Programmable Control for coal firing, shows the overall computing structure of the decision-making logic to serve a coal-fired steam-generating unit employing 7 pulverizer equipment groups and 1 elevation of oil warm-up guns. Each pulverizer equipment group includes a pulverizer and its motor, a coal feeder and its motor, the primary-air supply, the secondary-air supply, ignition system, associated valves and drives, dampers and drives, feedback sensing elements, and instrumentation.

A prepackaged and preprogrammed set of 9

logic processors arranged together with other control components into a self-sufficient system such as this can also be monitored by the plant central computer. Of the 9 processors, 7 (labelled A through G) serve the pulverizer equipment groups. One processor (W) is reserved for the warm-up elevation, and one processor (U) is dedicated to overall unit control.

The ring-type arrangement of logic processors A through G illustrates the functional interrelationships and actual interwiring. The functions and associated interface of each processor arranged in a ring are split into three parts. The larger part (shown as black space in the center) is concerned with the control of the pulverizer. The two smaller parts (shown crosshatched on both sides of the black space) are concerned with the *safety* of the pulverizer equipment group functions. But only the right-hand part takes care of the protection of its own pulverizer equipment group; the left-

Fig. 12 C-E Distributed Programmable Control for coal firing

hand part takes care of the protection of the neighboring pulverizer equipment to the left.

Processor U and processor W, located in the center of the ring, have, in addition to the control functions, safety sections serving the overall unit and warm-up functions. Logic processor U is dedicated to functions pertaining to overall unit control including furnace purge; interpreting and acting upon a number of unit trip conditions; first-out trip recording and indication; overall furnace flame failure protection; opening and closing of main fuel supply valve and ignitor fuel supply valve; establishing elevation start permissive conditions; ignitor fan control and scanner fan control; placing windbox auxiliary air dampers under analog modulating control and opening or closing them; and coordination of individual pulverizer equipment groups (placing them in service or removing them from service).

Although the processor network discussed here is designed to be completely self-sufficient, it has the capability of interfacing with the plant central computer and assuming the role of a satellite grouping. The one-way communication from processor U to plant central computer shown on left of Fig. 12 is primarily to emphasize that the plant central computer must not interfere with the well-defined safety program contained in the satellite processors.

Fig. 13 shows input/output channels for a programmable system, while Fig. 14 shows the central processing units for the same system.

As computer-based technology offers flexibility in carrying out logic modifications quickly, its most important feature is its potential for improving furnace safeguard system availability. This, in turn, will increase the margin of safety in firing a steam generator.

Fig. 13 **Input/output channels for a programmable system**

PROCESS CONTROLS

Plant operators retain the ultimate responsibility for the operation and protection of both utility and industrial steam generators. But as discussed, automatic safety systems are customarily installed to relieve operators of the task of instantaneously analyzing and reacting to a rapidly developing hazardous condition.

Safety systems improve unit availability by preventing improper operating sequences and by automatically shutting down equipment before damage can occur. But acceptable availability can only be achieved by installing control systems to *prevent* the plant-controlled variables from reaching the deviation from normal values which result in safety system action. The continuous, automatic regulation of controlled variables is the function of the process control systems.

Although it is still common to divide the process controls for a large steam generator into subsystems (such as combustion control, feedwater control, and steam temperature), a *coordinated* approach to process control has proven to be the most effective technique to achieve optimum boiler performance.

BOILER-FOLLOW SYSTEMS

For many years, the most common process control system employed on subcritical drum-type units was the boiler-follow system which relies heavily on feedback control principles.

With a boiler-follow system on a subcritical pressure unit a change in required electrical generation results in the following events:

1. The turbine control valves are repositioned to establish the new generation level, at the expense of a change in steam-generator energy storage level.

2. Changes in steam flow initiate changes in the

Fig. 14 **The central processing units for a programmable system**

flow of feedwater, fuel, and air on a feed-forward basis. Fuel is further modified by the feedback of throttle-pressure deviation from setpoint, which is an indication of the energy balance between the steam generator and the turbine. Feedwater is adjusted by drum-level deviation, which is a measure of the feed-water-flow/steam-flow balance.

3. The steam-temperature control systems respond to temperature deviations caused by steam-flow/fuel mismatches and heat distribution changes.

The large energy storage of drum-type units allows boiler-follow systems to be very effective as long as generation level (load) changes are small or are accomplished slowly.

COORDINATED-CONTROL SYSTEMS

The advent of the supercritical unit, with its relatively small energy storage, quickly dem-

Fig. 15 Typical master control panel for a coordinated-control system

onstrated the limitations of the boiler-follow system. The solution to this problem was the development of the coordinated-control system.

Fig. 15 shows a typical master control panel for a coordinated-control system.

The fundamental objectives of a coordinated-control system are as follows:

1. Operation of the steam generator and turbine generator as an integrated unit.

2. Application of control signals in a coordinated manner to minimize interactions between the controlled variables (unit generation, steam pressure, flue-gas oxygen, furnace draft, and steam temperatures) by appropriate and simultaneous operation of the manipulated variables (fuel, feedwater, airflow, flue-gas flow, turbine governor, and steam-temperature regulating equipment).

3. Manipulation of steam-temperature control devices so as to utilize the available thermal storage to minimize transient temperature disturbances.

4. In the case of coal-fired units, regulation of pulverizer airflow and temperature to insure proper drying, grinding, and transport of the coal to the furnace.

Fig. 16 shows the functional arrangement of a coordinated-control system for a supercritical unit. This design illustrates that the "required output" signal, which represents generation demand, goes directly to the steam-generator input variable as well as to the turbine governor. This parallel control arrangement is based on the principle that the only way to *permanently* change unit generation is to change the energy output of the steam generator.

The presence of any error between required output and actual generation will bias the steam-generator and turbine-demand signals in order to recalibrate the system for cycle changes. Similarly, throttle pressure error is used to recalibrate the balance between steam production and steam usage. Both of these error signals operate on a transient basis to compensate for the difference in response time of the boiler and turbine, allowing the faster responding turbine to minimize generation errors by modifying boiler energy storage levels.

THE C-E COORDINATED CONTROL SYSTEM

The preceding discussion summarizes the basic differences between boiler-follow and coordinated-control-type systems. The C-E Coordinated Control System (CCS) contains a number of additional features designed to provide several layers of defense between the direct regulation of the variables and the automatic shutdown actions of the FSSS system.

Each major subsystem, such as fuel, air, or feedwater, contains a flow tie-back loop to insure the process variable will quickly match required output. Redundant transmitters and comparison networks transfer the loop automatically to manual if a transmitter malfunction occurs. Bypass switches permit automatic operation while one transmitter is being calibrated.

Ahead of the flow loops are the ratio correction loops. Flue-gas oxygen corrects fuel/air ratio and main steam temperature corrects fuel/feedwater ratio.

When all process loops are well tuned and calibrated, and are functioning properly on automatic, the controlled variables will be maintained well within acceptable limits.

Various limit circuits are provided to take care of the times when this desirable condition does not exist.

In the case of fuel/air, a cross-limit circuit is provided which does not permit fuel demand to exceed measured airflow (plus tolerance) and does not permit airflow demand to drop below measured fuel flow (plus tolerance). This circuit is most commonly activated when a malfunction causes airflow and fuel-flow regulating devices to follow demand at different rates. On supercritical units, the fuel/feedwater ratio is limited by automatically

Fig. 16 **Coordinated-control system, signal flow diagram**

cutting back the fuel flow if waterwall outlet temperature exceeds a preset value.

Referring again to Fig. 16, note that the "output adjustment signal" (the desired generation value established by the operator or the load-dispatch system) must pass through several conditioning devices before emerging as "required output."

The first such device is the operator-set rate-of-change limiter. This device prevents the unit from accepting a load demand change at a rate which would create instability and a resulting unit trip.

Turbine governors automatically change unit steam flow in response to an electrical-grid frequency disturbance. To prevent the CCS from fighting the governor, and to match the boiler demand to the turbine action, the frequency bias conditioner is required. This circuit simply adjusts required output to match the governor action.

Limit actions occur when the CCS detects that one or more process variables cannot follow the output adjustment demand signal. If, for example, a feedwater pump were out of service, the limit circuit would not allow required

output to exceed the capability of the pumps in service. Without this limit, firing rate would be allowed to exceed feedwater flow, resulting in high waterwall-outlet temperature on a supercritical unit or loss of drum level on a subcritical-pressure unit. The limit circuits also act whenever such process variables as generation and throttle pressure deviate from their required values by a preset amount. These deviations are indications that the steam generator or turbine, or both, are unable to follow the desired output.

An extension of the limit circuits, which is not shown on Fig. 16, is the run-up and run-down circuits. These circuits act to return the required output within the capability of the unit when a change in boiler-unit conditions occur. For example, if all coal feeders are operating near maximum output and one feeder trips, the unit cannot maintain its existing load. The run-down circuit would automatically reduce load to a value within the capability of the existing feeders.

The run-back actions shown next are simply a more dramatic version of a run-down. The loss of a major piece of auxiliary equipment such as a feedpump or forced-draft fan may reduce the load-carrying capability of the unit to 50–60 percent of maximum continuous rating. When such an equipment loss is detected, the run-back circuit very rapidly reduces the required output signal to a value within the capability of the remaining equipment. Without such a circuit, a unit trip would almost certainly result.

One final protection circuit, which is the last line of defense designed to act before the safety-system limits are reached, is the deviation-limit system. This system continuously makes two separate and independent calculations of fuel/feedwater ratio and fuel/air ratio. Fig. 17 illustrates the fuel/feedwater concept. If both calculations verify that this ratio has exceeded allowable limits, the deviation-limit system directly operates the appropriate drive units to restore a permissible ratio. This system, which overrides manual control, should activate only when the operator has made a

Fig. 17 The deviation-limit system is a protection circuit which continuously monitors fuel/feedwater and fuel/air ratios to verify that these ratios have not exceeded allowable limits, as shown here for fuel/feedwater.

serious mistake or an automatic-control computational element has failed.

STEAM-TEMPERATURE CONTROL

On a supercritical unit, the primary (superheat) steam-temperature control is an integral part of the coordinated control because steady-state control of primary steam temperature is accomplished by establishing the proper ratio of firing rate to feedwater flow. Desuperheating sprays are used only for transient control. Fig. 18 shows a typical primary steam-temperature control scheme.

With a drum-type unit, the temperature entering the superheater is dictated by the drum-pressure/saturation-temperature relationship. Final control is accomplished by desuperheating sprays.

For both supercritical and drum-type units, reheat temperature is controlled by heat redistribution devices. The several boiler manufacturers have developed numerous techniques for this purpose, including flue-gas bypassing, gas proportioning, and excess-air variation. Fig. 19 shows three techniques which C-E uses most commonly: tilting nozzles, desuperheating sprays, and on oil-and-gas fired units, gas recirculation. Only during unusual conditions is reheater desuperheating by spray used, because of its deleterious effect on heat rate. On coal-fired units, fuel-nozzle tilting is the most common mechanism.

AN OVERVIEW

Primary measuring devices, transmitters, indicators, recorders, annunciators, and indicating lights can be integrated into a system which permits plant operators to continuously and conveniently monitor plant operating conditions. Push buttons, switches, and manual-loading stations can be combined with pneumatically and electrically powered regulating devices (such as valves and dampers) to provide the capability of starting up, maneu-

Fig. 18 **Coordinated-control system, primary-steam-temperature control**

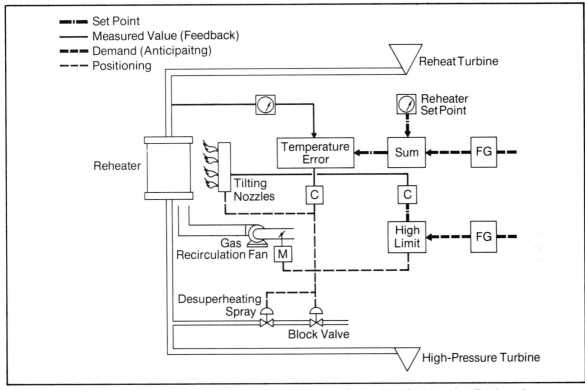

Fig. 19 **Three reheat temperature control techniques commonly used by Combustion Engineering**

vering, and shutting down a steam generator from a central location.

Using process control systems results in more precise control, thus increasing plant productivity and reducing cycling-life expenditures caused by process variable excursions. When a sophisticated process control is employed, such as the described Coordinated Control System, the steam generator and turbine generator act as a coordinated unit to further improve unit transient response and productivity. The CCS also provides several layers of limit systems designed to improve unit availability by preventing a process deviation from reaching a safety-system limit. Either hard-wired solid-state components or computers may implement the CCS.

Safety systems, such as the FSSS system described earlier, also contribute to plant automation while performing their primary function of protecting both plant personnel and plant equipment.

A well-designed automation system, with both firing system and process controls, will operate the unit in the same manner that the plant equipment designers would operate the unit if they were given the opportunity to do so. It is vital, therefore, that the control system designers thoroughly understand the process requirements and limitations and that the control systems are tailored to the specific equipment and plant-operational requirements.

FURNACE IMPLOSIONS

Earlier in this chapter, furnace explosions and the techniques to prevent their occurrence were discussed. In the mid-1970's, a new problem, which came to be known as a furnace *implosion,* appeared. Before discussing the impact of the implosion phenomenon on steam-generator control systems, the fundamental nature of the problem should be examined.

THE IMPLOSION PHENOMENON

Two basic mechanisms can cause a negative-pressure excursion of sufficient magnitude to cause structural damage. The first of these mechanisms is well understood.

Simply attach to a boiler an induced-draft (ID) fan that is capable of producing more suction head than the boiler structure is capable of withstanding. Next, through control malfunction and/or operator error, establish circumstances that result in this pressure capability being applied to the structure. An example would be opening the dampers on an operating ID fan with the forced-draft (FD) fan dampers closed, which can result in a destructive negative pressure with the boiler not being fired.

The second mechanism, the so-called *flame collapse* or *flameout* effect, is not generally understood. As a matter of fact, the unfortunate use of such terms as *flame collapse* has led to many distorted conceptions of the physical reality.

It is vitally important that the following explanation for the negative-pressure excursion which follows a fuel trip and loss of furnace flame be understood, because only through a basic knowledge of this mechanism can pitfalls and preventive techniques be realistically evaluated.

The physical state of the gases in a furnace or other subsystem at any instant in time can be described by the Perfect Gas Law as follows:

$$PV = MRT$$

where: P = absolute pressure
V = volume of system under consideration
M = resident mass (not mass flow)
R = the universal gas constant
T = absolute temperature,
    all in consistent units

(3)

Because V is fixed and R is approximately constant, P is directly proportional to the product MT. Thus, for two different conditions of pressure and temperature in a given boiler system, this approximate relationship holds:

$$\frac{P_2}{P_1} = \frac{M_2 T_2}{M_1 T_1}$$

(4)

During steady-state operation, P is held constant at approximately atmospheric pressure by balancing the resident mass M and the existing temperature T. Furnace temperature in a steam generator is not directly controlled and depends on the thermal balance between the *heat in* (in the form of burning fuel and heated air) and the *heat out* (in the flue gas and heat transferred to the pressure parts). The resident mass is automatically balanced by controlling the flue gas out of the boiler to maintain a given furnace pressure.

When the fuel input is terminated, this balance no longer exists. The flue gas being pulled out of the furnace by the ID fan is now being replaced only by preheated air rather than by the products of combustion in the firing zone. As a result of this situation, the average temperature of the gases resident in the furnace (or other subsystem) at any given time following the fuel trip will decrease rapidly. Because of the temperature drop, the pressure in the furnace starts to decrease (Fig. 20).

If the resident mass were to remain constant in quantity, the absolute pressure in the furnace would drop in direct proportion to the absolute temperature drop. A gage pressure of $-1.0''$ WG is equivalent to 406″ WG absolute. Thus, with a constant resident mass, a 10 percent change in absolute temperature would cause a 10 percent change in furnace pressure; that is, 40.6″ WG.

Fortunately, the natural characteristics of forced-draft and induced-draft fans and their control devices are such that a constant-resident-mass situation is virtually impossible to achieve.

Assume, for the moment, that all FD and ID fan dampers are fixed in position. As the furnace pressure begins to decay because of the temperature decay, the fans will move to different operating points on their respective performance curves. The FD fan will move in the direction of *increasing* volume; the ID fan, in

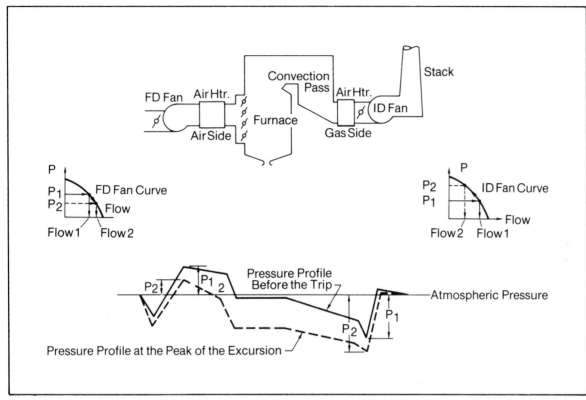

Fig. 20 Pressure profile in a balanced-draft unit before and after trip. Notice that the magnitude of the drop in furnace pressure at the peak of the excursion is higher than those at the FD fan discharge and the ID fan inlet. This is because of the difference in flow conditions at the time of the excursion

the direction of *decreasing* volume (Fig. 21).

The airflow through the windbox will *increase* because the lower furnace pressure appears to the FD fan to be a reduced system resistance.

The flue-gas flow will *decrease* because the lower furnace pressure appears to the ID fan to be an increased system resistance.

The net effect of this increase in airflow and reduction in gas flow is to increase the resident mass in the furnace, which tends to compensate for the temperature decay. This natural corrective action taken by the FD and ID fans is a key ingredient in the ability to contain furnace-pressure excursions to values that are within tolerable limits.

It should be apparent that the Perfect Gas Law does not recognize the difference between:

■ types of firing systems (corner, front and rear, slagging bottom);

■ coal firing, oil firing, or gas firing; and

■ balanced-draft or pressurized operation.

To understand, then, why the most serious implosion problems have been experienced with oil-fired, balanced-draft boilers, it is necessary to keep in mind that the key to holding furnace pressure constant is to maintain the product of resident mass and temperature constant.

On a *pressurized* boiler, the action of the FD fan during normal operation *pushes* the flue gases out of the furnace.

When the combustion process in such a pressurized unit is terminated, the resulting temperature decay causes the furnace pressure to drop rapidly. As soon as the furnace pressure drops below atmospheric pressure (ignoring stack effect), the flue gas will no longer leave the furnace but the airflow will continue to en-

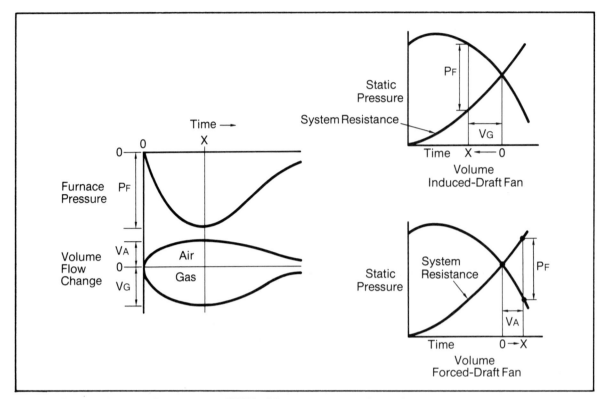

Fig. 21 Destructive negative pressure (DNP) with constant-speed centrifugal fans and dampers locked

ter. Moreover, any additional decrease in furnace pressure will cause a reverse flow down the stack, back into the furnace.

When firing is terminated on a *balanced-draft* unit, flue gas (with its mass at furnace temperature) will be pulled out of the furnace until the pressure there reaches a negative value which is directly related to the cutoff pressure of the ID fan corresponding to the temperature entering the fan. The higher the head capability of the ID fan, the larger the pressure excursions that may be experienced.

Thus, although some authors have attempted to treat the ID fan characteristics and the fuel cutoff as two independent effects, they are actually inseparable.

With respect to pulverized-coal and oil firing, the difference is one of the *rate* of temperature change. This rate depends on how fast a given percentage of the furnace volume undergoes a replacement of combustion products with preheated air. Coal-fired units have the following characteristics that produce a slower temperature decay:

1. The fuel cutoff is generally more gradual than with oil firing, because of the pulverized-fuel residual in the pulverizer and fuel piping.

2. The ratio of resident mass to mass-flow rate is higher than for an oil-fired boiler, because coal-fired furnaces are significantly larger in size than oil-fired-only furnaces.

THE "CULPRIT," THE INDUCED-DRAFT FAN

In connection with the implosion phenomenon, it is most important that engineers responsible for draft-system and furnace-framing-system design understand how an induced-draft fan operates, how it is controlled, and how it responds to changes in the inlet pressure that it "sees."

Induced-draft fans are used singly, or in multiples of 2, 3, or 4, to evacuate the products of combustion from a boiler furnace while main-

taining the pressure at the top of such a furnace about 0.2″ WG below atmospheric pressure. Centrifugal-type ID fans customarily are equipped with inlet vanes or inlet louver dampers for control of the volumetric flow of gas through them. (See Chapter 15.)

These devices have similar control characteristics (as compared to outlet dampers or variable-speed drives), but can have widely varying time-constants depending upon the type of actuator used to move them.

Fig. 22 shows the effect on the pressure/volume curve of such a fan when either vanes or dampers are closed to reduce the gas through-flow. On this curve, fan static-pressure capability is plotted against rated volume, and a system-pressure curve is shown—a simple square relationship of static pressure to volume (SP $\propto V^2$). The control device is regulated so that the required static pressure to satisfy the resistance of the physical system is developed at any given volumetric flow rate. But, at the same time, for the particular vane position, a fan characteristic curve is established such that the fan is capable of an infinite number of discrete static-pressure values versus any given volumetric flow.

If we consider an operating mode in which

the induced-draft-fan control vanes or dampers are capable of infinitely fast response, any change in the furnace pressure of a balanced-draft unit that is sensed by the system will cause the vanes to change position to maintain the required system static pressure exactly, and along the system-pressure curve. For instance, if there should be a reduction in furnace pressure (caused, say, by a decrease in the fuel fired and the corresponding combustion airflow), the vanes will immediately close to reduce the gas flow handled by the fan before the furnace pressure drops any further. With such infinitely fast vane control assumed, even with an instantaneous very large drop in furnace-pressure level (such as there could be if there were a master fuel trip or if the forced-draft-fan dampers were to accidentally close), the system curve will always be followed and the induced-draft fan will make instantaneous corrections to maintain furnace pressure at the level preset (below atmospheric).

Another condition can be postulated, in which the control vanes or dampers are maintained in a fixed position as boiler load varies; this is equivalent to a zero rate of damper response. When boiler load decreases (and fuel flow, airflow, and gas flow decrease corre-

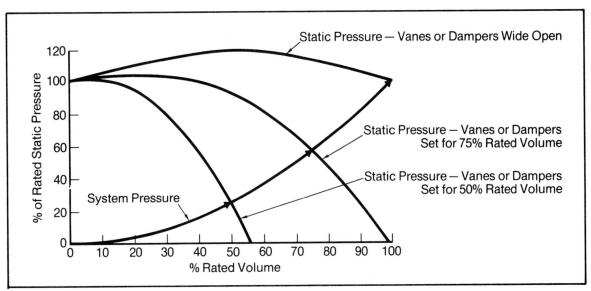

Fig. 22 The effect on an centrifugal-type ID-fan pressure/volume curve when either vanes or dampers are positioned to reduce the gas through-flow

spondingly), the developed fan static pressure increases following a static-pressure versus volume curve sloping upward to the left; furnace suction (pressure below atmospheric) increases rapidly. The obvious limit to the furnace suction that can be developed is the highest static-pressure value on the curve, which for damper settings below 50 percent, appears to be at or about the fan no-load cutoff value (the static head developed by a fan when its volumetric delivery is zero).

Under normal load-changing conditions, if fan vanes are maintained at a given position, either accidentally or purposely, furnace suction will vary, with the maximum static-pressure capability of the fan being the limit. Under these conditions, of course, forced-draft airflow continues, but is automatically varied with boiler firing rate.

Assume that a master fuel trip occurs under this condition of vanes-maintained-in-position. Assume further that the forced-draft fan dampers close quickly, so that there is a rapid decrease in the gas available to the induced-draft fan. The induced-draft fan will immediately ride up along the characteristic curve to the cutoff point; after reaching the cutoff point, reverse flow of gas down the stack will occur (at some indeterminable flow rate) until the furnace suction that has been established by the decrease in the average gas temperature is satisfied.

If the rate of reverse flow is not high enough, the furnace will fail structurally if the framing system is not capable of withstanding the low absolute pressure that results from the fuel trip.

Of course, what happens during a master fuel trip in which equipment is on automatic control is somewhere between the above two postulated situations. Fan dampers or vanes close in an effort to reduce the gas flow leaving the furnace, restricting the magnitude of the furnace pressure-level reduction. With good mechanical response to the control signal (particularly if an "early" signal has been received through the use of a feed-forward arrangement), fan static-pressure capability will match the furnace suction being developed as a result

of the reduction in furnace gas temperature, all while the volumetric gas flow through the fan is being reduced to zero. Ultimately, this frustrates any implosion tendency.

The above analysis applies to constant-speed centrifugal-type or vane-controlled axial-flow fans. A similar approach can be used in assessing the implosion potential of variable-speed centrifugal, or variable-pitch axial-flow fans.

CONTROL IMPLICATIONS

Implosion concerns have resulted in many new control-system developments. The search for the ideal implosion-prevention control scheme is still proceeding. Each steam-generator manufacturer has recommendations, and the National Fire Protection Association has issued NFPA 85-G on the subject.

Space does not permit going into the specifics of the control-system designs which are outlined in such recommendations. However, the following must be provided in any furnace-draft and combustion-control system:

1. The airflow to a furnace must be maintained at its pretrip value and must not be prevented from increasing by following natural fan curves; but positive control action to increase airflow is not allowed by NFPA.

2. The flow of combustion products from a furnace must be reduced as quickly as possible following a unit trip.

3. If the removal of fuel from the furnace can be over a 5- to 10-second period (rather than instantaneously), there will be a reduction in the magnitude of the furnace-pressure excursion that follows a unit trip.

Obviously, even the most carefully designed control system will be of limited value if all its components are not completely installed, if it has not been properly checked out or is in "poor tune", or if it has been inadequately maintained. It is essential, therefore, that protective control systems for large, high draft-loss boilers be properly designed, installed, tested, and maintained, and that plant operators consider these control systems to be vital.

INDUSTRIAL BOILER CONTROLS

The term *industrial boilers* covers a range of units from the single-burner, single-fuel package boiler to multiple-elevation field-erected units which fire 5 or 6 fuels. The degree of automation ranges from supervised local-manual to fully automated. Furnace safeguard supervisory systems for industrial units utilize the same hardware and documentation as utility units; only the degree of complexity varies.

The concept of a coordinated-control system is not generally applied to industrial units. Combustion, feedwater, furnace-draft, and steam-temperature control systems are often specified separately. Figs. 23 through 26 show samples of typical control systems.

As the number of elements in the control system increases, system complexity and cost

Fig. 24 **Furnace-draft control system**

Fig. 23 **Parallel-metering combustion-control system, flow tie-back, single fuel**

Fig. 25 **Three-element feedwater-flow control system**

Fig. 26 Typical steam-temperature control systems

increase, but control response to transients improves. The best system is selected by examining plant operating requirements.

FIELD-MOUNTED EQUIPMENT

All control systems, from the most basic supervised manual system to a completely automated system, make decisions based on information derived from field-mounted sensors and take action through field-mounted driven devices. Regardless of the care taken in establishing the control strategy, the accuracy of information from the field-mounted sensors and precision with which the driven devices act will always limit the quality of control. Despite its important role, this field-mounted equipment is often the most neglected area in control-system design, installation, and maintenance.

Many equipment-related problems are caused by selecting underdesigned components for the demanding service requirements of today's plants, as well as by improperly locating and installing hardware. The following are some points to remember, with respect to the power-plant environment, when applying field-mounted components.

MOISTURE

As a minimum, equipment should be rated NEMA-3 (National Electrical Manufacturer's Association), suitable for weather-resistant service. Some locations may require upgrading the enclosure rating to NEMA-4 (water-tight). For example, switches, contacts, and terminal strips in enclosures exposed to driving rains or frequent hosing should be protected in NEMA-4 enclosures, to prevent moisture-induced malfunctions.

HAZARDOUS LOCATIONS

If liquid fuels with a flash point of less than 100°F or heavier-than-air gaseous fuels are to be burned, special consideration should be given to electrical enclosures in areas where flammables or vapors may collect (see reference 1). Switching-contact arcs in open cabinets, or ignition of flammable accumulations in closed cabinets, can provide the energy to ignite external accumulations of flammable gases, with catastrophic results.

TEMPERATURE

Both the ambient and mounting-surface temperatures of a field-mounted component must be considered in maintenance troubleshooting—a point often overlooked when maintenance personnel inspect controls on a cool boiler during an outage. In general, wiring and equipment should be designed for 200°F service, though sometimes 150°F is acceptable for service components mounted 3 to 10 ft from the unit.

The overlapping responsibilities of mechanical and electrical designers frequently lead to temperature- and vibration-induced operating problems with firing equipment—such as dampers and vanes, actuators and controllers, scanners and igniter controls. Whenever possible, electrical or pneumatic components should not be mounted on windboxes, the furnace-wall casing, or the buckstay system; locate them where the ambient temperature and ventilation are favorable.

PRIMARY ELEMENTS

This category includes temperature and pressure sensors; gas, water, and steam samplers; and flow-metering elements. The control-system designer usually selects these components according to the requirements of the controlled variable. But changes in process flow rate, flow stratification, fluid temperature, and, sometimes, abnormalities induced by other equipment, affect the quality of the monitored variable. Examples: (1) Furnace-wall deslagger operation sometimes upsets the furnace-draft measurement. (2) Flow-metering locations satisfactory for flow rates at high loads may not be adequate at low loads because of stratification and backflow or eddies and shifts in the flow distribution.

When locating primary elements, it is important to be sure that

■ the new location is representative of the monitored parameter over the operating range

■ the sensing point remains free of contamination and cannot be influenced by the effects of parallel installation of primary elements

■ the new location is accessible for maintenance and diagnostic monitoring without interfering with process operation or control

■ the element is positioned so that calibration, lubrication, and other routine maintenance can be performed without dismantling

SENSING LINES

The response of sensing lines, as limited by their length and volume, is frequently overlooked in analyzing transmitter, positioner, and drive-unit performance. The size and length of these lines must not exceed the manufacturer's recommendations.

Also, averaging and redundant sensing should never be accomplished by manifolding. Instead, a transmitter should be provided for each sensing tap; the signal can then be averaged or compared downstream of the transmitters. This approach will prevent problems such as the loss of system redundancy caused by opening a manifolding header. Also, a slight difference in pressure between sensing taps can induce flow in the manifold sensing line. This tramp flow may contain contaminants such as flyash, and may cause an outage or compromise sensor accuracy.

If sensing-tap openings become contaminated, corrective measures include enlarging sensing-point openings to prevent bridging, adding a metered purge to keep the opening clear, or isolating the process opening by use of diaphragms and capillary sensing lines. Additionally, redundant measurements or isolation facilities can be provided, so that the primary element can be either replaced or cleaned on-line. Often a T-fitting for rodding out the sensor tap provides a satisfactory solution (Fig. 27).

Fig. 27 T-fitting for rodding-out sensor tap facilitates on-line removal of crud

PROBLEMS WITH SWITCHING ELEMENTS

High- and low-pressure limit switches, temperature-sensing and flow switches, solenoid valves, transmitters, and drive units comprise another segment of field-mounted hardware that frequently experiences mechanical problems.

Vibration and temperature, which cause most of the difficulties, can often be eliminated only by relocating switching elements. But, if a particular problem must be corrected while the unit is operating, vibration-absorption pads, fans, or heat-deflecting baffles can be used to ensure safe operation on a temporary basis. (Fig. 28).

Other problems with switching elements are setpoint drifting and deadband. There are two types of setpoint drifting: (1) A change in actuation point with service life, which can be identified during periodic maintenance and calibration, and (2) A change in the field-adjustable setpoint (where provided), which can vary with load and line vibration. The point at which the switch actuates is unpredictable and is usually not discovered by an operator until the unit is in service.

Deadband problems occur when the range of

Fig. 28 Instrumentation that may be sensitive to vibration should be mounted securely.

the variable accomplishing the switching is not great enough to actuate the switch. For instance, a switch closes but fails to reset to the open position as pressure reverses. Such a switch can be considered permanently closed because the process cycle is not broad enough to satisfy the deadband reset requirement. Such problems can be prevented by reviewing the process requirements with the equipment vendor before ordering a switch.

MAINTAINING FIELD-MOUNTED EQUIPMENT

Maximum reliability and safety during unit operation require that field-mounted components be maintained properly and that essential monitoring features be retained in working order to carry out corrective actions when they are needed.

Improperly set pressure switches, limit switches, positioners, and actuators cause countless delays in the start-up of essential power units. Many accidents and near-accidents have been caused by burned-out relays or jumpered components. Field reports continue to show that units are returned to service before control systems and their components have been serviced or checked out completely. Greater emphasis on controls maintenance is needed if the power industry expects to continue its excellent service record.

A well-organized instruments-and-controls field-maintenance program requires:

■ early planning, beginning during the preliminary design phase for a new unit;

■ thorough training of personnel;

■ monitoring the performance of station operations and maintenance personnel;

■ initiating and maintaining an "early warning" problem-analysis program;

■ developing and enforcing an inspection and maintenance schedule; and

■ establishing and maintaining an adequate maintenance and failure-documentation records system.

The controls-systems maintenance group can contribute significantly to improving plant productivity, but to be effective, it should be accountable directly to and receive close support from the generating station manager.[2]

OTHER POWER-PLANT CONTROL SYSTEMS

This chapter has dealt solely with steam-generator control systems. Given sufficient space, similar chapters could be written about the controls for flue-gas-desulfurization systems, precipitators, and ash-handling systems, all of which can be in the "steam-generator island." Increased controls sophistication is taking place in such areas, for the same reasons as outlined above.

The power industry will never be a high-volume user of state-of-the-art electronic equipment and cannot be expected, therefore, to play a significant role in electronics development. But the industry will take advantage of new developments, particularly in the area of distributed computer-based systems, as they become available.

Increasing demands for higher productivity and availability of steam-generating plants will provide new challenges for control-systems designers. The electronics industry will provide the tools; the power-generation controls engineers must provide the imagination.

REFERENCES

1. National Electrical Code; Chapter 5; Special Occupancies; Articles 500, 501. Boston: National Fire Protection Association, latest edition.

2. T. H. Cooper, et al., "Improve Control-System Reliability." *Power*, 121(8): 64–67, August 1977.

CHAPTER 15

Steam-Generator Auxiliaries

This chapter describes power-plant equipment such as fans, air heaters, sootblowers, and the boiler-water circulating pumps. This equipment is usually designated as boiler auxiliaries. Power-plant noise, which applies particularly to these and most other equipment peripheral to the boiler, also is covered. Other such components described in detail elsewhere include pulverizers, Chapter 12, ash-handling equipment, Chapter 16, and structural-steel design and erection, Chapters 6 and 19. Operational control system philosophy and design are included in Chapter 14, and the entire scope of boiler-related emission-control equipment is presented in Chapter 17.

Although boiler auxiliary components are secondary to the design of the boiler itself, they are absolutely essential to its operation. Together, they represent a very sizable portion of the overall steam-generator cost. As differentiated from equipment considered auxiliary to the remainder of a steam power plant, a *boiler auxiliary* is equipment which is an integral part of, or is required for the operation of, the boiler. For example, compressors for air sootblowers and certain sealing requirements, are part of the overall power-plant equipment and are not boiler auxiliaries. Pumps within the boiler circuit are boiler auxiliaries, but feedwater pumps are part of the power-plant cycle. In general, valves required for boiler operation are boiler auxiliaries, but steam stop valves, turbine throttle valves and most other valves related to the steam turbine and feedwater heaters are not.

Equipment is described here to help familiarize the reader with the different components and their specific applications in boiler work. The calculation of volumes handled and static pressures to be encountered with fans are given in Chapter 6. For sootblower selection, the designer must take into account the boiler configuration and the probable dirtying characteristics of the coal ash, as referenced in Chapters 2, 3, 6, 7, 8, and Appendix C. For air-heater sizing, air and gas flows and temperatures have to be calculated, as will allowable static pressure losses; for more information on such calculations see Chapter 6.

It is important to realize that there are instances in which some of this peripheral equipment is purchased separately from the steam-generator contract. However the boiler manufacturer has to be relied on heavily to provide basic steam generator performance data. The data is necessary for the proper selection and design of the peripheral equipment and other auxiliaries.

POWER-PLANT FANS

Regardless of fuel and method of firing, all boilers for electrical, industrial, or marine power generation use mechanical draft fans (Fig. 1). They supply the primary air for the pulverization and transport of coal to the furnace. They also supply the secondary and tertiary air to the windboxes for completion of combustion. Fans also remove the products of combustion from the furnace and move the gases through heat-transfer equipment and flue-gas desulfurization equipment. Sometimes, gas fans control steam temperature. Numerous small fans are used for sealing and cooling of ignitors, scanners, and other equipment.

Power-station fans are among the largest made: static pressures of 60″ WG and individual fan volumes of 1.5 million cu ft/min are common. And, usually, they are custom-designed with blade configuration and control systems highly sensitive to both owner preference and the evaluated cost of installed and operating power. Applications that require the largest fans (and thereby use greatest amount of plant power) on a boiler fall into four categories which combined account for more than half of the total boiler power requirements. The four fan categories are: forced draft, primary air, induced draft and gas-recirculation.

FORCED-DRAFT FANS

Forced-draft fans supply air necessary for fuel combustion, as calculated in Chapters 4 and 6, and must be sized to handle the stoichiometric air plus the excess air needed for proper burning of the specific fuel for which they are designed. In addition, they provide air to make up for air-heater leakage and for some sealing-air requirements. Forced-draft (FD) fans supply the total airflow except when an atmospheric-suction primary-air fan is used.

Radial airfoil (centrifugal) or variable-pitch axial fans are preferred for FD service. FD fans operate in the cleanest environment associated with a boiler, and are generally the quietest and most efficient fans in the power plant. They are particularly well-suited for high-speed operation. Most FD fan installations have inlet silencers for noise reduction with screens to protect the fans from any entrained particles in the incoming air.

EFFECT OF AIR TEMPERATURE

Both the air temperature at a power plant and its elevation above sea level affect air density, which in turn has a direct influence on the FD-fan capacity. If steam coils or other means of heating the air *ahead* of the FD fans are provided, the consequent air temperature to the fans must be taken into account. If hot-air recirculation is used for air-heater protection, then both the added volume of air and its higher temperature must be considered. As mentioned in the calculation sections of previous chapters, if air moisture exceeds 1 or 2 percent by weight (as can occur in high-temperature tropical installations) the resulting greater volume proportionately increases all fans on a unit.

PRIMARY-AIR FANS

Large high-pressure fans supply the air needed to dry and transport coal either directly from the pulverizing equipment to the furnace, or to an intermediate storage bunker. As de-

Fig. 1 **Construction view of four axial-flow type induced-draft fans serving a large pulverized-coal steam generator**

scribed in Chapter 10, primary-air fans may be located before or after the milling equipment. The most common applications are either pulverizer exhauster fans or cold (ambient temperature) primary-air fans.

The mill exhauster fan draws hot air from the secondary-air duct and through the pulverizer. The coal/air mixture from the pulverizer then passes through the fan and discharges into the fuel pipes which carry the mixture to the furnace for ignition. One fan is usually supplied for each pulverizer.

A materials-handling fan of the straight-blade type, the mill exhauster is sized for the maximum airflow needed by the pulverizer. It must develop sufficient pressure at maximum airflow to overcome the resistance of the air ducts, dampers, the pulverizer, and the fuel pipes to the furnace.

Located before the air heater, the cold primary-air fan draws air from the atmosphere and supplies the energy required to force the air through the ducts, air heater, pulverizer, and fuel piping. Usually two fans are supplied for each steam generator.

Cold primary-air fans for ambient-air duty are usually of the centrifugal airfoil type and, like FD fans, have silencers. In situations involving severe particulate or high temperatures, straight radial or modified radial fans are recommended.

With a cold-air system, the air volume handled by the primary-air fan is subtracted from the amount of air that must be handled by the forced-draft fan. Therefore, if coal is the only fuel being fired, the forced-draft fan may be made smaller because of the amount of air handled by the cold primary-air fan.

INDUCED-DRAFT FANS

Induced-draft (ID) fans exhaust combustion products from a boiler. In doing so, they create sufficient negative pressure to establish a slight suction in the furnace (usually from 0.2 to 0.5″ WG). This condition gives rise to the name "suction firing" or "balanced-draft" operation. These fans must have enough capacity to accommodate any infiltration caused by the nega-

tive pressure in the equipment downstream of the furnace and by any seal leakage in air preheaters. Chapter 6 gives the method of establishing volume and pressure specifications and tolerances.

As ID fans are now typically located downstream of any particulate removal system, they are a relatively clean service fan. In most instances, therefore, an airfoil centrifugal fan is selected. The airfoil designs can develop efficiencies of more than 88 percent and can have capacities greater than 1.5 million cu ft/min (CFM). The airfoil blade shape minimizes turbulence and noise. The blades and center plates may also be fitted with wear pads and replaceable nose sections for greater wear. Structural strength, particularly important in larger sizes, is excellent with this design.

Where greater wear resistance is needed because of dust burden or where a very conservative approach is desirable, a modified radial or forward-curved, backward-inclined design is used. Without unduly sacrificing efficiency, these blade shapes minimize dust build-up and reduce downtime for cleaning. They have low-noise characteristics, and their relatively simple design allows fabrication in special alloys should they be required for service downstream of a wet scrubber.

The ID fan is sometimes used as a booster fan with flue-gas desulfurizing (FGD) scrubbers. In one such arrangement, ID fans follow the precipitator or baghouse and another set of fans—the booster fans—follows the scrubber. With pressurized scrubbers, the booster fans are placed directly behind the ID's and *ahead of* the scrubbers, acting to "push" the gases through the FGDS.

GAS-RECIRCULATION FANS

Gas recirculation fans draw gas from a point between the economizer outlet and the air-preheater inlet, and discharge it (for steam-temperature control) into the bottom of the furnace. When controlling steam temperature on coal-fired units, a high-efficiency, high draft-loss mechanical dust collector must be installed ahead of the fan. If the recirculation fan on a coal-fired unit is only for standby or emergency oil firing, the dust collector is omitted.

Gas-recirculation duty provides the most severe test of a power-plant fan. The combination of heavy dust loads and rapid temperature changes demands the utmost in rugged, reliable fan design. Particularly important is how the fan hub is mated with the shaft; conventional shrink-fit may not be adequate. To cope with temperature excursions, fans with an integral hub are preferable. Straight or modified radials or forward-curved, backwardly inclined centrifugal wheels meet these needs the best.

If recirculation fans are to be turned on and off as a function of boiler load or the fuel being burned, turning gears are supplied to prevent thermal distortion of the rotor under cool-down conditions.

HOW FANS WORK

A fan is a volumetric machine which, like a pump, moves quantities of air or gas from one place to another. In so doing, it overcomes resistance to flow by supplying the fluid with the energy necessary for continued motion. Physically, the essential elements of a fan are a bladed rotor and a housing to contain the incoming air or gas and direct its flow.

ENERGY FACTORS

Because a fan does work it demands energy to operate. The amount of energy depends on the volume of gas moved, the resistance against which the fan works, and machine efficiency. Chapter 6 gives the method of calculation of air and gas volumes. It is important to calculate such volumes at the actual pressure or suction existing at the fan *inlet*.

FAN PRESSURE RELATIONSHIPS

Draft, pressure, draft loss and pressure loss were defined in Chapter 6 which also differentiated between velocity pressure and static pressure: total pressure was stated to be the algebraic sum of velocity pressure and static pressure. Specifically related to fans, total pressure is the air pressure that exists by virtue of the degree of compression and the rate of motion. When applying these definitions to fan performance, there are distinct relationships that exist between each variable.

Fan total pressure is the difference between the total pressure at the fan outlet and the total pressure at the fan inlet. *Fan velocity pressure* is that corresponding to the average velocity at the specified fan outlet area. *Fan static pressure* is the difference between the fan total pressure and the fan velocity pressure. Thus, it is the difference between the static pressure at the fan outlet and the total pressure at the fan inlet. *Static pressure rise*, sometimes mistaken for fan static pressure, is the static pressure at the fan outlet minus the static pressure at the fan inlet. The difference between fan static pressure and static pressure rise is the inlet velocity pressure.

POWER

With the equation for fan work and some basic physical constants, the equation that expresses air horsepower can be developed.

$$Ahp = \frac{V \times H}{6356}$$

(1)

where V is the volumetric flow through the fan in cu ft/min and H is the head or pressure difference (in inches of water) across the fan. The air horsepower may also be designated as either static or total. Because the resistance to be overcome in fan application is primarily static pressure, the fan pressure developed is usually referred to in terms of static head. On this basis, the calculated fan power is known as *static air horsepower* (Ahp_s). When the power calculations are based on *total* head, fan power is referred to as the *total air horsepower* (Ahp_t) and is equivalent to the power output.

$$\text{Fan Mechanical efficiency } (\eta_t) = \frac{Ahp_t}{\text{power input}}$$

(2)

or, transposing,

Power input (brake or shaft hp) $= \dfrac{Ahp_t}{\eta_t}$

$$= \dfrac{V H_t}{6356 \eta_t} \tag{3}$$

The power input formula assumes that air is an incompressible fluid. But the fact that air is compressible must be recognized when designing for high pressure differentials. The fan power formula then becomes

$$\text{Power input, hp} = \dfrac{k_c V H_t}{6356 \eta_t} \tag{4}$$

where k_c can be taken from Fig. 2, which is based on adiabatic compression.

Density

Because they affect gas density, pressure and temperature of the air or gas also influence power output and efficiency. A change in density changes total and static pressure and their subsequent conversion into inches of water at standard conditions. Remember that head and horsepower vary inversely as absolute fluid temperature and directly as absolute

Fig. 2 Compressibility factor for use in calculating fan power consumption, assuming adiabatic compression

fluid pressure (or directly with fluid density)—and that adjustments often must be made for pressure and temperature variations when calculating performance or selecting a fan for a particular application.

SPECIFYING FAN OPERATING CONDITIONS

The problem of specifying the required operating conditions for fans at various load points is usually the responsibility of the boiler FGD system, or particulate-removal-equipment supplier. The fan manufacturer assumes responsibility only for producing the volumetric flow and pressure specified. If the fan and system are incorrectly matched, the fan will not deliver the desired flow or pressure. Once the fan has been installed, it is difficult to increase its capability significantly because of physical limitations such as motor and impeller size. To select the appropriate fan for a given application, the fan vendor needs to know the density, flow and pressure requirements of the system at various points of operation and whether there are any fan speed limitations. If any of these variables change, it can affect the fan selection.

FLOW

The gas flow through the fan is usually expressed as a volumetric flow rate. It is necessary to determine the flow rate in actual cu ft/min (acfm) at the inlet to each fan from the density at the fan inlet and the mass flow rate (lb/hr). Proper corrections for plant elevation and actual conditions of local pressure at fan inlets must be made to the calculated air and gas volumes, as described in Chapter 6.

PRESSURE

On balanced-draft units, the required static head for the FD fan is the sum of all the series resistances in the secondary-air system, including cold-air duct, steam air heater, air preheater, air metering device, hot-air duct, dampers and windbox pressure drop. For pressurized units, the additional loss from the furnace to the stack outlet must also be included in determining total system resistance. ID fans must provide a static head equal to the series resistance from the furnace to the stack outlet, including resistances of superheater, reheater, boiler bank, economizer, air preheater, dust-collecting equipment, scrubbers and all duct-work. For primary-air (PA) fans, static pressure requirements are determined by the resistances through the inlet duct and air preheater, the pressure drop through the pulverizer, and the resistance through the fuel piping to the furnace.

"SPECIFIED" CONDITIONS

The volume flow (acfm) and static pressure ("WG) calculated by the boiler or scrubber manufacturer, as previously discussed, give the actual required fan capacity under ideal operating conditions. Besides the requirements at full load, the boiler or scrubber manufacturer should also calculate performance requirements at several other partial load points to evaluate power consumption, select the control equipment, and assure a fan that will operate at maximum efficiency at the desired normal output of the steam-generating unit. Also, the fan manufacturer must have a clear understanding of the system resistance over its entire range to ensure that a fan will operate at all points along its curve from the point of view of stability, sound, and efficiency.

Usually a margin or safety factor is added to the maximum continuous (MCR) volume and pressure requirements to arrive at maximum design or "specified" rating. Fan tolerances ordinarily used by C-E are given in Chapter 6.

TYPES OF FANS

From the point of view of fluid mechanics, fans represent a class of turbomachines designed to move fluids such as air, gases and vapor against low pressure. From the point of view of mechanical design, fans have a very light casing because inlet pressures are atmospheric or lower. Simplified hydraulic forms and welded steel plate are generally encountered in fans.

Direct-connected drives most often are used in power-plant work with control obtained through variable-speed motors, hydraulic couplings, or variable inlet vanes.

Fans are broadly classed as either centrifugal or axial, according to the flow direction. The centrifugal (radial) fan moves air perpendicular to the rotational axis of the impeller; the axial-flow fan moves air parallel to the rotational axis of the impeller.

CENTRIFUGAL FANS

Centrifugal fans use blades mounted on an impeller (or rotor) which rotates within a spiral or volute housing. Blade design determines fan characteristics, so by using blades of different shapes, a fan engineer can select an appropriate fan design. There are three basic blade types: forward curved, straight (radial and radial tipped) and backward curved (airfoil or flat). A velocity vector diagram at blade tip (Fig. 3) indicates that backward curved blades produce low velocities for a given tip or peripheral speed, and that forward curved blades give high velocity. Radial blades and radial-tipped blades lie between these two extremes. The backward curved blade type, therefore, operates at greater motor speeds than the other types for a given duty and is well adapted to direct drive with motors or steam turbines.

Fig. 4 shows some commonly used blade shapes. In general, blade type limits fan speed. Thus, the backward-blade machines can operate at a relatively higher speed than the for-

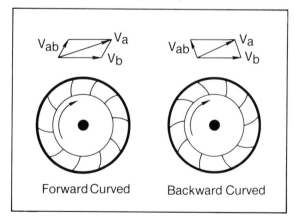

Fig. 3 **Velocity vector diagrams comparing forward-curved and backwardly curved centrifugal-fan blades. At same tip velocity (V_b) each type blade produces different air velocity (V_a). Vector V_{ab} is air velocity relative to the blade .**

ward-curved design. Blade selection depends on speed limitations, allowable noise levels, efficiency demanded by specified load conditions, and desired fan performance characteristics in the most likely range of operation. In addition, the maximum attainable mechanical efficiencies and tolerance of the blade to corrosion and erosion are selection factors. Table I shows the effect of blade type on both maximum possible efficiency and fan resistance to flyash erosion. Notice that increasing the efficiency of a centrifugal fan sacrifices its erosion resistance.

Once the optimum fan has been determined, the aerodynamic selection process yields width, diameter and speed of the fan wheel. These parameters then become factors for subsequent elements of the fan design. In general, the fan wheel dimensions determine the basic dimensions of the fan housing and inlet boxes.

Centrifugal-Fan Design

A once popular centrifugal fan arrangement (Fig. 5) was a single-speed motor drive which controlled flow by inlet vanes or inlet louvers. The centrifugal fan in this instance is sized for "specified" conditions and is throttled by the inlet vanes to allow the fan to provide the flow and pressure required at lower operating loads.

As fuel costs and equipment efficiency have become increasingly important, new arrangements for centrifugal fans have developed. Because the welded blades of a centrifugal fan are not easily adjusted, the only other means of controlling flow and pressure is to vary the

speed of the fan. Two-speed motor drives, turbine drives and fluid couplings all have been used with varying success on centrifugal fans, and have helped to increase their efficiency at lower loads. These arrangements do, however, add more moving parts to the fan system, with a potential negative effect on reliability.

The variable-speed and the variable-frequency wound rotor motors are fan drives that allow varying the speed from full to zero in infinite intervals; they improve dramatically low-flow efficiencies. As discussed elsewhere in this chapter, speed variation is the ideal way to change fan operating characteristics; thus, for centrifugal fans, these motor designs are of great interest.

Centrifugal-Fan Construction

Fan scrolls and inlet boxes are of welded steel construction. The housing and the inlet boxes have either removable sections or are split for access and removal of the rotor (Fig. 6). The rotor wheel is of all-welded construction. After final machining, the rotor is usually statically and dynamically balanced and installed on its shaft in the manufacturer's plant (Fig. 7).

AXIAL-FLOW FANS

Axial fans at various boiler loads can maintain far higher efficiencies than constant-speed

Table I. Effect of Blade Type on Erosion Resistance and Efficiency

Blade Type	Typical Max. Static Eff., %	Tolerance to Erosive Environment
Straight	70	High
Forward Curved	80	Medium to High
Backward Curved	85	Medium
Airfoil	90	Low

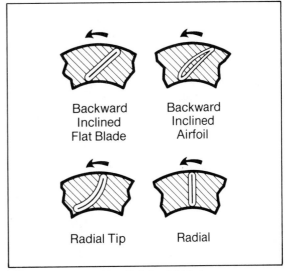

Backward Inclined Flat Blade Backward Inclined Airfoil

Radial Tip Radial

Fig. 4 Centrifugal (radial) fan blade types

Fig. 5 **Airfoil-blade centrifugal fan with inlet-vane control**

Fig. 6 **Airfoil-bladed centrifugal fan showing inlet boxes and housing split for rotor removal**

centrifugal fans. As fuel costs continue to rise, their higher initial expense has been offset by operational cost savings over the life of the plant. However, a detailed evaluation is required to show the advantages of using axials in any given situation.

In the most common axial arrangement (Fig. 8), the fan operates at constant speed and the angle of the blades on the hub is adjusted to vary flow; no inlet vanes are required for control. This enables the axial fan to develop, for each point of operation, a unique aerodynamic configuration that is as efficient as possible.

Either a mechanical or hydraulic mechanism adjusts blade pitch while the fan operates at its design speed. Mechanical type pitch-change mechanisms are, however, usually insufficient to properly control fans of the size required for utility applications. Variable-pitch axials are best suited to PA, FD, ID or booster-fan applications on large industrial and utility boilers. As stated earlier, axial fans are not appropriate for small fan requirements or for gas recirculation.

Axial-Fan Construction

Variable-pitch moving blades provide a wide range of flow with satisfactory operational efficiency. Because the fan and its built-in components work under high peripheral speed, and thus great centrifugal force, mechanical reliability is as important as aerodynamic performance. The centrifugal force of a moving blade, for example, can be more than 150,000 lbs.

Fig. 9 shows the structure of a typical two-stage axial ID fan. An overhung runner boss, with blade-actuating levers and an oil hydraulic piston and cylinder, supports the moving blades. At the free end of the rotating cylinder a control valve is attached.

The variable-pitch scheme shown in Fig. 10, includes an oil-hydraulic control that can be operated both manually and automatically. In automatic operation, an electric drive responds to a signal from the automatic plant controller and moves the control spool in the control valve through a linkage of levers. The control valve consists of a rotating sleeve attached

Fig. 7 Centrifugal-fan rotor undergoing static balancing in manufacturer's shop

Fig. 8 Two-stage variable-pitch axial-flow fan for induced-draft service

directly to the hydraulic cylinder and a non-rotating spool linked to the external control unit. With the displacement of the spool, pressurized oil flows, accompanying the cylinder movement; the oil is fed back directly to the control valve. Thus, an accurate location of the blade pitch is obtained.

A thrust roller bearing at the blade root supports the centrifugal force of the blade. The bearing is one of the most critical elements, as it fluctuates under severe static loading. Such working conditions are most strenuous on ball or roller bearings, which require substantial attention in design, with life tests to simulate actual operating conditions.

FAN CHARACTERISTIC CURVES

Fig. 11 shows a typical set of constant-speed characteristic curves for a centrifugal fan with backwardly inclined blades. Although by applying theory of similitude the performance of

Fig. 9 Construction view of two-stage axial-flow fan with upper housing not yet in place

Fig. 10 Schematic arrangement of pitch control for adjustable blade axial-flow fan

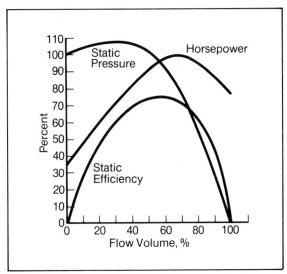

Fig. 11 Chart showing typical constant-speed characteristics for a fan with backwardly curved blades. Pressure decreases as fan capacity goes up; this expands the range of stable operation. Horsepower characteristic is non-overloading.

a single fan of a given type may be used to determine the characteristics of a complete line of sizes, each separate type must be tested independently. The curves are for one speed only; when a constant-speed motor drives the fan, it will operate somewhere on the characteristic curves, depending on the resistance imposed by the system through which the air passes. The system resistance, therefore, acts as an automatic control on the fan and will limit the amount of overload that can be developed, despite the flatness of the pressure characteristic. The amount of overload depends also on the shape of the horsepower curve.

To fully appreciate the significance of fan characteristic curves, realize that every fan is restricted to that performance defined by its curve. The fan *must* operate at a point that lies somewhere on the characteristic plot. For example, if the head required for a given volume is less than that specified by the curves, additional resistance must be placed in the system; otherwise, the fan will put out more capacity until it reaches a point on the characteristic curve at which the head matches system resistance. The fan has no choice; it must operate at a point on the curve where head, capacity and system resistance balance.

**DEVELOPMENT OF
FAN PERFORMANCE CURVES**

Fan performance curves are normally developed from base test curves, which, in turn, are developed from test data recorded under controlled laboratory conditions. For continuity throughout industry, as well as for ease of understanding and ready comparison, test data are corrected or adjusted to what is known as standard conditions. Standard conditions for fan design work denote that all flow, pressure and power values are at 70°F and sea level, with air density of 0.075 lb per cu ft.

Normal curve format consists of a graph which has the air or gas volumetric flow numerically on the abscissa or horizontal axis, with both static pressure and brake horsepower numerically on the ordinate or vertical axis. Two separate curves—volume versus static pressure, and volume versus power—are plotted on each performance curve.

Several other variables can be incorporated on the constant-speed performance curves. Such things as static or mechanical efficiency, the horsepower or pressure at various temperatures, altitudes or densities can all be plotted to illustrate actual conditions. Finally, in rating from a curve, the same fan design must be retained. That is, a radial-blade centrifugal-fan test curve cannot be used to rate to a backwardly-inclined-blade centrifugal fan.

APPLICATION OF CHARACTERISTIC CURVES

Fig. 12 illustrates the application of typical centrifugal-fan characteristic curves to a fan problem in which points A, B, and C are calculated requirements at four load points on a given boiler. The line through them defines the system resistance. The point where this line intersects the static pressure characteristics of any fan, at any given speed, determines the point on the characteristic at which the fan will operate, if both curves are plotted for the same density. However, the fan can operate only on its characteristic curve. If any error has been made in calculating point D—in volume or pressure, or temperature—that point will not fall on the characteristic curve and the fan may not meet the requirements when operating at that particular speed.

For example, if 10 percent more volume is needed at the same pressure, point D will be displaced to the right, but the available pressure at the fan head at the same time drops 14 percent and the fan cannot satisfy the requirements. Similarly, if the volume is correct but 10 percent more pressure is needed, the volume that the fan would deliver at the greater pressure would be only about 90 percent of the requirements, because the fan can operate only on its characteristic curve for a given speed and density condition.

To provide excess capacity it is customary to specify the volume and pressure in excess of the actual calculated requirements and thereby obtain a larger fan. Suppose a portion of the pressure characteristic of this larger fan,

operating at the same speed and density, is represented by line FG in Fig. 12. Then it is apparent that this size fan would be selected by the manufacturer if the purchaser specified 24-percent excess volume. At the same time the fan would satisfy the requirement of point E, which requires 8-percent excess volume and 17-percent excess pressure. The only advantage in attempting to define point E on the extrapolated system resistance curve, instead of point F or G, is that the power requirement given by the manufacturer will then represent a closer estimate of the larger fan under actual operating conditions than if point F or point G had been defined for fan selection. The fan finally chosen can, however, satisfy the requirements of all three points, if sufficient power is available from the drive.

Speed Variations

For a given fan, a family of characteristic curves can be obtained by varying the fan

Fig. 12 **Use of characteristic curves as applied to problems of centrifugal fan selection**

speed. The nature of each curve remains the same because the change in operating speed merely shifts the curve by a proportionate amount. A graph like that of Fig. 13 results if system resistance is plotted on the same grid as the family of curves for different fan speeds.

FAN CONTROL

Very few applications permit fans to operate continuously at the same pressure and volume. Therefore, to meet the requirements of the system, some means of varying fan output becomes necessary. Capacity control of a fan can be achieved in two ways:

■ controlling the aerodynamic flow into or within the fan

■ controlling the speed of the fan

The first method refers either to altering the flow of gas into the eye of a centrifugal-fan wheel as with inlet vanes, or changing the internal aerodynamics by altering internal geometry as with controllable pitch axial fans. The second method refers to any speed-changing device such as a turbine, fluid drive, multiple-speed motor or an electronically adjustable motor drive connected to the fan.

Fig. 13 Fan speed of a centrifugal fan can be varied so that output pressure matches system resistance for desired volumetric flow; this conserves energy.

VARIABLE INLET VANES

Sometimes variable inlet vanes (Fig. 14) are used to control fan performance by providing swirl to the fan impeller, saving significant power. Variable inlet vanes tend to be slightly more effective in saving power than parallel blade inlet box dampers. When furnishing variable inlet vanes for either centrifugal or fixed-pitch axial fans, fan manufacturers provide a complete performance envelope showing the effect of vane position on fan performance and power. Fig. 15 shows the typical percentage range in power reduction along a constant system resistance line as a percentage of design flow for a backwardly-inclined airfoil centrifugal fan.

An inlet-vane-controlled centrifugal fan is selected to produce full specified flow and pressure with no inlet vanes present. Inlet vanes then throttle down this maximum performance capability so that the fan can operate over the range of normal boiler operating load points. Fig. 16 illustrates the effect of this type of control system, which is extremely sensitive at the lower load conditions. Extremely minor changes in inlet vane openings have a dramatic effect on the flow produced by the fan, whereas at higher loads it requires increasingly larger movement of the inlet vanes to have any effect on the flow produced by a centrifugal fan.

AXIAL-FAN BLADE PITCH CONTROL

The axial-flow fan can control flow at constant speed by varying the blade angle of the fan (Fig. 17). The effect is to create a unique aerodynamic configuration for the fan at each point of operation so that the fan is operating at maximum possible efficiency. As the blade angle is adjusted from minimum to maximum position, the flow change is nearly linear (Fig. 16). Another aspect of control rests in the response time of the fan. Most axial-flow fans can move the blades a full stroke, from the maximum open to fully closed position in 30 seconds. This means that under the normal boiler operating range, an axial fan can respond or move from maximum continuous conditions to zero flow in approximately 20 seconds.

Fig. 14 Inlet vanes give an initial spin to air entering a centrifugal fan. By adjusting angle of vanes, the degree of spin and volumetric output are regulated.

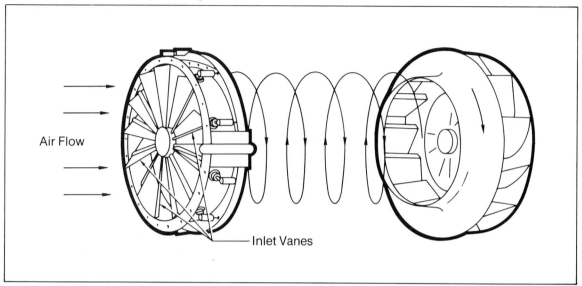

Fig. 15 Typical airfoil blade centrifugal-fan performance characteristics—constant-speed with variable inlet-vane control

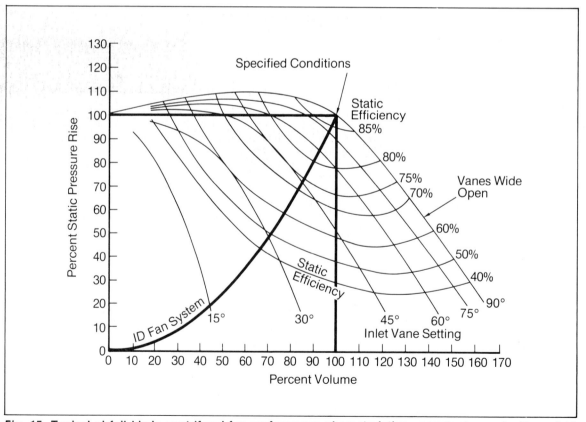

SURGE OR STALL LIMIT

The surge limit of a centrifugal fan is that point near the peak of the pressure curve corresponding to the minimum flow rate at which the fan can be operated without instability. The stall limit of an axial fan is that point near the peak of the pressure curve at a particular blade angle corresponding to the minimum flow rate at which the fan may be operated without separation of airflow over the blades. A fan must not be operated in the surge or stall region or serious damage can occur.

An aerodynamic characteristic of all axial fans (just as with an airplane), stall is understood by few. A stall occurs when the angle of attack of the fan blade (or airplane wing) exceeds a certain value in relationship to air velocity. When this angle of attack value is exceeded, airflow becomes separated from the convex side of the blade. Centrifugal force then throws air trapped in this separated portion in a radial direction, to the outer tip of the blade. At this point, pressure builds up until it is relieved through the blade tip clearance. This process creates a very unstable and oscillating pressure force on the blade, and can cause very severe vibrations throughout the entire fan. In Fig. 18, the flow separation points occur at the upper end of the several blade-pitch lines, with the dotted lines extending downward and left to the recovery point, where another reversal takes place. At low blade angles, the fan tends to get noisy and somewhat unstable, but it no longer is subject to stalling.

FAN SPEED CONTROL

Controlling the fan speed is potentially the most efficient form of capacity control. The only significant inefficiency that a speed control system can introduce to a fan results from the inefficiencies of the speed control system.

All speed control systems yield certain operational/reliability improvements to large fans in induced-draft service. They include

■ reduction in erosion approximately proportional to the ratio of the squares of the impact velocities

■ reduction in mechanical shock at start-up

■ adjustability of speed to any point within the operating speed range

Fig. 17 **Close-up of adjustable airfoil blading of an axial-flow fan**

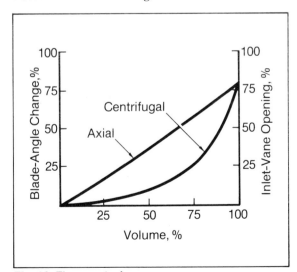

Fig. 16 **Flow control**

■ reduction in potential fan system-oriented problems (fan/foundation, fan/ductwork, fan noise) at reduced running speeds

■ reduction in electrical power surge on motor start-up

The primary disadvantage of adjustable-speed drives is their cost which, depending on unit size, can be significantly more than a single-speed motor drive with inlet-vane control. Also, adjustable-speed drives add additional components to the drive train which require more careful consideration of system dynamics to avoid torsional oscillations or other undesirable phenomena.

Fluid-Drive Speed Control

For speed adjustment, fluid drives are either hydrokinetic or hydroviscous. In hydrokinetic operation, an impeller attached to the driving motor accelerates oil particles and impinges them against a runner attached to the driven fan. Speed is adjusted by changing the volume of oil in the system and thus the transmittable torque. The hydroviscous method is similar in principle, but relies for speed change upon the increase in torque transmitted by the oil used between alternate rows of driver/driven plates that are forced closer together.

Fluid drives have been used extensively where speed changing was required on large centrifugal fans. They are more efficient than single-speed inlet-vane control as volume output drops below about 75 percent. They are, however, the least efficient adjustable speed method of gas volume control, giving away essentially a percent of efficiency for each percent of speed reduction. They also add another mechanical device in the drive train which increases the cost of installation, requires cooling equipment, and possibly increases initial fan size due to slip at full speed.

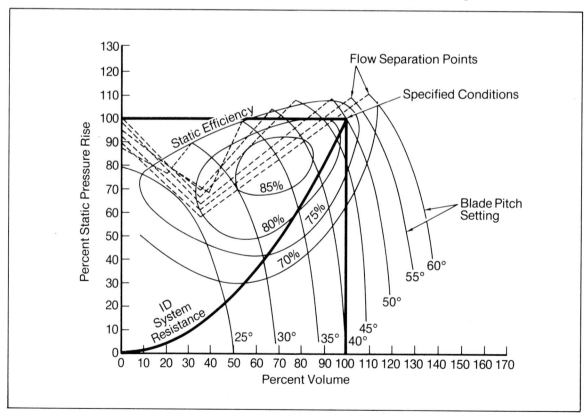

Fig. 18 Typical axial-flow fan performance characteristics with variable-pitch blade control

Two-Speed Motor Drives

As a centrifugal fan is vaned or dampered down from the specified point, its efficiency falls off rather rapidly. If, however, at the normal operating point, fan speed is changed to a lower base speed and the vanes or dampers reopened, a system efficiency is achieved which matches the original full load levels. This is the principle of application of two-speed motors to power fans. Many two-speed motors have been applied to fans to gain the overall high efficiencies available from two running speeds. Also, the two-speed motor drive is the least expensive and least complex speed control method. An objection frequently voiced is that operators hesitate to change to the lower speed until far below the designed load limit, which of course negates the planned economy of the system.

Variable-Speed Drives

A variable speed system significantly improves fan efficiency during periods when the boiler is operating at less than its maximum load. A centrifugal fan can be equipped with an adjustable-speed drive, a control and monitoring system. The speed control range can be tailored to a particular installation and drive system costs can be optimized. By equipping a fan with both adjustable speed capability and inlet vanes, the fan output can be tailored to match all possible boiler operating conditions.

Slip-ring (or wound-rotor) motors provide step changes in speed by connecting the motor windings to an adjustable external resistance through slip rings and brushes. By changing rotor circuit resistance, the motor speed/torque characteristics can be adjusted to fit changes in load conditions. With no resistance in the rotor circuit (rings-shorted condition), the wound-rotor motor will operate exactly the same as a squirrel-cage motor.

Another important difference is the starting characteristics of the motor. The wound-rotor motor inrush current can be as low as the magnetizing current—normally about 30 percent of rated current. Most other induction motors draw a very high (600 to 700 percent of rated)

current during start-up. This lower current characteristic can provide significant savings in the electrical distribution system. It also eliminates the need for long intervals between motor starts which are needed to dissipate the heat generated by the high starting current. Wound-rotor motor current is essentially proportional to the load torque.

Synchronous motor adjustable-frequency systems use static electronic control equipment to adjust frequency and voltage. The synchronous motor is an AC device with two sets of windings, one fixed in the stator (frame) and the other wound around field poles which are fixed to the rotor in pairs. For a given frequency, the number of poles determines the speed of the motor. To run the synchronous motor, the stator windings are energized by connection to an AC power source. The rotor field pole windings are excited by a DC power source. A magnetic coupling then exists between the stator and the DC field pole windings which are separated only by a small air gap. The windings in the stator when energized with an AC power source set up a rotating magnetic field around the stator. The magnetic DC fields on the rotor couple with the rotating AC field and, thus, mechanically follow the rotating AC stator field. This causes the rotor to turn at the same speed as the rotating AC field.

Sometimes, when a supply of exhaust steam is available, boiler fans can be driven by steam turbines. Such an arrangement is frequently used in industrial plants to achieve an efficient heat balance—as well as drive the fan. Speed variation is feasible down to about 35 percent of rated turbine speed.

FAN SELECTION

Once the boiler or scrubber engineer determines the pressure and flow required by the system at rated load, at the specified condition (with margin) and at various load points, this information can be plotted and the fan selected. A centrifugal fan will have its specified point fall within the area of maximum efficiency. At this point, the fan is operating wide-open with no restrictions. To achieve the lower load points, inlet vanes are closed to throttle the maximum capability of the fan. As the fan performance moves down the system resistance line, it moves through areas of constant efficiency that fall perpendicular to the system resistance line.

The characteristic curve for an axial fan is considerably different from that of a centrifugal fan. Given exactly the same system resistance curve, an axial-fan designer will select a fan that operates at maximum efficiency at boiler full load. If normal fan performance tolerances have been used, the fan will usually have the capacity to achieve the specified requirements. If higher-than-normal tolerances have been applied, a less-than-optimum selection will have to be made, in which full boiler load does not fall inside the maximum efficiency area. The oblong or egg-shaped areas on the axial-fan curve are the areas of constant static efficiency. It is important to note that these areas for the axial fan are oblong in a direction approximately parallel to the system resistance line rather than perpendicular to it, as with the centrifugal fans. Changes in flow requirements along the system curve cause only slight changes in efficiency compared to the significant changes in efficiency for constant-speed centrifugals. The lines that are perpendicular to the system line on the axial curve depict the angle of the blades at that point of operation.

COMPARISON OF FANS AND FAN CONTROLS

Table II summarizes the available fans and operational control equipment; generally, with increasing efficiency of either draft equipment or controls, cost increases. Fig. 19 shows the power consumed by the various designs over the full range of capacity.

In comparing the several types, both capital and operating costs must be established over the anticipated load range. The cost of fans, controls, drives, silencers, foundations, switchgear and other auxiliaries, plus any differences in ductwork, have to be obtained for equal specified capacities and sound-pressure levels. Based upon the relative power-consumption curves, the operating hours at the individual load points for the entire life of the unit must be multiplied by the associated power consumptions of the fans being compared. Maintenance costs also must be considered by analyzing available historic data.

FAN SIZE SCALE-UP

Most fan designs are developed using models of moderate size and input power. The performance obtained from the model provides an information base to calculate the performance of larger fans that are geometrically similar to the model. If only the basic fan laws are used to make these conversions, (with no correction for compressibility of air) the larger fan, in many cases, will perform better than predicted, providing that all geometric kinematic, and dynamic similarity requirements are satisfied. Geometric similarity requires not only linear proportionality but also requires complete angular similarity without omission or addition of parts.

The three main performance factors of flow, speed, and head are linked in the concepts of specific speed and specific diameter.

Specific speed is that rpm at which a fan would operate if reduced proportionately in size so that it delivers 1 cfm of air at standard conditions, against a 1″ WG static pressure.

Fig. 19 Comparative fan power consumption versus volumetric flow with various types of control

Specific diameter is the fan diameter required to deliver 1 cfm standard air against a 1" WG static pressure at a given specific speed. From the fan laws we get these equations:

$$\text{Specific speed } (N_s) = \frac{\text{rpm (cfm)}^{1/2}}{(SP)^{3/4}} \quad (5)$$

$$\text{Specific diameter } (D_s) = \frac{D\,(SP)^{1/4}}{(\text{cfm})^{1/2}} \quad (6)$$

Table II. Available Types of Fans and Fan-Control Equipment

Centrifugal Fans
Radial
Radial-tip
Backwardly Inclined Solid
Backwardly Inclined Airfoil

Increasing Efficiency Over Normal Operating Range

Axial Fans
Fixed Pitch
Adjustable Pitch
Variable Pitch

Flow Control
Single-Speed Motor
  Outlet Damper
  Inlet Louver
  Inlet Vane
Two-Speed Motor
Fluid Coupling
Variable-Speed Turbine Drive
Variable-Speed Motors

Increasing Efficiency At Partial-Loads

where flow in cfm is at standard conditions, SP is static pressure (in. of water), and D is the diameter of the fan in inches.

Table III shows the parameters for designing to "specified" pressure and volume.

In the case of axial fans, maximum flow can be achieved by proper selection of the rotating-blade tip diameter, so an increase in tip size results in a shift of the entire fan curve along the flow (horizontal) axis to the right. Maximum pressure can be achieved by selection of the proper hub diameter, so an increase in hub size would result in a shift of the entire fan curve along the pressure (vertical) axis upward. The system-resistance requirements given the fan designer remain the same, so by selecting the proper hub and blade sizes, the fan characteristic can be shifted along the system resistance, so that boiler full-load conditions occur in the area of maximum efficiency. A centrifugal fan's characteristic similarly can be shifted along the system resistance line.

FAN LAWS

How a change in any operating condition affects a fan can be predicted by a set of rules known as the fan laws. These are summarized in the box on the next page and apply to fans of the same geometric shape and operating at the same point on the characteristic curve.[1]

FANS OPERATING IN SERIES

Infrequently it is necessary to install two or more fans in series in the same system. Every fan in series handles the same weight of air or gas, assuming negligible air loss or infiltration between stages.

In theory the combined volume-pressure

Table III. Effect of Fan Parameters on Performance Capabilities

	Axial	Centrifugal
To increase volume:	increase blade tip diameter	increase wheel width
	increase rotational speed	increase rotational speed
To increase pressure:	increase rotor diameter	increase wheel diameter
	increase rotational speed	increase rotational speed
	increase number of stages	

FAN LAWS

1. For a given fan size, system resistance, and air density:

   A—When speed varies,

   (a) Capacity varies directly as the speed ratio.

   (b) Pressure varies as the square of the speed ratio.

   (c) Horsepower varies as the cube of the speed ratio.

   B—When pressure varies,

   (a) Capacity and speed vary as the square root of the pressure.

   (b) Horsepower varies as the 1.5 power of the pressure.

2. For constant pressure:

   When density varies, speed, capacity and horsepower vary inversely as the square root of the density; that is, inversely as the square root of the barometric pressure, and directly as the square root of the absolute temperature.

3. For constant capacity and speed:

   When density of air varies, horsepower and pressure vary directly as the air density; that is, directly as the barometric pressure, and inversely as the absolute temperature.

4. For constant mass flow:

   A—When density of air varies,

   (a) Capacity, speed and pressure vary inversely as the density; that is, inversely as the barometric pressure, and directly as the absolute temperature.

   (b) Horsepower varies inversely as the square of the density; that is, inversely as the square of the barometric pressure, and directly as the square of the absolute temperature.

   B—When both temperature and pressure vary,

   (a) Capacity and speed vary as the square root of (pressure × absolute temperature).

   (b) Horsepower varies as the square root of (cube of the pressure × absolute temperature).

curve of two fans operating in series is obtained by adding the fan pressures at the same volumetric flow. (Fig. 20). In practice there is some reduction in volume due to the increased air density in the later stages. There also can be a significant performance loss from non-uniform flow into the second stage fan.

FANS OPERATING IN PARALLEL

Fans commonly operate in parallel in the same system, particularly when large volumes of air or gas must be moved. The combined volume-pressure curve in this case is obtained by adding the volumetric capacity of each fan at the same pressure (Fig. 21). Each fan handles only part of the volumetric capacity. The total performance of the multiple fans will be less than the theoretical sum if inlets are restricted or the flow into the inlets is not straight.

Some centrifugal fans have a pressure-volume curve with a positive slope to the left of the peak pressure point. If fans operating in parallel are selected in the region of this positive slope, unstable operation can occur. Fig. 21 shows the combined volume-pressure curve of two such fans in parallel. The closed loop to the left of the peak pressure point is the result of plotting all the possible combinations of volume flow at each pressure. If the system curve intersects the combined volume-pressure curve in the area enclosed by the loop, more than one point of operation is possible. This may cause one of the fans to handle more air than the other and could cause a motor overload if the fans are individually driven. This unbalanced flow condition tends to reverse readily and fans will intermittently load and unload, with the possibility of damage to the fans, ductwork or driving motors.[2]

When paralleling two variable-pitch axial-flow fans, care must be taken to keep both units out of the stall region. Since this area generally is not near the boiler resistance line, avoiding a stall situation is relatively easy. With two fans

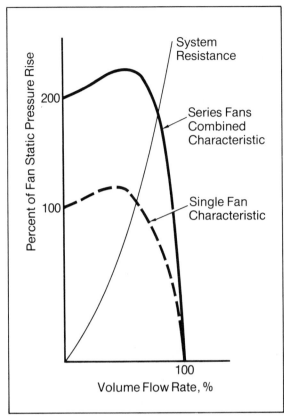

Fig. 20 Typical characteristic curve of two fans operating in series

Fig. 21 **Parallel fan operation**

operating, the resistance line for one fan is influenced by the other fan, as well as by boiler conditions. This means that the two fans together will develop the pressure required to overcome the boiler resistance, but that their volume flow need not be equal.

GAS-FAN EROSION AND CORROSION

Erosion is the loss of fan material through mechanical action of particulate matter in the flue gas impinging on or abrading the fan surfaces during operation.

Corrosion is the loss of material through the reaction of various chemicals in the flue gas coming in contact with the fan.

Erosion is determined not only by tip speed, but also by the properties of the impeller and the particulate matter in the gas. Factors such as ash loading, particle size, composition, den-

sity, hardness, shape, surface texture, velocity and impact angle—as well as impeller material, hardness, and use of wear plates—influence erosion rates.[3,4] Chapter 22 covers the repair of eroded fan blades in detail.

It is significant that fans for induced-draft service have become progressively more efficient as more efficient dust-collection devices have been installed. Airfoil bladed fans could not be used with particulate-collection efficiencies below 95 to 97 percent; axial-flow fans required even higher efficiencies. Now, with dust loadings as low as 0.03 grains/ standard cu ft, the use of more sophisticated equipment is practical. During this same period of development, there had been technical developments on erosion-resistant materials for fan blades, as well as the increased usage of variable speed drivers, which results in further reduction of erosion.

FAN EROSION

The loss of fan wheel material poses two serious threats to fan reliability. First, any change in the rotor mass distribution, especially at the outer extremities, can cause unbalanced forces and high vibrations. Second, a loss of material on highly stressed fan elements such as blades and side plates can cause structural damage and lead to catastrophic failure.

The centrifugal fan designer can consider several alternatives one of which is modifying the fan-blade type and speed. As described earlier, some fan blades are more resistant to erosion than others. Also, the ability of any given fan to resist erosion is proportional to at least the square of the relative velocity of the gas passing the blading. The principal fan wheel areas attacked by erosion are the blades and the center plate. Heaviest erosion occurs in the area where blade and center plate are joined. Erosive wear on these critical parts can be reduced by applying a larger fan running at lower speed which can meet aerodynamic requirements at lower gas velocities.

Another alternative would be to modify the fan inlet conditions where it appears that ductwork design has led to differential erosion of a fan. It is possible for flyash leaving a precipitator to be channeled down a particular leg of a duct and to concentrate in one fan of a multiple-fan installation, or even in one of the inlets of a particular fan. In such cases, erosion is very uneven and the affected areas are subject to rapid deterioration.

As a third alternative, repairable liners can be used to control erosive effects on airfoil fans (Fig. 22). This method consists of designing blades with two layers of material, the outer layer being easily repaired in the field with welding. Periodic inspection is required to determine when repairs are necessary. In addition, airfoil blades can be furnished with extra thick nose pieces.

As a fourth alternative, replaceable liners to bear the brunt of erosive forces can be provided on fan blades. It is essential that, in the design of a fan, the added weight of the liner plates be accounted for in the stress calculations for the structural members such as the blade and side plates, as well as in specifying the moment of inertia of the motor.

Because coatings can affect the physical properties of fan structural material, and cracks in coatings can propagate into critical fan members, tests must be performed using proposed spray coats and actual fan structures before such coatings are used.

FAN CORROSION

The problem of chemical corrosion of fans has to be accounted for in the design and operation of ID and booster fans downstream of wet scrubbers. Although early experience with corrosive gases entering fans was limited to chemical process plants, the use of FGD systems has brought the problem to the utility industry.

Experience has been excellent with fans of standard carbon-steel or low-alloy-steel construction, where the entering flue gas has been properly dehumidified and heated above the temperature of adiabatic saturation (which is about 130°F). On the other hand, "wet" fans handling scrubber effluent gas without reheating to at least 30°F above saturation temperature have undergone severe corrosion. High-alloy metals used to manufacture such rotating

Fig. 22 **Airfoil blades of a centrifugal fan with repairable weld-metal liners**

equipment have proven a very expensive alternative to flue-gas drying and reheating.

ACOUSTICS

Controllable-pitch axial fans exhibit a much different noise characteristic than centrifugal fans for similar duty. As shown in Fig. 23, a controllable-pitch axial-fan noise signature can have more acoustic power in the high frequencies due to the large number of rotor blade/stator blades passages in fan operation. This factor must be considered in the design of any noise suppression devices for the axial fan. Because axial fans have a slightly higher total noise sound-power level than centrifugal fans, more acoustical treatment is sometimes needed Power-plant noise and attenuation are discussed further later in this chapter.

AIR HEATERS

The functions of combustion-air heaters have been described in Chapters 5, 6, and 12. Although justified by the increased efficiency resulting from lower exit-gas temperatures and the higher flame temperature in the boiler furnace, air heaters also make pulverized-coal firing practical by providing the drying and transporting medium.

Two principal types of air heaters are in use: the tubular recuperative type and the regenerative type, typified by the Lungstrom® air preheater. The choice of the size and type of air

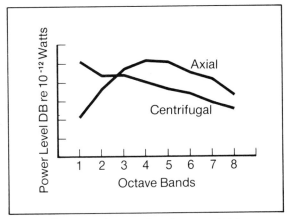

Fig. 23 Fan sound power level comparison

heater depends on economic and engineering factors. The economic factors include the original cost of the air heater, the maintenance costs, the cost of the fuel, and the cost of the fan power resulting from air-heater draft losses. The engineering factors include the air temperature required for combustion and/or pulverized coal drying, as well as unit reliability and installation space requirements.

TUBULAR AIR HEATERS

Fig. 7 in Chapter 8 shows a typical application of a tubular air heater to an industrial boiler. The heater is arranged for vertical gas flow through the tubes. Air flows horizontally across the tubes, usually 2 or 3 inches in diameter and in a staggered relationship for optimum heat transfer. The air passes over all the sections of the air heater in sequence, the effect of which is to provide counterflow heat transfer. Tube sheets at top and bottom support and guide the tubes. Most frequently, the bottom tube sheet or sheets form the structural support; the upper tube sheet is welded to the outside casing; and the tubes pass through slightly oversize holes in the upper sheet which allows for expansion when the equipment is brought up to temperature. Many designs for use with sulfur-bearing fuels have separated cold-end sections, to reduce the cost of tube replacement in the event of excessive corrosion.

In contrast to regenerative designs, tubular or recuperative type air heaters have more severe cold-end corrosion problems. With variations in cleanliness of the tube wall, entering air temperature, and flow intensities on gas and air sides, very low metal temperatures and correspondingly severe corrosion can occur. Although the tube-metal temperature may be considered to be the arithmetic average of the air temperature entering the air heater and the gas temperature leaving, actual field measurements have shown metal temperatures as low as 120°F below the mean of the air and gas temperatures. Such conditions can result in deposits that reduce heat transfer and increase draft loss until they are removed, usually by water washing.[5]

REGENERATIVE AIR HEATERS

The Ljungstrom air preheater transfers sensible heat in the flue gas leaving the boiler to the combustion air, through regenerative heat-transfer surface in a rotor which turns continuously through the gas and air streams at from 1 to 3 rpm (depending on diameter.) The principle is illustrated schematically in Fig. 24.

Fig. 25 illustrates the major components of a large vertical-shaft Ljungstrom air preheater designed for gas flow downward and airflow upward. The rotor, packed with Ljungstrom transfer surface, is supported through a lower bearing at the cold end of the air preheater and guided through a guide-bearing assembly located at the top or hot end of the air preheater.

Depending on its size, the rotor has either 12 or 24 radial members, which are attached to a center post. The rotor compartments are closed with a shell plate as shown in Fig. 25. The rotor sealing system contains simple leaf-type labyrinth seals bolted to the rotor radial members at both the hot and the cold ends. The radial seals compress against radial plates, again located at both the hot and the cold ends of the rotor. To complete the system, axial seals are positioned at the peripheral end of the radial members of the rotor. There are also leaf-type labyrinth seals used with axial sealing plates. This system effectively separates the air stream from the flue-gas stream. Both the radial and axial sealing plates can be adjusted during operation for maximum effectiveness.

The air preheater design can accommodate any steam-generator duct arrangement. The air preheater ducts and heating surface can be positioned for either vertical or horizontal flow. The vertical-shaft air preheater can be arranged for flue-gas flow upward or downward, while the horizontal air preheater can be arranged for gas-over-air or air-over-gas at the option of the plant designer.

The electric motor provides drive action through a speed-reducer pinion gear which engages a pin rack attached to the periphery of the rotor. Pin rack drives are also used on air heaters for both industrial and utility service.

Ljungstrom air heaters are designed with rotor diameters from 7 to 65 feet. The smaller units are completely shop assembled, while the larger utility size units are arranged for convenient field assembly.

Heating Surface Design

The heating surface of a Ljungstrom preheater uses combinations of flat or formed pressed-steel sheets with corrugated, notched or undulated ribbing. When in combination, they form longitudinal passages of the most desirable contour for the predetermined spacing. The surface design and arrangement provides only point contact between adjacent plates. Although the gas and airflow are turbulent, the smooth path for their travel through the rotor offers low resistance. As an approximate rule, one inch in height of standard Ljungstrom heating surface recovers about as much heat as two feet of surface in a tubular heater with equivalent resistance to gas and air flow. The compact arrangement of light metal sheets permits a large amount of effective heating surface to be

---

AIR HEATER TEMPERATURE TERMINOLOGY

Exit-Gas Temperature with Leakage (corrected)—This is the observed or measured exit-gas temperature and includes the dilution effect of leakage through the air-heater seals.

Exit-Gas Temperature No Leakage (uncorrected)—This is the temperature at which the gas would leave the heater if there were no leakage in the heater. This temperature cannot be measured directly, but is arrived at by accounting for the cooling effect of the leakage air by calculation. (See Chapter 6.)

Gas Drop—Temperature of the gas entering heater minus temperature of the gas leaving heater (not including leakage).

Air Rise—Temperature of the air leaving heater minus that of the air entering heater.

Temperature Head—Temperature of the gas entering heater minus air temperature entering heater.

Gas Side Efficiency, percent =
$$\frac{Gas\ Drop}{Temperature\ Head} \times 100$$

Fig. 24 Details of regenerative air preheater, bisector type

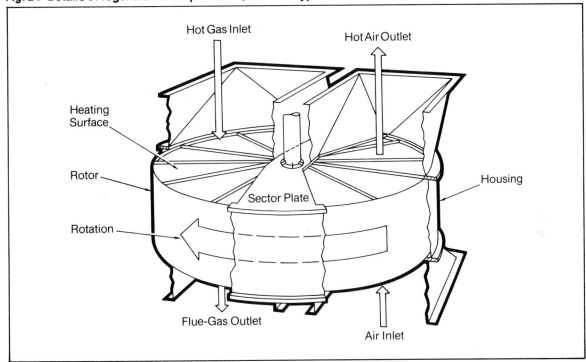

Fig. 25 Ljungstrom regenerative air preheater, bisector design for vertical air and gas flow

---

FACTORS AFFECTING REGENERATIVE AIR-HEATER PERFORMANCE

Entering Air Temperature

A change in entering air temperature will cause the exit-gas temperature to change in the same direction. Changes in entering air temperature result in a change in temperature head which directly affects the drop in gas temperature. For example, if the entering air temperature increases 10°F, the exit-gas temperature will increase by (10 × gas side efficiency) °F.

Entering Gas Temperature

A change in entering gas temperature causes the exit-gas temperature to change in the same direction. Changes in entering gas temperature result in a change in temperature head which directly affects the drop in gas temperature. For example, a 10°F increase in entering gas temperature will cause the exit-gas temperature to increase by 10 × (1 − gas side efficiency) °F.

Gas Weight

An increase in gas weight to the heater will result in a higher exit-gas temperature, while conversely, a lower exit-gas temperature results from a lower gas weight entering the unit.

Pressure Drop Across Air Heater

The air and gas side pressure drops will change approximately in proportion to the square of the air and gas weights through the heater. If excess air is greater than anticipated, the air-heater pressure drop will be greater than expected. A build-up of heating element deposits will result in higher air heater resistances with the consequence of an increase in pressure drop. Pressure drop will also vary directly with the mean absolute temperatures of the fluids passing through the heater as a result of changes in density.

Air Heater Leakage

A change in the temperature of the fluid leaking past the seals will, by reason of density change, have a slight effect on the amount of leakage. Variations in pressure levels between the high and low pressure sides of the heater will, likewise, alter the air heater leakage. An increase in the pressure differential will increase the leakage while a decrease in pressure differential will reduce the leakage. Improper settings of the heater radial and circumferential seals will also result in an increase in leakage.

---

placed in a relatively small rotor. The metal sheets are factory packed in containers.

Normally, the heating surface is divided into two or more layers (Fig. 26). Advantages resulting from layering the surface include

■ the ability to provide a field-removable cold-end section, usually 12″ in height, that can undergo severe corrosive duty and be first reversed in position, and then replaced

■ varying the spaces of surfaces throughout the preheater sections can satisfy different operating demands

■ the sheets in each layer may be of different materials, each to accommodate the temperature and other conditions particular to its zone

Rotor Design Details

The heat-transfer surface and rotor structure are the heart of the Ljungstrom air preheater.

Large rotors have 24 self-supporting compartments extending the full length of the heater axially and fabricated as separate modules; the 15° compartments consist of two side plates connected by a series of circumferential stay plates and grating.

The cut-away of a vertical rotor assembly (Fig. 27), illustrates the simplified field erection possible with this rotor design. The rotor post is placed upon its bearings and the 24 rotor modules are then pinned in place, a technique that eliminates any field welding. With this type of rotor, it is customary to install the basketed heating surface in each individual module. This is done in the manufacturing plant before the unit is shipped.

AIR LEAKAGE

Air may leak into the gas in a Ljungstrom preheater in three ways:

■ leakage into the gas chamber resulting from entrainment in the rotor passages

■ leakage at the periphery of the rotor through the clearance space between the rotor and the housing and then into the gas passage

■ leakage across the radial seals into the gas passage

Fig. 26 Heating surface of Ljungstrom regenerative-type air preheater

To reduce leakage at the periphery of the rotor, a deflectable sector plate is used on the hot end of the larger airheaters.

The deflectable sector plate provides a flexible sealing surface which forms a curved shape approximating the rotor curvature under hot conditions. Acting as a cantilever beam, the sealing surface is attached to a framework at the inboard end of the support beam. The entire assembly rides on a roller at the inboard end to accommodate thermal expansion along the axis of the sector plate. The sealing surface at the outboard end will track the rotor as it goes through boiler load changes. This surface is deflected by means of motor-driven jacks located at the outboard end of the sector plate.

As the greatest pressure differential and the denser air exist at the cold end of the preheater where the gas exits and the air enters, the largest portion of the leakage is at this end, and does not pass through the preheater. Thus the performance as to either heat recovery or draft loss is not measurably affected.

TRISECTOR AIR PREHEATERS

In Chapters 5 and 12, the discussions of the direct-fired pulverized-coal system included the necessity of air heating for coal pulverization. Ordinarily, hot air supplied to the pulverizers furnishes the heat to dry the coal and is used to transport the pulverized fuel to the furnace. This portion of the total air for combustion is called the primary air (Fig. 28).

The trisector air preheater is used on large coal-fired boilers where a cold primary-air fan is desirable. The preheater is designed so that by dividing the air-side of the preheater into two sectors (Fig. 29), the higher pressure primary air and the lower pressure secondary air may be heated by a single air preheater. Some advantages of the trisector over arrangements having separate primary- and secondary-air preheaters include

■ no gas-biasing dampers and controls

■ because average cold-end temperatures can be maintained using only secondary-air preheater coils, the requirement for primary-air steam coils is eliminated

Fig. 27 Ljungstrom modular rotor for large vertical-flow air preheaters

Full Sector Module
Retaining Pin
Tension Fitting
Rotor Post Assembly
Compression Fitting

Stay Plate
Module Shell Plate
Full Sector Side Removal Container
Bolted Flange Assembly

■ fewer sootblowers and water-washing devices are required with one heater in lieu of two

■ even with a large variation in primary airflow, there is relatively little effect on overall heat recovery, because heat not recovered in the primary section will be picked up in the secondary section

The trisector is equipped with an additional radial sealing plate and an axial sealing plate separating the primary and secondary air streams. The trisector heater is readily adaptable to varying coal moisture content. The size of the primary-air opening depends on the coal being fired and its moisture content, with a 35° or 50° primary air opening normally used.

EFFECT OF THERMAL GRADIENTS ON STRUCTURAL DEFORMATION

The transfer of heat from the hotter gas stream to the cooler air stream creates temperature gradients which cause thermal distortions

Hot Secondary Air

Hot Gas

Hot Primary Air

Cooled Gas

Secondary Air
Primary Air

Pulverizers

Fig. 28 Trisector air heater arrangement

Fig. 29 **Ljungstrom trisector air preheater, vertical- shaft arrangement**

- Gas Sector
- Secondary Air Sector
- Primary Air Sector

throughout the structural members. The relative distortion of the various components affects the clearances between the seals and sealing surfaces controlling leakage of air to the gas stream.

With fixed seals and a fixed sealing plate, rotor turndown would make a sizeable opening between the leaf-type radial seal and the sealing plate. To close this opening during operation, the air preheater includes a sealing plate controller which senses the position of the periphery of the rotor during operation and automatically positions the sealing plate to maintain an average clearance of 1/16".

Rotor turndown closes the seal opening between the cold-end radial seals and the cold-end sealing plate. In the same manner, the axial seals maintain minimum clearance during operation with the axial sealing plate. Therefore, all rotor seals are designed to maintain a close running clearance regardless of mode of boiler operation.

ROTARY REGENERATIVE AIR PREHEATER LEAKAGE

Direct leakage is that quantity of air that passes into the gas stream between the radial and circumferential seals and sealing surface

as a result of the static pressure differential between the air and gas streams. The leakage across the sealing system is directly proportional to the square root of the pressure differential but also depends on the air and gas density.

Entrained leakage is that quantity of air contained in the rotor as it passes from the air side to the gas side and from the gas side to the air side. The quantity of entrained leakage depends on the rotor depth, rotor diameter, and rotor speed.

Whether direct or entrained, leakage has no effect on the heat-transfer efficiency of the Ljungstrom air preheater. There is no difference in the heat transferred to the air stream from the gas stream because of leakage, as discussed in Chapter 6. However, the gas temperature leaving the preheater is diluted or decreased by 10°F to 20°F by the mixture of the cooler air with the hotter gas stream.

DESIGNING FOR LOW EXIT GAS TEMPERATURE

While efficiencies can be improved by adding surface to reduce the air heater exit gas temperature, this practice lowers the cold-end metal temperatures and the dew point of the flue gas. Consequently, steel construction materials are subject to corrosion from sulfuric acid as moisture condenses in the presence of sulfur in the gas.

The rate of acid condensation depends on the sulfur content of the fuel, firing procedures, excess air, and the presence of moisture. The acid dew point varies with the concentration of sulfur trioxide in the flue gas. High-sulfur coals result in the existence of a dew point at a higher temperature, thus exposing more of the air-heater surface to corrosion and fouling.

Typical acid dew points for coal are between 280° and 320°F. For coal firing, fouling potential increases as the temperature decreases. Water condensation causes a marked increase in dew-point meter response at 140°F or below. This does not necessarily mean as severe corrosion in the water dew-point range, as compared to the acid condensation range, although rapid fouling would likely take place at the water dew point. With low-sulfur coal, the corrosion and fouling potential is low and restricted to the extreme cold end of the air preheater.

A number of means have been developed to minimize the rate of corrosion, as well as provision for replacement or corroded surface. Because corrosion occurs on the lowest temperature surface, air-heater designs have been developed which incorporate replaceable cold-end sections. Other means to minimize corrosion are aimed at increasing the metal temperature. One such arrangement directs a portion of the preheated air to the inlet of the forced-draft fan and recirculates it through the air heater. Thus, the temperature of air leaving the fan and entering the air heater is increased, correspondingly increasing the cold-end metal temperature.

Air bypass around the air heater is used to a limited extent. With reduced airflow, metal temperatures within the air heater are higher because of the influence of the higher gas-to-air ratio. Also, because the overall recovery is less as a result of the reduced airflow, gas outlet temperature rises, causing a rise in the cold-end metal temperature.

The prevalent means of increasing cold-end metal temperature, discussed in detail in Chap-

ter 6, is the use of steam air heaters located in the cold-air duct between the FD fan and the air heater. These increase the temperature of the air entering the heater, correspondingly causing an increase in the metal temperature. Steam bled from the turbine is used as the heating medium in the steam air heater. In supplying heat to the cold air, steam is condensed and the condensate returned to the appropriate stage of the feedwater bleed heating system.

To assist specifiers and operators in arriving at reasonable cold-end temperatures, average cold-end temperature (ACET) guides are published. These guides take into account the variables of fuel type, sulfur content, and the effect of excess air. A guide for coal firing was presented as Fig. 4 in Chapter 6.

CLEANING AIR HEATER HEAT-TRANSFER SURFACES

Cold-end deposition occurs when boiler flue gases reach the condensation temperature. The flyash in the flue gas can combine with moisture and sulfur derivatives to form a fine-grained deposit or scale on the cold-end heating surface. Sootblowing can remove and control regenerative air-heater cold-end deposits provided those deposits are not subjected to moisture.

Moisture can be introduced as drainage from water-cooled gas analysis probes, economizer and boiler tube leaks, and unprotected FD fan inlets through which rain can enter the air heater. Leaking steam-sootblower and water-washing shutoff valves add to the problem. But the most frequent source of external moisture is the sootblowing steam. Moisture in this blowing medium can be eliminated by selecting a steam source with controlled pressure and temperature to provide dry steam to the sootblowers at all times.

Air-heater element fouling also can result from the carryover of material from the economizer and the subsequent lodging of the larger particles in the heating surface, particularly at the air-heater hot end.

Regenerative air preheater fouling can be limited by controlling the cold-end temperature level and by the use of proper maintenance procedures and cleaning equipment. The primary requisites for this purpose are sootblowing and washing equipment, a dry blowing medium, an adequate water supply, and a good drainage system.

SOOTBLOWING

Three types of sootblowing equipment are presently furnished and installed on air preheaters. Power-driven sootblowers which have nozzles mounted on a swinging arm are used extensively, while a stationary multi-nozzle type is used occasionally on package air preheaters (Fig. 30). On air preheaters above 32 ft. in diameter, retractable sootblowers are installed as standard equipment.

Fig. 31 illustrates a large power-driven device, supplied as either a single- or twin-nozzle soot-blower. The nozzle arm, which moves slowly over the face of the heating surface, is controlled by a gear-driven mechanism powered by an electric motor through a speed reducer. The blowing cycle consists of one pass across the heating surface, either from the rotor periphery to the rotor post or from the post to the periphery.

Retractable blowers of the same type as used in boiler convection passes (see the next section of this chapter) are installed on large-diameter air preheaters. These, as well as the other types described, are generally located at the cold end where deposition usually occurs. The equipment is most often located at the gas-outlet side to eliminate flyash from being carried into the windboxes. They are installed either as an integral part of the air-preheater duct or in the gas-outlet ductwork immediately adjacent to the unit.

SOOTBLOWING MEDIA

Superheated steam (approximately 300°F superheat) or dry compressed air is the recommended cleaning medium. Although saturated steam, which contains some moisture, has been used occasionally, superheated steam has been found to be more effective for sootblowing.

Although compressed air is considered to be

Fig. 30 Stationary multinozzle sootblower for package-type air preheaters

the premium cleaning medium, its merits do not stem from an inherent cleaning ability, but from the moisture deficiency as compared with steam. In fact, under dry discharge conditions, the kinetic energy of a steam jet at 200 psia is approximately twice that of air at the same blowing pressure. So a steam source must be selected to have pressure-temperature conditions which, by proper control measures, may be used to provide dry steam to the air-preheater sootblower. If a steam source is of undesirable quality, unwanted moisture will be introduced to the air-heater surface.

The steam blowing pressure should be 200 to 250 psig. When using air, care should be taken to install a proper line of traps and separators to remove moisture from the blowing medium. Pressure at 180 psi is recommended.

A steam-sootblowing piping system should include an automatic drain valve, thermocouple, and an automatic admission valve to the blowers. The automatic drain valve is open to free drain discharge until the temperature-sensing thermocouple indicates steam of adequate quality.

WATER WASHING

In cases where sootblowing cannot readily remove residual deposits, it sometimes becomes necessary to water wash the heating surface to maintain acceptable draft losses through the air preheater. In some instances this may be required more frequently than during the scheduled boiler outages.

Most deposits forming on the air-preheater heat-transfer surface are highly soluble in water and, therefore, are easily removed by washing with a sufficient quantity of water. A high-penetration, stationary multi-nozzle device is the standard washing apparatus and is available for all air-preheater types and sizes.

Adequate drainage is necessary before planning to wash an air heater. Washing can be on either the air or gas side, depending upon which has best drainage.

Out-of-service washing is simply washing the preheater in a cold state during periods when the boiler has been shut down. During shutdown is the best time to control the washing operation and to make a thorough inspection of the heating surface, both during and after washing. The rotor can be turned at normal speeds. If it is necessary to restrict the discharge of water to one side of the air heater, however, an auxiliary drive will be required to reduce rotor speed. Surfaces should be exam-

Fig. 31 **Large power-driven air preheater sootblower. Nozzle arm swings in an arc across the face of the heat-transfer surface.**

ined frequently during the washing process. After the deposits are removed, the unit should be allowed to dry completely before being returned to service.

In-service isolated washing consists of reducing boiler load and isolating one preheater by means of dampers while the boiler remains on the line by using the other preheaters and fans. After the isolated air preheater is completely washed, the procedure is reversed allowing all the gas and air to flow through the clean preheater while another unit is isolated and washed in the same manner. The isolated method of washing air preheaters has been found to produce excellent results both from the standpoint of cleanliness and time.

Normally, about ⅔ boiler load can be maintained during isolation of one preheater for washing. Fig. 32 shows the arrangement for the isolated washing procedure. The rotor speed is

controlled in a manner similar to that used for out-of-service operation.

On-stream in-service washing is carried out while allowing gas and air to pass through the preheaters. This is only feasible where drains are located to eliminate the moisture entering the dust collectors, precipitators, windboxes, and boiler. The preferred location for operation is in the air side, especially with an electrostatic precipitator. On-stream washing should not be done when gas passes are plugged.

The speed of the air-preheater rotor should be reduced to 1/15 rpm by means of an auxiliary drive unit before admitting water to the washing devices. The slow speed permits the wash water to drain from the rotor and heating surface before the wash water enters the other stream. To insure coverage of all heating surface, the washing cycle must consist of at least one revolution of the air-preheater rotor.

Fig. 32 **Arrangement for in-service air-preheater washing with one preheater isolated**

An intermediate-pressure, high-volume wash is sometimes necessary to remove particles of insoluble material that are carried from the boiler by the gas stream, the larger ones becoming wedged in the flow passages of the hot-end heating surface. These obstructed passages then fill up with flyash, which restricts flow. This type of deposit accumulation is difficult to remove with the usual washing equipment. Special equipment using a high-energy jet has been developed for this purpose. The procedure is similar to that followed in a regular out-of-service washing using standard washing devices. Water nozzles are moved radially across the surface, allowing sufficient time for the rotor to complete at least one revolution between each movement of the nozzle of the sootblowers.

BOILER SOOTBLOWER

One of the most important boiler auxiliary operations is the on-line fireside cleaning of heat-absorbing surfaces. Not only is it important for proper heat transfer, but also to prevent sections of the boiler from becoming severely plugged. Plugged sections can restrict gas flow and cause load limitation. Tube erosion due to high local velocities also can occur.

Sootblowing systems are required on coal and oil fired furnaces. Natural gas is a clean-burning fuel with a very small percentage of entrained dust and therefore does not require sootblowers. Oil has a low ash content which produces a thin water-soluble deposit on the furnace walls that is normally removed by annual water washing. Furnace-wall sootblowers are, therefore, not required on oil-fired units. In the superheater and reheater sections of an oil-fired unit, ash deposits do accumulate on the tubing surface. This is especially true of high-vanadium oils where fuel oil additives are used to combat high-temperature corrosion. But in doing so, ash deposits in the high-gas-temperature areas increase markedly. Ordinarily quite friable, such deposits are easily removed with sootblowers.

Of the major fossil fuels, coal alone requires large complements of permanently installed sootblowing equipment. Coals and the ash resulting from combustion vary widely throughout the world, and even from region to region of most countries; thus, depending on certain properties, boilers burning varying fuels require different sootblowing systems. In the boiler furnace, the concentration of wall blowers depends upon such factors as the ash-fusion temperatures. The lower these temperatures are, the more likely the ash will adhere to the furnace walls and accumulate. The percentage of ash in the coal is another factor in the design of the furnace wall-blower system, with higher-ash coals requiring greater and more concentrated coverage.

FURNACE-WALL SOOTBLOWERS

A short single-nozzle retractable blower, called a wall blower, removes the ash deposited on the walls of furnace chambers (Fig. 33). It is a short-stroke lance which penetrates the furnace wall one to two inches. Supported by wall boxes welded to the furnace tubes, it moves down and up with the tubes as they heat and cool. The single nozzle at the tip directs a supersonic high-energy jet of superheated steam or air tangent to the furnace face of the water-wall tubes, dislodging the slag deposits. The lance rotates through 360° and cleans approximately a five-foot radius; the effective radius depends upon how tenacious the deposit is. Some coals with difficult-to-remove slag require wall-blower spacing to be closer; the maximum cleaning radius may be only 3 to 4 ft. Blowing frequency depends on the rate of slag build-up, but frequencies in the 4- to 8-hour range are common. Fig. 34 shows a large pulverized-coal-fired unit with typical wall-blower coverage.

CONVECTION-SURFACE SOOTBLOWERS

Superheater, reheater, and economizer sections are cleaned with long, fully retractable lances which penetrate the cavities between major heat-absorbing sections. Industrial and marine boilers use nonretractable blowers with multiple nozzles, which rotate, allowing each nozzle to clean a tube row.

Fig. 33 Typical retractable furnace-wall sootblower

The long retractable type sootblower is the most effective way to clean radiant and convective heating surface. It normally uses two 180°, opposed cleaning nozzles at the tip which emit a high-energy jet of superheated steam or compressed air perpendicular to the lance. While the lance traverses the boiler, it rotates, forming a helical blowing pattern (Fig. 35) which effectively cleans the tubes and spaces between tubes in a superheater, reheater, or economizer bank. In widely spaced platenized sections, these nozzles are angled slightly, leading and lagging the perpendicular to gain more dwell time on the tube surface. The effective range of retracts depends upon the gas temperature in the area to be cleaned and the ash characteristics of the particular fuel being fired. Therefore, the maximum effective cleaning radius varies from 4 to 9 feet. It is difficult to relate cleaning radius to blowing pressures because of various nozzle combinations. Blowing pressures depend not only on supplying a flow for cleaning but, in high-temperature zones, supplying an even greater flow for cooling.

Fig. 36 shows a retractable blower on one side of a large utility boiler; this blower penetrates half the width of a 90-ft wide boiler. The blower typically uses a two-point support which allows for boiler expansion. A wall box welded to the tubes supports the front of the lance; the platform structure supports the rear.

SOOTBLOWER OPERATION

The type of deposits in the radiant and convection sections of the boiler can vary from very hard tenacious slag to a dry powdery coating. The most important coal properties affecting the severity and rate of ash build-up are ash softening and fluid temperatures, percent ash in the coal, and the percent sodium in the coal ash. Coals with high percentages of ash, low ash-fusion temperatures, and high percentages of sodium in the ash are the most difficult to keep clean. The blowing sequence and frequency of the retract system must be adjusted during initial operation by starting with an assumed sequence of blowing and a frequency of, say, one complete cycle per 8-hour shift. After observing fouling patterns either through observation doors (on line), or by gas-side inspections during shutdowns, the operator can modify the blowing pattern to that which best suits the boiler for the coal being fired. It is common for certain retracts to be blown more frequently than others, either singly or in groups. Once the pattern is established, it can be programmed in the sootblower system and run automatically. Fig. 34 also shows typical retractable sootblower locations.

The air preheaters are also cleaned by soot-blowing as described in the previous section on air preheaters. The ash at this point in the system is usually dry and the particles small enough to pass through air preheater elements.

Fig. 34 Typical coal-fired unit showing furnace-wall and long retractable sootblower locations

BLOWING MEDIA

The two blowing media are steam and compressed air, with both being equally effective in deposit removal. The utility normally makes the choice based on plant economics. In the case of air, large compressors must be installed with an integrated piping system around the boiler. Steam systems are usually supplied from the boiler through a pressure-reduction station so that, after pressure reduction, a dry superheated steam is available at the soot-blower nozzle. Steam has the advantage of availability whenever the boiler is in operation. With air, there is always the possibility that the blowing medium will be lost if the compressor is out of service.

Water as a medium is not generally recommended for sootblowing and is considered as a last resort for particularly troublesome slag deposits. Thermal shock from water may reduce tube life due to cyclic fatigue.

FURNACE TEMPERATURE PROBES

Fig. 37 illustrates a typical retractable furnace probe for monitoring gas temperatures at the top of a furnace. The probe is inserted during the lighting-off period and remains in the furnace until reheater steam flow has been established. Its design is based on that of the long retractable sootblower, but without the rotating feature. It traverses back and forth across the

Fig. 35 Retractable sootblower cleaning pattern

Fig. 36 Long retractable sootblower for cleaning convection surface of a 750-MW steam generator

Fig. 37 Retractable probe for measuring furnace gas temperature

furnace or convection pass as it's driven by a single electric motor.

As a probe senses temperatures, it also transmits its position. A thermocouple mounted on the end of the lance measures gas temperatures. The standard thermocouple is suitable for temperatures to 1850°F.

For lance extensions below 16 ft and gas temperatures of 1200°F or lower, there is no need for cooling the lance. Automatic retraction from the recorder alarm protects the lance at excessive temperatures. When air cooling is required, the lance is supplied with an inner lining for optimum cooling.

Introduced into the traveling carriage, the cooling air passes through a small annular space between the lance wall and the inner liner. It then is discharged from a nozzle into the furnace. Mounted back from the end of the lance, the nozzle is slanted away from the thermocouple, so that discharged air will have no effect on the temperature readings.

SOOTBLOWER CONTROL SYSTEMS

The mode of sootblower operation depends upon the size and capacity of the boiler unit and the number of blowers installed. Small industrial boilers using few sootblowers cannot economically justify the use of automatic control systems; manually operated blowers are used. On the other hand, large industrial and central-station boilers can justify various degrees of automatic control.

The sootblower control systems of the early 1960's basically required the blowing of each sootblower, one blower at a time, in some predetermined operating sequence. Each blowing cycle was started manually by the operator or automatically by a 24-hr clock. Therefore, only a simple sequencing device was required to start each blower.

In the later 1960's and early 1970's, transistorized logic elements, hardwired into unique control circuits, replaced these electromechanical sequencing systems. Essentially, the control was still a sequencing system, but additional functions were added as necessitated by the increased boiler cleaning requirements.

The control systems were limited only by the ability of their logic to perform the more complex operations and still retain an economic, relatively small package designed for high reliability. Because of the greater number of sootblowers in the typical system, it became necessary to operate several types of sootblowers simultaneously. Common systems operated the furnace wallblowers together with the superheater and reheater blowers. In addition to operating the wallblowers and retractables simultaneously, multiple blowing of each type of sootblower was also incorporated into the control system. It would be impossible otherwise to operate the sootblowers often enough, to maintain essential boiler cleanliness.

In systems with over 200 sootblowers, programmable controllers frequently are installed so that proper automatic sequential operation of the system can be accomplished after ash-deposition patterns are established under operating conditions. With properly programmed blowing sequence, ash deposits on the furnace walls are minimal and the combustion gases are cooled to the required temperature before entering the convection pass.

Sootblower control panels are now designed for easy modification of the automatic sequential operation. This gives the operator maximum flexibility to maintaining the cleanliness of a unit. Essential parameters for such a sootblower control package include

■ equipment to automatically start each sootblower in the system

■ a method to cancel the operation of any sootblower in the system

■ a way to determine easily which sootblowers have been selected to operate, and their programmed operating sequence

■ the complete capability to monitor and display the operation of each sootblower

■ the capability to monitor all the essentials of the sootblowing system and prevent continued sootblower operation if the system is not functioning properly and abort the operation of any sootblower if a malfunction occurs

■ a method to select and alter various blowing

routines as required by the boiler cleaning·
requirements

■ the ability to operate all of the sootblowers simultaneously

■ a means of manually overriding the automatic routines

Ideally, a sootblower control system would respond automatically to conditions of load, temperature, pressure and fuel to provide for the most efficient boiler operation. However, because of the number of input variables and the questionable validity of signals and the complexity of process manipulation, this has not been technically feasible to date. Sequential control with the boiler operator as the decision maker has been used for the majority of sootblower systems. With the advent of more complex blowing operations, the hard-wired solid-state logic systems have taken over some of the decision making. It is extremely beneficial to minimize operator attention and still operate the sootblowers efficiently. Effective performance of any soot-blowing control system depends on its ability to make complex decisions with a minimum of operator input.

BOILER-WATER CIRCULATING PUMPS

Boiler circulation pumps are an integral part of the furnace-wall circulation system on the Controlled Circulation® and Combined Circulation® units. By using pumps in the circulation flow path, the total quantity of water circulated can be apportioned and distributed throughout the furnace heat-absorbing surfaces to suit all the conditions of operation. Boiler circulation pumps also give the operator the capability of insuring positive circulation for a wide variety of pre-operational procedures and off full-load plant cycling conditions.

Most boiler circulation pumps have certain basic similarities. All are vertical, single-stage, centrifugal type with overhung impeller and are designed for constant-speed operation without throttling. The hydraulic end consists

of a single vertical suction and either single or double horizontal discharge (Fig. 38).

The pump case and associated isolation valves are entirely supported by the boiler circulation-system piping, which permits unrestricted expansion movement during boiler start-up and shutdown. Butt-weld joints between pump nozzles, valves, and piping are designed to withstand the combined moments and forces resulting from dead weight loads and differential boiler expansion. Only the connections for auxiliary station services of seal water, cooling water, and electric power supply must be flexible to accommodate pump expansion movements. The pump drives share the basic electrical characteristics of low starting torque, induction squirrel-cage motors, designed for full-voltage across-the-line starting.

Fig. 38 Vertical single-stage centrifugal pump for boiler-water circulation

DESCRIPTION
OF BOILER CIRCULATION PUMPS

Pumping water at or near saturated temperature and at high pressure requires pumps of special design because of the possibility that shaft seal leakage water may flash rapidly into steam. For this service, three types of boiler circulating pumps have been used. The zero-leakage pump is driven by a wet motor, cooled and lubricated by recirculated water at system pressure. The stator windings are immersed in the high-pressure water. This unit is also known as a glandless submerged motor pump.

The second type employs a canned motor housed within a pressure vessel common to the pump itself. It too is a glandless or zero-leakage type of pump. The third type employs a conventional motor drive. Shaft sealing is accomplished by a stuffing box with packing or a shaft mechanical seal, supplemented by an injection sealing-water arrangement.

ZERO-LEAKAGE
BOILER-WATER PUMPS

Controlled Circulation boilers of the type described in Chapter 7 are designed with glandless pumps in which the electric motor and the pump are enclosed in a common pressure casing (glandless meaning that there are no stuffing boxes or mechanical seals around the pump shaft). These zero-leakage pumps are of two main types: those with stator enclosures, but with the rotor immersed in water (known as dry stator or "canned" pumps) and those in which water at system pressure is circulated through the stator windings (known as wet stator or "submerged motor" pumps). In both designs, the high-pressure water in the motor is recirculated through an external heat exchanger and then through the rotor gap and acts as a lubricant for both thrust and journal bearings, and as a cooling medium for removing the heat generated by the motor losses.

SUBMERGED MOTOR RECIRCULATING PUMPS

The motors of these pumps are wound with waterproof insulated cable. The motor power is supplied through pressure-tight cable inlets. As shown in Fig. 39, the internal high-pressure water content is circulated through an external heat exchanger to keep the motor cool and provide bearing lubrication. Circulation is accomplished by an auxiliary impeller, integral with the thrust disc and located at the base of the motor. The design also includes a thermal barrier for minimizing the flow of heat from the pump to the motor. Provision is made for controlling the temperature within the submerged motor by

- restriction of conduction and convection between pump and motor by reduced cross-sectional areas, and by mounting the pump above the motor

- heat exchange through a closed-circuit pipe system and external heat exchanger

The electrical leads exit the motor casing through pressure-tight sealed glands to an external terminal box at atmospheric pressure. The main supply cable is connected to the motor phases inside this terminal box.

The entire pumping element—the drive motor, pump shaft, thermal barrier and overhung impeller—can be installed or removed from the pump casing without disturbing the casing or its piping connections.

The pump shown in Fig. 40 is of the diffuser type with a spherical casing. The materials and construction of the pressure-retaining parts— pump casing, heat barrier, forged motor case, and all bolted flanges—are in accordance with *ASME* Section I requirements.

The motor shaft of this pump is fitted with two chromium-plated chrome-steel sleeves running in water-lubricated journal bearings. A double-acting Kingsbury-type thrust bearing locates the rotor assembly axially and takes up any residual thrust. Both the radial journal bearings and the axial thrust bearings are self-adjusting, thus ensuring equal bearing loads.

CANNED-MOTOR PUMP

The canned-motor, boiler-circulating pump is a zero-leakage pump designed to circulate boiler water at high temperature and high pressure. No shaft seals are required. The motor and pump components are designed as an integral pressurized unit, sealed by a gasket and studs.

The impeller is rotated by an AC polyphase, squirrel-cage induction motor. The spaces between the stator and rotor and around the bearings are filled with the cooled system water. A heat barrier between the pump and motor limits the conduction of heat from the high-pressure hot water being pumped, to the high-pressure internal motor water. The dry stator winding is completely isolated from the high-pressure water by a corrosion-resistant "can" lining the stator bore.

The stator assembly consists of the bearing assemblies, the stack of laminated steel punch-

Fig. 39 **Schematic of a typical glandless wet-motor boiler-water circulating pump**

ings, the three-phase insulated copper winding, the outer pressure shell, and stator can. The rotor assembly contains a shaft, squirrel-cage type rotor body, auxiliary impeller, rotor journals, and thrust runner. The main impeller is mounted on the rotor shaft extension. Secured to the lower end of the shaft, the thrust runner carries the weight of the rotor assembly and absorbs the axial hydraulic thrust. The pump motor with its integral pump shaft and impeller can be withdrawn from the pump casing without disturbing the casing or its piping.

In operation, high-pressure cooling water in the motor cavity is circulated by the auxiliary impeller mounted on the rotor shaft. This water is circulated from the auxiliary impeller up through the gap between the rotor and stator, through the upper guide bearing, out to the external heat exchanger, back into the motor

Fig. 40 Single discharge spherical-type C-E/KSB pump for supercritical-pressure steam generator. Pump casing design pressure is 4500 psig.

through the piping connections to the auxiliary impeller suction in the hollow shaft end. Some of the auxiliary impeller discharge is circulated down through the lower guide bearing and the thrust bearing and then back to the auxiliary impeller suction.

Low-pressure cooling water is circulated through the external heat exchanger. When the pump is idle, but pressurized with high-temperature boiler water in the pump casing, conducted heat is removed by motor-fluid convection flow through the heat exchanger.

INJECTION-SEAL PUMP DESIGN

This controlled-leakage boiler-water circulating pump is mounted vertically with a rigid shaft designed to carry its own thrust. No thrust load is transmitted to the motor, which is entirely supported by the pump. The internal pump materials are selected to accommodate expansion encountered at high temperatures, and to provide corrosion resistance.

Essentially, the pump contains the following main components: casing, stuffing box, pressure breakdown assembly, bearing assemblies and pump shaft with impeller. The pump casing is supported by the suction and discharge piping to which the casing nozzles are welded. A direct-drive coupling connects the pump motor to the pump shaft. The vertical induction motor is of open drip-proof construction for indoor installation, or a weather-protected type for outdoor installation.

The suction pressure and temperature at the pump are virtually the same as the boiler operating conditions. The injection seal reduces the pressure and temperature at the stuffing box packing by injecting cool water at high-pressure into the annulus formed by the shaft running clearance. The injection water serves as a thermal barrier against conducted heat and as a means of keeping the boiler water from entering the close clearances of the throttling sleeve and floating seals. The floating seals and the packing control the leakage at the stuffing box. The injection water, free and clear of foreign particles, can be supplied from the discharge of the boiler feed pump or any other source that can supply a pressure differential of 50 to 100 psi over the discharge of the boiler circulating-water pump. A supplementary booster pump of limited capacity is provided with a takeoff point from the boiler feed-pump discharge to supply the additional pressure necessary for sealing the boiler circulating pump. The booster injection pump has a bypass system for operation at partial loads.

OTHER AUXILIARY EQUIPMENT

Although this chapter has discussed fans, air heaters, sootblowers, and boiler-water circulating pumps, it has only scratched the surface as far as the multiplicity of ancillary equipment involved in a large steam-generator installation. For instance, there are hundreds of pumps in a power plant in addition to the boiler-water pumps. Two others are sometimes found in the scope of supply of the boiler manufacturer: the feedwater pump and the fuel-oil pump. Some considerations in the specification of feedwater pumps are of direct interest.

FEEDWATER-PUMP DESIGN

If the feedwater pump is a constant-speed pump, driven either by a separate motor or from the main turbine shaft, it will produce about the right pressure at full load but a very high pressure at low load. This means extra duty for the feedwater regulator which is sometimes furnished by the boiler manufacturer. Adequate pressure will be available for superheater desuperheaters, but spray valves in the steam temperature control system are affected.

If the feedwater pump is motor driven with a variable speed device, outlet pressure will match boiler system resistance and feedwater regulators may or may not be used. If they are not used, superheater spray water pressure is low at low loads, and this must be considered in the design of spray control valves. Also, if feedwater regulators are not used, and boiler circulating pumps are of the type requiring injection water at shaft seals, there may not be enough pressure at low loads for this purpose, and it may be necessary to add one or more booster pumps in the injection water lines.

If feedwater pumps are variable speed using a separate turbine drive, the steam is taken from one of the bleed points on the main turbine at or above the point of reheat return. This reduces the quantity of steam in the reheater and affects the design of the reheater.

BOILER-RELATED VALVES

Hundreds of valves for high-pressure steam, water, compressed-air and oil duty are part of the scope of most boiler contracts. The *ASME* Boiler and Pressure Vessel Code and *ANSI* Code B31.1 for power-plant piping govern the design and application of most of the valves.

Because boiler valves experience extremes of temperature and pressure as well as widely varying conditions of operation, the valve manufacturer must give close attention to the materials of construction. For valve parts these may range from low-carbon steel through the low and medium chrome alloys to stainless steel, in both castings and forgings.

Safety valves are regulated by the *ASME* Code. For boilers operating below the critical pressure, superheater safety valves are customarily set to pop before boiler safety valves. This assures maximum possible flow through the superheater, thus protecting the tubes.

Feedwater valves contain stop and check valves near the economizer inlet. Ordinarily these valves are wide open. Blowoff valves are located at low points in the boiler, such as the lower waterwall supply header, for rapid removal of sludge collected at these points. Continuous blowdown and chemical feed valves serve to limit and control concentration of impurities in the water in the main steam drum. Sampling valves provide a continuous record of steam and water purity.

On Controlled Circulation boilers there is a large motor-operated gate valve at the inlet of each boiler circulation pump, with an optional valve at the outlet.

Boilers operating at supercritical pressures involve special considerations that differ from *ASME* Boiler and Pressure Vessel Code requirements for subcritical-pressure boilers.

POWER-PLANT NOISE

This final section discusses the problem of noise and its suppression in a large pulverized-coal fired power plant. Generally, the motors, and the rotating equipment they drive, are the source of most noise.

Noise is unwanted sound with a severity that varies with space and time. For example, it is worse at night when the masking effect of background sounds is reduced.

The human ear is more sensitive to high than to low-pitched sounds. Because of this, high frequency noise is normally the greatest offender, particularly if it contains a pure note.

An essential feature of the human sense of hearing is that to perceive a just noticeable difference in volume requires a discrete change of about 10 percent in the subjective noise level on the decibel (dB) scale. Therefore, worthwhile reductions in noise levels should probably involve 5- to 10-fold decreases.

PHYSICAL LEVEL SCALES OF NOISE

The human ear is a frequency meter, a sound analyzer, and an intensity meter. Conveniently, we describe our sensations, sometimes in physical, sometimes in psycho-physical terms, but neither provides terminologies that alone seem suitable for classifying all sounds.

Physically, a pure note is a single harmonic wave. Sound is produced by adding together several, but not too many, pure notes. Too many produce noise. The human ear, to some degree, can separate sound into pure notes, but apparently only if the frequencies involved are well separated. The intensity of specific frequencies then becomes important.

The quantity usually measured in acoustics is the RMS—root-mean-square *sound pressure* (P). The weakest sound pressure perceptible to the average human ear is very small, about 0.0002 microbar. In comparison, the greatest sound pressure perceived without pain is about 1000 microbars. The human sense of hearing covers a wide dynamic range.

The human ear responds to changes in sound pressures, but it is the ratio rather than the absolute difference between two intensities or two frequencies that produces the distinct subjective sensation. In noise measurement, it is practical, therefore, to adopt a relative scale of sound pressure, such as the decibel (dB) scale. The decibel is defined as 10 times the logarithm to the base 10 of the ratio between two quantities of power. (The factor 10 converts bels to decibels.) Thus, as sound power is related to sound pressure squared, the common scale for noise measurement becomes:

Sound Pressure Level (SPL) =

$$10 \log_{10} \frac{P^2}{P_o^2} (dB) = 20 \log_{10} \frac{P}{P_o} (dB)$$

$$(7)$$

where P is the actual pressure measured and P_o some reference value, conventionally the threshold of human hearing (0.0002 microbar or 20 micropascals). The use of this equation reduces the range of sound pressures to 0 to 120 dB, 0 dB indicating the reference value and 120 dB an approximate "maximum" level for pain-free stimuli (during short exposures).

NOISE CRITERIA

The dB term, unfortunately, is also used to designate levels of sound power, sound intensity, and in ratings simulating human response such as the *A, B,* and *C "weightings"* and the *Noise Criteria Curves.* To avoid confusion, reference values should never be omitted.

Some common sound levels are listed in Table IV. Most daily activities take place within ¼ of the scale, from 50 to 85 dB. This covers any sensation between pleasantly quiet and annoyingly noisy. A noise attenuation of a few dB will be most pronounced within this narrow range. At the top and the bottom of the scale, as much as 10 or 15 dB attenuation (*i.e.,* 10% of full-scale) is hardly noticeable.

LOUDNESS AND NOISE NUISANCE

There is no simple relationship between the physical measurement of a sound pressure level and the human perception of sound. In Fig. 41, each curve represents one of constant

Table IV. Typical Sound Pressures and Sound Pressure Levels

P (μ bar)	SPL (dB ref. 0.0002 μ bar)	Source (long time average)	Distance (ft)
2,000	140	Threshold of pain	
	130	Pneumatic clipper	6
200	120	Threshold of discomfort	
	110	Automobile horn	20
20	100	New York subway train	Inside
	90	Motor bus	Inside
2	80	Traffic on street corner	
	70	Conversational speech	3
0.2	60	Typical business office	Inside
	50	Quiet residence	Inside
0.02	40	Library	Inside
	30	Whisper	5
0.002	20		
	10		
0.0002	0	Threshold of hearing	

Fig. 41 Normal equal loudness contours for pure tones

subjective loudness equal to the physical dB level at a standard noise frequency of 1000 Hz. These "equal loudness contours" are an international standard. Sound-level meters are made with electronic filters which can integrate sound energy in such a way that the filter characteristics (Fig. 42) reflect the subjective response of human hearing. The ensuing noise level (measured in decibels on the A-scale, dBA) is then a good measure of the subjective loudness of the sound provided there are no discrete tones.

Prolonged exposure to noise results in a temporary threshold shift, TTS. It has been suggested that 12 dB TTS (P_o-0.0002 microbar) should be the maximum permissible short-

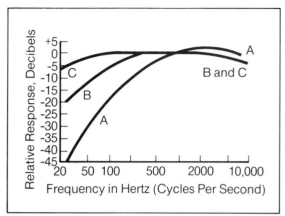

Fig. 42 The standard weighting curve for sound level meters

term noise exposure for given noise ratings (N) as a function of TTS at 2000 Hz. For example, exposure to noise rating N-90 should not exceed 2 hours. If the subject becomes exposed for any longer periods, hearing-conservation aids should be provided.

NOISE MEASUREMENT

Most sound-level meters are now equipped with frequency weighting networks to determine overall sound pressure levels at a certain location. However, for abatement purposes, more thorough investigations are often required. Therefore, the next step is to make a frequency analysis of the noise. Usually, the instruments are provided with filters that divide the noise spectrum into 8 to 10 electronically-controlled, well-separated bands. The frequency analysis is then simplified to discrete dB measurements for each band.

In noise studies, the position of observation with respect to the source is of utmost importance, and so is a detailed knowledge of the surroundings. The effects of reflections from wall surfaces and the contribution of the other sources must be known. In fact, to do a noise study properly, one should operate in a free field and, in a standardized way, locate the observation points around the source to account for sound directivity. As measurements usually cannot be made under these conditions, it is extremely important, from the point of view

of noise guarantees on equipment, to stipulate not only the noise spectrum, but the exact location at which it applies. Specifying distance from casing or center of the noise source is generally inadequate, as the sound spectrum invariably changes around the source.

In specifying noise ratings, it must be realized that at the present state of the art there are no set regulations, only suggested ones, and that each of the several possible ratings has limitations. No sound measurement is that accurate. Plus or minus 2 dB or less in sound power level is insignificant, particularly in the low frequency bands where differences of up to 4 dB should be disregarded.[6]

There seems to be a trend toward the use of sound power level ratings. These indicate the actual acoustic power radiated from a source. From these data, the audible sound pressure levels can be predicted with an accuracy dependent on how well the physics of the surroundings is understood, and one can predict the need for extra abatement measures such as silencers, barriers or plenum chambers.

References 7, 8, 9 and 10 are publications applicable to fan sound ratings, methods of calculating fan sound ratings from laboratory data, and methods of testing sound power from air-moving devices.

NOISE SOURCES

To determine the nature of an offending noise and to make silencing worthwhile, it is necessary to examine the spectral distribution of sound levels at various frequencies. In a power station, nearly every frequency within the audible area is represented. The dominating frequencies differ at different locations within the plant. Where low frequency noise dominates, the offender is likely to be the furnace, fans, reciprocating compressors, or pulverizers. High-frequency noises dominate at positions where gas or steam is emitted at high velocity through valves and vents.

There are two principal sources of sound within a fan. The first source is the blade passing tone which is generated by the impeller blades. The frequency of the blade passing tone is equal to the number of times per second a blade passes a stationary object.

$$F_{BP} = \frac{(rpm)\,(number\ of\ blades)}{60}$$

(8)

The loudness of the blade passing tone depends on the width of the fan impeller and the distance between a blade and the cutoff or the stator vanes. The second major source is the turbulence created by the fan while adding energy to the airstream. This sound is generally broad band in character.

There are three primary paths by which sound radiates from a fan; namely, through the inlet, the outlet, and the fan housing. Sound radiated from the fan inlet and outlet is approximately at the same sound power level. Sound radiated by the housing is normally at a lower sound power level than that radiated from either the fan inlet or outlet. If the fan inlet(s) and/or outlet are ducted, some of the sound is radiated into the system while some of the sound is transmitted through the duct wall to the surroundings. In the case of FD fans with open inlets or inlet boxes, sound passes directly through the openings to the surroundings. The sound radiating from the fan housing is transmitted directly to the surroundings. For effective sound control, it is necessary to consider all three of the sound paths in accordance with the amount of sound power being transmitted from each.[4]

1. SPL — Inside Enclosure
2. SPL — Outside Wall
3. SPL — Silencer Outlet
4. SPL — 600-Ft Away, Both Fans at Full Load

Fig. 43 Calculated abatement of sound pressure levels for two FD fans for a 500-MW boiler. Each fan is housed in a 30-ft wide × 45-ft long × 35-ft high enclosure of 8-in. masonry.

Fig. 44 Large centrifugal forced-draft fan with silencers mounted on inlet boxes

NOISE REDUCTION

Basically, there are two ways of abating noise. One is to assume the existing process cannot be modified and to isolate the sound from nearby inhabitants by enclosures, barriers, etc. The other is to examine thoroughly the nature of the noise and to modify the process or replace the offending component with a less noisy one. In practice, both methods may be required since 10 to 20 dBA reductions are difficult to obtain except early in the design.

In most cases, separation of source and receiver is also only possible during the early design stage. Doubling the distance halves the sound pressure, *i.e.*, reduces the sound pressure level by 6 dB. For this reason, it may be attractive to include a "buffer zone" rather than silencing equipment.

In general, most problem noises are at a fairly high frequency. Therefore, the best results are obtained with double structures (inner steel and outer lead linings with porous glass fibre material between). This method prevents the build-up of reverberant sound levels. However, the structure must be leaktight. With 30 dBA reduction, for example, only one thousandth of the noise energy that hits the inside of an enclosure escapes to the outside. A similar quantity would be emitted through a hole 1/1000 of the wall area. Therefore, small leaks between panels and around openings for supply pipes must be avoided. Also, the wall must be vibrationally isolated from the mechanical sound-source, or, because of its larger area, the noise emission produced by the vibration may be worse than the initial noise.

An example of the noise attenuation that can be achieved by enclosing two 500,000-CFM FD fans for a 500-MW boiler in 30 ft × 45 ft × 35 ft enclosures of 8-in. block masonry is shown in Fig. 43. At 600 ft (free field assumed), the noise is reduced to a mere whisper.

Fig. 44 shows inlet silencers attached directly to the inlet boxes of an airfoil-type centrifugal FD fan. Such silencers are often used in lieu of acoustical enclosures.

REFERENCES

[1] Richard D. Madison, ed., *Fan Engineering: An Engineer's Handbook*, 7th ed. Buffalo: Buffalo Forge Co., 1970.

American Blower Corp. and Canada Sirocco Co., Ltd., *Air Conditioning and Engineering: A Treatise on the Technique of Conditioning and Mechanical Movement of Air and the Transmission of Power For the Health and Comfort of Human Beings and Efficiency of Production in Industry*, 2nd ed. Detroit: American Blower Corp., 1955.

R. D. Moyer, "Fans Laws Simplify Performance Calculation," *Power*, 90(8): 77–79, August 1946.

[2] Air Movement and Control Association, *Fans and Systems*, AMCA Publication 201. Arlington Heights, IL: Air Movement and Control Association, 1977.

[3] R. Kotwal and W. Tabakoff, "A New Approach for Erosion Prediction Due to Fly Ash," *ASME Paper No. 80-GT-96.* New York: American Society of Mechanical Engineers, 1980.

[4] H. Sugano, M. Nakajima, and N. Yamaguchi, "Factors Affecting Blade Ash-Erosion in Axial Induced Draft Fans," *ASME Paper No. 80-JPGC/Pwr-7.* New York: American Society of Mechanical Engineers, 1980.

[5] E. F. Rothemich and G. Parmakian, "Tubular Air-Heater Problems," *ASME Paper No. 52-A-124.* New York: American Society of Mechanical Engineers, 1952. Also in: *Transactions of the ASME,* 75:723-728, July 1953.

[6] Air Movement and Control Association, *Power Plant Fans: Specification Guidelines*, AMCA Publication 801. Arlington Heights, IL: Air Movement and Control Association, 1977.

[7] "Test Code for Sound Rating Air Moving Devices" *AMCA Standard 300.* Arlington Heights, IL: Air Movement and Control Association, 1967.

[8] "Methods of Calculating Fan Sound Ratings From Laboratory Test Data," *AMCA Standard 301.* Arlington Heights, IL: Air Movement and Control Association, 1976.

[9] Air Movement and Control Association, *Application of Sound Power Level Ratings for Ducted Air Moving Devices,* AMCA Publication 303 (Application Guide). Arlington Heights, IL: Air Movement and Control Association, 1979.

[10] "Method of Testing In-Duct Sound Power Measurement Procedure for Fans," *ASHRAE Standard 68-78.* New York: American Society of Heating, Refrigerating and Air Conditioning Engineers, 1978.

CHAPTER 16

Ash Handling Systems

Chapter 3 presented both the physical and chemical properties of coal-ash and the effects that ash in its various forms can have on the operation of a boiler. This chapter describes the equipment being used for the collection and transport of ash from pulverized-coal-fired steam generators. Heat losses, power consumption, and water use in operating this equipment also are considered. Only through complete understanding of the design and operation of ash-handling equipment, as well as the comparative features of the many available types, can the very large systems currently being installed be made both more reliable and more economical to operate.

There are essentially two types of ash produced in a furnace: bottom ash and flyash. Bottom ash is slag which builds up on the heat-absorbing surfaces of the furnace, superheater, reheater, and economizer that eventually falls either by its own weight or as a result of load changes or sootblowing. With low ash-fusion temperatures, a large amount of molten slag can adhere to the furnace walls and subsequently fall through the furnace bottom. (See Fig. 1) Other ash becomes entrained with, and carried away by, the flue gas stream and is collected in economizer or dust-collection equipment hoppers. This is called flyash.

The amount of air-borne ash passing through the furnace depends on the dust-bearing capacity of the combustion gases, on the size and shape of the particles, and on the density of the ash relative to that of the upward flowing gas. Fig. 2 shows the effects of particle size on terminal velocity[1] which is the rate at which particles of various diameter settle in still air.

Fig. 1 A large pulverized-coal-fired furnace viewed from above. Ash and slag falling from the walls pass through the bottom opening into a bottom-ash hopper or conveyor.

Coarser particles fall more rapidly than fine. Thus, for a given upward velocity, fine particles will leave the furnace and coarse particles either will drop to the bottom or be thrown from the center of the furnace toward the bounding furnace walls. For example, according to the curve, particles larger than 0.011 in. diameter (not passing through a 50-mesh screen) can be expected to fall to the bottom when the vertical velocity of the gases in a furnace is 10 ft/sec.

In this regard, a situation occurs in the design and operation of large pulverized-fuel furnaces that is of interest. As furnace plan areas increase for a given quantity of heat input (NHI/PA), to accommodate a very poor fuel, for example, the upward gas velocities correspondingly decrease. At the same time, the furnace wall area becomes greater, leading to the possibility of larger accumulations of slag or ash on the walls for a given heat input. The greater ash deposits and lesser upward velocities that result mean that more ash will fall to the furnace bottom.

FACTORS
IN SYSTEM SELECTION

Many factors determine the method of handling and storing coal-fired power-plant ash. They include

- fuel source and ash content
- plant siting (land availability, presence of aquifers, adjacent residential areas)
- environmental regulations
- steam-generator size
- cost of auxiliary power
- local market for ash
- cementitious character of the ash

Ash quantities and properties, both physical and chemical, determine the type and size of an ash-handling, storage, transport, and disposal system. They also provide an indication of the environmental impact associated with ash disposal; establish overall system constraints, and influence disposal site design. Peak ash production rates (based on 100 percent capacity

factor) are used to size ash-handling and transport systems. On the other hand, average ash production rate, which considers the projected plant capacity factor over the operating life of the plant, is used to size disposal sites.

FUEL SOURCE AND ASH CONTENT

A major factor affecting the choice of an ash-handling system is the type of fuel to be fired. Fig. 3 shows the wide variation in ash "fired" into a furnace as a function of fuel ash content and moisture. For example, a boiler firing a 15-percent ash subbituminous coal generates almost three times the total ash as the same size unit burning a 10-percent ash, high-calorific-value, medium-volatile coal.

It is usually more meaningful to define ash content as it relates to energy input rather than on the basis of a weight percentage of the coal alone. The pounds of ash per million Btu fired is arrived at by the formula:

$$\frac{\text{ash (as a \%)}}{\text{HHV (Btu/lb)}} \times 10,000 = \text{lbs ash}/10^6 \text{ Btu}$$

(1)

Relating the ash to be handled directly to the required heat input gives a realistic relation-

Fig. 2 Velocity of air borne particles (specific gravity 1.2) falling through still air at 70°F

ship to the amount that must be handled as bottom ash as well as that handled as economizer and precipitator ash. It also gives an insight to the potential rate of ash that has to be handled in the furnace and on convective surfaces.

PLANT SITING

The available water supply and locations of an ash disposal site, relative to the power plant, can greatly affect the design and cost of ash disposal. An ample water supply and a great deal of land are prerequisites of many ash-handling systems.

If land for a plant is limited, ash storage bins or small dewatering ponds can be used for temporary holdup. Trucks or rail cars then are used to carry the ash away. If there is insufficient water, the flyash must be collected by one of the available dry systems while bottom-ash is collected in a recirculated water system.

ENVIRONMENTAL REGULATIONS

Federal, state and local effluent regulations probably have the greatest impact on installations today and in the future. For example, Table I lists typical limitations for bottom-ash and flyash transport water.

Fig. 3 Relative ash amounts with various types of coals, compared to Eastern bituminous coal with 10% ash as a base (corrected for boiler efficiency). Figures in parentheses are as-received moisture contents (by weight) in the coal.

The TSS (total suspended solids) limitations usually are the most difficult to meet, resulting in a trend toward dry flyash systems[2]. But this consideration does not preclude storage ponds to which flyash can be trucked or conveyed pneumatically. Dust is controlled with water sprays and no net effluent is created.

ASH COLLECTION POINTS

After the combustion process in solid-fuel-burning furnaces, the ash collects or is collected in several areas (Fig. 4).

Hoppers or conveyors in troughs are used under the furnace bottom to collect the material falling from the furnace heat-absorbing surfaces. This material can be in either a dry or molten state. If dry, it can be collected in water-impounded or dry receivers. If molten (from wet-bottom furnaces) it must be directed into a water impoundment.

Hoppers also are used under the pulverizer-rejects discharge spout. These collect high-density pyrites and tramp iron separated from the coal during pulverization.

Hoppers under the rear convection pass and air heater(s) of the boiler are commonly called economizer and air-heater hoppers. It is here that coarser particles drop from the gas stream with directional changes in the gas flow.

Flyash hoppers included under the precipitators or baghouses collect the material extracted from the flue-gas stream by these particulate-removal devices.

TABLE I. Typical Effluent Limitations

Bottom-Ash	Oil and Grease	1 mg/ℓ × Flow (max) 0.75 mg/ℓ × Flow (avg)
Transport	pH	6–9
Water	TSS	5 mg/ℓ × Flow (max) 1.5 mg/ℓ × Flow (avg)
Flyash	Oil and Grease	0
Transport	pH	6–9
Water	TSS	0

QUANTITIES OF ASH

Most pulverized-coal-fired steam generators are dry-bottom units in which 20–40 percent of the ash from the coal falls to the furnace bottom. Sixty to 80 percent of the ash leaves the furnace as flyash. Most of the flyash is collected in economizer hoppers and one of several available dust collection systems.

However, with some fuels less than 20 percent bottom ash has been measured, while with certain lignites more than 45 percent bottom ash has been reported. As a guide to establishing the size of the equipment in the total ash-handling system, typical collection quantities (mass basis) are used.

For example, the 20–40 percent figure can vary according to experience with the type of fuel burned. With low- and medium-volatile bituminous coals, a 15–20 percent bottom ash figure is appropriate. With a high-volatile bituminous coal a 20–30 percent bottom ash figure is used. Systems for subbituminous coal and lignite are sized using a 30–50 percent bottom ash figure.

The economizer and air heater ash hoppers each are sized to collect about 5 percent of the flyash while a precipitator, fabric filter or other equipment would be sized to extract 80 to 100 percent of the flyash from the flue gas.

Note that the sum of all the assumed collection-point values can exceed the total ash in the coal by 50 percent or more because of the lack of precision of the individual factors, and to allow for variation in fuel quality.

ASH DENSITY

Flyash density depends primarily on particle size, particle structure, and carbon content. In general, the relatively large, coarse particles containing a high percentage of carbon have a low density. These particles commonly have a porous or lace-like structure and result from the partial combustion of the pulverized coal. It appears that the volatile portion burns out, leaving black coke-like particles. These particles have densities of about 35 to 65 lb/ft^3 (true density). The finer ash particles, which tend to be low in carbon content, have much higher densities, usually ranging from 90 to 180 lb/ft^3 (true density).

In the hot state, freshly collected ash is normally very fluid with a lower density than cold ash—generally between 30 to 50 lb/ft^3 bulk density. The fresh ash is aerated as the individual particles are exposed to the gas. With standing and cooling, de-aeration occurs and the ash compacts. It becomes less fluid and can approach bulk densities as high as 90 lb/ft^3. When

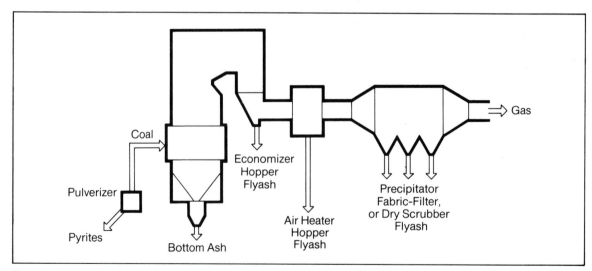

Fig. 4 Ash must be collected and transported from at least the five points shown. In each location, the physical and chemical characteristics of the ash vary.

cold, subbituminous coal ash, which is very fine, will usually have loosely packed bulk densities between 65 and 85 lb/ft³. Bituminous coal ash, on the same basis, will have a density between 60 and 70 lb/ft³.

The bulk density of dry bottom ash, as initially dropped into an ash receiver, can be as low as 40 to 45 lb/ft³, but it can compact to above 75 lb/ft³. A value of 55 lb/ft³ bulk density is used for establishing bottom-ash hopper storage capacity. Pulverizer rejects, when principally iron pyrites (iron disulfide, FeS_2), will have a bulk density of at least 135 lb/ft³.

TYPES OF SYSTEMS

The three principal methods of moving ash from the collection points to the on-site disposal or storage location are hydraulic, pneumatic, and mechanical. In a hydraulic system, a stream of water conveys the ash in a closed pipeline or open sluiceway. Commonly, a jet or centrifugal pump provides the motive force. A pneumatic system transports the ash in a stream of air or flue gas induced by either an upstream pressure or a downstream vacuum. The oldest technique for ash removal is the mechanical method, the most rudimentary form being a shovel or hoe, with the more sophisticated type being mechanical scraper or flight conveyors.

Two basic philosophies have evolved throughout the world for removing ash from coal-fired boilers:

■ collection, storage and *periodic* removal, usually called intermittent removal systems

■ collection and *continuous* removal, commonly termed continuous removal systems

Ash-handling systems are further differentiated by their conveying frequency and the conveying medium. The major systems are:

1. Bottom ash
   a. Water-impounded hopper with wet pipeline or sluiceway, to a pond or closed recirculation system—intermittent, hydraulic
   b. Dry hopper, dry pipeline—intermittent, pneumatic
   c. Submerged scraper conveyor—continuous, mechanical
2. Pyrites (Pulverizer Rejects)
   a. Hoppers with wet sluicing (pipeline or open trough)—intermittent, hydraulic
   b. Hoppers with manual removal—intermittent, mechanical
   c. Hoppers with dry vacuum removal (infrequently used)—intermittent, pneumatic
3. Economizer
   a. Dry pipeline—intermittent, pneumatic
   b. Dry flight or screw conveyor—continuous, mechanical
   c. Wet pipeline using receiving tanks below economizer hoppers—continuous, hydraulic
   d. Dry pipeline using receiving tanks below economizer hoppers—continuous, pneumatic
4. Flyash
   a. Dry pipeline, vacuum—intermittent, pneumatic
   b. Dry pipeline, pressure—intermittent, pneumatic
   c. Dry/wet pipeline, vacuum—intermittent, pneumatic/hydraulic (water exhausters)
   d. Dry, screw or flight conveyor—continuous, mechanical

BOTTOM ASH SYSTEMS

A wet bottom-ash system collects and hydraulically or mechanically removes ash falling from the furnace heat-transfer surfaces. One type—a water-impounded hopper (Figs. 5 and 6)—receives, quenches, and stores ash from the furnace. In this system the ash is intermittently drained by discharging the water-ash mixture through an outlet gate to clinker grinders that reduce the size of the materials to facilitate transport to disposal by jet or centrifugal pumps.

The principal reasons for water-impounding include the following:

■ to break up large pieces of slag by thermal

Fig. 5 **C-E Water-filled intermittent-removal ash hopper**

Fig. 6 **Cross section of C-E water-filled ash hopper under a pulverized-coal boiler**

shock as they fall into the pool of approximately 140°F water

■ to keep the ash and slag submerged so that they do not fuse into large unmanageable masses that would result if they were exposed to furnace heat

■ to provide a resilient medium to decelerate the large pieces of slag

■ to assist in the evacuation of ash (from the intermittent-removal type of hopper) by reducing its effective angle of repose

INTERMITTENT-REMOVAL BOTTOM-ASH HOPPER

On most pulverized-coal-fired units above 400,000 lbs of steam/hr, intermittent-removal bottom-ash hoppers are of the V, W, or triple-V design. This design has hopper floors sloping at angles of 35 to 55 degrees allowing gravity to help remove ash from the hopper. During ash removal the high-pressure water to the jet pump is turned on and the clinker grinder is started. The control system opens the hydraulic-cylinder-controlled sluice gate and the ash flows from the hopper through a grinder into the jet pump, then to a transfer tank, dewatering system, or settling pond. Alternatively, a centrifugal materials-handling pump evacuates the hopper and transports the ash to the disposal system.

Operating experience with water-filled hoppers has shown that most of the ash will flow toward and through the sluice gates by gravity; however, large slabs of fused ash do occur that will not move by gravity alone. Their removal requires the assistance of high-pressure (125 psig) water-jetting nozzles located on the slopping floors of the hopper. In addition, jetting nozzles in the wall opposite each sluice gate break up the arching and packing of the ash that may occur at the gate.

Whenever practical the hopper should have a volume corresponding to the ash produced during 12 hours of operation at full boiler load while firing the lowest-heating value and highest-ash-content fuel for which the boiler is designed. This guideline is based on the normal practice in the U.S. of emptying ash hoppers once each 8-hour shift. Depending upon the fuel ash content and the boiler load, the usual time required to evacuate a bottom-ash-hopper is one to three hours. The hopper volumetric capacity is measured below a mean ash level which is usually 12 to 24 inches below the normal water level, depending on the bottom-ash hopper width (see Table II and Fig. 7).

It is important to realize that the ash falling from the furnace walls does not pass through the furnace bottom opening in equal increments along the length of that opening. Fig. 8 shows that, for a large "open" furnace (one without a center wall), all of the ash from each sidewall falls through the first 3 or 4 feet of the bottom opening; the ash falling from the front and rear walls can be assumed to distribute fairly equally along the furnace width. Thus, as shown by the figure, about 25 percent of the total ash to the furnace bottom will go through the 3 to 4 ft portion near the side wall, and less than 2% of the bottom ash will go through each remaining foot of the bottom "slot". It is of utmost importance to take this distribution into account when designing bottom-ash receiving equipment. The normal water level should be at least 30″ below the horizontal plane of the furnace tubes forming the furnace throat opening (A in Figs. 7 and 9); this dimension is with the boiler pressure parts in the hot (expanded)

TABLE II. Determination of Effective Ash Level*

Hopper Width Inside Refractory (See Fig. 7)	Effective Ash Level (EAL) Below NWL, ft
7'-0″	0.8
8'-0″	1.0
9'-0″	1.2
10'-0″	1.4
11'-0″	1.6
12'-0″	1.8
13'-0″	2.0
14'-0″	2.2

*An interpolation can be made for other hopper widths.

Fig. 7 Effective ash level below normal water level varies as a function of ash hopper width (See Table II)

condition. This distance minimizes the amount of water that may splash on the furnace tubing. The hopper is designed with 5 to 10 feet end-wall submergence to provide a deep pool of water at this critical portion of the hopper.

Depending upon the boiler width and headroom available, the hopper configuration should adequately provide the needed storage capacity. Centerwall boilers must have an odd number of sections. This places the center of a hopper section underneath the centerwall so that there is maximum submergence to collect the ash properly from both sides of the wall.

For ease of maintenance, the ash hopper should be designed so that the entire hopper and its discharge equipment are located above grade. Pits must be avoided, but if they are used to put the sluice piping below basement floor level, their depth should be limited to a maximum of 3 feet.

OVERFLOW WEIRS

To maintain the normal water level (NWL) in the hopper, an NWL overflow should be provided. The bottom opening of the weir is at the normal water level, Fig. 10. To protect from overfilling the hopper and possibly wetting the boiler tubes, there is a second, independent "high-water-level" overflow. The opening at the bottom of this weir is a minimum of 6 inches above the NWL weir. A conductivity device in the outlet box from the high-level overflow provides an alarm when high overflow occurs.

ASH-HOPPER CONSTRUCTION

Ash hoppers are constructed of carbon-steel plate with structural framing similar to that of the furnace walls. A high-temperature water-resistant gunned or cast refractory, supported by stainless-steel anchors, lines the sides and bottom slopes. Alternatively, on the sloped bottom portions of the hopper, acid-resistant bricks backed by concrete can be used.

Fig. 8 Approximate distribution of pulverized-coal bottom ash along the furnace hopper opening

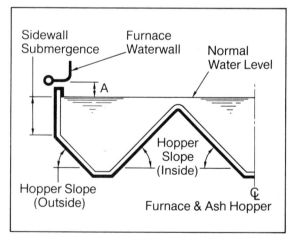

Fig. 9 Schematic arrangement of half of a triple-vee water-impounded bottom-ash hopper. Dimension A is defined with boiler in cold condition and with boiler structural supports assumed undeflected.

Fig. 10 Arrangement of bottom-ash hopper overflow weirs and piping

A water seal-trough around the upper periphery of the ash hopper, together with the seal plates hung from the boiler tubes, provides a seal against furnace pressure fluctuations and accommodates the downward expansion of the furnace. Nozzles located throughout the seal trough periodically flush accumulated sludge and sediment from the trough bottom.

REFRACTORY COOLING

At the top of the hopper is a water-distribution assembly for cooling the hopper refractory that extends above the normal water level (Fig. 11). The curtain of water flowing over the refractory face also retards refractory deterioration during extended periods when the hopper is drained of water during boiler operation. The water distribution pipe must be equipped with a deflection shield to prevent water from being sprayed on the furnace tubes. Periodic flushing of this pipe with a high-volume water flow through a drain connection in each section insures that pieces of ash do not clog the holes.

Fig. 12, a flow diagram for a single-V type bottom-ash hopper, shows all of the water-flows entering and leaving this hopper. Op-

Fig. 11 Distribution-pipe system for refractory cooling water

Fig. 12 **Flow diagram of single-vee bottom-ash hopper**

timum operation of a water-impounded hopper can be achieved by maintaining the water level at all times, even while discharging the ash. In this way, the design makes use of all the advantages of water impounding and establishes the maximum possible net-positive suction-heat on the jet (or centrifugal) pumps at the optimum moment. The only time the water level

has to be lowered with this arrangement is when it's necessary to visually inspect the hopper interior or to remove over-sized pieces manually. Each end of the hopper should be equipped with access doors for maintenance.

HOPPER SLUICE GATES

Bottom ash hopper sluice gates (Fig. 13) (usually $24'' \times 24''$) allow for periodic removal of bottom ash from the hopper. Around the discharge gates are water-tight steel enclosures which flood when ash is being discharged. These enclosures are equipped with access doors, observation ports, and floodlights and are designed to withstand negative and positive pressures. A vent pipe equipped with two vacuum breakers provides vacuum/pressure protection. Positive-pressure protection is achieved by allowing the water in the enclosures to enter the vent pipe to discharge into the bottom-ash hopper. A loop in the vent-pipe above the hopper water level prevents water backflow from the hopper to the enclosure. Vacuum protection is provided by check valves located at the top of the vent-pipe loop.

The gate is hydraulically lifted by a cylinder designed for water service. Limit switches indicate a fully open or fully closed position.

Fig. 13 **C-E bottom-ash hopper sluice gate**

High-wear areas in the sluice gate enclosure are often made of ceramic or stainless-steel.

CLINKER GRINDERS

Single- or double-roll clinker grinders are provided at the outlet of each sluice gate. The grinding elements are made from heavy-duty abrasion-resistant materials, such as work-hardened manganese steel or heat-treated high-chrome steel. Ash is ground by a shearing, splitting or crushing action to facilitate hydraulic or pneumatic transport (Figs. 14 and 15).

Because of the severe duty, relatively frequent replacement is required for the wear-prone internals of these crushing machines. It is important to provide easy access for their removal while the steam generator is operating. The design shown in Fig. 14 and 15 provides an easily removed front panel for such access allowing maintenance personnel to replace worn grinding elements without entering the enclosure.

Shaft bearings are spherical roller type with provisions for forced lubrication. Shaft seals have continuous seal-water flow during periods of both grinder operation and shutdown. A close-tolerance throttling bushing impedes the flow of small ash particles into the stuffing box.

JET PUMPS

A jet pump is a venturi-type solids/fluids transport device with no moving parts (Figs. 16 and 17). The pump has an inherent low efficiency but this is offset by its non-overloading characteristic, ease of maintenance, and lack of rotating parts. For these reasons, the majority of hydraulic bottom-ash and mill-rejects systems use jet pumps instead of centrifugal pumps.

To minimize the effects of abrasion, the jet pump is made of abrasion-resistant alloys. The inlet section is heat-treated nodular iron (minimum Brinell hardness of 400); the combining tube (diffuser), high-hardness cast chrome-nickel alloy material, to a minimum Brinell of 550.

A jet pump is supplied at the outlet of each clinker grinder; alternately, a mechanical cen-

Fig. 14 Single-roll clinker grinder for reducing size of bottom-ash; hammers and anvils are replaceable through removable access panel.

trifugal pump can be used. The accompanying box lists the advantages of each.

As more high-ash coal is used for steam-generator fuel—producing greater ash loading on bottom-ash systems—suppliers recommend another sluice gate, grinder and pump for each hopper section. The purpose of this redundant equipment is two-fold: first, to increase the overall system reliability and, second, to in-

Fig. 15 C-E single-roll clinker grinder showing external tripod bearing supports

Fig. 16 Schematic arrangement of jet pump for handling abrasive solids

crease the rate of ash-removal when quicker-than-design evacuation is desired.

PIPING, FITTING, AND VALVES

Ash slurry piping is supplied in several forms. Included are
■ centrifugally cast chrome-iron alloy with hardness ranging from 280 to 400 BHN (Brinell hardness number)
■ surface-hardened carbon-steel piping
■ fiberglass-reinforced plastic pipe lined with abrasion-resistant material
■ basalt-lined steel pipe

Ash in a water slurry usually travels along the bottom portion of pipes in saltation flow; that is, it alternately "rests" (settles out) and "jumps" (becomes re-entrained in suspended flow). Thus, most wear on slurry piping is on the bottom third (the lower 120° arc) of the pipe. Directly downstream of elbows, piping wear is higher than in straight runs because of the turbulence and impact created at the elbow; this calls for more frequent replacement of downstream runs.

Whenever there is a change in direction in the slurry piping, the fitting located at the change of direction will undergo accelerated wear as a result of turbulence and solids-impact erosion. Thus, fittings, such as 45° and 90° elbows and laterals, are normally constructed from alloy castings that range from 450 to 550 BHN (Fig. 18).

Material hardness alone cannot provide long life at points of change in direction. To add ad-

Fig. 17 C-E jet pump for bottom-ash transport

Fig. 18 Chrome-nickel alloy 90° elbow with integral wearback helps reduce wear from solids-impact erosion and turbulence experienced with changes in flow direction.

ditional life to the fitting, the impact area has a thicker cross-section than the normal conveying pipeline. This thicker section is commonly termed an *integral wearback*.

Fittings can have connections that are either plain-end or bevelled-end. When plain-end sections are used, piping harnesses prevent the fitting from dislodging due to the reactive

---

COMPARISON OF JET PUMPS VS. CENTRIFUGAL PUMPS

ADVANTAGES OF JET PUMPS

- A jet pump is a simple device. There are no moving parts; it is made up of only three principal components: nozzle, body, and diffuser. This makes maintenance and replacement easier and less expensive than for a centrifugal pump.
- A jet pump can handle air without any deleterious effects; lack of suction head is never a problem.
- A jet pump is self-regulating. The amount of suction material depends on the discharge head. The higher the discharge head, the less suction material will be taken—when there is no suction flow, the only flow through the pump is the motive (clear water) flow. This makes for a self-cleaning action. If the discharge line becomes clogged, the flow of more material into the pump is limited so that the motive flow can flush the line.
- There are no rotating parts subject to erosive ash.

ADVANTAGES OF A CENTRIFUGAL PUMP

- A centrifugal pump can obtain much higher volumetric capacities than a jet pump. A typical jet pump has a practical limit of about 3,500 gpm discharge flow. Centrifugal pumps can produce flows of 35,000 gpm and higher.
- A centrifugal pump has a higher efficiency than a jet pump. Stated in another way, the power required for a centrifugal pump to convey a given flow at a given head is considerably less than the power required to give the jet-pump motive fluid the required head and flow to convey the given mixed water/slurry head and flow.
- No separate motive-water pump is required.

loads of the conveying medium. Bevelled-end fittings do not require friction-type couplings to secure the fitting to the pipe.

In conveying water-ash slurries, it may be necessary to divert flow or isolate branch lines when multiple sluice lines exist. Industry practice is to provide heavy-duty knife gate valves for this service because of their profile characteristic. That is to say, when the knife-gate valve is open, its orifice matches the diameter of the sluice pipe in which it is installed. Minimizing the turbulence through the valve reduces erosion. In addition, the insertion of the valve in the line requires no special adaptors or fittings. Also, knife-gate valves can have bonnets to prevent leakage from the packing, and flushing ports for cleaning the seat and the gate before closing. Manual handwheels or pneumatic operators are commonly used to open and close knife gates. Automatic knife-gate systems can have limit switches to provide feedback to the control system.

When the sluice conveying line is made of alloy cast pipe, the couplings between fittings, valves, and plain-end pipe are manufactured by ash-system suppliers. Where two sections of plain-end pipe meet, commercial pipe couplings can be used.

Any slurry piping system must be designed with minimum and maximum velocities in mind. The minimum velocity is that required to convey the particle in the pipeline without settling. This velocity is a function of the specific gravity of the material being conveyed, the pipeline size, and the slurry concentration. Typical ash-slurry pipeline velocities are

- bottom ash—7 to 8 ft/sec
- economizer ash—6 ft/sec
- pyrites—9 to 10 ft/sec
- flyash—4 ft/sec

DISPOSAL OF BOTTOM ASH FROM HYDRAULIC SYSTEMS

Hydraulic ash systems dispose of the ash-and-water slurry in various ways, depending on the overall plant layout, ecological considerations, and available disposal areas.[3] As previously mentioned, the ecological considerations are presently a major influence on decisions made about the means of disposal of ash and slurry.

Most steam-generating plants require either a recirculating system or monitoring (and treatment, if required) of pond blowdown. Recirculating systems frequently include dewatering equipment for the mechanical separation of bottom ash and water.

DEWATERING SYSTEMS

Ash from a conveying sluice line can be deposited into dewatering bins. As the ash settles, it displaces water which overflows into a trough extending around the circumference of the bin top. The overflow water drains by gravity to the recirculation basin or waste drain.

A series of baffle plates, concentric with the outer shell of the bin, prevent ash carryover and undesirable turbulence in the overflow trough. Submerged beneath the water level, the inner baffle inhibits the finer material from reaching the overflow. The second baffle, extending above the overflow trough, creates a barrier to retain the floating material before it reaches the overflow trough. Eventually, floating material settles and is discharged through the sluice gate after the bin is dewatered.

Dewatering bins are installed in pairs. When one bin is filled, the input flow is diverted to the empty bin. After a short period of natural settling, a level of surface water will exist. This surface water is drained off through vertical decanting pipes or floating decanters.

After the surface water is drained, the lower drain valves in the decanting pipes are automatically opened, resulting in a slow, controlled draining of water from the ash in the bin. Depending on the composition of the ash and the desired moisture content, this process generally takes less than eight hours. With proper filtration, settling, and chemical treatment, the overflow water can be recycled to the bottom-ash system in what is essentially a closed loop.

It is important to protect dewatering bins from freezing by providing heaters at the bottom. Also, the lower cone section of the bin normally has vibrators to aid in removing the dewatered ash.

CONTINUOUS-DEWATERING EQUIPMENT

In lieu of the intermittent-dewatering bins just described, continuously operating dewatering systems are available using equipment similar to the submerged scraper conveyor, discussed later in this chapter. With continuous-dewatering apparatus, ash is periodically removed and sluiced from a batch-storage (intermittent-removal) ash hopper to the remote dewatering scraper conveyor. The conveyor dewaters the ash to the same extent as with a dewatering bin and places it on a belt conveyor for further handling. Water from the dewatered ash overflows the conveyor vessel and is treated further as with dewatering bins.

SETTLING AND STORAGE TANK

The discharge water from the dewatering device normally is routed into a settling basin or tank. To separate the ash fines low velocities are maintained throughout the basin or tank which are designed for maximum retention time. Any agitation is confined to a small area. Water and ash fines are deposited into the center of the settling tank after passing through a cyclone-type separator and baffles. As the ash fines settle into the tank, the displaced water overflows into a trough which extends around the circumference of the top of the tank. The overflow water drains into the center of the ash-water storage tank. As in the case of the dewatering device, it is important to protect the settling tanks from freezing.

STORAGE OR SURGE TANK

In a recirculating system, an ash-water storage tank provides sufficient volume to absorb the volumetric fluctuations of the hydraulic ash removal system. In addition, this tank provides further separation of fines by maintaining a low velocity. Again, freeze protection must be provided. Centrifugal pumps recirculate the discharge water from the surge tank to supply the jet pumps and other requirements for water in the system.

PONDS OR FILL AREAS

Where geological and siting conditions permit, ash can be pumped to ponds or fill areas. Any ash-receiving pond needs a large capacity to permit the ash to settle by gravity. The design of such ponds can include recovery and reuse of the water in the ash removal system.

DRY BOTTOM-ASH HOPPER SYSTEM

Dry bottom-ash hopper systems for intermittent removal are used when there is no need to provide for water impoundment—and less automation is acceptable. A rule of thumb is that dry bottom-ash hoppers are generally practical on units rated below 400,000 lbs/hr of steam.

Customarily constructed of carbon-steel plate, these hoppers, like the hoppers used in a wet system, have a water-seal trough, complete with flushing nozzles. Unlike water-impounded hoppers, dry hopper slopes must be steep to insure that the dry ash flows to the discharge openings.

The inside of the hopper steel plate is lined with several inches of insulation. Anchors, normally of stainless-steel and welded to the hopper plate, are used to hold 4 to 6 inches of gunned refractory lining forming the inside of the ash hopper.

Ash is periodically removed from the hopper through a series of water-cooled discharge gates. Each gate has a sealed enclosure, a pneumatic operator, an access door, observation port, and floodlight.

At the discharge of the ash gates, grinders may be provided to reduce any large clinkers to a size that can be handled by a pneumatic or hydraulic conveying system. The grinders are similar in construction but normally smaller than the grinders under the wet bottom-ash hoppers. Instead of grinders, sizing grids for manual handling may be placed at the discharge gate outlet.

THE SUBMERGED SCRAPER CONVEYOR FOR CONTINUOUS REMOVAL

Another method of bottom-ash removal uses a flight conveyor of heavy construction submerged in a water trough below the furnace.

With the submerged scraper conveyor (SSC), ash continuously is evacuated mechanically so there is no long-time storage in the water impoundment beneath the furnace. After discharge from the SSC in a dewatered condition, ash is usually transported by belt conveyors. The major advantages of the SSC are

- reduced water usage (no transport water)
- reduced power consumption (by eliminating the high-pressure sluicing water required by the jet pumps)
- low boiler setting height

The C-E Combusco submerged conveyor was used in the 1920's for ash removal from stoker-fired boilers. Presently, the C-E/EVT SSC offers similar continuous ash removal from pulverized-coal units.[4] It serves the same functions as the intermittently emptied refractory-lined ash hopper, that is, it seals the furnace bottom, quenches the falling ash and removes it from under the furnace.

The most widely accepted SSC configuration has two separated compartments in which the flights and chains move (Fig. 19). The upper (wet) chamber, containing three to six feet of water, receives the ash falling from the furnace and conveys it up the dewatering slope. At the top of the dewatering slope, the flights reverse direction, dumping the conveyed ash. They then return through the dry chamber below; this has open sides to facilitate inspection while the equipment is operating (Fig. 20).

Generally, the maximum speed of the scraper conveyor is about 20 feet per minute, with a 4-to-1 or 6-to-1 turndown ratio. Operation at low speed, as a function of low boiler load or low ash content, reduces power consumption and abrasive wear on both flights and supporting surfaces.

Travel wheels, when furnished, support the entire conveyor; they ride in tracks or on rails located in the power-plant floor. The dewatering slope on the ash-removal conveyor leads to a transfer chute or hopper, in which a conventional clinker grinder reduces the size of the ash. From the transfer chute, the size-reduced ash is deposited on a belt conveyor.

CONVEYOR CHAIN DESIGN

A common SSC chain is the double-stranded round link or ship's-type chain made from alloy steel, annealed and carburized to a 550–600 BHN hardness. Chain couplings, of the same material as the chain, are designed for ash-handling service. The chain is supplied in matched sets and undergoes stringent quality control and testing to insure a long service life. Useful life is a function of chain lengthening caused by wear of the inner portion of the links. The lengthening can result in a mismatch of the chain to the driving sprocket.

OTHER DESIGN FEATURES

The flights are commercially available structural angles attached to the chains by fittings provided by the chain manufacturer.

The upper trough of the conveyor has overflow boxes to regulate the height of the water above the flights. Cooling water is added to maintain a normal 140°F (maximum 160°F) temperature. In this respect, the submerged scraper conveyor uses exactly the same amount of cooling water as a water-impounded hopper because the heat presented to the equipment is exactly the same.

Dewatering slopes are at an angle between 25 and 45 degrees. The actual physical configuration depends on the unobstructed space available, boiler-house structural-steel design considerations, and the method of handling the ash after it leaves the conveyor.

SETTING HEIGHT OF STEAM GENERATORS AS AFFECTED BY THE BOTTOM-ASH SYSTEM

The operation and maintenance of bottom-ash hoppers and associated auxiliary equipment are easier and better when no equipment is located in sub-basement-floor pits. But, by eliminating such pits it is sometimes necessary to have boiler setting heights up to 35 feet to accommodate the intermittent-removal, water-impounded bottom hopper. (*Setting height* is the vertical distance from the basement floor level to the centerline of the horizontal furnace-wall tubing directly above the ash-removal equipment; this dimension is measured with the steam generator in the "cold" condition, before expansion has taken place.)

Such generous setting heights are not necessary with the submerged scraper conveyor. When SSC's are specified before the boiler is purchased, the setting height can be adjusted to save substantial amounts in the cost of boiler structural steel, piping, and ductwork.

Fig. 19 **Submerged scraper conveyor for bottom-ash removal (C-E/EVT SSC)**

COMPARISON OF CONTINUOUS- AND INTERMITTENT-REMOVAL BOTTOM-ASH EQUIPMENT

Continuous mechanical removal permits lighter equipment, reduced power consumption compared to hydraulic evacuation, and eliminates the need for conveying water. It's also possible to observe the ash-removal process without drawing down the water-level. Continuous removal provides "auto-dewatering" without the use of dewatering vessels.

In addition, operational control systems for continuous removal are simpler than are those on an intermittent-removal system. Moreover, the reduced height of the boiler above the basement floor has a savings potential in fuel piping, ductwork, structural steel, and building costs. There is also an advantage in being able to move the conveyor to the side at times when the boiler is out of operation. This feature facilitates access to the interior of the furnace through the furnace bottom opening; nor are the high-pressure pumps or water piping of the intermittent hopper (Fig. 12) required.

Because the SSC is designed for *continuous removal*, provision must be made for *continuous receiving* of the ash dropping from the top of the dewatering slope by belt conveyors or other similar mechanical devices. The usual intermittent-removal hopper system in the U.S. is operated only 20 to 30 percent of the time; there is thus a period during which the equipment is not in operation and is available for inspection and maintenance.

Redundancy of mechanical conveying equipment downstream of the scraper conveyor should be considered to assure continuous ash removal. However, despite the fact that ash-storage is not considered in designing an SSC, it can be shut down for short periods to repair downstream equipment.

Fig. 20 **Submerged scraper conveyor for 740-MW bituminous-coal-fired steam generator 108 ft 3 in. long from head to "tail"**

PULVERIZER-REJECTS SYSTEMS

The pulverizer-rejects system collects and transports pulverizer rejects (principally pyrites and tramp iron) hydraulically from the pulverizers (also called mills). A typical system (Fig. 21) uses an enclosed pyrites-reject hopper located next to each pulverizer to receive and store the pulverizer rejects for intermittent removal. Removal and transport from the pyrites hopper is by a jet pump similar to the jet pumps used in bottom-ash sluicing, but smaller in size and conveying capacity.

Although the mill rejects may be pumped directly to a dewatering bin or pond, it is more common to have all the pyrites-removal jet pumps discharge to a local collection or transfer tank (Fig. 21). This arrangement permits emptying more than one hopper at a time.

From this central collection tank, jet or centrifugal pumps remove the pyrites-rejects to the dewatering equipment. Discharging mill rejects into bottom-ash equipment is not acceptable unless a method can be provided to prevent splashing of ash-hopper water onto the boiler tubes above the pyrites injection point. This splashing has caused stress-cracking failure of these tubes. With an SSC, it is practical to introduce mill rejects outside the water-seal plates, obviating the problem.

Plant maintenance and operating flexibility demands that the pulverizer-reject system be operable simultaneously with the main bottom-ash system.

When pressurized mills are used, it is a requirement of NFPA No. 85F, Para. 2-6.1 to design the rejects hoppers to withstand 50 psig (Fig. 22). To seal out pulverizer pressure during normal operation, a water-seal overflow box is used. This seal box is sized for 120 percent of the static pressure specified for the primary air fan.

Each rejects hopper must be equipped with a
- level indicator
- steel grate with approximately 1½″ square openings to capture large particles for manual removal
- floodlight (for pressurized hopper only)
- inspection port
- access panel
- discharge chute to connect the reject outlet on each pulverizer to the hopper. A pneumatically-operated gate valve is located in the discharge chute for isolation of the hopper. The pyrites slurry piping and fittings are similar to that provided for the bottom-ash systems.

With suction-type mills, the pyrites hopper is an open tank to store and collect the rejects (Fig. 23). On open hoppers, accessories such as floodlights and inspection ports are eliminated. On small steam generators equipped with suction mills from which there will not be a large amount of pulverizer rejects, a simple

Fig. 21 **Mill-rejects (pyrites) hydraulic transport system uses individual pipelines from each pulverizer to the transfer tank.**

wheelbarrow may substitute for hoppers.

The amount of rejects from a pulverizer varies greatly as a function of the type of coal, the type of firing system, the mill, and the way the mill is operated.

REMOVAL OF ECONOMIZER-HOPPER ASH

Economizer ash is usually over 700°F, and frequently coarse. It sometimes contains combustible material. This ash can have the physical characteristics of furnace-wall ash and the chemical characteristics of hygroscopic flyash. It is collected in a row of pyramidal hoppers beneath the boiler economizer section, usually at the point of the 90-degree turn in the combustion gas flow.

Formerly, economizer ash was most often handled dry, as an extension of the dry precipitator flyash system; but, exposed to in-leaking air, it could combust and form clinkers making it impossible for the ash to flow through the hopper outlets which usually were only 8 inches in diameter.

Economizer ash should be removed *continuously*, in a method analogous to the continuous removal of bottom ash from a hot furnace. Con-

tinuous removal gets the ash out of the hot environment of the hopper and prevents further combustion of any carbon it may contain. For low-calcium-content bituminous coals, water-filled tanks beneath each economizer-hopper outlet, Fig. 24, should be used. The ash is stored in these tanks for intermittent removal.

Unfortunately, wet holding is not feasible with economizer-hopper ash produced by certain high-calcium lignite or subbituminous coal. Some such ash shows pozzolanic and cementitious properties when dropped into or mixed with water, and may require very frequent evacuation from wet tanks to obviate the possibility of plugging. Utilities burning such "concrete-making" high-calcium coals have used dry transfer tanks below the economizer hoppers to achieve continuous removal without tank or line plugging problems.

It is important, then, to recognize that such flyash has the potential of producing synthetic

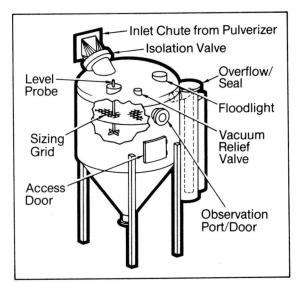

Fig. 22 C-E mill-rejects hopper for pressurized pulverizers

Fig. 23 Open-top rejects hopper for suction pulverizers

silicate rocks that cannot be redissolved and flushed out of tanks or transport lines. The ash is in the category of a pozzolan—siliceous or aluminous/siliceous material which in itself possesses little or no cementitious value but which will, in finely divided form and in the presence of moisture, chemically react with calcium hydroxide to form compounds having cementitious properties.

The best solution to the handling of economizer ash having concreting characteristics is to remove it continuously from the hoppers under the high-temperature gas zone into dry holdup/collecting tanks located beneath the economizer hoppers, so as to prevent burning or sintering. The ash can be removed from these tanks on an intermittent basis as a branch of the precipitator or baghouse pneumatic removal system. Alternatively, the flyash can be removed continuously from the hoppers by means of mechanical removal equipment, as discussed later in this chapter.

FLYASH REMOVAL SYSTEMS

Flyash from the hoppers serving air heaters, precipitators, and baghouses is removed intermittently by either vacuum (negative-pressure) or pressure (positive-pressure) pneumatic type systems, or combinations of the two. In addition, several types of continuous-removal systems such as flight conveyors or screw conveyors can be used.

VACUUM SYSTEMS

A vacuum system (Fig. 25) uses a mechanical blower, water exhauster, or a steam exhauster to create a vacuum which removes the flyash from the hoppers. A flyash-intake valve located at each hopper regulates the flow of the flyash. Flyash intakes have carbon-steel or cast-iron bodies and a swing disc which seals against a hardened seat. For maintenance, the outlet of each hopper has a manual isolation gate.

Each flyash intake is actuated automatically by the system logic which controls both the flow rate and quantity of flyash leaving the

hopper to avoid plugging the discharge line. Because the system operates on a vacuum, only one flyash intake and one conveyor branch line operate at any given time. As each hopper is emptied of flyash, the system will step to the next hopper in the same branch line. When all hoppers in a branch line have been emptied, the system will step to the next branch line. The system logic insures the proper sequence of events and positioning of valves.

The intake shown in Figs. 26 and 27 uses a microporous stainless-steel filter cloth which passes hot fluidizing air into the body of the intake at a controlled rate. The metallic fluidizing material is used because it does not plug or crack easily, as do some other media.

When a mechanical blower produces the necessary vacuum, flyash is taken to a silo where a cyclone separator and bag filter, in series, separate the air-ash mixture. To protect the blower it is important to collect most of the ash, which is then emptied from the silos into enclosed trucks or railcars.

The water exhauster (Fig. 28) is another method of transporting flyash through the conveying line. High-pressure water supplied to the water-exhauster inlet nozzles creates the

Fig. 24 **Water-filled tank beneath economizer hopper receives low-calcium-content ash for cooling and intermittent flushing.**

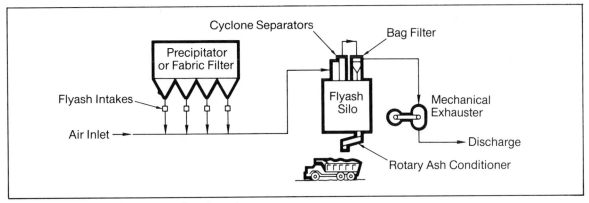

Fig. 25 **Dry pneumatic-vacuum flyash system**

transport vacuum; flyash, air, and water are mixed in the exhauster venturi. Water exhausters normally have hardened ductile iron bodies, wear-resistant liners and stainless-steel nozzles. Diffusers are hardened ductile iron.

Fig. 26 **C-E fluidizing-type flyash intake for regulating flyash flow from collection hoppers (fluidizing-air plenum is removable for precipitator washdown)**

Following the water exhausters, an air separator is provided to separate and vent the air from the flyash-water-air mixture (Fig. 29). Separators are made of cast iron or carbon steel with an abrasion-resistant basalt or ceramic liner. The separator discharge is elevated sufficiently to allow the ash-water slurry to flow by gravity to a pond or disposal area. Flyash slurry is never discharged to a dewatering bin because it is very difficult to settle out the fine flyash particles in the dewatering bin; most fine particles would pass over the overflow weir.

Fig. 27 **Flyash intake (see Fig. 26) installed**

Fig. 28 **Water exhauster for vacuum removal of flyash (ash and water are combined in exhauster for transport as a slurry to disposal; upper flange is high-pressure water inlet; dry ash enters left end)**

PRESSURE SYSTEMS

In a pressure system (Fig. 30), an air-lock feeder transfers flyash from a hopper at a low pressure to a pipeline conveyor at a higher pressure. Compressors or blowers provide the airflow and pressure to convey the flyash.

These feeders are designed with a storage capacity based on the desired conveying rate, ash density and number of hoppers to be conveyed in a given unloading sequence. The volumetric feeders are controlled to empty each selected group of hoppers on a staggered cycle, thus providing uniform loading into the conveyor system. Fluidizing air at the inlet and outlet of each feeder insures ash flow.

Vacuum transport systems usually move flyash in a quite "airy" mixture (dilute phase), but the consistency of the mixture can vary with a positive-pressure system. For example, the mixture might be in a dilute phase, a combination dilute and dense phase (much more ash than air) or the mixture may begin as a dense phase and gradually change to a dilute phase at the discharge end.

Many low-velocity, dilute-phase systems operate at some time in a dense phase because dense phase occurs whenever saltation takes place in a pipeline.

AIR-LOCK FEEDER OPERATION

It is customary in dilute-phase flyash transport to use the collecting hoppers for storage; the air-lock tank is used only during the actual ash-moving process. Thus, the inlet valve to the pressure tank is kept closed until the transport cycle begins. This exposes the ash to the unheated tank metal for the shortest possible time, but keeps the ash in the collecting hoppers for the longest possible time.

In dense-phase transport, the inlet valves of the pressure tanks are kept open whenever the tanks are not full. The ash, then, leaves the area that is heated by flue gas and drops into the tanks, normally unheated, until the tank level

Fig. 29 **Dry pneumatic flyash transport system using water exhausters as vacuum producers**

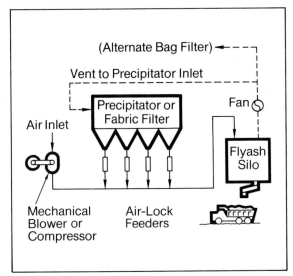

Fig. 30 **Dry pneumatic-pressure flyash system**

indicator causes the inlet valve to close; the filled tank remains at essentially atmospheric pressure until its turn in the transport "queue" is signalled. The time that the ash remains in the tank before fluidization and transport will depend on the filling/emptying status of any other tanks on the same conveying line.

COMPARISON OF VACUUM AND PRESSURE SYSTEMS

Selecting a vacuum or pressure flyash re-

moval system for a given unit depends on an evaluation of

- conveying rate
- altitude
- number of hoppers to be evacuated
- distance to be conveyed

A vacuum conveying system is normally preferred over a dilute-phase pressure system because less equipment is used under each hopper: one flyash intake versus two flyash intakes and an air-lock tank. Also, a vacuum system uses the more positive means of suction to evacuate the flyash from the hoppers whereas a pressure system uses gravity alone to move the ash from the hopper to the feeders. Of course fluidization and rappers are available, but to be effective they must be used properly.

A vacuum system also has the advantage of being able to indicate, from the conveying-line vacuum switches, whether a given hopper is full, empty, plugged or ratholed. This is not possible with a pressure system as multiple hoppers are being evacuated similtaneously.

However, the practicality of a vacuum system is limited by the amount of pressure differential that is available for conveying. The actual pressure drop increases as the conveying rate increases; thus, if all else is constant, higher conveying rates may require a pressure

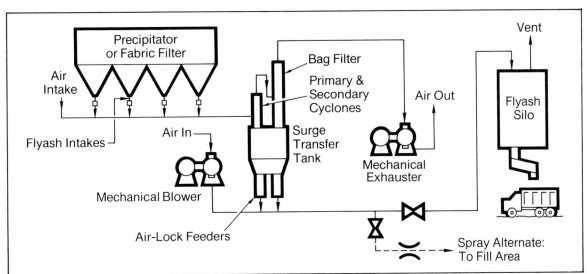

Fig. 31 **Vacuum-to-pressure dry pneumatic flyash system**

system. (Theoretically, a vacuum system can almost always be used by installing many vacuum-producing devices and pipe-lines in parallel.) When plants are at high elevations, the available pressure decreases (at 7000 feet, approximately 5″ Hg. are lost over that of sea level), thus limiting the application of vacuum systems. In addition, the pressure will drop as conveying distance increases, making a pressure system the more feasible.

To understand a pneumatic transport system, it is important to realize that conveying distance is the total developed length of the pipeline. In pneumatics, the pressure drop through an elbow can easily be the equivalent of 50 feet of pipe; therefore, the optimum system would have a minimum number of elbows.

VACUUM/PRESSURE SYSTEMS

When the number of precipitator or baghouse collection hoppers is relatively high (say, 20 to 40, or more) and the conveying distance dictates a pressure system, it is usually economical to provide a vacuum-pressure system, Fig. 31. In this system, a transfer silo is located close to the precipitator or baghouse and the flyash moves by vacuum from the hoppers to the transfer silo. At the discharge of the silo, a set of air-lock feeders form the pressure system to convey the flyash by pressure to the main ash storage silos. The capital and maintenance cost is reduced because of less equipment under the hoppers (one flyash intake per hopper vs. two flyash intakes and the air-lock tank). This reduction in equipment under the hoppers can more than offset additonal costs associated with the transfer silo and the positive pressure blowers. On the other hand, a vacuum-pressure system uses more power than a straight pressure system.

FLYASH HOPPER DESIGN

Pneumatic ash-removal systems *are not designed to handle wet material.* Thus, it is critical in the design and operation of hopper systems to maintain collected material sufficiently above the water or acid dew point

to keep it absolutely dry, so that it *will be* free-flowing.

Dry dust in hoppers ordinarily will flow freely by gravity and be transported pneumatically without difficulty. But to do so, it

- must be kept essentially at the temperature at which it was collected
- must not be exposed to any moisture
- must not compact from its own weight to cause bridging above the hopper outlet
- must have no clinkers formed as the result of oxidation of any combustibles in the ash

In power-plant operation, it is frequently difficult to keep the ash free-flowing. With the boiler at full load, temperatures as low as 90°F have been reported in hoppers of cold precipitators (those that follow the boiler air heaters). Similarly, temperatures 20° to 40°F above *ambient* have been recorded in the hoppers of "hot" precipitators (those located *ahead* of the boiler air heater).

The problem in the industry is even more severe with the high-calcium ash associated with certain subbituminous coals and various lignites. In addition to being highly hygroscopic, such ash shows pozzolanic and cementitious properties when exposed to moisture.

Hoppers under precipitators and baghouses should be considered only as funnels. Because of difficulties with removing flyash that has been stored for a long time while exposed to flue gas containing moisture and sulfur, recommendations state there be no specified storage time in collecting-equipment hoppers.[5]

Minimum hopper outlet size should be 12 inches (diameter or square). In any case, 6-inch or 8-inch outlets should be avoided wherever possible, unless with identical fuels such sizes proved successful.

The ideal hopper is square in horizontal cross section. Minimum outlet-chute or hopper valley angles should be 55 degrees from the horizontal; 60 degrees if space allows. In any case, hopper sides should have a minimum slope of 60 degrees. In addition, for precipitators, rounded inside valleys are desirable with approximately a 4-inch inside radius.

Such rounded corners are not as necessary with fabric filters because the continuous air changes promote ash movement.

Stainless-steel linings at hopper corners or along the hopper's entire lower portion facilitates emptying. Because of size of fields, or where a given row of hoppers serves more than one field, it may be necessary to include baffles in the precipitator. Such baffles should be properly designed and positioned with respect to hopper outlets to prevent bridging. Generally, the baffle plates should terminate 18 inches or more above the hopper outlets.

HOPPER FLUIDIZING DEVICES

Properly located fluidizing devices can help evacuate hoppers (particularly precipitators), if these devices are well-maintained and reliably supplied with dry air preheated above dew-point temperatures. If not, fluidizers will only aggravate evacuation by caking the ash, and provide unwanted surface areas for ash accumulation and bridging. Where significant percentages of combustibles are present in the collected flyash, the fluidizing-medium supply must be non-oxidizing to prevent destructive hopper fires.

The fluidizing devices referred to are those located inside the hopper, away from the walls and extending out into the dust stream; they are not those in the hopper walls or those integral with the flyash intake valves.[5]

HOPPER VIBRATORS

When their operation is properly controlled, hopper vibrators can help prevent bridging and ratholing. In the automatic operation of vacuum pneumatic systems, vibrators should be regulated by ash-evacuation controls to insure operation only when an "empty hopper" signal is generated and the evacuation cycle is completed. Routine use of the vibrators during evacuation of damp ash will further compact the ash and make evacuation difficult.

It should be possible to manually operate the vibrators from each hopper to assist maintenance personnel during emergency evacuation.

WEATHERPROOF ENCLOSURES FOR HOPPERS

Many owners add skirts to precipitators or baghouses to keep wind and weather from reducing the hopper metal temperatures. Such enclosures are highly recommended, although reducing the heat loss from the hoppers can be accomplished equally well by judicious use of insulation and lagging.

Skirts also are instrumental in preventing hopper plugging. They

- keep ash-handling hardware from being chilled to low ambient temperatures
- provide warmed air from the "hopper room" for pneumatic transport of the flyash, particularly with vacuum systems
- allow inspection and maintenance under protected conditions
- provide a plenum for hot air ducted from the top of the boiler house, which then makes heated transport air available without additional energy consumption.[5]

CONTINUOUS REMOVAL OF FLYASH

The ideal flyash-removal system is one that takes ash from the receiving hoppers at the same rate as it enters. The hoppers then effectively become *chutes* and there is no time for cooling, deaeration, or compaction to occur.

There are virtually no such systems in U.S. utility power plants, and only a few in certain industrial boiler or process applications. The majority of multiple-dust-outlet precipitators and baghouses have their removal systems intentionally designed for intermittent removal to minimize the power consumed by the ash-transport system. Such an approach ignores the harmful impact on the reliability of collection equipment when hoppers are used for storage.

Utility plants in Europe report good experience with continuous removal as have some industrial installations in the U.S. In these systems flyash is transported by either mechanical or air-fluidized conveyors, instead of by pneumatic-conveying equipment. It appears that a principal feature of such continuous-removal devices is that, with proper valving, they do not allow any substantial amount of air

Fig. 32 Mechanical flight conveyor for dry moving of flyash and economizer ash

to leak into the precipitator or baghouse hoppers. This feature maintains the gas temperatures in those hoppers above the dew point.[5]

Air-fluidized conveyors can be used only if the flyash remains fluid under all conditions of start-up, normal load, or shutdown. Although these conveyors are a form of continuous removal, there have been numerous problems in keeping the ash completely dry during start-up. Also, if ash clinkers form, they are impossible to fluidize and transport.

Two types of *mechanical* conveyors have been used for conveying flyash—screw conveyors and flight conveyors. Often prone to wear, screw conveyors are usually used for ash transport only when conveying a relatively small quantity of material. Flight conveyors (Fig. 32) move the ash in a dust-tight casing using elements linked by a single or double strand of chain. The units are sized either on a volumetric basis or on an *en masse* basis in which the material is conveyed in bulk, without agitation. Flight conveyors have been successfully operated for many decades on coal-fired units, both in North America and Europe. They are relatively insensitive to problems such as moisture in the flyash and flyash clinkers (which may force outages in other types of systems).

With continuous conveying devices, the system can combine the mechanical conveyor with a pneumatic pipeline. Mechanical devices have the ability to move the ash "uphill" to the top of a storage silo.

FLYASH RECEIVING AND STORING EQUIPMENT

Flyash storage silos and their related accessories form an integral part of ash-handling equipment. Silos are made of concrete or steel, depending upon size, seismic condition, and plant economics.

On vacuum systems, equipment is required to separate the flyash from the conveying air stream before it can be discharged into the silo. This equipment, located on top of the silo, normally has several stages of separation.

AIR/FLYASH SEPARATION EQUIPMENT

Dual-cyclone continuous-separation modules are the primary mechanism to separate the flyash from the conveying air. The module contains a primary and secondary cyclone separator (Fig. 33). The centrifugal action exerted by the cyclone forces the flyash to drop as the lighter airflow is extracted from the top. By using an airlock the storage silo is never under vacuum and the module can function continuously.

The bag filter receives the flow from the separation modules and acts to precipitate the remaining flyash from the conveying air stream. This tertiary separation protects the vacuum pump from unnecessary particulate carry-over.

Fig. 33 Dual-cyclone module for continous separation of flyash and transport air (used on vacuum-pneumatic systems)

The bag filter usually features reversed-air cleaning with a good air-to-cloth ratio.

The vacuum-producing device (blower, vacuum pump, exhauster) which has pulled the flyash air mixture down the pipeline and through the discharge equipment, is located at the side or underneath the silo.

On a pressure system, somewhat simpler filtration equipment is used. Vent fans and motor drives are mounted on top of the storage silo. The vent fan should be designed to handle not only all the air displaced in the silo by the conveying input stream and silo fluidizing air, but also the static head required to transport it back to the precipitator inlet duct. The vent fan places the silo under a slight negative pressure, eliminating the possibility of blowing dust out of the silo. Vent-fan operation can be synchronized with that of the conveying blowers. Alternately, the vent fan can discharge to a bag filter atop the silo.

SILO FLUIDIZATION

Flyash, when not allowed to agglomerate and when fluidized with heated air, takes on the flow properties of a fluid. To expedite flyash removal, troughs with fluidizing air are provided at the bottom of the silos. Traditionally, the fluidizing medium was constructed of canvas or porous stone. But recently, the industry has been using porous laminates of sintered stainless-steel-wire cloth such as used in the C-E flyash intake. This provides a microporous filter that allows controlled amounts of heated air to pass and fluidize the flyash. The possibility of stress cracking that is common with fluidizing stones is eliminated with this metallic material. Because of the microporous construction, the metallic cloth is highly resistant to blinding; in addition, water will not penetrate into the porous openings. This will allow washing of equipment with water without having to remove the fluidizing media.

Fluidizing-air blowers and associated heaters provide the required air to the fluidizing air troughs. Care must be taken to properly size the blowers to account for a full head of flyash in the silo.

Fluidizing hoods, normally one above each silo discharge opening, minimize the possibility of avalanching, which would adversely affect the operation of the unloading equipment.

Silo discharge equipment is designed so the flyash can be removed dry into enclosed vehicles, or so that it can be moistened (to 12–15 percent moisture by weight) for transport in open vehicles. It is increasingly common for flyash to be sold for use in landfills, roads and the cement industry.

Telescoping ash discharge chutes convey flash dry from the storage silo to a removal vehicle stationed below. Normally, each chute is capable of extending a full eighteen feet using a motor-driven-winch retract system. A blower and piping in each chute vent, back into the silo, any fugitive dust released during the unloading process. An air-operated gate controls the inlet flow to the chute and is placed just below a manual maintenance gate. A clean-out compartment should be included between the maintenance gate and control gate. This compartment should contain a grid to trap large clinkers that may form in the silo, and an access door for their subsequent removal.

Flyash Conditioners

Rotary ash conditioners, Fig. 34, add moisture to the flyash discharged from the storage silo into open-top vehicles. The conditioning and moisture prevents any fugitive-dust nuisance. An orifice feeder controls the rate at which the dry material moves from the silo into the mixing drum of the conditioner. A series of atomizing nozzles within the drum spray the material with water as the drum rotates. A longitudinal scraper bar along the full length of the drum plows damp material from the side of the drum, causing it to be mixed thoroughly with the spray water. The continuous tumbling action of the wetted material within the drum results in minimal dust at the conditioner out-

let. Stop plates prevent any tendency for dry material to cascade through the drum before being thoroughly mixed with water. Mounted on a central support, the scraper bar and stop plates are readily removed.

OPERATIONAL CONTROLS

Ash-handling controls range from completely manual to completely automatic systems of either the relay, solid state, or programmable-controller type. Figs. 35 and 36 show a typical free-standing control panel for a relay system.

When selecting the type of control system and the degree of automation that should be employed, many factors should be considered. First, the more automated the plant, the less attention paid by the plant operators. If little attention is paid to ash systems, breakdowns are inevitable and, when breakdowns occur,

Fig. 34 Sectional side elevation of C-E rotary-type flyash conditioner

the operators may lack enough knowledge of the system to take corrective action. For intermittent-removal bottom-ash and pyrites systems many utilities select a push-button automatic system where the operator, at a local panel, performs the ash-removal sequence. The operator can judge by the crushing sound of the grinder, whether each hopper section has been emptied. If a problem arises, the operator is on hand to analyze it and take action.

In some cases density meters are installed in the discharge line of each bottom-ash hopper section to record the amount of time it takes to empty each section. By comparing the time to empty one section with that of other sections, it's possible to spot signs of trouble.

Similarly, on a vacuum pneumatic system, the operator can make a check by examining the strip chart that records the vacuum in the pneumatic pipeline. As vacuum can be related to the ash flow, the operator can easily determine the removal rate and time required to empty each hopper. Inconsistencies in removal time and/or removal rate per hopper are signs of a problem.

On multifield precipitators, programmable

controllers can be used to advantage. As the front fields will collect ash at a much faster rate than the rear fields, the operator may choose to alter the sequence in which hoppers are "visited" by the ash removal system. Such adjustments accommodate unequal distribution across the fields, or compensate for fields being removed from service.

Continuous removal systems obviously require the least sophisticated controls but on/off switches, indicating lights, and alarms should be provided. Programmable controllers are rarely justified.

MATERIAL- AND ENERGY-BALANCE CONSIDERATIONS

Water-impounded ash-receiving equipment beneath a furnace, as previously stated, helps to quench the ash as it falls from the furnace and to transport it to a disposal point. The thermal shock to the hot ash as it enters the low-temperature water helps to break up the large pieces while submerging the ash prevents sintering during the time that it may be stored (with intermittent-removal systems).

Fig. 35 C-E control console for an intermittent-removal bottom-ash system and vacuum-pneumatic flyash system

Fig. 36 Rear view of free-standing control console in Fig. 35

Fig. 37 Steady-state heat-balance diagram for furnace bottom-ash receiver

Part of the heat released in the furnace is transmitted to the ash hopper by radiation from the burning fuel, but most of the heat input is from the sensible heat given up to the water by the hot bottom ash falling from the furnace. The ash-systems engineer must perform a heat balance to determine the flow of cooling water required to absorb the incoming heat and maintain the water temperature at a predetermined level.

Field experience indicates that the temperature of the impounded water should be optimally about 140°F, and should not be higher than 160°F. Temperatures at this level are effective in rapidly cooling and fracturing the falling ash. Lower temperatures require more cooling water; higher temperature may prove uncomfortable or unsafe in the area around the bottom-ash receiver.

BOTTOM-ASH COOLING SYSTEM DESIGN

Heat is removed from bottom-ash hoppers or submerged conveyors by

■ evaporation of water from the surface of the water pool

■ the heat removed in the water going out the overflow or leakage points

■ the heat removed with the accumulated bottom ash as it is discharged

■ the heat loss by radiation and convection from the outside metal surfaces

The last loss is small and is usually neglected in view of the unknown accuracy of some of the other assumed factors.

Fig. 37 is a simplified heat-balance diagram around a bottom-ash receiver, in this case, a submerged scraper conveyor with continuous ash removal. The heat balance forms the basis for the calculation of the cooling-water flow needed to maintain a temperature of about 140°F (60°C). In Fig. 37

$$Q_{in} = Q_{out}$$

(2)

where

$$Q_{in} = Q_{ash\ entering} + Q_{furnace\ radiation} + Q_{inlet\ water} = Q_{ae} + Q_{fr} + Q_{iw}$$

and

$$Q_{out} = Q_{overflow\ water} + Q_{ash\ leaving} + Q_{evaporation} + Q_{external\ radiation\ loss} + Q_{water\ in\ ash\ leaving} = Q_{ow} + Q_{al} + Q_e + Q_{er} + Q_{aw}$$

MASS AND ENERGY TERMS

Before equating and simplifying the above inputs and outputs so that they can be mathematically manipulated, it is necessary to define and discuss them further.

HEAT IN THE BOTTOM ASH

The mass of bottom ash, M_{ba}, is the collection rate, lb/hr or kg/hr.

$$Q_{ae} = M_{ba} \times C_{ash_1} \times (T_{hot\ ash} - T_r)$$

(3)

where

C_{ash_1} = specific heat of the ash at the mean temperature between $T_{hot\ ash}$ and T_r

$T_{hot\ ash}$ = the temperature of the falling ash or slag as it enters the water pool

T_r = reference temperature for defining heat contents

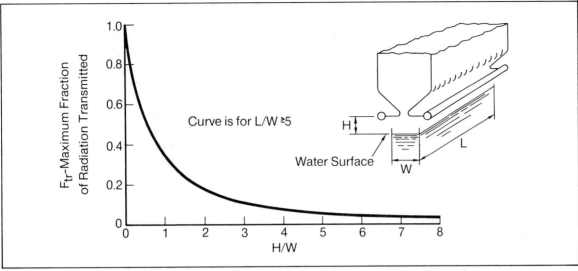

Fig. 38 Curve to determine fraction of radiation transmitted to ash-receiver water surface

The temperature of ash leaving the bottom of a furnace depends on the thickness of the pieces dislodged from the walls, the face-metal temperature of the furnace walls, the temperature of the sootblowing medium, the distance of fall, and the average gas temperature surrounding the material during its fall. For pulverized coal fired in suspension (without the use of furnace-bottom grates), the temperature is estimated to be between 1200°F and 1800°F, averaging 1500°F. Obviously, the validity of the heat-balance calculation depends on this temperature to a great extent.

The heat of the cooled bottom ash exiting the collection device is

$$Q_{al} = M_{ba} \times C_{ash_2} \times (t_{out} - T_r)$$

(4)

where

C_{ash_2} = specific heat of the ash at the mean temperature between t_{out} and T_r

where

t_{out} = temperature of the water and ash leaving

FURNACE RADIATION TO THE IMPOUNDED WATER

Furnace radiation passing through an opening in the hopper bottom varies with firing rate, furnace and firing-system configuration, and the effective center of the fuel-admission nozzles or burners in operation (measured vertically above the furnace-bottom opening). The heat transfer is

$$Q_{fr} = A_{fa} \times R_f \times F_{tr}$$

(5)

where:

A_{fa} = furnace hopper-bottom aperture above the ash receiver

R_f = radiation rate through furnace aperture, Btu/hr-sq ft

F_{tr} = fraction of radiation transmitted to water surface through the space between the furnace bottom and the water, Fig. 38.

A typical value for R_f, the heat radiated through the bottom aperture to the space above the impounded water, is 20,000 Btu/hr-sq ft. Fig. 38 shows that the radiation reaching the water surface decreases as that surface is located farther away from the aperture, as would be expected.

HEAT IN COOLING WATER

The mass of incoming cooling water, from all sources (including any refractory-cooling

16–31

water or SSC bearing-flush water), is designated M_{iw}.

$$Q_{iw} = M_{iw} \times C_{iw} \times (t_{iw} - T_r) \tag{6}$$

where:

T_{iw} = incoming water temperature

C_{iw} = incoming water specific heat

The mass of cooling water leaving, M_{ow}, includes any outward leakage, but not the water entrained by the exiting bottom ash; the latter is shown as M_{aw}, the mass of heated water leaving with the ash.

$$Q_{ow} = M_{ow} \times C_{ow} \times (t_{ow} - T_r) \text{ and}$$
$$Q_{aw} = M_{aw} \times C_{ow} \times (t_{ow} - T_r) \tag{7}$$

where

C_{ow} = specific heat of water leaving

t_{ow} = temperature of the impounded water

HEAT LEAVING IN EVAPORATED WATER

The rate of evaporation from a water pool below a large coal-fired furnace is a complex function of the water temperature, the temperature of the radiating gas, and the other factors involved in the determination of the radiation rate. In general, rates between 4 and 10 U.S. gallons/day-sq ft are to be expected. Large pieces of slag falling into the water can result in additional localized evaporation, which is neither calculable or separable from the overall effect. It is calculated by

$$Q_e = A_w \times R_e \times h_{fg} \tag{8}$$

where

A_w = total area of ash-receiver water surface

R_e = evaporation rate per unit of surface area

h_{fg} = latent heat of vaporization of water at T_{ow}

SIMPLIFICATION OF THE HEAT-BALANCE EQUATION

If T_r, the reference temperature, is equal to t_{ow}, the water temperature in the water pool, Q_{al}, Q_{ow}, and Q_{aw} go to zero, then,

$$Q_{ae} + Q_{fr} + Q_{iw} = Q_e,$$
$$\text{or}$$
$$Q_{ae} + Q_{fr} = Q_e + |M_{iw} \times C_{iw} \times (t_{ow} - t_{iw})| \tag{9}$$

Note that the mass of water leaving, M_{ow} must not be less than zero; that is,

$$M_{ow} = (M_{iw} - M_{aw} - M_e) \geq 0 \tag{10}$$

where

M_e = mass rate of evaporated water

In a closed-loop cooling-water system, M_{ow} is the amount of water that must be cooled and recirculated. The extent of physical cleanup and chemical treatment applied to this recirculated water is principally a function of what the system heat-transfer and pumping equipment can tolerate. Generally, the cleanup required for the low-pressure cooling stream of an SSC is much less than that for an intermittent-removal hopper with slope jetting nozzles, which use water at high pressure.

Recirculation equipment size and cost are sensitive to the ash temperature and quantity, the furnace radiation absorbed, and the evaporation rate, as shown above. It is important that economic comparisons of such loops be based on equivalent boundary conditions, which include, in addition, the inlet water and impounded water temperatures.

It is fairly accurate, for these heat-balance calculations, to use 0.25 Btu/lb-°F for the specific heat of ash, 1.0 as the specific heat of water, and 1014 Btu/lb as h_{fg} at 140°F.

COOLING-WATER FLOW VARIATION

Two inputs to the equation can vary widely, greatly affecting the cooling-water flow. First, the bottom-ash collection is a function of

■ quantity of fuel burned (boiler load and heating value of the coal)

■ percentage of ash in the fuel

■ percentage of the total ash that falls to the furnace bottom

Second, the cooling water temperature can vary substantially from summer to winter, and with geographical area.

The designer is faced with the problem of deciding what should be used for ash-collecting rates and the water temperature to the hopper. The common design approach requires excess water because the designer uses *maximum* values for all calculations. Systems so designed will pump and treat excessive quantities of water when the unit is burning a good fuel in winter when the cooling water is cold.

The potential difference in cooling water usage is illustrated in Table III. This data considers only the water necessary to cool the incoming ash (not taking into account the radiation and evaporation heat exchange), to point out how great is the difference between the two postulated conditions.

If the ash-system was designed to provide the maximum cooling water at all times, the pumping power consumption would be considerably greater than needed. Because the purpose of the cooling water is to maintain the ash-hopper water at a temperature such as 140°F, it is logical to regulate the flow on a demand basis. This is done by monitoring the overflow water temperature and modulating a supply valve. The system design has to provide for the worst case (maximum cooling water), but the actual water use will only be as required, thereby saving pumping power and the cost of cleanup of the ash-receiver overflow water under many load conditions.

PROPER INSTALLATION

It is important to state that any ash-removal system must be installed, set up, checked out, and deemed ready for use by a plant startup crew. There have been many reports of damage to boiler pressure parts and precipitator elements, with consequent unit shutdowns caused by well designed ash-removal systems that were not ready for use.

Also, ash, by nature, is a very abrasive material and wear and replacement of worn components are inevitable. Plant personnel must perform regular inspections of these wear components and make replacements as necessary.

TABLE III. Cooling Water Usage*

	High Use	Low Use
Coal burned, lb/hr	750,000	200,000
Ash content, percent	25	10
Cooling water temperature, °F	90	50
Ash down, percent	50	30
Bottom ash collection, lb/hr	93,750	6,000
Cooling water flow, U.S. GPM	1,275	45

*Approximate, based on absorbing heat from incoming ash at 1500°F only; no radiation or evaporation considered. Ash receiver water temperature 140°F.

REFERENCES

[1] E. H. Tenney, "Pulverization and Boiler Performance," FSP-54-7, *Proceedings of the Fourth National Fuels Meeting*, Feb 11 to 13, 1931, pp. 55–65. Chicago, Illinois: The American Society of Mechanical Engineers. 1931.

E. G. Bailey, "Present Status of Furnace and Burner Design for Pulverized Fuel," FSP-50-72, *Transactions of the American Society of Mechanical Engineers*, September to December 1928, p. 177. New York: The American Society of Mechanical Engineers.

[2] W. E. Loftus, "Ash Handling, Storage and Utilization," *Proceedings of the American Power Conference*, 38:707–717, 1976. Chicago: Illinois Institute of Technology. 1976.

[3] J. G. Singer and A. J. Cozza, "Material and Energy Balances of Ash-Handling Systems," Presented at the Joint Power Generation Conference. Dallas, Sept. 10–13, 1978; published as Combustion Engineering publication TIS-5822, Windsor, CT: Combustion Engineering Inc., 1978.

[4] J. G. Singer and A. J. Cozza, "Design for Continuous Ash Removal: Alternative Concepts in Ash Handling," *Proceedings of the American Power Conference*, 41: 544–553, 1979. Chicago: Illinois Institute of Technology. 1979.

[5] Joint Technical Committee of the American Boiler Manufacturers Association and Industrial Gas Cleaning Institute, Inc., "Design and Operation of Reliable Central Station Flyash Hopper Evacuation Systems," *Proceedings of the American Power Conference* vol 42, 1980. Chicago: Illinois Institute of Technology. 1980.

CHAPTER 17

Power-Plant Emission-Control Systems

This chapter presents the various types of commercially available equipment for the control of particulate and gaseous effluents. No reference is made to national or local legislation or regulations because of the probability of change from year to year. Such regulations are best found in the U.S. Federal Register or obtained from the local environment-regulating agencies in other countries.

ENVIRONMENTAL FACTORS IN POWER PRODUCTION

The installation of highly efficient precipitators, baghouses, and flue-gas desulfurization systems (FGDS) has become increasingly necessary; power-plant owners must include them in their planning to obtain permission to start construction of a new facility. Additional controls that are applied to other gaseous emissions such as oxides of nitrogen, and to liquid and solid wastes that result from the processing, handling, and disposal of fossil fuels and their products of combustion add considerably to the complexity and cost of installation, operation, and maintenance of power plants.

Changes in fuel availability as well as air-quality standards have impacted significantly on the electric-utility industry. Discounting in-

flation, the cost of installation of a major facility has more than doubled since the imposition of environmental laws. Because of permits needed to satisfy ecological statutes, and the time taken to debate these in public, the time required to construct a fossil plant has increased 2 to 3 years.

Besides the emission-control equipment described in this chapter, a coal-fired power plant must have

■ very high static-pressure ID fans or additional FGD booster fans to accommodate draft requirements

■ flue-gas reheat to increase the buoyancy of gases from an FGD system to insure adequate dispersion of the residual SO_2, NO_x, and particulate matter exiting from the stack

■ FGD solid-waste beneficiation, handling, and disposal systems

■ more sophisticated treatment of raw water, makeup water, and waste water

■ condenser cooling-water systems that do not add heat to inland or coastal waters.

The auxiliary power requirements of equipment to satisfy environmental regulations may demand from 9 to 14 percent of the total installed capacity of a large power plant.

POWER-PLANT EMISSIONS

Three classes of emissions are judged significant from an air-quality standpoint: particulate matter, sulfur oxides, and nitrogen oxides. Historically, particulate matter has received the greatest attention because it is easily seen and often labeled a public nuisance. The concern about sulfur oxide comes from its possible health effects and from its potential to damage vegetation. Oxides of nitrogen are also significant because they participate in complex chemical reactions that lead to formation of photo-chemical smog in the atmosphere.

PARTICULATE EMISSIONS

Emissions from coal-fired boilers vary considerably depending on the ash content of the coal and the type of firing. A pulverized-coal-fired unit can be expected to have 60 to 80 percent of the coal ash normally leaving the furnace with the flue gas. The balance of the ash leaves through the boiler bottom-ash removal system, hoppers under economizers and air heaters, and pulverizer rejects hoppers. Fig. 1 illustrates the exceedingly high efficiency required of particulate-collection equipment for high-ash-content coals and very low effluent ash levels.

As flyash is nonhomogeneous in properties such as specific gravity and particle shape, size is very difficult to describe in absolute terms. Methods for determining this property include photomicrographs, sedimentation, and elutriation devices. Flyash is the combination of inert or inorganic residue in pulverized-coal particles with varying amounts of carbon or coke particles resulting from incomplete combustion. In general, the inorganic ash particles consist primarily of silicates, oxides and sulfates together with small quantities of phosphates and other trace compounds. Particle size varies from below 0.01 micron diameter to over 100 microns. Fig. 2, based on test data,[1] shows the size distribution between the 2 and $50 \mu m$ diameters.

SULFUR-OXIDE EMISSIONS

As fuels burn, most of the sulfur content is converted to the sulfur oxides SO_2 and SO_3. As explained in Chapter 2, the quantity of sulfur varies widely for different coals and may range from less than 0.5 to over 5 percent. In general, 90 percent or more of the sulfur in the fuel will oxidize to gaseous sulfur oxides. Typically, concentrations will be 0.1 to 0.25 percent by volume in the products of combustion. The fur-

Fig. 1 Required particulate-collection efficiency versus inlet ash concentration

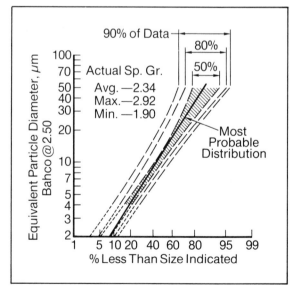

Fig. 2 Flyash particle-size distribution in pulverized-coal-fired boilers

ther conversion of SO_2 to SO_3 ranges from 1 to 4 percent. The formation of SO_3 in a boiler is a complex process and is believed to be influenced by the oxidation of SO_2 by molecular oxygen, oxidation of SO_2 in the flame by atomic oxygen, and catalytic oxidation of SO_2.

NITROGEN-OXIDE EMISSIONS

During the combustion process in a conventional steam generator, oxides of nitrogen (collectively referred to as NO_x) form in the high-temperature region in and around the flame zone. The oxidation of both atmospheric nitrogen (thermal NO_x) and nitrogen contained in the fuel (fuel NO_x), is the cause. The rate of formation is influenced by the temperature and the oxygen present. Reducing the flame temperature and the excess air can help control thermal-NO_x formation. Fuel NO_x is related to the available nitrogen in the fuel and is most significantly influenced by the oxygen concentration in the combustion region.

In addition to the information on post-furnace NO_x control in this chapter, refer to Chapter 4 for a discussion of NO_x formation and to Chapter 13 for techniques to reduce NO_x in furnaces.

PARTICULATE EMISSION CONTROL

Particulate emission control deals with methods of removing particles dispersed in effluent gases of power, industrial process and commercial plants. These dispersions, commonly referred to as aerosols or dispersoids, have through general use come to include all particles in air or other gases.

Dispersoids are characterized by their physical, chemical, and electrical properties, their particle size and structure, rate of settling under gravity, optical activity, the ability to absorb an electrical charge, the surface-to-volume ratio and the chemical reaction rate. Particles larger than 100 microns are excluded from consideration because they settle rapidly. On the other hand, 1-micron particles settle slowly and are regarded as permanent suspensions.

Dispersoids are generally classified as dust, smoke, fumes and mists. Fig. 3A indicates the common dispersoids and the typical particle size for each classification. Fig. 3B notes the devices for collecting the various classifications of dispersoids.

INFLUENCE OF COAL AND COMBUSTION CHARACTERISTICS

The varying coal characteristics described in Chapter 2 have a dominant effect on the removal efficiency of particulates. The variation in ash content, ash composition, ash resistivity and particle size distribution requires an engineering evaluation of collection principles to reduce emissions to required levels.

INFLUENCE OF VOLUMETRIC GAS FLOW

No matter what type of flyash collector is to be installed on a boiler, it is essential that it be designed for the correct gas volume.

Manufacturers design and size their equipment based upon their experience with this equipment. This experience includes tests on both laboratory or pilot-plant equipment, and full-scale equipment. The joint American Boiler Manufacturers Association (ABMA) and Industrial Gas Cleaning Institute (IGCI) survey has shown there to be a difference in the gas volume of gas that is measured by the pitot tube and in the volume of gas that is calculated from a stoichiometric balance.[1]

The pitot tube consistently indicates a higher volume. The manufacturer of the dust-collection equipment, therefore, must ascertain that the gas volume for equipment design has been stoichiometrically calculated and be aware that the value may differ from a volume measured by a pitot tube in the operating installation. It is vital that proper corrections be made for plant elevation and local negative pressure ahead of the induced-draft fan, to arrive at the actual gas volume. (See Chapter 6.)

Because performance is so dependent upon gas volume, the question as to which technique to use for field testing to guarantee verification becomes very important. The ABMA member companies use the heat-balance techniques of

ASME PTC 4.1, Steam Generating Units. The IGCI member companies use *ASME* PTC 21, Dust Separating Apparatus, which uses the pitot-tube techniques. Under ideal conditions, where both techniques have been used, volume variations of about 5 percent have been observed, the pitot-tube technique being higher. With less than ideal conditions, as much as 15 percent variation has been observed, again the pitot-tube technique being higher. (See Chapter 21 for more on gas-volume measurement.)

MEASUREMENT TECHNIQUES

It is difficult to analyze size distribution of fine particulate matter because flyash is non-homogeneous. The varying specific gravity and particle shape make it difficult to describe size in absolute terms. Many methods, including photomicrographs and various sedimentation and elutriation techniques, have been used to determine size distribution. The ASME Performance Test Code Committee has selected

terminal settling velocity to characterize flyash particulate emmissions from furnaces.

TERMINAL VELOCITY

Particle terminal velocity is a significant parameter in the design of mechanical separators that use inertial or centrifugal forces to separate dust from a gas stream. It includes the effect of particle shape and specific gravity for each particle. Its determination is important for heterogeneous dusts of varying shape and specific gravity. Determination of terminal velocity for a centrifugal classifier is included in *ASME Performance Test Code* 28.

Flyash characterization also includes methods for bulk electrical resistivity, insitu resistivity and particle size.

BULK ELECTRICAL RESISTIVITY

Particulate resistivity can be determined in a high-voltage conductivity cell in which a sample of known thickness is placed between two

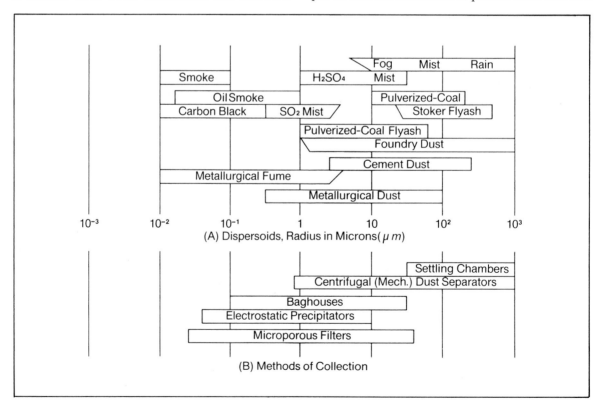

Fig. 3 Classification of dispersoids and methods of collection

oppositely charged electrodes. Guard rings eliminate fringe effects. The potential between the two electrodes is increased and the voltage and current noted until an electrical breakdown occurs. The resistivity is then calculated and reported in ohms per cm at 85 to 95 percent of the average breakover.

IN-SITU RESISTIVITY

A combination high-voltage and ground-potential probe, inserted in the gas stream, has a negative high-voltage probe consisting of a flat disc concentric about a needle-point electrode. The needle-point electrode precipitates the particulates electrically from the dispersoid. The flat charged disc is separated from the needle point so as not to affect the precipitation of particulate onto a grounded electrode. After a short time, the charged disc is lowered to entrap the precipitated particulate between it and the grounded electrode. Calculation is the same as bulk electrical resistivity.

Fig. 4 **Principle of cyclone-separator operation**

DUST COLLECTION BY MECHANICAL MEANS

Although cyclone-type mechanical collectors have a long history in boiler service, their use is now limited to small stoker-fired units because of their relatively low collection efficiency. Mechanical collectors can be either the dry cyclone collector or the wet scrubber.

MECHANICAL CYCLONE COLLECTORS

These devices achieve particulate removal by centrifugal, inertial, and gravitational forces developed in a vortex separator. The dust-laden gas is admitted either tangentially or axially over whirl vanes (Fig. 4) to create a high velocity in the cylindrical portion of the device. Particles are subjected to an outward centrifugal force and an oppositely directed viscous drag. The balance between these two forces determines whether a particle will move to the wall or be carried into the vortex sink and be passed on to the clean-gas outlet tube.

The high-velocity, downwardly-directed vortex is reversed at the bottom of the cylindrical section. In this reversal, inertia and gravity as well as centrifugal force inject the dust into the hopper. The action of the reversed-gas circulation takes place over a small diameter but at a relatively great velocity.

This inner vortex has an axially upward component which carries the spirally flowing gas to the outlet pipe at the upper center of the separating unit. Because these collectors depend primarily on differential inertia, collection efficiencies vary with particle size, density, gas temperature, and pressure drop through the apparatus. Efficiencies are very high on material greater than 20 microns ($20 \mu m$) in size, but drop off rapidly as particles approach the minus 10 range. The overall collection efficiency of a cyclone can be estimated when the particle-size distribution of the dust and the allowable pressure drop are known. Fig. 5 relates collection efficiency to particle size. In normal boiler operation, differential-pressure requirements for mechanical collectors are from 2 to 5″ WG.

WET SCRUBBERS

Dust scrubbing is an extremely complex process with no proven theoretical analysis to compare with those for dry mechanical separation, electrostatic collection or filtration.

In the analysis of scrubbing particulates, a number of important facts are known. First, the dust particle must impact on the water droplet. The impaction efficiency is a function of the dimensionless group $\dfrac{(Vr\ Vs)}{Dg}$ where Vr is the relative velocity between the water droplet and the dust particle, Vs is the setting velocity for the dust particle, D is the diameter of the water droplet in microns, and g is the acceleration of gravity. As g and Vs are constant for a dust particle of a given size, target efficiency is a direct function of the relative velocity and an inverse function of the droplet diameter. If the collection efficiency depends critically on relative velocity and droplet size, then collection efficiency must also be a function of the power supplied to the unit.

Phase transfer for small particles require high energy inputs, usually in the form of greater pressure drops across the scrubber. Low-pressure-drop scrubbers, such as spray towers, collect coarse dust in the range of 2 to 5 microns. High-pressure-drop venturi scrubbers are effective in removing 0.1 to 1.0 micron particles.

Typically, a scrubber operating at 6″ WG pressure drop should capture practically 100 percent of the particles greater than 5 microns, and about 90 percent of the particles in the 1 to 2 micron range.

Fig. 6 shows typical efficiency curve for a wet scrubber operating at 6″ WG pressure drop.

VENTURI SCRUBBERS

In a venturi scrubber, dust laden gases are wetted continuously at the venturi throat. Flowing at 12,000 to 18,000 fpm, the gases produce a shearing force on the scrubbing liquor due to the initial high velocity differential between the two streams. This shearing force causes the liquor to atomize into very fine droplets.

Impaction takes place between the dust entrained in the gas stream and the liquid droplets. As the gas decelerates, collision continues and agglomeration of the dust-laden liquor droplets discharge through a diffuser into the lower chamber of a separator vessel. Impingement of the stream into the liquid reservoir removes most of the particulate.

A venturi-type scrubber operating in the pressure range of 30 to 40″ WG can collect nearly 100 percent of 0.2 to 1.0 micron particles.

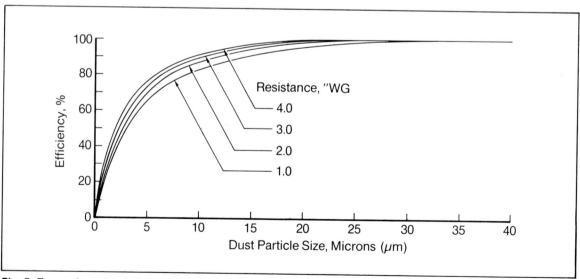

Fig. 5 **Form of mechanical dust-collector efficiency curve versus particle size**

ELECTROSTATIC PRECIPITATION OF DUST

In electrostatic precipitation, suspended particles in the gas are electrically charged, then driven to collecting electrodes by an electrical field; the electrodes are rapped to cause the particles to drop into collecting hoppers. This process differs from mechanical or filtering processes in which forces are exerted directly on the particulates rather than the gas as a whole. Effective separation of particles can be achieved with lower power expenditure, with negligible draft loss, and with little or no effect on the composition of the gas.

In the United States, the control of emissions began with preventing or minimizing nuisance smoke. Such control required equipment capable of only 70 to 90 percent efficiency. Later, the need to protect induced-draft fans by reducing entrained flyash emitted from utility boilers led to precipitators being built for power plants. The first such application was in 1923.[2]

The early users of electrostatic precipitators, then, installed them to

■ recover a valuable product, such as lead, copper, or saltcake

■ eliminate a nuisance, either visual or damaging to crops

■ protect process equipment, such as induced-draft fans.

As initially applied, precipitators were designed to provide a minimum plate area at low cost; designs used interlocking or opzel collecting plates and hanging weighted-wire discharge electrodes. Roof-mounted gang-rapping vibrators removed particulate from the collectors.

To meet a demand for ultra-high efficiency collectors of rugged construction and high reliability, European manufacturers in possession of the basic patents disseminated by Frederick Gardner Cottrell developed the rigid-frame precipitator. Actually, this design more closely approximated Cottrell's original design than did the U.S.-style weighted-wire designs. The term *rigid-frame* refers to the rugged pipe-frame or mast-construction discharge electrode, which largely precludes wire breakage. The basic design incorporates: segmented collecting plate configurations and profiles for close fabrication tolerances over heights more than 40 feet, rigid discharge electrodes, and much greater division of rapping, often with individual rapping for each discharge frame.

ELECTROSTATIC COLLECTION TECHNIQUE

Fig. 7 shows in simple fashion the principle of electrostatic precipitation. The process applies an electrostatic charge to dust particles with a corona discharge and passes them through an electrical field where the particles are attracted to a collecting surface. The basic elements of a precipitator include a source of unidirectional voltage, corona or discharge electrodes, collecting electrodes and a means of removing the collected matter.

PRECIPITATOR TYPES

Single-stage (Cottrell type) precipitators combine the ionizing and collecting step (Fig. 8A). In the more common plate type, the electrodes are suspended between plates on insulators connected to a high-voltage source. A voltage differential created between the discharge and collecting electrodes develops a strong electrical field between them. The flue gas is passed through the field and a unipolar discharge of gas ions, from the discharge electrode, is attached to the particulate matter.

***Fig. 6** Wet-scrubber fractional efficiency curve*

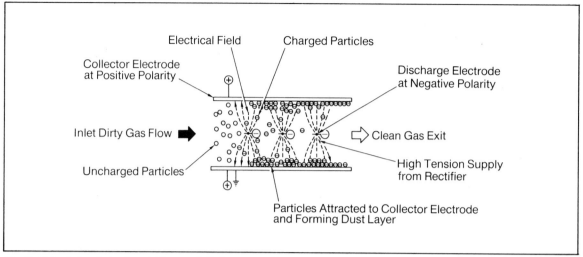

Fig. 7 **Principle of electrostatic precipitator operation**

The unipolar discharge of gas ions (normally negative charge) occurs at a critical voltage at which air molecules are ionized. The ionization is visible as a corona at the discharge electrode. The negative air ions move towards the positive collecting electrode; the positive air ions migrate toward the discharge electrode. In this movement, the air ions become attached to neutral particles carried by the gas stream. The charge is the force that moves flyash to the appropriate electrode. The particles attached to the positive electrode dissipate their charge and become electrically neutral. The particulates on the collecting electrode are removed mechanically by rapping or washing.

In the two-stage precipitator, the ionizing and collecting stages are separated (Fig. 8B). This design is used for low particulate loadings and minimum ozone generation.

Single-stage precipitators are classified as either weighted-wire or rigid-frame units.

Weighted-wire units work well on high-sulfur coal and easily removed particulates and have economic designs. The rigid-frame pre-

(A) Rigid-Frame Single-Stage Precipitator   (B) Two-Stage Precipitator

Fig. 8 **Electrostatic-precipitator types**

cipitator is better suited to applications where high-resistivity ash is to be collected and large collecting areas are needed. The term rigid frame comes from the discharge electrodes being suspended in rigid support frames. These units have high reliability and low maintenance, which combined caused a significant shift to rigid-frame equipment.

PRECIPITATOR DESIGN FACTORS

Precipitator designs consider
- specific collection area (SCA)
- treatment time
- gas velocity
- number of fields
- automatic voltage control (AVC)
- hopper size and slope.

Specific Collection Area (SCA)

The SCA relates the size of one precipitator to another in terms of the effective collecting-electrode surface area per thousand cfm (cubic ft/min) of gas treated. The area considered is the flat projected surface of both sides of the collecting electrodes; the gas volume is the actual volume at the design operating temperature and power-plant elevation. Depending upon the physical, chemical, and electrical characteristics of the coal ash, precipitator SCA's range from 300 to 1000 for collection efficiencies above 99.5 percent.

Treatment Time

This refers to the length of time a particle will spend in the presence of the collecting electrodes, at design velocity, if it were allowed to traverse the entire length of the precipitator. The treatment length is not the total front-to-rear dimension of the "box", but is rather the horizontal dimension from the plane of the front face of the first collector to the rear plane of the last surface less any space for walkways.

Gas Velocity

Gas velocity is a critical design parameter. It is calculated by dividing the actual gas volume (at design temperature and elevation) by the face area of the precipitator immediately in front of the first collecting electrode. Effective plate height in feet is multiplied by the inside face-to-face dimension between the side-wall casings to give the face area.

Designs for low-sulfur, low-sodium coals use velocities between 3 and 4 ft/sec. For high-sulfur, high-sodium coals, velocities on the order of 5 fps are used.

Number of Fields

For reliability, precipitators are divided into fields, each of which is an independent electrical section in the direction of gas flow. Systems with a large number of fields (5 or 6) are not seriously impaired by the loss of a single field.

Automatic Voltage Control

The AVC system keeps the precipitator operating at its peak voltage. Such systems can be either analog or digital. Digital control systems are able to maintain higher precipitation voltage potential between the discharge electrode and the collecting plate than analog systems.

Hopper Size and Slope

The proper design of the collecting hoppers forming the floor of a precipitator is important because a breakdown in hopper outflow that results in overfilling can severely damage the electrical internals. The ABMA and the IGCI have made comprehensive recommendations[3] concerning the design and heating of precipitator and fabric-filter hoppers, and their flyash-removal systems. These recommendations help the industry avoid costly outages attributable to these portions of the collection/transport complex.

PRECIPITATOR DESIGN ANALYSIS

It is traditional to consider the semiempirical Deutsch-Anderson equation in the analytical design of a precipitator for efficiencies up to 98 percent. Above that level performance can be predicted accurately by a modified form of the Deutsch-Anderson formula.

Electrostatic-precipitator collection efficiency is related to the total surface of the collecting electrodes per unit volume of gas (the SCA) and is directly proportional to the particle migration velocity. Efficiency in the Deutsch-Anderson equation, is determined by

$$\eta = \left(1 - e^{\frac{-Aw}{V}}\right)100$$

(1)

where

η = efficiency of collection, %

e = base of natural logarithms (2.718 . . .)

A = collecting-electrode surface area, ft^2

w = migration velocity, fps, and

V = actual volumetric gas-flow rate, in 1000 ft^3/sec (at temperature and elevation)

Although important to an understanding of the precipitation process, the Deutsch-Anderson equation does not satisfactorily predict performance for a known ash at higher or lower efficiencies than an actual test point. That is because it relies entirely on Stoke's law and is properly applied only to average-size particles that are effectively the same size and experience the same force. The lack of correlation of analytical and field-performance data has been found to be specific to the variation in migration velocity and has led to the development of a modified equation:

$$\eta = \left[1 - e^{\left(\frac{-Aw}{V}\right)^k}\right]100$$

(2)

where w is now the empirical migration velocity at an observed lower efficiency, and k is a constant, approximately 0.5 but varying between 0.4 and 0.8 depending on the specific ash and application. The other terms are as defined for equation 1.

Migration or Drift Velocity

The drift velocity w, also called the "precipitation rate", is determined by the magnitude of the particle charge, the strength of the electrical field, and by Stoke's law for the drag of the particles.[2, 4] There is a significant dis-

crepancy between theoretical and practical values of w, with the theoretical being about twice the actual, or more.[5, 6] This loss of performance is caused by such factors as uneven gas flow, particle diffusion, electric wind, particle charging time and loss of particles from collecting surfaces by reentrainment.

Because of these uncertainties, and the effects on performance of concentration variations in SO_3 and sodium in the flue gas and the flyash, it is necessary to rely upon field experience with a variety of precipitator installations.[2, 5, 7] Where experience is limited, designs are established by means of experimental and pilot-plant test.[8, 9, 10]

EFFECT OF ELECTRICAL PROPERTIES

The electrical conductivity of flyash and the dielectric strength of the bulk ash are two properties important to the electrostatic-collection process. For effective operation, a small but definite electric current, in the form of corona gas ions, flows between the high-tension discharge electrodes and the collecting electrodes. This current must pass through the layers of collected ash which normally coat the plates. Therefore, the ash must be able to conduct the corona current to the grounded metal surfaces of the plates. The electrical conductivity required is very small; about 10^{10} mho. In practice, it is usually more convenient to express this in terms of *resistivity*, which is the inverse of conductivity.

The *dielectric strength* of the collected ash on the plate electrodes is also an important electrical property of the ash. The flow of the corona current through the ash layers produces a voltage or potential drop across the layers in accordance with Ohm's law. When the resistivity of the ash is in the critical zone (near 2×10^{10} ohm-cm), the voltage drop across the ash layer typically will amount to several kV. The existence of this voltage drop across the layer may be sufficient to cause it to break down electrically. When this happens, a spark flashes through the dust layer and is propagated to the discharge electrode. This is the source of the intensified sparking which occurs with dusts of excessive resistivity. Clearly, the higher the dielectric or breakdown strength of the dust layer, the higher the resistivity which may be tolerated for a given amount of corona current. Thus, dusts of relatively high breakdown strength are less sensitive to resistivity effects than dusts of low dielectric strength.

For flyash, the dielectric strength of the bulk ash in ¼ to ½ in. thick layers ranges from as low as a few hundred V/cm up to as high as 20 kV/cm. The average value of dielectric strength is in the 5 to 10 kV/cm range.

Ash Resistivity

Experience has shown that coal ashes with resistivities above 5×10^{10} ohm-cm are difficult to collect. Low resistivity (less than 10^7 ohm-cm) ash tends to sweep out the precipitator, but such low resistivities are rarely encountered. The area between 10^8 and 2×10^{10} ohm-cm usually is normal for satisfactory and predictable precipitator design.

The factors that affect resistivity are sulfur content of the coal ash, flue-gas temperature and moisture, and such ash constituents as sodium, potassium, calcium, alumina, silica and iron oxide.

Ash resistivity is inversely proportional to the concentration of sulfur trioxide and water in the flue gas and the sodium, potassium and carbon in the ash. It is directly proportional to the ash constituents of calcium, magnesium, alumina and silica. Peak ash resistivities occur between 250° and 450°F, depending upon coal-ash characteristics. Above 450°F to 550°F, the ash resistivity is inversely proportional to the absolute temperature, while below 250°F to 300°F, the resistivity is directly proportional to the absolute temperature.

Low-resistivity ash is a problem because the ash easily loses its charge after being collected on the plates. The uncharged particles are then reentrained in the flue gas. High-resistivity ash does not readily lose its charge when collected on the plates and the agglomerated ash can be very difficult to remove. When a deep enough deposit collects on the plate, back-corona develops on the ash surface and the precipitator can no longer collect efficiently.

Back-corona is extremely detrimental to precipitator performance. It occurs when a particle migrates to the collecting surface but fails to dissipate its charge, causing a high potential gradient in the dust layer on the surface of the plate. This layer disrupts the electrical field that induces migration, and repels particles of like charge attempting to migrate to the collecting surface. If the potential gradient across the layer gets sufficiently high, it promotes current conduction of diametrically opposed polarity to that of the discharge electrode.

Measurement of Dust Resistivity

Dust resistivity, to have any possible value to a precipitator design engineer, must be measured with the dust under the same gas and temperature conditions as those at which the precipitator will operate. And the packing density of the dust should be the same as that of the dust layer deposited on the precipitator collectors. It will be appreciated, then, that the measurement of dust resistivity is subject to considerable problems, making it very difficult in practice to relate absolute precipitation efficiency to dust resistivity.

Fig. 9 indicates the in-situ bulk resistivity of a variety of fuels as related to temperature. Although there is a significant difference between many of the ash samples tested at temperatures below 400°F, it appears that, above 600°F, most ash will have resistivities below the level of incipient back corona.

For this reason some precipitators have been located *between* the boiler economizer and the air heaters, in what is called the "hot" position, instead of downstream of the air heaters, the ordinary "cold" position. Hot precipitators are used to avoid back corona, to minimize the heavy rapping that is sometimes needed at lower temperatures, and to increase the effective migration velocity.[11,12]

The structural and mechanical design of hot precipitators is more critical than that of equipment to be operated at the 300°F temperature level. Designs should minimize thermal gradients and allow for differential expansion if such temperature gradients cannot be avoided.

The efficiency of hot precipitators can be seriously affected by low-sulfur, low-sodium and high-phosphorous coals. Adding sodium salts increases the electronic conduction and improves performance. Thus, ash composition influences operation of both low- and high-temperature precipitators.

Gas Conditioning

At preheater outlet temperatures, collected-dust resistivity is determined principally by surface conduction of an absorbed film on the particle surface. With flyash from low-volatile bituminous coal, for instance, surface conductivity is greatly affected as small concentrations of sulfur trioxide increase the moisture on the dust surface. Normally, for resistivity to be below the critical value of 2×10^{10} ohm-cm at airheater outlet temperatures of 250° to 350°F, there must be about 1.5 to 2.0 percent

sulfur in the fuel. Above 450°F, volume conduction predominates and the presence of sulfur is not critical.

To explain volume conduction: Below 450°F, *surface* condition affects resistivity. Above the 450° level, there is an excitation of the molecular structure as temperature causes the release of free electrons, thus increasing conduction through the ash layer. Although the presence of sulfur is then not a critical factor, sodium salts do become influential.

Migration velocity declines as resistivity increases (Fig. 10), as is characteristically typical of many low-sulfur subbituminous coals. Adding SO_3 to flue gas can reduce ash resistivity.[13] For some western U.S. low-sulfur coals, an increase of 30 ppm of SO_3 in the gas has reduced the flyash resistivity from between 10^{11} and 10^{12} to 5×10^9.

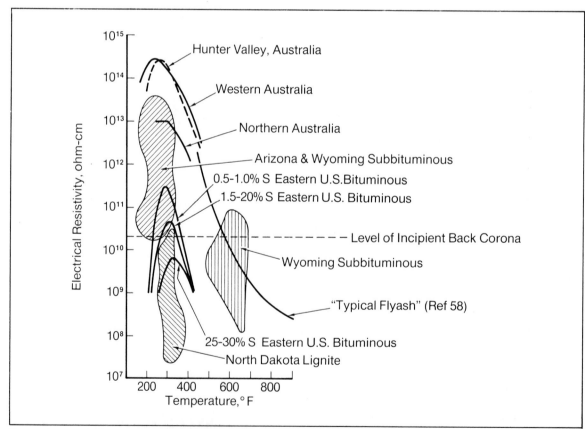

Fig. 9 **Composite of in-situ flyash resistivity data versus temperature, from several sources (Refs 8, 12, 57, 58)**

COHESIVE AND ADHESIVE PROPERTIES OF FLYASH

These properties of flyash are important for collection by electrostatic precipitators, where the ash forms in compacted layers on the electrode surfaces. Typically, these layers are about 0.5 in. thick, but may in some cases build up to 1 in. or more. Although some ash falls into the hoppers because of either the mechanical vibrations frequently present in plant structures or its own weight, rapping or jarring of the electrodes is usually necessary to effectively remove the collected ash layers. The ash generally breaks away in isolated patches, so that the collecting-plate surfaces present a somewhat spotty appearance.[6]

It is well known that fine solid particles tend to cohere and to form agglomerated masses which have a small but definite stability. The coherence of the particles is caused by molecular attractive forces at the points of contact of the particles. The degree of coherence is appreciable only for relatively fine particles of less than about 20 to 40 μm. Coarse or granular particles such as sand, for example, do not cohere in the dry state. On the other hand, fume particles, which typically are less than 1 μm in size, usually show a high degree of coherence.

The adhesion of particles to the collecting

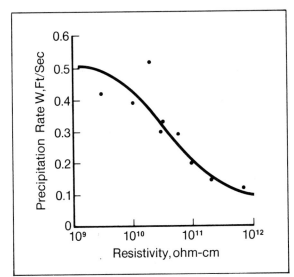

Fig. 10 Precipitation rate versus resistivity for representative group of flyash precipitators

electrodes is also the result of molecular attractive forces, and, similar to cohesion, the adhesive forces are larger for fine particles. Thus, the adhesion and retention of the collected layers of ash on the electrodes are determined basically by particle size, and increase with decreasing particle size. But other factors such as particle shape and composition also influence the adhesion and cohesion of particles. The presence of condensed moisture, with possible cementing effects, can also profoundly influence the build-up of particles on electrodes and other surfaces.

In electrical precipitators the rain of corona ions on the collected dust layers produces an additional retention force of major importance. These ions tend to charge the collected particles so that they are attracted to the collecting plates by relatively strong electric forces. Further, any particles that do escape from the collected layers of ash tend to be immediately recharged electrically by the corona ions and forced back to the collecting plates. The particle-retaining force of the corona current increases with the electrical resistivity of the particles and with the strength of the current. Thus it is often advantageous to operate precipitators at relatively high-corona current densities—particularly the outlet sections.[6]

Agglomerated masses of particles, removed from the electrodes by rapping, fall into the hoppers by the force of gravity. These agglomerated masses are bound together by molecular cohesive forces. For best performance, these falling agglomerates must be relatively stable and fall with as little loss of particles as possible. If the falling agglomerates have little coherence, some may break up and be redispersed in the gas stream, thus partially nullifying the collecting action of the precipitator.

The presence of coarse particles tends to reduce the cohesive and adhesive forces and, therefore, the agglomerating effect which holds masses of fine particles together. Excessive amounts of coarse, gritty particles in an ash make the ash difficult to hold on the collecting plates and also lead to loose, unstable agglomerates when the plates are rapped. On the other hand, the elimination of all coarse particles above 10 to 20 μm may in some cases make removal of the ash difficult. As there also will be a much greater tendency for the particles to build up on the discharge electrodes, a very fine ash containing no coarse particles presents a more difficult rapping problem.[6]

THE WEIGHTED-WIRE PRECIPITATOR

The weighted-wire type of electrostatic precipitator has been well described in references 2, 7, 14, 15 and 16. Typically, the collecting plates are as shown in Fig. 11 and the overall arrangement in Fig. 12.

RIGID-FRAME DESIGN FEATURES

In the rigid-frame design, the carbon-steel plates are constructed of profiled segments approximately 18 to 19 in. wide and up to 50 ft long. They attach at the top to back-to-back channels spanning the insulator housing, usually on 12 foot centers (Fig. 13). At the bottom,

anvil or spacer bars maintain plate alignment and act as anvils for plate rapping. The collecting-electrode plates are rapped individually by mechanical hammers indexed on a shaft driven from outside the precipitator shell. In a C-E rapping system (Fig. 14), the 6-by-16-ft collecting-electrode assemblies can be free to move or can be rigidly fixed. In either case, rapping accelerations are high.

Made from steel tubing, the individually suspended and rapped discharge frames are up to 24 feet long and are located one above the other. The discharge wire itself can be star-shaped, saw-toothed, or have another profile depending upon the manufacturer. Insulators carrying the high-tension support steel work are located in the insulator housing. There is no high-tension framing and, therefore, no access above the collecting plates. The discharge frames are individually rapped by mechanical hammers driven from outside the precipitator and are restrained front and rear, to maintain

Fig. 11 **Detail of collecting and discharge electrodes for weighted-wire precipitators**

Fig. 12 **Schematic arrangement of weighted-wire precipitator**

Fig. 13 **Collecting electrode system in C-E rigid-frame precipitators**

electrical clearances. With top suspension for all internals, expansion allowances are provided in the lower alignment steel work.

Rapping the Collection Plates

With a minimum force of 150G, 16- to 18-lb hammers individually rap collecting curtains. This intensity is essential when dealing with high-resistivity ash. Because plates are individually rapped, as opposed to gang rapping, puffing is virtually eliminated. Rapping losses are actually quite small as evidenced by measured stack emissions of about 0.002 grains/actual cu ft (ACF).

Emitting electrode frames are also individually rapped. The weight of the hammer and the type of rotation varies with manufacturer. The important item to note is that the intensity is greater than 50G on a half-size frame, with rapping taking place 30 times every hour. On weighted-wire precipitators a typical rap cycle is only 3 to 5 times per hour because of the light-weight discharge electrodes, typically less than 3 mm in diameter.

Discharge Electrodes and Collecting Plates

Selection of either spiked or star-studded electrodes depends on resistivity of the dust and anticipated dust loading. Star wires have a cross section of ¼ inch. Both type of electrodes are mounted in rugged pipe or tubular frames with horizontal struts on 5 to 7 foot centers (Fig. 15). As the wires of this discharge-electrode system do not project below collecting curtains, they are not as vulnerable to damage from overfilled ash hoppers. A collecting curtain consists of numerous 18- to 19-in. wide, roll-formed panels up to 48 feet long.

Internal Walkways

Walkways are provided before and after each electrical field at the collecting-electrode rapper elevation. Grate width is approximately 24 inches; clearance at shoulder height is 36 to 48

Fig. 14 **Operating mechanism for collecting surface rapping—C-E design**

inches depending on manufacturer's design. Internal ladders permit inspection and maintenance at all levels of this type of precipitator.

Box Girder/Insulator Compartments

These components, a minimum of 5 feet tall, span the full width of the precipitator. Inspection and maintenance of the high-voltage system are performed in these weather-tight enclosures. Separate weather enclosures are usually not required.

Precipitator Arrangement

After calculating the total collecting area of a precipitator, the application engineer must determine the shape of the box required to house the internals, Fig. 16. The beginning point is the computation of precipitator frontal area (width × height) using an acceptable gas velocity to the unit—ordinarily 3 to 5 ft/sec for a coal-fired boiler application. Once field height and number of gas passages have been deter-

Fig. 15 **Discharge-electrode wire frame assembly in C-E rigid-frame precipitator**

mined, required treatment length is figured. Selection is now complete if the equipment fits the allocated space envelope. Should the equipment extend beyond width constraints, alternative selections must be made.

There are four basic arrangements for locating precipitators in a given plot plan (Fig. 17):

- in-line
- cross-flow
- piggyback
- chevron

The preferred arrangement is in-line because of such advantages as:

- lowest capital cost
- good flow balance between chambers
- best gas distribution within a chamber
- lowest system pressure drop
- easy removal of internals in event of damage due to fires, explosion, or corrosion
- ease of erection and shortest time span to install a precipitator system

In laying out a plant, the rigid-frame precipitator has a decided advantage over a weighted wire unit because field heights can be 48 ft for the rigid-frame, and a maximum of 36 ft for the weighted-wire. In many instances a rigid-frame unit will fit in-line, whereas the weighted-wire design must be arranged in a less desirable fashion.

OPTIMIZATION OF PRECIPITATION RATE

Factors that affect precipitation rate are

- Plate design—as it affects dust reentrainment
- Rapping design—as it affects the ability to remove dust from the plates and electrodes. Heavy dust layers on the plate can result in formation of positive back corona which neutralizes the charging effect of the negative electrons; heavy accumulations on the discharge electrode restrict the emission of electrons from the wire.
- Gas distribution—poor gas distribution results in pockets of high gas velocity and in localized inadequate collection that adversely affects overall performance.

Fig. 16 **C-E rigid-frame precipitator**

Fig. 17 **Basic precipitator arrangements**

■ "Sneakage"—designs that allow small streams of dust-laden gas to skirt the precipitator by bypassing (sneaking) around the plates (through the hoppers, above the plates, or beside the plates) perform poorly. This factor becomes extremely important as efficiency specifications near 100 percent.

■ Electrode configuration and spacing—the shape and spacing of the electrode can drastically affect the amount of peak voltage and current achieved in the precipitator before sparking occurs. The selection of transformer/rectifier (T/R) sets with adequate kVA ratings and sensitive controls can affect this voltage and current.

■ Sectionalization—the amount of plate area per T/R set can affect the peak current and voltage achieved in an electrical section.

■ Alignment—the accuracy of the alignment between the plates and electrodes can also affect the peak current and voltage in the bus section. Voltage for the T/R operation is determined by the smallest space between plate and electrode anywhere in the electrical section.

FLYASH RECEIVING HOPPERS

During operation, the flyash accumulated on the collecting surfaces of the precipitator is periodically shaken loose, and dropped into the hoppers. The level of dust in each hopper will rise until that particular hopper is emptied. If, for any reason, emptying the hopper is delayed until the dust level approaches the elevation of the bottom of the discharge electrodes, they will be electrically short-circuited to ground through the mass of collected dust. The precipitator will cease functioning in a normal manner, but will continue to collect some dust as a settling chamber.

If the dust and flue gas entering the precipitator are reasonably well distributed, all precipitator hoppers in any row perpendicular to the gas flow will collect substantially the same quantity of dust per unit time. However, much more flyash will be collected in the rows of hoppers closer to the precipitator inlet than in the rows toward the rear of the precipitator.

The quantities can be approximated with reasonable accuracy by use of the Deutsch equation. An example is shown in Table I for four precipitators having overall efficiencies of 99.6 percent and from 3 to 6 rows of hoppers in the direction of gas flow. In modern flyash precipitators, then, the inlet row of hoppers can collect from 40 to 100 times as much flyash as does the rearmost row.[3]

FABRIC FILTRATION

Fabric filters, or baghouses, have a long history of applications in both dry and wet filtration processes to recover chemicals or control stack emissions. Available materials limited early baghouse installations to temperatures below 250°F, and air dilution was frequently used ahead of the baghouse. In addition, the chemical-resistance characteristics of the bags also curtailed fabric filtration. These two limitations retarded its development for many years, particularly as available precipitator equipment met the existing regulations.

Serious consideration of this technology began after 1970; interest heightened as installations on large coal-fired boilers demonstrated good operating characteristics and high particulate-removal efficiencies.

TYPES OF FABRIC FILTERS

Baghouses have a relatively constant collection efficiency but varying pressure drop, whereas precipitators have a relatively constant pressure drop but varying efficiency.

Table I. Percent of Flyash Collected In Each Row of Hoppers

| Row No. | Total number of rows, front to rear | | | |
	3	4	5	6
1	84.1	74.9	66.9	60.2
2	13.4	18.8	22.2	24.0
3	2.1	4.7	7.3	9.3
4	—	1.2	2.4	3.9
5	—	—	0.8	1.6
6	—	—	—	0.6
TOTAL	99.6	99.6	99.6	99.6

When dirty gas flows through a fabric, the particulate matter in the gas forms a "cake" on the fabric. This deposit increases both the filtration efficiency of the cloth and its resistance to gas flow. Thus, for continuous operation, a fabric filter must have some provision to periodically clean the deposit from the cloth.

Various fabric filter designs are available. Selection depends on gas temperature, particulate characteristics, and the type of cleaning mechanism for removing the collected dust from the cloth. Also, there are designations other than the following.[3]

Shaker

This oldest of filter designs uses vigorous shaking to remove the filter cake (captured particulate). The shaking causes the cake to fracture and fall into the collection and disposal hopper (Fig. 18). This method of cleaning has been applied to both inside collectors (those collecting particulate matter on the inside of the individual filter bags) and to outside collectors (those collecting the particulate matter on the outside of the individual filter bags).

The shaker design has been used where gas temperatures range from ambient to elevated levels—consistent with the cloth used. Cloth selection is critical and is normally limited to those materials capable of withstanding the vigorous shaking action without damage. Cloths for shaker-type filters must have proper weave construction, finish and weight.

Reverse Air

Originally developed to accommodate the relatively fragile cloths in baghouses operating at higher temperatures, this cleaning method is generally used with an inside-bag collector, although some variations can be found (Fig. 19). To relax and fracture the cake, a reversed flow of cleaned gases is passed through the cloth.

In the reverse-air system, clean flue gas taken from the outlet ductwork is blown in the direction counter to normal flow through the fabric of one or two compartments not in service. The cleaning frequency depends upon the porosity of the cake being formed, the inlet grain loading, and the predetermined allowable system pressure drop.

This design has been applied to a wide temperature range, from near ambient to more than 500°F, with appropriate cloth materials. An advantage of this system is the use of glass cloth which can withstand wide ranges in temperature without physical damage. The reverse-air system, being the most gentle method of bag cleaning, is compatible with most available bag materials.

Pulse-Jet

The pulse-jet outside collector filters the gases through the bag from the outside to inside. Wire or mesh frame cages support the bags (Fig. 20) to prevent their collapse during the filtering period. Cages vary in both design and materials of construction depending upon the composition of the gas being filtered, customer preference with respect to ease of handling, and the reuse of components.

Pulse-jet cake removal uses a short-duration pulse of compressed air injected into the open end of the filter bag. This air pulse causes a momentary expansion of the bag as the pulse wave travels the bag length. The action fractures the cake which falls into the collection and disposal hopper.

Generally, the cleaning action of a pulse-jet type of fabric filter is much harsher on the bags than other available cleaning methods. However, depending on the specific temperature

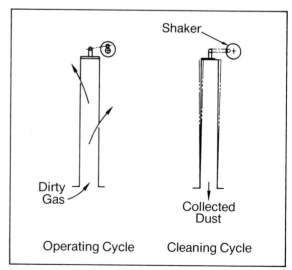

Fig. 18 **Shaker-type fabric collector**

and gas composition in an application, satisfactory fabrics are available.

Typically, this collector, when used to control a fugitive dust, is cleaned without stopping the gas flow to the unit. The online cleaning gives this equipment a significant economic advantage when compared to cleaning systems which operate only off-line.

EQUIPMENT DESIGN

Overall system design combines fabric materials and finishes most suitable to the cleaning system for the particular application. The ultimate choice of components and their arrangement within the system require complete knowledge of the process for which the fabric filter is to be used, and the limitations of available alternatives.

Baghouse design includes establishing criteria such as the air-to-cloth ratio and the bag aspect ratio. Currently, for reverse-air units for coal-fired plants, the gross air-to-cloth ratio will be 2.0 or less; "gross" is with all compartments operating. Net air/cloth will then be between 2.3 to 2.5 actual cfm/sq ft of fabric. For any given situation the gas volume to be designed for and the number of compartments out of service for the calculation of the net area have to be specified.

Bags used in power-plant fabric filters have an aspect ratio (height of bag divided by the diameter of the bag) of about 33 to 1. Extending this ratio makes it difficult to clean the bags. Other considerations include: bag inlet velocities, air-to-cloth ratio experience in field applications, bag-hanging hardware, damper design and the effect of compartmentalization on equipment sizing.

FABRIC FILTER MATERIALS

Specification of the weave, thread count, weight and finish for a particular filter bag material lists only a few of the combination of manufacturing processes that define the finished bag for a particular application. Fabric materials specifications include special attention to such properties as tensile strength, abrasion resistance, chemical resistance, and operating temperature as noted in Table II. Tensile strength measures the ability of the yarn or fabric to resist breaking when in direct tension. Abrasion resistance is its ability to withstand externally caused abrasion or that resulting from the internal rubbing of fabric fibers. Some materials exhibit excellent resistance while others are damaged easily. Coatings (finishes) can improve the abrasion resistance of fabrics.

Bag hardware usually consists of the cap for attaching the upper portion of the bag to the

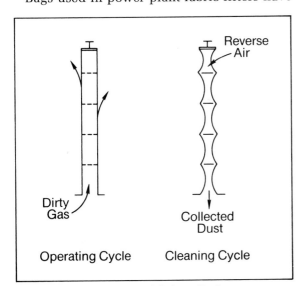

Fig. 19 Reverse-air type fabric collector

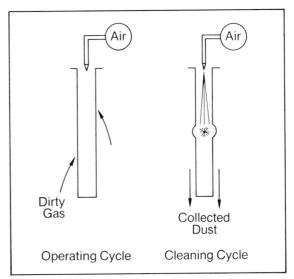

Fig. 20 Pulse-jet-cleaning type fabric collector

tensioning device connected to the upper frame, the clamp or snap ring to attach the bottom of bag to the thimble, and the rings which support the bag during reverse air cleaning. Although only a small fraction of the fabric-filter cost, bag hardware can cause problems if the wrong material is selected. Each of the components contacts the bag; if any should corrode, it may cause premature bag failure.

FABRIC-FILTER PERFORMANCE

Unlike baghouses, most other emission control forms depend upon either pressure drop or collection surface area to reach the required collection efficiency. Upsets to predicted gas volume or particulate loadings will typically cause the equipment to have higher emissions (despite maintaining the same fractional efficiency). Fabric filters do not behave in this fashion, because the collected material on the filter bags becomes the filtering medium that captures the incoming particles on its surface. Although upset conditions may change the flange-to-flange pressure drop, they do not materially change the final emission. Therefore, it can be said that a fabric filter represents a constant-emission control device.

The actual performance of a baghouse depends on specific items such as air-to-cloth ratio, permeability of the fabric (potential bleed-through), the nature of the particulate and, to some extent, the cleaning frequency. Careful selection of components can control emission levels to higher than 99.9 percent of incoming particulate, or outlet loadings lower than 0.005 grains per dry standard cu ft (at 60°F and 14.7 psia).

FABRIC-FILTER OPERATING PROBLEMS

A primary concern in the operation of fabric filters is bag life and bag replacement cost.[17] The initial cost of bags, excluding installation, can be 10 to 15 percent of the total baghouse cost (unerected)—a significant expense if bag life is short compared to the projected life of the equipment. Short life can be caused by various operating or design problems among which are the following.

■ Bag blinding, usually caused by operating a baghouse for long periods at or below the dew point. The effect is to plug or blind the fabric pores, with what might be considered "mud," impossible to remove even with repeated cleaning. As a result, the system develops high pressure differentials, possibly beyond the capabilities of the induced-draft fans.

■ Bag erosion, resulting from high-velocity streams of flyash-laden gases where the gas enters the bag. This problem is minimized by designing for lower air-to-cloth ratios; use of long thimbles at the bag tube sheet, and more frequent ash removal.

Table II. Fabric Material Properties

Fiber	Fiber Property		Chemical Resistance		Recommended Operating Temp., °F	
	Tensile Strength	Abrasion Resistance	Acids	Bases	Continous	Short-time
Cotton	Good	Average	Poor	Excellent	180	225
Polyethylene	Excellent	Good	Excellent	Excellent	190	190
Glass	Excellent	Poor	Good	Poor	500	550
Nylon	Excellent	Excellent	Poor	Excellent	200	250
Dacron*	Excellent	Excellent	Good	Fair	275	325
Acrylic*	Average	Average	Very Good	Fair	260	280
Nomex*	Very Good	Very Good	Fair	Very Good	400	425
Teflon*	Average	Below Average	Excellent	Excellent	450	500

*Trademark E.I. DuPont

■ Bag deterioration, often the result of a poor selection of material to properly accommodate the extreme operating parameters.

FLYASH HOPPER PLUGGING

The reliability and availability of electrostatic precipitators and fabric filters are affected adversely by problems in the dust-receiving hoppers and equipment beneath those hoppers for transporting flyash to disposal. A significant portion of the downtime of such dust-collecting equipment stems from problems with, and malfunctions of, ash evacuation systems.[3]

There is a paradox in the design of equipment for removing the collected flyash from the bottom of precipitators and fabric filters and conveying it away. Suppliers of ash-handling-systems design their equipment for "dry and free-flowing" material at the inlets of the ash-removal equipment. Yet, dust-collecting equipment can have mud or water flowing out of hoppers any time the hopper metal temperatures are below the water dew point (100° to 130°F, depending on fuel type and excess air in the products of combustion). This condition occurs commonly during boiler cold start-up, when many metal surfaces in the gas stream are at ambient temperature.

When sub dew point conditions occur, the hygroscopic flyash absorbs the acid or water produced and may agglomerate and cement into large pieces that either cannot pass through the hopper outlets or are too heavy to be conveyed.

EFFECT ON COLLECTING EQUIPMENT

Undetected and/or uncorrected hopper plugging can cause one or more of the following deleterious effects on precipitators:

■ bent or misaligned collecting surfaces

■ discharge-electrode burning

■ distorted or broken discharge-electrode frames

■ broken anvil bars

■ broken shaft or drive insulators

■ shorted high-voltage bus sections

■ lowered electrical-power output from bent or misaligned collecting- and discharge-electrode components

■ the formation of large, difficult-to-remove clinkers by high-temperature electrical fusing of the ash overflowing a hopper.

With fabric filters plugging can increased the gas velocities as hoppers fill above the inlet level, resulting in the possibility of re-entrainment of dust. This can result in excessive bag abrasion. With a completely blocked hopper, the compartment will no longer accept gas flow, and the other compartments will have to handle the volume, resulting in increased pressure drop. Lower collection efficiency may result.

With both precipitators and baghouses if a plugged hopper cannot be cleared and discharged through the ash system in a normal manner, the ash must be emptied onto the hopper-room floor or the ground (creating a fire and safety hazard) and manually removed.

SOLUTIONS TO THE PROBLEM

The problem can be solved by:

1. Removing the ash as continuously as possible so that it can remain hot and uncompacted, and unexposed to cold air.

2. Enclosing hopper areas and using maximum insulation thickness to reduce heat losses and cooling of ash-system hardware.

3. Modifying hopper design for improved outflow.

4. Heating hoppers such that the walls do not drop in temperature below the acid or water dew point.

5. Using conveying air with a temperature above the water dew point.

6. Preventing air in-leakage that cools the ash below the acid or water dew point.

HEATING OF PRECIPITATOR FABRIC-FILTER HOPPERS

The principal variables in the application of hopper heating are

■ external design temperature

■ internal design temperature

■ internal ash layer

- the extent and placement of heating elements
- the design electrical-heat density
- the thickness of insulation outside the heating equipment

Design operating temperature for hopper-heating equipment for boilers firing low- to medium-sulfur coals should be a minimum of 270°F. This is 10 to 15 degrees above the normally expected acid dew point. For units firing high-sulfur oils, hopper plate should be kept above 350°F. The heating equipment must be capable of maintaining such temperatures under the worst expected ambient conditions of temperature and wind velocity (for 97 to 98 percent of the time) and for the lowest anticipated interior gas-temperature.

Large portions of some hoppers customarily have not been heated because they are not flat or because of the problem of removal of heating elements in the event of access required to this equipment. Where such areas cannot be heat-traced, they should be completely insulated to avoid cooling of hoppers; doors, poke holes, strike-pad shafts, and vibrator mounting pads should be insulated as well as possible, both to minimize local ash buildups and to reduce corrosion.

Test reports of temperature measurements in operating precipitator hoppers indicate that gas or air temperatures as low as 90°F sometimes occur inside the hoppers, with the precipitator and boiler operating at essentially full load. Under such conditions, most of the heat loss from the hopper plate is not to the outside atmosphere, but rather to the *inside of the hopper*. That is, with substantially clean hopper plate (no measurable ash coating), the thermostat that actuates the electrical heating system will be activated on the basis of heat flow *into* the hopper. If such low internal temperatures are taken into account in the design of the heat-

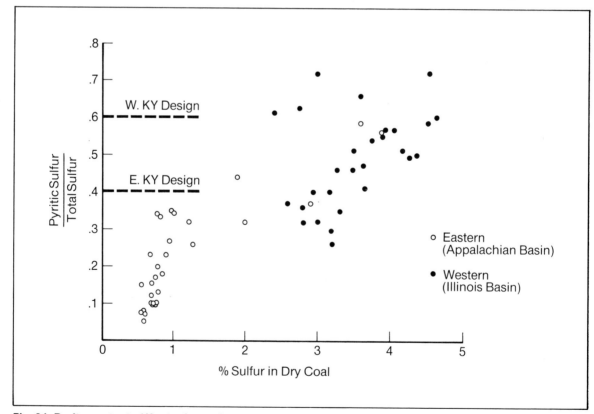

Fig. 21 **Pyrite content of Kentucky coal**

ing systems, considerably more electrical energy will be needed than to take care of external-temperature and wind conditions alone.[3]

CONTROL OF GASEOUS EMISSIONS

Sulfur in coal exists in two forms: organic and inorganic. The inorganic compound pyrite, FeS_2, is present as discrete particles within the fuel, and typically accounts for 20 to 50 percent of the total sulfur. Fig. 21 is illustrative of the variety of pyritic sulfur occurring in just one small area of the United States. The coals forming the basis for the plot are all from the state of Kentucky, which has two separate basins of formation. Pyrite as a percentage of total sulfur is from less than 10 to over 60 percent for the low-sulfur Appalachian basin coal, and from about 25 to 65 percent for the higher sulfur Illinois basin fuel. The milling and classifying operations associated with pulverized-fuel steam generators using pulverizers equivalent to the C-E bowl mill separate a substantial portion of the pyritic sulfur from the coal. (See Chapter 12) An additional amount of inorganic sulfur is retained in the bottom ash and the flyash leaving the boiler in solid form.

FORMATION OF SULFUR OXIDES

Contained in the polymeric and molecular structure of the coal, organic sulfur is oxidized during the combustion process and emitted from the furnace as gaseous oxides of sulfur.

The principal oxiding reaction leads to the formation of sulfur dioxide.

$$S + O_2 \rightarrow SO_2$$

(3)

In addition to SO_2, lesser quantities of sulfur trioxide, SO_3, are formed during combustion.

$$SO_2 + \tfrac{1}{2}O_2 \rightleftarrows SO_3$$

(4)

Typically, the ratio of SO_2/SO_3 in combustion gases ranges from 20:1 to 80:1. The chemical reactions that form sulfur dioxide and trioxide are substantially more complex than the overall reactions in Eqs. 3 and 4.

Explicit emission standards for the control of SO_3 do not exist. But as SO_3 is highly reactive and extremely hygroscopic compared to SO_2, it is capable of readily combining with water to form sulfuric-acid aerosol. The reaction is enhanced by the presence of fine particles which serve as condensation nuclei; the resulting aerosol is a principal constituent of visible stack plumes. Thus, opacity and particulate-emission regulations are an indirect method of restricting SO_3 emissions.

Studies show flue-gas desulfurization systems intended principally for SO_2 control are moderately effective in curtailing SO_3 emissions. Tests indicate that a venturi/spray-tower scrubber removes approximately 60 percent of the SO_3 in flue gas, with the removal efficiency essentially independent of the SO_3 concentration or scrubber operating variables.[18]

CONTROL OF SO₂ EMISSIONS

Historically, gaseous sulfur-dioxide emissions have been controlled by either dispersion or reduction. Dispersion of SO_2 and other pollutants through tall stacks is the oldest form of control. Under favorable meteorological conditions tall stacks can effectively limit ground level SO_2 concentration to local ambient air-quality standards. Thermal inversions or comparable short-term meteorological conditions can impair the effectiveness of dispersion as a control method. A further disadvantage of control by dispersion is that SO_2 and sulfates resulting from the atmospheric oxidation of SO_2 may accumulate to high background levels unacceptable in regional areas.

Reduction of sulfur emissions has been achieved through one or a combination of the following:

■ switching to lower-sulfur fuels

■ use of fuel desulfurization methods

■ use of flue-gas desulfurization systems

Switching to lower-sulfur fuels is not possible for most large fossil-fired steam-generating plants. More low-sulfur gaseous and liquid fuels are essentially unavailable to utilities.

Fuel desulfurization processes range from conventional coal washing to coal liquefaction and gasification. Coal washing is effective in reducing the pyritic sulfur in the coal. It cannot remove the organic sulfur from the coal matrix, and as such it is limited to sulfur reduction of less than 50 percent. Coal liquefaction and gasification are discussed in Chapter 24.

FLUE-GAS DESULFURIZATION SYSTEMS

Flue-gas desulfurization (FGD) began in England in 1935; the Battersea process used the alkaline Thames river water for scrubbing power-plant flue gas until the visible plume caused abandonment of the process early in World War II.[19] The technology remained dormant until the mid-1960's when it became active primarily in the United States and Japan. Since then, over 50 FGD processes have been developed, differing in the chemical reagents and the resultant end products. In the following section, we will describe some of the more prominent, giving appropriate references for the interested reader. References 4, 18, 20, 21 and 22 provide a comprehensive overview through the 1970's.

In the flue-gas scrubbing process, water evaporates from the scrubbing liquid as the flue-gas is cooled to the adiabatic saturation temperature. Under equilibrium conditions, a quantity of water must be added to the system to make up for the water loss.

In a recirculation system where scrubbing liquid is not bled from the system, the salts in the incoming make-up water gradually concentrate, eventually attaining infinite value. In any scrubbing system involving solids present in the flue-gas stream as flyash or as solids from the sorption of sulfur dioxide, a stream must be bled off to remove the solids and similarly prevent their buildup to infinite values in the system. The specific concentration of various chemicals in the scrubbing liquid in any given system depends on the sulfur in the coal, the flyash in the flue gas entering the scrubber, and the type of additive.

The evaporation that occurs in the flue-gas scrubbing process, then, results in pure water being discharged to atmosphere, and simultaneously, a concentration of solids in the bleed stream leaving the scrubbing system. Of these solids, the sulfates, sulfites, and chlorides are potentially the greatest problem.

One approach in categorizing FGD processes is to differentiate between nonregenerable, or "throwaway", and regenerable, or recovery, type processes. Throwaway systems produce waste products of various sulfur compounds that must be stored in ponds or treated for use as landfill. Regenerable systems recover the SO_2 in some commercially useful form such as elemental sulfur or sulfuric acid.

NON-REGENERABLE FGD PROCESSES

In the U.S., the overwhelming majority of commercial FGD systems are of the throwaway type. Included in this category are the lime or limestone, the double alkali, and the dilute sulfuric acid systems.

Lime/Limestone Scrubbing

Lime or limestone scrubbing is the oldest and most common method of flue-gas desulfurization. The first successful closed-loop lime/limestone process is credited to the English firm of J. Howden and Company, which during 1931-1933 conducted pilot-plant tests in which the scrubber effluent was recycled to the absorber; initially, scale formed in the absorber.[23] The critical breakthrough in system chemistry came in 1933 when the problem was identified as one of excessive gypsum ($CaSO_4 \cdot 2H_2O$) supersaturation in the scrubber. The solution was to add a crystallization tank and increase the liquid-to-gas (L/G, that is "L over G") ratio. Adding a crystallization tank operating at high solids concentration allows calcium-sulfur compounds to precipitate outside a scrubber. Because of precipitation reactions, the absorbent recycled to the scrubber has a lower concentration of scale-forming gypsum. A high L/G ratio minimizes the increase in supersaturation across the scrubber and thereby further diminishes the potential for scale formation.

In the mid-1960's, Combustion Engineering developed and marketed the limestone-injection scrubbing process. In this variation, pulverized limestone was injected into the furance simultaneously with the coal. The resulting calcined limestone (CaO) was entrained in the flue gas along with flyash. A water scrubber was used to remove the flyash, limestone and SO_2 from the flue gas. Several systems were placed into operation between 1968 and 1970, but persistent difficulties with scaling, poor additive utilization, and plugging of boiler convection surfaces prompted C-E to revert to the older Howden tail-end process.[24]

In a typical lime/limestone FGD system (Fig. 22) boiler flue gas enters the scrubber and contacts the absorbent slurry while sulfur dioxide and lesser amounts of oxygen are simultaneously absorbed. The spent absorbent returns to the reaction tank where the dissolved sulfur compounds are precipitated as calcium salts to which fresh limestone or lime slurry is added to regenerate the spent absorbent.

The size of the reaction tank provides sufficient time for precipitation of sulfur compounds and the dissolution of additive. The rate of additive feed is pH-controlled in lime systems. In limestone systems, the feed rate may be controlled either by pH, or according to SO_2 concentration and boiler load, or a combination of the two.

From the reaction tank, the regenerated absorbent slurry is recycled to the absorber. The slurry typically contains from 5 to 15 percent suspended solids consisting of fresh additive, absorption reaction products, and flyash. To regulate the accumulation of solids, a bleed stream from the reaction tank is routed to the solid/liquid separation equipment.

Typically, the bleed is routed to a gravity thickener where the suspended solids settle to the bottom and the clear liquid is drawn off the

Fig. 22 **Typical process flow diagram for lime/limestone scrubbing**

top and returned to the scrubber loop. The thickener underflow containing 25 to 50 percent solids can be pumped to a pond or may be further dewatered through vacuum filtration. The filtrate is returned to the scrubber loop. Alternately, the bleed from the reaction tank can be pumped directly to a settling pond where solids accumulate and clear liquid is recycled to the scrubber. Make-up water is added to the system to replace water evaporated by the hot flue gas and water entrained in the waste stream. The water is added as mist-eliminator wash, and as the additive slurrying medium.

Double-Alkali Systems

Like lime/limestone processes, in double alkali (or dual alkali) processes lime or limestone is consumed and a calcium sulfite/sulfate wet solid is produced as waste. They differ from the lime/limestone in that SO_2 is absorbed and waste-products are formed in separate components. The absorption and waste generation are separated by using an intermediate soluble alkali such as Na_2CO_3, NaOH, or Na_2SO_3. The separation serves two objectives. First, it permits scrubbing the flue gas with a clear solution allowing the rate of SO_2 absorption to proceed independently of lime or limestone dissolution rate. Second, it permits better control of the calcium-sulfur precipitation reactions in equipment specifically designed for this function. In theory, this improves the use of lime or limestone.

Double alkali FGD processes developed because they offered significant advantages over lime/limestone slurry processes. First, there are no suspended solids in the absorbent to contribute to scaling and plugging of internal scrubber components. Second, because of a high concentration of dissolved alkali species, there is minimal resistant to liquid-phase mass transfer. The practical implication of these factors is excellent SO_2 removal efficiency achieved with a simple scrubber at lower liquid-to-gas ratios.

Fig. 23 shows a typical double-alkali process. Clear alkali solution is circulated through the scrubber where SO_2 absorption and some oxidation take place. The absorbed SO_2 reacts with sulfite to form bisulfite:

$$Na_2SO_3 + SO_2 + H_2O \leftarrow 2NaHSO_3$$

(5)

The pH of the absorbent is typically between 6 and 8.5. Scrubber effluent, which contains a lower ratio of sulfite to bisulfite than the scrubber feed, is collected in the absorber sump. A bleed stream from the sump is pumped to the regeneration system where it is treated with

Fig. 23 **Simplified process diagram for double-alkali system**

lime or limestone. The absorber SO_2 is precipitated as calcium solids as follows:

$$Ca(OH)_2 + 2NaHSO_3 \rightleftharpoons CaSO_3 \cdot \tfrac{1}{2}H_2O$$
$$+ Na_2SO_3 + \frac{3}{2}H_2O$$

(6)

$$CaCO_3 + 2NaHSO_3 \rightleftharpoons CaSO_3 \cdot \tfrac{1}{2}H_2O$$
$$+ Na_2SO_3 + \tfrac{1}{2}H_2O + CO_2$$

(7)

The bisulfite is neutralized and active sulfite is regenerated. The sulfite-rich clear solution is separated from the precipitates in conventional solid/liquid separation equipment such as thickeners and vacuum filters. Waste calcium and sulfur componds are disposed and sulfite solution returned to the scrubber loop. Sodium lost as a result of entrainment in the waste solids is replaced with fresh sodium-carbonate addition.

Technically, the most serious difficulty with double-alkali processes arises from the irreversible oxidation of sulfite to sulfate.

$$Na_2SO_3 + \tfrac{1}{2}O_2 \rightarrow Na_2SO_4$$

(8)

When active sodium sulfite is converted to inactive sulfate, the capacity to absorb additional SO_2 is diminished. To restore dissolved scrubbing capacity, the inactive sulfate must be removed from the system while the sodium remains in solution. A direct purge of sodium sulfate from the system is unacceptable because it contributes to surface and ground water contamination. Additionally, the cost of replacing the lost sodium is further incentive against direct purge.

The methods for removing sulfate depend on the concentration of sulfite in the system. If the sulfite concentration is low, the system is said to operate in the dilute mode. In a dilute double-alkali system, sulfate may be removed according to the following reaction:

$$Na_2SO_4 + Ca(OH)_2 + 2H_2O \rightleftharpoons 2NaOH + CaSO_4 \cdot 2H_2O$$

(9)

In a concentrated double-alkali system with a high sulfite concentration, this reaction will not proceed appreciably and other techniques must be used to regenerate the inactive sulfate. In Japan, sulfuric acid is added in a separate reactor to force the following reaction:

$$Na_2SO_4 + 2CaSO_3 \cdot \tfrac{1}{2}H_2O + H_2SO_4 + 3H_2O \rightarrow$$
$$2NaHSO_3 + 2CaSO_4 \cdot 2H_2O$$

(10)

This mode of operation is often referred to as low-sulfate crystallization because the reactor operates at a pH of 2 to 3. Low-pH crystallization often can be combined with simultaneous forced oxidation to yield a marketable gypsum.

Double-alkali desulfurization systems in utility plants are limited because of the cost of sodium reagents, requirements for large solid/liquid separation equipment, and leaching problems associated with the disposal of wastes containing entrained sodium compounds. A number of industrial-size installations have been constructed and are operational.

Dilute Sulfuric-Acid

Developed in Japan, the dilute sulfuric-acid FGD process (Fig. 24) uses a dilute sulfuric-acid absorbent, iron oxidation catalysts and limestone to produce a remarketable gypsum end product.[25]

Boiler flue gas enters a venturi-type prescrubber for particulate removal and humidification. The saturated flue gas then moves to the absorber where a dilute solution of sulfuric acid in water absorbs SO_2

$$SO_2 + H_2O \rightarrow SO_2 \cdot H_2O$$

(11)

$$SO_2 + H_2O + \tfrac{1}{2}O_2 \xrightarrow{Fe^{+3}} H_2SO_4$$

(12)

To achieve complete oxidation, the absorber effluent is pumped to an oxidizing tower where air forces the SO_2 oxidation reaction in the presence of ferric iron. It is believed that the catalyzed oxidation reactions proceed:

$$SO_2 \cdot H_2O + 2FeSO_4 + O_2 \rightarrow Fe_2(SO_4)_3 + H_2O \tag{13}$$

$$Fe_2(SO_4)_3 + SO_2 + 2H_2O \rightarrow 2FeSO_4 + 2H_2SO_4 \tag{14}$$

To neutralize the sulfuric acid at a rate equal to its generation, a slipstream of oxidized liquor is sent to the gypsum crystallizer. The bulk of the liquor is recycled back to the absorber.

In the crystallizer, limestone is added to the acid solution to precipitate gypsum:

$$H_2SO_4 + CaCO_3 + H_2O \rightarrow CaSO_4 \cdot 2H_2O + CO_2 \tag{15}$$

The gypsum crystals are dewatered in a centrifuge and the mother liquor recycled to the absorber.

The dilute sulfuric-acid process has successfully produced marketable gypsum as an end product because of its use of liquid fuels which are low in ash and chlorides. With coal firing, it is uncertain if commercially pure gypsum can be produced economically.

The principal disadvantages of this process are high initial cost and a requirement for very high liquid-to-gas ratios. Because the process operates at an approximate liquor pH of 1, selection of highly acid-resistant construction materials is necessary. The corrosion at this pH level increases sharply in the presence of even small levels of chloride. Also, because of the low absorbent pH, typical liquid-to-gas ratios for the process are approximately 3 to 5 times greater than in lime/limestone processes.

REGENERABLE (RECOVERY) PROCESSES

Although regenerable FGD systems can produce marketable sulfur or sulfuric-acid

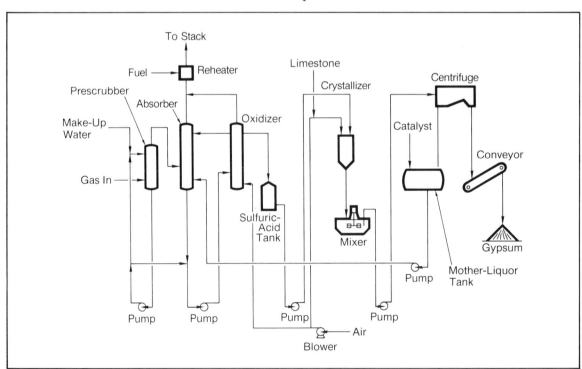

***Fig. 24* Dilute sulfuric-acid FGD process**

end products instead of essentially valueless wastes, such systems are more expensive and complex. They result in highly sophisticated chemical plants generally unattractive to electric-utility users.

Limited application of this technology results from several factors. First, regenerable processes are energy-intensive as reducing sulfur compounds to elemental sulfur requires thermal energy. Second, the decomposition processes require substantial amounts of reducing gases including hydrogen sulfide, carbon monoxide, or hydrogen derived from natural gas or other hydrocarbon feed stock.

Aside from the availability problem, there is a reluctance to handle large quantities of potentially toxic reductants like hydrogen sulfide in the power plant. Also, regeneration processes are difficult to justify unless it is impractical to dispose of large quantities of wastes, or there a secure market for the sulfur.

Magnesium Oxide

The magnesium-oxide FGD process, a wet-slurry regenerable/recovery system, is shown as a simplified flow diagram in Fig. 25. As with all regenerable processes, the flue gas must have the particulate removed to prevent buildup of inert solids and contamination of the final product. Ash-free flue gas is scrubbed

with a slurry of magnesium oxide and water in a suitable absorber. Depending upon specific process conditions, sulfur dioxide reacts with magnesium oxide, magnesium sulfite, or magnesium hydroxide to yield soluble magnesium bisulfite.

$$MgO + 2SO_2 + H_2O \rightarrow Mg(HSO_3)_2 \tag{16}$$

$$MgSO_3 + SO_2 + H_2O \rightarrow Mg(HSO_3)_2 \tag{17}$$

$$Mg(OH)_2 + 2SO_2 \rightarrow Mg(HSO_3)_2 \tag{18}$$

In the process, some oxygen is also absorbed into the slurry, an action that forms magnesium sulfate.

The magnesium bisulfite is neutralized with magnesium oxide to produce a magnesium-sulfite precipitate.

$$Mg(HSO_3)_2 + MgO + 11 H_2O \rightarrow 2MgSO_3 \cdot 6 H_2O \tag{19}$$

The magnesium-sulfite/sulfate crystals are withdrawn in a bleed stream from the absorber

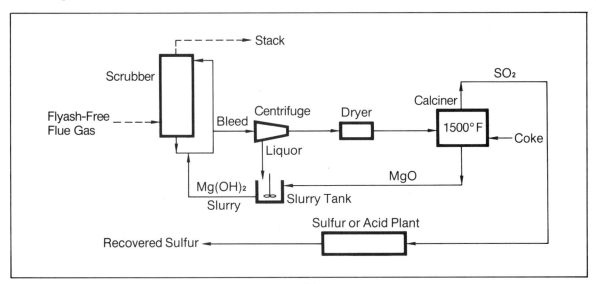

Fig. 25 **Simplified process diagram for magnesium-oxide recovery system**

loop and sent to a centrifuge for dewatering. The product from the centrifuge is thermally dried and the liquor is recycled to the scrubber.

Dried magnesium-sulfite/sulfate crystals are calcined, usually under a reducing atmosphere at approximately 1500°F, to regenerate magnesium oxide and a gas steam concentrated in sulfur dioxide. The calciner exit gas is treated for particulate removal and then used as the feed stream to produce sulfuric acid or elemental sulfur. The magnesium oxide is recycled to the scrubber. Commercial magnesium-oxide FGD systems have been built at Boston Edison's Mystic station, for an oil-fired boiler, and for coal-fired units at Potomac Electric Power Company's Dickerson station and Philadelphia Electric Company's Eddystone station. The systems removed much SO_2 with minor mechanical problems.

Sodium Sulfite

The sodium sulfite process (Fig. 26) is a regenerative FGD process which combines absorption of soluble SO_2 with thermal regeneration of sodium sulfite to produce either elemental sulfur or sulfuric acid.[26] A sodium sulfite solution absorbs SO_2 from the flue gas, thereby forming sodium bisulfite.

$$Na_2SO_3 + SO_2 + H_2O \rightarrow 2NaHSO_3 \tag{20}$$

A bleed stream is sent to the evaporator/crystallizer where sodium bisulfite is thermally decomposed to solid sodium sulfite and gaseous SO_2.

$$2NaHSO_3 \xrightarrow{\Delta} Na_2SO_3 + H_2O + SO_2 \tag{21}$$

The sulfur dioxide is stripped with steam to yield a concentrated product stream containing approximately 90 percent SO_2 and 10 percent water. This stream is further processed

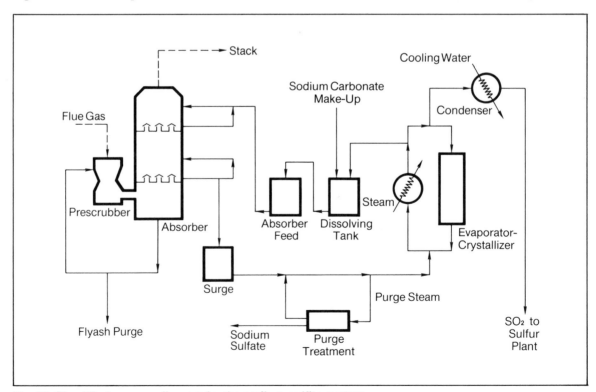

Fig. 26 Simplified process diagram for the sodium-sulfite system

17–32

to recover sulfuric acid or elemental sulfur. Sodium sulfite crystals are dissolved in water and recycled to the absorber. Sodium sulfate formed as a result of oxidation does not decompose in the evaporator and must be purged.

The sodium sulfite process has been applied since 1971 in Japan on several oil-fired industrial and utility boilers.[27] The only sodium sulfite processes prior to 1979 in the United States controlled SO_2 emissions from Claus sulfur and sulfuric-acid plants. Early in 1980 three systems had been installed on coal-fired boilers, all designed to produce elemental sulfur for ultimate use in sulfuric-acid manufacture.

Catalytic Oxidation

Catalytic oxidation (Fig. 27) is a dry regenerable FGD process which yields sulfuric acid. Flyash is removed from the flue gas with a high-efficiency hot electrostatic precipitator. The gas then passes through a catalytic converter where SO_2 is oxidized to SO_3 in the presence of vanadium-pentoxide catalyst. The

temperature of the gas must be increased to approximately 850°F to allow 90-percent conversion of SO_2 to SO_3. The flue gas passes from the converter through the air preheater where it is cooled to approximately 450°F. The gas is then scrubbed with recycled acid to form 80-percent sulfuric acid. A utility installation to demonstrate the technical feasibility of the system was terminated in 1975.[28]

Aqueous Carbonation

The aqueous carbonate process is a regenerable FGD process which produces elemental sulfur as a byproduct. Fig. 28 is a block diagram showing the various process subsystems. Flue gas is treated in a spray dryer absorber with an aqueous solution of sodium carbonate.

$$Na_2CO_3 + SO_2 \rightarrow Na_2SO_3 + CO_2 \tag{22}$$

$$Na_2CO_3 + SO_2 + \tfrac{1}{2}O_2 \rightarrow Na_2SO_4 + CO_2 \tag{23}$$

Fig. 27 **Flow diagram for the catalytic-oxidation process**

The spray dryer absorber is operated at a liquid-to-gas ratio of approximately 0.3 gallon per thousand cubic feet of gas. As a result, the water is completely evaporated and only solid sodium-sulfur compounds are discharged from the spray dryer. Cyclones and electrostatic precipitators collect the particulate leaving the spray dryer.

The collected solids are fed to a high-temperature refractory-lined reactor which contains a pool of molten sodium carbonate and sodium sulfite. In the reactor, sodium sulfite/sulfate solids are reduced to sodium sulfide in the presence of a reducing agent such as coke.

$$2Na_2SO_3 + 3C \rightarrow 2Na_2S + 3CO_2 \tag{24}$$

$$Na_2SO_4 + 2C \rightarrow Na_2S + 2CO_2 \tag{25}$$

$$C + O_2 \rightarrow CO_2 + \Delta \tag{26}$$

The sodium sulfide is quenched with water and dissolved and the solution is filtered to remove flyash and coke ash. Clear sodium sulfide solution is sent to a carbonate system where CO_2 from a molten salt reactor combines with the sulfide to produce sodium carbonate and hydrogen sulfide.

$$2NaS + H_2O + CO_2 \rightarrow 2NaHS + Na_2CO_3 \tag{27}$$

$$2NaHS + H_2O + CO_2 \rightarrow 2H_2S + Na_2CO_3 \tag{28}$$

The sodium carbonate is recycled to the spray dryer and the hydrogen sulfide is reduced to elemental sulfur in a Claus plant.

Specific subsystems of the aqueous carbonate process have been pilot tested, including the spray-dryer absorber and the regeneration subsystem.[29]

Activated-Carbon Absorption

Activated-carbon processes are dry regenerable FGD processes in which SO_2 is absorbed on activated-carbon granules in either fixed or fluidized-bed reactors. Sulfur dioxide is catalytically oxidized to SO_3 which undergoes hydrolysis and forms sulfuric acid in the carbon pores.

$$SO_2 + \tfrac{1}{2}O_2 + H_2O \xrightarrow[\text{Carbon}]{\text{Activated}} H_2SO_4 \text{ (Sorbed)} \tag{29}$$

The carbon, loaded with sulfuric acid, combines with hydrogen sulfide in a separate reactor to yield sulfur.

$$H_2SO_4 + 3H_2S \rightarrow 4H_2O + 4S \tag{30}$$

A third reactor removes the sulfur absorbed upon the carbon by reaction with hydrogen at 1000°F.

$$4S + 3H_2 \xrightarrow[\text{Carbon}]{\text{Activated}} 3H_2S + S \text{ (Product)} \tag{31}$$

The reactor off-gas, consisting of sulfur vapor and hydrogen sulfide, is cooled to condense out the sulfur.

The ability of the process to consistently remove SO_2 with acceptable carbon degradation has to be demonstrated at the prototype and commercial scale.[30]

Copper Oxide

The copper oxide process (Fig. 29) is a dry, fixed-bed, regenerable FGD process. Flue gas leaving the economizer is passed through a sorption vessel packed with copper oxide supported on alumina. At approximately 750°F, cupric oxide reacts with SO_2 and oxygen to produce copper sulfate.

$$CuO + SO_2 + \tfrac{1}{2}O_2 \rightarrow CuSO_4 \tag{32}$$

Fig. 28 **Aqueous carbonate FGD process**

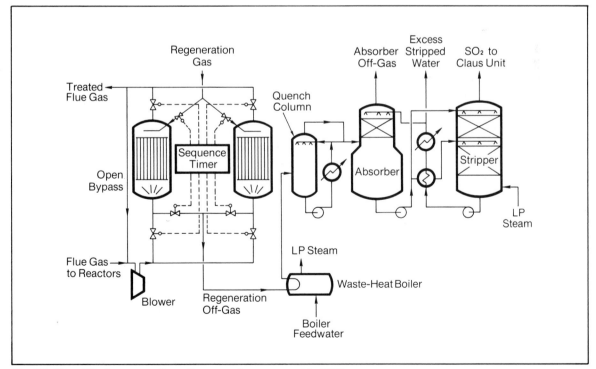

Fig. 29 **Simplified process flow diagram of copper-oxide FGD process**

When one sorption vessel is sufficiently loaded with sulfate, it is isolated from the flue gas and regenerated by adding hydrogen.

$$CuSO_4 + 2H_2 \rightarrow Cu + SO_2 + 2H_2O \tag{33}$$

The regenerated copper is oxidized to copper oxide when re-exposed to the flue gas. The SO_2 produced during regeneration is further concentrated in a water absorber/stripper system. Further reduction with hydrogen produces a hydrogen sulfide/sulfur dioxide stream which is processed through a Claus plant for conversion to elemental sulfur.

The basic concept of the copper-oxide FGD process was tested in 1967 at a Shell Oil refinery in the Netherlands.[31] Following successful demonstration, a larger system was installed in Japan on a 40 MW oil-fired boiler. The system has operated intermittently since 1973 with considerable downtime attributable to problems with construction materials. In the U.S. a pilot demonstration was installed on a coal-fired boiler at Tampa Electric Company's Big Bend Station.[32] The potential of the copper oxide process to reduce both SO_2 and NO_x emissions heightens its standing among other dry regenerable systems.

Ammonium Sulfite

The concept of using ammonia based solutions for SO_2 scrubbing dates back to the 1930's. Current versions of the process combine ammonium-sulfite scrubbing with regeneration to produce elemental sulfur in a Claus recovery system. The overall absorption reactions are

$$NH_3 + SO_2 + H_2O \rightarrow NH_4HSO_3 \tag{34}$$

$$NH_4HSO_3 + NH_3 \rightarrow (NH_4)_2SO_3 \tag{35}$$

$$(NH_4)_2SO_3 + SO_2 + H_2O \rightarrow 2NH_4HSO_3 \tag{36}$$

The absorber effluent is treated with ammonium bisulfate to produce SO_2 and ammonium sulfate.

$$NH_4HSO_3 + NH_4HSO_4 \rightarrow (NH_4)_2SO_4 + H_2O + SO_2 \tag{37}$$

$$(NH_4)_2SO_3 + 2NH_4HSO_4 \rightarrow 2(NH_4)_2SO_4 + H_2O + SO_2 \tag{38}$$

The ammonium sulfate is heated at approximately 700°F to release ammonia for recycle to the scrubber.

$$(NH_4)_2SO_4 \xrightarrow{700°F} NH_4HSO_4 + NH_3 \tag{39}$$

Ammonium scrubbing has been applied in the USSR and Japan on oil- and coal-fired boilers. In the United States TVA and EPA have conducted pilot plant studies of the process.

Although ammonium-based scrubbers can remove SO_2 efficiently, they generate fine aerosols which can result in excessive visible emissions. Collection of ammonium-sulfate aerosol represents a significant problem, although some advances in limiting aerosol emission have been reported. In addition to the visible emission problem, the economics of ammonium-sulfite system are not established.

LIME/LIMESTONE FGD SYSTEMS

In 1980, the U.S. Environmental Protection Agency regulations required that, for a typical 10,000 Btu/lb coal containing 3 percent sulfur and 10 percent ash, sulfur emissions be reduced by 90 percent and particulate emissions, by 99.7 percent. To meet such standards, and depending on local regulations, the type of fuel burned, and other site-specific conditions, utilities and large industrial boiler operators have to study all of the available flue-gas cleaning processes.

The viable options for particulate collection consist of electrostatic precipitation, fabric filtration, and high-energy wet scrubbing. The preferred options for SO_2 removal are lime/

limestone wet scrubbing and dry scrubbing. Integrated flue-gas cleaning systems consist of various combinations of particulate and SO_2 removal systems. Fig. 30 presents different possibilities for flue-gas cleaning systems.

ESP/Single-Stage Wet Scrubbing

The most common flue-gas cleaning system uses an electrostatic precipitator (ESP) followed by a lime/limestone wet SO_2 scrubber. After the flue gas has been treated in the precipitator, it passes through the induced fans and enters the SO_2 scrubber. If the required SO_2 removal efficiency is less than 85 percent, a fraction of the flue gas can be treated while bypassing the rest to mix with and reheat the saturated flue gas leaving the scrubber.

For higher sulfur fuels requiring SO_2 removal efficiencies of 90 percent or greater, the entire flue gas stream must be treated. Upon leaving the SO_2 absorption section, the flue gas is passed through entrainment separators to remove any slurry droplets mixed with the gas.

The saturated flue gas is then reheated approximately 25 to 50°F above the water dew point before it is vented to the stack.

Baghouse/Single-Stage Wet Scrubbing

For certain types of fuels, the size of an electrostatic precipitator to meet the 1980 standard becomes so large that fabric filters are a technical and economic alternative. The principal advantages of fabric filters are

- very high removal efficiency
- ability to collect fine particles
- insensitivity of collection efficiency to fuel characteristics

This latter advantage is significant because, contrary to the performance of a fabric filter, electrostatic precipitator performance is affected by the characteristics of the flue gas and flyash particles while fabric filter performance is not. Thus, fabric filters give the utility the option of switching fuels without modifying the particulate collection system. The major disadvantages of fabric filters include gas pressure

Fig. 30 **Power-plant flue-gas cleaning systems**

drops of 4 to 6″ WG and more maintenance compared with precipitators.

Two-Stage Scrubbing

Wet scrubbing can remove not only gaseous emissions but particulates as well. To collect flyash by wet scrubbing, a liquid is atomized to fine droplets which are then dispersed and mixed thoroughly with the flue gas. Atomization takes place by accelerating the gas through a venturi and using the momentum of the gas to shear the liquid into fine droplets. The initial large velocity differential between the liquid droplets and the flyash particles provides ideal conditions for collecting flyash by impaction and interception. Simultaneously with flyash collection, some of the SO_2 is absorbed in the venturi scrubber. A second-stage absorber accomplishes final SO_2 removal.[33]

Two-stage wet scrubbing is particularly attractive when collecting flyash containing appreciable amounts of calcium, magnesium, and sodium. To a certain degree, the alkali content of the flyash reacts with the absorbed SO_2 and reduces lime or limestone consumption.

The primary advantage of particulate wet scrubbers is low initial cost compared to electrostatic precipitators and fabric filters. A significant disadvantage is the high gas-side pressure drop. At very low emission levels, pressure drops in excess of 20″ WG are required for most applications.

Two-Stage Scrubbing Plus Electrostatic Precipitation

A recent innovation in flue-gas-cleaning technology consists of low-energy two-stage scrubbing followed by electrostatic precipitation for removing flyash and entrained moisture (Fig. 31). Developed by Combustion Engineering, Inc. in 1979, two-stage-plus scrubbing represents an economical alternative particularly when the alkali content of the flyash is appreciable.[34]

A Two Stage Plus module is shown in Fig. 32. Flue gas enters a low-pressure-drop venturi where the majority of the flyash is collected. The venturi typically operates at 3 to 5″ WG pressure drop. Sulfur dioxide is removed primarily in the second-stage absorber from which the saturated flue gas containing res-

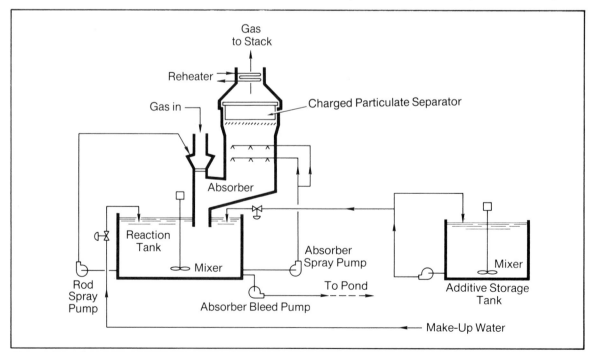

***Fig. 31* Two Stage Plus flow schematic**

idual amounts of flyash and entrained slurry is passed through a charged particulate separator (wet electrostatic precipitator).

Dry-Scrubbing Systems

Dry-scrubbing is an alternative to wet lime/limestone processes for use primarily in low-sulfur-coal applications. The term *dry scrubbing* is derived from the nature of dry waste products which do not require dewatering, and can be transported by conventional flyash han-

dling equipment (as described in Chapter 16).

Wet scrubbers normally operate at liquid-to-gas ratios of 30 or higher. In dry scrubbing, complete evaporation of the liquid is possible with L/G ratios of 0.3 to 0.4 gallons of liquid/1000 cu ft (actual) of flue gas.

Dry-scrubbing systems incorporate spray-dryer absorbers (Fig. 33). Flue gas is contacted with very finely atomized alkaline solutions or slurries. Absorption of SO_2 and evaporation of water occurs simultaneously. The product

Fig. 32 **Isometric cutaway of a Two Stage Plus module**

leaving the spray-dryer absorber consists of dried SO_2 reaction products and flyash. If classifying spray dryers are used, the coarser solids are discharged at the bottom of the spray dryer and the finer solids entrained in the gas. In nonclassifying spray dryers, all of the solids are entrained in the flue gas and ducted to the particulate collector.

Particulate collection takes place beyond the absorber in baghouses or precipitators. Dry SO_2 scrubbing offers several advantages such as minimal water consumption and the elimination of flue-gas reheat requirements (since the gas temperature is not lowered to the adiabatic saturation temperature as with wet scrubbing). On the negative side, dry processes rely on more expensive additives like lime or sodium carbonate. They appear to be limited economically to fuels having low to medium sulfur.

C-E Spray-Absorber Design

The Combustion Engineering dry SO_2 absorber is a co-current classifying spray dryer. Flue gas enters the top of the absorber through inlet assemblies containing swirl vanes.

The absorbent is injected pneumatically into the center of each swirler assembly by ultrasonic atomizing nozzles that require an air pressure of about 60 psig. Slurry feed pressures are 10-15 psig. The compressed air induces primary dispersion of the absorbent slurry by mechanical shear forces produced by the two fluid streams. Final dispersion is accomplished by shattering the droplets with ultrasonic energy produced by the compressed air used with a proprietary nozzle design. Then ultrasonic nozzles generate extremely fine droplets which photographic studies show have diameters that range from 10 to 50 microns.[35]

The flue-gas outlet design requires that effluent gases make a 180° turn before leaving the absorber. Besides eliminating product accumulation in the outlet duct, the abrupt directional change also allows the larger particles to drop out in the absorber product hopper. This design curtails the particulate loading to the fabric filter. Consequently, the number of cleaning cycles as well as abrasion of the filter media are reduced.

As compared with ordinary flyash collection applications, fabric filters together with dry scrubbing offer a broader choice of design options. In conventional flyash-collection applications, the fabric filter experiences flue-gas temperatures about 100° to 150°F higher than encountered in dry scrubbing. Filter media unsuitable at the higher temperatures can be used when the fabric filter follows a dry absorber. In particular, acrylic fibers become attractive due to their strength and flex characteristics, as well as their ability to support more vigorous cleaning methods like mechanical shaking. In

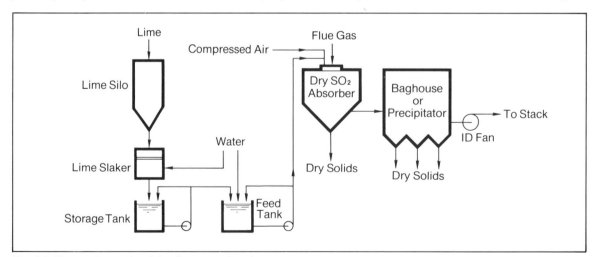

Fig. 33 **Flow schematic of dry flue-gas cleaning system**

dry-scrubbing applications, fabric filters with mechanically shaken acrylic bags represent a viable alternative to conventional reverse-air cleaned fiberglass filter houses.

WET-SCRUBBER DESIGN FACTORS

Lime/limestone-additive scrubber processes commonly use spray towers to absorb SO_2 from the flue gases. Whether operated in the countercurrent, co-current, or cross-current modes, such towers typically have few internals and very low liquid-residence time. The popularity of spray towers is attributable both to a better understanding of the chemical phenomena of wet scrubbing and to more restrictive particulate-emission standards.

The scrubbers designed by the British in the 1930's reflected the belief that high mass-transfer rates were required to absorb slightly soluble SO_2 gases. Thus, towers were designed with internals to promote liquid hold-up. In the 1960's, U.S. firms, acting on the British experience, adopted packed towers for simultaneous SO_2 and particulate removal.

More restrictive effluent-discharge regulations together with more efficient dewatering of waste solids made it necessary to operate FGD systems at higher concentrations of dissolved solids. In general, as the level of dissolved solids in lime/limestone slurries increases, the potential for scaling also increases. Scale formation in packed scrubbers can shut down an FGD system due to excessive gas-side pressure drop. The consequences of scale formation in spray-tower absorbers are considerably less severe.

Spray-Tower Design

Among the advantages of spray towers for lime/limestone FGD processes are
■ maximum turndown ratio
■ high allowable gas velocities
■ low gas-side pressure drop
■ low plugging potential
■ simple mechanical construction

The most common spray-tower design is the vertical countercurrent type in which the gas enters the bottom of the absorber and flows upward through perforated plates and ladder vanes, used to improve distribution of the entering gas. Poor distribution impairs SO_2 removal efficiency, increases the entrainment of slurry droplets, and increases pressure drop.

In the typical absorber, two to four stages of atomizing nozzles admit absorbent slurry into the gas. Designs usually have an optional spare stage. Depending upon the particular FGDS vendor, the nozzles are either hollow or full-cone spray type with capacities that range from approximately 500 to 1500 gallons per minute in large installations. Nozzles are designed to produce fine droplets over a large area at minimum spray-water pressure.

The sprayed slurry falls by gravity to the bottom of the absorber and is drained to a reaction tank. In the spray tower, above the spray stages, entrainment separators (demisting elements) separate suspended slurry droplets from the gas stream. Zig-zag baffles are the most common type of entrainment separators because they offer low pressure drop, simple construction, and good cleanability.

Mass-Transfer Concepts

Sulfur dioxide absorption in countercurrent spray towers involves mass transfer from the gas phase to the liquid phase. The design of spray towers and other FGD wet absorbers requires an understanding of mass-transfer.[36]

The rate of mass transfer, N, is determined by the mass-transfer driving force, $y - y^*$, and the resistance to mass transfer, $1/K_gA$. Symbolically, the relationship may be expressed as

$$N = (y - y^*) \div (1/K_gA) = K_gA (y - y^*) \tag{40}$$

where
N = rate of mass transfer across interface, mol/hr
y = concentration of SO_2 in gas phase, mol fraction
y^* = concentration of SO_2 in gas phase in equilibrium with the existing liquid-phase composition, mol fraction
K_g = gas-phase mass-transfer coefficient, mol/hr-ft^2
A = total interfacial area available for mass transfer, ft^2

From material-balance considerations, the rate of mass transfer may also be expressed by

$$N = GS \, \Delta y \tag{41}$$

where:

G = molar gas flux, mol/hr-ft²

S = cross-sectional area of tower, ft²

Δy = change in SO_2 concentration across tower, mol fraction

For any differential element of spray-tower height, dz, Eqs. 40 and 41 may be equated to give

$$GSdy = K_g(a)(S) \, dz \, (y - y^*) \tag{42}$$

where:

dy = differential change in SO_2 gas-phase concentration, mol fraction

dz = differential increment of tower height, ft

a = available interfacial area per unit volume of spray tower, ft²/ft³

Rearrangement of equation 42 gives

$$dz = \frac{G}{K_g a} \cdot \frac{d}{y - y^*} \tag{43}$$

where:

$K_g a$ = overall gas-phase mass-transfer coefficient, mol/hr-ft³

Eq. 43 may be expressed in integral form as

$$Z = \frac{G}{K_g a} \cdot \int \frac{dy}{y - y^*} = H_{og} \cdot N_{og} \tag{44}$$

where:

H_{og} = height of gas-phase transfer unit, ft

N_{og} = number of gas-phase transfer units

Z = total height of tower, ft

The overall mass-transfer coefficient, $K_g a$, may be evaluated by rearranging Eq. 44 to:

$$K_g a = \frac{G}{Z} \int \frac{dy}{y - y^*} = \frac{G}{Z} N_{og} \tag{45}$$

and then graphically solving the integral for the appropriate limits of y.

For spray-tower design it is essential to know the relationship between $K_g a$ and design variables such as gas velocity, tower height, number of stages, stage spacing, nozzle characteristics, and L/G. This information usually must be developed through pilot- and prototype-plant experiments. Fig. 34 illustrates how such experiments help.

The operating line, AC is based on test data, where points C and A are the gas-phase inlet and outlet SO_2 concentrations respectively. The slope of the line equals the liquid-to-gas ratio, L/G. The gas-liquid equilibrium line, BD, expresses the equilibrium relationship between SO_2 in the liquid and gas phases and is a function of variables such as temperature and liquid composition.

As mentioned, $K_g a$ may be obtained by graphically determining the integral in Eq. 45 to obtain N_{og}. Although details of this integration procedure are not included here, un-

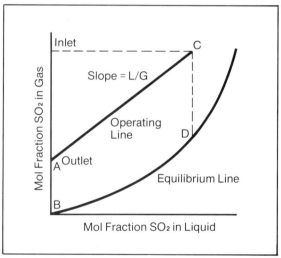

Fig. 34 **Determination of K₉a**

derstand that if the operating line AC and equilibrium line BD are close (due to changes in position of either the operating line or equilibrium line), the number of transfer units (N_{og}) will increase and make the removal process more difficult. As seen in Eq. 45, this situation would require an increase in $K_g a$ (G and Z being constant), or an increase in tower height, Z ($K_g a$ and G being constant). If the operating and equilibrium lines are further apart, the opposite relationships will exist.

Through a series of parametric experiments, a mathematical correlation between $K_g a$ and spray tower design variables can be established. One such correlation developed by Combustion Engineering[36] is

$$K_g a = K_o (Y_{in})^a (Z)^b (L/G)^c \left[\frac{C_d \Delta P}{D} \right]^d (V_g)^e (Mg, Cl)^f$$

(46)

Where:

$K_g a$ = overall mass-transfer coefficient, mol/hr-ft³

Y_{in} = Actual SO_2 concentration at inlet, mol fraction

Z = Spray tower height, ft

L/G = Liquid-to-gas ratio, gpm/1000 cfm (actual) at the outlet

C_d = Coefficient of discharge of the spray nozzle

ΔP = Pressure drop of liquid across the nozzle, psi

D = Sauter mean droplet diameter[37] of the spray liquid, μm

V_g = Superficial gas velocity, ft/sec

Mg, Cl = Concentration of magnesium and chloride in spray liquid

$K, a, \ldots, f$ = Correlation constants.

Eqs. 45 and 46 are used simultaneously with mathematical models of lime/limestone slurry chemistry to select the optimal spray tower.

LIME/LIMESTONE FGDS PROCESS CHEMISTRY

The chemistry of wet scrubbing of SO_2 from flue gas with lime/limestone consists of a complex series of kinetic and equilibrium-controlled reactions occurring in the gas, liquid, and solid phases. Although the overall reactions are commonly expressed as:

$$\text{Lime: } CaO + SO_2 \rightarrow CaSO_3$$
$$CaSO_3 + \tfrac{1}{2}O_2 \rightarrow CaSO_4$$

(47)

$$\text{Limestone: } CaCO_3 + SO_2 \rightarrow CaSO_3 + CO_2$$
$$CaSO_3 + \tfrac{1}{2}O_2 \rightarrow CaSO_4$$

(48)

considerably more detail is required to emphasize and understand the effect of several key process variables such as pH and soluble magnesium and chloride concentration on the chemistry of lime/limestone scrubbing.

The chemical reactions occurring in lime/limestone systems can be written in several different forms, depending on which aspects are being discussed. For this discussion, the reactions have been categorized as absorption, neutralization, regeneration, oxidation, and precipitation. Although written sequentially, many of these reactions occur simultaneously in an actual system. Significant reactions are

Absorption:
$$SO_2 + H_2O \rightarrow H_2SO_3 (HSO_3^- + H^+)$$

(49)

Neutralization:
$$H_2SO_3 + SO_3^= \rightarrow 2HSO_3^-$$

(50)

$$H_2SO_3 + HCO_3^- \rightarrow HSO_3^- + H_2CO_3$$

(51)

Regeneration:
$$Ca(OH)_2 + 2HSO_3^- \rightarrow Ca^{++} + 2SO_3^= + 2H_2O$$

(52)

$$Ca(OH)_2 + 2H_2CO_3 \rightarrow Ca^{++} + 2HCO_3^- + 2H_2O$$

(53)

Oxidation:
$$HSO_3^- + \tfrac{1}{2}O_2 \rightarrow SO_4^= + H^+ \tag{54}$$

$$SO_3^= + \tfrac{1}{2}O_2 \rightarrow SO_4^= \tag{55}$$

Precipitation:
$$(m + n)\,Ca^{++} + m\,SO_3^= + n\,SO_4^= + x\,H_2O \rightarrow$$
$$Ca_{(m+n)}(SO_3)_m(SO_4)_n \cdot xH_2O \tag{56}$$

$$Ca^{++} + SO_4^= + 2H_2O \rightarrow CaSO_4 \cdot 2H_2O \tag{57}$$

Replacing Eqs. 52 and 53 with the following regeneration reactions makes it possible to describe limestone scrubbing:

Regeneration:
$$CaCO_3 + HSO_3^- \rightarrow Ca^{++} + SO_3^= + HCO_3^- \tag{58}$$

$$CaCO_3 + H_2CO_3 \rightarrow Ca^{++} + 2HCO_3^- \tag{59}$$

The following text relates this chemistry to key aspects of FGDS design. Specifically covered are the effects of absorbent composition on SO_2 removal, scale control, oxidation and additive utilization.

Absorbent-Composition Effect

Vapor-liquid equilibrium between SO_2 in the gas and the absorbent liquid governs the amount of SO_2 absorbed from flue gas. If no soluble alkaline species are present, the liquid quickly becomes saturated with SO_2 and absorption is limited.

The neutralization reactions (50 and 51) remove sulfurous acid, H_2SO_3, from solution and allow the absorption reaction to proceed. In a spray tower, the soluble alkaline species in the spray slurry performs nearly all of the neutralization due to the extremely short liquid residence time. If an absorber has greater liquid holdup, some neutralization can be expected

from dissolution of solid calcium sulfite or limestone. Thus, factors affecting soluble alkaline species level in the spray slurry impact on the overall SO_2 removal capability of a lime/limestone FGDS. In the development of these processes, it is apparent that the three major factors affecting the soluble alkali level are pH, soluble-magnesium concentration, and soluble-chloride concentration.

Effect of pH

In general, with a lime/limestone FGDS, the higher the pH, the greater the sulfur-removal efficiency. Two factors are involved. First, by definition, a high pH increases the hydroxyl-ion (OH^-) concentration, which acts similar to sulfite and bicarbonate reactions 50 and 51. But at the pH ranges experienced in commercial systems—between 5 and 8—the impact of hydroxyl-ion neutralization is negligible. So it is the second factor, the impact that pH has on the sulfite/bisulfite and bicarbonate/carbonic-acid equilibrium reactions, that has the primary beneficial effect on SO_2 removal.

Figs. 35 and 36 illustrate the impact of pH on these equilibria. In the range of pH from 5 to 8, increasing pH shifts the sulfite-bisulfite equilibrium in favor of sulfite. Shifting the equilibrium towards the sulfite region by increasing pH is beneficial to SO_2 removal. A similar condition exists with the carbonic acid (H_2CO_3)/

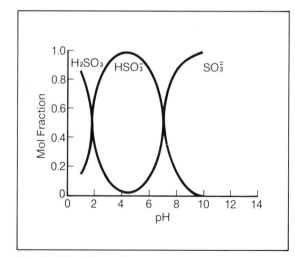

Fig. 35 **Bisulfite-sulfite ratio versus pH**

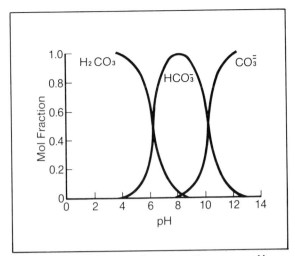

Fig. 36 **Bicarbonate-carbonate ratio versus pH**

bicarbonate equilibrium. Increasing pH favors existence of the bicarbonate ion which can neutralize sulfurous acid (reaction 51).

Effect of Magnesium

Magnesium enters the SO_2 scrubbing system through several mechanisms:

■ as an impurity in limestone

■ as a constituent of dolomite CaMg $(CO_3)_2$ additive

■ from coal-ash constituents solubilized in the scrubbing liquor

■ in the makeup water added to compensate for evaporation and other liquid losses.

The magnesium concentration depends on the total input from the various sources and upon the rate at which liquid leaves the system. In closed-loop operation, the accumulation increases until a magnesium compound, such as magnesium sulfite, precipitates. In a commercial system some liquid containing magnesium leaves with the solids. Thus, the degree of solids dewatering affects the concentration of magnesium in an FGDS. Recycle systems with vacuum filters for final solid/liquid separation operate at higher magnesium levels than those with a thickener only.[38]

The ultimate concentration of magnesium depends on the solubility of the magnesium in the additive and on the pH of the slurry. If calcined at too high a temperature, the magnesium has a relatively low solubility and is eventually removed with the effluent solids. Systems operating at an above-9 pH have a low Mg concentration due to the limited solubility of magnesium hydroxide (Fig. 37).

Commercial operation of FGD systems has shown that soluble Mg in the absorbing slurry significantly improves SO_2-removal efficiency (Fig. 38). The increase is attributable primarily to the higher soluble-alkali levels in the presence of magnesium. In normal lime/limestone spray-tower operation, little of the additive dissolves within the tower because it remains there such a short time. Thus, the amount of

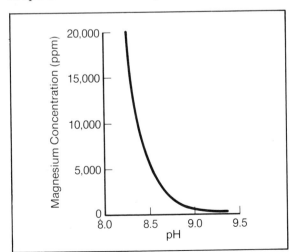

Fig. 37 **Magnesium solubility at various pH values**

Fig. 38 **Effect of magnesium on SO₂ removal efficiency**

sulfur-dioxide absorbed depends only upon soluble-alkali content. If the alkali concentration in any region of the liquid drops, the rate of the neutralization reactions 50 and 51 also drops. Ultimately, there exists a static equilibrium condition between gaseous and liquid SO_2 concentration.

Where magnesium exists, the soluble alkali level of the absorbent increases primarily because of the presence of sulfite and bicarbonate salts of magnesium. As these magnesium alkalies are significantly more soluble than the corresponding calcium alkalies, there is an increase in the sulfur-dioxide absorption capacity of the slurry. The solubility of magnesium alkali compounds depends on the pH concentration. In a lime-additive FGDS, therefore, the proper system operating pH is very important to take full advantage of the magnesium. Examination of the sulfite-bisulfite and carbonate-bicarbonate equilibria and the magnesium solubility curve indicates the optimum pH to lie in the 7-8 range. System operation at pH higher than 8 reduces the magnesium solubility and may prevent full use of the additive. Operation below a pH of 7 decreases the concentration of neutralizing bicarbonate and sulfite and the beneficial effect of magnesium on SO_2 removal.

Effect of Chloride

Chlorides generally find their way into an FGD system by one or both of the following: from the chloride present in the coal burned, subsequently dissolved as a hydrogen chloride gas (or as a salt in the scrubbing liquor) or with the make-up water, when cooling-tower blowdown or other plant waste water is used.

While magnesium improves SO_2 removal efficiencies by increasing the soluble alkalinity level of the scrubbing slurry, chloride has an opposite effect. Chloride ions combine with available magnesium and displace soluble sulfite and bicarbonate from solution. Many investigations have correlated SO_2 removal efficiency to "effective" magnesium concentration, not "actual" magnesium concentration. "Effective" magnesium concentration is defined as:

$$Mg_e = Mg - \frac{Cl}{2.92}$$

$$(60)$$

where:

Mg_e = effective Mg concentration, mg/l

Mg = actual Mg concentration, mg/l

Cl = actual Cl concentration, mg/l

Using Eq. 60, it can be shown that, in the presence of 10,000 mg/l of chloride, the beneficial effect of 5,000 mg/l of magnesium is reduced to the equivalent of only 1575 ppm magnesium. In a system where there is no magnesium present, increasing chloride concentration produces a minor improvement in SO_2 removal because of the higher ionic strength of the scrubbing slurry.

Scale Control

The principal compounds crystallizing in a flue-gas desulfurization system are calcium sulfite and sulfate (reactions 56 and 57). The major concern with crystallization of these compounds is the potential for scale formation on scrubber internals. Uncontrolled scale can plug the spray nozzles, mist eliminators, piping, and other equipment. Plugged systems must be shut down and cleaned.

As the crystallization of calcium sulfite is pH-sensitive, abrupt pH increases in critical system components must be avoided. Control of the spray slurry pH has curtailed sulfite scaling in commercial systems.

Control of calcium-sulfate scaling is more difficult, and the normal 3–9 pH range encountered in operation is not a factor influencing calcium-sulfate saturation or crystallization. Control of calcium-sulfate relative saturation depends on seed-crystal concentrations and crystallization time. Any increases in the relative saturation of calcium sulfate to high values can be conducive to heterogeneous nucleation and scaling of scrubber components.

Work on scale-control techniques performed by C-E and others in 1974 and 1975, revealed that there was an alternate mode of FGDS operation—subsaturated operation.[38,39] Under some conditions, coprecipitation of sulfate within the calcium sulfite crystal lattice can occur to such an extent that it removes all the sulfate formed by the process. When this occurs, the scrubbing slurry does not become saturated with calcium sulfate, and scale cannot form. The following sections will discuss various aspects of scale control including relative saturation and scale potential, supersaturated operation, and subsaturated operation.[39]

Relative Saturation and Scaling Potential

As the scrubbing liquor absorbs SO_2 from flue gas, it is in intimate contact with gases containing typically 3 to 5 percent oxygen. The reaction between the oxygen, which is absorbed, and the sulfite/bisulfite in the liquid leads to sulfate formation. Since there may be no accumulation of material at steady-state, sulfate must be continually purged from the system. Although sulfate may theoretically be purged entirely in the liquid phase, this mode is generally unacceptable from an environmental standpoint—large quantities of sulfate would be discharged into the local water.

In practice, sulfate is generally purged from lime/limestone wet scrubbers as relatively insoluble calcium salts which are dewatered and disposed of as solid waste. Thus, it is extremely important to control the reactions of crystallization which form the calcium-sulfate salts. If these reactions are not properly controlled, serious plugging can occur because of a hard scale of calcium-sulfate dihydrate ($CaSO_4 \cdot 2H_2O$, gypsum) that may form.

The equilibrium and kinetic factors in crystallization reactions involving calcium sulfate are complex. Slurries containing high concentrations of salts behave as non-ideal solutions and the relationship between the concentration of calcium sulfate and its equilibrium solubility is best defined in terms of activity coefficients. The activity is defined as becoming equal to the mol fraction; concentration or molality of the salt as infinite dilution is approached where it becomes unity. In a slurry, calcium sulfate does not behave ideally, hence the use of the activity in defining the solubility product, K_{sp}.

$$K_{CaSO4} \cdot 2H_2O = A_{Ca}A_{SO_4} = 1.9 \times 10^{-5} \text{ at } 50°C \tag{61}$$

where:

$K_{CaSO4} = A_{Ca}A_{SO_4}$ = solubility product of $CaSO_4$
A_{Ca} = activity of calcium ion
A_{SO_4} = activity of sulfate ion

If the activity product of the calcium and sulfate ions is less than the solubility product, the solution is said to be subsaturated. If the product is greater than Ksp, the solution is supersaturated. The ratio of the activity product to the solubility product is called the relative saturation (RS) and is used as a measure of the saturation level of a solution with respect to gypsum.

$$RS = \frac{A_{Ca}A_{SO_4}}{K_{sp}, CaSO_4 \cdot 2H_2O} \tag{62}$$

when:

RS < 1.0, solution is subsaturated;
RS = 1.0, solution is saturated;
RS > 1.0, solution is supersaturated.

The importance of gypsum relative saturation in designing lime/limestone wet scrubbing systems for scale-free operation is shown in the following discussions.

Supersaturated Operation—Gypsum Crystallization

Formation of calcium-sulfite and calcium-sulfate scale on scrubber internals can be a severe problem and, while control of calcium-sulfite scaling is possible by avoiding rapid increases in slurry pH, control of calcium-sulfate scaling is not a function of slurry pH.

Considerable effort was made in the early 1970's to establish an expression to describe the desupersaturation rate of calcium sulfate as a function of appropriate system design and operating parameters.[38]

In addition to developing a crystallization-rate equation, it was necessary to determine the level of calcium supersaturation that could be tolerated without causing scaling of internal surfaces in any operating scrubber.

A series of experiments to determine the critical supersaturation above which scaling can occur revealed that a high probability of scaling exists if the absorber effluent relative saturation exceeded 1.4. Thus, Fig. 39 shows the supersaturated operating range between relative saturation 1.0-1.4 where scale formation is unlikely and operational difficulties slight.

After establishing a calcium-sulfate-relative saturation region for scale-free operation, the industry worked on developing a crystallization rate expression.

A crystallization rate equation was developed from bench-tests

$$R = knS \tag{63}$$

where:

R = reaction rate
k = rate constant
n = number of seed crystals
S = driving force

Interpretation of the data collected suggested a driving force term of the form (RS − 1). It also showed that the rate was directly proportional to seed crystal concentration.

Further work was performed to calibrate the rate expression with data from full-scale, commercial FGD Systems.[39, 40] The rate expression may be used to predict the seed crystal concentration required to prevent calcium sulfate scaling. The rate of calcium-sulfate precipitation in the reaction tank, R, can be computed by material balance if the following information is known: SO_2 absorption rate, fraction SO_2 oxidized to $SO_4^=$, and reaction tank residence time. Sulfur dioxide absorption rate and reaction tank residence time are design parameters and fraction SO_2 oxidized can be predicted from various design models. The maximum relative saturation allowable in the absorber effluent is 1.4; values above this critical level will result in scale formation. By using information on the absorbent composition (such as magnesium and chloride concentrations), rates of oxidation, ionic strength/activity coefficient correlations and the level of saturation entering the absorber which will result in an absorber effluent saturation of 1.4 can be calculated. This value and the rate of calcium sulfate precipitation are used in Eq. 63 to predict the seed crystal concentration required in the reaction tank to maintain the absorber effluent relative saturation below 1.4. Thus, the solids concentration circulated to prevent scaling can be computed and used as an operating point.

Subsaturated Operation—Coprecipitation

Because crystallization is thermodynamically impossible from subsaturated solutions, the potential for scaling can be eliminated by operating the system at a relative saturation less than 1.0. Until recently, the only technique known to accomplish this was liquid blowdown. However, discharging large quantities of process water to the environment is generally unacceptable. Work by EPA has suggested an alternate method for purging sulfate from solutions that are subsaturated with respect to gypsum: coprecipitation of sulfate with calcium sulfite to form a mixed crystal.[41, 42] Although the exact nature of this mixed crystal is not fully understood, several interesting facts have evolved:

■ significant amounts of sulfate can be coprecipitated with calcium sulfite from solutions

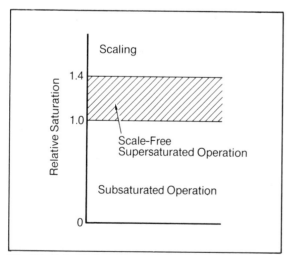

Fig. 39** **Relative saturation of gypsum as an indication of scaling potential

which are subsaturated with respect to gypsum

■ the mol ratio of sulfate to sulfite in the mixed crystal can be as high as 0.2–0.3

■ x-ray diffraction analysis of samples of the mixed crystal indicates only the presence of calcium sulfite hemihydrate ($CaSO_3 \cdot \frac{1}{2}H_2O$); no known calcium sulfate forms are observed.

Bench and pilot scale experiments aimed at studying this phenomenon lead to the development of mathematical correlations which related the amount of sulfate coprecipitated to various system parameters. An example of one of the more useful correlations is shown below:

$$MR = KA_{Ca}{}^x \cdot A_{SO_4}{}^y \tag{64}$$

where,

MR = mol ratio of SO_4 to SO_3 in the co-precipitated solid

A_{Ca}, A_{SO_4} = activities of calcium and sulfate iron, respectively

K,x,y = experimental constants

Numerical values for the experimental constants were determined to be

K = 231
x = 0.54
y = 0.76

Fig. 40 is a plot of over 60 bench scale experiments and several data points taken from full-scale commercial installations. The dependency of mol ratio (MR) on the activities of calcium and sulfate has been demonstrated over a wide range of solution compositions and kinetic conditions. The ranges studied included:

Calcium	60–6,000 mg/ℓ
Sulfate	600–20,000 mg/ℓ
Sulfite	100–6,000 mg/ℓ
Magnesium	0–5,000 mg/ℓ
Chloride	0–14,000 mg/ℓ
Sodium	100–5,000 mg/ℓ
Sulfite precipitation rate	0.15–2.3 millimol/ℓ-min.

The mathematical model can be used to predict the effect of oxidation on the level of gypsum saturation in a subsaturated lime/limestone FGDS.

The left side of Eq. 64 consists of the term, MR, the mol ratio of sulfate to sulfite in the co-precipitation solid. Because nearly all forms of sulfur leave the system in the solid phase, the ratio of sulfate to total sulfur in the solids equals the oxidation in the system. It can be shown that the following relationship exists between MR and system oxidation:

$$\frac{1}{MR} = \frac{1}{OX} - 1 \tag{65}$$

where:

$$OX = \text{fraction oxidized} = \frac{SO_4}{SO_4 + SO_3}$$

The right side of Eq. 64 contains terms for calcium and sulfate activity similar to the definition of RS. Thus,

$$MR = KA_{Ca}{}^x \cdot A_{SO_4}{}^y$$

(related to oxidation) (related to relative saturation)

(64)

Eq. 64 can, therefore, be used to relate relative saturation to system oxidation. As oxidation can be predicted by other design models, the level of gypsum saturation can be predicted using Eq. 64. Furthermore, the relationship is direct and by increasing the oxidation we increase the saturation.

Maximum Tolerable Oxidation

One particularly useful concept is that of maximum tolerable oxidation (MTO) which is the oxidation level that will cause a lime/limestone FGD system to run saturated with respect to gypsum (RS = 1.0). Maximum tolerable oxidation can be calculated using the proposed design equation. By using an equilibrium program or other experimental or theoretical techniques, the activities of calcium and sulfate for a saturated solution can be calculated. If these values are inserted into Eq. 64, it's possible to calculate the mol ratio of sulfate to sulfite in the coprecipitated solids in equilibrium with this solution. Oxidation can then be calculated from Eq. 65. For example, in a solution containing no magnesium or chloride, the activities of calcium and sulfate in a saturated solution are approximately 0.0049 and 0.0039 mol/ℓ respectively at 50°C; this translates to approximately 16 percent oxidation (Eq. 65).

If the system operates at 16-percent oxidation, the reaction tank will operate saturated with respect to gypsum, assuming that the precipitation reaction occurs in the reaction tank. Higher oxidation levels will result in supersaturated operation; lower oxidations will result in subsaturated operation. Thus, the MTO for a system containing no magnesium or chloride is 16 percent.

The design equation can be used to predict the relative saturation of gypsum for subsatu-rated systems as a function of magnesium and chloride concentrations, and temperature. As a consequence, it can also be used to predict whether a system will operate in the subsaturated mode. Calcium and sulfate ion activities can be predicted for solutions of various compositions (i.e., magnesium/chloride concentrations and saturations) and temperatures. Using these activities it is possible to calculate the mol ratio of sulfate to sulfite in the coprecipitated solid and, thus the oxidation required to produce that mol ratio.

Fig. 41 is a plot of relative saturation versus oxidation as a function of varying magnesium and chloride concentrations obtained by this method. The presence of chloride shifts the curves to the left resulting in high saturations for the same oxidation, while magnesium has the opposite effect. It also can be seen that the presence of chloride diminishes the beneficial effect of magnesium. In addition, the oxidation

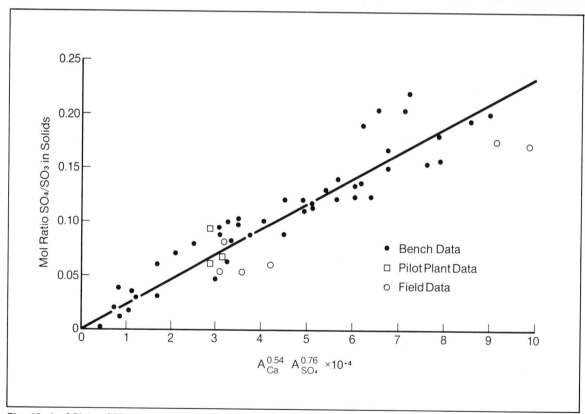

Fig. 40 $A_{Ca}^{0.54}$ $A_{SO_4}^{0.76}$ **versus mol ratio to SO₄ to SO₃**

that corresponds to relative saturation of 1.0 represents the maximum tolerable oxidation for subsaturated operation at these conditions.

Oxidation

In lime/limestone FGD systems, solutions containing sulfite $(SO_3^=)$ come in intimate contact with flue gas containing typically 3 to 50 percent oxygen. As a result, significant quantities of $SO_3^= (S^{+4})$ are oxidized to $SO_4^= (S^{+6})$. The rate at which sulfate is formed directly determines the required rate of sulfate purge at steady-state which in turn influences the level of calcium sulfate saturation. The relative amounts of sulfate and sulfite formed in the process also have implications in the ultimate disposal of FGDS waste product. In general, sludges containing high sulfate to sulfite ratios are more easily dewatered and result in a more stable disposal product. Thus, the rate of sulfate ion formation (rate of oxidation) has widespread implications on the performance and

reliability of wet SO_2 scrubbing processes. A quantitative understanding of the factors which contribute to sulfate ion formation is essential if lime/limestone wet scrubbing is to have optimum performance.

Two major oxidation process options exist: natural and forced. In natural oxidation, conversion results primarily from a reaction between soluble sulfite in the scrubbing slurry and oxygen in the flue gas. Only a minute amount of oxidation occurs from contact with atmospheric oxygen in open tanks, overflow weirs, and the like.

Several factors influence the rate of oxidation: oxygen concentration in the flue gas, ionic strength of the absorbent slurry, and the liquid-to-gas ratio in the absorber.

In forced oxidation, on the other hand, compressed atmospheric air is injected into the process (usually in the reaction tank) to promote oxidation and achieve oxidation effi-

Fig. 41 Effects of Mg and Cl on gypsum relative saturation as a function of oxidation

ciencies of 99-99+ percent. Forced oxidation improves the dewatering and structural characteristics of the waste product and reduces disposal costs. The following text discusses factors which influence oxidation in lime/limestone scrubbing systems.

Natural Oxidation

The major source of oxidation in a naturally oxidized FGDS is the absorber in which the oxygen in the flue gas reacts with the soluble sulfite in the scrubbing slurry. The reaction between oxygen and sulfite in the aqueous phase is very complex and can be greatly influenced by the presence of catalysts and inhibitors. The rate of the oxidation reaction is nearly always much faster than the rate of oxygen transfer to the liquid phase. Thus, oxidation in FGDS is generally mass-transfer limited and the rate of chemical reaction can be assumed to be instantaneous. Mathematical models of the oxidation process can then be expressed in terms of classical two-film mass-transfer theory.

An example of the type model which has been developed to describe the rate of oxidation in a spray tower absorber is

$$r_{NO} = \frac{2GC_oRT}{V_AP} \left[1 - \exp \left\{ \frac{K_La\,PV_T}{HG} \right\} \right]$$

(66)

where,

r_{NO} = rate of natural oxidation, mols/min-gal
G = gas flow rate, mols/min
C_o = oxygen content in flue gas, mols/gal
R = gas constant, gal/atm-mol-°R
T = gas temperature, °R
P = total pressure of gas, atm
K_La = overall volumetric mass-transfer coefficient, min^{-1}
V_A = volume of liquid in absorber, gal
V_T = absorber volume, gal
H = Henry's law constant, gal/atm-mol

All variables in Eq. 66, except K_La, are design parameters which are known or may be estimated. The overall mass-transfer coefficient cannot be determined on theoretical grounds

except in the most simple cases and must therefore be determined experimentally. C-E has developed mathematical correlations which predict K_La as a function of operating and design parameters for various absorber types. An example of the equation form used to predict K_La for spray-tower absorbers is

$$K_La = a\,(L/G)^{\,b}(I)^c\,(pH)^d\,(V_G)^e\,(Z)^f\,(C_o)^g$$

(67)

where,

L/G = liquid-to-gas ratio
I = ionic strength of absorbent slurry
pH = pH of spray slurry
V_G = superficial gas velocity in absorber
Z = height of contactor
a, b, c, d, e, f, g = experimental constants

With the oxidation rate known, the fraction of SO_2 oxidized can be calculated by dividing the oxidation rate by the SO_2 absorption rate. The fraction oxidized can then be used in the various scale-control models to arrive at appropriate operation conditions, and to predict the characteristics of the disposal product.

Forced Oxidation

Forced oxidation uses atmospheric air injected into the reaction tank of FGD systems. To achieve the best efficiency, the injected air must be finely divided into tiny bubbles to maximize the interfacial area. The dispersion is usually accomplished by using either sparge rings and radial turbine mixers, or jet eductors. With either arrangement, the ultimate problem is to define and predict the impact of various process design and operating parameters on the rate of oxidation. This can be achieved in a manner similar to predicting the level of natural oxidation occurring in an absorber. The two-film mass-transfer approach is:

$$r_{FO} = \frac{2G_AC_oRT}{h\,P} \left[1 - \exp \left\{ -\frac{K_La P\,h}{G_A\,H} \right\} \right]$$

(68)

where,

r_{FO} = rate of forced oxidation

G_A = airflow

h = height of reaction tank

Similar to the absorber natural oxidation model, all of the variables except $K_L a$ are known or may be estimated. A correlation describing $K_L a$ as a function of pertinent process variables for a sparge ring/radial turbine forced-oxidation system is as follows.

$$K_L a = K_2 (h)^a (I)^b (pH)^c (V_{air})^d (D)^e (P_M)^f \tag{69}$$

where,

K_2 = experimental constant

V_{air} = superficial air velocity in tank

D = tank diameter

P_M = mixer power input to tank

It is generally accepted that oxidation is increased by decreasing pH, increasing mixer power, increasing ionic strength, and increasing tank height.

Note that the total oxidation achieved in a forced oxidation FGDS is a function of the naturally occurring oxidation for which credit may be taken.

ADDITIVE UTILIZATION

Minimizing the amount of alkali additive required to obtain a desired SO_2 removal efficiency reduces the operating cost of an FGD system. To determine the factors influencing additive use, it is necessary to understand the additive dissolution process and the effect of system operating conditions, design, and additive properties on this process.

In a lime or limestone SO_2 scrubbing system, the addition of alkali is controlled to neutralize the SO_2 absorbed and precipitate the calcium-sulfur salts. Although in theory the amount of lime or limestone required is stoichiometrically equal to the amount of SO_2 removed, the kinetics of the limestone dissolution process dictates the use of excess additive to achieve the desired SO_2 removal efficiency.

Additive stoichiometry is usually defined as the mols of additive fed (excluding impurities) to a scrubber per mol of SO_2 absorbed (although it can be, and sometimes is, defined as the mols of additive fed per mol of SO_2 entering the scrubber). Additive utilization, then, can be expressed by the following relationship:

$$\text{Utilization} = \frac{1}{\text{Stoichiometry}} = \frac{\text{mols } SO_2 \text{ absorbed}}{\text{mols additive fed}} \tag{70}$$

Although not usually significant, the absorption of other acid gases such as HCl can influence utilization of the additive. Utilization then could be more broadly defined as the fraction of additive converted to reaction products in the scrubber. However, unless a detailed material balance is done, it is more straightforward to use Eq. 70 to calculate utilization from system operating data.

From Eq. 70, it can be seen that to increase utilization one must either reduce the additive feed rate while maintaining constant SO_2 absorption efficiency or increase the SO_2 removal efficiency for a given limestone feed rate.

The dissolution rate of alkali additives is inversely proportional to the solution pH; therefore, better utilization is possible by operating a system at low pH levels. However, as pointed out earlier, reducing the pH also can reduce SO_2 removal efficiency. Therefore, it is usually more productive to increase the absorber performance for the same system pH, or increase the additive dissolution and utilization at a constant system pH.

Lime Utilization.

Lime or calcium oxide (CaO) is obtained from calcination of limestone ($CaCO_3$). The conditions under which the limestone is calcined or "burned" can have a great impact on the reactivity of the lime produced. If the limestone is calcined at too high a temperature, the lime may become dead-burned and unreactive, making it unsuitable for FGDS use.

Because of the high reactivity of most commercially available lime, it is possible to achieve high utilization (as much as 95 percent) with minimum impact on the remainder of the system. The main design parameter in maximizing utilization is the pH of the scrubbing slurry. With pH maintained above 8.5, considerable carbon-dioxide absorption occurs because of the 10 to 15 percent by volume of CO_2 in the flue gas. Carbon dioxide reacts with lime in a manner similar to sulfur dioxide to form calcium carbonate. Calcium carbonate, being insoluble at high pH, precipitates thus preventing the calcium from reacting with sulfur dioxide. The following reactions summarize the effect of CO_2 absorption:

$$CaO + CO_2 \rightarrow CaCO_3\,(aq) \tag{71}$$

$$CaCO\,(aq) \rightarrow CaCO_3\,(S) \tag{72}$$

Data from a full-scale commercial FGDS indicate that a decrease in utilization from 95 percent to 85 percent may occur as pH is increased from 7.5 to 9.0. To reduce waste of the relatively high-cost lime, the pH of lime systems is generally held below 8.5.

Limestone Utilization

Limestone is usually less reactive than lime in FGD systems operating under identical conditions. For this reason, system modifications are needed to produce limestone utilizations in excess of 90–95 percent.

Limestone dissolution is a function of surface area of the suspended limestone and hydrogen-ion concentration (i.e., pH) of the solution as follows:

$$r = KA\,[H^+] \tag{73}$$

where

    r = rate of limestone dissolution, mol/ℓ-s
    K = experimental constant, s/cm^2
    A = surface area of suspended limestone, cm^2
    H^+ = hydrogen ion concentration (10^{-pH}), mol/ℓ

Use of Eq. 73 suggests two methods of in-creasing the limestone dissolution rate and, thus, utilization. First, by increasing the surface area, A, and second, by increasing the hydrogen-ion concentration (decreasing pH).

Large surface areas can be produced by finely grinding the limestone before it is injected into the system. Limestone is typically ground to 75 percent through 200 mesh in FGDS applications. Finer grinds, such as 75 percent through 325 mesh, are possible but more mill power is required. This is often cost-effective.

Limestone utilization can also be improved by operating at reduced pH's. As mentioned previously, this impairs efficiency—to maintain the same removal at reduced pH, the absorber design must be modified. For example, L/G may be increased (with higher pumping costs) or tower height may be increased (with higher capital costs). The cost-effectiveness of any adjustments must be examined.

It is also possible to use a two-stage operation in which the primary stage is operated at reduced pH to maximize lime/limestone utilization, and the second stage is operated at high pH to accomplish the required SO_2 removal. In this operation, limestone is fed to the second stage and the spent slurry from the second stage is fed to the primary stage before being bled off.

A final technique for improving limestone utilization is to increase residence time—at a fixed rate of reaction, the longer a limestone particle remains in the absorber/reaction-tank loop, the greater will be the fraction of the particle that dissolves.

The residence time of the solid particles in the process is a function of the particle inventory and the solids bleed rate. Because the bleed rate is fixed by the SO_2 absorption rate at steady-state, only the inventory can be adjusted. The solids inventory can be made greater by increasing the reaction-tank volume and/or the solids concentration. Because the slurry is abrasive, the solids concentration has a practical upper limit of approximately 15 percent. The relatively low cost of tanks and low mixer power requirements suggests that, in many situations, it is cheaper to increase the tank size to improve limestone use.

SPRAY-TOWER COMPONENTS

In addition to viable process chemistry, successful spray-tower performance requires the proper selection of system components. These consist principally of the tower shell, the slurry delivery subsystems (pumps, piping and nozzles), the mist eliminator, and the gas reheater. Each must be designed with materials for good reliability and performance in a corrosive and erosive environment.

With the cooperation of utility users, consulting engineers, vendors, and field-service representatives, C-E has developed the following standard features.

Tower Shell

Velocity considerations dictate the tower (Fig. 42) cross-sectional area. Although higher gas velocities through the absorbing section improve SO_2 removal, the maximum allowable velocity through the close-coupled mist eliminator section (about 10 to 11 ft/sec) sets a practical limit of 12 to 13 ft/sec through the absorbing section. A short transition piece with a gradually expanding area connects the mist eliminator section to the absorber section. The number of absorbing stages required to obtain the desired level of SO_2 removal governs the tower height.

The corrosive and erosive environment within the tower requires special materials. The tower shell and internal support members are constructed entirely of 316L austenitic stainless steel containing a minimum of 2.5 percent molybdenum. The 316L material provides several benefits.

■ Demonstrated corrosive resistance without stress corrosion or pitting. Accelerated corrosion tests verified this performance with chloride levels as high as 35,000 ppm.

■ Erosion resistance superior to other tested materials and nonmetallic coatings.

■ Maintenance ease so that high-wear parts can be replaced with minimal downtime.

■ Positive sealing around access doors and penetrations; unlike plastic-coated materials, smooth mating surfaces allow effective sealing.

Pumps, Piping and Nozzles

C-E uses independent absorption stages, each consisting of a spray pump, piping, manifold, headers, and spray nozzles (Fig. 42). If a spare spray pump is included, a complete spare absorption stage is also provided. This arrangement provides maximum flexibility and allows tailoring the spray flow to system requirements by removing absorption stages from operation in steps.

Rubber-lined centrifugal spray pumps provide erosion resistance and protection against unexpected process upsets in pH control. A tall reaction tank provides a large net-positive-suction head to prevent pump cavitation which can damage the rubber liner.

Fiberglass-reinforced plastic (FRP) spray piping with an abrasion-resistant internal liner provides abrasion/erosion resistance. The FRP is an inert material used for its corrosion resistance. FRP piping is easily fabricated and, unlike rubber-lined pipe, can be readily repaired in the field.

The manifold and headers are built of FRP for the flow and geometry requirements of each contract. Tapered manifolds and headers keep slurry velocities within allowable values (nominally 5 to 10 ft/sec).

The spray nozzles at each absorption stage are arranged in an even-spaced array which provides full spray coverage over the tower cross-section. The result of several years of testing various designs and materials, the nozzles provide a full-cone, wide-angle spray pattern, and are made of a wear-resistant cast refractory containing silicon carbide.

Mist Eliminator

The cleaned flue gas passes through a separation section with two stages: the bulk entrainment separator (BES) and the mist eliminator (Fig. 43). The BES consists of six-inch FRP vanes mounted at a 45-degree angle on two-inch parallel spacing. It extends across the entire face area of the spray-tower absorber.

The mist eliminator located above the BES is made from vee-shaped FRP vanes arranged in a series of chevrons across the gas flow path. Two

Fig. 42 **Spray-tower absorber module**

rows of chevrons assure droplet impingement and minimize mist carryover.

Retractable lances, which rotate 360 degrees, have pairs of opposed nozzles at the ends and midpoints; they are located between the BES and the lower level of chevrons. These lances provide high-energy jets of water to clean each vane. Efficient cleaning prevents excessive droplet carryover which would result from deposition on the vanes.

Flue-Gas Reheater

Combustion Engineering recommends inline carbon-steel gas reheaters.[33, 43] Compared to austenitic-stainless-steel reheaters, they are the least expensive to install; with proper maintenance, they are also the least costly to operate. C-E uses spiral-wound finned-tube heat exchangers identical to those installed in many high-pressure boilers. Staggered tubes combined with shallow overall depth ensure high heat-transfer efficiency as well as easy cleaning of the reheater.

Combustion has had excellent experience with its carbon-steel reheaters placed immediately downstream of the scrubbing equipment. The mist-eliminator system described above exposes the reheater to extremely small quantities of liquids and solids. And any solids that do collect on the reheater are removed easily by conventional air or steam sootblowers.

Because entrainment is immediately evaporated in the turbulent reheater, metal surfaces are kept warm and dry, a condition conducive to long life for a carbon steel heating surface. Although general corrosion will eventually require replacement of a carbon steel reheater, the danger of sudden failures due to stress corrosion is minimal.

REAGENT PREPARATION SYSTEMS

The reagent preparation systems for fluegas desulfurization include the handling, storage,

Fig. 43 **Spray-tower mist-eliminator system**

grinding, slurrying and feeding of the chemical after it has been delivered to the plant site. Additives such as lime, limestone, magnesium oxide, and sodium carbonate are prepared with such systems. Preparation of the most commonly used additives, lime and limestone, will be described in detail.

Limestone

Limestone is received as crushed rock, sized to about $\frac{1}{2}'' \times \frac{1}{2}''$, shipped, unloaded and stored like coal. The rock is ground to a fine powder (about 90 percent passing through 325 mesh) in either wet or dry pulverizers.

A closed-cycle, wet-grinding system (Fig. 44) is normally used to prepare limestone. The system includes classification so that oversized particles are recycled to the mill and accurate control of the top-size particles helps minimize the formation of superfines. The pulverized limestone is slurried and stored in large tanks where the solution is continuously agitated.

Limestone grinding is generally a batch process and the mill operates at maximum capability until the storage tanks are full.

Lime

Lime is generally available as pebble lime produced in $\frac{3}{4}''$ and $\frac{1}{2}''$ mesh sizes by the calcining processes. Commerical lime is typically 85–95 percent calcium oxide with 0 to 5 percent magnesium oxide and 0 to 10 percent inerts. The lime is generally fed from the silo to a slaker by a variable-speed gravimetric belt feeder. The slaker controls adjust the water flow rate to provide a 5 to 15 percent solids mixture of slaked lime which is pumped to an additive storage tank for use in the FGD system.

Reagent Feed Systems

FGD operation requires reagent feeding to the system at a rate proportional to the pounds of SO_2 removed. The feed rate should be varied to maximize the additive utilization during partial load operation or changes in SO_2 con-

***Fig. 44** Closed-circuit wet-grinding flow diagram*

centrations in the flue gas. This requires that the additive feed rate be metered and matched to the demand. For process control, a variable slurry feed system is desirable.

The control of a slurry feed does, however, have constraints to consider when designing the feed system. A settling slurry (lime or limestone slurry) is susceptible to pipe plugging during low flow, thus mitigating against high turndown ratios. High slurry velocities cause excessive component wear which limits slurry design velocities.

SCRUBBER SYSTEM WASTE DISPOSAL

Depending on the process used, a number of reaction products can result when SO_2 is absorbed from the boiler flue gases. Some of these byproducts may be salable while others may be waste products valuable only as landfill. When selecting a sulfur-removal process, it is important to consider local sales markets, applicable disposal regulations and available land for disposal. Markets for salable products such as sulfuric acid, sodium sulfate, sulfur, and pure gypsum are usually limited and may be distant from the power plant. Processes that produce a throwaway waste product are relatively simple. And, because the plant must already dispose of ash, it can readily dispose of FGDS byproducts.

Character of Solid Waste

The solid byproducts of a C-E system consist primarily of calcium sulfite, calcium sulfate, and flyash (Fig. 45) along with minor quantities of unreacted additive. Calcium-sulfite particles are generally present as thin platelets which often form aggregates with a rosette-like structure. Calcium-sulfate crystals are thick and rod-shaped while flyash particles are predominantly spherical.

The morphology of the waste solids strongly influences activities such as dewatering. For example, the thin platelike sulfite crystals settle slowly and tend to retain water in their clustered structure. The sulfite crystalline structure causes a pseudo-thixotropic behavior; sulfite solids which appear dry and stable may reliquefy and flow if vibrated. The rod-shaped

Fig. 45 Solid byproducts of FGD systems

sulfate crystals, on the other hand, settle more rapidly and retain less water than sulfite solids. Also, sulfate solids do not exhibit thixotropic properties. Flyash particles appear to respond to dewatering somewhere between that which takes place with sulfite and sulfate crystals.

The exact composition of the waste solids from a particular desulfurization system depends on several operating parameters. The ratio of sulfite to sulfate in the waste solids depends on the degree of oxidation in the FGDS, while the quantity of unreacted additive is a function of additive utilization. Flyash concentrations in the solids may be very low—if produced by a system with an efficient particulate collection device upstream of the FGDS—or very high if produced by an FGDS which removes both particulate and sulfur dioxide. Variation in waste-solid chemical composition cause corresponding variations in dewatering and handling which affect the design of disposal systems.

DISPOSAL PROCESS SELECTION

Fig. 46 diagrams several waste-disposal processes for FGD systems. Ponding and landfill are common methods for direct disposal of scrubber solids. But each method has unique advantages and disadvantages to be considered for a particular site. Estimates of the relative costs of ponding, physical stabilization and chemical fixation are given in Ref. 44.

Ponding

The most-used method for solid-waste disposal is wet ponding. The slurry bleed stream is usually pumped to a pond where the solids are allowed to settle and the clarified liquid returned to the FGD system. To reduce costs on long pipe runs, an intermediate dewatering step may be added to limit the quantity of material to be moved.

Ponding is simple, usually low-cost, and flexible in its ability to accept variations in solids. Its disadvantages are potentially high capital costs of land-acquisition in certain areas and

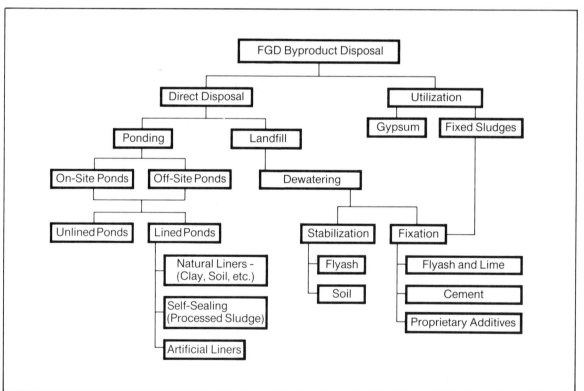

Fig. 46 FGDS waste-disposal alternatives

the possibility of leaching that might affect ground and surface waters. However, the environmental impacts can be limited by careful design and maintenance of dikes and dams to prevent contamination of surface waters and the addition of liners to protect ground water.

Liners may be: synthetic, such as polyvinylchloride sheeting or asphalt; natural soils, such as bentonite (a low permeability, high-swelling, clay); and processed sludge. For the latter, chemically-treated waste solids are used to line the pond before operation. These processes are similar to those discussed under landfill fixation methods.

Reclamation of a disposal pond could be difficult and expensive. With the possible exception of some sulfate sludges from forced-oxidation systems, the settled solids remain physically unstable, so that rain, snow and ground water could create a soft, hazardous mud-like area. As a result, a number of dry disposal processes have been developed to allow landfill disposal of sludges.

Dry Disposal

In a dry disposal system, liquid is removed from the scrubber bleed stream before disposal at the landfill. Site selection is easier for dry disposal because landfills can be constructed on slopes and other areas not suitable for ponds. On the other hand, dry disposal systems are more complex and costly because of the added dewatering and processing equipment.

Dewatering considerably improves FGDS waste solids for landfill. Table III lists optimum values for solids content necessary for maximum compacted density of sludges from several FGD systems.

Table III. Optimum Dryness for Compaction[44]

	Naturally Oxidized Limestone	Naturally Oxidized Lime	Forced-Oxidized Limestone
Solids Content (%)	74	71	77
Compacted Dry Density (lb/ft³)	82	73	88

Table III defines the ideal moisture-content percentages of each of these sludges at the time of disposal. However, it is difficult and, in some cases impossible, to mechanically dewater many of these sludges to these values. To increase the solids content, additional processing is required by either of two methods: physical stabilization or chemical fixation. Stabilization involves adding dry material such as flyash or soil to the dewatered sludge, thereby reducing its moisture content and improving its handling properties. Chemical fixation for stabilization adds dry materials both to decrease moisture content and cause cementitious reactions that improve the waste-product quality. Choosing a method depends on the type of waste solids, the future uses planned for the landfill area, and costs.

Dewatering Thickeners

Sludge is dewatered principally with gravity-type thickeners. The required thickener area and the solids content of the concentrated underflow are determined by the size, shape and specific gravity of the individual particles in the scrubber slurry. Using a flocculant to aid settling can reduce thickener area. Flocculants such as an ionic, high-molecular-weight, organic copolymer of acrylamide are very effective in reducing the area required for settling. Typical dosage rates are 30 parts of flocculant per million parts of dry scrubber solids. Flocculant has minimal effects on the percent solids of the underflow from the thickener.

Table IV lists typical thickener requirements and underflow concentrations for the various solid wastes from flue gas desulfurization systems. The equipment size and performance criteria are established using equations developed from laboratory and prototype settling tests applied to many waste solids.

Dewatering Filters

For most types of sludge, the thickener underflow has too low a solids content to allow its use as landfill; consequently, additional dewatering is required. Studies indicate that rotary-drum vacuum filters are reliable and economical for further dewatering thickener-underflow streams.

Performance of vacuum filters depends on physical and chemical characteristics of the waste solids and the concentration of solids in the feed stream to the filter. Table V lists typical size criteria and product dryness expected from slurries with the underflow concentrations given in Table IV. Other dewatering devices for FGDS waste slurries include centrifuges and pressure filters.

Water content greatly affects the ability to stabilize the solids. Smaller quantities of additives are required to process sludges with reduced water content. But the processing costs to dewater sludge increase greatly as more complex equipment is used to increase solids content. A trade-off exists between dewatering and additive costs, and the structural requirements of the final disposal site.

Processing Equipment

The equipment for mixing dewatered sludge with dry materials include additive hoppers and feeders, mixers, and conveying systems. Fig. 47 illustrates a typical system.

To add the physical-stabilization or chemical-fixing materials at the FGDS site requires that a blending system be constructed near the dewatering devices. If the sludge is to be mixed with soil or other material stored at the landfill site, the dewatered sludge has to be moved to the landfill for mixing. Although site-mixing cuts the quantity of material that has to be moved, handling the dewatered sludge may prove difficult if it is still fluid or thixotropic.

The type of solids will influence the choice of processing location. For example, sulfite-rich sludges that can be dewatered only to about 40-percent solids would be difficult to move before stabilization. Conversely, forced-oxidized (sulfate) sludge, dewatered to 70 percent, could be handled and moved easily.

Instead of installing a mixing system, it is possible to use earth-moving equipment at the landfill to layer the sludge and dry additives in thin layers, using a bucket and the track treads for blending. This method may be feasible to physically stabilize sludges dewatered so that they will no longer fluidize. However, because the mixing would likely not be uniform, it is doubtful that this technique could be used for chemical fixation which requires thorough mixing of alkali additive in the waste product.

Structural Properties of FGDS Sludges

Table VI compares structural and other properties exhibited by untreated sludges, physically stabilized sludges and chemically treated sludges when used as landfills. Evaluation of the structural properties shows that all sludges can be treated for disposal in a landfill. The degree of processing depends on the strength and permeability requirements of the final product. Either dry disposal with no processing or physical stabilization of sulfite sludges may affect the potential reuse of the disposal site because of a low load-bearing strength. It appears that forced oxidized (sulfate) sludges may develop satisfactory load-bearing strength through stabilization alone. All sludges can be treated with chemicals to produce structural landfill material. It should be noted that, in some cases,

Table IV. Typical Thickener Sizing and Performance Criteria

FGDS	Naturally Oxidized Limestone	Naturally Oxidized Lime	Forced-Oxidized Limestone
Unit Area, ft²/ton-day, Without Flocculant	70	110	5
Unit Area, ft²/ton-day, With Flocculant	12	25	4
Underflow Solids Content, %	35	30	50*

* High solids concentrations may not be pumpable

Table V. Typical Vacuum Filtration Sizing and Performance Criteria

	Naturally Oxidized Limestone	Naturally Oxidized Lime	Forced-Oxidized Limestone
Filtration Rate, lb/ft²-hr	100	40	160
Cake Dryness, % solids	55	40	70

Table VI. Landfill Properties of FGDS Sludges

	Dewatered Untreated Sludge[1]		Physically Stabilized Sludge[2]		Chemically Fixated Sludge[3]
	High Sulfite	High Sulfate	High Sulfite	High Sulfate	All Sludges
Unconfined Compressive Strength-ton/ft[2]	0	2.0	0.5[4]	2.5[4]	1.5 to 10.0[5]
Permeability, cm/sec	10^{-3}	10^{-4}	10^{-4}	10^{-6}	10^{-6} to $<10^{-7}$
Leachate Quality	Poor, may be high in chemical oxygen demand and major and trace elements.		Poor to fair, benefit primarily due to reduction in permeability over untreated sludges.		Good to excellent, reduction in permeability, increase in pH, and formation of cementitious compounds aid retention of soluble species.

[1] Mechanically dewatered, landfilled, no additives.
[2] Addition of low-alkaline flyash or soil to achieve optimum solids content for maximum compaction.
[3] Addition of low-alkaline flyash and lime, or high-alkaline flyash, to achieve optimum solids content and cause cementitious reactions.
[4] Sludges may have a potential to reliquify if exposed to water.
[5] Strength highly dependent on quantity and type of additive used.

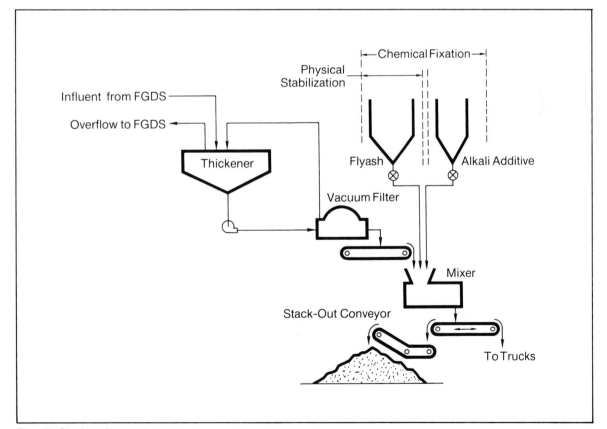

Fig. 47 **Sludge-disposal system**

permeability and leachate criteria may require the addition of chemicals even though physical stabilization would produce a product of acceptable strength. This may be the case for some forced oxidized sludges as well as sulfite sludges.[45, 46]

SLUDGE UTILIZATION

When evaluating disposal alternatives, the potential of using the waste as a raw material in other processes should be considered. Although many uses have been proposed, most are limited by technical or economic factors. The most promising appear to be

- gypsum as a wallboard material or a retarder in cement
- treated sludge in roads, dams, embankments and the like.

Two determinators are involved in considering waste as a raw material: first, is it possible to use the relatively large volume of waste material produced by a power plant; second, is the product competitive with established sources of the material? Use of wastes has not become widespread, but a limited number of markets may exist in selected areas.

CONTROL OF OXIDES OF NITROGEN

Because of more stringent regulations of NO_x emissions from combustion sources, boiler designs have been modified to reduce oxide formation through control of flame temperature—reduced excess air percentage, staged combustion, the use of overfire air, tangential firing, and gas recirculation. Some of these are described in Chapter 13.

Although these steps have been effective, and have been found adequate in many countries, any further reduction in allowable NO_x may require some form of post-boiler gas treatment. Many flue-gas treatment systems are in operation, principally in Japan, using both dry and wet systems on the effluent from oil- and gas-fired units. Now the processes developed for liquid and gaseous fuels have been applied to coal-fired boilers. In this section, some of these tail-end systems are discussed briefly.[47, 48]

In the most-developed dry NO_x systems ammonia is the reducing agent. Some systems complete the reaction over catalyzed surfaces at a low temperature; others complete the reduction at a relatively high temperature. One of the objections to applying the systems to coal-fired units is their sensitivity to particulate matter and the sulfur dioxide in the flue gas. Also, as a catalyst surface is ideally located between the economizer outlet and the air heater inlet, the process is intimately involved with the power generation cycle. Problems with these processes could then have an adverse impact on the basic boiler operation.

In addition, the long-term supply of ammonia (NH_3) for these processes may be a problem. For an effective $NH_3 : NO_x$ ratio, a 500-MW plant requires about 6,000 tons/year of liquid anhydrous ammonia to treat a flue gas containing 600 ppm of NO_x.

NO$_x$-REDUCTION PROCESSES

The major methods of dry NO_x removal include

- catalytic decomposition
- selective catalytic reduction (SCR)
- selective noncatalytic reduction
- absorption

Catalytic decomposition is a process that will remove 90 to 95 percent of the NO_x, depending on the effectiveness of the catalyst. In this process the reactions are

$$NO_{(g)} \xrightarrow{\text{catalyst}} \tfrac{1}{2}N_{2(g)} + \tfrac{1}{2}O_{2(g)}$$

(74)

In the selective catalytic reduction (SCR) process, a selective reduction of ammonia for NO_x exists and the reactions are generally expressed as

$$4NH_{3(g)} + 4NO_{(g)} + O_{2(g)} \rightarrow 4N_{2(g)} + 6H_2O_{(g)}$$

(75)

$$4NH_{3(g)} + 2NO_{2(g)} + O_{2(g)} \rightarrow 3N_{2(g)} + 6H_2O_{(g)}$$

$$(76)$$

Both metal- and carbon-based catalysts are used. The metal catalysts are either noble or non-noble. Noble catalysts are considered impractical because of their reaction with sulfur gases and their expense. Non-noble catalysts are less efficient, require higher temperatures (300° to 400°C), and are more resistant to sulfur gases. They also are expensive and do not promote N_2O production. However, the process achieves 90 percent or more NO_x removal.

Carbon-based catalysts are used for simultaneous NO_x and SO_2 removal. Carbon is used commercially as an SO_2 adsorbent and activated carbons have been developed with special structures for aiding the NO_x and NH_3 reduction reaction. Operating temperatures with these catalysts (200 to 250°C) are usually lower than for metal-based catalysts. The lower temperatures enhance SO_2 adsorption, while higher temperatures improve the efficiency of removing NO_x from the gas stream.

These systems normally require heating to attain a controlled-reduction temperature, have the potential for emitting ammonium sulfate into the air heater, and are generally sensitive to particulate fouling.

In selective noncatalytic reduction the ammonia reductant combines at an appropriate temperature, without any catalyst, to convert the NO_x to nitrogen and water. The overall reaction is

$$4NH_{3(g)} + 4NO_{(g)} + O_{2(g)} \rightarrow 4N_{2(g)} + 6H_2O_{(g)}$$

$$(77)$$

The optimum temperature at which ammonia is added is about 1850°F, but this can be reduced to about 1350°F by injecting hydrogen, either with the ammonia or just downstream of the NH_3 injection point. The process is limited by this narrow temperature range and the fact that temperature changes with varying boiler load. The use of hydrogen introduces storage, safety, and purchase problems. Also, the process reduces 60 to 70 percent of the NO_x while requiring a large molar volume of NH_3.

The *absorption process* removes SO_x and NO_x with an activated char, with the reduction occurring when the char is regenerated in a vessel at about 1250°F. The process is complex, has an NO_x removal of only 40 to 60 percent, and requires the handling of hot solids.

NO_x-REMOVAL PROCESSES

There are many NO_x-removal processes under development, or in pilot-plant or commercial-application stages. They are both dry and wet, with some of the latter in combination with SO_x removal. The majority of the processes have been developed in Japan, where the NO_x emission level has been set lower than the rest of the world.

The Exxon Thermal De-NOx Process

This system uses noncatalytic denitrification to reduce NO_x by reaction with ammonia. The optimum temperature range is 1700 to 1900°F, but this can be reduced to 1300–1400°F by adding an oxidizable gas such as H_2 to the NH_3. A maximum 70 percent NO_x removal has been obtained on an oil-fired unit.

Hitachi Process

This dry selective catalytic reduction system uses NH_3 as the reducing agent. Tests have been conducted on flue gas from coal-fired units.

The process operates at temperatures between 570 and 750°F (with 660°F being optimum) using a moving or parallel-flow bed. The catalyst, with a titanium oxide base, is reported to have a high tolerance to SO_3 and particulate matter. Ninety percent efficiency is predicted for an NO/NH3 ratio of 1.

Mitsubishi Heavy Industries—Dry SCR

The MHI process reduces NO_x with NH_3 over a catalyst, in a manner similar to the Hitachi system. The principal differences are in the catalyst formulation, reactor design, and process control. The process has been extensively applied to slipstreams of flue gas from coal-fired boilers. The reaction temperature ranges from 660 to 750°F, with parallel-passage reactors located upstream of a cold-side precipitator. A 90-percent reduction efficiency is typical of the MHI SRC process. As in all dry systems, there is a potential for fouling of the air heater by the sneakage of NH_3, resulting in ammonium-sulfate deposits.

FLOW-MODEL TESTS OF EMISSION-CONTROL SYSTEMS

Gas flow is fundamental to emission-control systems (electrostatic precipitators, scrubbers and fabric filters). It affects not only the system working efficiency but also the engineering design. The purpose of a model study is to investigate the flow characteristics, pressure loss, gas mixing and temperature distribution. Usually, a three-dimensional model to 1/16th scale is used to obtain engineering design informa-tion and to insure that performance predictions are met. With a flow model, the potential gas-flow problems of the design can be identified and engineering modifications recommended. A flow-model study also can analyze field problems, and is an economic way to select modifications quickly and accurately.[49]

MODELING THEORY

Whenever the flow of a fluid through a model is studied, there must be some assurance that the flow pattern in the model will closely correspond to the actual flow pattern at full scale. To attain the desired similarity, one should attempt to keep the Reynolds number for the flow in the model equal to the Reynolds number for the full-scale flow. The Reynolds number (Re) is a dimensionless ratio between the inertial and viscous forces existing in the flow pattern and is defined as $Re = \dfrac{\rho vD}{\mu}$, where ρ is gas density, V its velocity, μ its viscosity and D is

Fig. 48 **Precipitator flow model for test of flow-control devices**

the hydraulic diameter. The flow is usually considered laminar if the Reynolds number is less than 2000; it is turbulent if the Reynolds number is above 4000.

The industrial gases flowing through a commercial FGD system normally have a density and a viscosity on the same order of magnitude as density and viscosity for the air in the model. Therefore, to have the same Reynolds number in the scale model as the full-scale unit, the velocity of the air in the model must be 10 to 20 times greater than it is in the actual unit. This causes difficulties and uncertainties in the model study.

Due to the large size of most gas-cleaning systems, the Reynolds number is usually well into the turbulent region. Experience indicates that flow pattern and pressure losses for an FGD system can be reasonably predicted if turbulent, essentially incompressible flow, is maintained in the model.

To predict full-scale pressure losses from model studies, it is important to consider all correlating parameters. The physical flow boundaries and any devices inside the duct work must be modeled to very close tolerance. The flow must be in the incompressible region and most importantly, the Reynolds number effect must be determined.

In studying the pressure losses in closed channels, it is helpful to note that the losses generally occur from two effects; loss due to viscous forces and those due to a momentum change of the gas. The viscous losses occur in all segments of the duct while losses due to a momentum change are present only when gas velocity changes magnitude or direction. The boundary layer in the modeled system will, in general, be proportionately larger than the boundary layer in the full-scale system. This tends to make frictional pressure losses in the model higher than full-scale losses. Losses due to momentum changes are similar for both model and full-scale system because velocity patterns are similar. For these reasons, pressure losses predicted by the model tests are usually conservative.

In model studies, a number of instruments are used to measure such variables as velocity, static pressure, conductivity and the like. Many of the devices are similar or identical to the measurement equipment described in Chapter 21, and include hot-wire anemometers, pitot tubes and pressure transducers, and thermal-conductivity gas analyzers.

GAS-FLOW CONTROL DEVICES

In precipitator modeling, flow-control-devices such as vanes and perforated plates are studied. Vanes are placed in the turns of the ductwork ahead of the precipitator to smooth the gas flow and lower the pressure-loss coefficient.[50,51] Perforated plates are very effective devices used at the precipitator inlet to reduce turbulence and improve uniformity of gas flow. Basically, they provide the essential transition from large-scale persistent turbulence to small-scale nonpersistent turbulence. Horizontal or vertical vanes or gas-distribution panels may also be installed to obtain a desirable uniformity in flow.

In the final stage of modeling, flow visualization tests that use smoke traces, ground cork, and string tufts are conducted to locate gross flow aberrations, to study dust deposition in the ducts, and to study hopper sweepage. Various configurations of flow-control devices are evaluated until one is found that yields acceptable system-flow characteristics. Fig. 48 shows

Fig. 49 **A front view of a fabric-filter flow model**

a precipitator flow model with flow-control devices being tested.

Flue-gas scrubbers and fabric filters are modeled using the same techniques as for precipitators except that pressure drops across demisting elements and filter bags are simulated by perforated plates. Optimum turning-vane and baffle arrangements are determined, as are the size and configuration of gas-inlet and outlet plenums. A front view of a fabric-filter model is shown in Fig. 49.

DISPERSION OF EMISSIONS

Air pollution control is not entirely a question of the quantity of emissions. It is also related to the atmosphere's ability to assimilate them without adverse effects. Emission control by dispersion requires the optimum combination of such factors as stack height, buoyancy, climate and topography. Such control requires a study of atmospheric conditions surrounding the plant to determine airflow patterns and ventilating capabilities of the region. Model studies provide valuable assistance to predict the dispersion of combustion products and thereby maintain particulate or gaseous concentrations to prescribed levels.

Dispersion refers to the movement of parcels of gases, either vertically or horizontally, and their simultaneous dilution with fresh air.

WIND DIRECTION AND VELOCITY

Emissions are dispersed horizontally into the air as the parcel moves with the existing wind. Vertical dispersion results from an exhaust stack discharging a warm parcel upward to mix with fresh air at higher elevations.

Certain phenomena restrict these activities and must be considered when evaluating plant dispersion capability. One of the most severe natural impediments to proper dispersion is thermal inversion of the atmosphere. This atmospheric condition restricts vertical dispersion, and as there is generally little wind during an inversion, it tends to trap and concentrate emissions. Further complicating dispersion is topography such as valleys where emission concentrations can reach dangerous levels.

To disperse emmissions from boilers, stacks 800 to 1200 feet tall have been constructed. This height can be augmented by a high efflux velocity of 75 to 100 feet per second. These factors, coupled with the buoyancy of the hot flue gas, produce an effective stack height substantially greater than the physical stack height (Fig. 50). The effective stack height is the sum of the actual stack height plus the height effects due to velocity and buoyancy. If it is great enough, the effluent can "puncture" an inversion to disperse at higher elevations.

"Stack meteorology" has been used to study the factors affecting dispersion of gases from stacks or chimneys. For power plants, the dispersion of particulates and SO_2 must be estimated and compared to federal, state, and local ambient air-quality criteria and regulations.

Fig. 50 **Effective stack height equals actual stack height plus velocity and buoyancy factors**

Three different calculations are generally required to estimate a time-averaged concentration of a gas at a location downwind from the stack. First, the plume rise above the stack must be established; second, the dispersion of the gas before it reaches the downwind location must be found; and third, it is necessary to calculate the time average of the ground-level concentration.

DISPERSION CALCULATIONS

The rise of plumes above the top of a stack can be calculated with many formulas but results vary widely if these equations are applied to sources substantially different from those used in the original testing. Effective plume rise can be obtained from equations given in reference 52.

Small-volume sources having an appreciable exit velocity—but little temperature excess above ambient—are essentially momentum jets in a crosswind and the plume rise Δh may be calculated as:

$$\Delta h = D \left(\frac{V_s}{\overline{U}_s}\right)^{1.4}$$

(78)

where, in consistent units,

D = diameter of stack

V_s = vertical efflux velocity at release temperature (m/sec)

$\overline{U}_s$ = mean wind speed at actual stack height (m/sec)

As buoyant plumes have temperatures above that of the ambient air and involve a large volume release, they require a different calculation treatment. Under stable conditions Δh is

$$\Delta h = 2.9 \cdot \left(\frac{F}{\overline{U}_s G}\right)^{0.33}$$

(79)

where,

F = buoyancy flux = $gV_s\left(\frac{D}{2}\right)^2 \left(\frac{P_a - P_s}{P_a}\right)$ (m^4/sec^3)

G = stability parameter (sec^{-2})

g = acceleration of gravity (m/sec^2)

P_s = density of stack gas at stack top (mg/m^3)

P_a = density of ambient air at stack top (mg/m^3)

A neutral or unstable lapse rate implies a different turbulence regime and the recommended equation is

$$\Delta h = \frac{7.4h_s{}^{0.67}F^{0.33}}{u}$$

(80)

where h_s is the actual stack height in meters.

These equations include the plume-rise forces attributable to the thermal buoyancy of

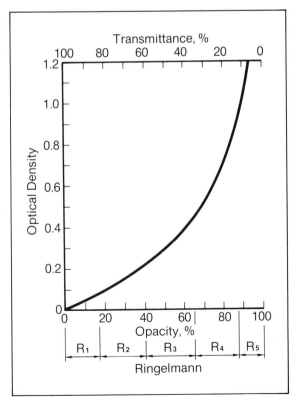

Fig. 51 Relationships between various optical emission-measuring units

the plume and the velocity momentum. The effective stack height (theoretical gas-release height) is the sum of the actual stack height and the calculated plume rise.

Theories based on the assumption that the mean concentration of material dispersed in a diffusion cloud follows a three-dimensional Gaussian distribution have been developed. A Gaussian formulation proposed by Cramer[53] is recommended by ASME and is generally accepted by industry, although other models are available.[54, 55]

OPTICAL PROPERTIES OF FLYASH

Although the optical properties of suspended particles do not affect collector performance, they are important because of their relationship to the visual appearance of stack emissions. Fine particles suspended in gases and exposed to a light beam scatter the light in directions other than that of the original beam and obscure or darken the light as viewed toward the light source. The visibility of stack emissions is due to both these effects.

It has been shown both theoretically and experimentally that the light-scattering and obscuring effects increase with the specific surface of the particles and the size or thickness of the stack plume. The specific surface is defined as the total exposed surface area of the particles per unit mass of dust or dispersoid. It is a function of particle size and increases rapidly with decreasing size of particles. For flyash, the specific surface usually will be between about 2,000 and 15,000 cm^2/g. As the fine ash emitted by most pulverized-coal boilers has relatively high specific surfaces, it is very effective in its light-scattering and obscuring properties. The high-volume gas flows associated with large boilers also contribute to emissions that have greater visibility above the stack.

Removing the coarser fractions of an ash usually will not appreciably reduce the visibility of stack emissions. For example, an inertial collector which removes 75 percent of the ash only slightly improves stack-discharge appearance. The finer particles below about 10 or 20 μm are not collected, and it is these particles with their high specific surface which cause most of the visibility.[6]

OPACITY

Opacity is the percent reduction of light intensity and is defined as:

$$\text{Opacity} = \frac{I_o - I}{I_o}(100)$$

(81)

where,

I = intensity of light reaching the observer

I_o = original intensity of the light

The reduction of light intensity when the light is X feet in length is the following:

$$I = I_o e^{-(bg + a)X}$$

(82)

where,

b = extinction coefficient

g = concentration of gases

a = extinction coefficient for particles (includes dust concentration)

The light path for a flue-gas plume is the plume depth (stack diameter). The extinction coefficient includes the absorption coefficient, scattering factors and diffraction factors that are known for small solid particles, oil mist, and gases.[56]

The required reduction of flue-gas loading due to opacity restrictions becomes the governing requirement when the stack diameter is increased beyond a critical dimension. This is because the light path X in the above equation becomes larger and, with a constant dust concentration, the opacity increases as the stack diameter increases. On large units, the required degree of dust loading reduction is greater than on small units. Fig. 51 gives the relationships between the Ringelmann number, opacity and transmittance in percent, and optical density.

REFERENCES

[1] "Criteria for the Application of Dust Collectors to Coal-Fired Boilers: The Results of an IGCI/ABMA Joint Technical Committee Survey," *Proceedings of the American Power Conference*, 29: 572–580, 1967. Chicago: Illinois Institute of Technology, 1967.

[2] Harry J. White, *Industrial Electrostatic Precipitation*. Reading, MA: Addison-Wesley, 1963.

[3] Joint Technical Committee of the American Boiler Manufacturers Association and the Industrial Gas Cleaning Institute, Inc., "Design and Operation of Reliable Central Station Flyash Hopper Evacuation Systems," *Proceedings of the American Power Conference*, 42, 1980. (To be published by the Illinois Institute of Technology, Chicago, 1981.)

[4] Kenneth Wark and Cecil F. Warner, *Air Pollution: Its Origin and Control*. New York: IEP, 1976.

[5] G. W. Penney, "Weaknesses in Conventional Theory of Electrostatic Precipitation," *ASME Paper no. 67-WA/APC-1*. New York: American Society of Mechanical Engineers, 1967.

[6] Harry J. White, "Effect of Fly Ash Characteristics on Collector Performance," *ASME Paper no. 54-A-259*. New York: American Society of Mechanical Engineers, 1954. Also in: *Air Repair*, 5: 37–50, 62, 1955.

[7] Sabert Oglesby, Jr. and Grady B. Nichols, *A Manual of Electrostatic Precipitator Technology. Part I—Fundamentals*. Report no. PB-196 380 (APTD-0610). Springfield, VA: National Technical Information Service, 1970.
Sabert Oglesby, Jr. and Grady B. Nichols, *A Manual of Electrostatic Precipitor Technology. Part II—Application Areas*. Report no. PB-196 381 (APTD-0611). Springfield, VA: National Technical Information Service, 1970.

[8] Kenneth J. McLean, *Survey of Australian Experience in Collecting High Resistivity Fly Ash with Electrostatic Precipitators*. Final Report. Report no. PB-221 139 (EPA-R2-73-258). Springfield, VA: National Technical Information Service, 1972.

[9] Kenneth J. McLean, "Some Effects of High Resistivity Fly Ash on Electrostatic Precipitator Operation," *Electrostatic Precipitator Symposium*, EPA, Birmingham, Alabama, 1971. Author address: University of Wollongong, P.O. Box 1144, Wollongong, New South Wales, Australia 2500.

[10] Z. Herceg and Kenneth J. McLean, "Efficiency of Electrostatic Precipitators and Relationship to Corona Voltage-Current Characteristics," Presented at the 64th Annual Meeting of the Air Pollution Control Association, Atlantic City, June 27–July 1, 1971, Paper no. 71–178. Pittsburgh: Air Pollution Control Association, 1971.

[11] Alan B. Walker, "Experience with Hot Electrostatic Precipitators for Fly Ash Collection in Electric Utilities," *Proceedings of the American Power Conference*, 36: 481–490, 1974. Chicago: Illinois Institute of Technology, 1974.

[12] Alan B. Walker, "Operating Experience With Hot Precipitators on Western Low-Sulfur Coals," *Proceedings of the American Power Conference*, 39: 582–594, 1977. Chicago: Illinois Institute of Technology, 1977.

[13] Harry J. White, "Resistivity Problems in Electrostatic Precipitation," *Air Pollution Control Association. Journal*, 24(4): 313–338, April 1974.

[14] Gilbert G. Schneider, et al., "Selecting and Specifying Electrostatic Precipitators," *Chemical Engineering*, 82(11): 94–108, May 26, 1975.

[15] Industrial Gas Cleaning Institute, Inc. *Terminology for Electrostatic Precipitators*, Publication no. EP-1, revised ed. Alexandria, VA: Industrial Gas Cleaning Institute, Inc., 1973.
Industrial Gas Cleaning Institute, Inc., *Basic Types of Wet Scrubbers*, Publication no. WS-3. Alexandria, VA: Industrial Gas Cleaning Institute, Inc., 1976.

[16] Y. Goland, "Mechanical and Structural Design Consideration for Internals in Electrostatic Precipitators," *ASME Paper no. 76-WA/Pwr-7*. New York: American Society of Mechanical Engineers, 1976.

[17] J. A. Hudson, et al., "Design Considerations and Initial Startup of Shawnee Baghouses," *Proceedings of the American Power Conference*, 42, 1980. (To be published by the Illinois Institute of Technology, Chicago, 1981).

[18] H. N. Head, *EPA Alkali Scrubbing Test Facility: Advanced Program*. Third Progress Report. September 1977. Report no. PB-274 544 (EPA-600/7-77/105). Springfield, VA: National Technical Information Service, 1977.

[19] Arthur L. Plumley et al., "Removal of SO_2 and Dust From Stack Gases," *Proceedings of the American Power Conference*, 29:592–614, 1967. Chicago: Illinois Institute of Technology, 1967.

[20] C. C. Leivo, *Flue Gas Desulfurization Systems; Design and Operating Considerations*. Volume II. Technical Report. March 1978. Report no. PB-280 254 (EPA-600/7-78/030B). Springfield, VA: National Technical Information Service, 1978.

[21] F. A. Ayer, comp., *Proceedings: Symposium on Flue Gas Desulfurization*, Hollywood, FL, 1977. Report no. EPA-600/7-78/058. Springfield, VA: National Technical Information Service, 1978.

[22] M. Smith, et al., *EPA Utility FGD (Flue Gas Desulfurization) Survey*. December 1978–January 1979. Report no. PB-299 399 (EPA-600/7-79/022c). Springfield, VA: National Technical Information Service, 1979.

[23] J. L. Pearson, G. Nonhebel, and P. H. N. Ulander, "The Removal of Smoke and Acid Constituents from Flue Gases by a Non-Effluent Water Process," *Institute of Fuel. Journal*, 8: 119–156, 1935.

[24] Elno M. Powell, et al., "Designing from Experience with 900 Mw of Air Quality Control Systems," Presented at the 67th Annual Meeting of the Air Pollution Control Association, Denver, June 9–13, 1974. Pittsburgh: Air Pollution

Control Association, 1974; Also published as *Combustion Engineering publication TIS-3998*, Windsor, CT: Combustion Engineering, Inc., 1974.

[25] T. M. Morasky, "Results from Evaluation of Chiyoda Thoroughbred /2/ (CP-121) Scrubber System," *Proceedings of the American Power Conference*, 42, 1980. (To be published by the Illinois Institute of Technology, Chicago, 1981).

[26] F. W. Link and W. H. Ponder, "Status Report on the Wellman-Lord/ Allied Chemical Flue Gas Desulfurization Plant at Northern Indiana Public Service Company's Dean H. Mitchell Plant," *Proceedings: Symposium on Flue Gas Desulfurization held at Hollywood, Florida, November 1977. Volume II. Report no. PB-282 091 (EPA-600/7-78-058b), pp. 650–664.* Springfield, VA: National Technical Information Service, 1978.

[27] J. Ando, "Status of Flue Gas Desulfurization and Simultaneous Removal of SO_2 and NO_x in Japan," *Proceedings: Symposium on Flue Gas Desulfurization, New Orleans, March 1976. Volume I.* Report no. PB-255 317 (EPA-600/2-76-136a), pp. 53–78. Springfield, VA: National Technical Information Service, 1976.

[28] E. A. Shultz, et al., "The Cat-Ox Project at Illinois Power," *Proceedings of the American Power Conference*, 34:484–490, 1972. Chicago: Illinois Institute of Technology, 1972.

[29] Donald R. Binns and Robers G. Aldrich, "Design of the 100 Mw Atomics International Aqueous Carbonate Process Regenerative FGD Demonstration Plant," *Proceedings: Symposium of Flue Gas Desulfurization held at Hollywood, Florida, November 1977. Volume II.* Report no. PB-282 091 (EPA-600/7-78-058b), pp. 665–694. Springfield, VA: National Technical Information Service, 1978.

[30] E. F. Aul, et al., *Evaluations of Regenerable Flue Gas Desulfurization Procedures. Volume II. Final Report.* Report no. EPRI-FP-272 (V.2). Palo Alto, Ca: Electric Power Research Institute, 1977.

[31] J. Pohlenz, "The Shell FGD Process," presented at the Third Annual International Conference on Coal Gasification and Liquifaction, Pittsburgh, Aug. 3–5, 1976.

[32] Allen D. Arneson, Frans M. Nooy, and Jack B. Pohlenz, "The Shell FGD Process Pilot Plant Experience at Tampa Electric," *Proceedings: Symposium on Flue Gas Desulfurization held at Hollywood, Florida, November 1977. Volume II.* Report no. PB-282 091 (EPA-600/7-78-058b), pp. 752–793. Springfield, VA: National Technical Information Service, 1978.

[33] Kelly Green, et al., "Commitment to Air Quality Control," *Proceedings of the American Power Conference*, 40:632–645, 1978. Chicago: Illinois Institute of Technology, 1978.

[34] James R. Martin, Khaldoun W. Malki, and Neil Graves, "The Results of a Two-Stage Scrubber/Charged Particulate Separator Pilot Program," presented at the 2nd Symposium on Transfer and Utilization of Particulate Control Technology, Denver, Colorado, July 23–27, 1979, sponsored by the Environmental Protection Agency, Particulate Technology Branch.

[35] James R. Martin, W. B. Ferguson, D. Frabotta, "C-E Dry Scrubber Systems: Application to Western Coals," *Proceedings of the American Power Conference*, Vol. 42, April 21–23, 1980; Chicago: Illinois Institute of Technology, 1980.

[36] D. C. Borio, et al., "Design of Spray of Tower Absorbers for Lime/Limestone Wet Scrubbers," *ASME paper no. 79-WA/Fu-9.* New York: American Society of Mechanical Engineers, 1979.

[37] Howard E. Hesketh, *Understanding and Controlling Air Pollution.* Ann Arbor, MI: Ann Arbor Science Publishers, Inc., 1972.

[38] Dante Frabotta and Philip C. Rader, "Lime/Limestone Air Quality Control Systems: Effect of Magnesium on System Performance," *ASME paper no. 76-WA/APC-10.* New York: American Society of Mechanical Engineers, 1976.

[39] Philip C. Rader, M. R. Gogineni and K. Poglitsch, "Co-precipitation: A Method for Gypsum Scale Prevention in Lime/Limestone Flue Gas Desulfurization Systems," presented at the 72nd Annual Meeting of the American Institute of Chemical Engineers, San Francisco, November 25–29, 1979; published as Combustion Engineering publication TIS-6396, Windsor, CT: Combustion Engineering, Inc., 1979.

[40] Philip C. Rader, et al., "The Role of Crystallization in the Design of Lime/Limestone Wet Scrubbing Systems for Flue Gas Desulfurization," Presented at the Symposium on Crystallization and Energy Systems, 83rd National Meeting of the American Institute of Chemical Engineers, Houston, March 20–24, 1977; published as Combustion Engineering publication TIS-5057, Windsor, CT: Combustion Engineering, Inc., 1977.

[41] Benjamin F. Jones, Philip S. Lowell, and Frank S. Meserole, *Experimental and Theoretical Studies of Solid Solution Formation in Lime and Limestone Scrubbers. Volumes I and II. Final Report.* Report nos. PB-264 953 (EPA/600/2-76/273a) and PB-264 954 (EPA/600/2-76/273b), respectively. Springfield, VA: National Technical Information Service, 1976.

[42] Benjamin F. Jones, Philp S. Lowell, and Frank Meserole, *Experimental and Theoretical Studies of Solid Solution Formation in Lime and Limestone Scrubbers. Volumes I and II. Final Report.* Report nos. PB-264 953 (EPA/600/2-76/273a) and PB-264 954 (EPA/600/2-76/273b), respectively. Springfield, VA: National Technical Information Service, 1976.

[43] R. P. VanNess, W. H. Kingston, and D. C. Borsare, "Operation of C-E Flue Gas Desulfurization System for High-Sulfur Coal at Louisville Gas and Electric Company, Can Run 5," *Proceedings of the American Power Conference*, 41: 656–664, 1979. Chicago: Illinois Institute of Technology, 1979.

[44] John C. Haas and Walter J. Lombardi, "Landfill Disposal of Flue Gas Desulfurization Sludge," presented at the NCA/BCR Coal Conference and Exposition III, Louisville, KY, October 19–21, 1976; published as Combustion Engineering publication TIS-4926, Windsor, CT: Combustion Engineering Inc., 1976.

[45] N. C. Mohn, et al., "Environmental-Effects of FGD Disposal—A Laboratory—Field Landfill Demonstration," *Proceedings: Symposium on Flue Gas Desulfurization held at Las Vegas, Nevada, March 1979. Volume II.* Report no. EPA-600/7-79-167b, pp. 835–857. Springfield, VA: National Technical Information Service, 1979.

[46] W. A. Duvel, Jr., et al., *State-of-the-Art of FGD Sludge Fixation.* Final Report. Report no. EPRI-FP-671 (Research Project 786-1). Springfield, VA: National Technical Information Service, 1978.

[47] Chuo Univ., Tokyo (Japan), NO_x Abatement for Stationary Sources in Japan. Annual Report. June 1978–June 1979. Report no. PB80-113673 (EPA-600/7-79/205). Springfield, VA: National Technical Information Service, 1979.

[48] H. L. Faucett, J. D. Maxwell, and T. A. Burnett, *Technical Assessment of NO_x Removal Processess for Utility Application.* Final Report. October 1976–July 1977. Report no. PB-276 637 (EPA 600/7-77/127) (EPRI/AF-568). Springfield, VA: National Technical Information Service, 1977.

[49] C. L. Burton and R. E. Willison, "Application of Model Studies to Industrial Gas-Flow Systems," *ASME Paper no. 59-A-280.* New York: American Society of Mechanical Engineers, 1959.

[50] Lewis F. Moody, "Friction Factors for Pipe Flow," *Transactions of the ASME*, 66: 671–684, New York. 1944.

[51] I. E. Idel'chik, *Handbook of Hydraulic Resistance—Coefficients of Local Resistance and of Friction.* Report no. AEC-TR-6630. Springfield, VA: National Technical Information Service, 1966.

[52] John R. Martin, *Recommended Guide for the Prediction of the Dispersion of Airborne Effluents*, 3rd ed. New York: American Society of Mechanical Engineers, 1979.

[53] H. E. Cramer, "A Practical Method for Estimating the Dispersal of Atmospheric Contaminants," *Proceedings of the 1st National Conference on Applied Meteorology*, Hartford, CT, October 28–29, 1957, pp. C-33–C-55. Boston, MA: American Meteorological Society, 1957.

[54] O. G. Sutton, "A Theory of Eddy Diffusion in the Atmosphere," *Proceedings of the Royal Society of London*, 135, Series A: 143–165, 1932.

[55] C. H. Bosanquet and J. L. Pearson, "The Spread of Smoke and Gases From Chimneys," *Transactions of the Faraday Society*, 32: 1249–1263, 1936.

[56] Philip A. Leighton, *Photochemistry of Air Pollution.* New York: Academic Press, 1961.

[57] Harry J. White, "Electrostatic Precipitation of Fly Ash; Part II, Section 3: Fly Ash and Furnace Gas Characteristics," *Air Pollution Control Association Journal*, 27(2): 114–120, Pittsburgh 1977.

[58] C. C. Shale, J. H. Holden, and G. E. Fasching, "Electrical Resistivity of Fly Ash at Temperatures to 1500°F.," *U.S. Bureau of Mines Report of Investigations 7041.* Washington: U.S. Government Printing Office, 1968.

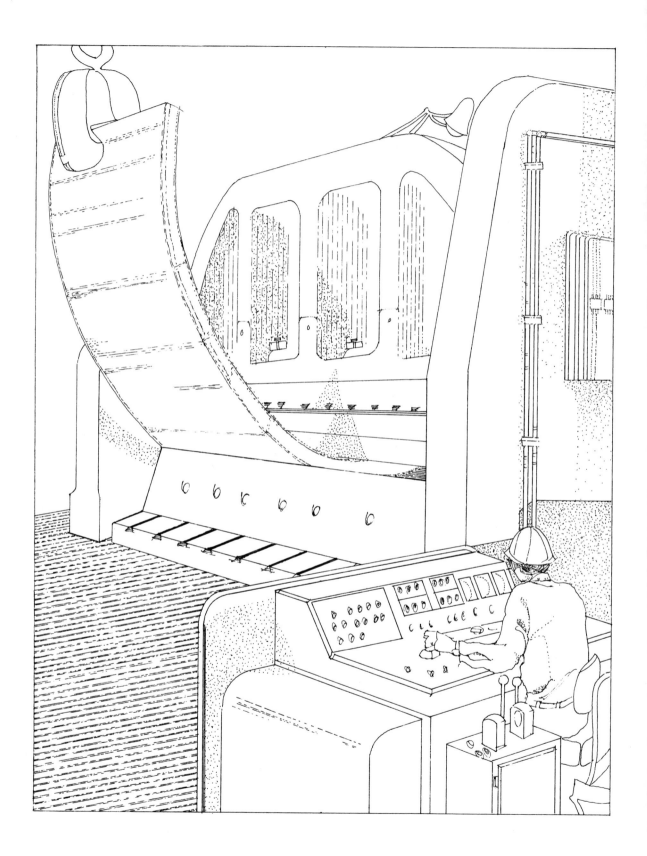

CHAPTER 18

Steam-Generator Manufacture

anufacturing boiler components requires extensive equipment, machinery, and facilities. Most of these fabrication operations involve the use of steel tubing and plate. As the tubing and plate are built into furnace-wall panels, superheaters and reheaters, drums, headers, pulverizers, ductwork, and structural members, various forms of welding are used. Heavy hydraulic presses are required to form segments of boiler drums and other pressure vessels, and machining likewise plays a vital part in the manufacture of boilers. Heat treatment, materials handling, inspection, and quality control are important adjuncts of the manufacturing operations.

THE INTERRELATIONSHIP BETWEEN PRODUCT DESIGN AND MANUFACTURE

The steam-generator engineer must be continually aware of the interrelationship between product design and manufacture. A design resulting in improved heat-transfer efficiency may be useless if the component cannot be fabricated economically and within the tolerances proposed. On the other hand, savings in manufacturing costs cannot be justified if they result in finished elements which do not meet

design objectives. The lines of communication between design and manufacturing functions must be maintained if overall production economy and high-quality products are to be the end results.

New-product design needs have significant effects upon manufacturing processes. Standardized production equipment may not be satisfactory, and new machines may have to be developed. The design of such equipment requires knowledge from many specialized fields, including production practices, component design, materials, metallurgy, and controls.

Since it is obvious that a large utility or industrial boiler must be transported to the jobsite in relatively small assemblies and sub-assemblies, most shipments are made by rail car. A large utility-type unit will have 10,000 tons of boiler parts and equipment and more than 4,000 tons of structural steel supports, and will require about 200 railroad cars and 100 trucks for shipment to the site.

ASME CODE CONSIDERATIONS

All U.S.-installed utility and industrial boilers are designed and manufactured in accordance with the rules of applicable sections of the American Society of Mechanical Engineers Boiler and Pressure Vessel Code, which is the professional standard in the United States and in many other parts of the world. The *ASME* Code is a set of regulations and guidelines incorporating many details for design, manufacturing, and field construction to assure safe construction of pressure parts of boilers. It is not a thermodynamic performance code. There is nothing in it that tells how big a furnace must be to burn a fuel or how large a drum is needed to get dry steam. The Code does concern itself with the materials of construction, the design aspects from a structural or pressure-parts standpoint, the fabrication rules (primarily welding), the rules for nondestructive examination, and certain rules for certification (which include third-party inspection).

This third-party inspection has been a feature of the Code since its inception. It is this which enables it to be a code rather than a standard. Construction of Code-stamped components must be by a manufacturer holding an *ASME* certificate of authorization. One requirement for such a certificate is the manufacturer's arranging for the services of an authorized inspector to verify that the components are constructed in accordance with Code rules. The inspector performs such inspections as he considers necessary in the shops of the boiler manufacturer, and when he is satisfied he so indicates by countersigning a certification sheet (the manufacturer's data report).

The materials in the pressure-retaining parts of the entire boiler structure range from carbon steel for drums, headers, and tubular products to the high-chromium, high-nickel austenitic stainless steels for "fire-exposed" parts of the superheater and reheater assemblies. Each material used in the pressure-retaining parts—drums, headers, tubing, piping, forgings, or castings—conforms to all the requirements of an applicable *ASME* Boiler and Pressure Vessel Code material specification. Furthermore, during fabrication of each material used, the rules relating to welding, material forming, and inspection of materials and the welds in them are dictated by the *ASME* Code. Within the framework of the Code establishing quality standards there is considerable latitude for selecting materials, welding process and procedures, types of inspection, and thermal treatments of welded assemblies.

FABRICATION OF STEAM-GENERATOR PRESSURE PARTS

Welding is the basic tool for fabricating boiler components. While elements of a skilled art are retained in some aspects, welding is a recognized technical specialty that requires substantial background in the fields of metallurgy, electrical, and mechanical engineering.[1]

In applying the welding process, metallurgical skills are necessary to determine the effects of chemical composition and metal structure on the weld properties. Electrical engineering skills are required in designing the welding power supply, welding controls, and related equipment. Particularly in automatic fusion welding, there must be precise control of the welding arc as well as the welding machine, and such control usually involves electronics. Skills in mechanical engineering are essential to design automatic welding equipment, where the machine designer must have knowledge of mechanics, hydraulics, pneumatics, and heat transfer.

In the sections that follow, the principal fabrication and welding operations for drums, headers, furnace walls, superheaters and reheaters will be described.

STEAM DRUM

The steam drum is a heavy-wall pressure vessel having hemispherical ends, with nozzles and nipples attached for incoming and outgoing water and steam. Fig. 1A illustrates a typical drum for a large boiler. In this figure, the drum is fabricated in three cylindrical sections, called courses, each welded to one another and with a hemispherical head welded to each end of the three-course cylinder. Fig. 1B and 1C show that each cylindrical section is made up of a thick plate (called the tube sheet) and a thin plate (called the wrapper sheet). The tube sheet is designed to withstand the

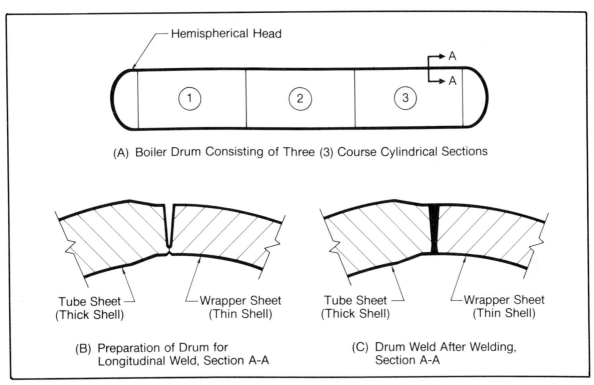

(A) Boiler Drum Consisting of Three (3) Course Cylindrical Sections

Tube Sheet
(Thick Shell)

Wrapper Sheet
(Thin Shell)

Tube Sheet
(Thick Shell)

Wrapper Sheet
(Thin Shell)

(B) Preparation of Drum for
Longitudinal Weld, Section A-A

(C) Drum Weld After Welding,
Section A-A

Fig. 1 **Details of a large boiler steam drum**

Fig. 2 **The internals separate water from steam, direct the steam to the outlets leading to the superheater, and provide an exit for the water to be recirculated through the furnace-wall system.**

Fig. 3 Ultrasonic tests are used to inspect plate material. Basically, this form of nondestructive testing uses ultrasonic sound waves to detect flaws in materials and welds.

Fig. 4 Mammoth presses can bend and form steel plate 20 feet wide and 15 inches thick. Here, a 6,000-ton hydraulic-beam press is used for hot-working of plates.

specified pressure and temperature as well as the necessary additional reinforcement to compensate for the weakening effect of the multiple holes drilled for the nipple attachments. The wrapper sheet is designed to withstand the same pressure and temperature parameters but, where openings are required for nozzles, the extra strength or reinforcement is provided by extra thickness in the nozzle forging. This type of steam-drum design provides the most economical use of materials. The internals are welded and installed as shown in Fig. 2. These internals separate water from steam, direct the steam to the outlets leading to the superheater, and provide an exit for the water to be recirculated through the furnace-wall system.

The Drum Plates

The drum plate, which is carbon steel conforming to *ASME* Specification SA 299 or SA 515-70 (both carbon steels), is first ultrasonically tested to assure required quality through the absence of large laminations or seams

(steel-making defects). The ultrasonic test is conducted using a 2.25-megahertz longitudinal wave directed from one plate surface to the other. In this manner, the entire volume of a 12-inch band completely around the plate and a 24-inch-wide strip centered on the longitudinal axis is tested. Fig. 3 shows the ultrasonic-testing equipment being used for examination of a thick drum plate. The forming operation begins only after the plate soundness has been assured by such ultrasonic tests and following a review of the test reports received from the steel supplier.

The plates are heated in a furnace at 1650°F, and each plate is then removed to the 6,000-ton hydraulic-beam press where it is incrementally hot-worked into the required shell-course segment based on the nominal inside diameter of the drum. When the bent plate has cooled to below 300°F, but not less than 72°F, it is then cold pressed to a specified, more precise contour than is possible to attain during the hot-pressing operation (Fig. 4).

Fig. 5 Each of the longitudinal edges of the bent plate is machine weld-beveled.

The next step is to machine the weld bevel on each of the longitudinal edges as shown in Fig. 5. To make up a cylinder or shell course, a series of tack welds join one bent plate with its slightly thinner (wrapper) counterpart. The longitudinal seams are welded using the automatic tandem submerged-arc process to deposit a succession of thin layers from the outside, all with a preheat of 300°F. In the welding process, a blanket of granular fusible material completely covers and shields the welding zone. Although referred to as flux, the material performs functions in addition to those of flux. Visibly, there is no evidence of current passing between the welding electrode and the component being welded. The electrode is not in actual contact with the component. The welding current is carried across the gap through the molten flux which is supplied automatically along the seam to be welded. The entire welding action takes place beneath the flux without sparks, spatter, smoke or flash. When the outer welding is completed, the inner side of the weld is back-gouged to sound metal using the electric arc-air process. Next, the weld is finished on the inside using the automatic submerged-arc process, Fig. 6. As the outside portion of each weld is applied, about 20 percent of the weld is deposited in one seam. The shell is then rotated so that a similar amount of weld can be deposited, with the required preheat, in the other seam; such a procedure helps to control distortion.

Each cylindrical course is fabricated in the same way. After welding, both the inside and outside of each longitudinal seam are ground flush and magnetic-particle inspected. This operation is followed by radiography using a 4-MeV (million electron volts) linear accelerator, Fig. 7. If necessary, repairs are made using low-hydrogen covered electrodes at 300°F preheat. Repairs are re-radiographed until the welding is completely satisfactory.

Drilling for Nipples and Nozzles

Next, each course is drilled for the nipples: first, the holes for nozzles are oxy-gas cut; then, both nozzles and nipples are welded into place using manual metal-arc welding with low-hydrogen covered electrodes.

Joining the Courses

A three-course drum, as we have described, is assembled by first joining two of the courses with a girth seam. Following this, these two joined courses and the remaining course each have a hemispherical head welded to one end. The circumferential welds are ground, magnetic-particle inspected, and radiographed. When the welds have passed inspection, each of the two assemblies is stress-relieved at 1150°F ± 25°F. After the internals are put into place, a final girth weld is made; this is locally stress-relieved, followed by magnetic-particle testing of all welds. Fig. 8 shows a typical steam drum ready for shipment.

HEADERS

Headers may be considered smaller-diameter versions of the steam drum just described, except that headers do not have steam-separation equipment in them. They collect water or steam from a group of tubes assembled either in panel form or as a group of individual tubes. Headers are made from plate-formed pipe, seamless pipe, or centrifugally cast pipe. The materials employed are low-carbon steel, carbon-molybdenum steel, and three types of chromium-molybdenum steel.

Fabricating the cylinder or shell from plate for headers differs somewhat from fabricating the drum shell course. To make a "plate-formed" header, the plate, after the required inspection, is cut to a predetermined size and the long edges of the plate are bent in a 14,000-ton hydraulic pull-down forming press. This bending operation may be done hot or cold, depending upon the plate thickness and the subsequent shell diameter.

After the plate edges have been bent and (depending upon the material) the plate has been heated in a furnace to between 1600 and 1750°F, the plate is pressed into a U-shape and then into a cylinder, slightly larger than the required size. The two longitudinal edges are trimmed and the cylinder is again heated and

Fig. 6 An automatic submerged-arc welder finishes the inside long-seam of the cylindrical course.

Fig. 7 Each cylindrical course is inspected by radiography. Any subsequent necessary repairs are re-radiographed until the welding is satisfactory.

Fig. 8 A typical steam drum is readied for shipment. High-pressure steam drums range in length to over 100 feet and weigh more than 500,000 lbs. Shipment of these drums require utilization of multiple rail cars.

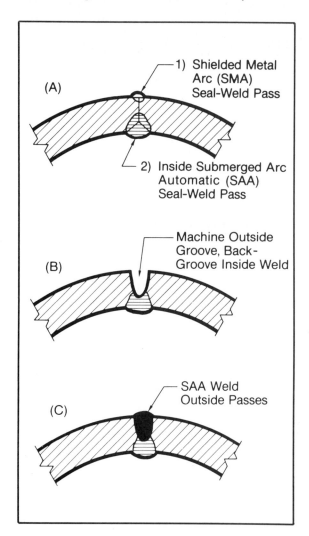

Fig. 9 Header longitudinal welding sequence

set in dies in a 2,000-ton hydraulic four-post press for final closing and sizing to specified outside diameter. (The long seam has yet to be welded.) The formed shell is then cleaned by grit-blasting and the long seam is fitted-up by depositing a continuous manual weld outside. Next, the shell is moved to the internal longitudinal seam welder, where the inside is finish-welded under the specified preheat conditions, Fig. 9A.

Machining the Shell

The longitudinal seam of the shell is then machined to produce a welding groove on the outside. During this machining, the manually deposited seal weld is removed and the inside automatic weld is machined to clean, sound metal, Fig. 9B. Later, with the specified preheat, the outside portion of the longitudinal seam is completed using the automatic submerged-arc process, Fig. 9C.

Upon completion of the inspection and upon acceptance of the weld quality, the cylinder is machined inside and outside to final required dimensions.

Depending upon the length of the finished header, cylinders and fittings are welded together and the ends may be closed in any one of three ways, by:

1. Butt-welding an elliptical or hemispherical cap on each end,

2. Welding a flat plate into each end of the cylinder assembly,

Fig. 10 **Tape-controlled drilling and checking of tube holes in a pressure vessel**

3. Forging each end of the cylinder closed (an operation called "wobbling").

The holes for nozzles and nipples are drilled in the headers (Fig. 10) and then the nipples of the desired shape are welded into the sockets previously machined during the drilling operation. After all welding has been completed, the assembly is stress-relieved. Fig. 11 shows a completed header with nipples, ready for rail-shipment.

FURNACE WALLS

C-E furnace walls are constructed of panels made of tubes joined by fusion welding. This construction provides a gas-tight "box" which contains the burning fuel and hot gases. Generally, panels are built up with four tubes, each 75-feet long, welded together simultaneously; single tubes and four-tube subassemblies are added successively to make up panels about 5-feet wide. Details of this fabrication and of the panel-processing welding machines (PPM) are shown in Figs. 12 and 13.

Fusion-Panel Welding

In the PPM, three welding arcs simultaneously deposit molten metal which solidifies to

Fig. 11 **Completed header for large boiler is securely loaded on a rail car for delivery to utility destination**

form the web between the tubes. Optimum web widths are in the ⅜ up to ⅝ in. range, and the welder can fabricate panels of ⅞ to 3-½ in. diameter tubes. The machine is capable of welding carbon and alloy tubing at rates up to about two feet per minute.

The fusion panel welder shown consists of a frame, three welding heads, tube drive, pressure rollers, copper chill bars, flux recovery and dispensing unit, filler-wire feed, tube feed-in rack and conveyor, and feed-out and storage racks.

The feed-in rack and conveyor position tubes and panel segments against a gate which aligns the tube ends. The alignment gate is then lowered and the tube drive activated. Held in alignment by contoured pressure and drive rollers, the tubes and panel segments pass under the three welding electrodes where weld wire and filler wire are fed into each arc. A water-cooled copper chill bar, under each welding arc and between the tubes, supports the individual weld puddles until they solidify to form the webs between the tube. At any time

during the welding cycle, the operator may stop or start one, two, or all three welding heads.

After the three webs are welded, the panel moves under automatic scaling hammers which remove the fused flux from the top of the weld. The panel is then discharged from the machine onto the feed-out racks where it is mechanically transferred to storage racks.

Provision for Openings in Tube Walls

It is necessary to provide openings in the tubular walls for sootblowers, insertion of instruments, and access. A special machine called an integral offset-bender makes small openings equal in width to one or two tube diameters. This machine actually cold-distorts tubes after the fusion-weld web joint between

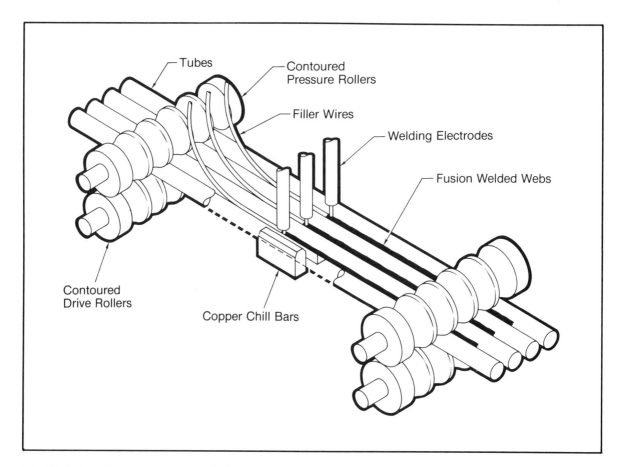

Fig. 12 **Schematic arrangement of fusion panel welder**

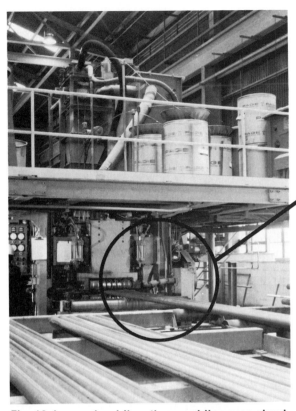

Fig. 13 In panel welding, three welding arcs simultaneously deposit molten metal which solidifies to form the web between the tubes. The machine can weld carbon and alloy tubing at rates up to about two feet per minute.

Fig. 14 An integral offset-bender makes small openings by cold-distorting tubes after the fusion-weld web joint between two tubes is cut.

two tubes is cut, Fig. 14. This pressing-form technique has reduced the use of hand-welded inserts that were a potential source of leaks.

To make larger or wider openings, sections are cut from the panel and then a prefabricated bent-tube assembly is welded back into the opening to permit steam or water flow to continue through the panel but in a path that provides the required opening as shown in Fig. 15. These 75-foot panels, containing attachments for buckstays and other structurals and for attaching insulation, are welded together in place in the field to the required height, width, and depth of the furnace. Generally, the field welds are made by manual shielded-arc welding or tungsten-inert-gas welding, individually or in combination. It should be noted that the welds joining the tubes lengthwise in the panel are intentionally slit in the shop for approximately 18 in. at one end to facilitate the precise alignment of one tube in a panel with its counterpart in the panel above or below, or for joining the tubes to headers or other connecting tubes already in place.

Solid and Peg Fins

Although the fusion-welded panel construction makes a gas-tight furnace enclosure, the space between tubes in the area of the furnace arch and in areas not exposed directly to furnace radiation are filled by either a solid fin or a peg fin. The solid fin is a flat strip of steel welded lengthwise to adjacent tubes where spacing greater than ⅝-inch can be tolerated The fins are joined to two tubes at one time by a machine having four separate automatic submerged-arc welders. The fins are welded on one side, then turned over; the back side of each previously made weld is again welded to provide a complete penetration weld. Peg fins, carbon steel pieces approximately 1½ in. wide with varying height, are electric-flash-welded to the outside of the tube. The "pegs" provide heat transfer to the tube and fill the space between adjacent tubes to retain refractory.

Rather than by bending individual tubes which are then welded together, welded-wall panels that make up the furnace arch, bottom, and roof section of the boiler are bent after they are formed into panels. Fig. 16 shows how these panel sections are mounted and bent on the shop floor during fabrication.

SUPERHEATERS, REHEATERS, AND ECONOMIZERS

These assemblies are made up of carbon steel, low-alloy steel, and nickel-chromium stainless-steel tubing. Material choice depends upon gas and steam temperatures to which the tube is exposed; it is selected in accordance with *ASME* Code rules and boiler manufacturer's design standards.

Shop Fabrication of Superheaters

To use materials effectively and economically, tubes up to 40-feet in length are joined by automatic metal inert-gas arc-welding to form a single tube up to 150-feet long, Fig. 17. The butt welds on this assembly are examined by fluoroscopy and, when acceptable, the tube enters an automatic bending line. Controlled by a previously prepared tape, this equipment bends the long tube at the required location (Fig. 18) and can be programmed to make either cold or hot bends. A superheater or reheater *section* is an assembly of such tubes, each bent to a particular pattern. C-E uses an electric induction pressure-welding process to form butt welds on the long prebent tubes to form element assemblies, Fig. 19. The induction pressure welds are inspected by ultrasonic testing.

In continuous-fin construction, two strips of steel are welded longitudinally to the tube on diametrically opposite sides. Fig. 20 shows the fin detail and the fin welding operation.

Shop Optimization

To save time and labor at the jobsite, panels such as superheaters and reheaters are joined to their respective headers in the shop prior to shipping in a process called "optimization" that is intended to make the most economical assembly for erection upon its arrival at the jobsite. To achieve this, the panels are welded to the tube extension or nipples on the header by a miniature automatic welding machine that rotates about the two tube ends, the axis of which is horizontal. This is called "orbital" welding; a photo of the orbital welding machine is shown in Fig. 21.

Unquestionably, optimizing shop work on superheater and reheater sections has led to lower forced-outage rates, which directly translates into higher availability. Modules up to 11-feet wide are available that require only field girth welds on the headers themselves. All field welding of tubes to header nipples has been eliminated. Moreover, shipping and erection rigs designed for use with these optimized sections have virtually eliminated any damage during either the shipping or erection stages.

The Economizer Section

The boiler economizer section is another type of tubular assembly, which may have its heating surface extended by fins. The amount of heat transfer and the type of fuel usually dictate the type of heating surface. C-E designs include spiral-finned tubes, continuous-finned tubes, and bare tubes (those without fins). The latter type is fabricated very much like a bare-tube superheater or reheater.

Fig. 15 To make larger or wider openings, sections are cut from the panel. A prefabricated bent-tube assembly is welded back into the opening.

Fig. 16 Entire tube assemblies that make up, say, the furnace bottom or nose section, are bent in panel form rather than by bending individual tubes.

NONDESTRUCTIVE EXAMINATION OF BOILER COMPONENTS

In describing the operations performed in the C-E boiler shops, reference has been made to the several types of nondestructive testing (NDT) for determining the integrity of the fabricated components. By definition, NDT is a means of inspecting an item without destroying its usefulness.

Several factors must be considered prior to selecting an NDT method:

1. Type of imperfection expected to be found: deterioration, cracking, surface, volumetric

2. Surface condition of areas to be inspected (inside and outside surfaces)

3. Orientation of defects: vertical to wall thickness or horizontal to wall

4. Permitted severity of imperfections: e.g., 2 percent wall, 5 percent wall, serviceable component

5. Suspected cause of defect: improper chemical cleaning, water treatment, draft, stress-associated, improper welding

Once the above conditions have been evaluated, the method of inspection can be determined. Table I lists the most universally used methods. All methods have limits and depend on the ability of the performing inspector. Yet regardless of the inspector's qualifications, destructive examination may sometimes be required.

Of the four methods, radiography is the acceptance tool for conformance of pressure parts to *ASME* Code requirements. Ultrasonic, liquid penetrant, and magnetic-particle testing, on the other hand, are used primarily to assure quality in manufacture.

RADIOGRAPHY

Radiographic inspection is the most common volumetric inspection method used in the boiler industry to determine the integrity of welds. Many factors can affect the value of a radiograph as an inspection method; a few are:

Fig. 17 Automatic metal inert-gas arc-welding machines join 40-foot lengths of tubes to form a single tube up to 150-feet long.

Fig. 18 After examination by fluoroscopy, tubes which have passed inspection enter an automatic bending line. Programmable for either hot or cold operation, this equipment bends the long tube at required locations.

Table I. Nondestructive Testing Methods

Method	Definition	Uses	Limitations
Radiographic	Uses electro-magnetic rays (X-rays and gamma rays) to penetrate material, recording on film imperfections in the material.	Used on any metal stock or articles as well as a variety of other materials to detect (and record on film) surface or subsurface imperfections. Film provides a permanent record of the discontinuities.	High initial cost. Requires electrical power source. Potential radiation hazard to personnel.
Ultrasonic	Uses ultrasound to penetrate material, indicating imperfections on an oscilloscope screen.	Used on metal, ceramics, plastics to detect surface and subsurface imperfections. When automated, permanent records are available. Also measures material thickness.	Moderately high initial cost. Interpretation of test results requires highly trained personnel.
Magnetic Particle	Uses electrical current to create a magnetic field in a specimen while magnetic particles indicate where the field is broken by an imperfection.	Used on metal that can be magnetized (ferro-magnetic) to detect surface or subsurface imperfections. Simple to use. Equipment is portable for field testing.	Cannot be used on metal that cannot be magnetized. Requires electrical power.
Liquid Penetrant	Uses a penetrating liquid to seep into a surface imperfection, thus providing a visible indication.	Used on metal, glass, and ceramics to locate surface imperfections. Simple to use and does not require elaborate equipment.	Does not detect imperfections beneath the surface of a specimen.

1. Thickness of the part
2. Radiation emitter physical size
3. Type radiation
4. Radiographic film selection
5. The distance the radiation source is placed from the subject
6. Quality of processing
7. The ability and experience of the person evaluating the radiograph
8. Nature of flaw and degree of acceptance criteria

A radiograph, by definition, is a shadow picture produced by the passage of X-ray or gamma rays through an object onto a film (Fig. 22). Normally, the radiation is produced by one of two methods:

1. Man-made radioactive isotopes, produced by placing an element into a nuclear reactor and bombarding it with radiation; for example, the stable element iridium 191 becomes radioactive iridium 192 after bombardment by radiation in a reactor.

2. X-rays are produced by the sudden stopping of high-speed electrons in a vacuum tube

ULTRASONIC TESTING

Ultrasonic testing (UT) is based on comparisons of the times it takes ultrasonic waves to travel through materials. After the test operator

Fig. 19 To form element assemblies, an induction pressure welder makes butt welds on the prebent tubes. As part of standard quality assurance procedure, ultrasonic tests check welds for flaws.

Fig. 20 In continuous-fin construction, two strips of steel are welded longitudinally to the tube on diametrically opposite sides.

Fig. 21 Miniature orbital welding machines join superheater elements to header nipples to make optimized superheater modules.

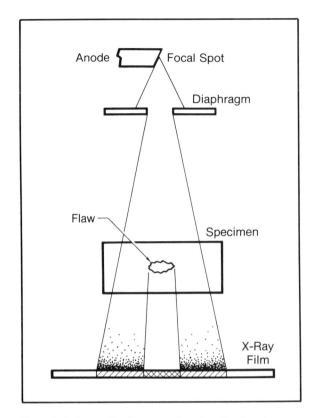

Fig. 22 **Schematic diagram showing the fundamentals of a radiographic exposure. The dark region of the film represents the more penetrable part of the object; the light regions, the more opaque. (***From Radiography in Modern Industry,* **published by Radiography Markets Division, Eastman Kodak Company.)**

establishes the time for an ultrasonic wave to pass through a good specimen of test material, flaws are detected by deviations from the standard time pattern. In Fig. 23, Time A corresponds to the wave entry into the material. Time B corresponds to wave reflection at the extremity of the test specimen. If a void within the component interrupts the sound wave, a portion of the sound is reflected back to the transmitter (transducer) as a mechanical signal. A piezoelectric element in the transducer changes the signal from mechanical to electrical. The electrical signal created by the element is then processed through the instrument and eventually will be produced as an electronic spike on the CRT of the ultrasonic instrument. In Fig. 23, an internal void would cause a wave disturbance to propagate to the surface (and the transducer) sooner than waves reflecting from the extremity at Time B. The electronic spike would show up on the CRT between Times A and B.

Ultrasonic testing is used for volumetric examination of welds and base materials for flaws. When inspecting materials, the sound wave is introduced into the part either normal to the surface or at predetermined angles, providing what is known as angle-beam inspection.

Many factors affect the results of the ultrasonic inspection:

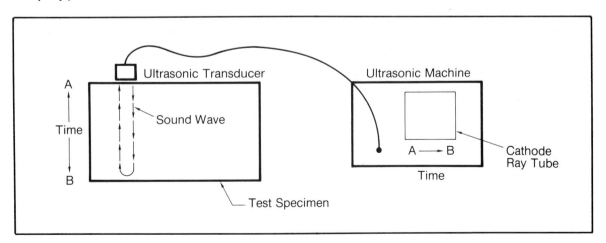

Fig. 23 **An ultrasonic transducer changes electrical energy to mechanical energy and mechanical energy to electrical energy.**

1. Selection of calibration reflectors
2. Ultrasound transmitter/receiver selection
3. Material composition
4. Surface condition (smooth vs. pitted)
5. Choice of equipment
6. Ability of the inspector

C-E ultrasonically tests all superheater and reheater tubes and electric-resistance-welded boiler tubes. Other ultrasonic tests are carried out on plate material over four inches thick, induction pressure welds, base material in the lifting-lug area, and nozzle welds, which are tested on a sample basis.

MAGNETIC-PARTICLE TESTING

Magnetic-particle testing is a dry-powder, magnetic-field technique to detect surface defects in

■ welds of fusion-welded panels

■ butt joints on plates 1¼ inch or less in thickness

■ back grooves of multipass submerged-arc welding

■ machined longitudinal weld preparations of plate-fabricated pipe

■ longitudinal and circumferential drum welds after interstage and following final heat treatment

■ nozzle welds, and

■ internal and external attachments

LIQUID-PENETRANT TESTING

Liquid-penetrant testing is a widely used non-destructive test applied to nonporous materials. Its success depends on the ability of a penetrating liquid to enter a surface opening by capillary action, and remain in the opening after the surplus penetrant on the surface is removed. A developer is then used to draw the penetrant out of the opening, back to the surface of the nonporous material.

The visibility of surface imperfections to the operator is increased by the addition of a dye, which may be either a visible dye which can be viewed in normal white light or a fluorescent dye that must be viewed under black light.

In contrast to the magnetic-particle testing method, which normally is used on ferrous materials, the liquid-penetrant method is primarily applied to austenitic stainless-steel and other non-magnetic materials. In providing assistance to manufacturing and quality-control people in a boiler shop, its major field of use is in giving indications of the length of imperfections that are open to the tested surfaces of such materials.

Among the present uses of liquid-penetrant testing are (a) checking of austenitic weld deposits between composite austenitic-ferritic tubes in furnace-wall panels; (b) checking of induction pressure welds where stainless steel is used on one side or both sides of the joint; and (c) as a check method for classification of ghost indications that have been detected by magnetic-particle testing.

OTHER MANUFACTURING PROCESSES

Many aspects of the fabricating process have been omitted in this brief description of a typical steam-generating supplier's pressure-part manufacturing facilities. Details of many types of welding, of heat-treating methods of welded assemblies, and of the inspection and quality-control procedures must, for example, be treated as separate subjects outside the scope of this text. Moreover, in addition to the extensive equipment required for pressure-part fabrication as described in this chapter, a steam-generator manufacturer must have facilities for making castings (for pulverizers and ash-handling components) as well as facilities for fabricating ductwork, firing equipment, buckstays, and structural steel.

REFERENCES

[1] An authoritative work on this subject is the *Welding Handbook* issued in several volumes and revised periodically by the American Welding Society, United Engineering Center, New York.

CHAPTER 19

Field Erection of Power-Plant Equipment

This chapter describes the field-construction activities associated with the erection of a coal-burning steam generator and other portions of a modern power plant. The information is of a general nature and does not reflect the detailed design and construction of a specific unit. Rather, it represents common features of much of the 400-MW to 900-MW equipment currently being installed throughout the world. Fig. 1 shows such a large positive-circulation coal-fired unit as will be referred to throughout the chapter.

PLANNING AND ORGANIZING FOR FIELD CONSTRUCTION

An electric utility or large industrial organization will prepare the design criteria and scope documents, the detailed engineering specifications, and other technical data needed for a complete plant. This work is accomplished either by a consulting-engineering firm retained to do the architectural and engineering design, or by in-house personnel performing all or part of it.

On most projects, many different vendors supply equipment and services; some of them do their own erection on the plant site. As a result, the owner or engineer issues many specifications to the various suppliers of the plant components—the steam generator, turbine-generator, condenser, emission-control equipment, ash-handling equipment, fans, pumps, piping, and valves. After equipment selection and purchase, the owner frequently will have the engineer-consultant continue as the constructor, supervising the several contractors and subcontractors.

Some of the crafts involved in the erection work are boilermakers, ironworkers, pipefitters, millwrights, electricians, insulators, operating engineers, sheet metal workers, carpenters, teamsters and laborers. These personnel are hired at the local jobsite at the beginning of the project or as the work progresses and are released once the portion of work requiring their craft is completed.

The erection of a utility steam generator is a major portion of the work in the total plant. About 65 percent of the time, the company that supplies the boiler also constructs it. Early in the project, the erecting company sets up a field organization headed by a construction manager who is experienced and knowledgeable in boiler erection and who holds the authority to make decisions necessary to the operation. The construction manager's staff consists of construction and welding supervisors, field

Fig. 1 Side elevation of large coal-fired steam generator for high-subcritical-pressure operation

engineers, quality-control engineers, field accountants and clerical personnel. Although all construction personnel are charged with maintaining a safe operation, a safety engineer may also be employed as well as a labor-relations specialist, if deemed necessary by the contractor.

It is the responsibility of this organization to plan and schedule the work in accordance with the overall project requirements; to perform the work as designed in a safe and timely fashion, assuring an adequate flow of materials, manpower, and money to avoid any delay; to verify the attainment of specification and code requirements; and to provide the documents and reports necessary to monitor the work.

FIELD ERECTION OF A BOILER

One of the first activities of the field-erection phase is the verification of the accuracy of all concrete foundations for the boiler. All column-to-column dimensions, anchor-bolt lo-cations, and concrete elevations are measured and verified against the drawings.

STRUCTURAL STEEL ERECTION

Since a boiler structure is sometimes 250 feet high, very large cranes are needed for erection. Main cranes with boom heights of 280 ft and lifting capacities of 250 tons or more are common. One crew of ironworkers can erect about 40 tons of steel a day with one such crane.

Because of the large quantity of boiler steel (often greater than 4000 tons for a 600-MW unit), boiler components, plus other plant equipment and materials, it is usually impossible or uneconomical to store all the boiler items within reach of the main crane. Storage in a yard area will therefore be required for the construction materials and additional equipment: one or more cranes of lighter capacity, cherry pickers (small rubber-tired mobile cranes) and flatbed trucks.

There are basically two ways of erecting boiler steel. One is the tier method, shown in Fig. 2. The other is the cube method. In the tier method, each elevation is completed to the splice point before another elevation is started. In the cube method, sections of the steel are built up to different elevations starting from the turbine deck and progressing back toward the stack. The structure is built in a horseshoe shape, leaving an open area for the crane to back out as work is completed.

The large sizes of some of the boiler components, such as the ductwork, deaerator tank, and sootblowers, require that these components be installed as the building structure is erected. For this reason, close coordination between the material suppliers and the constructor is essential.

It is desirable in many instances for the boiler erector also to erect the boiler support steel. This facilitates the planning of erection sequences, and firm dates for finishing elevations can be planned with a minimum of coordination problems or schedule disruptions. If the steam-generator supplier does not erect the structural steel, it is important that the supplier be consulted so that steel erection and boiler-

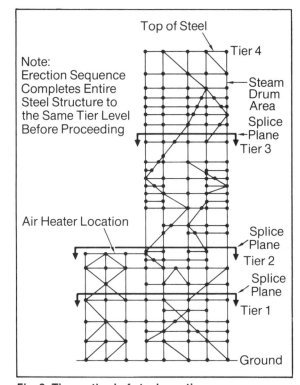

Fig. 2 **Tier method of steel erection**

Fig. 3 Erection sequence of the main boiler girder: 3A, main girder being lifted off the ground; 3B, main girder at an angle to the steel; 3C, main girder being set on the support columns; 3D, main girder in place, ready for tie-in steel

components installation are coordinated, to preclude structural-steel blocking of the component installation.

The steel erection begins with the main boiler columns, usually starting on the turbine and steam-drum sides of the unit. Then the main girders are erected. They support the main boiler sections and the steam drum from the top of the unit. There are usually 5 or 6 main girders spaced about 24 feet apart. Girder sizes range from 6 to 20 feet high, 100 feet long, with weights approaching 160 tons. For structural members of these sizes, shipping to the jobsite becomes a problem, since railroads have height and weight limitations.

MAIN-GIRDER ERECTION

Main-girder erection is one of many rigging problems of the structural-steel erection process. The most accepted method of lifting the heavier girders is to use two cranes in the furnace cavity. Lifting lugs are bolted to the top flange of the girder to attach it to the crane's load blocks. Fig. 3A shows such a girder raised off the ground with the two cranes. Because the girder rests on top of the structure columns, its total length is longer than the open area between the columns. This requires the girder to go up at an angle to fit between the steel. This can be seen in Fig. 3B. Once the girder is raised above the column tops, one of the cranes moves its boom forward while the other goes backward to bring the girder parallel to the front of the boiler. The girder can then be set down on the column tops as seen in Fig. 3C. At this time, the top flange of the girder is very close to the tubular framing on the boom. If the girders begin to swing and touch the boom, the boom could collapse. Once the girder is in place, (Fig. 3D), intermediate steel can be installed to tie all of the upper steel together. Coordinated radio communication, highly experienced operating engineers and rigging supervisors, and first-class equipment are imperative for successful girder erection.

STEAM-DRUM INSTALLATION

The steam drum can be raised into position at the top of the boiler once the main girder steel

has been erected. The drum, shown in Fig. 1, is hung just below the main girder steel by means of huge U-bolts that encircle the drum. Steam drums currently being used may be 7 feet in outside diameter, over 100 feet long, and weigh as much as 300 tons.

RAISING A DRUM

As shown in Fig. 4, the drum is often raised at an angle to the ground, because the bay may not accommodate the full drum length. Based on the lifting lugs welded on the drum in the shop, the location of the support steel for the load blocks can be determined before construction is started. A set of "cat heads" (a temporary support for the upper portion of the block-and-tackle arrangement which is used to raise the load) rests on top of the support steel, through which the upper load block is pinned. The block can rotate according to the angle of the drum. The rigging usually consists of 1-inch cable with up to 17 parts of line on each set of blocks.

The steam drum is usually brought inside the furnace cavity on a railroad car and off-loaded with the lifting blocks. In the absence of a railroad track, the cranes used for steel erection can off-load the drum and "walk it" to the lift area. The line-pull two-drum hoist that is used for lifting is usually located on the ground with the two load lines following a column line up to

Fig. 4 **Lift of steam drum in boiler cavity. (Note deaerator tank already in place)**

the top blocks hanging in the cat heads. Because of the inner dimensions of the structural steel and the location of the cat heads, an outhaul such as that shown in Fig. 4 may be used to keep the drum from drifting into the steel work. Proper location of all rigging is important because of the height of the boiler and the lifting distance, which can be well over 200 feet.

"DRIFTING" A DRUM

On some jobs, it is advantageous to erect the platform steel that is under the steam drum along with the boiler structural steel. This can involve steel in excess of 200 tons that can be put up more efficiently at that time.

When steel has been erected such that the drum cannot be lifted vertically from the ground, the steam drum must be raised up in the boiler cavity to a height just below its final elevation and then drifted into the drum-bay area. This will require 2 sets of cat heads and blocks, and an extra set of lugs on the drum. Fig. 5A shows the drum located in the boiler cavity with the first set of rigging attached to the drum. To the left of the drum is the platform steel that the drum will be drifted over. Fig. 5B shows the drum up to the drift elevation with the second set of rigging being attached to the second set of lugs while the first set still supports the load. The temporary planks on the platform steel provide a work area and also support the hanger rods. Fig. 5C shows the load being transferred from the boiler cavity to the drum bay, with the load equally distributed in all four blocks. In Fig. 5D, the drum is being raised to its final elevation, with the second set of rigging supporting the entire load and the first set slacked off.

PRESSURE-PARTS SUPPORT-STEEL ERECTION

While the steam drum is being erected, the pressure-parts support steel (upper region of Fig. 1) can be installed. This steel, located at the top of the unit, supports all of the weight of the boiler. Unlike conventional structures that are built from the ground up, most modern boilers are built from the top down, with the whole boiler suspended by hanger rods from the main girders. This permits the boiler to expand downward as much as 15 inches as it heats up during the start-up of the plant. The correct setting of the pressure-parts support steel is very important because every part of the boiler is located with respect to this steel. It controls all elevations and is continually used as a reference to align the different components as they are erected.

INSTALLATION OF UPPER HEADERS AND LINKS

Next, the upper headers and links are hung just below the pressure-parts support steel. They may include the main steam lines to the turbine, the crossover links from the different stages of the superheat and reheat systems, the economizer lines to the steam drum, and the riser tubes from the waterwall outlet headers.

By the time these components are raised, the crane used to erect the boiler steel has usually been moved to the back of the unit and cannot reach the areas where these components will be located. Therefore, most are raised from the ground inside the furnace cavity using block and tackle (a set of pulleys in a frame). The components are then hung on their respective hanger rods, which support the different boiler components, or are lashed temporarily to the pressure-parts support steel. The sequencing of component installation requires extra care on units where there are multiple riser tubes to the steam drum from the side-wall headers. These pipe sections are usually 6 inches in diameter and as long as 40 feet. They are very flexible and may contain several compound bends.

Other pipes between the various superheater and reheater headers are often 30 inches in diameter, with sections weighing as much as 10 tons. They require proper sequencing because of the difficulty of moving them once they have been positioned between the existing hanger rods. Fig. 6 shows some completed main steam and reheat piping to the turbine. At this point in the installation of the boiler, no pressure-part final welding has been started. All work has involved the placement of equipment.

Fig. 5. Erection sequence of steam drum being drifted into place: 5A, drum in boiler bay with first set of rigging attached; 5B, second set of rigging being attached to steam drum; 5C, drum being drifted over from the boiler bay with the second set of rigging; 5D, drum raised to its final elevation with the second set of rigging

The downcomers from the steam drum to the suction manifold, as shown in Fig. 1 and Fig. 7, are raised into place after the above-mentioned work is completed. Usually arriving on the jobsite in 60-foot sections, downcomers are about 16 inches in diameter and weigh as much as 7 tons per section. Each downcomer requires about 3 sections. Rigging must be located underneath the steam drum itself, because the downcomers are welded directly to the drum nozzles. Clips are welded on the ends so that threaded rods can be inserted to raise or lower the downcomer a few inches for proper positioning for welding.

As soon as the downcomers are in place, boilermaker welders can begin the fit-up and welding procedures that will ultimately join the downcomers to the drum. A joint can be finished in about 1½ days if a two-person crew works on each weld. An automatic welding machine (a welding tool mounted on a track that follows the joint) saves considerable time and makes an essentially perfect weld.

SUPERHEATER AND REHEATER MODULES INSTALLATION

The next boiler components to be installed are the superheater and the reheater pendant modules. Fig. 1 shows their locations within the boiler. These modules, which require some of the most difficult rigging on the boiler, contain sections of tubes bent in complex configurations and welded together on a common section of header. Each module can measure as much as 10 feet square and 55 feet long and weigh up to 70 tons. They arrive on the jobsite partially encased in shipping rigs that are also used to upend the module to a vertical position.

A large crane and a cherry picker are needed to off-load the modules from the railroad car to a flatbed truck, which brings them into the furnace area. A set of 75-ton capacity blocks are rigged above the final position of the module. The lower block is attached to a special spreader beam, shown in Figs. 8A and 8B. The lower end of the module is picked up with a cherry picker, while the main load blocks raise the header end. The flatbed trailer is removed and the main blocks continue to raise the upper end of the module, while the cherry picker lowers the other end, thus orienting the module in a vertical position for final raising. Rotation to the vertical position is accomplished quite easily with specially designed rods between the high-crown end bar of the module and the spreader beam. The cherry picker and shipping

Fig. 6 Main steam and reheat piping to the turbine

Fig. 7 Downcomer piping from steam drum

frame are then removed and the module is lifted with the 75-ton blocks (Fig. 9).

Because of the thick-wall tubes required to retain high-pressure steam, the superheater modules are much heavier than reheater modules. When a complete section of superheater modules is in place, the header sections are fitted together and prepared for welding. Girth welds made on the header sections connect the different superheater modules. (Fig. 10).

Depending on the location of the modules in the furnace and the structural steel underneath them, it is sometimes necessary to drift a module into place. To transfer the load to its final position, this lift requires two sets of blocks attached to a steel plate pinned to the module. Generally, this procedure is required when the load is raised or "picked" inside the boiler cavity with the final location of the component in the back pass of the boiler.

COMPONENT LIFTING CONSIDERATIONS

During the erection of the boiler components, hundreds of lifts are made inside the furnace cavity. This necessitates changing the location of rigging almost every time a pick is made. It is often helpful to locate a crawler crane inside the furnace area that has the capacity to boom in and out and swing around to change its location. A crawler is very useful and can be used throughout 70 percent of the steam-generator construction.

The elevation of the previously erected pendant sections limits the height of the crane. Getting the crane in and out of the furnace is about a 2-day job and requires a 30- by 24-foot opening in the side of the steelwork. As the crane is being brought in, the boom is laid all the way down, parallel to the ground. A line is dropped down inside the furnace and attached to the end of the boom. The two lower pins on the front boom section are removed and the section is lifted with the line and rotated around the upper two pins. This puts the top section at a 90-degree angle to the rest of the boom. The rig is driven further into the furnace area for the length of another section and two more pins are removed. The second section is raised to the vertical position and the first two pins are replaced. This is repeated until all of the crane is in the furnace cavity

Fig. 8A Rigging for superheater and reheater modules

Fig. 8B Raising of superheater and reheater modules

Fig. 9 **Superheater module lift within boiler**

Fig. 10 Last module being fit into place. Girth welds will be made between the header sections.

with the boom reassembled in the vertical position. It is removed in the same way. Fig. 11 shows a completed crane within the furnace.

When most of the boiler is completed and there is no more head room available for the crane (about the time that the two lower headers are attached), it is removed.

Another method of lifting inside the furnace is with a guyed derrick located on top of the unit above the main girders. Guyed derricks can rotate 360 degrees on a bull wheel (the lower support for the derrick) and can boom out in any position. A system of guy wires is tied off to boiler steel at different points to support the mast from which the boom is rigged. When the boom is needed on the other side of a guy wire, the boom must be brought up to the vertical position parallel to the mast. Then, by rotating the bull ring, the complete crane is moved to a new position and the boom again lowered.

Other rigs used for lifting in the boiler area are stiff-leg derricks, Sky-horse cranes, ringer and crawler cranes, and travel lifts. All these are used in different ways and in varying capacities.

Some units presently being erected have very tall furnace heights, with top of structural steel in excess of 350 ft, which no conven-

Fig. 11 A completed crane boom within the furnace. Note the waterwall panels enclosing the furnace.

tional crawler crane can reach. These heights sometimes require a "kangaroo" tower crane that sits in the center of the furnace opening and can be used to erect the structural steel and some of the boiler components. The tower rests on a poured concrete base, held down with anchor bolts and tied off to the structural steel in several different places. The tower is a square structural member and, with the crane, can free-stand 160 ft above any tie-offs. The crane is then capable of jacking itself in the air 14 ft and inserting another section of tower for the crane to sit on. Fig. 12A, looking up inside the furnace cavity, shows the tower with its 2 tie-offs to the steel and the crane on top.

Fig. 12B shows the crane after it has erected the main girders and some of the fill-in steel. While the structural steel has been going up, the coal bunkers, ductwork, air heaters and other components have also been erected. The crane has 160 ft of boom and can reach almost all sections of the boiler area. With the crane located on top of the boiler, most of the steel can be erected in the tier method.

BUCKSTAY ERECTION

Once the primary crane has been installed inside the furnace, one of its first jobs is setting buckstays at different elevations. The buckstays are structural shapes or trusses that restrain movement of the waterwalls caused by fluctuation in furnace pressure. Buckstays may be all horizontal or may form a system of large vertical steel members combined with small horizontal members.

On boilers with both types, the main vertical buckstays, which are sometimes 3 feet wide and come to the jobsite in 60-foot sections, are hung from the pressure-parts support steel. Between these are 8-inch horizontal buckstays that are supported by the vertical buckstays.

SOOTBLOWER ERECTION

A crawler crane raises the sootblowers, typical locations of which are seen in Fig. 1, and sets them on the grating at their correct elevations. The type of fuel to be burned determines the number, type, and location of the blowers.

Fig. 12A Tower section and tie-offs for the "kangaroo" crane

Fig. 12B Crane on top of the unit with the main girders in place

Mounted horizontally, they have a long round tube or lance that is rotated by a driving motor. The sootblowers clean the walls and elements of the steam generator during operation.

One type of sootblower is the wall blower, which extends into the boiler only a few inches to clean the fireside of the waterwalls. A second type is the long retractable blower, which can be inserted up to a distance of either full boiler width, or one half the width of the boiler, depending upon available space and owner preference. These blowers extend between the sections of the superheater, reheater and economizer to clean the convection heat-absorbing surfaces.

WATERWALL ERECTION

Once the sootblowers have been laid on the grating temporarily, the waterwalls which form the sides of the furnace can be erected. The waterwalls are sections of tubes that are fusion welded together into a gas-tight panel. They conduct a mixture of steam and water upward as heat is applied from the furnace side. The walls extend from the base of the boiler (just above the ash hopper) up to the steam-drum level.

Waterwall panels come from the shop with the upper headers already attached. When two panels are joined in the field, only one girth weld is needed on the header. This eliminates the need for numerous field welds between header nipples and the panel tubes. Such shop prefabrication saves substantially in field erection time. In addition, it is a well accepted fact that shop welds cost less and are of higher quality than field welds, which are often performed under adverse weather or logistic conditions. Other examples of shop prefabrication of waterwall panels are welding of buckstay stirrups, installing insulation pins, and fitting seal boxes on the observation openings.

Another helpful shop procedure is the application of white paint to each panel to brighten the interior of the boiler during erection. This technique, as shown in Fig. 13, improves working conditions.

Typically about 12 feet wide and 80 feet long, waterwall panels are brought into the furnace on a flatbed truck. Because they are so long and flexible, the biggest problem with these panels is upending them. Two lines are needed. The crane in the hole lifts the top line; a cherry picker, the other, in much the same way the superheater modules are upended.

Sometimes, a special lifting device distributes the weight so the panel will not buckle. This requires that several slots be cut in the welded web between the tubes. A bar welded to a small T-beam is inserted and pinned on the back. This device assists in keeping the panel straight along its width during upending process. When the panel is vertical, it is lifted up to its final position.

Fig. 13 Installation of waterwall panels. Vertical and horizontal buckstays are visible.

Fig. 14 Installation of roof tubes within furnace cavity

The desuperheater (or desuperheaters) is raised and put in place at this time. Before the superheated steam goes through the finishing superheater assemblies, it passes through the desuperheater. Through a system of spray nozzles that inject water into the steam, the desuperheater controls the temperature of the steam delivered to the turbine.

ROOF-TUBE ERECTION

After the waterwalls are in place, the roof tubes, see Figs. 1 and 14, can be erected usually in either of two ways. One approach uses single tubes that fit between the vertical elements. In other areas with larger openings, full roof-tube panels can be raised from the ground with a set of blocks and a tugger, rather than with a crane.

While the roof tubes are being fitted into place, the intermediate waterwall panels are lifted and fitted below the upper panels. Generally, they are attached to the upper panels by a system of threaded rods and clips that are welded to the welded webs between the panel tubes. When this temporary hanging system is used, final panel spacing for weld-out can be done with the threaded rods.

Fig. 15 The structural framing between the furnace "nose" and the vertical front wall of the convection pass of a large high-pressure steam generator

SUPPLEMENTARY FRAMING

Fig. 15 shows the structural framing between the furnace "nose" and the vertical front wall of the convection pass of a large high-pressure steam generator. All of the steelwork shown is supported by the pressure parts; both the pressure parts and these structural members have to be designed to withstand the loads imposed, as well as both positive and negative gas pressures as dictated by codes and owner specifications. The horizontal tubing in the top of the picture forms the floor of the gas pass directly behind the furnace nose.

AIR PREHEATER ERECTION

While the rest of the work is being done on the boiler, the air preheaters, usually two per steam generator, can be erected at the rear of the unit. (See Fig. 1 for their locations.) The air preheaters are heat exchangers made of heat-absorbing metal baskets assembled on a rotor that is turned by a drive. Hot flue gases leaving the boiler pass through one side of the heater. Incoming cold air from the forced-draft fans passes in counterflow through the other side. The baskets are heated by the hot flue gases and rotate into the cold air stream to raise the temperature of the incoming air. Various seals prevent the gas and airflows from mixing.

The air preheater is most often oriented with a vertical shaft. Its main parts are the bearing, bearing supports, baskets, oil circulating system, drive motor, seals, casing and insulation. On some projects, it is economical to fabricate the main sections of the preheater on the ground and raise them into place in the structural framework with a crane from behind the unit. This method is very satisfactory if a large capacity crane, such as the one shown in Fig. 16, is available. The extremely accurate measurements required are performed by millwrights. This includes setting the clearances between the rotor and seals, aligning the bearing and support structure and setting the rotor motor and roller pins. Boilermakers erect the main housing and raise the air preheater into place. They also level and set the preheater in its final position in the boiler, as shown in Fig. 17. Once the preheater rotor and other parts are assembled, the heat-absorbing baskets are raised and moved into place.

ECONOMIZER ERECTION

While the air preheater is being erected, the economizer, located just above the air preheater (see Fig. 1), can be erected. This is a heat recovery device designed to transfer heat from the exiting flue gases to the incoming boiler feedwater. The economizer consists of an interconnected horizontal tube array. The upper ends of each economizer assembly connect to the outlet header, which is already in place above the roof tubes.

Two types of economizer transfer surface are in common use: one consists of a pair of longitudinal fins located 180 degrees apart along the top and bottom of the horizontal tube; the second is bare tubing, similar to horizontal low-temperature-superheater surface.

Finned economizer tubes require careful handling because of the heat-absorbing fins. They are grouped together in modules of 3 to 8 elements, each with saddle supports installed to hold them together. They are raised into place from the ground with a tugger rigged in the area of the outlet headers. Pins and rods usually support the assemblies directly to lugs welded to the bottom of the intermediate headers. Because the economizer tubes are often fabricated in a staggered pitch to increase heat transfer and minimize space requirements, fitting the last few elements sometimes presents a rigging problem. It is difficult to pass hoisting falls through the staggered tubes. This often means that the already installed elements must be spread apart and the side walls must be moved out.

WINDBOX-ASSEMBLY ERECTION

After the intermediate waterwall panels are in place, the windbox assemblies, shown in Fig. 18, can be brought into the furnace and positioned for lifting.

The rigging of a furnace windbox assembly is one of the most difficult tasks on the project because of the weight, shape and balance points of the assembly. When the windbox comes from the shop, sections of waterwall tubing are attached to it, with the bends in the tubing prefit around the windbox. These are welded into the already erected wall panels and help support the windbox. Additional hanger rods support the back side of the assembly. The average weight of the assembly is 25 to 30 tons. It is raised in place using the crane in the furnace.

Fig. 16 Assembly of air preheaters on the ground

Fig. 17 Air preheaters in place inside the building

Because the back side of the windbox contains control arms, ductwork and insulated panels, it must be cribbed up on the low-boy truck when it is brought into the furnace cavity.

Special lifting lugs are also installed in the shop to make the windbox assembly hang as close to plumb as possible while it is being raised. To ensure that the tip of the crane boom does not hit the waterwall panel above, special care must be used when attaching the assembly to the hanger rods.

PULVERIZER ERECTION

Coal feeders, coal pulverizers, and the coal piping to the windbox are usually erected as part of the steam-generator contract.

If shipping schedules permit, coal pulverizers such as those shown in Fig. 1 can be set in place in sections as the structural steel is set. On a large unit, there are usually 6 to 10 coal pulverizers which are located on both sides or in front of the boiler at ground level. Generally,

one pulverizer on each side is not installed until most of the required material has been moved into the furnace cavity.

A typical bowl mill (Fig. 19) contains about 6 sections, the first of which is the poured concrete foundation with four large anchor bolts. The mill base, which contains the gear case on many mills, is set on top of the foundation. The mill side assembly, where the grinding bowl is located, is installed on top of this. The separator body, which contains the 3 roller journals and covers, goes on top of this. The separator, where the coal is classified cyclonically to the desired fineness, is next. The very top of the mill is the multiple-port discharge assembly. Here, coal is fed into the mill from a central feeder pipe and pulverized coal is discharged to the coal piping through the peripheral ports.

Mills weigh up to 150 tons and are up to 30 feet high. The crane that erects the structural steel can easily set the heavy sections of each

Fig. 18 Windbox assemblies erected in place

Fig. 19 Erection of bowl mills

mill. The lighter internals can be installed later. If the use of a crane is impractical, the different mill parts can be rolled into place on a track and jacked in position. Ironworkers and millwrights do most of the construction work on the mills, with the latter doing all of the alignment and settings because of the close tolerances that are required.

Simultaneously with the work on the bowl mills, hanging and setting of the coal piping to the furnace can also be progressing. Welded joints and Victaulic couplings join sections of the pipe. Fig. 20 shows the final tightening of a Victaulic coupling on an elbow that connects to a windbox assembly.

SUCTION-MANIFOLD ERECTION

The suction manifold, also shown in Fig. 1, is raised into place next. It is the collecting header that distributes the water from the downcomers to the boiler circulating pumps.

The suction manifold is hung from the downcomers, which are welded to the steam drum. The downcomer leads join the top of the manifold. Lugs are provided on the downcomers, (and also on the nipples of the manifold), so that threaded rods can be inserted to hold the manifold after it is lifted. These can also be used to adjust the weld gap for proper fit.

The manifold is usually lifted into place using the crane in the furnace cavity. If the crane is not used, blocks must be rigged under the steam drum with the rigging reaching down the full height of the boiler to hoist the manifold into place.

The boiler circulating pump assemblies are usually raised and temporarily rigged before the manifold is raised. As the lift is only about 8 tons for each pump assembly, the crane in the furnace can be used for this operation.

It is often advantageous to fit a number of pump components together on the ground first. The discharge valves can be welded onto the pump casings (Fig. 21) before erection. The pump casing is a volute-shaped chamber into which the pump impeller fits. The pumps force the water from the manifold through discharge links into the lower waterwall headers. Check valves at the pump outlets prevent water flow from backing up into an idle pump.

Fig. 20 Fuel pipe connections being made to furnace windbox

Fig. 21 Volute and pump assembly with a discharge valve on each side

A monorail can be used to install the electric motors and pump rotors. Millwrights perform the critical alignment of motors and pumps.

DUCTWORK ERECTION

Ductwork erection must be completely integrated with boiler erection to avoid problems in fitting ductwork sections into the structural steel framework.

The boiler ductwork, as indicated in Fig. 1, consists of two main systems, the air-supply system, which includes the primary and secondary air and the furnace-windbox ducts, and the flue-gas system, which includes the backpass ash hopper and ductwork to the air preheater, precipitators, absorbers (if included), induced-draft fans, and stack.

The hot-air ductwork from the air preheater to the windboxes, along with the burner connection duct, contains some of the biggest pieces of equipment on the boiler. Because of the sizes involved, ductwork is generally assembled on the ground (Fig. 22) with sections installed simultaneously with the structural steel. Hanger rods and expansion joints in the ductwork allow for thermal expansion. Some ductwork sections are 20 feet by 30 feet in cross section. At this size, internal stiffeners are often needed to provide strength during shipping and erection.

The gas-system ductwork extends from the bottom of the economizer to the exit side of

Fig. 22 Ductwork fabricated on the ground

the air preheater. It also includes the ductwork from the air preheater to the induced-draft fans, to the gas cleaning equipment, and to the stack. Most of this ductwork is installed after the air preheater is in place, usually with the same crawler crane that set the air preheater.

Dampers to isolate equipment or regulate airflow or gas flow to and from the boiler are installed with the ductwork.

LOWER WATERWALL HEADER ERECTION

Typically, the lower waterwall headers are the last major lifts made inside the boiler and are installed after most of the already noted welding has been completed. The headers are up to 3 ft in diameter, extend the full width and depth of the furnace, and weigh as much as 60 tons each. During boiler operation, once the water reaches the suction manifold from the downcomers, it is pumped into these headers and up the waterwalls. Because these headers are so heavy, a large cherry picker is brought to the furnace to help the crane make this final lift. Once headers are in position, they are hung with hanger rods from the waterwall structure.

WELDING OF ERECTED COMPONENTS

Thus far, as the boiler erection has proceeded, the different components have been raised and hung by hanger rods or temporary rigging. After a group of components is installed, the fit-up and welding must be performed. Except for the structural steel, which is most commonly bolted together, almost everything else on the boiler is welded.

Several different welding procedures are used in the field on jobs of this size. The most extensively used is the manual metallic-arc type in which a flux-covered rod of filler material, used as an electrode, is consumed in the weld. Another type is the gas-shielded process, which consists of an externally supplied gas blanket (usually of argon) with a separate bare filler rod. In another kind, metal inert gas

(MIG), a special machine feeds a core of bare wire into the weld area. The shielded-arc process is mainly used to complete the root or first pass of a pressure weld in waterwall tubes, elements and piping. The manual metallic-arc process is used to finish and cap out these welds and to complete welds with backing rings. This process is also used to weld ductwork, steel sections, wall webs, and plate. The MIG process is used for completing seams in waterwall panels and ductwork.

Radiographic analysis of field welds can be a contract requirement to satisfy code, manufacturer, or owner specifications. (See Chapter 18 which describes radiography requirements in a steam-generator manufacturing facility.) For this analysis, X-ray film is placed on one side of the weld and a radioactive source is temporarily placed on the other side. When the film is developed, any flaws in the weld will be evident. A weld flaw, depending on its size, may have to be ground out and rewelded.

If the radiographs are satisfactory and the size of the weld requires it (according to Code standards), a stress-relieving process is used to relax any residual stresses caused by the high welding heat in the area. This process involves the placing of heating coils, gas burners or finger elements around the weld area, which is covered with layers of insulation to contain the heat. Thermocouples are attached to the weld joint to monitor the temperature, which is raised to a predetermined stress-relieving temperature, typically 1150°F, at a certain calculated rate and held there for a required amount of time (a function of the thickness of the weld). The temperature is then lowered to the ambient temperature at a controlled rate. The stress-relieving process is then complete.

ADDITIONAL CONSTRUCTION WORK

When the lower headers have been set in place, the cherry picker and the crane are removed from the furnace. Then the lower waterwall panels are brought in and raised into place, and the downtake system from the suc-

Fig. 23 Precipitator during final construction

Fig. 24 The erection of a stainless-steel absorber

tion manifold discharge valves is installed.

Additional work that can proceed simultaneously in other sections of the boiler is attaching the buckstays to the waterwalls, bolting the sootblowers to the waterwalls, connecting the piping for the sootblowers, and welding safety valves to the steam drum and outlet leads to the turbine. At this stage, a "punch list" of work that must be completed before the hydrostatic test should be compiled, so that all responsible contractors can be aware of unfinished items.

ERECTION OF STEAM GENERATOR AUXILIARY EQUIPMENT

Other equipment that is worked on during boiler erection are precipitators, absorbers, fans and the stack. The precipitator is located downstream of the steam generator proper and removes the solid particulate from the flue gases. It rests on a structural-steel frame which is also tied into the main support members for the precipitator. The hoppers are erected first and lowered into the steel from above with a crawler crane. The hoppers are usually subassembled on the ground and erected as one piece. The main supports, sides and internal

bracing are put up next along with the inlet and outlet ductwork. The collecting and discharge electrodes, or other types of internals, are then erected. The inner roof, weather roof, and electrical components finish the main sections. Work on alignment, wiring and checkout is required before the unit is complete. Fig. 23 shows a nearly finished precipitator.

Absorbers, such as the one shown in Fig. 24, are installed as required by local environmental regulations necessitating removal of sulfur oxides from the stack gases. Because of the large amount of ductwork and tanks, it is usually easier to erect the absorber at the same time as its structural-steel support framing. Fig. 25 shows the tanks with much of the ductwork in place. Once the main sections are up, the internal piping and spray sections can be installed. Because of the potentially corrosive atmosphere inside the absorber, a noncorroding material, such as austenitic stainless steel, is usually used. Such stainless steel requires special handling and welding requirements not needed on carbon-steel equipment.

On large utility units, there are usually two forced-draft fans that move combustion air through the air preheater and into the boiler

Fig. 25 Section of absorber steel and ductwork

Fig. 26 Induced-draft fans under construction

through the windboxes and two or more induced-draft fans that pull the hot gases from the boiler and into the stack.

Fig. 26 shows two induced-draft fans partially completed. Once the support foundations are poured, the lower rotor housing, bearing supports, and rotor are installed. Then the remaining inlet chambers and outlet boxes are put together and connected to the supply and discharge ductwork. Millwrights set and align the rotor, a critical job because of the close tolerances required.

ERECTION OF MECHANICAL EQUIPMENT

On some projects, the mechanical equipment is also included under the scope of the boiler erector. Most of this work proceeds while the boiler is being erected and includes the turbine generator, miscellaneous pumps and valves, the water-treatment systems, the boiler feed pumps, and the condenser to name but a few.

The turbine generator is a large section of the mechanical work and requires almost the same time span for erection as the boiler. Fig. 27 shows a turbine under construction with most of the components already in place. The overhead gantry crane (upper left corner of Fig. 27), one of the first pieces of equipment erected, is used to raise and set most of the turbine except the stator.

Because the stator is so heavy (200 to 400 tons), a special lifting rig is usually brought to the site just for this one lift. The design of the particular rig usually dictates where the stator will enter the building. Fig. 28 shows a stator entering through an access opening from the ground. This rig uses a system of "Lucker" grip-type jacks with steel cables to lift the stator from the railroad car and up approximately 70 ft to the turbine-pedestal floor. Once the stator is up to elevation (Fig. 29), special rolling beams are put under the stator. The stator can

Fig. 27 Turbine pedestal with most components set in place

Fig. 28 Stator lift rig with "Lucker" jacks used to raise stator from ground level to turbine floor be lowered a few inches onto special heavy-duty rollers and rolled from the lift frame onto the concrete turbine floor. The stator is transferred to the generator hole and lowered again using the upper section of the same lift rig.

HYDROSTATIC TESTING AND INSULATION

During hydrostatic testing, water is pumped into the complete water and steam circuits of the boiler and raised to the pressure of 1½ times the nominal operating pressure. This pressure is held for a specified period of time and then lowered to the design pressure and held there for another period. The entire boiler, including piping, valves, wall panels, and drums, is then inspected for leaks. If any are found, the pressure is dropped, the water is drained out, and the defect is repaired. The entire process is then repeated until no more leaks are apparent. A steam-generating unit is "built in accordance

Fig. 29 **Stator being prepared to be brought out onto the turbine floor**

with the ASME Boiler Code" only when it has successfully passed such a hydrostatic test of the entire unit, either in the shop or in the field.

The erector engages the services of a steam-boiler inspection and insurance agent who is responsible for verifying the inspection and assuring the integrity of the boiler to the owner. The owner usually has its own insurance representative on the job at the same time to look over the records and ensure that proper inspection and tests are performed.

Once the hydrostatic test is complete, the insulation and lagging installation can proceed. Insulation blankets or blocks are installed on all piping, waterwalls, drums and ductwork. Metal lagging is installed over the insulation for protection of equipment and personnel. A coating of refractory is troweled on the top side of the roof tubes and a steel "skin" casing is welded over the top.

If the unit is an outdoor unit, the lagging serves to protect the boiler from the weather as well as to provide a satisfactory appearance. If the unit is an indoor unit, the boiler is completely enclosed by an outer building. This is desirable in cold climates, making initial erection and subsequent maintenance easier in the winter months.

ERECTION-COMMISSIONING INTERFACE

With most of the major work done on the boiler, boilout and acid cleaning of the inside of the tubes can be done. Chemicals are circulated through the boiler for prescribed lengths of time and then drained from the boiler. These procedures remove internal scale from water-bearing systems and assure free water passage in all tubes, headers and drums. (See the following chapter for a description of boilout and acid-cleaning of high-pressure boilers.)

Installation of boiler-drum internals may now be completed and access openings closed.

The contractual responsibility for the erection phase is usually complete at this point; however, support crafts for assisting test and start-up engineers may be necessary to take care of items that require modification and/or replacement during commissioning.

CHAPTER 20

Basic Principles of Operation

The operation of a multi-million-dollar steam generator and its associated power-plant equipment requires the constant exercise of intuitive reasoning and sound engineering judgment. It is in *operation* that all of the factors that went into the design and construction of the facility are put to the test.

A principal objective of proper operation is sustained service between outages while, at the same time, obtaining the highest possible efficiency from all the plant components.

Operation of a steam generator is a balance of inputs to outputs: the better the balance, the smoother the operation. Producing steam from a boiler requires that the weight of water entering the boiler equal the steam leaving, and firing the furnace requires a balance of fuel and air. To equalize these inputs and outputs, one must understand the system, not just the network of hardware that comprises the system. This understanding is the principal ingredient of successful operation.

Too often in recent years, operators have confused operation with control-system management. The operator must realize that a control system is hardware assembled to make operation easier, faster, and safer. All large steam generators require operators, and the control of all major functions can be switched from automatic to operator control. To be effec-

tive an operator must know not only what he or she is doing but why it is done and what results from the operator's action.

SAFETY, A PRIME OPERATING CONSIDERATION

The prime consideration for all operation is the safety of people and equipment. Whenever there is any doubt about an unsafe condition, the operator must take immediate action to return the unit to a known safe condition even if it means tripping the unit.

The loss of a unit even during peak-load requirements is not as important as a human life or the downtime for a major repair and the two most dangerous conditions remain the same today as throughout the history of steam generation: the loss of water and the explosive mixture of fuel and air. Both result from an imbalance: the first from less water than steam produced, even if some of that steam is escaping through a tube leak; the second, from too little air for the fuel present.

Safe operation, then, is a result of comprehensive training programs for operators, well-designed furnace safeguard systems, and an effective preventative-maintenance program.

BASIC OPERATING PRINCIPLES

In this section, certain basic operating guidelines for overall effective operation of a large coal-fired unit are discussed.

STEAM TEMPERATURES

Maintaining desired primary and reheat steam temperatures requires considerable operator attention. Even the best control systems do not anticipate all of the factors affecting steam temperature. Despite the equipment installed for controlling superheater and reheater steam temperatures, certain conditions may produce abnormal steam temperatures.

For instance, with a new coal-fired unit, it may be necessary to operate for a considerable time before normal furnace seasoning allows the unit to make predicted steam temperatures. "Normal furnace seasoning" is often defined as the condition of furnace-wall slag or ash deposits which remains after sootblower operation. Low steam temperatures may also result from:

- insufficient excess air
- higher-than-design feedwater temperature
- reheater inlet temperature lower than specified
- an externally fouled superheater or reheater
- leaking desuperheater spray water
- poorly adjusted controls.

On the other hand, high steam temperature may result from:

- an "over-seasoned" furnace
- too high an excess-air percentage
- feedwater temperature lower than specified
- reheater inlet temperature higher than specified
- irregular ignition or delayed combustion
- poorly adjusted control equipment.

As already indicated, the operating variable with the greatest effect on steam temperature is the cleanliness of the radiant and convective heat-absorbing surfaces. Although all modern coal-fired steam generators are equipped with automatic sootblower systems, the judicious supplemental manual operation of certain blowers can improve overall unit operation. It can save valuable blowing medium and reduce required maintenance by minimizing the number of blowing cycles. To be most effective, a program requires periodic furnace observations. Based on such observations and performance results, selective sootblowing can lead to better steam-temperature control and reduce the possibility of troublesome accumulations in portions of the furnace.

BOILER EFFICIENCY

An effective operator is constantly striving to obtain maximum efficiency from a unit. To do this, he or she must be aware of the effect of all operating variables, and the adjustments required to maximize efficiency.

Two items within operator control that affect boiler efficiency are dry-gas loss and unburned-fuel loss.

DRY-GAS LOSS

Usually the largest factor affecting boiler efficiency, dry-gas loss increases with higher exit-gas temperatures or excess air values. Every 35° to 40°F increment in exit-gas temperature will lower boiler efficiency by 1 percent. A 1-percent increase in excess air by itself only decreases boiler efficiency by 0.05 percent. On most boilers, however, increased excess air leads to higher exit-gas temperature. Consequently, increases in excess air can have a twofold effect on unit efficiency.

Usually, coal-fired units are designed to operate with 20 to 30 percent excess air. To operate a boiler most efficiently, therefore, an operator must have a reliable means of assessing the quantity of excess air leaving the boiler. In-situ oxygen recorders that measure the oxygen at the boiler or economizer outlet, are the best information source. They must, however, be checked daily for proper calibration and maintained as necessary. The operator should sustain the required excess air by making sure the controls are in the correct mode or by manual bias of the fuel-to-air ratio.

UNBURNED-FUEL LOSS

On gas- or oil-fired units unburned-fuel loss should be negligible, whereas unburned loss on coal-fired units can be appreciable. The boiler manufacturer will predict unburned-fuel loss and these values can usually be maintained with correct operation. There is no easy way to continuously monitor unburned carbon in the ash. Obtaining such values involves the time and manual effort of laboratory analysis of a flyash sample. The significant point is that the laboratory feed back the information to the operators. If values are consistently high, the plant operations department should develop a program to pinpoint what is causing the high unburns and how to improve the condition.

Usually, high unburns can be traced to the mixing process of the fuel and air in the furnace. Once the source is found, attention must be focused on what corrects it. For example, one cause of poor mixing of fuel and air could be inadequate windbox to furnace pressure. If this is so, monitoring pressure to keep it in line is easier than waiting for the periodic feedback of laboratory results.

There are two other items having an effect on boiler efficiency that an operator can do little about. These are the moisture-in-fuel and hydrogen-in-fuel losses, and the steam-generator radiation loss.

MOISTURE LOSS

Although the moistsre loss of the stack gases is considerable, the loss comes from fuel moisture and hydrogen, and the moisture in the air, which are realities not within operator control. The moisture in coal consists of inherent moisture and surface moisture. Although attention to the care of coal from the mine to the coal bunker can minimize the surface-moisture pickup with resultant increase in boiler efficiency, this is seldom within the boiler operator's control. A reduction in exit-gas temperature will decrease the moisture loss as well as the dry-gas loss.

RADIATION LOSS

On large, well-insulated steam generators, the efficiency loss due to radiation is about 0.2 percent at full load. As the same total heat is lost throughout the load range, radiation loss increases with decreasing loads. Considering only radiation losses, operating several units at low load may be less economical than taking one off. But other things must be considered such as sudden additional load demands and the amount of fuel required to return the unit to service.

See Chapters 4 and 6 for further discussion of the above heat-loss items.

AIR HEATERS

As already noted, lower exit-gas temperature is the most positive means for increasing boiler efficiency. The limiting factor is usually the air heater and for purposes of this discussion, observations will be focused on the Ljungstrom® regenerative air heaters.

For maximum effectiveness the air heater must be kept clean, the baskets must be replaced when acid corrosion has deteriorated enough material to affect performance, and the seals must be adjusted to minimize air and gas leakage. Proper operation of air heaters requires certain instrumentation. Pressure-drop indicators across both the air and gas sides must be available to the operator as well as temperature indicators for gas and air, both entering and leaving. Pressure drops are the best guide on the need to operate the air-heater sootblowers. Once pluggage progresses too far, sootblowers will not remove the deposits and the air heater will have to be removed from service for cleaning.

Faulty operation causes most air-heater corrosion. The air-heater manufacturer supplies a chart with recommended average cold-end temperatures to keep the metal above the dew point for the amount of sulfur in the fuel. The "average cold-end temperature" is defined as the arithmetical sum of the temperature of the air entering the air heater plus the gas temperature leaving the air heater, divided by two. Consistent operation below the dew point rapidly corrodes air heater baskets. Steam or water air heaters or bypass ducts control the cold end temperature. (See Chapter 6.)

High exit-gas temperatures leaving the air heater are often an indication of air bypassing the air heater. This can be from poorly adjusted seals or excess pulverizer tempering air. Pulverizer systems for example, are designed to dry coal of a specified moisture. If the coal has less than designed-for moisture or the mills are at partial capacity, mill tempering air will bypass the air heater and result in higher exit-gas temperatures leaving the air heater.

THE ECONOMIC IMPACT OF OPERATION

The most effective way to achieve maximum boiler efficiency in day-to-day operation is to embark upon an education campaign for plant management, supervisory staff, operators and maintenance personnel. If everyone knows the economic impact of operational variables on fuel costs, this knowledge can lead to significant fuel savings.

Too often campaigns to improve efficiency are carried out by only one group. Tests are performed to collect data rather than to establish "bogies" for day-to-day operation. The people performing the tests do not communicate the results to the rest of the plant, but rather to the company files. It is important, then, to review test results with the unit operators and to establish operating procedures that will take advantage of what is learned from the tests.

Re-starts are expensive. It requires considerable fuel to get a unit up to pressure and bring it on line. Extra maintenance and on-line attention that keeps downtime to a minimum can pay off in fuel savings. Retaining heat in the boiler during a weekend shutdown when there is no demand for steam can save fuel. A boiler can retain a good deal of heat if its isolation dampers are in good condition and are closed tightly. One word of caution—purging requirements both before bottling and prior to light off must be adhered to. The loss of the unit because of an explosion will be infinitely more costly than any heat saving from failing to purge.

START-UP
FROM COLD CONDITION: GENERAL

Prior to light off of any boiler, a supervisor of operations should inspect the unit exterior. All doors should be checked, cleared of tags, and then shut. Valves should be correctly positioned for start-up in accordance with the steam-generator manufacturer's valve operating diagram. All areas must be free of debris that will hinder expansion. If repair work was done during the outage, special care must be taken to assure that no permanent ties were made to the furnace structure which will impair expansion. Account for all personnel.

At this point, safety tags can be removed from breakers. As the boiler is filling with treated water, all vents should be open, as noted on the manufacturer's valve operating diagram. On a thermal-circulation unit, the water level should be brought to where it just shows near the bottom of the water glass. On a Controlled Circulation® unit, the water level should be brought near the top of the gage glass; this will prevent the water from dropping from sight when the first boiler-water circulating pump is started. The drainable portions of all steam-circuit headers, connecting links and piping should be drained through lines free from back pressure. Reheater drains and vents are opened so that residual moisture will be boiled off. These reheater drains and vents will have to be closed prior to raising a vacuum in the condenser.

During warm-up and until the unit is carrying load, there will be little or no steam flow through the superheater and reheater. To protect the superheater and reheater metals, the temperature of the gas leaving the furnace should be limited to the manufacturer's recommendation, usually 1000°F. The firing rate must be limited to satisfy this requirement. Thermal-circulation boilers can be warmed up at a rate that does not exceed a saturated-steam temperature rise of 200°F per hour. Controlled Circulation boilers have no saturation steam temperature rise limitation, only the furnace exit-gas limitation previously stated. Most modern boilers have traversing thermocouples to monitor furnace exit-gas temperature during warm-up; older units may use temporary thermocouple probes for each start-up or have conservatively established firing limitations based on prior testing.

Before light off, the operator should check all instrumentation and furnace safety systems. Steam-generating units differ too much to be able to give detailed start-up procedures. The operator must be familiar with all manufacturer's instructions and the plant operating procedures.

Usually the equipment will start in this sequence. Air heaters and boiler-water circulating pumps (on positive-circulation units) will be started first. Next the induced-draft fans, followed immediately by the forced-draft fans. On most units, furnace draft will be established and then transferred to automatic draft control. Airflow is raised to at least 30 percent of full load airflow, and the unit purged for at least five minutes to remove any unburned fuel or combustible gases.

During start-up, airflow should be maintained at 30 percent of full load airflow to assure an air-rich furnace mixture and to prevent any settling out of explosive mixtures. Once the unit is purged, oil pumps may be started and gas or oil trip valves opened. At set intervals, the operator should check the proper function of any furnace safeguard system. Regardless of how much urgency there is for getting the unit returned to service, no interlock should be jumpered or bypassed.

Never attempt to light off any fuel nozzle without the required ignition-energy source for that nozzle. Any time an operator has doubt about safe combustion in the furnace, he or she should trip the fuel and purge the furnace before relighting.

As pressure is raised, periodic inspections are necessary to assure that the unit is expanding as it should. If oil is the warm-up fuel, air-heater sootblowers should be operated frequently to keep the heating surface clear of flammable deposits.

Once the unit is on line, load may be picked up as swiftly as pulverizers can be brought into service. The usual restriction in most power plants is the warm-up and load-rise limitations of the turbine. (See Chapter 7.)

START-UP
FROM COLD CONDITION:
DRUM-TYPE UNITS

On drum-type units, maintaining drum water level is of prime importance. Normally, the operator carries out this function in the manual mode until pressure is raised. Before light off, drum water level should be brought in sight. It is best to start firing with a low water level because, as the water starts heating, it will expand. Drum vent valves should be wide open so that the air will vent from the drum. Superheater and reheater should be drained of any condensate wherever possible and then the valves opened or closed according to the valve operating sheet.

For a Controlled Circulation boiler, two of the circulating pumps are started to initiate circulation. To minimize flashing of steam in the downcomers, additional pumps are not started until the boiler water reaches 250°F.

The unit is now fired in accordance with the established furnace safeguards. During the warming period, the economizer recirculating line valves are open. The water will swell as it is heated and the operator will manually blow down the boiler as required to maintain sight of the water in the gage glass.

The firing rate will be controlled to keep the furnace exit-gas temperature below the recommended value, usually between 900°F and 1000°F.

When drum pressure reaches 25 psig, it can be assumed that all air has been purged from the drum and water circuits. The operator can close the drum vent valves. As pressure increases, it is necessary to progressively throttle the superheater drains and vents and to increase the firing rate as required.

If there is evidence of steaming in the economizer by erratic drum control during feeding of water, the operator must be certain that the recirculation line is open. On thermal circulation units it may be necessary to feed more water than required to maintain level in sight and to blow down to control level.

Start rolling the turbine as soon as the minimum permissible start-up pressure and temperature, specified by the turbine manufacturer, are reached. When bringing the turbine to speed, the firing rate must continue to be controlled to prevent the furnace exit gas from exceeding its limit. Once the turbine is synchronized and minimum load established, this limit can be removed. The gas temperature probe is withdrawn and the firing rate increased as required. Usually by this time all superheater and reheater vents and drains are closed. If drum water level is still under manual control, it should now be placed on automatic control.

LOAD AND PRESSURE CONTROL

Opening or closing the turbine control valves increases or decreases the load on a drum-type unit. Changing the firing rate regulates the pressure. In theory, for increasing load the operator will open the turbine control valve. If no other action were taken, the flow to the turbine would increase and the superheater outlet pressure would decrease. Upon seeing the outlet pressure drop, the operator would increase the fuel and air inputs.

Because of the increased steam flow, the water level in the drum would change. Initially, the level would rise due to surging, but shortly it would fall rapidly because more steam is removed than water enters.

A trained operator will anticipate these interactions. As the turbine control valve is opened, the operator will simultaneously increase fuel, air and feedwater flow. A well-designed and executed operational control system will perform the same as will such a trained operator. In addition, there are many other considerations involved in a load change. The more experienced and trained the operator, and the more sophisticated the control system, the more anticipation there is to all the subsystems and hardware such that smooth operation results.

SHUTTING DOWN

Time requirements and procedures for shutting down a boiler depend on the nature of the shutdown (normal shutdown to cold, normal shutdown to hot standby, emergency shutdown) and whether the unit is to be entered.

For a scheduled shutdown, steam pressure can be reduced to the limit of the turbine before the unit is taken off line. Thermal circulation units should not exceed a cool-down rate of 150°F per hour of saturated steam temperature decrease. Controlled Circulation units can be rapidly cooled if the circulating pumps are left in service. Normally, the drum vents are opened at 25 psig and the boiler is not drained until water temperature is below 200°F.

SUPERCRITICAL-PRESSURE BOILERS

Although much of the discussion of drum-type operation pertains also to supercritical-pressure boilers, there are some differences. The supercritical boiler needs an even more precise balance of inputs to outputs, because it does not have the flywheel effect that the boiler drum affords the subcritical-pressure unit.

START-UP

Although the firing system start-up and operation are the same as for a drum-type unit, the fluid system start-up is completely different. The supercritical boiler is furnished with an integral start-up system. The unit is initially fired, warmed up, and brought to partial load on the bypass system.

The Combined Circulation® unit, one type of supercritical-pressure steam generator, isolates the waterwalls from the superheater with boiler throttling (BT) valves (Fig. 1). To gain good control at low flow, there are boiler throttling bypass (BTB) valves around the BT valves. For initial warm-up and supply of steam to the turbine, the BT and BTB valves are closed. To vent fluid, a separator is installed, external to the boiler, with a line from the waterwall to the separator valved off by a boiler extraction valve (BE). Since it is advantageous to start the turbine with low-pressure steam, steam pressure is reduced through the BE valve to the separator. There is a line from the top of the separator to bring the steam to the super-heater, with a check valve to prevent backflow during high-load operation. The check valve is referred to as a steam-admission valve (SA).

A line to the condenser called a water drain valve (WD) removes water and controls water level in the separator tank.

As the boiler is warming up, steam is produced in the separator tank, but very little steam goes to the turbine. A line from the top of the separator tank to the condenser carries the excess steam from the separator. A control valve called the spillover (SP) regulates separator pressure during start-up. For detailed guidelines on the start-up of supercritical units see the adjoining box, "Recommended Supercritical Unit Start-Up Procedures."

LOAD CONTROL

The method of controlling the operation of Combined Circulation supercritical boiler differs from the drum-type boiler. The turbine control valves do not regulate the load; rather the load is regulated by flow. To raise or reduce load, the operator varies flow with the boiler feed pump.

PRESSURE CONTROL

The pressure on a supercritical boiler is controlled by the turbine valves, which operate initially as back-pressure valves. The only

Fig. 1 Schematic diagram of a supercritical boiler

RECOMMENDED SUPERCRITICAL-UNIT START-UP PROCEDURE

1. The feed pump establishes a flow (5 percent of maximum continuous rating) through the economizer and the waterwall. The BT and BTB valves are closed. The flow is brought through the BE down to the separator. The flow continues through the WD valve to the condenser. The WD maintains level in the separator.

2. The boiler circulating pumps are running to provide protection for the waterwall.

3. The boiler is lit off and gradually the waterwall temperature is raised to the point that the turbine can be rolled.

4. As the temperature of the fluid from the waterwall rises, steam will be generated in the separator. Steam will flow through the SA valve and through the superheater. This excess steam is bled off through the SP valve to the condenser. The SP controls the steam pressure in the separator.

5. When the waterwall reaches the proper temperature, the turbine can be rolled and put on the line using steam from the separator. The flow is now through the economizer, the BE valve, the separator, the SA valve, and out through the superheater.

6. The next step is to raise the waterwall temperature high enough to prevent a dip in steam temperature when the boiler is transferred to once-through operation.

7. When the waterwall temperature reaches this point, the flow is transferred from the BE to the BTB valves. The boiler is now operating as a once-through boiler and the separator is no longer in use. The pressure in the waterwalls is controlled by the BTB valves.

8. The turbine valves are set for approximately 30-percent flow. As the load increases, the superheater pressure will gradually rise until it reaches full throttle pressure.

9. When the throttle pressure reaches the design valve, the turbine valves are placed on automatic to control boiler pressure.

variable that the turbine valves monitor is throttle pressure, approximately 3500 psig for most operating supercritical units. In normal operation (above 30 percent), these valves are the only boiler pressure control. To raise pressure, the valves close and to decrease pressure the valves open.

STEAM-TEMPERATURE CONTROL

The superheater outlet temperature on a supercritical-pressure boiler is controlled with firing rate which is increased to raise outlet temperature and decreased to lower it. Although this is an effective means of temperature control, the response time to correct a temperature deviation is too long for smooth operation.

To improve the response, desuperheater water is injected between superheater stages. The injection water is taken at the economizer inlet at full boiler feedwater temperature so there is no cycle efficiency loss. Although the injected water gives fast response, the ultimate temperature control is balancing firing rate to feedwater rate.

The injection water essentially bypasses the waterwalls and economizer. When the superheater temperature is high, the operator or control system will reduce the firing rate and open the spray valves simultaneously until the temperature returns to the desired level.

Usually, for a Combined Circulation unit, adjusting the reheater outlet temperature follows the same procedure as for a drum-type unit. With a C-E tangentially fired unit, the process involves tilting the fuel and air nozzle and maintaining furnace cleanliness by sootblowing.

CLEANUP

Because a supercritical unit has no steam drum to separate the impurities in the waterwalls from the essentially pure steam in the superheater, a waterwall cleanup procedure must precede each start-up. The procedure involves circulating condensate through the polisher, feedwater heater train, economizer, waterwalls, separator, and drain system back to the condenser. The water is monitored for iron concentrations with the flushing continuing until the manufacturer's limits are obtained.

PULVERIZER OPERATION

Although several types of pulverizers are used to grind coal for power-plant service, the majority used in modern steam generation are a rotating bowl-type using direct firing. Refer to Chapter 12 for a description of this pulverizer.

In operation, four areas must be understood and monitored, the foremost being lubrication of the gearing and bearings. Airflow, mill temperature and fineness are the other three.

LUBRICATION

With the exception of the roller journals and exhauster (if so equipped), the mill is completely lubricated from one system in the worm gear housing. The worm-shaft bearings are flood oiled from a bath of oil in the gear case. The circulation is either by an external pumping system or by an internal pump that is a part of the gearing system. The lubricant must meet the manufacturer's specifications and be non-foaming and noncorrosive.

Periodic inspection of the gear-housing oil

A - Gear Case Level Gage
B - Optical Oil Flow Indicator
C - Oil Supply Header Pressure Gage
D - Oil Supply Header Pressure Switch
E - Sump Oil Temperature Thermometer

Fig. 2 Simplified pulverizer diagram showing lube-oil system temperature is required. For most of the recommended lubricants, oil temperature is maintained at about 150°F. If it is above this temperature, the oil level may be too low; if so, it should be promptly refilled with oil of the same manufacture and type as already in the housing. High oil temperature could also result from a breakdown of the lubricant or sludging. If so, change the oil. It could also be because of scale formation in the cooling coil, insufficient quantity of cooling water, or temperature of the inlet cooling water too high.

The operator should check the oil in the return glass after each mill start-up, and daily for mills in continuous service.

MILL OPERATION

To place a mill in service, start the mill, allow it to come up to speed, and bring mill outlet temperature up to recommendations before starting the feed of coal. Make sure there is proper ignition energy adjacent to the fuel nozzles supplied by the mill being put in service. Start the feeder with a fairly high feed rate setting. After the mill begins to grind, reduce the feed rate to the desired amount. The feeder drive must be interlocked with the mill motor so that, if the mill power is interrupted, the feeder will shut down.

Mill-outlet temperature should be maintained as high as possible without exceeding the safe limits of the type of coal ground. This temperature may be as low as 130°F with lignites and as high as 180°F for low-volatile bituminous coals. Low mill-outlet temperatures often indicate mill overload which is usually accompanied by other indications such as high motor amperage or high mill differential pressure.

PULVERIZER FIRES

Pulverizer fires can range from nondestructive to highly destructive, dependent mainly on how soon the fire is detected and what action the operator takes. Basic causes of pulverizer fires are excessive mill temperatures; foreign combustible material such as rags, paper or wood; settling out of coal in the pulverizers, or excessive accumulations of pyrites or coal in the mill base area.

If detected early, the fire can usually be extinguished easily by shutting off the supply of hot air, increasing or keeping the coal feed constant, and adding water or an inert gas.

Generally, an uncontrolled increase in mill outlet temperature signals a fire so it is important that a fast-responding thermocouple, set up to alarm, monitors the mill-outlet temperature. Any rapid increase in the temperature calls for immediate action. The mill hot-air gate should be shut at once and the cold air increased to keep airflow at design. The coal feeder should be placed on hand control, and the coal feed increased to the maximum without overloading the mill.

After this action, if the mill-outlet temperature does not drop within a couple of minutes, water or an inert gas such as CO_2 can be injected into the mill. When the mill temperature has lowered and all signs of fire disappeared, the feeder may be stopped, but the mill should remain running to purge the system completely. Next, the mill should be stopped, and the entire milling system inspected and cleaned of any accumulations. Check the lubricants in the mill base and rollers for any evidence of carbonizing. Recheck compression of journal springs by means of a hydraulic jack. If everything is satisfactory, the mill may be returned to service.

During normal pulverizer operation the pulverizer system has a fuel-rich mixture and an explosion is unlikely to occur. Most pulverizer explosions occur during initial feed of coal to the mill, interruptions of coal feed, or when shutting off the feed of coal. A mill explosion requires an explosive mixture and a source of ignition. This source can be from a fire in the mill, smoldering coal or an overheated mill. This is why it is so important to continue the feed of coal during a mill fire and until the fire has been extinguished. Coal has been known to smolder for many hours after a mill fire. Consequently, the careful inspection of all internal sections of a pulverizer system which has experienced a mill fire is necessary.

Before starting the coal feeder to a mill, it is

important that the mill outlet temperature be no higher than its normal operating temperature.

SLAGGING AND FOULING

Chapter 3 describes ash characteristics and their effect on slagging and fouling. This section will cover what the operator can do to control slagging and fouling. Successful boiler operation depends to a significant extent on the ability of the operating staff to understand how certain operating variables relate to fuel properties and furnace-sizing criteria. Consequently, Chapter 3 on ash characteristics and Chapter 7 on furnace design must be understood if slag is to be controlled.

Those operating variables that influence slagging and fouling are unit load, excess air, fuel fineness, and secondary-air distribution. Changing any one, however, will not eliminate operating problems completely. Although the individual variables affect boiler performance, they must be studied collectively to determine the effectiveness of a given program. This normally requires thorough testing, which may be accomplished best with the assistance of the steam-generator supplier.

LOAD

The higher the load, the higher the heat input to the furnace, and the greater the potential for slagging and fouling; therefore, the most direct way to reduce slagging is to curtail load. But this is not always possible, because the rated output may be necessary to meet electric-generation or process requirements. Changes in excess air, fuel fineness, and secondary-air distribution are less-drastic methods for minimizing slagging and fouling.

EXCESS AIR

At high oxidation states, iron compounds in the ash melt at a higher temperature than at lower oxidation states. Therefore, for bituminous coals, which are frequently high in iron content, there is a significant difference in fusion temperatures measured in reducing (oxygen-starved) and oxidizing (oxygen-rich) atmospheres. Subbituminous coals normally contain less iron and exhibit a smaller difference in melting temperatures produced in oxidizing and reducing environments. This means that, if slagging is a problem with high-iron coals, furnace deposits can be reduced dramatically by increasing the amount of excess air. As a rule of thumb, the higher the fusion temperature, the drier the slag in the furnace, and the easier it is to remove.

FUEL FINENESS

Slagging conditions often can be improved by proper control of pulverizer fineness and classification. Since coarse coal particles take longer to burn, they are more prone to producing slag. High retention on the +50 mesh often increases slagging tendencies. See Chapter 12 for a detailed discussion of the fineness recommended for optimum pulverized firing of various ranks of coal.

SECONDARY-AIR DISTRIBUTION

Because several different types of firing systems are in use, it is difficult to generalize on the subject of air distribution in the combustion zone. Basically, the objective is to provide good mixing of fuel and air so combustion is efficient, and local zones with reducing atmospheres are avoided. In units with tangential firing, for example, slagging sometimes can be reduced by increasing secondary airflow to fuel compartments.

OTHER OPERATIONAL MEASURES

If the coal contains a substantial amount of ash with a tendency to slag and/or foul heat-transfer surfaces, particular attention must be given to equipment capable of cleaning the furnace walls and convection-tube banks. Failure to remove deposits at the proper time may result in a chain reaction of deteriorating events. For example, excessive furnace slagging results from not using the wall blowers at proper intervals. This condition imposes higher gas temperatures in the convection sections because of the reduced rate of heat absorption in the furnace.

In turn, the higher gas temperature causes the flyash to become sticky, increasing deposition in the convection sections. Depending on gas temperature and ash properties, the retractable sootblowers may not be able to remove these deposits. Ultimately, sections of the convection pass may become plugged. Unless load is reduced at this point, it may not be possible for the induced-draft fans to maintain the proper amount of excess air. This causes additional slagging, and the cycle repeats.

Modern sootblower systems have programming techniques so proper sequential operation of the blowers—on an automatic basis—can be established after ash-deposition patterns are verified during preoperational tests. Through programming, ash deposits on the furnace walls generally can be held to a minimum, and combustion gases cooled sufficiently before they enter the convection pass.

SOOTBLOWER OPERATION

A major guideline to reliable sootblower operation is that plant personnel should not wait until large deposits develop before operating blowers. Waiting too long between operations can seriously hamper the effectiveness of sootblowers. Observation of furnace conditions at least twice per shift helps eliminate unexpected problems (Fig. 3).

For maximum effectiveness, the blowing se-

Fig. 3 Operators must observe fires, evaluate slagging, and listen for tube leaks.

quence must be established to favor those sections of the furnace that foul easiest. Only by careful observation can these areas be identified. If some areas of the furnace are particularly prone to fouling, supplemental remote-manual operation of selected blowers can save valuable blowing medium and reduce system maintenance by minimizing the number of blowing cycles. In addition, the sootblower manufacturers,who offer many variations in nozzle arrangement, size and incidence angle may help solve some of the problems.

Because the sootblower system is so important for reliable, full-power operation of a coal-fired unit, this equipment must be maintained in good operating condition. Realize that blowing pressure can change, especially if valve travel is used for pressure regulation. Thus, air or steam pressure should be checked frequently with blowers of this type, especially when furnace observation shows a buildup in deposits. Sootblowers with adjustable orifices are not so sensitive and will usually retain their settings indefinitely.

FEEDWATER/BOILER WATER

Because internal tube corrosion and deposition are major causes of costly forced outages, operators must be continually alert to the hazard of water neglect. All plants must establish and adhere to a feedwater and boiler-water treatment and control for their system. Chapter 11 describes the chemistry of water treatment in detail. Rather, this section describes the cautions that must be taken to minimize corrosion and deposition.

OXYGEN CONTROL

Oxygen control is the most important element in feedwater control. Oxygen concentration in the feedwater must be regulated to minimize the formation of preboiler corrosion products which inevitably end up as deposits on heat-transfer surfaces in the boiler.

Oxygen levels are more likely to exceed recommended limits during start-up, shutdown, and low-load operation. At these times low-pressure feedwater heaters and related extraction piping are often under negative pressure, and any leaking valves, pumps or flanges will provide a path into the system.

Excess oxygen is removed from the system by the deaerator, not through chemical additives. Such deaerators have manufacturer's guarantees for levels of oxygen leaving the deaerator.

Oxygen leaving the deaerator should meet these guarantees at all times or the manufacturer should be contacted for his recommendations to bring it back in line. Adequate steam should be available to the deaerator during unit start-up so oxygen is purged from the feedwater. If adequate auxiliary steam is not available because there are no other sources of steam in the station, peg the deaerator with steam from the boiler drum until turbine extraction steam is available.

To minimize the formation of preboiler corrosion products, the oxygen concentration in feedwater should be maintained at less than about 5 parts per billion (ppb) during unit operation. But acceptable feedwater oxygen levels during steady-state operation do not necessarily mean that oxygen concentration is within safe limits. During various phases of operation, conditions can exist that may result in excessive amounts of oxygen. Thus, use of dissolved-oxygen monitors is important, particularly during load swings and start-up operations. And do not be lulled into a false sense of security if oxygen levels are excessive only for a short time. Considerable damage can still occur, a fact that those responsible for plant operation must be aware. Periodically, plant procedures and controls should be evaluated to ascertain that all sources of oxygen contamination have been eliminated.

pH CONTROL

Of equal importance with oxygen is the control of boiler-water pH. Small deviations from the recommended boiler-water limits will result in tube corrosion. Large deviations can lead to the destruction of all furnace wall tubes in a matter of minutes.

CAUSES OF HIGH AND LOW PH

The primary cause of acidic and caustic boiler-water conditions is condenser leakage. Raw cooling water that leaks into the condenser eventually ends up in the boiler water. The water source determines whether the in-leakage is either acid-producing or caustic-producing. Fresh water from lakes and rivers, for example, usually provides dissolved solids that hydrolize in the boiler-water environment to form a caustic, such as sodium hydroxide. By contrast, seawater and water from recirculating cooling-water systems with cooling towers contain dissolved solids that hydrolize to form acidic compounds.

Strict tolerance levels on condenser leakage should be established for all high-pressure boilers. Set a limit of 0.5-ppm (parts per million) dissolved solids in the feedwater for normal operation; allow from 0.5 to 2 ppm for short periods only. Shut down the steam generator immediately if the surface-condenser leakage produces more than 2 ppm of dissolved solids in the feedwater.

Another potential source of acidic and caustic contaminants is the makeup demineralizer, where regenerant chemicals such as sulfuric acid and caustic may inadvertently enter the feedwater system. Chemicals incorrectly applied during boiler-water treatment also can be corrosive, as for example sodium hydroxide used in conjunction with sodium-phosphate compounds to treat boiler water. Corrosion can occur if the sodium hydroxide and sodium phosphate are not added to the water in the proper proportion.

IMPORTANCE OF WATER ANALYSIS

A comprehensive water-analysis program should be maintained to assure that feedwater and boiler-water chemistry is held within prescribed limits. Continuous, automatic analytical instrumentation is preferred. If automatic analyzers are unavailable or are not operational, conduct water tests daily for pH and oxygen in the feedwater and for pH, PO_4 and total solids in the boiler water. A condenser leak-detection system is of particular importance in any high-pressure steam cycle. When installing this type of system on multishell condensers, individual analyzers must be provided for each shell.

The operator must remember that many potential tube failures can be avoided by continuous attention to the control of the water and steam environment throughout the station.

COMMISSIONING FUNCTIONS

Before a new unit can be put in service, the entire system must be cleaned to remove oil, grease, siliceous material, mill scale, rust, and any other debris. The condensate and feedwater system is cleaned before the boiler so that none of the debris or dirt is carried into the boiler. This part of the system is mechanically cleaned, then given an alkaline flush and sometimes, an acid wash.

The economizer and boiler will be given an alkaline boilout followed by an acid cleaning.

Finally, the superheater, steam piping and reheater will be cleaned by a three-phase scavenging with steam. It is important that each of these processes be conscientiously undertaken and result in as clean a system as is possible. If not, operating problems are sure to develop when the unit goes into service.

PREBOILER CYCLE

All preboiler systems of high-pressure boilers must be thoroughly flushed with a hot alkaline solution to remove oils, siliceous materials and particulate matter which are present following fabrication, storage and erection. It is important that these materials be removed prior to initial operation; otherwise, they will be carried into the boiler. Optimum plant operating conditions will be realized rapidly after start-up if the preboiler equipment is satisfactorily cleaned.

The condensate system, feedwater system and the shell side of all heaters should be included in the alkaline cleaning. This cleaning involves the following basic operations:

1. Manual cleaning of the condenser, all feedwater heaters and the deaerator storage tanks.

2. Gross flushing to waste to remove the bulk of loose material.

3. Preheating of circulation water to increase temperature to 200°F.

4. Circulation of alkaline solution at 200°F (0.5 percent tri-sodium phosphate, Na_3PO_4).

5. Rinse to remove alkaline material.

6. Wet lay-up solution addition and circulation to protect metal surfaces until initial operation.

Cleaning the preboiler cycle normally requires the installation of temporary piping to establish circulation through the system. It is also desirable to install temporary piping to bypass portions of the system, such as the boiler feed pump and deaerator storage tank, which may be damaged by or trap large quantities of loose particulate material. Circulation is normally established with a condensate pump which takes suction from the condenser hotwell, or a special pump of equivalent capacity. Flow is through the condensate and feedwater systems and is returned to the hot-well through temporary piping or through the shell side of heaters. Strainers are placed at the suction of all pumps used during cleaning to protect them from suspended particles. The strainers are checked periodically during the circulation period and cleaned if necessary.

The condenser, condenser hot-well and deaerator storage tank have to be mechanically cleaned to remove loose debris before any chemical cleaning is started. Mechanical cleaning will consist of sweeping and hosing down all surfaces, and removing all loose material by vacuuming, shoveling, or any other convenient means.

A solution containing 5,000 ppm tri-sodium phosphate (5 lbs Na_3PO_4 per 1,000 lbs H_2O) and a detergent are recommended for the hot alkaline cleaning of the preboiler cycle. The cleaning is carried out at about 200°F. Samples are obtained periodically and tested for silica and oil concentrations. The cleaning is continued until the chemical checks indicate no further increase in the silica and oil concentrations. This process is normally accomplished in 6 to 8 hours.

Following the alkaline cleaning, the system is thoroughly rinsed to remove the alkaline material, and refilled with condensate of demineralized water containing 100 ppm hydrazine for wet lay-up of those systems containing copper alloys.

In completely copper-free systems (supercritical boilers), 200 ppm hydrazine and 10 ppm ammonia should be added to the water for wet lay-up. The system should be isolated and stored wet under nitrogen until ready for the next phase of start-up, usually chemical cleaning of the boiler.

CHEMICAL CLEANING OF BOILERS

The internal surfaces of a boiler in contact with water or steam must be kept clean to assure an efficient transfer of heat in the generation of steam. Several cleaning procedures are available to assure a removal of foreign matter introduced into the boiler during the manufacturing process, erection of the equipment and in operation. The general cleaning processes are alkaline boilout and acid washing.

Alkaline boilout removes contaminants commonly found in a boiler following its shop assembly or field erection: lubricants, oil, rust, sand, metal fragments and assorted debris.

Acid cleaning removes scales and deposits formed on internal heat-transfer surfaces in contact with water. This procedure dissolves compounds resulting from contaminants in the feedwater delivered to the boiler. Acid cleaning is also used to remove mill scale and corrosion products.

ALKALINE BOILOUT

The basic reason for an alkaline boilout of a boiler is to remove water- and alkali-soluble and saponifiable compounds from the water side surfaces of the unit. These compounds may include lubricants used in the erection of the boiler and in some instances, protective coatings applied to prevent atmospheric rusting following shop fabrication.

Most lubricants used in boiler construction are water soluble and do not offer any difficulty to removal during boilout. Non-water-soluble oils and greases are introduced in small quantities into the boiler from oil-lubricated equipment and workmen's clothes. Every effort should be made to minimize the introduction of oil and grease into the boiler because the quantity of these materials determines the length of cleaning and the degree of difficulty in obtaining clean surfaces.

Sand, loose mill scale and corrosion products formed on the tube surfaces during erection and following the hydrostatic test are removed by blowdown during boilout.

Chemicals Used for Boilout

The chemicals used for boiling out a steam generator vary in composition. Generally, some combination of the following chemical compounds is used during an alkaline boilout: caustic soda, soda ash, sodium phosphate, sodium sulfite and sodium nitrate. Sodium sulfite reduces oxygen corrosion and sodium nitrate is added to prevent the possibility of caustic embrittlement. Soda ash and sodium phosphate are most commonly used because of the ease of handling. Potassium salts can be substituted for the sodium form.

Organic detergents are added to improve the effectiveness of the alkaline boilout. These materials must be used with care and according to the supplier's recommendation. Their indiscriminate use may lead to foaming and carryover of chemical to the superheater. The temperature stability of the organic detergent should be ascertained before use in a boiler.

The amount of detergent normally used ranges from 0.05 to 0.1 percent by volume.

The use of sulfite and nitrate is a refinement in the boilout procedures. Using them has not been shown to be a prime necessity. The principal chemical action is the reaction of the alkaline chemicals with non-water-soluble oils and greases. Exprience has shown that an effective boilout for drum-type boilers can be attained by any of the following combinations:

1. Soda ash — 4000 ppm
   Sodium phosphate — 4000 ppm
2. Sodium hydroxide — 2000 ppm
   Sodium carbonate or
   Sodium phosphate — 2000 ppm

3. Sodium phosphate   5000 ppm
   Caustic soda   500 ppm
4. Sodium carbonate   2000 ppm
   Sodium phosphate   4000 ppm
   Caustic soda   2000 ppm

The first combination is most commonly recommended for boilout of high-pressure boilers. In some instances, a chemical such as sodium silicate is included in the boilout formula. Although this is an effective additive, it is not recommended for use in high-pressure boilers. High silica concentrations have been observed during initial operation when metasilicate was used in the boilout formula.

For once-through boilers, the boilout solution is composed of 5,000 to 10,000 ppm of sodium phosphate. Other formulations and combinations of chemicals can be satisfactorily employed for boilout, as dictated by local water-pollution control requirements. Such revised formulations should be reviewed by the boiler manufacturer prior to use.

Boilout Procedure

Preparatory to boiling out, the chemicals to be added to the boiler should be dissolved completely before introduction into the unit. In thermal (natural) circulation units, these chemicals are most suitably introduced into the boiler by blending them with water as the unit is being filled. This insures a homogeneous concentration throughout the boiler. In positive (pumped) circulation boilers, the boilout chemicals may be pumped into the boiler without concern about proper mixing with the fill water. The boiler-water circulation pumps will insure proper mixing.

Gradual heating of the boilout solution in the boiler is accomplished by the use of ignitors and warm-up burners. This assures a more even heating of the boiler surfaces. Steam pressure is raised to increase the saturation temperature and, thereby, the thermal circulation of the boiler water; this promotes good mixing of chemicals in the boiler circuits. The boiler pressure is raised to about one fifth of the normal operating pressure, or 300 psig, which ever is lower. A pressure of not less than 100 psig is recommended for lower-pressure industrial boilers. Excellent results have been obtained in boiling out at a pressure range of a few pounds to 100 psig with positive-circulation boilers, in which the ability to circulate is not related to pressure.

The quantity of oil and grease found in a boiler determines the duration of the boilout with boilout periods of 8 to 24 hours being common. During the pressure-holding period, boiler-water solids are purged by blowdown at about 4-hour intervals. A chemical balance is re-established at the end of each purging of boiler water if the chemical concentration decreases to below one-half of the initial value. At the completion of boilout, the boiler is cooled slowly, drained, flushed free of residues, and inspected for cleanliness. If the boilout was unsuccessful and oil and grease are still present, subsequent acid cleaning of the boiler will be ineffective. If an internal inspection still shows oil or grease in the drum, the boilout procedures should be repeated.

ACID CLEANING

As an important part of the commissioning of a new unit, initial acid cleaning is included in this section. But as there will be future needs for acid cleaning to remove operational deposits, the discussion incorporates both initial acid cleaning and future acid cleanings.

Removal of preoperational and operational deposits from the internal surfaces of steam-generator tubing and other components has become an increasingly important maintenance problem in modern equipment. Because mechanical cleaning is virtually impossible in modern boilers, the effective application of chemical-cleaning solvents has become a necessary tool of the power-plant operator.

The primary reasons for boiler chemical cleaning are to prevent tube failures and to improve unit availability. Tube failures in low-pressure boilers are normally the result of creep which occurs when internal deposits produce excessive metal temperatures. A much smaller quantity of deposit will create difficulties in high-pressure boilers. Caustic corrosion and hydrogen damage, which only occur in the presence of deposits, can cause tube failures at temperatures well below the creep limit. Deposits originating both from fabrication and during operation must be considered potential problems.

Boiler manufacturers recommend that boilers operating above 900 psig be acid cleaned prior to initial operation. Also, because of the nature of chemical-recovery-boiler operations, the recommendation dictates that the lower 450 and 600 psig units be acid cleaned initially.

Mill and Operational Scale

All of the pressure parts of a steam generator may be subjected to heat treatment of some sort during fabrication or erection—during forming operations, stress relief, welding, or bending. Whenever carbon or low-alloy steels are subjected to high temperatures in the presence of air, oxidation occurs; the oxide produced is known as mill scale Fig. 4. Mill scale on boiler tubing is normally very thin with the exception of areas near welds and bends. Even where mill scale is initially uniform, its brittleness upon cooling can produce flaking. The resulting non-uniform surface is undesirable from the standpoint of corrosion susceptibility. During operation, mill scale can be readily eroded from the steam-generating surfaces and sub-

Fig. 4 **Typical mill-scale thickness on tubes installed in modern high-pressure boilers. Scale thickness illustrated 0.5 mils, at 75X**

sequently redeposited in critical areas. Preoperational acid cleaning removes the mill scale and serves to remove atmospheric rust which inevitably accumulates during erection.

The type of operational scale found in steam generators is related to the quality of feedwater supplied to the boiler. In industrial boilers, the principal deposits are calcium and magnesium phosphates, calcium and magnesium silicate, complex silicates as acmite or analcite, quartz, oxides of iron and copper, and organic matter. In utility boilers, the principal deposits are corrosion products, and iron and copper oxides.

Chemical Cleaning Procedures

Only experienced personnel with up-to-date equipment and a detailed procedure to follow should perform chemical cleaning operations.

The procedure should include:

1. The system layout with proper identification of all equipment to be used.

2. A step-by-step description of the functions to be performed. These should be specific for the solvent used for the cleaning.

3. Precautions to be taken against possible inadvertent contamination of equipment not included in the cleaning system.

The utility operators, cleaning vendor, and boiler manufacturer must cooperate closely for a successful operation. Mutual prior approval of cleaning procedures and assignment of responsibility are desirable. Although respective responsibilities may vary from job to job, they can be generally classified as follows:

1. Normally, the cleaning vendor will supply all of the chemicals and equipment necessary to deliver the solvent to the boiler at a controlled concentration and temperature. Vendor personnel will generally operate the equipment and supervise the overall cleaning. They will perform the necessary chemical analyses during solvent introduction and monitor the spent solvent to determine when the cleaning has been completed.

2. Utility personnel must operate all permanent plant equipment. They are responsible for determining metal temperatures and maintain-

ing proper temperatures throughout the cleaning period. The utility normally supplies the necessary water and steam and sets up the solvent-delivery and waste-disposal systems. An important operator responsibility is to assure that the solvent is not inadvertently introduced to any other part of the steam plant.

3. The boiler manufacturer has the responsibility to provide a boiler that can be cleaned safely and effectively. The boiler must be designed with an adequate filling, draining, and venting capacity. The boiler manufacturer should establish a standard cleaning procedure for the specific boiler that should emphasize the hazards involved and the limitations on the use of specific components. They should be informed of any unusual use of boiler components and be ready to review any cleaning procedures that involve unusual steps or solvents.

The precautions relative to acid cleaning are common to all solvents currently used in practice. The metal temperature of the boiler is raised either by heating water using auxiliary burners or by circulating water which has been increased in temperature by the addition of live steam. The addition of heat by the use of burners is prohibited when the boiler is filled with inhibited hydrochloric acid. This is to prevent a destruction of any inhibitor due to localized application of heat. A similar precaution is required when organic acids are used for cleaning purposes. The only exception is when an organic alkaline solvent (e.g.; such as ammonium EDTA) is used for cleaning the boiler. The boiler is fired to raise the solvent temperature to approximately 275°F.

Selection of Cleaning Solvents

Solvents are selected for their ability to remove boiler deposits. Hydrochloric acid remains the principal solvent used in chemical cleaning. Its wide use is largely related to its lower cost, its availability, and its versatility. It has the ability to remove most of the various deposits normally encountered in boiler tubes even in a stagnant condition.

Although hydrochloric acid is commonly employed for dissolving iron oxide, some organic acids and organic alkaline solvents can also effectively perform the same function. These latter solvents are particularly useful in situations where specific circumstances prohibit the use of hydrochloric acid. Some of the solvents which have been developed, extensively evaluated, and employed in boiler cleanings are (1) ammoniated citric acid (ammonium citrate), (2) formic-hydroxyacetic (glycolic)

Table I. Effect of Velocity on Scale Removal of Various Solvents

Solvents and Cleaning Conditions	Static	Velocity				
		0.03 fps	0.1 fps	1 fps	2 fps	3 fps
Hydrochloric acid (5%) 6 hrs, 160–170°F	C	C	C	C	C	C
Phosphoric acid (3%) 6 hrs, 212°F	C	. . .	C	C	C	. . .
Ammonium citrate (3%) 6 hrs, 200–220°F	U	U	U	C	C	C
Formic hydroxyacetic acid (3%) 6 hrs, 275–280°F	. . .	U	U	C	C	C
Ammonium EDTA (3%) 6 hrs, 275–300°F	. . .	U	U	C	C	C

NOTE: U = Scale not removed (estimated 20–100% of scale remaining)
       C = Scale completely removed (estimated 95–100% of scale removed)
           All samples 5–10 mils scale

acid, (3) ammonium EDTA, and (4) sodium EDTA.[1]

In general, the criteria used to select solvents include:

1. Materials of Construction—The inhibited solvent selected must be compatible with the tube material. For example, hydrochloric acid cannot be used to clean superheaters and/or reheaters because of the possibility of stress-corrosion cracking of stainless-steel materials.

2. Deposit Compositions—Deposit compositions could include iron oxide, copper, zinc, nickel, aluminium, silica, as well as solids from condenser cooling water. Large amounts of silica in the deposit present problems. Ammonium bifluoride is one additional chemical (in conjunction with the solvent) used to remove silica-based materials. Copper complexors must be used with hydrochloric acid to avoid copper plating during the cleaning if small amounts of copper are present. If there is a large amount of copper in the deposit (greater than 10 percent by weight) a multi-step procedure will be necessary. Ammonium bromate has been shown to be an effective solvent to remove deposits with significant amounts of copper.

3. Geometries—Organic solvents are effective under dynamic conditions, usually when velocities are greater than 1 ft/sec. The effect of velocity and circulation on various solvents is illustrated in Table I. Complex circuits such as found in some superheaters and reheaters require special attention to assure removal of all air pockets and positive flow in all circuits.

4. Methods of Disposal—Environmental regulations can greatly affect disposal. The costs and methods of disposing cleaning wastes have a strong influence in the selection of a solvent.

Tube samples should be taken and given to a chemical cleaning vendor to allow determination of the best solvent and cleaning procedure. The thickness, porosity, texture, and composition of the deposit all may affect individual solvent effectiveness and normal cleaning procedures may have to be modified. It is also a good practice to remove additional tube samples after the cleaning to verify that the cleaning was successful.

Determining the Need for Chemical Cleaning

Utility boilers should be cleaned at least once every 3 to 5 years. The empirical relationship given in Table II correlates the amount of deposit on a tube with the cleanliness of the boiler. Tube samples should be taken at yearly intervals from the high-heat-flux areas of the boiler (for example, several feet above the windbox) or other areas that have in the past been prone to deposition.

The information obtained from inspecting the tube samples, in conjuction with operational factors, is used to aid in deciding the need for cleaning. These factors include the number of start-ups, the number of periods with condenser leakage, chemistry deviations, and length of outages.

Table II. Relationship of Analyzed Deposit Quantity to Unit Cleanliness

Boiler Type	Internal Deposit Quantity Limits*		
	Clean Surfaces, mg/cm²	Moderately Dirty Surfaces, mg/cm²	Very Dirty Surfaces, mg/cm²
Supercritical units	Less than 15	15–25	More than 25
Subcritical units (1800 psig and higher)	Less than 15	15–40	More than 40

*All values are as measured on the furnace side of tube samples and include soft and hard deposits.

Note: For all practical purposes, 1 mg/cm² = ~ 1 g/ft².

Chemical cleaning of industrial boilers should also be performed on a periodic basis. The primary purpose for cleaning these units is to prevent buildup of deposits to the point where overheating may occur.

In cases where deposits consist of hardness salts, it is imperative to periodically examine tube samples from the unit to establish the need to clean.

In those units where iron oxide and copper are the main impurities in the feedwater, the information in Fig. 5 can be used as a guide in determining the need to clean. However, good practice would still dictate periodic examination of tube samples to confirm the analytical evaluation.

Acid Cleaning Procedure

In thermal (natural) circulation boilers, no effective circulation can be obtained at the low solvent temperature of 150°F to 170°F. Therefore, the distribution of acid strength and temperature is obtained by blending concentrated inhibited acid and hot water as the solution is injected into the boiler. Superheaters are flooded with condensate prior to the addition of acid to prevent the spillage of the solvent to this section. Thermal circulation boilers are

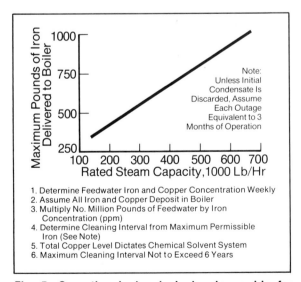

1. Determine Feedwater Iron and Copper Concentration Weekly
2. Assume All Iron and Copper Deposit in Boiler
3. Multiply No. Million Pounds of Feedwater by Iron Concentration (ppm)
4. Determine Cleaning Interval from Maximum Permissible Iron (See Note)
5. Total Copper Level Dictates Chemical Solvent System
6. Maximum Cleaning Interval Not to Exceed 6 Years

Fig. 5 Operational chemical cleaning guide for industrial-type boilers (based on demineralized or evaporated makeup water)

generally cleaned by the soaking process. Samples are taken periodically to check the degree of reaction in the boiler.

Boilers are soaked for a period of 4 to 6 hours. The acid is drained by pressurizing with nitrogen. This step is taken to prevent the oxidation of cleaned surfaces during this time. Water is used to displace nitrogen in rinsing the metal surfaces of acid. The rinse water is subsequently displaced with nitrogen. Two rinses are usually sufficient to attain a pH that is between 5 and 6.

The boiler is then filled with water contain-

AVOIDING SUPERHEATER CONTAMINATION

1. The entire cleaning piping layout should be examined to identify all possible areas where any solutions from the boiler could enter the superheater or reheater. Such connections should be eliminated so contamination of the superheater does not occur. Possible leaking valves and pressure levels that might result in backflow must be avoided.

2. Control and monitoring of drum level is of paramount importance.

3. Water used to fill or "backflush" the superheater should be demineralized or of condensate quality.

4. Possibility of preboiler (feedwater train) cleaning solutions "hiding-out" in lines, manifolds or tanks to be used, in, or interconnected to, water fill-lines should be considered before starting the preboiler cleaning operation.

5. Suspicion of contamination warrants a careful assessment of water (or condensate) quality at appropriate locations in the superheater (e.g., locations nearest point of suspected entry). If evidence of contamination exists, firing should be discontinued until a judgment can be made as to the seriousness of the contamination. If doubt exists, the prudent course of action is to water-flush (condensate quality) the superheater and/or reheater.

ing soda ash, 1.0 percent solution. The water is adjusted to the operating level and the temperature is raised to correspond to a pressure of about 100 psig. About 2 hours are required to effect neutralization of the acid and passivation of the metal. The boiler is drained and inspected at the conclusion of the wash period.

Controlled Circulation and Combined Circulation boilers can be cleaned efficiently because the circulation pumps can be used to equalize acid temperatures and concentrations throughout the boiler. The acid is circulated intermittently with one pump during the cleaning, which normally requires 4 to 6 hours.

Organic-type acids are frequently used to clean once-through boilers. At the conclusion of such a cleaning, the boiler is rinsed with water. When the system has then been purged of acid, condensate containing ammonia and hydrogen is circulated to effect neutralization.

Because of the close proximity of the superheater to the drum and the potential of corrosion from the cleaning solvents, particularly on the austenitic alloys, avoiding contamination of the superheater is important. If the superheater is known or suspected to be contaminated, the cleaning should be temporarily halted and the superheater flushed to remove the contaminants. The boiler should never be fired with suspected contaminants in the superheater. For precautions necessary to avoid superheater contamination see the accompanying box.

SUPERHEATER/REHEATER CLEANING AND FLUSHING

Although pre-operational cleaning of the steam-generating section in a high-pressure boiler is strongly recommended, superheater and reheater cleaning is not. The need to eliminate deposit-forming materials is related primarily to their effect on the corrosion problems that are common in waterwalls. We know of no case where the presence of initial mill scale has contributed to failures in superheaters and reheaters or difficulties in turbines. Normal mill

scale on tubing is thin, adherent, and not readily eroded by dry steam. Particulate matter and construction debris constitute the major portion of the foreign material present in any superheater or reheater at this point in its life. Because solvents do not efficiently dissolve most particulates, this method of cleaning is not considered completely satisfactory for placing a superheater and reheater in condition for operation. As steam blowing has proven effective in removing particulate matter, debris, loose oxide, and atmospheric rust, it is recommended for any pre-operational cleaning of superheaters and reheaters regardless of other procedures employed.

The need to clean a superheater or reheater at some point in its operating life by using well-engineered programs containing solvent techniques or water flushing cannot be overlooked. Because of the geometry, superheater and reheater cleaning requires special attention. Frequently, these sections contain nondrainable, nonventable sections that are difficult to clean unless the operator has a clear understanding of flow mechanics.

The problem in cleaning superheater or reheater surfaces is to assure that there is positive flow through all the parallel circuits. This is necessary for (1) effective cleaning, and (2) assurance that the solvent can be completely displaced at completion. This requirement applies even when simple water washing is employed for removal of soluble salts. Positive flow can be assured with a relatively low flow of water if the entire section can be initially filled. When a portion of the loop is nonventable, the difficulty exists because of trapped air. Air blockage which develops in nonventable areas will prevent effective cleaning and make it impossible to completely flush unless special procedures are employed to assure complete filling. Fig. 6 illustrates the filling problem. A well-engineered fill-flush program for the individual unit undergoing the cleaning, and the confirming of effective filling prior to cleaning solvent injection, are required if desired cleaning results are to be obtained and damage prevented.

POST-ACID-CLEANING ACTIVITIES

Before the main steam-lines are blown, the steam and lower drums should be inspected. The drums should be flushed of any loose sediment. The internals to the gage glass should be flushed and then blown out. Accessible headers should be inspected and flushed with clear water.

If the primary and secondary separators were not placed in the drum, they are installed. On Controlled Circulation units, each orifice and screen is installed in the lower drum. Each orifice is then checked with a go/no-go gage. Any header handhole caps which were removed or not previously welded are welded in place.

Acid cleaning connections are removed or valved off, and temporary piping removed. The chemical feed and continuous blowdown piping should be flushed and blown out. When all work is completed in the upper and lower drums, they must be inspected to ensure that there is no foreign material remaining. New gaskets should be installed on all drum manholes before closing.

Next, the boiler circulating pumps are prepared for operation as called for by the manufacturer's instructions.

STEAM-LINE BLOWING

The purpose of blowing the main-steam lines and the reheat-steam lines before starting up a new unit is to remove any foreign material remaining in the superheater, reheater and steam piping after erection is completed. Considerable damage can result if such material enters the turbine during initial operation.

On older units, the need for steam-line blowing should be considered following major pressure-parts repairs which introduce the possibility of foreign material into the system.

RESPONSIBILITY

Because prevention of damage to the turbine is the prime concern, the responsibility for determining the effectiveness of the steam-line blowing operation rests with the turbine manufacturer's representative. During this process the unit should be operated in accordance with recommended procedures, with all control systems and protective interlocks functioning.

The design, fabrication and installation of any temporary piping system used for the purpose of steam-line blowing, as well as protection against overpressure or overtemperature, require careful attention by qualified engineers.

GENERAL

Ideally, to obtain optimum cleaning, the flow conditions in the system during steam-line blowing should equal those during normal operation at maximum load. Because it is impossible to exactly duplicate these conditions when blowing through the piping to atmosphere, it is desirable to produce equivalent conditions by using lower pressure steam with a flow rate such that the product of steam flow times velocity will equal that under normal full-load conditions. The determination of the total obtainable flow quantity must be based on flow resistances in the entire system, including the temporary piping. Customarily the designer of the blowing system makes this determination. Most high-pressure units obtain satisfactory results with blowing pressure in the 600- to 800-psig range. The actual steam

Fig. 6 **Typical schematic of a nondrainable, non-ventable superheater section where air blockage will occur. (A) The air-blocked circuit(s) will remain stagnant because the unsupported water column H produces a pressure equal to and opposite to the pressure drop between headers P₁ and P₂. (B) Air blockage will be eliminated only when the flush rate is such that the pressure drop between the inlet and outlet headers because of flow exceeds the height of the unsupported water column H.**

blow is executed in three phases: main steam, cold reheat and hot reheat.

To prevent foreign material from being transported from one section and deposited in the next, it is important that the system be blown in sections, each section being blown separately. Particular care must be taken when blowing the reheater. If the reheater were to be blown immediately in series with the superheater, material too large to pass through the reheater tubes would remain lodged in the reheater inlet header and cause blockage of reheater tubes, with resulting overheating and failure of reheater tubing when the unit goes into operation. For this reason it is recommended that the temporary piping be arranged such that the main steam lines can be blown to atmosphere first. Similarly, the cold-reheat lines should be blown to atmosphere before they are connected to the reheater inlet header. Only after these precautionary measures should steam be admitted to the reheater for blowing through the hot reheat lines.

The temporary piping is often equipped with shutoff valves which are used as blowing valves. With this arrangement, the superheater and the upstream portion of the temporary piping are maintained at drum pressure at all times when not actually blowing. If the unit is equipped with main-steam stop valves, these may be used as blowoff valves, if the valve design permits this type of service. When more than one steam line is provided in any section, consideration should be given to arranging the temporary piping so that each line may be blown separately. In such situations, the piping system should be investigated to ensure that flow unbalances and expansion stresses at connections do not become a problem.

Impact specimens, installed in the blowoff piping during the final blows, give an indication of the cleanliness of the section. Polished square bar stock suitably mounted and supported has been used effectively for this purpose. The degree of pitting of the specimen surface following a blow determines the end point of the blowing cycle for the particular section.

PRECAUTIONS DURING STEAM-LINE BLOWING OPERATION

1. The process of steam-line blowing imposes abnormal and severe conditions upon the steam generator and steam piping. Large, rapid temperature changes occur during each blowing cycle. This cycling of temperature is far more severe than is incurred in normal operation. Thermal stresses may be excessive in the heavy-wall portions of the system, such as drums, headers and piping. It is prudent to consider this fact when performing the blowing procedure and to limit the number of blowing cycles ("blows") to the minimum consistent with cleaning the system.

2. Firing of all main fuel must be discontinued during all blows. It is permissible to keep ignitors and/or warm up guns in service during the blows in order to speed up reestablishment of the desired blowing pressure after a blow is completed. On Controlled Circulation boilers, circulating pump(s) must be kept in service during the entire blowing process. If a boiler circulating pump loses suction because of low drum water level, it must be shut down. If all pumps are stopped because of loss of suction, the blow must be terminated immediately.

3. Since the temporary steam-line blowing piping may be designed for lower pressure than the steam generator, care must be used to prevent overpressuring this piping during the entire steam-line blowing operation. The pressure in the temporary piping should be monitored continuously and the operators should be alert to prevent overpressure.
It is recommended that a means of overpressure protection be provided in the temporary piping, such as safety valves set at the design pressure of the temporary piping.

4. It is difficult to avoid carryover from the steam drum to the superheater during the steam-line blowing operation. Therefore, to avoid deposits of solid materials into the superheater, boiler water should not be treated with non-volatile chemicals during this process.

OPERATING PROCEDURES

The unit is started in the normal manner, following the cold start-up procedures. All normal recommendations and limitations with respect to pumps, fuel-firing equipment, ash-handling equipment, drains, and vents should be followed, as if the unit were being started for synchronizing the turbine. Before starting the first blow in each section, the economizer recirculating line valves should be closed. Because the steam-blowing operation is the first occasion that the unit is fired at any significant rate, the start-up as well as the steam-line blowing must be conducted with great care.

The unit must be brought up much slower than during subsequent normal start-ups, while all equipment is checked and expansion movements monitored closely. When the unit is fired, the furnace exit-gas temperature limitation must not be exceeded.

During the blows, the drum water level will be subject to extreme fluctuations. As the temporary blowoff valve is opened, the drum water level will rise rapidly and may disappear from sight in the gage glass. As the blow progresses, the drum water level will reappear and may drop out of sight so it is important that the drum water level is established at or slightly above normal operating level before the start of each blow. Feedwater flow must be established as soon as the water level drops back in sight, to prevent excessive low water level with resulting suction loss of the boiler circulating pumps. After the procedure is completed the temporary piping is removed, and final piping connections are made. The unit is now ready for the next commissioning function—setting safety valves.

SAFETY-VALVE SETTING

All safety valves installed on boilers or other pressure vessels should be test-operated before the boiler or vessel is placed in service. This test should involve a check of the proper functioning of the valves as to correct opening pressure, correct blowdown, proper mechanical operation without chatter, and clean closure without leakage.

BLOWING THE MAIN-STEAM LINE— PHASE I

The actual blow is started when the unit reaches the specified blowing pressure, usually 600 to 800 psig. However, the first blow is always at reduced pressure to check out the temporary piping system and its supports and anchors. All main-fuel firing is discontinued. The temporary valve or main-steam valve is opened fully to blow through the superheater, main-steam piping and the temporary blowoff piping to waste.

When the drum pressure drops to about 200 psig, the blowoff valve is closed. The firing rate is increased, and the cycle repeated as often as necessary until cleaning is satisfactory as indicated by inspection of the impact specimen.

BLOWING THE COLD-REHEAT LINE— PHASE II

The blowoff piping is now modified with a temporary connection from the main-steam piping around the high-pressure turbine to the inlet of the cold-reheat piping. Temporary blowoff piping is installed at the reheater inlet. Blowing is executed in the same manner as the main-steam line, but now the blow is through the superheater, main-steam line, cold-reheat line and the temporary blowoff piping to waste. Again, the first blow is at reduced pressure, with subsequent ones from 600 to 800 psig down to 200 psig drum pressure. This cycle is also repeated until the impact specimens are satisfactory.

BLOWING THE HOT-REHEAT LINES— PHASE III

The temporary blowoff line at the outlet of the cold-reheat piping is removed, and the cold-reheat piping is permanently connected to the reheater. A temporary blowoff connection is installed at the hot-reheat piping as close to the turbine as possible and piped to waste. The same blowing procedure is used as in phases I and II. When the specimen results are satisfactory, the steam blows can be considered successful.

In checking opening pressure and blow-down, a calibrated pressure gage must be used and the location of its connection on the vessel, header, or other component must be such that the pressure it indicates is a true indication of the pressure existing at the safety-valve inlet, both when it opens and when it closes. When valves are located on headers or steam lines through which steam is flowing, the test pressure gage should be connected near the valve to eliminate any effect of pressure drop resulting from the flow. In some cases the flow of steam being relieved through the valve itself could produce a significant pressure drop.

For high-pressure boilers (above approximately 1200 psig operating pressure) a manufacturer's representative should initially test and adjust safety valves. Certain local codes require that only licensed people may make adjustments on safety valves. Check with the insurance carrier before making any adjustments on safety valves. The setting or adjustment of safety valves should be done only by a competent person familiar with their construction, operation, and maintenance. A written report should be made of all testing and adjustment of safety valves. This should record the opening pressure, closing pressure and/or blowdown and give an indication of correct functioning of the valves as they are left. In addition, it should include the name and title of the responsible plant observer and the name and title of any insurance inspector, or state or local boiler inspector who witnesses the test and adjustment. The name of the valve vendor's representative making adjustments, if any, should also be included as well as the nameplate data (serial number, set pressure, blowdown, and valve location) of each valve on the unit. The operating company should retain the report as a permanent part of their records.

Before testing safety valves for the first time on new units, the steam lines will have been blown to eliminate as much of the foreign material as possible from the superheater and reheater and from the connecting piping to prevent damage to the safety valves. Damage to the valve seating surfaces from grit blasting by

particles of mill scale and weld beads, and such is common during initial testing. Adequate steam blowing prior to popping valves will minimize possible damage. Valves mounted on the dead end of headers are particularly prone to this damage. Inspection and manual clean-

---

PROCEDURES PRIOR TO SAFETY-VALVE SETTING

Before firing the unit for setting the valves, check the following:

1. That hydrostatic test plugs have been removed from the safety valves. If a problem of scheduling a valve vendor's representative for removal of hydrostatic test plugs is involved, the plug from one valve must be removed prior to the first fire. All plugs must be removed before the unit is brought up to full pressure for the first time.

2. That there is no physical interference which would prevent functioning of the safety valves. Expansion of the unit should be considered in this check.

3. That the exhaust stacks from the valves are firmly supported and restrained and that no physical interference which will put external stresses on the valves exists between exhaust stacks and the valves in the cold position, hot position or in between.

4. That the exhaust elbow attached to the valve body is not of excessive length in the horizontal run (maximum recommended—24") which may result in abnormal stresses being put on the valve body due to the reaction force when the valve is blowing.

5. That the drain piping from the valve body and drip pans, elbow, etc. is installed and discharges into a location which will prevent injury to personnel when the valve is blowing.

6. That, if flexible hoses are used between the exhaust elbow and exhaust stack, they be of sufficient length and installed so that they do not become "solid" in any position of the valve.

7. That all components of the safety valves are in place and secure, such as manual lifting gear and adjusting ring pins.

ing of the header by vacuum hose and/or magnets through the valve nozzle, with top works removed, is sometimes necessary. With maximum attention given to removing debris before initial popping of the valve, better success will be obtained with initial valve setting.

Leakage of safety valves in operation usually results from one or more of the following:

1. Seating-surface damage

2. Externally imposed stresses on the valve body which distort the seating surfaces

3. Operation at pressure too close to the set pressure of the valve. The valve manufacturers recommend a minimum difference between popping pressure and operating pressure of 5 percent of the popping pressure. With less than 5 percent difference on a continuous basis, problems with leakage and resulting high valve maintenance may be expected.

Safety of personnel and prevention of equipment damage should be the prime concern when testing and adjusting safety valves. Tremendous forces are involved when these valves operate. All precautions necessary to contain these forces and prevent accidents must be taken. For the initial popping of each valve all personnel should be kept at a safe distance from the valve. A rope should be attached to the manual lifting gear so that an uncontrollable valve chatter can be prevented from doing serious damage if it should occur.

Before starting the actual setting, refer to the latest section of the ASME Boiler and Pressure Vessel Code applicable to safety valves.

HYDRAULIC-JACK METHOD FOR SAFETY-VALVE SETTING

The use of a hydraulic jack has made setting safety valves easier. These jacks can be bought or rented from the valve manufacturers. This method was developed originally for setting supercritical pressure valves so that the lift could be limited to reduce damage to the seating surfaces.

The hydraulic-jack system contains a pump, hydraulic piston, yoke, turnbuckle and pressure gage. The hydraulic piston overcomes some of the safety-valve spring force so that the valve may be set at lower steam pressures.

This method has also been used widely on reheater safety valves as well as with high-pressure valves (drum and superheater) on drum-type boilers. But it must be remembered that this method only tests the popping pressure, not blowdown or the valve action itself. The disadvantages of not testing actual blowdown and the valve operation are outlined in the adjoining box, "Problems Avoided by Blowdown Testing."

Safety-valve manufacturers indicate that they check each valve with steam for blowdown, and that a cold setting of the blowdown rings can be made extremely close if the instruction manual is followed closely. However, C-E recommends the hydraulic jack method for supercritical or reheater applications.

PROBLEMS AVOIDED BY BLOWDOWN TESTING

1. Insufficient blowdown can result in chatter, which can produce extensive damage to the seating surfaces and other valve parts.

2. Excessive blowdown can result in operating problems in getting a valve to close above the normal operating pressure once it pops. The ASME Boiler Code requires that the low-set drum valve shall have no more than 4 percent blowdown and that other drum valves may have longer blowdowns but none shall close lower than 96 percent of the set pressure of the lowest-set drum valve.

3. The valve could fail to reach full lift because of some mechanical problem. This would not be known and hence its capacity might be restricted when it was really needed.

4. The valve could hang open because of a mechanical problem and bleed the pressure completely off the boiler during operation.

5. The exhaust-stack arrangement would not be subjected to a full-flow test before the unit goes on the line. Serious problems and possible damage can result if sizing is insufficient or the supports are not adequate.

After the unit has been chemically cleaned, steam lines blown and safety valves set, the boiler is ready for supplying steam to the turbine.

One of the necessities of effective operation is the periodic "walk down" of a steam generator during operation. This requires that the operator keep his or her eyes and ears open for unusual conditions and report any findings (Fig. 7). Potential damage to equipment can be avoided if abnormal conditions are detected in time. The operations department should develop a checkoff list specific to the station.

PROBLEMS IN OPERATION

In spite of adherence to the general procedures and observance of the cautions presented in this chapter, operational problems still occur. Tube ruptures can happen from a variety of reasons. The size and location of the break will determine what action is necessary. On a drum-type unit, the best method for shutting down will be dictated by the ability to maintain normal water level in the boiler and the need for the boiler in service.

If water level can be maintained, the unit can be kept in service until after a peak, or service may be stretched to a weekend outage. There is, however, the ever-present danger of high-pressure water from a break cutting other tubes. If the rupture can be visually observed, to ascertain that it is blowing out into the furnace and not damaging other tubes, the unit may be able to operate for a long time providing sufficient treated make-up water is available.

Unlike a waterwall tubing leak, a leak in a superheater, reheater, or economizer element requires greater attention. Because of the physical arrangement of such surfaces, steam cutting of adjacent tubes can result in making a major repair job out of what might have been a simple and short one. Economizer ruptures, if left unattended, can lead to plugging of the economizer and air heater, as the water mixing with the flyash can set similar to concrete.

A leak in a waterwall of a supercritical unit can result in rapid and extensive damage, not only to the leaking tube, but also to nearby tubes. Thermocouples are installed on individual outlet tubes and representative inlet tubes to alert the operator to such leaks. Any decision to operate a once-through unit with a known waterwall tube leak must be made with the full knowledge of the serious damage that may be incurred.

FURNACE EXPLOSIONS

Furnace explosions usually occur during start-up, shutdown, or low-load operation. Generally, they result from the accumulation of unburned fuel in the furnace because of incomplete combustion, loss of ignition, or fuel-valve leakage. An explosion occurs when the proportion of unburned fuel and air is in explosive range, and some heat source increases the temperature of the mixture to the ignition point. Unburned fuel which causes such fires can accumulate in the furnace in several ways: at leaky fuel inlet valves on idle windbox compartments; when the fire is extinguished and

Fig. 7 **Check each sootblower during weekly walk down.**

the fuel is not shut off promptly; when the fuel doesn't burn as rapidly as it enters the furnace; or if difficulty occurs in establishing ignition.

EXPLOSION PREVENTION

Because most explosions occur during periods of low fuel input, maintaining a minimum of 30 percent of full-load airflow is important to insure an air-rich mixture and to sweep out any accumulation of unburned fuel. Other preventive measures to take include

■ Be sure that all liquid or gaseous fuel valves are tightly shut on idle fuel compartments

■ Watch the fires closely at low loads and shut off all fuel immediately if proper combustion is not maintained. Most modern units have flame scanners to trip the unit automatically when poor ignition occurs. The scanners must be properly maintained. They should never be removed from the safety system or their outputs defeated

■ Always use the required ignition energy

TYPICAL OPERATOR WALK-DOWN CHECKLIST

■ Look for unusual traces of either coal dust, oil, flyash or water.

■ Look for valve and valve packing leaks.

■ Look for any unusual conditions such as discoloration, hot spots on casing and ductwork, or vapor leaking out.

■ Open all inspection doors and note any slag accumulations.

■ Listen for tube leaks in the furnace. (This is only possible to do on balanced-draft units.)

■ Check for unusual noises, overheating, and adequate lubrication of all motors and driven equipment.

■ Look for leaks in gage glasses and water columns.

■ Check that no sootblowers are stuck in the unit and that there are no leaks in the sootblower lines.

■ On tilting tangential units, make sure that the tilt setting is the same on all corners.

■ Check the secondary-air damper settings to make sure that all dampers are the same on a given elevation.

■ At the firing levels, check for coal, fuel oil or gas leaks. See that warm-up guns are retracted. Note any flyash leaks. Report any oil spills so that they can be cleaned up before a fire occurs.

■ Check with a hand touch all vertical coal piping for possible plugging or overheating. A cold pipe on a mill in service is a good indication of plugging.

■ Inspect furnace just above ash pit to make sure there is no bridging across bottom.

■ Check level of water in ash hopper and bottom seal trough.

■ At the pulverizers-
a. Check gear-case oil temperature, flow and level.
b. Check for excessive spillage or malfunction of pyrite system.
c. Look for any indication of mill fires.
d. Listen for unusual noise.
e. Check for coal leaks.

■ At the airheater-
a. Check the air-heater sootblower to make sure that it is not leaking when the control valve has closed.
b. Check drive motor, support and guide-bearing lubrication and cooling water.
c. Inspect cleanliness of air side through observation door.

■ At least once a week, a more extensive checking should be done such as:
a. Listen for badly leaking safety valves.
b. Check the sootblower cycle by walking down the unit as each blower operates to make sure it is functioning correctly and the packing is tight. Make sure all blowers are blown during a cycle.
c. Put all ignitors and retractable oil guns in service and check to make sure they are operating correctly.
d. Start and stop any idle equipment to make sure it is ready if needed.

source when placing any pulverizer in service

■ During low-load operation keep *adjacent* pulverizers in service

■ Regularly check the proper functioning of any furnace safeguard system

■ Never defeat any portion of a safeguard or interlock system

■ On a unit trip, purge the furnace before shutting off the fans

■ Empty the pulverizers of all coal before bottling up the unit.

UNINTENTIONAL FIRES EXTERNAL TO THE FURNACE

One of the most destructive events in steam-generator operation is uncontrolled ignition of fuel in an area external to the furnace. Such fires have taken place in air heaters, ductwork, windboxes, precipitators, hoppers, and fans. In the immediate vicinity of the boiler, such fires have occurred when oil is being burned.

Generally, fires in air heaters, back-end ductwork, precipitator and induced-draft fans take place when a unit is being brought up to load after a start-up from cold. With inadequate fuel-oil atomization and/or poor mixing of the oil with combustion air, unburned oil distillates will carry to the back of the unit and deposit on the relatively cold back-end surfaces. Later, when load is raised, these deposits will volatilize as temperature increases, and can ignite. Once such a fire starts, extinguishing it is difficult. The metal baskets in an air heater, for example, will continue to burn even after the oil is consumed. The only method of putting out such a metal fire is to flood it with as much water as possible.

Combustion Engineering has always recommended air-atomized light oil or steam-atomized heavy oil for light offs of a cold unit. If mechanical atomization of oil is the only means available, special observation of the furnace outlet is necessary when firing with a cold furnace. One method of detecting the carryover of distillates involves air-cooled probes at the furnace outlet which can be periodically extracted and examined.

Anytime there is doubt as to the quality of an oil fire during a cold light off, the air heater and other back-end surfaces should be examined. If oily deposits are found, all firing should cease until the surfaces can be thoroughly cleaned with a hot detergent solution.

Uncontrolled ignition occurring around the windbox area, external to the unit, usually results from oil spills when guns are removed or when valves or gaskets are permitted to leak. Therefore, oil spills should be cleaned and leaky oil valves or gaskets should be corrected immediately. Any plant which tolerates accumulation of spilled oil around the burner area is in danger of a serious destructive fire.

OPERATOR TRAINING

A well-trained operations crew means maximum plant availability and optimum unit efficiency. Such a crew is developed by a carefully designed training program which should be a step-by-step learning process. First, there must be an understanding of the fundamentals and principles involved. The individual equipment components and subsystems that comprise the unit must be taught in detail. And, finally, overall generating-unit operation must be discussed fully.

To be effective, a program should be versatile; new operators as well as more experienced personnel should be able to benefit from it. Flexibility is important too; a program that can be used individually or in classroom situations has a distinct advantage. Programs geared to specific equipment should be accurate and to the point. See Figs. 8 and 9.

THE SYSTEMS APPROACH

A well-planned operator-training program looks at the energy supply system as a "system," not just as a network of hardware. Part of that system is the people who manage, operate, and repair the network of hardware and equipment for the owner.

Many operating cost variables can be controlled by plant operating personnel throughout the useful life of the facility. Good

Fig. 8 **Part of operator training includes classroom presentations covering fundamentals of system equipment and unit operation. A well-planned operator training program looks at the energy supply system as a "system," not just as a network of hardware and equipment joined together.**

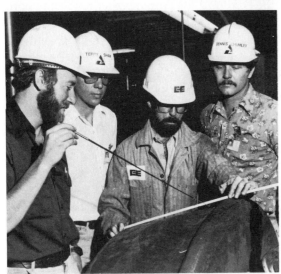

Fig. 9 **Experienced training specialists provide on-the-job training, an essential part of any comprehensive training program.**

operating techniques, for example, extend wearing-part cycles. Fuel usage also depends upon operating technique, as does effective preventive maintenance.

The question of operating-personnel quality is of great concern today, because of the increase in unit size, complexity, and automation. The trend is for fewer personnel to be involved in responsible operation of increasingly larger power plants.

The elements necessary to establish a successful systems training program include prerequisite conditions such as knowledge of the system, what it is, how it works, who uses it, what it is for. This is followed by a needs analysis that tailors the program to the specific requirements of the system and the student population. Then the training program must be designed to meet these requirements. Systematic verification of training program effectiveness is vital. Experience has taught that, if the above elements have been successfully applied, it is reasonable to expect demonstration of student operating competence and a high level of student retention of new knowledge and skills.

A prerequisite to a successful program is a cooperative understanding of the objectives and program goals. This is generally accomplished by giving presentations outlining the program goals and methods to station management personnel and officials of the production and maintenance unions. C-E's experience is that these presentations have resulted in excellent dissemination of program information, a high degree of interest, and active participation and cooperation at all levels during the survey. The inclusion of union management has achieved the same resultant support and cooperation and assures reasonable support for subsequent training program activities.

THE NEEDS ANALYSIS

The training requirements analysis is generally based upon data gathered from questionnaires provided to all operating personnel and from a survey of the power station. The survey includes a review of plant configuration, technical documentation, operating procedures and directives, operator job requirements, and, where applicable, review of licensing requirements. These data are analyzed by educational psychologists and training specialists who then prepare a population description of the average student, identify job-knowledge requirements and performance objectives, and identify motivational factors to be considered in training systems design.

The availability of operators for training, with the exception of a new station starting up, represents a significant factor to be considered in a training system design. The complexities of current manning levels, rotating shift schedules, and overtime opportunities complicate the arrangement of an effective training schedule.

Performance measurement criteria applied to training design are:

■ Evaluate the effectiveness of instruction and course material

■ Evaluate the level of each student's achievement and provide necessary additional assistance if required

■ Review and reemphasize important areas of course material

■ Establish procedures for scoring individual students to avoid possible union conflicts

THE ROLE
OF THE POWER-PLANT SIMULATOR

Training material, equipment, and facility requirements necessary to support the training program should be specified in the design of the program. Of great value to any operator training program is a compact, portable power-plant simulator. See Fig. 10. This device is designed to demonstrate the concept of a total operating plant.

These simulators allow dynamic demonstrations of overall power-plant systems operation; automatic combustion control system operation; turbine/generator control system operation; and operation of feedwater and fuel control systems. Practice exercises can be provided through the insertion of selected malfunctions and load variations to improve operator ability to diagnose abnormal conditions and initiate corrective action. The application of these simulators to the training program is always in the context of specific

Fig. 10 **A power-plant simulator for a Controlled Circulation unit**

Fig. 11 **Simulators provide a highly effective demonstration of plant operational concepts and the application of problem solving logic to determine corrective action to be taken when plant equipment malfunctions.**

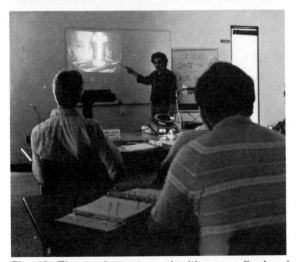

Fig. 12 **The equipment used with an audiovisual training program is portable and easy to operate; at any time operators can use it individually for plant system reviews.**

power-plant operating procedures and as a reinforcement of the training material being taught at the time, Fig. 11.

OTHER SUPPORT MATERIALS

An audiovisual training program is also very effective. Fig. 12. It combines sight and sound which greatly increases retention. Such a program can be used throughout the life of the unit for retraining operators and initial training of replacement operators.

COMPLETENESS

The training program design is complete when the following components have been accounted for: curriculum, lesson plans, training aids, note-taking guides, simulator, study texts, quizzes, tests, practical exercises (plant walk down and simulator operation), and the teaching team has demonstrated practice-teaching exercises.

PROGRAM VALIDATION

The next step in the process is to provide for program validation. In general, an initial course instruction is provided to a "pilot" class. This is to validate training course content, length of lessons, emphasis, and overall time schedules and objectives. Validation is accomplished by administration of pretests at course start to establish operator entry knowledge, and post-tests at course completion to measure gain in knowledge. Evaluation of training effectiveness through course audit by technical specialists, analysis of test results, and review of student course critiques are additional validation measures. Course material should be revised as necessary based on the results of validation measures.

CHAPTER 21

Testing and Measurements

In the modern power plant, measurements are made for three reasons: (1) to monitor various phases of power-plant operation, such as input and output flows, inlet and outlet water and steam temperatures, and power consumptions and power consumptions of auxiliaries, (2) to test individual equipment or systems for purposes of initial acceptance and (3) to check performance following a period of operation. This chapter concerns the latter-type measurements, many of which are governed by the comprehensive series of *ASME Performance Test Codes*[1]. Supplemented by additional tests of special character, the *ASME Performance Test Codes* are of considerable interest to manufacturers and users of power equipment, and the results of such tests aid in the evaluation and improvement of designs.

An engineer participating in power-plant testing must become aware of the nature of experimental errors, learn how a single error may influence the results calculated from multiple measurements, and gain some knowledge of the effect of instrument selection in minimizing measurement uncertainty. For best results, the engineer must be willing to question why certain procedures or instruments are used and to change them only if he can find better methods. Most important, the engineer must become skillful in interpreting test results and in drawing appropriate conclusions.

POWER-PLANT TESTING AND MEASUREMENT CHARACTERISTICS

Power-plant testing differs in one important respect from product quality control, to which it is sometimes compared: most tests fall into the single-sample category. Unlike the repetitive tests made of product dimensions, most power-plant tests consist, for example, of individual readings taken over a period of time during which some unwanted variations may be introduced. Except for a few unusually well-equipped laboratories, large-scale power-plant tests cannot be repeated a sufficient number of times to gain the statistical reliability expected for quality control. Furthermore, the cost of conducting certain full-scale tests can be in the hundreds of thousands of dollars.

UNCERTAINTY ANALYSES

When tests are costly in terms of manpower, time, and equipment, the uncertainty analyses made in advance help establish procedures and manpower assignments. They can also help determine how uncertainties propagate into the results. In their pioneering article on this subject, "Describing Uncertainties in Single-Sample Experiments,"[2] S. J. Kline and F. A.

McClintock show that a given reduction in a large uncertainty is far more important than the same numerical reduction in a small uncertainty. This technique also guides selection of appropriate measuring instruments prior to the start of experimental work. But consideration must also be given to adequate cross checks while the experiment is being conducted.[3]

ADVANCE PLANNING OF FIELD TESTS

Advance planning of field tests is becoming increasingly important. Under some circumstances, it is possible to set forth a fixed objective for overall accuracy and plan instrumentation accordingly.

More often, however, field tests are performed under less than ideal conditions, so the engineer must be capable of making a judicious selection of existing and special measuring instruments. If the objectives and desired end results are well defined, some of the plant control-panel instrumentation may be used, perhaps jointly with special calibration or by checking against standard sources.

Large sums of money may be spent in devising special measuring equipment for a particular part of a test, but these expenditures may be largely wasted if supporting measurements are substantially less precise. Minimally therefore, the engineer should be familiar with the main sources of error and their effect upon the results of the test performed.

By making an error analysis in advance of conducting tests, the engineer can determine crucial points of measurement and select his instruments accordingly.[4] He can also predict effects of propagation of errors on calculated results and obtain a much greater overall consistency in testing activities. In test reports, the combination of an error analysis with interpretation of results adds to the usefulness of tests as a design tool.

Tests and measurements, as indicated earlier, require a great deal of engineering thought. Their value is greater if the engineer is willing to ask searching questions and make all possible analyses before testing is begun. Finally, skill in reporting test results is crucial, particularly in the interpretation of what was observed. Important advances in engineering and science have resulted from skepticism of "obvious" results and perception of new factors that previously went unnoticed.

STEAM-GENERATOR TESTING

When applied to boiler study, testing activities range from daily performance observations using station supervisory instruments to unusual conditions with specialized measuring apparatus. In this latitude, the scope of any single test and the measurement techniques used depend upon the kind of testing information being sought.

Since individual phases of a design problem may range from a completely scientific solution with exact relationships between variables to empirical approaches with variables only generally related, test work for design information is intended either to determine magnitudes and limits of these variables or to establish their cause-and-effect relationships. Although a research laboratory can supply experimental information for basic investigations and observe behavior in many types of models, testing on full-scale units is vitally necessary to verify data thus obtained. Although tests of small industrial boilers may actually be carried out in a laboratory, for large utility-type boilers the power plant itself becomes the testing laboratory. In some cases where unusual fuels are being studied, large quantities of that fuel may be shipped long distances so that tests conducted in a boiler will have the desired firing-equipment and design characteristics.

Although emphasis is on the testing of large central-station boilers, many of the measuring techniques are equally applicable to smaller units installed in marine, industrial, and institutional power plants.

OPERATIONAL TESTING

After a design has been completed and a boiler erected, the initial operating period provides the first opportunity to determine whether it meets performance guarantees. Handled as a normal function of a technical-service organization, this acceptance work may include such items as determination of unit capacity, steam-temperature control range, draft losses and pressure drops, and overall efficiency. If deficiencies exist, some additional testing may be necessary to guide corrective action to meet contractual performance.

When a unit in a central station goes into commercial operation, it becomes an integrated part of a system. It is normal utility practice to determine the unit heat-rate characteristics at this time and periodically later. In these days of high costs, optimum system efficiency is important, and information from these incremental-load cost studies on each unit provides the basis for determining daily load distribution among system plants.

In some central stations, a control-room data-logging computer calculates heat-rate information almost instantaneously. Not only does such rapid information availability permit more detailed analysis of performance, it also supports decision-making for optimal unit operation under such conditions as extreme low loads or loss of a feedwater heater.

In addition to evaluating performance and results, operational testing covers the more detailed aspects of routine operation such as start-up procedures, adjustment and maintenance of unit control systems, and safe-limit monitoring of operating variables.

DETERMINING TEST CONDITIONS

The test objective governs the test condition which can be at either constant or transient load. Historically, the role of the newer, larger units in utility-system steam plants has been one of base loading at design rating, with system load fluctuations being taken care of by the older and smaller equipment. Consequently, in the past, new unit design emphasized steady-state operating characteristics. In recent years, however, the relationship between required short-term peak capability and off-peak capacity has changed. Because peak load has out-distanced off-peak load growth, there is in-

creasing interest in transient characteristics of the largest and most modern units. Many will, at times, operate at reduced load, and may even be shut down for weekends and other periods of low electrical demands.

Constant-load testing is needed for evaluation of unit heat absorption, heat-transfer parameters, unit efficiency, and heat rates. Transient testing is required for controls-response study and adjustment, and in connection with quick start-up and shutdown procedures.

TESTING MEASUREMENTS

Steam-generator design and operation revolve about three basic premises, any one or all of which may be involved in a test program.

- heat liberation
- heat absorption
- mechanical means to accomplish heat liberation and absorption.

HEAT LIBERATION

Heat liberation results from combustion of a fuel with oxygen in the air. This implies testing to obtain knowledge of fuel properties and combustion characteristics; establishing this means theoretical fuel-air-products relationships from fuel analysis and combining equations and from the actual combustion requirements in an operating furnace. Together with the combustion efficiency, such things as pulverizer (or other fuel-burning equipment) power and capacity requirements, ignition stability, and ash deposits must be evaluated. Testing for heat liberation requires considerable attention to fuel and flue-gas sampling to obtain representative data.

HEAT ABSORPTION

Heat absorbed by unit components reduces the flue-gas heat level. The reduction can be determined from gas-temperature measurements and specific-heat data. Similarly, the unrecovered heat quantity entering the stack is a loss and must be determined. Solid and gaseous stack emissions are other factors receiving considerable attention because of flyash disposal problems and air-quality considerations. To size fans and exhausters adequately, system resistance appearing as pressure and draft losses must be known. In summary, these are the most common areas of test work in the fuel-air cycle.

For a successful design, heating surface must be properly allocated among furnace, superheater, reheater, economizer, and air heater so that the desired heat absorption will be achieved and yield the expected relationships of capacity and steam temperature. Since in modern boilers the furnace represents the most important part of the evaporative surface, its performance is a key factor. The furnace must be sized to be capable of maximum design evaporation yet provide flue gas at the temperature level necessary to superheat and reheat the steam to a desired level over the operating range. Because of the series-type processes involved, miscalculation at any point will upset performance in all the other sections.

TESTING OF MECHANICAL EQUIPMENT

High availability and low maintenance costs are prime requirements for steam-generating equipment. Therefore, materials have to be selected for long-life operation at elevated temperatures and pressures. Since in-service pressure parts and structural-mechanical equipment are subjected to erosion, abrasion, expansion, and vibration, their design requires knowledge of the magnitudes and character of these factors. Only field and laboratory experience will yield this information.

MEASUREMENTS RELATED TO HEAT LIBERATION

Fuel-flow measurement depends upon the fuel state and the desired accuracy. Solid fuels, such as coke and coal, can be measured by scales. Many plants, between the coal-storage silos and the pulverizers, have gravimetric feeders suitable for test purposes. Such scales or feeders must be calibrated before and after tests, in accordance with PTC 19.5, Measurement of Quantity of Materials, Chapter 1.

METHODS OF MEASURING FUEL FLOW

For general test purposes, fuel oils are metered with volumetric instruments of the displacement rotating-disc type. Heavy grades of oil must be heated for proper atomization in burners, and where moderate accuracy is satisfactory, the resultant viscosities permit use of such meters even with these oils. If on the other hand, flow error of less than 4 percent is required, meter calibration is necessary using the intended oil at operating temperature and with a similar piping arrangement. The foaming tendency and volatilization of some oils may prevent their accurate metering by this method.

Using level change in large uncalibrated storage tanks as a flow index is at best an approximate method. For efficiency tests, weigh tanks are the most accurate means of direct measurement, but their use is generally regarded as impractical with large flow rates. Their cost also prohibits widespread use.

For gaseous fuels, orifice-flow measurement is most common. It gives highly accurate results if the actual installation has sufficient approach straight lengths and if it conforms to design of pressure taps and orifice-pipe size relationships.[5]

TECHNIQUES FOR FUEL SAMPLING

In arriving at a representative sample, the inhomogeneity of most fuels requires careful attention to sampling techniques. Accepted standard practices may be found in the latest revisions of *ASTM Standards* D 2013, Preparing Coal Samples for Analysis and D 2234, Collection of a Gross Sample of Coal.

In general, solid-fuel sampling procedures involve collecting small increments at regular intervals over the test period, and reducing their aggregate to obtain laboratory-size samples by successive quartering or riffling. For some coals, intermediate steps include crushing to definite screen sizes and mixing.

Since surface moisture of coal may vary considerably, separate samples are taken and sealed immediately for moisture-only determinations when high test accuracy is required.

This practice is mandatory for efficiency tests and desirable for any high-moisture fuel tests because the normal handling in aggregate reduction can produce significant moisture loss of the sample. Aggregate analysis is then adjusted for the average special moisture value to arrive at the as-fired analysis. The need for such care is readily apparent in weighed-coal tests when the heat input is directly affected by such moisture loss.

Sampling of other solid fuels such as wood and bark should be made with similar care to avoid moisture loss.

With most pumped-liquid and gaseous fuels, the problem is one of possible overall change during the test period rather than inhomogeneity at any instant. Thus, sampling at a single point with fixed extraction rate for the entire test period should be adequate except where known stratification exists as in waste fuel ducts or in residual fuel lines.

ANALYZING FUEL CHARACTERISTICS

In its broadest sense, fuel analysis refers to determination of all physical and chemical properties of a fuel.

Solid Fuels

The basic type of chemical analysis for coal is the proximate, which describes the fuel in weight percent of fixed carbon, volatile material, ash, and moisture contents. In the ultimate analysis, the fixed carbon and volatile material contents are reported in terms of total carbon, hydrogen, oxygen, nitrogen, and sulfur, this form being required for calculation of fuel-air quantities.

Fuel analysis and high-heat-value determination are made in accordance with the Test Code for Solid Fuels PTC 3.2 and *ASTM Standards*.[6] This is a constant-volume determination. Because the fuel is burned at constant pressure in the steam generator, the high heat value at constant volume as determined in the bomb-calorimeter must, therefore, be converted to a constant-pressure high heat value. Throughout the Codes, this high heat value for constant pressure combustion is referred to as the high heat value. (When testing by the input-output method, only the high heat value and the moisture content of the fuel are required.)

Generally, *fuel sizing* refers to crusher-prepared coal sizing measured with screens of ⅛-inch opening and larger, and is of importance mainly for fuel-bed distribution problems in stoker firing. *Coal fineness* usually means suspension-burning sizes and, for pulverized coal, involves sieving of 50- to 200-mesh (openings per inch) particle sizes. In both cases, a series of screen sizes is used, with the fractions retained or passed by each size being reported. Knowledge of the size consist or overall fraction relationship rather than just one size is required. For example, in pulverized-coal firing, combustion efficiency (carbon loss) can be more affected by larger size consist, whereas grinding power is more closely related to the finer size percentages.

Another physical property related to pulverizer performance is ease of grinding or *grindability index*. This is determined from the amount of power required to pulverize a prepared sample of the test coal in the laboratory. The results are then compared with a standard sample. In the Hardgrove method, the standard is 100 with decreasing numbers indicating progressively harder grinding coals.[7]

Liquid Fuels

Oil fuels are reported in an ultimate analysis together with higher heating value and sample density, viscosity, and flash point. Density can be stated as either standard specific gravity, referred to water, or degrees API, the two terms being readily convertible. Additional properties are pour point, sediment, and the presence of solid impurities such as metallic salts. These properties may influence pumping, storage, slagging, and corrosion problems.

In general, the ultimate analysis is sufficient to determine fuel-air relationships for by-product liquid fuels such as pulp-mill black liquor, refinery wastes, pitch and others. But operating problems may require special tests in addition to the standard physical property determinations.

Gaseous Fuels

Gaseous fuels are usually combinations of saturated and unsaturated hydrocarbons, and their analysis is reported as a mol or volume percent of these constituents. Common analyses include low-temperature distillation, mass-spectrometer, and adsorption methods. From this constituent analysis, high heating value at standard volumetric conditions and saturated or dry can be calculated by using standard heating values of constituents. Where gas samples of large volume can be provided easily, the classical method of heating-value determination, by calorimeter, is feasible. For instance, recording calorimeters are often found at transmission-line entry points to users' plants for billing purposes.

Fuel-Air Proportioning

Combustion airflow measurement and regulation are requisite to good operation because of the desire to burn a fuel with optimum air quantity. Some air in excess of the theoretical

Fig. 1 **The basic means of volumetric flue-gas analysis is by Orsat apparatus. In this method, a known volume of gas is exposed to absorbent solutions for carbon dioxide and oxygen.**

quantity for complete combustion is always required, the amount depending upon the fuel and firing method. Although ideally the lowest excess air is desirable, there are many conditions under which high excess air results in more economical plant operation. If, for example, constant steam temperature is to be maintained at low ratings, increased gas mass flow may be required over heat-transfer surfaces. Increasing excess-air is one way of accomplishing this.

Airflow Measurement

Knowing the quantities of air required and fuel products formed in terms of weight or volume rates is not necessary from an operating point of view. The operator wants to know these quantities relative to the theoretical amounts for the fuel rate being burned. Operating indexes, therefore, are designed to show the percent excess-air or relative percent total-air quantities. On the other hand, for engineering design purposes, these air and gas rates are necessary to properly size fans, ducts, and heat-transfer equipment.

In routine operation, airflow measurement is accomplished through pressure or draft differential sensing of a gas or air-side component, or by means of flue-gas analysis. In either case, field calibration of the metering equipment is ultimately based upon test flue-gas analysis. Flow measurement by pitot-tube techniques is somewhat restricted in boiler air-flue gas-flow problems because duct configuration and low static-impact pressure difference generally limit the resulting accuracy. More importantly, the flue-gas analysis method is superior because of its simple interpretation for overall airflow. However, pitot measurements become necessary for study of air of flue-gas distribution within a system.

Excess-Air Determination by Flue-Gas Analysis

The fundamental method of volumetric flue-gas analysis is by Orsat apparatus, in which a known volume of gas is sequentially exposed to absorbent solutions for carbon dioxide and oxygen. Measuring sample volume between stages indicates the constituent volume percentages and the remaining nitrogen. Trace gases such as argon are included with nitrogen, while sulfur compounds such as sulfur dioxide and trioxide are absorbed together with carbon dioxide. For most fuels, their effect on the gas-analysis results is negligible in excess-air determination.

The resultant gaseous products for complete combustion of a fuel using several excess-air values are calculated from the ultimate fuel analysis and chemical combining equations. Plotting the volume percentages of carbon dioxide and oxygen thus formed permits excess-air determination by volumetric gas analysis. As a matter of fact, within certain restrictions, excess-air can be determined without the fuel analysis, because the available oxygen in products is a direct measure of excess-air and, when compared to the nitrogen, will indicate percent excess-air. For fuel oil or many bituminous coals, oxygen measurement using graphical means such as Fig. 2 is sufficient to indicate excess-air with acceptable accuracy.

The practical uniformity of this oxygen-excess-air relationship over a wide range of fuels makes it extremely useful in both single and combination fuel firing. Moreover, it is responsible for the widespread use of flue-gas oxygen analyzers for operating and test purposes. These devices employ either catalytic combustion of a known gas and the uncombined oxygen in a flue-gas sample within a temperature-sensitive electrical circuit, or magnetic-field distortion due to paramagnetic qualities of the oxygen in the flue-gas sample. In both cases, the effect is proportional to sample oxygen content, and permits calibration of the instrument-output signal in terms of oxygen percent.

Detecting Unburned Combustibles

In modern fuel-burning practice, unburned gaseous combustibles in flue gas are generally nonexistent; however, they can occur with certain operating conditions. Even in these cases, the extremely low quantities to be found (less than 0.10 percent) are usually beyond the accu-

racy of Orsat work and require detection by chemical reaction-calorimetric methods or laboratory analysis of small samples by mass-spectrometer and adsorption techniques. In either case, to avoid misleading results, the samples must be collected with extreme care to circumvent sample contamination. For example, the sampling probe should be a quenching type since hot-probe materials may act as combustion catalysts in the flue gas, thus indicating no combustibles when they are present. Conversely, probes and sample containers should be free of oil films, high-vapor-pressure stopcock grease and the like, since these materials may indicate traces of combustibles when there are none in the flue gas.

TEMPERATURE MEASUREMENTS

Temperature-measurement techniques differ depending upon temperature level, fluid

Fig. 2 Percentage relationship of oxygen (O_2), carbon dioxide (CO_2) and excess air. (Orsat analyses for a given fuel should plot on a straight line parallel to the guidelines.)

stratification, physical accessibility, and accuracy desired.[8]

Generally, two methods are common in steam-generator testing:

1. filled-system thermometers and

2. thermoelectric and electrical resistance effects.

These two methods are direct in that they involve fluid-temperature level attainment by the sensing element. On the other hand, calibration difficulties arising from variations with different fuels and furnace equipment prevent frequent use of indirect techniques, such as utilization of optical or radiation effects accompanying temperature level of the fluid.

The most common of the filled-system thermometers, mercury and other liquid-in-glass thermometers use volume expansion. Their usage in gas-air work is restricted to ambient-level temperatures and, when stratification does not exist, in ducts. As a variation of the volume-expansion class, gaseous-bulb type instruments, commonly found in operating instrumentation, also measure accompanying pressure change. Although this type instrument permits remote indication, it is a fixed-

Fig. 3 **Mercury and other liquid-in-glass thermometers are used in gas-air work for sensing low- and moderate-temperature levels.**

position device, usually requiring field calibration by another means.

The most versatile temperature-measurement devices are those in the second group. Both thermoelectric and electric-resistance type techniques are readily adaptable to remote measurement, thus enabling monitoring of many points from a single location. Of the two, the thermocouple is more widely used because of its simplicity and low cost.

THE THERMOCOUPLE

Thermocouple measurement employs the thermoelectric effect, a phenomenon whose alternate effects were first observed respectively by Seebeck and Peltier in 1821 and 1834. An electromotive force (emf) is developed if a circuit comprising two different wires has the two junctions at different temperatures. The magnitude of the emf depends on the wire materials and is proportional to the temperature difference between the junctions. Thus, knowing the temperature at one junction and considering the wire materials, the temperature at the other junction can be determined. Special laws govern the effects of intermediate metals and temperatures.[9]

Numerous metals are available for thermocouple materials with selection being based on emf developed, expected mechanical life in the atmosphere and temperature involved, calibration constancy, and cost. The most common types are copper-constantan, iron-constantan, chromel-alumel,[10] and platinum-platinum-rhodium; their upper limit temperature ratings for general service are 400, 1100, 1800 and 2700°F respectively.

Several engineering societies[11] have developed detailed specifications covering temperature-emf relationships and standard accuracy limits. Experience with chromel-constantan thermocouples also indicates suitability of this combination for measurements up to 1600°F with high emf developed.

Thermocouple emf can be measured with either a millivolt galvanometer or a null-balance potentiometer. However, in the galvanometer system, the thermocouple circuit resistance is an additional factor and complicates the measurement, whereas in the null-balance system no current flows in the thermocouple circuit, the measurement being of the opposing emf. Being simpler, the latter system is more widely used.

THE RESISTANCE-BULB METHOD

The resistance-bulb method involves known temperature-electrical resistance change characteristic of a material, usually nickel or platinum, using a Wheatstone bridge type measuring circuit. This method can be made extremely accurate and is used in temperature standards work. However, the high cost of sensing elements and measuring circuit restricts its use to laboratory calibration work or field test work where high precision is required, such as measurement of fractional parts of degrees.

USING THERMOCOUPLE PROBES

Generally, flue-gas temperature measurement is made with thermocouple probes. This requires the hot junction to reach fluid temperature level, which means the fluid contacting the thermocouple must be flowing at a sufficient rate to supply heat lost by conduction from the hot junction along lead wires and radiation to colder surfaces. The magnitude of these heat losses will depend upon probe design, including probe temperature and relative orientation of the hot junction, and temperature differential between the hot junction and the heat receiving surfaces. Physical properties of flue gas also have an effect.

Thermocouple measurement of gas-air temperature in most ducts is simplified for the following reasons.

1. Temperature level is below 700°F and does not require water-cooling of probes for mechanical strength.

2. Ducts are insulated to prevent heat loss and the interiors of ducts are essentially at fluid temperature.

At a temperature level of 700°F, an error of 15°F is commonly found with bare thermocouples in proximity to economizer heating surface at 500°F.

At gas temperatures higher than 700°F, watercooling of probes is necessary for mechanical strength reasons, and the leadwire conduction heat-loss increases. More significantly, higher temperature levels correspond to areas with heat-transfer surfaces such as economizer, waterwalls, superheater, and reheater, the surface temperatures of which vary between 500 and 1100°F. As a result, the radiation error of a bare thermocouple junction increases severely until at the furnace outlet (with gas temperature of 2000°F) the bare thermocouple error is about 200°F.

To compensate for radiation and conduction heat loss in furnace gas-temperature work, the thermocouple junction is shielded with a thin ceramic cylinder through which a high gas flow is induced. In turn, the shield is subject to the same heat-loss effects and, by increasing the number of annular shield layers, the thermocouple junction can be brought to within ± 5°F of true gas temperature. Usually the fuel determines the limit to the size and number of

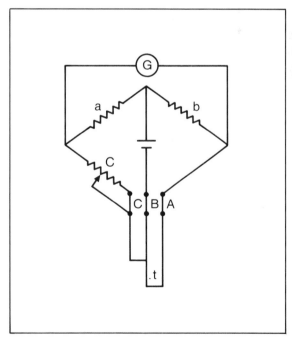

Fig. 4 **Resistance thermometers have as their sensing element a resistor usually made of pure-metal wire. Here, a diagram of a typical simple balanced-bridge type of instrument using a Wheatstone bridge is shown.**

shield openings. With high-ash coals serious plugging can occur in a short period when shields with small openings are used.

THE ORIFICE PROBE

Another type of furnace gas-temperature measuring device is the orifice probe, in which the hot gas is drawn through two metering orifices in series, with deliberate cooling of the gas occurring between them. By measuring the two orifice-flow rates and cold-gas temperature, the initial gas temperature can be calculated since weight flow is constant and the orifice-flow differentials indicate volume flow, which is a function of temperature. The advantage of this type measurement is that it eliminates thermocouple radiation error.

MEASUREMENTS RELATED TO HEAT ABSORPTION

Heat absorption values are used in developing the surface heat-transfer relationships and are determined from test steam-temperature and flow measurements, together with gas temperatures and flows. Additional performance items in the water-steam cycle are pressures, pressure drops, and quality-purity determinations. Circulation studies in furnace waterwalls and flow distribution between circuits are other examples of water-steam cycle testing.

WATER AND STEAM FLOW

Both steam output and feedwater flow are obtained by pressure-differential measurement across flow nozzle or thin-plate orifice sections. The two flows are equal except for losses such as blowdown and injection leakoff. Of the two, however, feedwater measurement is generally more reliable than steam flow because orifice coefficients are more positively established for the former.

The recording flow meters found in most plants employ commercial orifices or flow nozzles. Overall accuracy is usually plus or minus 2 percent of full scale, unless the installation has been calibrated against a special test orifice. These test orifices are plant primary standards, usually installed in low-pressure, low-temperature condensate points in the feedwater cycle to avoid undue extrapolation of original calibration data. Their calibration is performed with laboratory weigh tanks, and extrapolation of flow coefficients to the condensate conditions of flow, temperature and pressure is usually accomplished on the basis of Reynolds number and other dimensionless criteria.

While a few central stations have reheat steam flow meters, it is more common to determine this quantity from primary steam-water flow, high-pressure heater heat balance and the appropriate turbine gland corrections.

For test of heat-absorption surface characteristics, it is usually sufficient to use the operating feedwater recorder as these characteristics are essentially constant for rating changes within meter accuracy, and the fuel-air-gas flow data are related to this base value by heat balance.[12]

Another method of flow measurement sometimes used is pitot-tube technique. Variations of the standard air-gas type are usually preferred for manufacturing reasons, and these are commonly used in some circulation studies where a low-resistance measuring element is required. These devices are usually not suitable for total unit flow measurement because of structural and flow-pattern uncertainty reasons.

Weigh tanks are rarely found in large utility installations because of unit size and consequent cost. Flow nozzles and orifices are taking over their functions. However, the weighing facilities are necessary as primary references in standard laboratories where the nozzle calibration work is performed.

TEMPERATURE MEASUREMENT

The common devices for temperature measurement are thermocouples, resistance-bulb elements and thermometers. The general statements on this subject made previously under gas and air measurements also apply to steam and water measurements.

Some aspects, however, present more serious problems than in the gas-air work. Since in this case the fluid pressures are also high, the measuring elements are rarely exposed directly to the fluid stream. Measurement is commonly made by bottoming contact with a metal well which projects into the stream and provides the necessary mechanical strength. Several well designs are shown in the *ASME Performance Test Code,* Supplements on Instruments and Apparatus, PTC 19.3 and in a paper by J. W. Murdock.[13]

Another method of fluid-temperature determination is surface-temperature measurement of the containing steam or water line. This method is only possible where there is no heat transfer because of temperature gradient effects from hot gas and steam-film. In these zero heat-flux areas, the tube-wall gradient usually presents no problem in measurement, although even here precautions should be taken against boundary effects.

Thermocouples are commonly peened directly into the tube metal or attached by welding the hot junction to the metal. In a well application, spring loading of the element is more practical. In both these cases, the thermocouple is grounded and measurement of a number of points must be by separate circuits since series connections can form unknown loops using boiler metal as a third wire.

PRESSURE AND PRESSURE DIFFERENTIALS

The fundamental pressure and pressure-differential measuring device is the visible liquid column. Although its use is limited to column heights which are practical, the foolproof simplicity of the method is the reason for its retention as a reference. Glass-faced mercury manometers are used for pressure-differential work up to line pressures of 2000 psig, especially for orifice-flow nozzle differential measurements. Some range flexibility exists through use of liquids whose densities are between those of water and mercury. A variation of the visible column, used for pressures over 2000 psig, is a column inside a tube or jacket with a float indicating liquid level through

mechanical linkage or magnetic pointer.

Deadweight instruments employ incremental weights acting on a given-sized piston which floats when the liquid and weight pressures are equal. In deadweight gages, the liquid pressure is line pressure, its value determined from the weight total. In deadweight testers, the liquid is in a closed system with the pressure acting on the instrument to be calibrated and on the weight piston from which the pressure value is determined.

The most common steam-water pressure measuring device is the Bourdon gage, the simplest form of which is a bent flattened tube that tends to straighten itself when internal pressure is applied. Motion of the tube end is transmitted through linkage to a pointer which sweeps a graduated scale. The concept of mechanical motion or distortion due to fluid pressure is common to all pressure elements; the

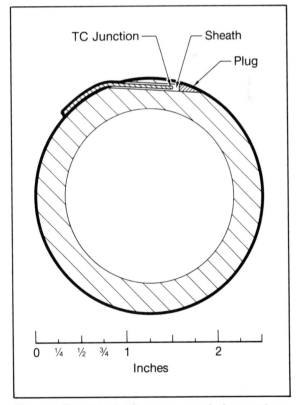

Fig. 5 **Thermocouples are used for surface-temperature measurement of tubing containing fluids at high pressure.**

differences occur in the way this force is translated into a signal. Development of this idea is found in diaphragms, bellows and cylinders whose motions are linked to and described by pointers, strain gage wires, varying resistance bridges, differential transformers, and other mechanical or electrical signal generators.

Such combinations of devices are known as pressure transducers. Their sensitivity, linearity, repeatability, and hysteresis are characteristics to be evaluated in selecting a combination for any specific application.

ADDITIONAL PERFORMANCE MEASUREMENTS

The steam-generator pressure parts are the means by which heat liberated in combustion of the fuel is absorbed by the steam-water fluid. Since the process is one of heat flow, it must be apparent that temperatures of the various equipment items are the basic criteria for design once the desired pressure is stated.

The thermocouple is by far the most-used piece of test apparatus in steam-generator study. Its adaptability for remote measurement of many widely separated points permits investigations and control otherwise impossible. Usage is not limited to pressure parts but includes structural parts as well.

Aside from temperature considerations, steam-generator equipment is subjected to abrasion and erosion and to vibration forces. The first two are generally long-term processes requiring correlation of metallurgical laboratory studies with prolonged operating experience. The main function of field-test activity in this area is to establish the magnitudes of existing factors such as temperature, gas-flow velocity patterns, ash-fuel character and concentrations.

With the increase in unit size and desire for balance between strength and weight, vibration forces have received considerable attention because of their destructive effects. Standing waves in flue-gas passages induce structural and pressure-parts vibrations. Test activity in this area is required for corrective work and to provide design criteria to avoid

Fig. 6 **In its simplest form, the Bourdon gage, a common steam-water pressure measuring device, is a bent flattened tube that tends to straighten itself when internal pressure is applied.**

susceptible arrangements. Gas vibrations are measured with traversing pressure transducers and oscillographic measuring circuits or mechanical vibration graphing devices, depending upon conditions. The latter are also used for structural and casing members.

Another problem related to temperature factors is equipment expansion between hot and cold positions. These movements are generally measured with trams or dial gages depending upon the application. For instance, since waterwall headers on certain units are expected to move downward as much as 15 inches, and other parts lesser amounts, unrestrained movement is essential.

GAS-FLOW MEASUREMENT TECHNIQUES

Considerations of corrosion and erosion of surfaces, formation of deposits, and undesired stack emission evoke interest in gaseous and particulate products of combustion. In attempting to control these effects, test work establishes the character of the emissions and control methods required.

Besides the usual gaseous combustion prod-

Fig. 7 **One method of flyash sampling involves the use of a sharp-edged nozzle through which a gas sample is withdrawn.**

ucts, oxides of nitrogen and sulfur, that are significant from the standpoint of air quality, are formed. Also, dew-point temperature elevation reflective of the presence of sulfur trioxide in flue gas is important for air-heater and dust-collector corrosion and plugging.

Particulate stack emissions vary with fuel and firing method. For example, flyash from coal-fired units may range in size from less than one micron to 50 mesh.

Flyash samples are taken with a sharp-edged nozzle which is pointed upstream and through which a gas sample is withdrawn. For accurate sampling, the withdrawal rate must equal the flow rate at the undisturbed point in the duct; that is, the sampling must be carried out isokinetically.

THE NEED
FOR ACCURATE MEASUREMENT
OF GAS FLOW

The information in the final portion of this chapter is included because of the profound effect that the quantity of gas being handled has on the sizing and cost of the gas-treatment equipment.

The determination of *total* quantities of gaseous and solid constituents in the gases leaving a steam-generator depends upon an ac-

curate quantitation of the gas flow itself. For instance, in the sampling of dust, the amount of material caught in a sampler is reduced to a dust concentration of, say, pounds of dust per 1000 pounds of gas. The total quantity of dust being emitted by the source, then, is the product of dust concentration and total gas flow by weight.

STACK SAMPLING FOR FLOW QUANTITATION

Present U.S. Codes for stack sampling are *ASME PTC 21, Test Code for Dust Separating Apparatus,* which has been combined with *ASME PTC 27, Determining Dust Concentration in a Gas Stream.* Both codes describe the equal-area zone method used to subdivide a duct, flue, or stack for velocity measurement and dust sampling. This technique permits the simplified approach of arithmetic averaging of velocities. The total quantity of gas flow is then determined by

$$Q = A_{duct} \times V_{avg}$$
where Q = cu ft per min,
A = duct area in sq ft and
V_{avg} = gas velocity, ft per min.

(1)

The above technique is further permitted by *ASME PTC 19.5, Fluid Velocity Measurement.* However, this last code introduces a discussion of the errors produced by encountering relatively non-uniform velocity distributions. Several analytical methods of velocity averaging are described and evaluated.

OTHER VELOCITY MEASUREMENT METHODS

Measurement of Solids in Flue Gases by P. G. W. Hawksley defines the approach of the British Institute of Fuel[14]. This publication discusses the effects of nonsymmetrical gas-flow distribution and boundary-layer profiles. It should be noted that the equal-area zone method, as typically used, can easily miss the boundary-layer flow profile. Very small incremental areas would be required for the velocity probing device to "see" all of the boundary layer. However, traversing time can be reduced if the boundary layer is evaluated in detail for one test only and then used to correct coarser subsequent traverses. This approach is justifiable since each flue or stack will have its own characteristic boundary layer which is a function of the specific system geometry and flow turbulence. There have been occasions where boundary layers representing 5 percent of the flue diameter have produced flow errors of some 10 to 20 percent.

ASME PTC 19.5 also presents and discusses the use of various types of velocity measuring devices which can be used in flues and ducts for flow quantitation. Cup-vane meters, propeller meters, and several other devices are discussed along with pitot-static tubes and hot-wire anemometers. This section will concern itself primarily with the use of pitot-static tubes (and modifications thereof) and hot-wire anemometers.

VARIATION IN RESULTS
USING PITOT-STATIC MEASUREMENT

Pitot-static tube velocity measurements have been coupled with the equal-area technique for many years. The results of total gas flow can be quite varied, and interesting, if care is not given to the selection of the measurement plane, or consideration given to developing and evaluating the complete flow pattern. Table I[15] presents the results of several total gas-flow measurements using the pitot-static tube and equal-area techniques as called for in the above standards. The results listed are derived from a typical utility steam-generator installation operating at constant load. As noted, the flow as measured can vary from 104 to 150 percent of rated value.

POWER-PLANT FLOW PATTERNS

Industrial ductwork and flues are designed to connect pieces of equipment at the minimum cost and minimum space requirements. The resultant flow patterns quite often deviate from the desired uniform and unidirectional condition required for accurate quantitation of flow. Flow separation and reverse flows, often found in the major runs of flues, are corrected only by

Table I. Gas-Flow Measurement:

Gas flow measured at different locations in accordance with methods given in *ASME* PTC 27 and by using a pitot-static tube. Observe the gross divergence of measured values and the necessity for careful choice of measurement point.

Measurement Point	Gas Flow CFM	% Rating
Rated Value	300,000	100
Mechanical-Collector Inlet	383,000	128
Mechanical-Collector Outlet	449,000	150
Induced-Draft Fan Inlet (Precipitator Outlet)	313,000	104
Induced-Draft Fan Outlet	424,000	141

major pressure drops such as an air heater or excessively long runs of duct work.

Flow patterns in stacks and fans frequently are highly productive of vortex energy. A basic problem associated with vortex formation is that vortices will persist for many diameters downstream from the source. Vorticity has a very strong effect on dynamic-flow measurement devices.

Occasionally, reverse or negative flow may be encountered. A question then arises as to how to calculate the total volume flow rate from this type of data. Fluid-flow continuity requires that all velocity points, both normal direction and reverse flow, be arithmetically averaged and applied to the total cross-sectional area of the plane of measurement. If this is not done, the recirculated gas flow (the negative values), which can represent 5 to 15 percent of volume throughput, will increase the positive flow values by the same amount and produce a measured flow that is high.

VELOCITY MEASUREMENT

The classical and long-term approach to the measurement of fluid velocity has been by pitot tube. Several references[16-19] are available which describe the developing history of this device. Appendix E, Velocity Calculations by Graphical Methods, presents graphs that can be used for quick determination of gas velocities from pitot-tube readings.

THE PITOT TUBE

The typical flow-measurement device is the pitot tube shown in Fig. 8. The impact or total-pressure hole is the most useful part of the probe. Hydraulically, the impact pressure is the true sum of the local static and dynamic (velocity) heads. Also, the impact hole can have a cone of response of some 60 to 70 degrees. Therefore, accurate angular positioning of the probe for total (impact) pressure measurements is not critical. However, positioning of the probe parallel to the flow direction is very critical for static-pressure measurement. The static-pressure-tap reference surface should be parallel to the flow stream-lines. Also, ideally, the flow stream-lines should be straight and parallel. Any flow stream-line which is not parallel to the static surface will induce an impact or reverse-impact, dynamic pressure at the static hole and create an associated error.

One practical problem associated with the pitot tube is the right-angle bend and probe tip length. This configuration requires large holes in the flue, or duct wall, or some awkward probe handling by the user. The bend also makes it difficult to probe the flow at the near side, or access wall, of the flue. Large holes in

the flue wall are, in turn, difficult to seal to prevent leakage errors. Another problem associated with the standard pitot tube is the tendency for the small holes to plug in flues with heavy dust loadings.

THE STAUSCHEIBE PITOT TUBE

To eliminate such problems, stack samplers have used the "Stauscheibe" or Type S pitot tube shown in Fig. 9. Because the reverse-

Fig. 8 A pitot tube for fluid-velocity measurement with pressure connections and readout shown schematically

Fig. 9 The Stauscheibe or Type S pitot tube

impact method is used to read the static pressure, this probe will produce a new velocity head reading $h = KV^{-2}/2g$ where K will be greater than 1.0. A velocity correction factor C_v is taken to be 0.854 or 0.855. However, C_v is not constant, but is a function of velocity. Cole[18] recommends $C_v = 0.870$ at 10 ft/sec and 0.885 at 3 ft/sec. C-E has found that C_v is 0.855 only for velocities of 20 ft/sec and higher. Cole shows that there are many variations of C_v with probe manufacture and, therefore, each Type S probe should be calibrated in a known flow stream and a curve of C_v vs velocity prepared.

THE FECHHEIMER PROBE

A directional pitot tube, see Fig. 10, has been developed using the work of Fechheimer.[19] This probe is basically a reverse impact probe, but makes use of properties of the flow field around a cylinder. Two additional static, or Fechheimer, taps are located on the "forward" face of the cylinder. Two sets of differential readings are required. The probe is rotated in the gas stream until the velocity taps read positive and the two additional static taps are nulled. The probe is then "looking" directly at the flow-velocity vector and the angle can be recorded.

The Fechheimer probe is very sensitive to the problem of flow moving along the length of the stem when the stem is not exactly perpendicular to the flow field. Folsom evaluates this condition, called "stem effects," in reference 19. The probe used in C-E's laboratory places the sensing cylinder at the end of the airfoil stem which will tend to bleed off stem flow before it reaches the pressure sensing holes. This modification minimizes, but does not eliminate, the induced stem errors. The velocity correction factor, C_v, for this probe is not as dependent on small differences in manufacture as is the Type S probe. In this case, the value of C_v is typically 0.78 for probe Reynolds numbers in excess of 100.

THE HOT-WIRE ANEMOMETER

A device now often used for measurement of industrial fluid velocities is the hot-wire or hot-film anemometer. A single hot-wire system is described in PTC 19.5. The hot-wire anemometer has the advantage of high sensitivity

Fig. 11 **The hot-wire or hot-film anemometer offers the advantage of high sensitivity at very low velocities, producing an electric readout and a measurement of turbulence.**

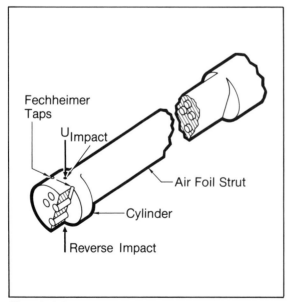

Fig. 10 **A Fechheimer directional pitot tube**

at very low velocities, producing an electric readout and a measurement of turbulence. A disadvantage is its incapability of measuring directional flow in complex flow fields. It is also fragile and can easily be broken in flues with heavy dust loading. This last problem can be overcome by the use of a hot-film anemometer. The hot-film anemometer operates with the characteristics of the hot-wire, but sacrifices the ability to measure very high turbulent frequencies. Since high-frequency response is typically desirable only in aerodynamic wind-tunnel studies, it is rarely needed for industrial flow evaluation.

INSTRUMENT CALIBRATION

All devices should be calibrated to insure a reasonable level of accuracy. The standard pitot tube will deviate from the theoretical Bernoulli response of $C_r = 1.0$ as a function of wear. The Stauscheibe and Fechheimer probes produce values of C_v which will also vary as a function of velocity and wear. The hot-wire and hot-film response is typically some function of V^n where n is less than 1.0 and will vary with dirtiness. Also, each device is dependent on gas composition. Using these dynamic devices requires that the gas density be known and the hot-wire requires the further evaluation of gas thermal properties. Fortunately, the probes can be calibrated in air and analytically corrected for gas properties.[20]

PROBE DYNAMICS AND TURBULENCE

To simplify energy calculations, flow turbulence is usually considered to be a random, but isotropic process. Typically, flow in industrial flues produces two distinct turbulence characteristics described as rolling and vortex flow.

ROLLING FLOW

Many installations include sharp corners and other abrupt discontinuities which will produce the turbulent roll. This roll is characterized by fluctuating velocity components μ and v usually coplanar with the major flow vector. A third component w is perpendicular to

the main-flow vector and is usually of smaller magnitude. Isotropic turbulence, which is defined as $\mu = v = w$, is difficult to find in industrial work.

VORTEX FLOW

Although vortex flow can be produced by stack entrances and fan discharges, it can also be produced by two rolling turbulence patterns intersecting at an angle. It is difficult to characterize vortex flow in linear-velocity vector notations. Typically, all turbulence is characterized when possible by the combined values of intensity (μ/U), frequency, and scale or size of the major eddies.

EFFECTS ON VELOCITY MEASUREMENTS

Turbulence, when applied to a dynamic device such as the standard pitot tube, will introduce a series of basic errors in the interpreted reading. The first is mathematical in that the reading produced by the pitot tube is a "head" of $V^2/2g$, while the result required is the velocity or V.[1.0] Fig 12 shows that, when measuring a turbulent or fluctuating velocity, the head measured will be the root mean square (RMS) value of the wave form and will always be higher than the head produced by the "average" velocity. Second, this problem is complicated by the flow dynamics of the resistance of the small-size pressure taps and tubing, the

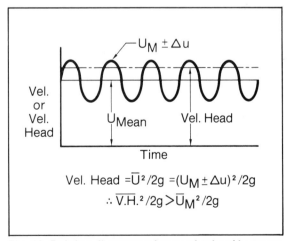

Fig. 12 **Pulsing-flow wave forms obtained in measurements of fluctuating velocities**

compressibility of air or gas in the tubes (where applicable), and the inertia of the indicating fluid. These effects are additive such that, in turbulent flow fields, when using fluid dynamic devices, the velocity as read will always be higher than the actual velocity being measured.

VELOCITY READOUTS

The problem of flow resistance can be partially corrected by using large sensing holes in the probe, close coupling of the readout device to the probe, and a readout device of low displacement volume and inertia. The readout device should also be capable of producing an electrical output signal. The signal can be recorded, for later analysis of the mathematical RMS effect on the velocity reading.

An approach to the mathematical evaluation of turbulent effects on velocity readings is given in the *ASME Performance Test Code* 19.5 Paragraph 57, which specifies isotropic turbulence and the RMS approach. It is relatively easy to apply this guide if the signal is sinusoidal. However, if the signal is not sinusoidal, turbulence effect is difficult to evaluate. This problem can be resolved by using a true RMS voltmeter to produce a true RMS reading independent of the applied wave form.

The effect of flow-steam vorticity has just the reverse effect on the velocity readout. Vorticity represents a well-ordered flow field of significant curvature. Flow curvature, in turn, produces a very definite radial pressure gradient. If the radius of curvature of the flow is of the same order of size as the measuring device, the device will not be measuring either the correct dynamic or static pressures. Vorticity of small size and high-intensity can, therefore, contain a significant amount of dynamic or pressure energy which will not be read if the measuring device is physically larger than the size of the turbulent vortices being produced.

Unfortunately, there is no easy way to evaluate the effect of vorticity on measurements of dynamic flow. Therefore, vorticity should be minimized or eliminated by egg crates or screens if no other flow-traversing station without vorticity is available.

Recommendations on reducing the major sources of error in obtaining total gas-flow rates, based on the above, are given in "Quantitation of Stack Gas Flow" by C. L. Burton.[21]

DRAFTS AND PRESSURE LOSSES (AIR AND GAS)

Draft and pressure losses in steam generators and gas-treatment equipment are recorded in routine and special test operations because they indicate the system resistance which fans must overcome.

Test measurement is usually of draft differential rather than draft alone. Aside from convenience in direct reading, a restriction must be observed in that draft measurement is with reference to some atmospheric pressure. Since atmospheric pressure changes with elevation (approximately one-inch water gage per 100 ft), all draft gages must be at the same elevation or readings corrected for elevation; otherwise, an error of as much as 10 percent can be introduced.

Measurement is with inclined and U-tube liquid manometers. Duct walls and casing connections are usually suitable; the maximum error due to impact would not exceed one velocity head which is less than 0.1-inch water gage in most cases. Since condensation and ash plugging in connecting lines is the most common source of error in draft measurement, the importance of adequate line pitch, drain connections and blowout fittings cannot be overemphasized.

STEAM-GENERATOR EFFICIENCY

The desire to achieve process completion with maximum economy is basic in any technical effort. One measure of performance in steam generators is overall or gross efficiency defined as the ratio of heat output (heat absorbed) to heat input.[22] A heat-balance diagram as shown in Fig. 13 indicates the corollary is efficiency = 100 − percent losses.

The *ASME Performance Test Code* for Steam Generating Units allows efficiency tests that use *only* the chemical heat in the fuel as input. It does not, however, give an explicit definition of boiler efficiency on such a chemical-heat basis where heat credits are to be taken into account. In such practice, the heat diagram and efficiency become as in Fig. 14.

Present day units are large, and the water, steam and fuel quantities associated with them are so great that their measurement with high accuracy is extremely difficult. Weighed water and fuel tests are seldom feasible on these units, and the results with operating instrumentation are subject to commercial meter accuracies. Hence, the input-output method is often unsuitable for an accurate test of very large stationary boilers, because it requires accurate measurement of the quantity and heating value of the fuel, and of the heat absorbed by the steam generator.

Besides costing less, efficiency measurement by the heat-loss method has several advantages over the input-output method. It is more informative since it establishes the individual losses for comparison with expected performance.

Regarding accuracy, the total *losses* are only 10 to 20 percent and fuel sampling and analysis errors affect the end results slightly, whereas in the input-output method these errors are at least four or five times as significant. Also, the basic losses measurements are simple: fuel analysis, exit gas temperature, entering air temperature, and refuse combustible content. Minor items in the heat losses can be obtained from sources such as *ASME Performance Test Code* PTC 4 which contains detailed instructions on test procedures and results calculations.

In order to achieve the objectives of a boiler test in accordance with PTC 4, agreement must be reached, before the test, on the definition of efficiency, the general method (heat loss or input-output), the heat credits and losses to be measured, and the heat credits and losses to be assigned where not measured. In addition, allocation of responsibility for all performance and operating conditions affecting the test

Fig. 13 Basic heat-balance diagram and efficiency relationships

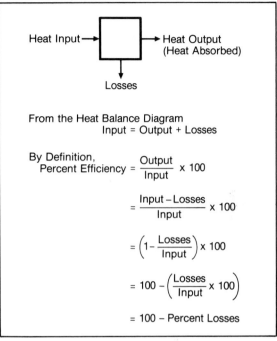

From the Heat Balance Diagram
Input = Output + Losses

By Definition,
Percent Efficiency = $\dfrac{Output}{Input}$ x 100

$= \dfrac{Input - Losses}{Input}$ x 100

$= \left(1 - \dfrac{Losses}{Input}\right)$ x 100

$= 100 - \left(\dfrac{Losses}{Input} \times 100\right)$

$= 100 -$ Percent Losses

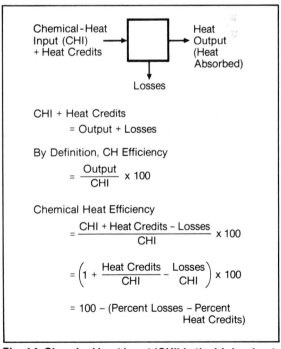

CHI + Heat Credits
= Output + Losses

By Definition, CH Efficiency

$= \dfrac{Output}{CHI}$ x 100

Chemical Heat Efficiency

$= \dfrac{CHI + Heat\ Credits - Losses}{CHI}$ x 100

$= \left(1 + \dfrac{Heat\ Credits}{CHI} - \dfrac{Losses}{CHI}\right)$ x 100

$= 100 -$ (Percent Losses − Percent Heat Credits)

Fig. 14 Chemical heat input (CHI) is the higher heating value of the fuel fired in the boiler above a stated reference temperature.

must be established, as well as acceptable operating conditions, number of load points, the direction of test runs, and any basis for rejection of runs.

Before a test is started, it must be determined whether the fuel to be fired is substantially as intended. A reliable, accurate efficiency test for purposes of equipment acceptance depends upon the fuel being in close agreement with that for which the steam-generating unit was designed. Significant deviations in fuel constituents and heating value can result in appreciable inaccuracies in heat-loss calculations and resulting efficiencies. Although the magnitude of deviation that is tolerable is difficult to establish, it should be recognized that fuel-

analysis variation producing changes in heating value on the order of 10 percent can alter final calculated efficiency about 1 percent.

The Test Code does not include consideration of overall tolerances or margins on performance guarantees; test results are to be reported as computed from test observations, with proper corrections for calibrations. Allowances for errors of measurement and sampling are permissible provided they are agreed upon in advance and are clearly stated in the test report. The limits of probable error on calculated steam generator efficiency are to be taken as the square root of the sum of the squares of the individual effects on efficiency.

Whenever allowances for probable errors of

As noted earlier in this chapter, a research laboratory has a variety of test instrumentation to supply experimental information for both basic investigation and for observation of behavior of less than full-size equipment. At C-E's KDL laboratories, this specially designed Gas Analysis System (GAS) is used to evaluate the products of combustion in several fuel-burning facilities. Water-cooled probes continuously extract a gas sample from the flame or the stack, as desired. From the probe, the sample gas is ducted to the conditioner/ analyzer through a heated sample line that maintains the sample temperature above its dew point. When the sample enters the GAS cabinet, it passes through one of two conditioners which prepare it for analysis by lowering its dew point by accurate blending with dry air and by removing particulate. Various internal instruments then analyze the conditioned sample for up to six flue-gas constituents: CO, CO_2, SO_2, NO/NO_x, O_2, and total hydrocarbons (THC).

measurement and sampling are to be taken into consideration, the reported test results shall be qualified by the statement that the error in the results may be considered not to exceed a given plus or minus percentage. Table II taken from PTC 4 is included as a guide to show the effect on efficiency of measurement errors (exclusive of sampling errors). The measurement-error range in the table is not intended to be authoritative but conforms approximately with experience. The values in the table are not intended for calculation of test results.

Table II. Probable Measurement Errors and Resulting Errors in Efficiency Calculations*

Measurement	Measurement error, percent	Error in calculated Steam Generator Efficiency, percent
Input-Output Method		
(1) Weigh tanks (calibrated scales)	±0.10	±0.10
(2) Volumetric tanks (calibrated)	±0.25	±0.25
(3) Calibrated flow nozzle or orifice including manometer	±0.35	±0.35
(4) Calibrated flow nozzle or orifice including recorder	±0.55	±0.55
(5) Coal scales—batch or dump (calibrated)	±0.25	±0.25
(6) Uncalibrated flow nozzle or orifice including manometer	±1.25	±1.25
(7) Uncalibrated flow nozzle or orifice including recorder	±1.60	±1.60
(8) Fuel heating value (coal)	±0.50	±0.50
(gas and oil)	±0.35	±0.35
(9) Reheatflow (based on heat balance calculations)	±0.60	±0.10
(10) Superheater outlet temperature (calibrated measuring device)	±0.25	±0.15
(11) Superheater outlet pressure (calibrated measuring device)	±1.00	±0.00
(12) Reheater inlet and outlet temperature (calibrated measuring device)	±0.25	±0.10
(13) Reheater inlet and outlet pressure (calibrated measuring device)	±0.50	±0.00
(14) Feedwater temperature (calibrated measuring device)	±0.25	±0.10
Heat-Loss Method		
(1) Heating value (coal)	±0.50	±0.03
(gas and oil)	±0.35	±0.02
(2) Orsat analysis	±3.00	±0.30
(3) Exit gas temperature (calibrated measuring device)	±0.50	±0.02
(4) Inlet air temperature (calibrated measuring device)	±0.50	±0.00
(5) Ultimate analysis of coal (carbon)	±1.00	±0.10
(hydrogen)	±1.00	±0.10
(6) Fuel moisture	±1.00	±0.00

*Taken from ASME PTC 4.

SUMMARY SHEET	ASME TEST FORM FOR ABBREVIATED EFFICIENCY TEST		PTC 4.1-a (1964)

	TEST NO	BOILER NO.	DATE
OWNER OF PLANT	LOCATION		
TEST CONDUCTED BY	OBJECTIVE OF TEST		DURATION
BOILER MAKE & TYPE	RATED CAPACITY		
STOKER TYPE & SIZE			
PULVERIZER, TYPE & SIZE	BURNER, TYPE & SIZE		
FUEL USED MINE	COUNTY	STATE	SIZE AS FIRED

PRESSURES & TEMPERATURES

1	STEAM PRESSURE IN BOILER DRUM	psia	
2	STEAM PRESSURE AT S. H. OUTLET	psia	
3	STEAM PRESSURE AT R. H. INLET	psia	
4	STEAM PRESSURE AT R. H. OUTLET	psia	
5	STEAM TEMPERATURE AT S. H. OUTLET	F	
6	STEAM TEMPERATURE AT R H INLET	F	
7	STEAM TEMPERATURE AT R.H. OUTLET	F	
8	WATER TEMP. ENTERING (ECON)(BOILER)	F	
9	STEAM QUALITY % MOISTURE OR P.P.M.		
10	AIR TEMP. AROUND BOILER (AMBIENT)	F	
11	TEMP AIR FOR COMBUSTION (This is Reference Temperature) †	F	
12	TEMPERATURE OF FUEL	F	
13	GAS TEMP. LEAVING (Boiler) (Econ.) (Air Htr.)	F	
14	GAS TEMP. ENTERING AH (If conditions to be corrected to guarantee)	F	

UNIT QUANTITIES

15	ENTHALPY OF SAT. LIQUID (TOTAL HEAT)	Btu/lb	
16	ENTHALPY OF (SATURATED) (SUPERHEATED) STM.	Btu/lb	
17	ENTHALPY OF SAT. FEED TO (BOILER) (ECON.)	Btu/lb	
18	ENTHALPY OF REHEATED STEAM R.H. INLET	Btu/lb	
19	ENTHALPY OF REHEATED STEAM R.H. OUTLET	Btu/lb	
20	HEAT ABS LB OF STEAM (ITEM 16 – ITEM 17)	Btu/lb	
21	HEAT ABS. LB R.H. STEAM (ITEM 19 – ITEM 18)	Btu/lb	
22	DRY REFUSE (ASH PIT + FLY ASH) PER LB AS FIRED FUEL	lb/lb	
23	Btu PER LB IN REFUSE (WEIGHTED AVERAGE)	Btu/lb	
24	CARBON BURNED PER LB AS FIRED FUEL	lb/lb	
25	DRY GAS PER LB AS FIRED FUEL BURNED	lb/lb	

HOURLY QUANTITIES

26	ACTUAL WATER EVAPORATED	lb/hr	
27	REHEAT STEAM FLOW	lb/hr	
28	RATE OF FUEL FIRING (AS FIRED wt)	lb/hr	
29	TOTAL HEAT INPUT $\frac{(\text{Item } 28 \times \text{Item } 41)}{1000}$	kB/hr	
30	HEAT OUTPUT IN BLOW-DOWN WATER	kB/hr	
31	TOTAL HEAT OUTPUT $\frac{(\text{Item } 26 \times \text{Item } 20)+(\text{Item } 27 \times \text{Item } 21)+\text{Item } 30}{1000}$	kB/hr	

FLUE GAS ANAL. (BOILER)(ECON)(AIR HTR) OUTLET

32	CO₂	% VOL	
33	O₂	% VOL	
34	CO	% VOL	
35	N₂ (BY DIFFERENCE)	% VOL	
36	EXCESS AIR	%	

FUEL DATA

	COAL AS FIRED PROX. ANALYSIS	% wt		OIL	
37	MOISTURE		51	FLASH POINT F*	
38	VOL MATTER		52	Sp. Gravity Deg. API*	
39	FIXED CARBON		53	VISCOSITY AT SSU* BURNER SSF	
40	ASH		44	TOTAL HYDROGEN % wt	
	TOTAL		41	Btu per lb	
41	Btu per lb AS FIRED				
42	ASH SOFT TEMP.* ASTM METHOD			**GAS**	% VOL

	COAL OR OIL AS FIRED ULTIMATE ANALYSIS				
43	CARBON		54	CO	
44	HYDROGEN		55	CH₄ METHANE	
45	OXYGEN		56	C₂H₂ ACETYLENE	
46	NITROGEN		57	C₂H₄ ETHYLENE	
47	SULPHUR		58	C₂H₆ ETHANE	
40	ASH		59	H₂S	
37	MOISTURE		60	CO₂	
			61	H₂ HYDROGEN	
	TOTAL			**TOTAL**	

COAL PULVERIZATION

				TOTAL HYDROGEN % wt	
48	GRINDABILITY INDEX*		62	DENSITY 68 F ATM. PRESS.	
49	FINENESS % THRU 50 M*		63	Btu PER CU FT	
50	FINENESS % THRU 200 M*		41	Btu PER LB	
64	INPUT-OUTPUT EFFICIENCY OF UNIT %	$\frac{\text{ITEM } 31 \times 100}{\text{ITEM } 29}$			

HEAT LOSS EFFICIENCY

		Btu/lb A.F. FUEL	% of A.F. FUEL
65	HEAT LOSS DUE TO DRY GAS		
66	HEAT LOSS DUE TO MOISTURE IN FUEL		
67	HEAT LOSS DUE TO H₂O FROM COMB. OF H₂		
68	HEAT LOSS DUE TO COMBUST. IN REFUSE		
69	HEAT LOSS DUE TO RADIATION		
70	UNMEASURED LOSSES		
71	**TOTAL**		
72	EFFICIENCY = (100 – Item 71)		

* Not Required for Efficiency Testing

† For Point of Measurement See Par. 7.2.8.1-PTC 4.1-1964

Printed in U.S.A. (10/74)

This Test Form (C-36) may be obtained from ASME, 345 E. 47 St., New York, N.Y. 10017

ASME Performance Test Codes: Since its first publication in 1915, *ASME Performance Test Code* 4.1, Steam Generating Units, has been a recognized guide for procedures of boiler testing. The boiler boundary diagram as well as the forms on the following pages are reproduced from the 1964 edition of PTC 4.1.

PTC 4.1-b (1964)

ASME TEST FORM
CALCULATION SHEET   FOR ABBREVIATED EFFICIENCY TEST   *Revised September, 1965*

OWNER OF PLANT	TEST NO.	BOILER NO.	DATE

30 HEAT OUTPUT IN BOILER BLOW-DOWN WATER = LB OF WATER BLOW-DOWN PER HR × $\dfrac{\boxed{\text{ITEM 15} \quad \text{ITEM 17}}}{1000}$ = ... kB/hr

24 *If impractical to weigh refuse, this item can be estimated as follows*

DRY REFUSE PER LB OF AS FIRED FUEL = $\dfrac{\% \text{ ASH IN AS FIRED COAL}}{100 - \% \text{ COMB. IN REFUSE SAMPLE}}$

CARBON BURNED PER LB AS FIRED FUEL = $\dfrac{\text{ITEM 43}}{100}$ .... $- \dfrac{\boxed{\text{ITEM 22} \quad \text{ITEM 23}}{........ \times ....}}{14,500}$ = ...

NOTE: IF FLUE DUST & ASH PIT REFUSE DIFFER MATERIALLY IN COMBUSTIBLE CONTENT, THEY SHOULD BE ESTIMATED SEPARATELY. SEE SECTION 7, COMPUTATIONS.

25 DRY GAS PER LB AS FIRED FUEL BURNED = $\dfrac{11CO_2 + 8O_2 + 7(N_2 + CO)}{3(CO_2 + CO)}$ × (LB CARBON BURNED PER LB AS FIRED FUEL + $\tfrac{3}{8}$ S)

= $\dfrac{11 \times \overset{\text{ITEM 32}}{.....} + 8 \times \overset{\text{ITEM 33}}{.....} + 7\left(\overset{\text{ITEM 35}}{.....} + \overset{\text{ITEM 34}}{.....}\right)}{3 \times \left(\overset{\text{ITEM 32}}{.....} + \overset{\text{ITEM 34}}{.....}\right)}$ × $\left[\overset{\text{ITEM 24}}{.....} + \dfrac{\overset{\text{ITEM 47}}{.....}}{267}\right]$ = ...

36 EXCESS AIR † = 100 × $\dfrac{O_2 - \dfrac{CO}{2}}{.2682N_2 - (O_2 - \dfrac{CO}{2})}$ = 100 × $\dfrac{\overset{\text{ITEM 33}}{.} - \dfrac{\text{ITEM 34}}{2}}{.2682(\text{ITEM 35}) - (\text{ITEM 33} - \dfrac{\text{ITEM 34}}{2})}$ = ...

HEAT LOSS EFFICIENCY	Btu/lb AS FIRED FUEL	$\dfrac{\text{LOSS}}{\text{HHV}} \times 100 =$	LOSS %
65 HEAT LOSS DUE TO DRY GAS = $\dfrac{\text{LB DRY GAS}}{\text{PER LB AS FIRED FUEL}}$ × C_p × $(t_{lvg} - t_{air})$ = $\overset{\text{ITEM 25}}{......}$ × 0.24 $\dfrac{(\text{ITEM 13}) - (\text{ITEM 11})}{......}$ =		$\dfrac{65}{41} \times 100 =$	......
66 HEAT LOSS DUE TO MOISTURE IN FUEL = $\dfrac{\text{LB }H_2O\text{ PER LB}}{\text{AS FIRED FUEL}}$ × [(ENTHALPY OF VAPOR AT 1 PSIA & T GAS LVG) − (ENTHALPY OF LIQUID AT T AIR)] = $\dfrac{\text{ITEM 37}}{100}$ × [(ENTHALPY OF VAPOR AT 1 PSIA & T ITEM 13) − (ENTHALPY OF LIQUID AT T ITEM 11)] = ...	......	$\dfrac{66}{41} \times 100 =$	......
67 HEAT LOSS DUE TO H_2O FROM COMB. OF H_2 = $9H_2$ × [(ENTHALPY OF VAPOR AT 1 PSIA & T GAS LVG) − (ENTHALPY OF LIQUID AT T AIR)] = 9 × $\dfrac{\text{ITEM 44}}{100}$ × [(ENTHALPY OF VAPOR AT 1 PSIA & T ITEM 13) − (ENTHALPY OF LIQUID AT T ITEM 11)] = ...	......	$\dfrac{67}{41} \times 100 =$	......
68 HEAT LOSS DUE TO COMBUSTIBLE IN REFUSE = $\overset{\text{ITEM 22}}{......} \times \overset{\text{ITEM 23}}{......}$ =		$\dfrac{68}{41} \times 100 =$	......
69 HEAT LOSS DUE TO RADIATION* = $\dfrac{\text{TOTAL BTU RADIATION LOSS PER HR}}{\text{LB AS FIRED FUEL} - \text{ITEM 28}}$ = ...	......	$\dfrac{69}{41} \times 100 =$	......
70 UNMEASURED LOSSES **	......	$\dfrac{70}{41} \times 100 =$	......
71 TOTAL	......	......	......
72 EFFICIENCY = (100 − ITEM 71)	......	......	......

† For rigorous determination of excess air see Appendix 9.2 — PTC 4.1-1964
* If losses are not measured, use ABMA Standard Radiation Loss Chart, Fig. 8, PTC 4.1-1964
** Unmeasured losses listed in PTC 4.1 but not tabulated above may by provided for by assigning a mutually agreed upon value for Item 70.

Printed in U.S.A. (10/74)   This Test Form (C-37) may be obtained from ASME, 345 E. 47 St., New York, N.Y. 10017

FIG 1 STEAM GENERATING UNIT DIAGRAM

This diagram for boiler tests serves as a key to the numerical subscripts used throughout *ASME Performance Test Code* 4.1, steam generating units

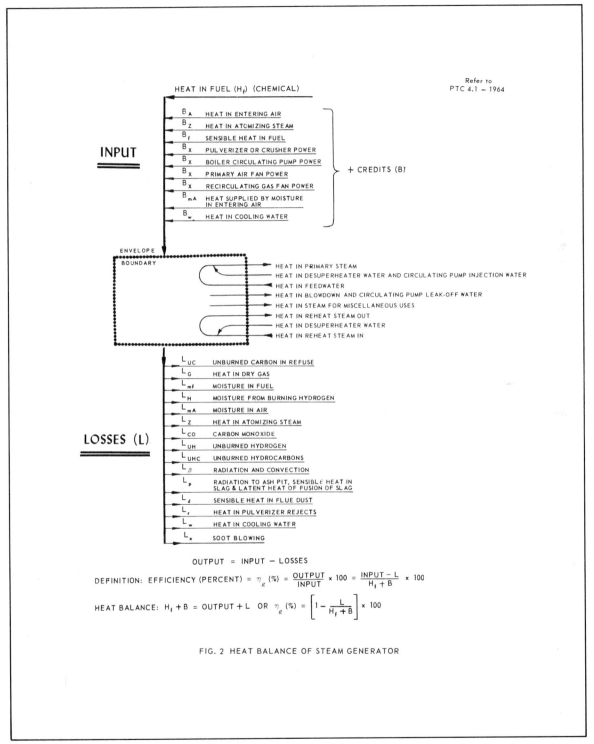

HEAT IN FUEL (H_f) (CHEMICAL)

Refer to
PTC 4.1 – 1964

INPUT

B_A — HEAT IN ENTERING AIR
B_z — HEAT IN ATOMIZING STEAM
B_f — SENSIBLE HEAT IN FUEL
B_x — PULVERIZER OR CRUSHER POWER
B_x — BOILER CIRCULATING PUMP POWER
B_x — PRIMARY AIR FAN POWER
B_x — RECIRCULATING GAS FAN POWER
B_{mA} — HEAT SUPPLIED BY MOISTURE IN ENTERING AIR
B_w — HEAT IN COOLING WATER

+ CREDITS (B)

ENVELOPE
BOUNDARY

HEAT IN PRIMARY STEAM
HEAT IN DESUPERHEATER WATER AND CIRCULATING PUMP INJECTION WATER
HEAT IN FEEDWATER
HEAT IN BLOWDOWN AND CIRCULATING PUMP LEAK-OFF WATER
HEAT IN STEAM FOR MISCELLANEOUS USES
HEAT IN REHEAT STEAM OUT
HEAT IN DESUPERHEATER WATER
HEAT IN REHEAT STEAM IN

LOSSES (L)

L_{UC} — UNBURNED CARBON IN REFUSE
L_G — HEAT IN DRY GAS
L_{mf} — MOISTURE IN FUEL
L_H — MOISTURE FROM BURNING HYDROGEN
L_{mA} — MOISTURE IN AIR
L_z — HEAT IN ATOMIZING STEAM
L_{CO} — CARBON MONOXIDE
L_{UH} — UNBURNED HYDROGEN
L_{UHC} — UNBURNED HYDROCARBONS
L_β — RADIATION AND CONVECTION
L_p — RADIATION TO ASH PIT, SENSIBLE HEAT IN SLAG & LATENT HEAT OF FUSION OF SLAG
L_d — SENSIBLE HEAT IN FLUE DUST
L_r — HEAT IN PULVERIZER REJECTS
L_w — HEAT IN COOLING WATER
L_x — SOOT BLOWING

OUTPUT = INPUT – LOSSES

DEFINITION: EFFICIENCY (PERCENT) = η_g (%) = $\dfrac{\text{OUTPUT}}{\text{INPUT}} \times 100 = \dfrac{\text{INPUT} - L}{H_f + B} \times 100$

HEAT BALANCE: $H_f + B$ = OUTPUT + L   OR η_g (%) = $\left[1 - \dfrac{L}{H_f + B}\right] \times 100$

FIG. 2 HEAT BALANCE OF STEAM GENERATOR

A heat balance diagram showing the significance of boiler testing

REFERENCES

[1] *ASME Performance Test Codes:* PTC 1, "General Instructions," PTC 2, "Code on Definitions and Values"; PTC 3.1, "Diesel and Burner Fuels"; PTC 3.2, "Solid Fuels"; PTC 3.3, "Gaseous Fuels"; PTC 4.2, "Coal Pulverizers"; PTC 4.3, "Air Heaters"; PTC 21, "Dust Separating Apparatus"; PTC 27, "Determining Dust Concentration in a Gas Stream," New York: American Society of Mechanical Engineers, latest edition.

[2] S. J. Kline and F. A. McClintock, "Describing Uncertainties in Single Sample Experiments," *Mechanical Engineering,* 75(1): 3–8, Jan. 1953.

[3] W. A. Wilson, "Design of Power Plant Tests to Insure Reliability of Results," *Transactions of the ASME,* 75: 405–408, May 1955.

L. W. Thrasher and R. C. Binder, "A Practical Application of Uncertainty Calculations to Measured Data," *Transactions of the ASME,* 79: 373–376, Feb. 1957.

S. Baron, "The Effect of Measurement Errors on Plant Performance Tests," *Combustion,* 25(8): 49–54, Feb. 1954.

[4] J. H. Born, Jr., "The Effect of Measurement Errors in the Accuracy of Steam Generator Efficiency Calculators," *ASME Paper 60-WA-301.* New York: American Society of Mechanical Engineers, 1960.

[5] "Orifice Metering of Natural Gas" *ANSI/API 2530. AGA Report no. 3.* New York: American National Standards Institute, latest edition.

American Petroleum Institute, *Oil Pipeline Construction and Maintenance,* 2nd ed. Austin: University of Texas, 1973.

ASME Performance Test Codes, PTC 19.5, "Supplements on Instruments and Apparatus," New York: American Society of Mechanical Engineers, latest edition.

[6] *ASTM Standards,* Part 26, *Gaseous Fuels; Coal and Coke; Atmospheric Analysis.* D 2015, "Test for Gross Calorific Value of Solid Fuel by the Adiabatic Bomb Calorimeter"; D 2961, "Test for Total Moisture in Coal Reduced to No. 8 Top Sieve Size (Limited Purpose Method)"; D 3172, "Proximate Analysis of Coal and Coke"; D 3173, "Test for Moisture in the Analysis Sample of Coal and Coke"; D 3174 "Test for Ash in the Analysis Sample of Coal and Coke"; D 3177, "Test for Total Sulfur in the Analysis Sample of Coal and Coke"; D3178, "Test for Carbon and Hydrogen in the Analysis Sample of Coal and Coke"; D 3180, "Calculating Coal and Coke Analyses from As-Determined to Different Bases"; D 3286, "Test for Gross Calorific Value of Solid Fuel by the Isothermal-Jacket Bomb Calorimeter"; D 3302, "Test for Total Moisture in Coal"; Philadelphia: American Society for Testing and Materials, latest edition.

[7] See Chapter 11, "Fuel Burning Equipment," for more information.

[8] *ASME Performance Test Codes,* PTC 19.3, "Temperature Measurement," New York: American Society of Mechanical Engineers, latest edition.

[9] P. H. Dike, *Thermoelectric Thermometry,* 3rd ed. Philadelphia: Leeds and Northrup Co., 1958.

[10] Chromel and alumel are chromium-nickel and aluminum-nickel alloys respectively. Constantan is a copper alloy.

[11] *ASTM Standards,* Part 44, "Magnetic Properties; Metallic Materials for Thermostatic; Electrical Resistance, Heating, Contacts; Temperature Measurement; Illuminating Standards," Philadelphia: American Society for Testing and Materials, latest edition.

[12] American Society of Mechanical Engineers, *Fluid Meters, Their Theory and Application,* 6th ed. New York: American Society of Mechanical Engineers, 1971.

[13] J. W. Murdock, "Power Test Code Thermometer Wells," *Transactions of the ASME. Journal of Engineering for Power,* 81, Series A: 403–416, 1959.

[14] P. G. W. Hawksley, et al., *Measurement of Solids in Flue Gases,* 2nd ed. London: The Institute of Fuel, 1977.

[15] Harry James White, *Industrial Electrostatic Precipitation.* Reading, Mass: Addison Wesley, 1963.

[16] W. B. Gregory, "The Pilot Tube," *Transactions of the ASME,* 25: 184–211, 1904.

[17] W. C. Rowse, "Pilot Tubes for Gas Measurement," *Transactions of the ASME,* 35: 633–703, 1913.

[18] E. S. Cole, "Pilot Tube Practice," *Transactions of the ASME,* 57: 281–294, 1935.

[19] R. G. Folsom, "Review of the Pilot Tube," *Transactions of the ASME,* 78: 1447–1460, Oct. 1956.

[20] C. J. Fechheimer, "Measurement of Static Pressure," *Transactions of the ASME,* 48: 965–977, 1926.

[21] C. L. Burton, "Quantitation of Stack Gas Flow," Reprint from *Journal of the Air Pollution Control Association,* 22(8): 631–635, Aug. 1972.

[22] *ASME Performance Test Codes,* PTC 4.1, "Steam Generating Units," New York: American Society of Mechanical Engineers, latest edition.

BIBLIOGRAPHY

Buna, Tibor, "Combustion Calculations for Multiple Fuels," *Transactions of the ASME,* 78: 1237–1249, Aug. 1956.

Bostic, J. A., and Long, W. F., "Code Testing of Large Boilers: Input-Output or Heat-Loss Method," *ASME Paper No. 60-PWR-5.* New York: American Society of Mechanical Engineers, 1960.

Cohen, L., and Fritz, W. A., Jr., "Efficiency Determination of Marine Boilers: Input-Output Versus Heat-Loss Method," *Transactions of the ASME. Journal of Engineering for Power,* 84, Series A: 39–43, Jan. 1962.

Vuia, R. E., "Performance Testing of Large Steam Generators," *ASME Paper No. 62-WA-267.* New York: American Society of Mechanical Engineers, 1962.

CHAPTER 22

Maintenance and Repair of Steam-Generating Equipment

A good maintenance program is one of the keys to reliability of any steam generator. To be successful, such a program requires managerial ability, expertise, imagination, planning, training, and the commitment of top management. In addition, maintenance must be closely integrated with both the operation and engineering functions.

MAINTENANCE FORESIGHT

Because plant layout can either facilitate or impede a maintenance program, maintenance personnel should be a part of the initial design team to insure the plant layout facilitates maintenance. Ideally, the person who will be ultimately responsible for plant maintenance should be a member of the design team.

Only during the design stage can truly adequate space be allocated for maintenance. As equipment is located, maintenance personnel must have space to remove the largest replaceable part easily. The steam generator should have enough access doors so that all areas may be entered easily for inspection. Access doors and aisles also must be large enough to accommodate components that must be moved to a maintenance area. Sufficient headroom is a must. Overhead trolleys and cranes for mainte-

nance should be designed *into* the plant rather than retrofitted. All high-maintenance items should have adequate laydown and work areas adjacent to the equipment. Models can help the designer plan for accessibility (Fig. 1).

Designers responsible for piping and electrical work must be aware of areas requiring accessibility for maintenance. Often piping and wiring are field-run from drawings having notes advising construction personnel of special maintenance requirements.

EQUIPMENT MANUALS: AN ASSET TO EFFECTIVE MAINTENANCE

It is important at the time equipment is purchased to specify operation and maintenance manuals which are complete, detailed, and specific to the piece of equipment supplied. Material that does not contribute to an understanding of the design, care, operation, and maintenance of the equipment should be excluded. Manuals should include

- step-by-step disassembly procedures

- step-by-step reassembly procedures

- preventive maintenance and lubrication instructions

- lists of all special tools required and instructions on their use

■ tabulated dimensional data on settings, clearances, and adjustments

DETERMINING THE NEED FOR SPARE PARTS

Often, a complement of spare parts is ordered with the initial purchase. If not, spares should be purchased before the equipment is placed in service. Items critical to plant production should receive special consideration and, for these items, it may be prudent to maintain spare subassemblies. At time of purchase, the owner should ask for complete instructions from the manufacturer for error-proof ordering of replacement parts. Catalogs specific to the equipment and with exploded view drawings help in selecting appropriate spare parts.

In addition, there should be a system for tracking spare parts. Many large plants maintain a replacement-parts inventory on a computer. If establishing an in-plant program is not feasible, equipment manufacturers are prepared to rent computer services for tracking spare parts supplied by them.

Manufacturers can provide guidelines for ordering spare parts based on field experience. Even so, one must realize that all equipment of a given type does not wear at the same rate, be-

Fig. 1 **Models help lay out a pulverizer lane for optimum maintenance access .**

cause different local conditions can alter wearing life drastically.

As orders arrive, responsible personnel should inspect maintenance material carefully. A defective part may sit in a storeroom for years before the defect is discovered—just at the time of need. Also, to assure correctness and completeness, all the incoming parts should be checked against purchase orders before the parts are stored.

IN-SERVICE MAINTENANCE

To insure that a unit is available on demand requires a constant effort by the maintenance staff. They must implement a day-to-day preventive program while the unit is in operation, establish a well-planned and properly executed inspection program for scheduled outages, and be prepared to handle all forced outages or equipment breakdowns as soon as they occur.

On-line maintenance functions are just as important as those performed during an outage. If properly undertaken, not only do they add to unit reliability, but they also save valuable downtime. On-line maintenance includes lubrication, seal and packing replacement, and repair of any component that has been removed and replaced with a spare.

Proper lubrication is critical for rotating auxiliaries. Usually, the most complete part of any correlated maintenance manual is its lubrication instructions. The manufacturer's recommendations for lubrication should be followed, with substitute oils or greases used only if they meet all specified properties. Each plant must develop and adhere to routine lubrication schedules. Major lubricant suppliers will work with a plant staff to develop a program which allows the most flexibility. Such a program would minimize the types of necessary lubricants, the amount of each kept in the plant, and the best reordering schedules. This lubrication is such an important part of any maintenance program that records of work that has been done should be kept by using checkoff sheets.

Good communications between the operations and maintenance groups is essential. The day-to-day in-service maintenance program must be closely coordinated with plant operators, who are to inform the maintenance crew of problems and potential problems. For example, maintenance should be informed of slight drops in pressure or temperature which could indicate inefficient operation or deterioration of machinery. In addition to such visual signals, operators inspecting equipment often detect problems by unusual sounds, smells, or tactile sensations.

Similarly, the maintenance crew must inform operators of any equipment being repaired. Often in the case of several sootblowers needing repair, the operator decides which blower is crucial to operation and requests maintenance to give that blower priority.

Fig. 2 **A plant should have three complete journal assemblies stored on transport dollies .**

PULVERIZER MAINTENANCE

Although it is beyond the scope of one chapter to describe the maintenance of the various equipment that can be overhauled while a generating unit continues in service, a major component usually overhauled on-line is a pulverizer. The life of mill parts depends on many factors which vary considerably from one plant to another. The main factors are the abrasive characteristics of the coal, operating hours of individual mills, and mill loading as a percent of maximum capacity. Although plants usually install spare pulverizers, two or more of which may be idle at reduced boiler loads, pulverizer outage time for maintenance should be kept to a minimum so that all pulverizers are always ready for service.

Because an effective pulverizer maintenance program must be adjusted on the basis of actual plant operating experience, it is essential to maintain an accurate log of each pulverizer's running time, stoppages for removal of foreign material, maintenance work and inspections. Maintenance must be staggered so that all pulverizers do not require work at the same time.

Rolls and grinding rings are the major replaceable items. (Later in this chapter, there is a further discussion of roll and ring wear.) With good planning and preparation, it is possible to overhaul a pulverizer, renewing the ring and rolls as well as repairing or replacing other wearing parts, in a few days.

As part of its spare-parts complement, a plant should have three complete journal assemblies including journal-opening covers (Fig. 2). Frequently, such assemblies are interchangeable on all mills in the station and can be stored on transport dollies in the mill overhaul area. Following a mill overhaul, worn journal assemblies that have been removed are rebuilt with new grinding rolls.

To accommodate transport of worn journals and overhauled assemblies simultaneously, six transport and storage dollies should be on hand. Storing segmented bowl-ring assemblies on pallets (one complete ring per pallet) permits hoisting to the mill platform in one lift. Frequently used bolts, nuts, and washers are kept in bins in the mill overhaul area. Two journal-assembly hoisting fixtures should be fabricated and stored adjacent to the journal overhaul and storage area.

Once a mill has cooled and been tagged out-of-service, access doors are removed and the mill-base access door is opened. To further cool mill parts, an air mover often is used to ventilate the mill through the mill-base door. When all three journal assemblies have been removed, there is free access to the inside of the mill, and a worn bull ring or worn separator-body liners can be removed rapidly. When all obviously worn parts have been stripped from the mill, the remaining parts are carefully inspected for repair or replacement.

When the repair work inside the mill has been completed, the overhauled journal assemblies are installed. All access doors are closed, the mill is cleared of all "hold" tags, and it is started without coal to facilitate adjustment of the grinding-roll-to-ring clearance. When this adjustment has been completed, the mill is released for normal service.

THE ANNUAL OUTAGE

For any power plant, the major part of its unified maintenance program is the scheduled annual maintenance outage. The objectives of the first-annual planned outage are to inspect equipment, recommend repairs, and establish a data base from which to develop a preventative maintenance program. Although subsequent annual outages will concentrate on repair work, a review of these three procedural items must be part of every outage.

Whether accomplished by plant personnel or a maintenance contractor, a well-planned outage program begins as much as a year before the scheduled downtime. The planning and the jobsite organization must include well-defined communication channels (Fig. 3). With an outside contractor, advance communication with the plant staff is crucial to the success of the operation. The plant staff must follow the contractor's work closely so that spare parts, engineering changes, and new material selections are expeditiously handled.

THE PRE-OUTAGE STAGE

Several months before a scheduled outage, the group responsible for the inspection and the work must jointly plan the inspection schedule with plant personnel. In preparation for the outage, personnel assemble tools, scaffolding, spare parts and other required materials. Also during this period, the engineers in charge of work during the outage examine existing unit operating and maintenance records, and discuss with all plant personnel those areas requiring particular attention.

PRE-OUTAGE INSPECTION ITEMS

Usually, while the unit and its auxiliaries are still operating, a complete visual inspection is

Fig. 3 **A successful outage must include a good organization with well-defined communication channels .**

performed to detect any obvious items requiring maintenance or more detailed investigation during shutdown. All items are noted and a list compiled.

Operational checks of certain equipment and systems also are conducted to ensure each is functioning properly—or requires adjustment, repair or replacement. Included are

■ fuel-burning equipment such as tilting mechanisms, windbox dampers, coal gates, and oil or gas valves

■ furnace-safety-control and ignition systems

■ combustion and feedwater-control systems

■ sootblowing equipment

In addition, the settings on safety valves are checked. Control and isolation valve performance is verified and any packing leaks recorded. The condition of activators is checked to be sure oil seals are secure and lubricating oil is not contaminated with water or flyash.

All permanent thermocouples, such as those on superheater and reheater tubing and water-wall panel outlets, are checked to isolate any defects requiring repair during the outage.

Readings from expansion trams in important areas should be recorded for comparison with readings taken during the outage when the unit is cold, and after its return to service. These readings are used to confirm free and proper expansion of the unit.

SCAFFOLDING

For outages in which extensive inspection and repairs to the furnace are planned, fixed scaffolding temporarily installed both outside and inside the furnace can save time and money. In the past, craft personnel have experienced considerable difficulty using sky-climbers and have questioned their efficiency and safety. When extensive repairs are planned for furnace and penthouse areas, scaffolding rental fees are more than offset by savings in working-hours. Adapted for quick installation, such scaffolding is modular and made of tubular carbon steel with steel loops at the end of each section (Fig. 4). Fixed-length sections are

Fig. 4 Interior view of unit with modular scaffolding system. Note easy entrance and access to all areas .

safety-locked to one another by inserting steel wedges into the loops.

Basically, the scaffolding for interior access provides a solid platform near the top of the furnace. Typically, ten or more scaffold towers, each with three working platforms, are positioned at the front of the furnace adjacent to each side of the superheater division panels. Scaffolding is also provided across the unit at the front and rear of the superheater or reheater pendent assemblies.

Furnace waterwalls are scaffolded from the lower slopes to a point approximately 6 feet below the lowest element tubing of the superheater division panels. Walkway levels are provided at approximately 7-foot intervals, beginning at the bottom wall-blower elevation and continuing to the top elevation of wall blowers. An extension of the waterwall platform at convenient working elevations provides interior access to the windbox. Exterior scaffolding also can be used at the penthouse front wall near the roof header and superheater links, at the sootblowers for lance removal, and at the economizer outlet ductwork.

As typical views of scaffolding show (Fig. 4 and 5), maintenance and repair personnel have easy access to the unit during an outage. This provides two significant improvements over previous methods. Repair personnel can enter the interior more safely than by using cable-hung equipment. Equally important, continuous access to all areas is possible and various crafts do not have to compete for access. This significantly reduces the time required to transport personnel and materials to areas to be repaired. Finally, scaffolding allows a more complete and thorough inspection.

THE OUTAGE STAGE

During the outage, every portion of the unit requires inspection. Scheduled repairs are then accomplished by a critical-path analysis to assure all repairs are completed. Key areas to be inspected are the pressure parts, the fuel-firing and transport equipment, boiler casing and structural supports, and such sub-systems as ash-handling and sootblowing equipment.

PRESSURE PARTS: EXAMINATION OF EXTERNAL SURFACES

Within the furnace, external surfaces of tubing are examined for erosion, metal wastage, swelling or developing problems in critical areas such as the firing zone and near sootblowers. Suspicious areas are investigated further by cleaning with sandblasting and then checking wall thicknesses by micrometer, or measuring thicknesses ultrasonically. See Fig. 6. This type inspection also covers

■ critical superheater and reheater sections
■ economizer tubing
■ steam-cooled-wall surfaces and waterwall hanger tubing in the gas passes.

PRESSURE PARTS: EXAMINATION OF INTERNAL SURFACES

The steam drum must be entered and thoroughly inspected for deposits, loose parts, erosion, and areas that may allow internal bypassing of water or steam. Conditions found in the boiler drums may dictate inspection of waterwall headers and other internal surfaces for evidence of corrosion or deposits.

Any lower waterwall headers large enough to have access ways should be inspected. Waterwall distribution orifices and screens are examined closely for deposits. Orifices are checked for proper size with go/no-go gages.

Samples of furnace-wall tubing may be removed from various locations a short distance above the uppermost fuel nozzles. Such samples are examined internally to determine surface condition and to detect any deposits.

FIRING EQUIPMENT

During the internal inspection of the furnace, the condition of the fuel and air nozzles is determined and any serious deterioration (Fig. 7) noted for replacement or repair.

Tilting fuel and air nozzles should be operated through their range while being observed from inside the furnace. Binding, nonparallelism or other malfunctions should be corrected. The tilt mechanism is also inspected from inside the windbox to determine the condition of the linkage.

Windbox dampers are inspected from within

to determine that they operate through their normal stroke and that damper-blade movements correspond correctly to external linkage movement. No binding should be evident.

If there are retractable oil guns, the retracting cylinders must be operated to verify proper movement. The clearance of oil guns and condition of the ignitor-horn also should be checked from inside the furnace.

Extensive pulverizer maintenance is not always scheduled during an outage. In any case, a general inspection of the mills must be made. Particularly, inspect all shutoff dampers related to the pulverizers for proper operation.

Coal-pipe elbows in critical locations are examined internally for wear. In particular, the final elbow at the fuel nozzle must be inspected and the wear pattern noted. Defective kicker blocks should be replaced or relocated. Riffle distributors throughout the system are inspected for wear and replaced or rotated as necessary. Coal-pipe orifices are checked for signs of wear.

The feeders must be inspected as recom-mended by the manufacturer to implement any necessary adjustments and maintenance. Any damaged belts must be repaired.

CASING AND ROOF ENCLOSURE

The roof enclosure also is inspected and the condition of pressure parts, hangers, and other pressure-part supports is recorded. Any damage or leakage of the furnace roof casing and seals should be corrected. Condition of insulation and pipe seals should be recorded.

The roof support steel and hanger rods within the air space between the roof deck plates and insulation are checked for corrosion.

Any leaks or damage of the external casing of the entire unit noted during the pre-outage stage are repaired as necessary.

The skin casing and seals within the dead air space behind the deflection arch are inspected as are the casing, seals, and support steel within the dead air space beneath the sloping furnace bottom. All are inspected to determine general conditions and to note any maintenance that should be performed.

Fig. 5 **View of vertical modular scaffolding system**

OTHER AREAS OF CONCERN

Drip shields and seal plates at the furnace bottom must be inspected and repaired. The bottom-ash hopper and the balance of the ash-handling system are inspected as recommended by the manufacturer.

To the extent possible, all gas and air ducts are examined internally and externally for corrosion, erosion and leakage (Fig. 8).

The entire sootblowing system is checked—any malfunctioning equipment noted during the pre-outage operational check is further investigated. During the internal furnace inspection, sootblower effectiveness and any tube erosion from sootblower operation are noted so that sootblowers can be adjusted as necessary.

Boiler-water circulating pumps are inspected to manufacturer's recommendations.

Air-heater elements, seals, bearings, drives, and lubrication systems are checked.

Malfunctioning or leaking safety valves noted during the pre-outage operational check must be investigated and corrected.

The control system inspection includes calibration checks, stroking of drive units, and a general inspection of system components. Any malfunctioning components of the furnace safety system found during the pre-outage operational check are further investigated. Flame-scanner tubes are removed, inspected, and cleaned thoroughly.

All fans must be inspected (Fig. 9) for the condition of the bearings and their lubrication as well as the rotor and the associated dampers and/or inlet vanes. In addition, the induced-draft fans are examined for erosion, corrosion and/or deposits. Finally, all observation ports and access doors are checked for tightness.

THE POST-OUTAGE STAGE

After the unit is returned to service, the repair work is checked under operating conditions. For example, all permanent thermocouples on superheater, reheater, and waterwall individual tubes are observed to confirm proper operation.

As the unit is brought on the line, all control systems should be observed functionally to make any necessary adjustments (Fig. 10).

All valves repaired or repacked during the outage should be observed for proper operation and performance. Re-tighten all packing nuts with extreme care after each valve has reached normal operating pressure and temperature. Do not touch a valve if there is any indication that the valve was not packed properly.

Take an inventory of all recommended spare parts and forward a list of shortages to plant purchasing for ordering.

DOCUMENTATION

Documentation is an important phase of any maintenance program. All findings, both good and bad, should be noted in a comprehensive report which covers all pre-outage, outage, and post-outage inspection and repair.

THE PRE-OUTAGE REPORT

The pre-outage-inspection documents contain a review of unit history, visual inspections, a walkdown of the unit while in operation, a checkout of all thermocouples, ignitors, fuel-burning equipment, safety valves, and

Fig. 6 **Tubing is measured ultrasonically for wall thickness .**

sootblowers. Any items requiring further inspection or repair are noted.

THE OUTAGE REPORT

The outage report is tangible evidence of all that transpired. It is the basis for any necessary changes in operation, design or repair methods. It is the basis for all subsequent outages. It is the source of spare-part requirements. Outage documentation includes detailed reports, both quantitative and qualitative, describing conditions of both pressure and non-pressure parts of the unit. Fig. 11 shows a typical section of an outage report.

The engineer in charge of the outage should compile the report. An effective report might include sketches, marked prints, or photographs which can be useful where ideas or concepts rather than physical objects are being described for the record.

THE POST-OUTAGE REPORT

The post-outage documents describe conditions immediately after restart, such as thermocouple temperature measurements and expansion data. The final and most important documentation lists the recommendations of the inspection team, as well as an engineering department review of those findings. Such recommendations include spare parts to order in preparation for the next outage.

After all the planning, inspection and documentation have been completed, a critique provides all those involved in the outage an opportunity to review their findings and determine improvements for future outages. A frank, open exchange sets the stage for the next outage and also the plan for continuing work throughout the coming operating period.

THE FORCED OUTAGE

A forced outage requires as much or more planning than a scheduled outage, but by its nature, it allows the least time for planning. Consequently, a plant maintenance group must be prepared with an emergency plan formulated before a failure occurs. This plan should be in writing and periodically updated.

The plan should list alternatives such as renting equipment, borrowing equipment from

Fig. 7 **Fuel and air nozzles are inspected from inside the furnace.**

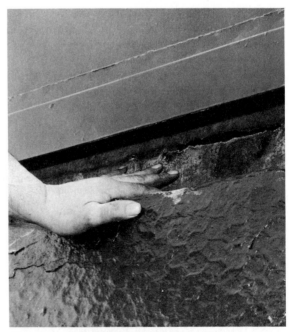

Fig. 8 **Look for corrosion, erosion or leakage on fan casings.**

another division or utility, use of alternate production methods, or purchase of power. Because downtime is critical, plan details and schedule must be worked out immediately. Plant personnel should have lists of other critical work that can be done during an outage.

Pressure-part failure is a major cause of forced outages. Since the unit must be cooled before it can be entered, the cooling time can be used for planning. As the repair of the failure will be the critical path in returning the unit to service, other maintenance must be done only if it does not interfere with the repair.

To save time during cool-down, crews can move parts, tools and scaffolds close to access doors. Usually, it is possible to determine the area of the failure and its general magnitude from the outside and, if a leak is small, sky-climbers, bosun chairs, or two-man scaffolding are generally adequate. If the steam generator has cable holes extending through the roof enclosure, considerable time can be saved because the roof enclosure does not have to be cooled for entry. For safety reasons, it is important that the cables be cooled if they are to pass through the hot enclosure; compressed air is

the usual cooling medium. If the damage is extensive and requires major repair work, more elaborate scaffolding may be necessary.

The importance of failure records cannot be over-emphasized. The cause of a single failure may not always be determined and an isolated random failure may be of little significance. But several similar failures may indicate serious problems affecting future availability. Good maintenance, then, requires not only that a failure be repaired but also that every effort be

Fig. 10 Control systems are adjusted as the unit is returned to service .

Fig. 9 Fan rotor is removed for inspection .

made to determine the root cause of the failure.

To retrieve information easily, an effective record-keeping procedure separates the logs for the superheater, reheater, economizer and waterwall. Patterns and trends are easily spotted when presented graphically such as on sketches showing elevation and plan views (Fig. 12). Numerals or dates of the chronological occurrence of a failure can be added.

REPAIR WELDING
FOR PRESSURE PARTS

Plant management and maintenance supervisors must bear in mind the legal formalities involved in the repair of boiler pressure parts.

In the United States, the National Board Inspection Code (NBIC) provides guidelines and rules for repairs and alterations to boilers and pressure vessels after they have been placed in service. NBIC rules, including the involvement of the Authorized Inspector (AI), are only mandatory in those states, cities, and provinces which have adopted the NBIC, or where required by the owner or the insurance carrier.

Jurisdictional requirements involving the AI vary widely. Most jurisdictions require the owner to obtain the AI's acceptance before repair or alteration. However, the NBI Code places the responsibility of coordinating the acceptance inspection on the contractor.

Anyone that is required to do pressure-part welding—owner, contractor or manufacturer—must use approved welding procedures done by qualified welders.

GUIDELINES FOR WELDING REPAIR
OF LOW-CARBON STEEL TUBES

A damaged tube should be cut out at least 2 in. on each side of the defective area. The minimum replacement tube length should be no less than 6 in.

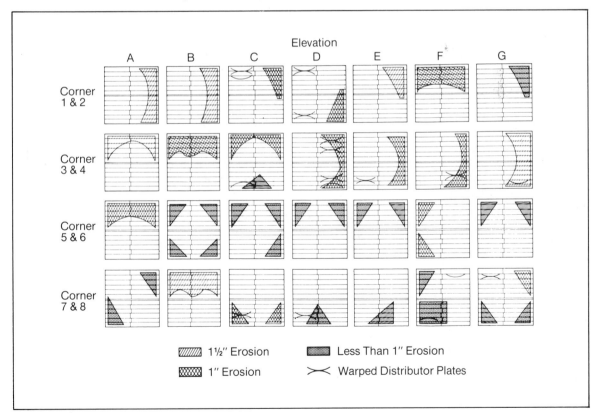

Fig. 11 **Typical section of outage report**

Backing rings must not be used to weld any heat-absorbing tubes carrying water or a mixture of steam and water. Without a backing ring, the first pass of the weld must be made by gas tungsten arc or oxy-acetylene. The weld passes may be completed by either process, or by shielded metal arc.

Window welds may be used for repair work if access is difficult (Fig. 13). The first pass of a window weld must be made by gas tungsten arc or oxy-acetylene.

Fit-up of the weld joints is important. Although it is difficult to obtain accurate cuts on furnace tubes, it is important to get the existing tube ends squared and correctly chamfered, and to cut the replacement tube to the correct length. A tube-end scarfing tool should be used when possible.

Allow for shrink in welding. Remember that the weld metal and parent metal are melted in the welding process and the molten metal shrinks as it solidifies. (A butt weld in a tube will shorten the total tube length about 1/16 in.)

Use a clamp or guide lug to hold one end of the replacement tube in alignment while the first weld is made. Do not tack weld both ends of the replacement tube, particularly if the existing tubes are rigidly supported. As a general rule, first complete the weld at the lower end of the replacement tube. Do not start welding the upper end of the replacement tube until both the replacement and existing tubes have cooled to ambient temperature.

GENERAL GUIDELINES FOR ALLOY TUBE REPAIRS

If a damaged alloy tube must be replaced, it is always preferable to weld the replacement tube to an existing tube end of the same alloy and the same wall thickness.

Before removing the damaged tube, check the manufacturer's material diagram and locate shop welds used to join the damaged length to tubes of different material or different wall thickness. If at all possible, make the cuts to remove the damaged tube at least 6 in. from the shop weld, thus leaving a "safe end."

CUTTING OUT A SHOP WELD

If necessary to cut out a shop weld joining tubes of different material and/or wall thickness, special attention must be paid, since all qualified butt-welding procedures require the two tube ends to have the same internal diameter (ID) at the weld root. In some cases, the thicker wall tube may be bored to match the ID of the thinner wall tube as shown in Fig. 14. But the thicker wall tube may be bored only if the strength of the tube, after reducing the wall

Fig. 12 Waterwall failure locations (viewed from inside boiler)

thickness, is at least equal to the strength of the thinner wall tube at the same operating temperature.

A ferritic-alloy tube must not be bored to match a thinner-wall austenitic alloy tube. The only satisfactory method is to use a connector of austenitic alloy tube having the same wall thickness as the ferritic-alloy tube. One end of the connector is bored to match the wall thickness of the existing austenitic-alloy tube.

FIT-UP AND SHRINK ALLOWANCE

Shrinkage in welding alloy tubes is similar to that for carbon-steel tubes. Allowance must be made for expansion from preheating which will close the root gap slightly.

For shielded metal-arc welding with a backing ring, it is essential that the root-gap opening be sufficient to assure full penetration and fusion with the backing ring during the first pass. For gas tungsten arc welding, a zero root-gap opening is permitted. However, there must be no pressure exerted between the two tubes. It is advisable to allow enough clearance to avoid actual contact at the root-gap opening after the two tubes are preheated.

REPAIR OF TUBES ROLLED INTO HEADERS OR DRUMS

If a replacement length of tubing requires a weld within 2 or 3 feet of the rolled end, removing the rolled joint and cutting the replacement tube to fit into the tube hole will avoid the stresses from weld shrinkage. This procedure is particularly effective in straight tubes or tubes welded to adjacent tubes. In cutting the replacement tube, allow for the normal projection through the tube hole plus 1/16 in. for shrinkage of the weld. Complete the weld in the replacement tube, allow the tube temperature to cool to ambient, and then roll the replacement tube end into the header.

![Fig. 13 window welds diagram]

Fig. 13 **Window welds may be used to repair damaged tubes when access is difficult .**

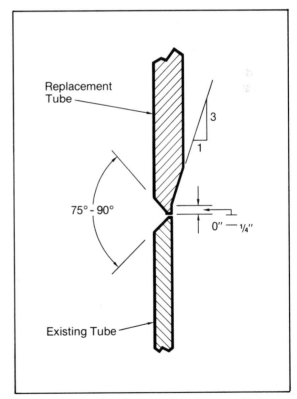

Fig. 14 **Fit-up detail to install replacement tube section with wall thicker than existing tube**

REPLACING A TUBE LENGTH IN A FIN-WELDED FURNACE WALL

First, the bar or fin along the damaged tube length must be removed by flame cutting. Because it is difficult to make a clean flame-cut in the weld attaching a bar or fin to a tube, it is preferable to make the cut just at the edge of the weld, approximately 1/8 to 1/4 in. from the damaged tube.

Overheating of the tube may have caused a longitudinal crack. In this case, the tube has swollen and the wall thickness reduced. If visual inspection indicates swelling and reduction of the tube-wall thickness at the crack, a complete replacement of the damaged tube length is the best solution. On the other hand, a circumferential crack suggests a failure due to excessive stress applied by expansion restriction, bending, or fatigue. Although such cracks can be repaired by welding, unless the cause of failure is diagnosed and corrected it is possible for a similar failure to occur at or near the original crack.

REPAIR OF TUBE BLISTERS

Internal deposits cause blisters on the furnace wall or boiler tubes. Generally, they occur in boilers operated with a high percentage of make up in the feedwater. A blister forms because an internal deposit increases tube metal temperature until metal creep occurs. As the heated area swells, the internal deposit cracks off and the tube metal temperature returns to normal. The process may be repeated several times before the blister ruptures.

Commonly, a large number of tubes are blistered and not noticed until one of the blisters cracks open. To avoid a massive tube-replacement job, particularly where replacement tubes are not immediately available, blisters can be worked down to the original tube radius. Follow these general guidelines:

Remove the damaged tube, then carefully cut away enough of the bar or fin to allow chamfering the tube end for welding around the sides of the replacement tube joint (Fig. 15).

After the tube welds are completed, weld the bar or fin to the replacement tube. If the gap be-

tween bar or fin is too great for easy bridging, insert a low-carbon-steel welding rod for a filler. The spaces in the bars or fins, at the tube joints, are built up with deposited weld metal. Be sure no cracks exist in these deposits before making the final weld to the tubes.

REMOVAL OF TUBE SAMPLE FOR METALLURGICAL OR CHEMICAL EXAMINATION

When a metallurgical or chemical examination is necessary to determine the cause of tube failure, special precautions are required to remove a defective tube from any type of welded-wall furnace. The defective portion of the tube should not be heated by flame cutting. To avoid such heating, the tube should be flame-cut at a point at least 6 in. away from the damaged area. In a furnace wall with bars or fins welded between tubes, it is preferable to cut the bars or fins with a saber saw or thin disc metal-cutting wheel. If these tools are not available, the bars or fins may be flame cut approximately 1/2 in. from the tube length required for the sample.

After removing the damaged tube from the

Fig. 15 **Welding detail for replacing a tube length in a fin-welded furnace wall**

furnace, the ends may be cut off to reduce shipping weight of the sample. Use a dry hacksaw. Cutting oil will contaminate any deposits and render a useful chemical analysis impossible. Be sure the sample is clearly marked to show which end was at the top and which side was toward the fire (Fig. 16).

COMPONENT MAINTENANCE

Although it is beyond the scope of this treatment to describe the overhaul of all steam-generator components and auxiliaries, a brief discussion of pump, fan, and control-system maintenance is offered for general information.

PUMP MAINTENANCE

Various types of pumps are used with a steam generator. For high-pressure recirculation-type boilers, single-shaft centrifugal pumps driven by a wet-stator induction motor move boiler water at pressures and temperatures exceeding 4000 psig and 650°F. Because the motor is enclosed within the pump casing and is filled with boiler water at full system pres-

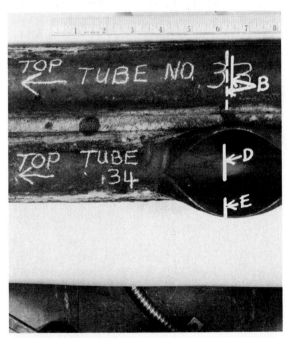

Fig. 16 **Make sure tube samples are clearly marked**.

sure, no seals are used between the pump and motor. A baffle, plus close clearances between the shaft and motor casing, prevents solids in the boiler water and hot water from passing into the motor. Through an external heat exchanger, recirculating water in the motor cavity cools the submerged motor.

Although manufacturers generally recommend an annual inspection for such pumps, local conditions help determine the proper interval for a given unit and installation. Periodic inspection of the pump in service usually reveals when an overhaul is needed. Some indications are an above normal noise level, high motor temperature, vibration, unusual starting or fluctuating current, reduced head across the pump, leaks from the pressure casing, or a drop in the winding resistance.

At most stations, one of the pumps is dismantled every few years. During disassembly, the motor and pump impeller are lowered as one assembly. The impeller can then be removed from the shaft and the rotor assembly taken from the housing. The assembly is placed horizontally on V blocks at floor level. An inspection is made with as much disassembly of subsections as observation dictates.

Although other pumps on steam generators might handle a cooler liquid at essentially ambient conditions, they may require much higher maintenance if the fluid being handled is more corrosive or erosive than pure boiler water. For example, heavy-duty centrifugal pumps are used to move a slurry solution of limestone and flyash in flue-gas desulfurization systems. The wear rate of these pumps can be substantial and is a function of the severity of the pumping duty and of the abrasive properties of the materials handled. The life of wear parts such as impellers and liners varies greatly. For instance, steel impellers and bodies have had very short life with highly acidic and abrasive solutions. If a new make or different type of pump is used, it should be opened regularly and the parts inspected to establish the life of wear parts.

When handling abrasive fluids, parts other than the impeller and housing are also subject to excessive wear. Shafts and gland seals and even the bearing must be inspected much more frequently. Bearing housings should be opened and inspected at least once a year.

FAN MAINTENANCE

Steam generators require many types and sizes of fans. The largest are used for forced- and induced-draft service, and for moving primary air to pulverizers for drying the coal. These fans can be of either centrifugal or axial-flow design, as described in Chapter 15. Bearing failure, one of the biggest problems with fans, usually is caused by either poor lubrication or excessive vibration. As stated previously, it is important to follow the lubrication requirements specified by the manufacturer.

If it occurs when a fan is initially started, vibration may be the result of inadequate foundations or unsuitable ductwork configuration or design. On the other hand, after operation, rotor imbalance often causes vibration. The imbalance can be a result of flyash accumulation in eroded blades, water, blade erosion, or uneven thermal growth of the wheel. But the possibility of changes in alignment or shifting foundations cannot be discounted.

An outage inspection program permits correction before a dangerous condition exists. The blades and associated ductwork systems should be examined for erosion, corrosion, or cracks (Fig. 17). If cracks are found in any blade, it is wise to magnetic-flux all of the blades for cracks. Fan dampers are as important as the fan itself, for deteriorated dampers can cause poor fan control.

Damper bearings are exposed to the same hostile environment as the fan wheel. Because flyash can penetrate the bearing lubricant, damper bearings must be inspected frequently and cleaned when the lubricant is contaminated. Dampers not in constant use, such as isolation dampers, may freeze in place and become useless. Exercising idle dampers can avoid this condition.

Some erosion of induced-draft fans on coal-fired boilers is to be expected. For centrifugal fans, erosion is generally most severe at the leading edge of the blades and at the joint between the blades and center plate. Axial-flow fans have the heaviest erosion on the front outer tip of the blade. Erosion primarily affects the structural integrity of the fan, but it can also cause imbalance.

For severe duty, replaceable wear plates are bolted or welded to centrifugal fan blades. At each outage the wear plates are checked and are replaced when worn halfway through. If wear plates are allowed to erode to a point that damage occurs to the blade material, repair cost and outage time can be greatly increased.

Although wear plates can reduce the effects of erosion, it is controlled best by flyash removal upstream of the fans. Again, an effective maintenance program determines and corrects the cause of maintenance sometimes initiated by equipment other than that actually experiencing the problems.

A most important part of any fan repair is the rebalancing and final cleanup. Besides the

Fig. 17 **Fan rotor blades with heavy erosion**

normal dangers of rotating equipment, fans present an additional hazard in their ability to draw in, not only air or gas, but loose material. Solid objects can pass through the fan and either damage the rotor or discharge the debris as projectiles. Therefore, upon job completion, all ductwork must be inspected to locate any foreign material.

CONTROL-SYSTEM MAINTENANCE

Historically, because of limited manpower and funds, power-plant control-system maintenance has been limited to repair of known deficiencies. With greater emphasis on plant reliability and availability, preventive maintenance programs have grown.

Such a program should begin with a continuous process of recalibration, repair or replacement while the unit is on the line. By relying on a redundant component, transferring a control loop to manual, or by temporarily defeating the component's function, most control system components can be recalibrated, repaired or replaced on line (Fig. 18). Periodic maintenance can prevent unit high or low furnace-pressure trips caused by drifting cali-

bration of transmitters and switches, or by plugged sensing lines between the furnace tap and the transmitters.

A power-plant annual outage offers the opportunity to perform a more complete overhaul of the control system. Usually scheduled well in advance, this work includes the recalibration of field devices such as transmitters; pressure, temperature, and position switches; control valves; speed controllers; damper drives; and thermocouple inputs. If there are known problems in the control system, additional work is done. For example, a dry-run of the furnace supervisory safety system should be conducted if some digital logic is not performing correctly, or a calibration and retuning of an analog loop may be in order if poor control is observed during previous operation.

Because the control system is the power-plant component that, as its proper function, trips a unit off line, its role is critical to plant operation. Often, unit trips are attributed incorrectly to control-system malfunctions when, in fact, the control system has sensed an abnormal condition and responded correctly.

Fig. 18 **Periodic maintenance of control hardware can prevent costly trips .**

EROSION AND ABRASION

On coal-fired units, one of the biggest maintenance requirements is the repair or replacement of parts worn by the erosion or abrasion of coal and ash. Abrasion is the "sandpaper" effect of solid particles moving parallel to, and in contact with, a boundary surface. Abrasion tends to occur at the high spots on the boundary surface and has little effect on the surface matrix. Therefore, a boundary surface containing a small hard-particle matrix will give the best life.

Erosion, on the other hand, occurs from the impact of energy particles. The solid particles strike the wall freely, and cut portions of the boundary or wall material. Hard or erosion-resistant particles in the wall matrix will not protect the less-resistant balance of the matrix. Consequently, many abrasion-resistant materials are not erosion resistant (Fig. 19).

In coal-fired steam generators and auxiliaries, the major wear is from erosion, which occurs in the fuel preparation and delivery system and in the backpass convection section. Although the grinding parts of the pulverizer wear from abrasion, wear in the other parts of the coal milling and transport system is principally due to erosion. The wear in the steam generator itself is almost all by erosion.

PULVERIZER WEAR

As discussed in Chapter 12, the C-E bowl mill pulverizes coal by subjecting it to a grinding force between a rotating bowl and spring-loaded stationary rollers. The bowl has a segmented wear-ring for easy replacement and the rolls are fairly easily removed from their journal assembly for replacement.

The rate of abrasive wear of the grinding parts depends on the type and quantity of impurities in the coal. Considerable laboratory research and field development of materials have reduced the wear and increased the availability of these components. An abrasion-resistant nickel-chromium white cast iron is used for the pulverizer grinding parts. Depending on the abrasiveness of the particular coal being

ground, rolls and rings may both have to be replaced at the same time or it may be possible to obtain twice the life from a ring as from a set of rolls (Fig. 20).

For highly abrasive coals, a hard-surface overlay which is applied to either new or worn parts has proven effective in increasing roll and ring life. The overlay must be at least ½ in. thick. For used rolls, overlays up to 1 in. thick are possible to return the roll to its original diameter. If overlays exceeding ½ in. are applied to new rolls, special undersize rolls should be used to obtain design roll diameter.

Other pulverizer parts subject to wear include the various liners fabricated of abrasion-resistant steel plate or high-nickel castings. These must be checked for metal loss at the same time as the rolls and rings.

COAL TRANSPORT PIPING

With more frequent use of highly abrasive coals, pulverized-coal pipeline wear has become a problem. The rate of wear is a function of

■ particle characteristics: hardness, sharpness, and size
■ particle velocity
■ angle of attack of particles
■ properties of the piping material

Fig. 21 shows the standard material selection for the coal-transport piping which provides cast-iron elbows at the pulverizer or exhauster outlet and at the windbox inlet. All straight

Fig. 19 **Erosion and abrasion in coal piping**

piping and bends between these points are of commercial carbon-steel pipe. All bends and elbows are designed to a two-pipe-diameter radius, except the windbox inlet elbow, which has a one-pipe-diameter radius.

Victaulic couplings are used on the toggle sections provided to accommodate the vertical expansion of the steam generator, and also for connecting to the cast-iron elbows and orifices. The balance of the piping is welded.

Because erosion potential is greater at and after bends, wear-resistant nodular-iron deflector blocks are positioned in selected elbows to both absorb coal particle impingement and redistribute solids flow concentrations (Fig. 21). Experience dictates initial location of deflector blocks but they can be repositioned in the field to match the elbow wear pattern. System pressure-drop considerations limit the number of deflector blocks that may be installed.

Sometimes, pipeline flow characteristics are so complex that deflector blocks cannot be completely effective. In these installations, the more serious pipeline erosion usually occurs in specific bends and in the first 2 to 3 ft of straight pipe directly following the bends. In such areas, special wear-resistant components are used for highly abrasive coals.

Such wear-resistant materials have been installed in, or in place of, elbows and bends on operating units and have been evaluated for erosion losses. Some are

- nihard elbows
- steel elbows lined with alumina
- steel elbows with silicon carbide
- steel elbows lined with basalt
- double wall steel elbows with "lobster-back" wear surface
- heat-treated (carburized) steel elbows

Fig. 20 **Checking roll wear**

Fig. 21 **Coal-piping elbow with deflector blocks**

Fig. 22 **Typical lined 90-degree steel elbow**

EXPERIENCE WITH WEAR-RESISTANT PIPING MATERIALS

Nihard is a nickel-chromium nodular white cast iron. Nihard elbows and bends, used in troublesome locations, will generally last two to four times the life of cast-iron bends.

Fig. 22 shows a typical ceramic lined elbow which may be a fabricated mitered elbow or a modified standard steel bend. A steel casing encloses the wear-resistant lining and satisfies code pressure requirements. The lining is secured in place with epoxy or similar cement. An advantage of the steel-casing design is that the ends can be prepared for any attachment design including welding, flanging, or Victaulic end preparation.

The two most promising ceramics are alumina (Al_2O_3) and silicon carbide (SiC) both with excellent erosion resistance. The expected wear-resistant life of either ceramic is a minimum of four times the life of cast-iron and perhaps far greater. But the service life will also depend to some degree on the type of mortar or epoxy and the stress survival of the insert castings.

One type of alumina lining is a sintered alumina ceramic tile, hexagonal in shape, about 1 in. across the face, and arranged on mesh backing. These sheets of tiles, 1/2-in. thick, are epoxy-cemented in place within the fabricated steel elbow. The inside diameter of the lined elbow is identical to the pipeline in-side diameter; the outside diameter is approximately 1½ times greater.

A volcanic rock, basalt, is fused and annealed into liners of various shapes and thickness. It has excellent abrasion resistance and is good for straight coal pipes. But as basalt has poor erosive-impact wear resistance, it is not recommended as a lining for elbow or bend installation.

Fig. 23 shows a double-backed elbow with a wear-resistant concrete filling the void between the two surfaces. The steel elbow and the outer containment cover are made from elbow torus fabricating dies. Such elbows have been in service for years with no sign of wear.

Disadvantages of the "lobster-back" elbow are cost and space requirements. It takes two complete elbows and considerable shop labor to construct one wear-back elbow, and results in a component 2 in. greater in outside radius.

Two steel elbows carburized to 700 Brinell hardness, installed for test evaluation, showed excellent abrasion and erosive-wear resistance. However, welding the elbows or attachments to the elbows is difficult and flange weld failures have been experienced. Also, the costs of carburizing large elbows appear prohibitive.

EROSION AND ABRASION FROM FLYASH

Approximately 60 to 80 percent of the ash resulting from the burning of coal leaves the furnace with the combustion gases. Gas

Carbon Stl. A 113 GrC 90° Steel Elbow to Be Altered as Shown After Filling

Carbon Stl. Die Formed Elbow

Section at Ends of Elbow

After Filling

Victaulic End May Be a Weld End or Flanged

Typ. Both Ends After Filling

Fill from Both Ends With Available Hard Wear Concrete

Fig. 23 **Double-walled wear-back outlet elbow assembly in steel coal-piping**

velocities must not exceed specified limits in order to control erosion from the ash particles. Depending on both the quantity of ash and its composition, the velocity is generally limited to 50 to 60 ft/second.

Two components in flyash that appear to contribute most to flyash erosion are silica (SiO_2) and iron oxide (Fe_2O_3), both relatively hard abrasive oxides. While silica is ordinarily present at higher percentages than iron oxide, iron oxide is more dense and, consequently, produces a greater impact influence.

Flyash erosion is a term that, in general use, includes flyash abrasion. All tubing erodes when subject to a flyash-laden gas stream. As long as the wastage rate (the loss of metal in a given time) is low, the polishing effect is not considered significant. When the wastage rate becomes excessive, premature tubing failures can occur. Although some erosion is experienced on superheaters and reheaters, most erosion has been on economizers, which usually are horizontal tubes with closer spacing than the superheaters and reheaters.

ECONOMIZER EROSION

In general, predicting where excessive flyash erosion might occur for any given unit is difficult, because such erosion is related to nonuniform flow of flue gas and uneven distribution of flyash in the backpass area associated with centrifugal forces acting on the ash particles during gas-turning.

Many factors affect flyash erosion, which is a very complex process. It is directly proportional to ash loading and is influenced by the relative amounts of abrasive constituents—the silica, alumina, and iron oxide compounds—in the flyash. Most investigators have found that the erosion rate is an exponential function of particle velocity to between the 3rd and 4th power. Gas-side pressure drop (which is a combined function of gas velocity, turbulence, and heating-surface configuration) also influences erosion.

Gas velocity through a tube bank is a function of unit operating load, excess-air level, and the amount of free (net) gas-flow area within the bank. Therefore, unit operation much above maximum continuous rating and design excess air aggravates the potential for flyash erosion. Also, any action that results in the reduction of flow area, such as localized flyash plugging, will increase gas velocity and the erosion potential by concentrating flyash in an area adjacent to the plugged area.

When a unit develops an economizer erosion problem, it is necessary to establish the cause. To add more localized baffling, tube shields, or other devices without regard to the causes may produce only short-term improvements.

If examination of the unit and its operation indicates that such factors as operating load, excess-air level and presence of plugging are not abnormal, then the addition or modification of baffles or tube shields or other devices is justified.

On some economizers where excessive erosion has occurred across the rear of the backpass, a combination of erosion-control methods has been used (see Fig. 24). Collectively, they have abated excessive erosion. Some methods used include

■ adding filter baffles to obtain a more uniform flyash distribution across the economizer

■ adding slag fences to prevent economizer plugging

■ installing plates or screen to block open areas

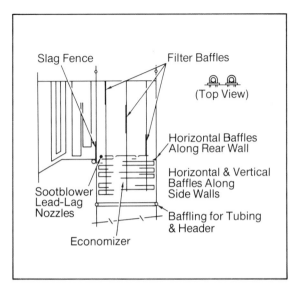

Fig. 24 **Erosion reduction methods in economizer**

and stop channeling of the flyash

■ adding additional sootblower equipment to maintain cleanliness of the economizer section

■ sequencing the sootblower in the upstream convection sections to blow from top to bottom and rear to front

MAINTENANCE STAFFING

The size of a plant maintenance staff varies with the number and size of units, fuel used, quality of the labor, and extent of outside supplemental help. Large coal-fired stations may have several hundred people employed in maintenance and still hire contractors for major overhauls. Some utilities have roving crews to supplement plant labor when required. Whether to use outside labor or be self-sufficient can only be determined by plant management. But no matter how much outside contract labor is employed, the final responsibility must rest with the station staff. Unless the station staff oversees the work done, there is little chance for a cohesive maintenance program.

TRAINING FOR MAINTENANCE

Training maintenance personnel is vitally important to the successful operation of any plant. Many months before a plant goes into service, maintenance crews should be selected and trained.

Although there are fewer available programs for maintenance people than for operators, the plant should explore all training aids and methods. Many manufacturers have courses and workshops in equipment maintenance and the use of special tools and procedures.

The plant maintenance staff should be used for initial setup of equipment because working with the manufacturers' representatives provides invaluable training. Money spent on vendor servicing can be wasted if no one in the plant knows what is being done. Thus, a plant maintenance supervisor, as well as maintenance mechanics, should be assigned to each vendor representative.

LONG-RANGE PLANNING AND SCHEDULING

Nothing is more important in maintaining a plant than scheduling maintenance intervals. The more crowded and busy the maintenance chief's schedule is, the more the need to take time for long-range planning and scheduling. Such forward thinking includes asking questions which define future needs.

■ What jobs are next in line?

■ On what dates do they have to be started or completed?

■ Which person is going to do what?

■ What equipment and material are needed to get the work done?

■ What problems or roadblocks will they run into?

Equally important, an optimum maintenance program calls for replacing some parts before they are completely worn out so as to take advantage of scheduled outage time. A cost/benefit analysis is one way to decide when to change critical parts; that is, the cost of the life remaining in the component is weighed against the cost of subsequent loss of production if that equipment is out of service again.

For fast-wearing or particularly vulnerable parts, consider substituting new materials or redesigned parts. Improved materials can prolong life and lead to much less maintenance labor. With higher labor costs, materials once considered too expensive are now cost savers. Even plants that seldom rely on manufacturers' representatives for aid in maintenance should periodically ask the manufacturer about new developments in materials and techniques. For instance, high-nickel material or tungsten-carbide overlays on steel have been most effective in prolonging life of steel parts. Ceramics are used in many applications. Initially these were used only on stationary parts but, with improved epoxies, some can now be used on rotating equipment as well.

Wise maintenance supervisors, then, will investigate new materials or other ways to cut maintenance costs. And they will allot some time for discussions with vendors' salespeople to find out what new products may be a solution to difficult maintenance problems.

CHAPTER 23

Availability and Reliability

In many respects, the electric utility is unique. Its product, the day-to-day output of electric energy, is supplied on demand with no opportunity to be inventoried or stored. Thus, its network of generation, transmission and distribution equipment through which the product is delivered must have high operating integrity to assure optimum reliability of supply, which is the industry's highest priority.

In addition, because of the long lead time required to add new capacity to the system, it is necessary for the industry to plan to add generating equipment years in advance of service dates to supply future electric loads. Further, the utility industry ranks among the most capital-intensive in terms of dollars of investment per dollar of revenue. This chapter explores the implications of reliability of supply in the generation of steam for fossil-fired power plants.

AVAILABILITY

The availability of an electric power plant is important to both utility economics and system reliability. Improving availability only slightly can save considerably on reserve generating capacity and the cost of replacement power.

As one measure of reliability, availability statistics have attracted much attention as the utility industry emphasizes producing the most energy for the least cost.

The importance of high plant availability has spurred the U.S. Department of Energy (DOE), the Edison Electric Institute (EEI), and the Electric Power Research Institute (EPRI)—acting as the research arm for participating utilities—to pursue programs that identify means of improving plant performance. Even state and federal legislation concerning electrical-plant reliability already has been enacted.

In very dramatic terms the world energy crisis has reinforced the tremendous importance of power-generating plant availability. The upward surge in fuel costs has been felt in virtually all energy sources with a significant impact on the political-socio-economic status of the U.S. and many other countries.

PERFORMANCE INDICES

The utility industry uses four recognized indices to evaluate power-plant productivity which, in essence, is a measure of the ability of a plant to produce electricity on demand. As defined by EEI, the four major power-plant performance indices are

Capacity Factor =

$$\frac{\text{Total Gross Generation in MWhr}}{\text{Period Hours} \times \text{Maximum Dependable Capacity}} \quad (1)$$

$$\text{Availability Factor} = \frac{\text{Available Hours}}{\text{Period Hours}} \quad (2)$$

$$\text{Equivalent Availability} = \frac{\begin{array}{c}\text{Available Hours}\\ -\,(\text{Equivalent Forced}\\ +\,\text{Scheduled Outage Hrs.})\end{array}}{\text{Period Hours}} \quad (3)$$

Forced Outage Rate =

$$\frac{\text{Forced Outage Hours}}{\text{Service Hours} + \text{Forced Outage Hours}} \quad (4)$$

where:

Maximum Dependable Capacity = the dependable unit capacity in winter or summer, whichever is smaller.

Available Hours = the period of time during which a unit or major piece of equipment is capable of service whether it is actually in service or not.

Period Hours = the clock hours in the period under consideration (generally taken as one year).

Service Hours = the total number of hours the unit is actually operated with the breakers closed to the station bus.

Forced Outage Hours = the time in hours during which a unit or major equipment is unavailable because of a forced outage which is the occurrence of a component failure or other condition requiring that the unit be removed from service immediately, or up to and including the next weekend.

MEASURING PERFORMANCE

Each equation identifies only a portion of performance measurement for a generating unit. No single index tells the overall performance story for a unit, a fact that is apparent from Fig. 1. The annual availability factor establishes only the percentage of time during the year that the unit was *capable* of producing power. This factor includes time when the unit was capable of generating power, but was not in service because more efficient units were being used. Thus, the availability factor *does not* measure the ability of a unit to operate at a specific power level when called upon by the utility. Rather, it measures only the capability of the unit to produce at a power level ranging from 0 to 100 percent of its rated capacity.

The equivalent availability index provides for an adjustment of the availability factor by accounting for the effect of partial deratings (losses in MW output capability) from partial forced and scheduled outages. Essentially, the index is equivalent to the percentage of the year during which the unit was available for operation at full capacity.

What equivalent availability does not indicate is whether an outage is either forced or planned. A forced outage is generally more costly in terms of both replacement power and the ability of the utility to supply system loads. The forced outage rate measures this performance. Capacity factor is, in effect, the "bottom line" result and also includes discretionary cutbacks in output by a utility.

Each index, therefore, is limited to defining a specific aspect of power-plant performance. To evaluate the overall performance of a power plant requires subjective and collective review of these four indices.

UNIT SIZE AND AVAILABILITY

It was commonly accepted in the early 1960's that as fossil-fired generating capacity matured, availability would improve. This expectation did not materialize as data from EEI substantiates (Fig. 2).

Using the four indices previously defined, the graphs of Fig. 3 plot the productivity of coal-fired units 400 MW and larger, over a 10-year period. These historic data also verify the trend toward lower availability as boiler ca-

Fig. 1 **Factors affecting productivity of power plants** [1]

pacity increased. This tendency holds for the other major plant components such as the steam turbine, the generator, and the condenser. Similarly, the forced-outage rate goes up as unit capacity increases.

On the average, supercritical-pressure boilers installed in the last two decades have performed with lower reliability than have drum-type units. On the other hand, availability statistics of 3500-psig steam generators entering service in recent years compare very favorably with those of drum-type subcritical pressure boilers of comparable age and capacity. Nevertheless, better equipment performance will be required at both pressure levels in future capacity additions.

UTILITY VIEW OF AVAILABILITY

A major reason for improving availability in electricity production is a matter of economics which essentially relates to the high cost of constructing power-generating facilities. The

Fig. 2 **Availability vs unit size — cumulative EEI data 1966–1975** [2]

basics of power-plant economics are discussed in Chapter 1.

Fig. 4 illustrates the rise in capital investment from $183/kW to $1266/kW for a three-unit coal-fired plant where each unit is 750 MW in size. The illustration is based on estimates prepared in 1968 and 1978. In view of environmental requirements and economic and political realities, these costs can only increase and there is little incentive for utilities to build more units than absolutely needed.

Better plant availability will have a large effect on construction or deferment of new plants. The opposite side of the coin is that long-term outages from repeated boiler tube leaks, turbine-blade failures or other plant equipment problems could force a utility either to install additional capacity or to purchase replacement power (if available) at higher cost.

RESERVE MARGINS

One measure of adequate generating capacity is the reserve margin in excess of the peak load demand. This margin offers a hedge against unanticipated demand growth, forced outages, derating and other contingencies. In the United States, a reserve margin of 20 to 22 percent is generally considered acceptable.

Usually certain regions have much less reserve than others, accentuating the requirement for highly reliable generating facilities. In all cases, outages of base load (the most efficient capacity) increase generating costs.

AVAILABILITY AFFECTS COSTS

The payback for improving the availability of a typical 500-MW coal-fired plant is shown in Table I. For each 1 percent improvement in operating availability, a utility avoids coal-fired replacement-power from less efficient generation of about $60,000/day. Should the replacement energy come from oil-fired capacity, the incremental costs would be substantially higher. By improving its forced outage rate, a utility can reduce the system reserve

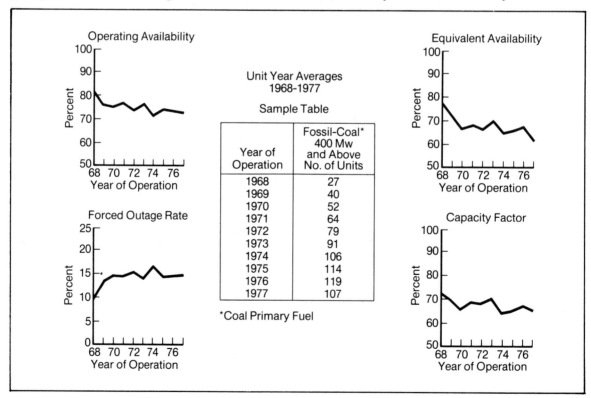

Fig. 3 **Performance trends of fossil coals-fired units 400 MW and above** [3]

Table I. Improvement in Availability of a 500 MW Coal-Fired Unit

Replacement Power	Incremental Cost, $/Day	1% IMPROVEMENT	
		$/Yr	Over Life of Plant*
Coal	60,000	220,000	. 1,300,000
Oil	180,000–360,000	650,000–1,300,000	3,800,000–7,600,000

*Capitalized at 17%

margin as shown in Table II. Even at $700/kW incremental cost for a 500-MW installation, the utility benefits greatly from a lower system reserve.

The conclusion is clear: one of the alternatives available to the electric power industry for increasing generating capacity at least cost is to improve plant productivity.

FACTORS CONTRIBUTING TO POOR AVAILABILITY

EEI data collected during the period 1964 to 1973 showed that the availability of drum-type steam generators, 500 MW in size (and above), averaged more than five percentage points higher than supercritical units. Contributing to this situation was the fact that most supercritical boilers were designed for, and operated with, pressurized rather than balanced-draft furnaces. Other factors influencing the decline in unit availability in this period were

■ rapid escalation of unit size: Anticipating rapid load-growth requirements, the electric utility industry during the late 1960's and early 1970's ordered coal-fired units with MW ratings much higher than they had been operating. Without the benefits of design and operating experience on these larger size units, boiler designers made extrapolations from design parameters established on smaller units.

■ economic considerations: As improvements in availability were emphasized less in that era, many coal-fired units were purchased primarily on the basis of low bid or rapid delivery. This market climate tended to deter considerations for greater design conservatism and equipment redundancy.

■ declining coal quality: The decline in coal quality and consistency has adversely affected boiler availability. Lower calorific value and higher ash content require more fuel to produce the same unit output. This increased fuel and ash input further burdens coal pulverizers, furnace sootblowing and ash-removal equipment, and gas-cleaning systems such as electrostatic precipitators, baghouses and scrubbers and affects the forced outage rate (Fig. 5).

AN APPROACH TO AVAILABILITY IMPROVEMENT

To help utilities improve on unit availability and obtain maximum reliability from steam generators, C-E formed an Availability Task Force to investigate how best to use EEI, NERC and other data-gathering systems.[6] A study showed that these data were capable only of providing the component cause for outages and load reduction and were not able to provide information as to why a component failed. Without information on the cause of the component problem, it was not possible to determine whether there existed a deficiency in design, manufacturing, maintenance or operation. Therefore, C-E established its own program to provide the necessary information.

Table II. Improvement in Forced Outage Rate (FOR)

1% Decrease in FOR Permits
1.25% Decrease in System Reserve Margins

Size of New Unit	Value of Lower Reserve Margin
500 MW	$4,375,000*

* @ $700/kW incremental cost

This program gathers information on the cause of outages and load reductions in nine major equipment categories related to steam generators. Included are

- waterwalls
- superheater/reheater
- economizer
- furnace sootblowing/bottom-ash removal equipment
- convection section sootblowing/flyash removal equipment
- boiler controls
- fans
- pulverizers
- boiler circulating pumps

This information helps identify trends in problems that occur from deficiencies in design, fabrication, operation, or maintenance. Derived from these data is the knowledge that waterwall, superheater, reheater, and economizer tubing leaks account for 80 to 90 percent of all forced outages, whereas coal pulverizing systems account for approximately 50 percent of equivalent downtime hours in load reductions.

Questionnaire-type reporting forms were designed to obtain the maximum amount of information to indicate the basic cause of failure in each of the designated categories. In addition to the date of the incident and the length of outage or load reduction, the questionnaire identified the failed component, gave its detailed location within the unit and within the specific assembly or component and solicited any opinions as to the type or mode of failure, as its cause, if definitely determined.

The program was limited to coal-fired units of 390-MW capacity and larger in consideration of the amount of effort required in data recording by the utilities. The program is expected to improve the performance of the new, large capacity coal-fired units currently operating, and thereby set the pattern for optimal performance of generating capacity in the future.

PROBLEMS AND IMPROVEMENTS

The underlying causes of failures producing forced outages may be difficult to identify, but their correction requires such an identification. Treatment of symptoms will neither cure a disease nor correct a disorder. Chapter 22 covers the importance of determining the root cause of incidents causing forced outages.

In the case of waterwall tube ruptures, poor feedwater quality is often the major contributing factor. With increases in operating pressure, feedwater quality becomes even more critical. The recommendation is a maximum of

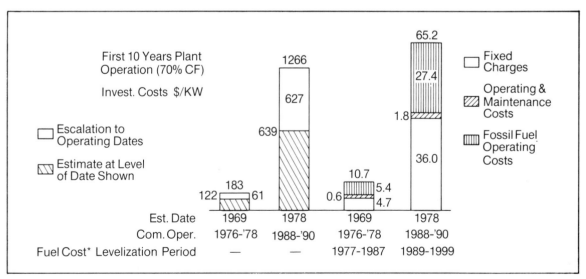

Fig. 4 Coal-fired plant investment costs and levelized power costs [4]

50 ppm of total dissolved solids in drum type units. Most operators follow this practice.

Degradation of coal properties adversely affects the capability of boiler auxiliaries, but its direct effect on availability is difficult to quantify. Component capability, e.g., pulverizers, fans, economizer, and air heaters frequently limit unit capacity and reduce generating reserves. If auxiliaries are operated continuously at or near their peak capability without proper maintenance, problems generally develop.

Casing and ductwork leaks also adversely affect availability, particularly on pressurized coal-fired units. Therefore, the industry has almost unanimously accepted balanced-draft operation. At the same time a concerted effort was initiated to improve furnace and ductwork design to prevent leaks.

Fusion-welded construction has replaced the peg-finned construction of the nose arch and the zone between the nose arch and rear furnace wall has been redesigned, eliminating peg finning and skin casing. Fusion and fin welded tubing used on the extended sidewalls and rear pass walls has eliminated the casing burnouts in these areas. Additionally, the design of ductwork and expansion joints has been improved.

Furnace framing design criteria have been increased significantly to provide greater protection against implosion.[7]

BOILER-WATER CIRCULATING PUMPS

A zero-leakage boiler circulating pump design, the wet-motor pump, has been widely accepted based on successful experience on utility units since 1960. As with any complex electro-mechanical equipment, the successful development of a larger, more durable design, results in part, from service experience. The wet-motor design is fundamentally simpler than either the canned-motor or injection-seal type and has permitted extensive on-site maintenance or modification at moderate cost

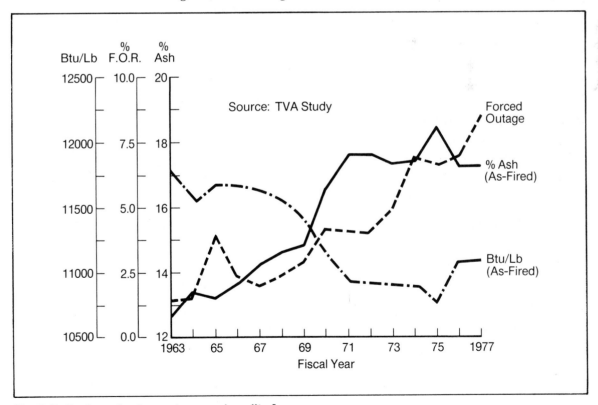

Fig. 5 **Boiler forced outage rate vs coal quality** [5]

and minimum pump downtime.

Outstanding reliability, extended maintenance intervals, and proportionally reduced maintenance cost and pump downtime are the results of over twenty-five years of wet motor experience and design evolution. Loss of boiler availability because of boiler circulating pumps, according to EEI records for the period 1965 through 1974, was less than 0.03 percent.

FANS

Damage to fan housings, duct work, and stack liners, resulting from fan-induced duct vibrations caused by pressure pulsations in centrifugal fans also is a significant problem.

To avoid this situation, C-E has been specifying equipment that does not emit damaging pulsations. An example is the specification of vane-controlled fans instead of louvered-damper-controlled fans whenever possible. Damper-controlled fans are more susceptible to stalling and consequent large emitted pressure pulsations. A second example is the specification of dorsal fins or an equivalent in all vane controlled fans. Without this corrective device, some installations experience destructive levels of vibration. These and other methods were detailed at the 1975 American Power Conference in a paper[8] entitled, "A Summary of Experiences with Fan Induced Duct Vibrations on Fossil Fired Boilers." Specifying equipment with these features limits the selection, but has markedly reduced fan/duct vibration incidents.

CONCLUSION

In designing for availability, it is imperative that information be gathered from all operating units no matter how long they have been in service. While large utility systems offer the best opportunity for maintaining and analyzing records, follow-on services program must reach out to every user in the world. New fuels and methods of combustion are already in the making and the evolution in designs and their application must continue if the availability of existing and future systems is to be improved.

REFERENCES

[1] "Availability Patterns in Fossil-Fired Steam Power Plants," EPRI Report #FP-583-SR, November 1977, Electric Power Research Institute, Palo Alto, CA.

[2] "Report on Equipment Availability for the Ten Year Period 1966–1975," Task Force of Prime Movers Committee, Edison Electric Institute, Washington, D.C. 1976.

[3] "Report on Equipment Availability for the Ten Year Period 1968–1977," Task Force of Prime Movers Committee, Edison Electric Institute, Washington, D.C. 1979.

[4] R. R. Bennett and D. J. Kettler, "Dramatic Changes in the Costs of Nuclear and Fossil-fueled Plants," Ebasco Services Inc., New York, N.Y. Sept. 1978.

[5] "Availability Improvement Program," Division of Power Products, Tennessee Valley Authority, Knoxville, TN. 1977.

[6] W. H. Clayton, V. Llinares, Jr., and G. C. Thomas, "C-E Availability Data Program," *Proceedings of the American Power Conference*, Vol 42, 1980, Chicago: Illinois Institute of Technology.

[7] S. S. Blackburn and D. E. Lyons, "Design for Availability—An Update," *Proceedings of the American Power Conference* 39: 349–368, 1975, Chicago: Illinois Institute of Technology.

[8] C. H. Gilkey and J. D. Rogers, "A Summary of Experiences with Fan-Induced Duct Vibrations on Fossil-Fueled Boilers," *Proceedings of the American Power Conference*, 37: 728–734, 1975, Chicago: Illinois Institute of Technology.

BIBLIOGRAPHY

Morong, T. M. and Patterson, R. L., "Designing for Plant Availability at the Navajo Generating Station," *Proceedings of the American Power Conference* 37: 436–446, 1975 Chicago Illinois Institute of Technology.

Thimot, George and Krikawa, Joseph F ; "Maintaining Availability on Supercritical Coal-Fired Steam Generators," paper presented at the ASME-IEEE-ASCE Joint Power Generation Conference, Buffalo, New York, September 19–22, 1976; Combustion Engineering Publication TIS-4896.

CHAPTER 24

Advanced Methods of Using Coal

Traditionally, fossil fuels have supplied most of the world's energy requirements and predictions to the year 2000 indicate that the U.S.—as well as many European and Asiatic countries—will continue to rely heavily on these fuels. In many countries federal laws require that new fossil-fired power plants, exclusive of gas-turbine plants, burn coal as the primary fuel. At the same time, environmental regulations governing plant emissions, particularly SO_x, NO_x and particulates, frequently demand emission control systems.

Although coal is the most abundant fossil fuel in the U.S., users find it increasingly expensive to burn and, at the same time, meet federal regulations regarding power-plant emissions. As a result, developments in the U.S. emphasize advanced coal-utilization methods that will meet these government regulations at the least cost.

Emission-control methods that facilitate the use of coal in power plants can be classified as:

- pre-combustion processes
- concurrent combustion processes
- post-combustion processes

Pollution control before combustion is accomplished either by partial oxidation of the coal to produce a clean gas, or by producing a "clean" fuel through coal liquefaction processes. Sulfur and ash are removed in these processes. The use of coal to produce a gas is not a new idea; it has been used in one form or another for over 200 years. But its use in the U.S. had almost disappeared by 1930, because natural gas was abundant and cost very little. Diminishing supplies and rising costs have now renewed the interest in coal gasification to produce substitute natural gas (SNG) and low- and medium-calorific-value (LCV and MCV) gas. Likewise, coal liquefaction is not a new technology, but it is only in limited commercial use in the United States. Large-scale production of synthetic liquid fuels from coal began about 1910 in Germany with the Fischer-Tropsch process, which is still used to produce a variety of fuels.

In fluidized-bed combustion, a concurrent-combustion emission-control process, much of the sulfur is removed during combustion by a sorbent material (limestone). In this process NO_x production is low because of the low temperature at which the combustion reaction takes place. Fluidized-bed combustion has been under development since the 1950's with the principal intent to demonstrate the economy of the coal/limestone system for sulfur-oxide control as compared with post-boiler wet scrubbing.

A coal-fired magnetohydrodynamic (MHD)

system also is a control process that takes place concurrently with combustion of the coal. It is the direct conversion of kinetic and thermal energy in an ionized gas to electrical energy. Although the least developed of the new systems, it has the potential for maximum efficiency for the generation of electric power and thus will use less coal. A potassium seed used in the MHD power generation captures the sulfur which then is separated chemically when the seed material is recovered. Oxides of nitrogen are controlled by staged combustion similar to that used in a pulverized-coal-fired boiler.

Post-combustion control processes are in extensive use today for SO_2 and particulate control. Lime/limestone scrubbers for SO_2 removal and equipment for particulate removal are described in Chapter 17.

Processes and equipment for removing the NO_X from flue gases leaving a boiler are developmental. In the U.S., most new steam generators do not require post-combustion NO_X removal because it is possible to meet the current (1981) NO_X standard with proper firing-system design (see Chapter 4).

In this chapter are presented theory and status of hardware being developed for the coal gasification and liquefaction processes, and the fluidized-bed and MHD technologies. It should be emphasized that these four developments have been demonstrated as operating systems, although not necessarily on a large-scale commercial basis.

Fig. 1 **Coal gasification options**

COAL GASIFICATION FOR POWER-PLANT FUEL

In the United States, coal gasification developments have concentrated on second and third generation processes. Such processes are expected to be suitable for producing large quantities of substitute natural gas that could supplement, or replace, dwindling supplies of natural gas. Although initial developments in the United States emphasized gasification processes that produced substitute natural gas (SNG), such processes do not appear to be the proper approach for producing bulk electric power. The intermediate destination of SNG is a pressurized pipeline for long-distance distribution of the gas; thus high-pressure, oxygen-blown gasification processes, which produce significant amounts of methane directly and tend to produce carbon monoxide and hydrogen in the approximate ratios desired for methanation, understandably are favored for SNG production. But LCV gasification of coal has the greatest potential for meeting both environmental and economic goals of a fuel for firing boilers.

Coal is gasified by burning it in a controlled deficiency of oxygen. Because there isn't enough oxygen to complete combustion, the process produces a flammable gas consisting of carbon monoxide and hydrogen. When pure oxygen is used in this process, there results a medium calorific value (MCV) gas with a heating value of approximately 275-300 Btu/scf (standard cubic foot). This compares to natural gas which, because of its high methane content, has a heating value of 1000 Btu/scf.

When air is used to gasify coal, the large amounts of nitrogen in the air dilute the product gas, resulting in a low calorific value (LCV) gas with a heating value of approximately 100-125 Btu/scf. With both methods, the impurities are readily cleaned from the raw gas and the result is a clean fuel particularly suitable for electric power generation (Fig. 1).

MCV gas can also be used as a synthesis gas for chemical feedstock, or the calorific content can be further up-graded in additional processes to produce other types of synthetic fuels. Neither LVC nor MCV gas is suitable for distribution through existing natural-gas pipeline networks, although MCV gas might be economically transported over short distances in specially constructed pipelines.

THE COAL GASIFICATION PROCESS

There are usually two steps to most coal gasification processes. In the first step, devolatilization, through heating of the coal, produces an LCV gas and char. The second step, gasification, reacts the hot char with a deficiency of air or pure oxygen, and frequently with steam, producing an LCV or MCV gas, which can be cleaned or further upgraded to a high calorific value (HCV) product.

DEVOLATILIZATION

When coal is heated, it undergoes the following reaction:

$$\text{Volatile Matter} \xrightarrow{1100°F - 1500°F} CH_4$$
$$+ C(\text{char}) + HC + \Delta H \tag{1}$$

where HC indicates hydrocarbons higher than CH_4, and tars. This reaction is exothermic; that is, heat is evolved. High pressure and relatively low temperature favor methane formation. After devolatilization, large quantities of carbon remain as char. To produce methane from char requires hydrogen which the steam-carbon reaction supplies.

GASIFICATION

Char reacts with steam, producing hydrogen and carbon monoxide:

$$C + H_2O + 58,400 \ \frac{\text{Btu}}{\text{lb mol } H_2O} \xrightarrow{1700°F} CO + H_2 \tag{2}$$

This reaction is highly endothermic, that is, a large amount of heat must be supplied to sustain the reaction. Part of this heat can be supplied by the hydrogasification reaction.

HYDROGASIFICATION

Char reacts with hydrogen to form additional methane:

$$C + 2H_2 \xrightarrow{1700°F} CH_4 + 39,200 \ \frac{\text{Btu}}{\text{lb mol}} \tag{3}$$

This reaction is exothermic. After hydrogasification, the balance of the energy required to produce hydrogen by the steam-carbon reaction is supplied by reacting char with either air or oxygen.

OXIDATION

Burning some char adds the necessary heat to the gasifier:

$$C + O_2 \longrightarrow CO_2 + \Delta H \tag{4}$$

All of the above reactions can occur simultaneously throughout a reactor, or each reaction may be localized in a region of a reactor or in a separate vessel. Most gasification processes, however, are carried out so that the heat released by oxidation, hydrogasification, and devolatilization balances the heat required by gasification and the sensible heat of the overall reaction products. If the reactions are carried out in separate regions or reactors, some mechanism is required to transfer heat between these regions. The gas composition produced by a gasification process depends primarily on the nature of the coal and on the temperature, pressure, and gas composition in the regions where gasification, hydrogasification, and devolatilization occur.

OBTAINING HCV PRODUCT GAS

The raw gas can be an LCV or MCV gas depending upon whether air or oxygen is used to oxidize the char. If oxygen is used, an MCV gas with a high heating value (HHV) of 275 to 350 Btu/scf is produced. If air is used, an LCV gas with an HHV of 90 to 160 Btu/scf can be produced. When high-calorific-value gas is the objective, raw gas is treated to remove tar and dust and is passed over a shift catalyst to adjust the hydrogen/carbon-monoxide ratio to three-to-one in preparation for the methanation step.

$$CO + H_2O \rightleftarrows H_2 + CO + 14{,}100 \frac{Btu}{lb\ mol\ H_2O}$$

(5)

At higher temperature (1200°F), this reaction proceeds to the left and, at lower temperatures, to the right. The shift usually takes place in its own vessel, over a catalyst, between 900°F and 1000°F. To minimize methanator size and improve catalyst life, the acid gases (carbon dioxide and hydrogen sulfide) must be removed first. Following the acid-gas removal step, the methanation reaction

$$3H_2 + CO \xrightarrow{Ni,\ 500°F - 900°F} CH_4 + H_2O + \Delta H$$

takes place by combining hydrogen and carbon monoxide over a catalyst between 500°F and 900°F. Methanation is strongly exothermic, but because it is carried out at low temperature, the heat is used to generate steam for use outside the gasifier. After the methanation step the gas is dried, giving an HCV gas with a heating value in the range of 900 to 1000 lb Btu/scf.

When LCV gas is the objective, raw gas is treated to remove tar (when present) and dust is further treated to remove H_2S. The product is an LCV, low-sulfur gas that can be used for boiler fuel or industrial processes. Production of this gas is less complicated and thus less expensive than producing HCV gas. The shift conversion is not needed, and a simple gas

cleanup system can be used because a methanation step is not required.

As the primary objective of HCV gas processes is to produce a substitute natural gas that can be piped economically over long distances, there are important differences in the characteristic properties of a pipeline gas and an LCV power plant fuel produced by a gasification process. Table I summarizes these differences. A major difference among the gasification processes using the steam-carbon reaction is the method of adding heat. It can be done in a number of ways; electrically heat the bed, add oxygen or air, or transfer hot inert fluids or fluidized solids to the bed. Along with the addition of heat to the gasifier, another significant difference is the type of gasifier, or the way in which coal and various gases are brought into contact. Multiple-stage contacting arrangements make better use of the devolatilization and hydrogasification reactions.

GENERAL PROCESS DESCRIPTION

Figure 2 summarizes the general process for producing a high- or low-calorific-value gas from coal. First, the coal is dried and crushed to the desired size. For some types of gasifiers, caking coal is oxidized and/or devolatilized superficially to prevent sticking and agglomeration of particles, and is then sent to the gasifier. Other pretreatment methods may include placing the coal in a fluidized bed of air, or a combination of steam or nitrogen mixed with air; air is most often used. (Entrainment gasifiers do not require pretreatment.)

Gasification is the next step. Whereas basic reactions are the same for each process, differ-

Table I. Fuel-Gas Properties for Pipeline (HCV) Gas and LCV Gas

	Pipeline Gas	LCV Gas
Heat Content, Btu/scf	900–1000	90–160
Pressure, psig	1000 at pipeline	0–300
Temperature, °F	70	70–1800
Composition	Mostly CH_4	$CO, N_2, H_2, CO_2, H_2O, CH_4$
Sulfur	1 ppm	100 ppm
Particulates	0.01 lb/10^6 Btu	0.03 lb/10^6 Btu*

*Reduction of particulate to 0.008 lb/10^6 Btu is required for use in a gas turbine.

ences occur in the coal feeding systems, reactor configurations and the methods of adding heat. After gasification, the process changes depending upon whether a high or low heat value gas is desired.

If an HCV gas is desired, the raw gas from gasification is upgraded in a series of steps as described earlier. If an LCV gas is to be the final product, the raw gas from gasification is treated to remove fines and sulfur products.

GASIFIER TYPES

There are three generally recognized types of coal gasification equipment: (1) fixed-bed (2) fluidized-bed and (3) entrainment. These have significantly different characteristics which influence commercial applicability.

FIXED-BED GASIFIERS

Fixed-bed gasification is somewhat analogous to stoker-fired combustion of coal or to coke-oven operation. Satisfactory operation is

achieved only with coals of suitable size and caking characteristics. Although adding coal pretreatment and mechanically stirring the fuel bed widens the range of coals that may be processed, a fixed-bed unit is not workable for all types of coal. As with stokers, physical size limitations for this type of equipment dictate a multiplicity of individual gasifiers for a large-capacity installation and large isolating valves in the gas ductwork.

Several types of commercial fixed-bed gasifiers are producing synthesis gas for various chemical processes and for other uses. Former town-gas plants, for example, generally were served by fixed-bed gasifiers.

FLUID-BED GASIFIERS

Fluid-bed gasification processes have been demonstrated with laboratory equipment, relatively small pilot plants, and small industrial installations. Fluidized beds have an attractive operating characteristic: the entire reactor vol-

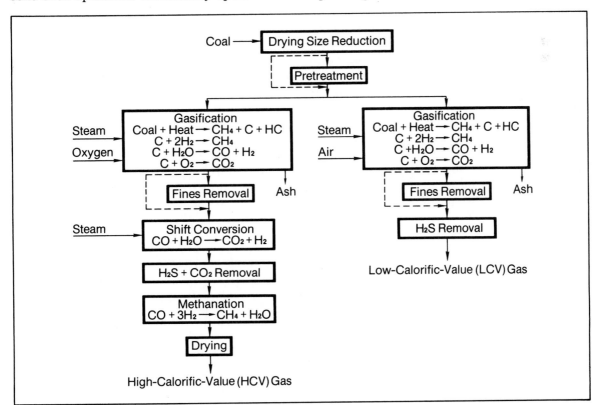

Fig. 2 **General process scheme for producing HCV or LCV gas**

ume operates at a substantially uniform temperature which, by design, can be the optimum temperature for the desired gasification reactions. In addition, the coal feed needs only to be crushed and dried. However, the gasifier produces a substantial amount of char which must be burned in some other device to achieve maximum coal utilization. Frequently these operating conditions are met with multiple fluid beds operated in tandem; one bed dries, one gasifies, and one burns residual char.

Some fluidized-bed processes have additional fluid beds to regenerate reactant material such as the sulfur-removing limestone circulated in the gasification bed. The hardware for feeding and circulating abrasive char, ash, and limestone at temperatures of 1500°F to 1900°F into and among such fluidized beds is entirely developmental, and presents significant operational control problems.

ENTRAINMENT GASIFIERS

Entrainment gasificaton processes use finely pulverized coal, gasifying it at relatively high temperatures as it is carried through the gasifier in suspension by the air, steam, and product gases. The process is very similar to firing boilers with pulverized-coal. At least three entrainment-type gasification processes have been in commercial operation, but on a relatively small scale, gasifying from 2 to 15 tons of coal per hour—some oxygen-blown and some air-blown. The air-blown versions produce gas of 80 to 110 Btu/scf heating value. All types op-

erate at essentially atmospheric pressure. Not size-limited as are other types, the entrainment gasifier is a simple, flexible system that can be scaled up for large electric-generating plants.

POWER-PLANT APPLICATION

For many years, boilers have successfully fired various types of low heat-content gaseous fuels including blast-furnace gas, refinery regenerator waste gas, and coke-oven gas, with heating values ranging from 40 to 600 Btu/scf. Industrial gas turbines have been fired by blast-furnace gas which also has been fired in electric utility boilers.

To gasify coal economically for electric-power production, the coal must be transported to the electric generating plant for on-site gasification. The primary reason is that, in addition to producing a clean fuel, the gasification process generates large amounts of heat. To attain the high efficiencies necessary for economic base-load power generation, this heat must be recovered by functionally integrating the gasification plant with the electric generating plant (Fig. 3).

In an integrated electric power-plant application, the gasification system is part of a two-stage coal combustion process. In the first, or gasification stage, the coal is partially reacted with a deficiency of oxygen to produce a low-heating-value fuel gas that can be readily cleaned. In the second stage, the cleaned fuel gas is burned in a boiler and/or gas turbine for the generation of electric power. Heat pro-

Fig. 3 **Integrated coal-gasification/steam-cycle power plant**

duced in the gasification stage is recovered by generating steam; therefore, the gasifier has a common need with the power boiler for heated air and feedwater. The gasifier steam is merged with the steam generated in the power boiler. Such integration is necessary for high plant efficiency regardless of whether the gasification system is retrofit to an existing power plant to replace oil or natural gas as the fuel, or whether the system is applied to a new steam or combined-cycle power plant.

With boiler modifications, LCV gas can be used in existing electric utility power plants to replace oil or natural gas fuels when they are unavailable, or to replace coal to provide an environmentally clean system without the use of scrubbers. When replacing oil or gas fuels, the LCV gasification plant should be integrated with the power plant as described above. Without this integration, there may be a downrating of the plant because the compact oil- or gas-fired boiler designs usually cannot achieve full load with the high-volume, low-heating-value gas. Units designed for full-load coal firing can accommodate LCV gas without downrating, if induced-draft fan capability is not a limiting factor.

There is another option for retrofit of oil- and gas-fired plants and that is the use of MCV gas. When a gasifier is fired with oxygen rather than air (eliminating the inert nitrogen from the gas), a gas of 275 to 350 Btu/cu ft is produced. With this gas, full load can be achieved with minimum modification to any oil- or gas-fired boiler. This has advantages in certain power-plant retrofit situations where an LCV gas substitution is not possible. This will include

■ existing steam plants where integration of a new gasification plant is not practical

■ existing gas-turbine plants not readily convertible to use a low-heat-content gas

■ centralized gasification facilities to service a number of generating plants through limited-distance specially built pipelines

Of the committed fossil-fuel-fired steam generation capacity in the USA, some of the newer coal-fired plants have been equipped with flue-gas desulfurization systems. It can be expected that all future plants will be required to meet the same environmental considerations. Approximately 100,000 MW of the installed capacity consists of oil- and gas-fired units that were placed in operation since 1960. Approximately 40,000 MW of these are larger than 100 MW in size and have the potential to be converted to coal firing. However, conversion of these units to direct coal firing is not practical due to severe downratings that would result. But, conversion to an integrated coal gasification system is practical.

Atmospheric-pressure gasification systems can be incorporated into combined-cycle power plants, Fig. 4, without an excessive heat-rate penalty for fuel compression for the gas turbines and with a decided advantage in accessibility and availability over pressurized gasifiers. Atmospheric-pressure systems can achieve 99.7 percent carbon utilization from the coal fired. Gasifier efficiency for an integrated system is about 96 percent, taking credit for steam generation and gas sensible heat.[1,2]

THE C-E PROCESS

The C-E gasification process is an air-blown, entrained-flow process operating at atmospheric pressure. Coal is pulverized and transported pneumatically to the gasifier where it is partially combusted in a deficiency of air and converted to a product-gas stream containing char and H_2S. Coal ash is fused and tapped from the bottom of the gasifier as molten slag. The product-gas stream leaving the top of the gasifier is cooled and ducted to a particulate removal system where the char is removed from the gas and recycled back to the gasifier for consumption. The cooled char-free gas is then sent to a Stretford absorber where the H_2S is removed from the gas and converted to elemental sulfur. The cleaned gas stream, free of particulates and sulfur with a heating value of about 110 Btu/scf, is suitable for fueling steam generators, gas turbines, or industrial process equipment without the need for stack gas cleanup systems. (See Fig. 5.)

The key component of the plant is the gasifier

Fig. 4 **Integrated coal-gasification/combined-cycle power plant**

Fig. 5. **Diagram of C-E coal gasification process**

Fig. 6 **Atmospheric-pressure entrained-flow coal gasifier**

which adheres closely to the proven design practices used by C-E for utility boilers (Fig. 6). Coal is prepared in a conventional pulverization system to a fineness of 70 percent through a 200 mesh seive and then transported by air to the gasifier reactor. Approximately one-third of the pulverized coal feed, and all of the recycled char from the particulate removal system, is blown tangentially into the combustor section of the gasifier reactor and totally burned with air under slightly substoichiometric conditions. High temperatures are maintained in the combustor to melt the ash in the coal and recycled char. The molten ash drips through a slag tap hole in the floor of the combustor into a water-filled tank; there it is quenched and sluiced to disposal.

The hot gases formed in the combustor swirl upward through the necked-down diffuser zone. Their heat devolatizes and then gasifies the remaining two-thirds of pulverized coal feed blown into the lower portion of the oxygen-deficient reductor section just above the neck. Devolatization and gasification reactions throughout the height of the reductor are endothermic causing the product-gas temperature to fall to approximately 1700°F before it reaches the top of the reductor. The raw gas is then cooled and heat is recovered in a series of tube banks in the same manner as flue gases are cooled by superheaters, reheaters, and economizers in conventional boilers.

GASIFIER CONSTRUCTION

Temperatures within the gasifier are high, varying from a maximum of 3200°F in the combustor to approximately 300°F upon completion of raw-gas cool-down. Refractory-lined, fusion-welded, water-cooled tubular walls enclose the gasifier in a gas-tight envelope. Steam is generated in these walls, collected in a boiler drum, and subsequently superheated in the cool-down section of the gasifier. Except for the refractory inner lining, which is supported by the water-cooled tube walls, this is the same construction that C-E uses for large coal-fired utility boilers.

Following its cool-down to approximately 300°F, the raw gas leaves the gasifier and passes through two cleanup systems, the first to remove the particulates being carried out of the reductor, and the second to strip the hydrogen sulfide (H_2S) from the raw gas which was formed from the sulfur in the coal during the oxygen-deficient gasification reaction. A number of commercial options which will provide high-efficiency particulate collection and H_2S removal with subsequent conversion to elemental sulfur are available for use for these two subsystems. Coal feedstock used in the gasifier and site-specific conditions of the gasification plans influence the selection.

PROCESS MODIFICATION FOR MCV GAS

Modification of the C-E process for medium heat-value gas production centers around the coal preparation system and the gasifier. Coal pulverization is essentially the same but the pulverized coal is fed to the gasifier differently. Rather than transporting the coal with air, a dense phase coal transport system is used to eliminate the effects of air dilution.

An oxygen separation plant is also required to supply pure oxygen to the gasifier reactor. This necessitates a new ductwork system around the gasifier as pure oxygen will replace the air used to burn the coal and char in the combustor. Additional modifications to the gasifier vessel, the gasifer cooling train, and the raw gas cleanup systems also are required to compensate for the difference in product-gas weight. The same general design practice used for air-blown LVC gasifiers is followed.

GASIFIER PILOT PLANT

A C-E pilot plant for an entrained flow, atmospheric pressure, air-blown gasifier was built to demonstrate the ability of the process and equipment to make LCV gas from coal and to provide the design information for scaleup of the equipment to commercial size. The 8 sequential units of the plant are scaled-down versions of the same process units that would be incorporated in a commercial-size plant.

Fig. 7 is a photograph of the completed pilot plant and Fig. 8 is a flow schematic which illustrates the interrelationships of all the principal equipment. Material flow in Fig. 8 generally is from left to right.

The plant has operated with a Pittsburgh seam coal, which is a high-sulfur, bituminous caking coal. Table II tabulates typical gas analyses obtained during test runs. Note that the CO content was higher than anticipated, and there was methane plus other useful hydrocarbons produced for extended periods. These constituents raised product-gas heating value to higher than predicted values. Hydrogen sulfide in the product gas has consistently been reduced from about 2300 ppm in the raw gas to levels ranging from 10 to 50 ppm in the clean gas. No tars or oils have ever been found in the product gas.

Fig. 9 shows the C-E atmospheric-pressure

Fig. 7 Coal-gasification pilot plant

Table II. Range of Product Gas Compositions from Pilot Plant

Components	Predicted, Vol. %	Initial Results, Vol. %
CO_2	4.4	3.0–12.5
CO	22.9	7.5–30.0
H_2	10.0	5.0–9.5
N_2	62.7	58.0–74.0
CH_4	0.0	0.0–3.0
Other Hydrocarbons	0.0	0.0–1.0
H_2S	100 ppm	10–50 ppm
HHV	106 Btu/scf	40–145 Btu/scf

entrainment gasifier suitable for large-scale plants of 275 to 300 MW capacity, depending upon the plant cycle with which it is used. It looks like and is built like a utility boiler—it is air blown and tangentially fired, using conventional fuel supply and firing equipment, pulverizers, convection heating surface, and

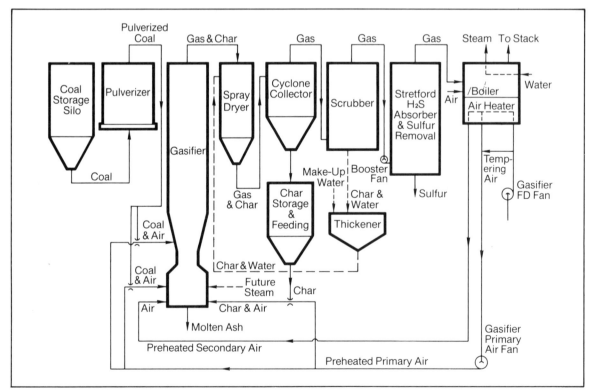

Fig. 8 Schematic flow diagram of atmospheric-pressure entrained-flow air-blown gasifier

fans. The steam/water circulation system of the gasifier may be designed for any desired operating pressure, and can be integrated with the steam/water circulation system of the plant's main power boiler as outlined in sub-section Power Plant Application.

The gasifier shown is about 180 feet tall with a maximum cross-sectional dimension of about 30 feet. The furnace, or reaction chamber, consists of gas-tight, fusion-welded, tubular waterwalls which support a thin inner refractory lining. A reduced-cross-section throat called the diffuser zone separates the reaction chamber into an upper and lower zone and minimizes mixing of reactants between the upper and lower zones.

The heat-recovery sections at the gasifier outlet includes heat-transfer surfaces to meet the specific cycle requirements of the power plant. To offset the potential for gas-side corrosion, low-temperature superheater sections have stainless-steel bare tubing. The

Fig. 9 Coal gasifier for utility power plant

economizer section has carbon-steel tubes and outside aluminizing to prevent corrosion. The particulate-removal equipment for each plant includes spray dryers, multicyclone units, gas coolers, wet scrubbers, and a thickener (for scrubber underflow), all similar to that installed in the pilot plant. A Stretford sulfur-removal system completes gas cleanup.

THE ECONOMICS OF ENTRAINMENT GASIFICATION

A modern 2 to 3 gigawatt coal-fired electrical-generating installation is one of the largest integrated materials-handling and processing plants in existence. Typically, such plants burn the coal at normal atmospheric pressure. The necessary peripheral equipment such as conveyors, feeders, pulverizers, firing equipment, fans, ductwork, sootblowers and ash-handling equipment are fully developed for these sizes and firing pressures. The atmospheric-pressure entrained gasification process uses much of this developed technology.

To examine its performance and economics, this process has been studied as part of several 600-MW power plants. The gasification and gas cleanup systems are essentially the same for all plants. Heat absorbed in the gasifier is used to generate a portion of the steam for the power cycles. The LCV product gas leaves the gasifier at 1700°F and is cooled to 300°F by convection heat exchangers located in the rear pass of the gasifier unit. The recovered heat is added to the steam power cycle or is used to preheat gasifier air or boiler fuel. The clean product gas, at 112 Btu/scf, meets both environmental requirements and gas-turbine fuel specifications. See Ref. 4 for comparative heat notes and economics of these plants.

EPRI conducted studies to compare the economics of "over-the-fence" retrofits of an existing gas-fired boiler and an existing oil-fired combined-cycle plant using an oxygen-blown C-E gasification system.[5] The studies do not imply that such a retrofit is an economical direct substitute for oil and natural gas if those fuels are still available for power production. However, it can be concluded that the retrofit of an existing gas-fired boiler or an oil-fired combustion turbine with an oxygen-blown C-E gasifier is cost competitive—in terms of cost of electricity produced—with a new replacement pulverized-coal-fired power plant equipped with a stack gas scrubber if oil or gas is no longer available. Capital requirements for the retrofit, however, are lower than those for the new pulverized-coal-fired plant. With the high cost of capital that appears to be ahead of us in the 1980s, this is an important factor.

INDUSTRIAL PLANT APPLICATIONS

In addition to power-plant applications, there are potential industrial applications for the gasification process, both air-blown (LCV gas) and oxygen-blown (MCV gas). Applications include the chemical industry (soda ash calcining, coal-to-methanol), oil industry (oil field flooding), paper industry (paper drying and general plant heating), metals industry (steel, lithium) and many others currently using natural gas or oil.

It is estimated that the potential market for gasification in industrial applications may be about 5 quads per year. (A quad is one quadrillion, or 10^{15} BTUs.) This is equivalent to about 500 gasification plants, each processing from 1200 to 1500 tons of coal per day.

The similarities between firing a boiler with pulverized-coal and the process of entrainment gasification are many. Similarities include:

- entrainment gasifiers are best suited for scale-up to the sizes required to achieve economy of scale in large power plants

- most, if not all, coals can be processed without special pretreatment

- virtually all char produced can be recycled to, and consumed in, the gasifier. There is no net char production and carbon utilization exceeds 99 percent

- ash disposal is minimized by fusing the ash into a molten slag in the gasifier. After water quenching, the coal ash is in an acceptable form for hydraulic transport and disposal

- entrainment gasifiers do not produce unwanted tars and oils in the product gas because of inherently high operating temperatures

Liquefaction of Coal for Boiler Fuels

Table III reveals that the elemental analysis of coals differs from oil and natural gas in that coal has

- a much lower hydrogen-to-carbon ratio

- higher concentrations of heteroatoms; i.e., oxygen, sulfur and nitrogen

Table III. Comparison of Chemical Properties of Coal with Other Premium Fossil Fuels

| | Ultimate Analysis* | | | | | | |
	S	H	C	N	O	H/C Atom Ratio	State at Room Temp
Bituminous, High-Volatile A	1.4	5.6	85.0	1.50	6.5	0.79	Solid
Bituminous, High-Volatile C	0.6	5.4	78.8	1.6	13.6	0.83	Solid
Lignite	0.9	5.2	72.0	1.3	20.6	0.86	Solid
Natural Gas	. . .	24.2	75.8	. . .	. . .	3.83	Gas
Crude Oil	. . .	11.7	86.4	1.14	0.6	1.62	Liquid
Gasoline	. . .	14.0	86.0	. . .	. . .	1.94	Liquid

*Moisture- and Ash-free

-In addition, coal as fired commonly has between 10 and 25 percent ash content and, for a wide range of coals, as high as 35 percent moisture content.

The primary objective of all liquefaction processes is to remove coal ash and increase the hydrogen/carbon ratio either by adding hydrogen and/or by reducing carbon content. It is also desirable to decrease the nitrogen, sulfur, and oxygen of the coal thereby reducing the production of nitrogen and sulfur oxides and increasing the quality of the derived product.

There are three methods for converting coal to clean burning and more environmentally acceptable liquids: direct liquefaction, indirect liquefaction and pyrolysis.

In direct liquefaction, hydrogen is added to the coal matrix to increase its hydrogen/carbon ratio. Depending on processing mode, the resultant coal-derived fuel product can be a high-melting-point solid, a heavy-residual-like coal-derived oil, or an all-distillate material. In indirect liquefaction, the coal matrix is completely consumed by gasification using oxygen and steam. The resulting product gas contains mainly hydrogen and carbon monoxide and can, after purification, be recombined to produce liquid products in (1) Fischer-Tropsch synthesis, (2) methanol synthesis, or (3) methanol synthesis followed by methanol conversion to gasoline. Pyrolysis involves heating coal in the absence of air, thereby achieving devolatilization and leaving behind a carbon-rich char. Depending on operating conditions, the pyrolysis process produces various proportions of oils and gases. Fig. 10 is a schematic flow diagram of these methods.

DIRECT LIQUEFACTION

In direct liquefaction processes, the addition of hydrogen increases the hydrogen-to-carbon ratio of coal. The liquefaction and hydrogenation of the coal can occur with or without catalyst. The main advantages of using a catalyst are more-efficient hydrogen utilization (less gas make) and lower product sulfur, nitrogen, and oxygen content.

Typical liquefaction reactor-system operating conditions, in either catalytic or noncatalytic processes, are pressures of 1500 psig and higher, and temperatures in excess of 800°F. The boiling range of the main product of a direct liquefaction process is related to the severity of the liquefaction system operating conditions. In general, higher pressure and temperature, and lower coal throughputs, increase distillate product yields and hydrogen consumption while decreasing residuum yield. The higher quality, all-distillate products are naturally more expensive to produce. Table IV lists typical properties of solid, residual and distillate-type boiler fuels.

Fig. 10 Coal liquefaction processes

The properties of the coal feedstock can also significantly influence the products of a direct liquefaction process. In general, bituminous coals are well suited as feedstocks, but a detailed petrographic analysis is useful in a preliminary assessment of the reactivity of a particular coal. The quantity and composition of the mineral matter in the coal also influence the ultimate product-yield distribution. When producing boiler fuels, younger lignitic and subbituminous coals have higher organic-oxygen contents than bituminous coals and require as much as 25 percent additional hydrogen consumption for the formation of water by deoxygenation. Because the extra water formed has no fuel value and hydrogen generation is costly, their higher oxygen content is a significant liability, only partially offset by their lower cost versus bituminous coals.

Although direct liquefaction was practiced on a commercial scale in Germany before and during World War II, more modern versions of this technology have been developed.

INDIRECT LIQUEFACTION

The indirect coal liquefaction route to clean liquids is a multistep process. In the first step, coal is gasified with oxygen and steam to produce a raw synthesis gas. Appropriate treatments such as purification to eliminate sulfur compounds, shifting to adjust the hydrogen/ carbon-monoxide ratio, and removal of carbon dioxide are required to prepare the raw gas for synthesis. The conversion of the purified raw gas to methanol or other liquid hydrocarbons is accomplished catalytically. The various methods available for conversion of synthesis gas to clean liquid products include the methanol and Fischer-Tropsch (F-T) processes.

Fischer-Tropsch synthesis yields a broad spectrum of products such as hydrocarbon gases and liquids, alcohols, aldehydes and ketones. Extensive treatment of the hydrocarbon liquids is required to produce salable gasoline, diesel and fuel oil. As the main products are transport fuels, this technique probably would not be used to produce boiler fuels.

In addition, although Lurgi gasification followed by F-T synthesis represents commercialized technology, the thermal efficiency of the total process including gasification is significantly lower than the projections for direct liquefaction if all-liquid fuels are required.

Widely practiced commercially, the methanol process uses synthesis gas produced by steam reforming of light hydrocarbon feeds. As the first-half of the technology is similar to that for producing synthetic natural gas (SNG) from coal by gasifiers, both of the major steps required to produce methanol from coal have been practiced commercially. Methanol is

Table IV. Properties of Typical Boiler Fuels from Direct Liquefaction Processes

Process:	SRC-I	SRC-II	H-Coal	CFFC
Type of Fuel:	Solid	Distillate	Distillate	Heavy Oil
Type of Process:	Noncatalytic	Noncatalytic	Catalytic	Catalytic
Pour Point, °F:	50 (Melting Point)	25	20	65
HHV Btu/lb:	15,700–16,000	17,300	17,500	16,800
Approximate Boiling Range, °F	850 +	400–800	400–975	400 +
Weight %				
Hydrogen	5.9	7.8	9.0	6.8
Sulfur	0.8	0.3	0.03	0.3
Nitrogen	2.0	0.9	0.4	1.2
Ash	0.15	Nil	Nil	0.05

being considered as a motor fuel for automobiles and other vehicles using gasoline or diesel fuel. It has also been extensively tested as a fuel in oil-fired power plants.

PYROLYSIS

In pyrolysis, complex thermal reactions decompose and rearrange the original coal structure. Three phases are produced: gases (H_2, CH_4, C_2H_4, CO, CO_2, H_2S, NH_3, and N_2); liquids (water, tar, and light oil); and solids (char). The gaseous and liquid phases have been preferentially enriched in their hydrogen content while the solid or char contains a lower hydrogen content.

The composition and yield of the pyrolysis product are influenced by how the coal is heated and the maximum pyrolytic temperature. In the low-temperature carbonization (850°F to 1300°F), the quantity of gaseous products is small and that of the liquid products is relatively large; therefore, liquefaction processes use low temperature. In high-temperature carbonization (1600°F +), the yield of gaseous products is larger than the yield of liquid products and the production of tar is relatively low.

Typically, coal is crushed to the required particle size. Then, in the pyrolysis step, heat is applied to drive off water, gases, and liquid hydrocarbons. The oil is recovered and sent to hydrogenation for upgrading to either fuel oil or synthetic crude. Gas also is recovered, purified, and can be used as plant fuel, hydrogen plant feedstock, or converted to pipeline gas and sold. The residual char remaining after pyrolysis contains significant amounts of carbon, all the ash, and most of the sulfur present in the original coal.

One disadvantage of the pyrolysis technique is that only one-third of the coal is converted to liquids, which generally require hydrotreatment to be environmentally acceptable. Another disadvantage of the pyrolysis route is the necessity to use the char in some other process. Historically, the char produced from the carbonization of coal has been used mainly for metallurgical coke in the steel industry.

APPLICABILITY OF COAL LIQUEFACTION FOR BOILER FUELS

Liquid fuels from coal have been produced commercially for many years by the pyrolysis and synthesis-gas processes. Although the pyrolysis process is simple, it yields multiple products (gas, oils, and tars) and leaves a considerable amount of unreacted carbon as a char. To produce an economical process, some use is required for this char; but it is not a desirable fuel with all the volatiles gone and most of the undesirables, such as sulfur and ash, remaining. The Fischer-Tropsch process is well known and is currently in commercial operation at the SASOL plant in South Africa but its primary products are transport fuels.[6] Efforts in coal liquefaction development are therefore towards direct liquefaction processes.

Applicable to most domestic coals regardless of sulfur content, direct liquefaction can produce a clean boiler fuel which can meet SO_2 emission requirements without stack gas scrubbing. Attaining an acceptable level of nitrogen-oxide emissions is more difficult. Because of their high fuel-bound nitrogen content, a residual-type fuel oil or a noncatalytic distillate fuel oil cannot meet NO_X emission requirements without boiler firing-system modifications. However, an all-distillate type fuel produced from catalytic-type direct liquefaction should satisfy NO_X emission requirements without boiler modifications.

The benefits of clean-boiler-fuel-from coal to the power producer include

■ its similarity to fuels already familiar to the industry

■ only minor, if any, changes to existing oil-fired power plants would be needed to accommodate this new clean fuel

Siting problems with new power-plants would be reduced considerably in comparison to conventional coal-fired units. Less land area would be needed since provisions for solid coal handling and storage, SO_2 removal, and ash disposal would be unnecessary.

The boiler fuel product would be of approximately constant quality with uniform heating value regardless of the coal source. This would help standardize the design of the new fossil-fueled boilers. The liquefied product is readily stored in tanks, and would permit the coal conversion plant to operate at a steady production rate despite any fluctuating demand in the utility generating plants. Conversely, a coal liquefaction plant shutdown, for maintenance or inspection, would not necessarily force a utility power-plant to shut down.

CLEAN BOILER FUEL BY DIRECT LIQUEFACTION

C-E Lummus has developed a Clean Fuel from Coal (CFFC) process for production of boiler and transportation fuels (Fig. 11). It is a catalytic direct-liquefaction process. The following description of a commercial plant for producing a residual-type boiler fuel is illustrative of this type of process.

Based on pilot-plant operations with a high-

volatile bituminous coal, overall heat and material balances were made to establish operating requirements and thermal efficiency. This resulted in a plant capable of producing 25,000 barrels per day of low-sulfur, low-ash product suitable for use in power generation. This quantity of clean fuel product could continuously generate 750 MW of power for 330 days/year based on a power-plant heat rate of 9030 Btu/kWhr.

The key features of the CFFC process are

■ catalytic hydrodesulfurization of coal to produce a refined liquid coal product containing 0.34 percent sulfur or less

■ special ash separation to produce a clean fuel product containing less than 0.1 percent ash

In the coal preparation area, raw coal is crushed and dried to 3 percent moisture then slurried in a mix tank with de-ashed pasting oil from the antisolvent de-ashing unit. From

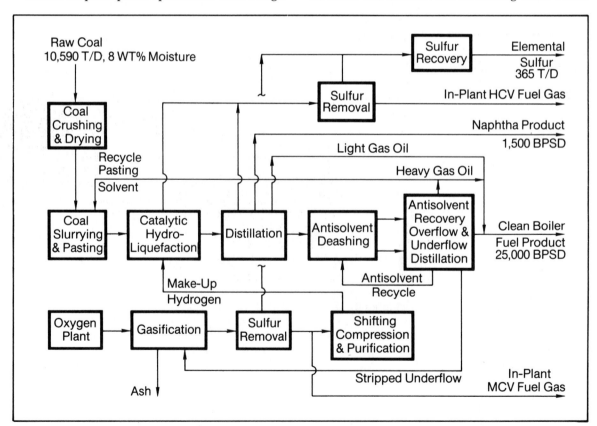

Fig. 11 Simplified flow diagram—clean boiler fuel by the C-E CFFC process

the mix tank the coal slurry is sent to the pasting tank where the temperature and residence time combine to partially dissolve the coal into solution. Continuous recirculation in a heated loop keeps the contents of the pasting tank hot.

The partially solubilized coal solution is sent to the catalytic hydroliquefaction section where it is mixed with a hot, combined makeup and recycle hydrogen stream. In the expanded-bed catalytic reactors, the coal solution is desulfurized and converted into gaseous and distillable as well as nondistillable liquid products. Approximately 75 to 80 percent of the sulfur contained in the coal slurried to the reactors is converted to H_2S. In addition, most of the oxygen and a portion of the nitrogen in the coal is hydrogenated to water and ammonia, respectively. The chemical hydrogen consumption is 2.2 lb per 100 lb of moisture- and ash-free (maf) coal fed to the hydroliquefaction reactors.

Table V. Clean Fuel Product Properties

Sulfur Content, weight %	0.34
Ash Content, weight %	0.05
Pour Point, °F	65
Sp. Gr. 170/60°F	1.100
Sp. Gr. 268/60°F	1.060
Conradson, weight % Carbon	25.0
Flash Point (PM CC), °F	215
Fire Point (COC), °F	265
Higher Heating Value, Btu/lb	16,800 ± 200
Viscosity, Saybolt Universal Seconds	
at 140°F	5900
at 180°F	864
at 210°F	325
Elemental Analysis (Ash-free basis), %	
Carbon	88.78
Hydrogen	6.84
Sulfur	0.34
Nitrogen	1.21
Oxygen (by diff.)	2.80
Chlorine	0.025
Trace Metal Analysis, ppm	
Sodium	5.7
Vanadium	1.0

After heat recovery, the reactor effluent is separated into gaseous, aqueous liquid and ash-containing liquid product streams. The high-pressure gas stream is desulfurized, partially purged, and recycled back to the reaction system where it joins with the makeup hydrogen. The aqueous liquid is stripped for ammonia and hydrogen sulfide removal.

The ash-containing liquid product stream is fractionated to recover gaseous light hydrocarbons, an aromatics-rich naphtha, and a light atmospheric gas oil. The gaseous light hydrocarbons are compressed, desulfurized, and mixed with recycle hydrogen purge gas to form a high-calorific-value in-plant fuel gas.

The bottoms from the fractionator are sent to the de-ashing unit where they are contacted with an antisolvent. Solids agglomeration, promoted by the presence of the antisolvent, together with gravity settling, separates an underflow stream which contains essentially all the ash in the coal fed to the liquefaction section. The overflow stream from settling is fractionated to recover antisolvent and pasting oil and residual product. The underflow stream is also fractionated for the recovery of antisolvent and pasting solvent. The excess heavy gas oil over and above that needed as pasting solvent is blended with the light gas oil and residual product to form the clean boiler-fuel product. Table V shows the properties of the clean-fuel product. After purge and makeup, recovered antisolvent is recycled to the gravity settler.

The ash-rich underflow stream in the form of a hot pumpable residual oil/solids slurry is routed to a gasification system for conversion into a hydrogen-carbon monoxide rich gas mixture suitable for makeup hydrogen production. The gasifiers operate on the partial oxidation principle; the ash-rich underflow is combusted in the presence of steam with less than the stoichiometric amount of pure oxygen.

Sulfur in the gasifier feed is converted primarily to hydrogen sulfide in the reducing atmosphere of the gasifiers. Gasifier effluent, after heat recovery and particulate removal, is desulfurized so that a portion of it can be used as in-plant fuel gas. The balance of the synthetic gas is compressed, shifted, and purified by carbon dioxide removal. The resultant makeup hydrogen stream is compressed and sent to the reaction system.

The liquefaction complex is supported by extensive offsite facilities which include tankage, steam generation and cooling water systems, makeup water treating, waste water treatment, flare system, plant and instrument air, firewater system, buildings and warehouses.

The plant is environmentally acceptable in that all gases fired in process heaters and steam boilers will be essentially sulfur-free, waste waters will be treated to remove particulates and chemicals as required, and the ash from the gasification area will be sterile and pose no odor, oil or tar emission problems.

NEW DE-ASHING TECHNIQUE

One of the main steps in the CFFC process is a method to separate ash or solids from the coal solutions liquefied by hydrogenation. An efficient operation consisting of an antisolvent-promoted, gravity settling of solids, has been developed that completely eliminates the need for mechanical equipment such as rotary filters, centrifuges, or flotation cells.

Sulfur compounds formed in the liquefaction/gasification steps and separated in the various sulfur-removal operations are sent to a Claus unit for conversion to elemental sulfur. But the Claus-unit tail gas does contain some unconverted sulfur compounds. A secondary cleanup process converts this tail gas to meet sulfur dioxide emission requirements.

Antisolvents which have a boiling point below 600°F and a Watson characterization factor greater than 9.75 are preferred in the process. Straight-run kerosene distillates from petroleum are highly satisfactory. Such antisolvents are not consumed in the process, but are continually recycled.

For the de-ashing process, topped feedstock (consisting of recycled pasting solvent, coal liquids, unconverted coal and ash) is mixed with antisolvent. The resulting mixture flows continually to a gravity settler operating in the 500°F to 600°F range and at a pressure sufficient to maintain its contents in liquid state. An overflow stream containing substantially no ash and an ash-enriched underflow stream are simultaneously and continuously withdrawn from the gravity settler.

High-ash bituminous middlings, containing as much as 23 percent ash, have been successfully processed to yield a fuel containing less than 0.1 percent ash.

PROCESS DESCRIPTION

The process-flow block diagram, Fig. 11, depicts the process configuration. The plant complex is composed of three major parts: coal preparation, a coal liquefaction section, and a gasification section. Table VI shows the feed coal analysis.

The complex is designed to charge 10,000 tons of coal per day and to produce as its major product 25,000 barrels per day of a clean fuel product containing less than 0.35 percent sulfur. Byproducts consist of 1,500 barrels per day of naphtha and sulfur recovered from the various desulfurizing processes. The plant's fuel requirement is supplied by light, gaseous hydrocarbons formed during hydroliquefaction together with fuel gas generated from the gasification of the ash-rich underflow.

The gross thermal efficiency of the plant, defined as

$$\frac{\text{HHV of C5 + product}}{\text{HHV of coal fed to complex}}$$

Table VI. Analysis of Bituminous Coal Used in the C-E Lummus CFFC Design

Constituent	As-Received Wt.%	Dried Feed to Liquefaction Wt.%
Carbon	62.6	66.2
Hydrogen	4.6	4.9
Nitrogen	1.1	1.2
Sulfur (Total)	3.7	3.9
Mineral Matter (Sulfur-free)	9.2	9.7
Organic Oxygen	10.5	11.1
Water	8.3	3.0
	100.0	100.0
High Heating Value (HHV) 11,600 Btu/lb		

is approximately 70 percent, based on an 8-percent moisture coal with a high heating value of 11,600 Btu/lb. This figure does not reflect the electrical power consumption for plant drives and other in plant uses.

FLUIDIZED-BED COMBUSTION

For decades fluidized-bed reactors have been used in non-combustion reactions in which the thorough mixing and intimate contact of the reactants in a fluidized bed result in high product yield with improved economy of time and energy. Although conventional methods of burning coal also can generate energy with very high efficiency, fluidized-bed combustion can burn coal efficiently at a temperature low enough to avoid many of the problems of conventional combustion.

The outstanding advantage of fluidized-bed combustion (FBC), then, is its ability to burn high-sulfur coal in an environmentally acceptable manner without the use of flue-gas scrubbers. A secondary benefit is the formation of lower levels of nitrogen oxides compared to other combustion methods. In addition, low bed temperatures help eliminate the potential for slag formation on the water-cooled walls of the furnace (an operational advantage) and

high heat-transfer in the fluidized bed permits a more economical boiler design.

DESIGN PRINCIPLES

A fluidized bed is a layer of solid particles kept in turbulent motion by bubbles created by air being forced into the bed from below (Fig. 12). A fuel may be added and burned in this bed. Although the fuel will make up less than 1 percent of the bed, all of the solid particles introduced are quickly heated by the churning action of the bed. If heat absorbing surface is submerged in the bed, the temperature of the solid bed particles can be controlled at a predetermined level. The hot solids and gases surround the heat absorbing tubes, and their intimate contact results in a high heat-transfer coefficient. This is the fundamental design principle of a fluidized-bed boiler. An FBC unit can be fired with many types of fuel including the lower-grade coals, municipal solid wastes, coal-cleaning wastes, agricultural wastes, peat, and other fuels difficult to burn by conventional methods.

From an environmental point of view, a most valuable feature of fluidized-bed combustion is the ability to burn coal in a bed consisting of heated limestone. The calcium oxide from the calcination of the limestone absorbs the sulfur

Fig. 12 **Schematic diagram of fluidized-bed-combustion boiler**

dioxide being released from the burning coal. The result is a dry calcium-sulfate waste product. Maximum sulfur capture occurs when the bed is maintained at temperatures between 1500°F and 1600°F.

The low combustion temperature in the fluidized-bed boiler permits burning coal and other high-ash fuels at temperatures below their ash softening point. Furnace slagging and associated heat-transfer surface fouling are virtually eliminated. Unlike a conventional boiler, therefore, the fluidized-bed boiler design is not as dependent upon the chemical and physical properties of the coal ash and can burn a much wider range of fuels with less operational difficulty. But this does not mean that any given fluidized-bed boiler can burn any fuel with the same unit output or performance. The bed must be properly designed to adjust for the fuel heating value, reactivity, sulfur content, and ash quantity.

Another benefit from the low combustion temperature of a fluidized-bed boiler is the reduced production of nitrogen oxides (NO_x). At these low temperatures, thermal NO_x does not form by direct oxidation of atmospheric air. In addition, NO_x production from fuel nitrogen is suppressed. This results in very low overall NO_x stack emissions.

There are two general classifications of fluidized-bed combustors: atmospheric and pressurized. As the names imply, the atmospheric FBC operates at or very near atmospheric pressure, while the pressurized FBC operates at pressures generally between 3 and 10 atmospheres. Although elevated-pressure operation results in increased efficiencies, it introduces significant technical difficulties. Thus, there has been a much broader effort concentrated on the development of atmospheric fluidized-bed boilers.

FBC BOILER DESIGN PARAMETERS

The design of fluid-bed boilers must take into account several features characteristic of the FBC process. The operation of the bed itself, the methods of fuel feed and ash removal, the heat-transfer rates, and the control of particulate carryover all differ radically from pulverized coal and even stoker firing.

BED EXPANSION

The bed height is one of the few controllable parameters available to the fluid-bed operator. The expanded-bed height is normally set so that the in-bed tubes are fully covered, which assures the maximum use of the submerged tube surface. During operation, the expanded-bed height can be adjusted through changes in limestone feed rate and bed drain rate.

Bed expansion is due primarily to bubble-gas holdup measurable by the excess gas-velocity ratio which is the ratio of the velocity in excess of the minimum fluidization velocity, divided by the minimum fluidization velocity,

$$\frac{U_o - U_{mf}}{U_{mf}}$$

Fig. 13 shows a plot of bed expansion ratio (active to static bed height) versus excess gas-velocity ratio. The low bed expansion at high velocity ratios is a result of the small particle sizes. With small particles, the bed is considered to be in the fast-bubble regime; the many small bubbles of gas produced result in the low bed expansion.

HEAT TRANSFER

One of the most important advantages of fluidized-bed combustion is the high heat-transfer coefficient from the bed to an immersed surface. The ability to predict heat-transfer coefficients accurately is essential in designing boilers. A large amount of literature is available on the prediction of heat transfer in fluidized beds. Caution is required, however, in applying these analyses to coal-fired fluidized beds, since most analyses are based on beds operating at low temperatures (less than 500°F) and on bench-scale equipment.

The total heat transfer to the immersed bed tubes consists of a direct radiation component and a combined solids-gas convection component. Direct radiation is a function of bed and tube surface temperatures. The convective heat-transfer component in a fluidized bed depends on the thermophysical properties of the fluidizing gas and bed solids, bed temperature and, to a lesser extent, on the bed particle size.

Fig. 14 is a curve of the Nusselt number versus the product of Archimedes number and Prandtl number derived from experimental test results. The Fig. 14 curve represents the following correlation:

$$Nu = \frac{h_c d_p}{k_g} = .31\,(Ar)^{.27}\,(Pr)^{.33}$$

$$(6)$$

where

d_p is the harmonic mean particle diameter

h_c is the total overall heat transfer coefficient (excluding radiation)

k_g is the gas thermal conductivity

Nu is the Nusselt Number

Pr is the Prandtl Number

Ar is the Archimedes Number

Eq. 6 indicates that the overall convective heat-transfer coefficient is a weak function of particle size and that there is no significant dependence of the heat-transfer coefficient upon the superficial gas velocity through the bed.

The small (8 percent) reduction in the convective heat-transfer component over a range of superficial velocities from 5 to 9 ft/sec is due to two competing effects. Increasing the gas velocity increases particle mixing. The faster the particles move, the less their temperature drops below the bulk bed temperature while in the vicinity of the heat-transfer surface. This results in increased heat transfer to the immersed surface. At the same time, as gas velocity is increased, the bed voidage increases, resulting in less solids contact and less heat being transferred to the immersed surface, thus decreasing the heat-transfer coefficient. The net result is effectively a constant transfer coefficient over a large range of velocities.

COMBUSTION EFFICIENCY

Understanding the interrelationship of critical operating variables affecting combustion efficiency in the bed also is necessary. Three factors influence this efficiency:

■ loss of carbon in the elutriated solids (governed by bed carbon loading, bed particle size, and superficial gas velocity)

■ loss of carbon in the bed-drain stream (which is determined by bed carbon loading and inert-material feed rate)

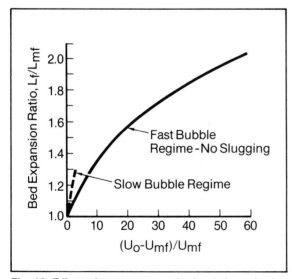

Fig. 13 Effect of excess gas velocity ratio on bed expansion

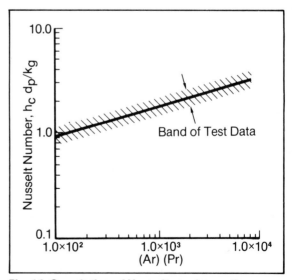

Fig. 14 Correlation of Nusselt number vs the product of Archimedes number and Prandtl number

■ loss of carbon as carbon monoxide (CO) due to incomplete combustion

The overall combustion efficiency has been determined to remain constant with increase in excess-air level ranging from 0 to 50 percent.[7,8] The combustible loss is estimated from the carbon loss due to CO in the exit flue gas and the elutriated combustible loss from carryover of unburned carbon. Total combustible loss is expressed as a weight percentage of the total carbon in the feed. In general, if the particle combustion is purely diffusion-limited, then the overall combustion efficiency should show little or no temperature dependence. Tests with bed temperature between 1400°F and 1650°F indicate this lack of dependence of efficiency on bed temperature. Recycle of elutriated particles captured by a mechanical-cyclone dust collector results in a 3 to 4 percent increase in the overall combustion efficiency. The value of overall combustion efficiency without recycle is about 92 percent whereas that for recycle is about 95 percent.

Combustion in the Bed

It is essential to be able to predict the amount of in-bed heat release so that the heat transfer surface can be designed accurately for the heat release expected in each zone.

Conditions for the burnout of char in the fluidized zone are favorable because of the good solids mixing and long residence time. But conditions for the combustion of volatile products may be less favorable because of the potential for release near the top of the bed. Unburned CO, volatile products, and fine char particles may escape the bed and reduce the proportion of combustion in the bed. It is highly desirable to optimize the proportion of combustion occurring in the bed to take advantage of the high heat transfer rates and, at the same time, to use to the fullest the above-bed volume for convective heating.

The percent of the total input-fuel energy released in the active bed zone is a weak function of excess air, active bed height, bed temperature, and superficial gas velocity. At a bed temperature of 1550°F, about 63 percent of the coal chemical energy is released in the bed under recycle operation.[7]

Freeboard Combustion

The freeboard zone is the region between the top of the bed and the first convective surface. Its primary function is to allow the larger particles ejected from the bed to decelerate and fall back into the bed. It also provides additional gas-to-gas and/or gas-to-solid contact so that combustion of CO, volatiles, and char particles, and absorption of SO_2 can take place.

The proportion of combustion taking place in the freeboard is about one-third of that in the bed. Splashing of the particles that are too large to be elutriated and that eventually fall back in the bed provides good solids mixing and promotes char combustion in the freeboard.

In the freeboard, the extent of char combustion depends upon the amount of solids holdup which in turn depends upon the amount of solids ejected into the freeboard by the bursting bubbles at the bed surface. However, the char elutriation rate from the bed rises slightly with superficial gas velocity and the extent of char combustion in the freeboard appears to be very nearly constant.

SULFUR-DIOXIDE REMOVAL

The chemical reactions involved in the sulfur-removal process, essentially calcination and subsequent sulfation of the limestone, are temperature-dependent. Optimum sulfur capture is achieved at a bed temperature of 1550°F.

Fig. 15 shows sulfur removal related to the major variables of bed temperature and calcium-to-sulfur mol ratio (Ca/S). Under optimum conditions sulfur removal of 90 percent can be achieved with a Ca/S ratio as low as 1:1. In practice, the actual Ca/S ratio is likely to be somewhat higher to account for the variations in bed temperature that will be encountered during normal operation.

PARTICULATE CARRYOVER

FBC units have large amounts of particulate matter leaving the furnace. This material comes from the coal ash char and limestone feed. Depending upon whether material collected in the cyclone is reinjected back to the bed, flue gases at the boiler outlet can contain high grain loadings. Usually, after passing through an air heater, the flue gases receive final particulate cleanup in a fabric filter.

NITROGEN-OXIDE GENERATION

Nitrogen oxides are generated from two sources: fuel nitrogen and atmospheric nitrogen. In FBC boilers, combustion temperatures are too low for any significant thermal-NO_X generation. The release of fuel nitrogen compounds, therefore, govern NO_X emissions.

This conversion occurs at very low efficiency. Actual emissions are generally in the 0.2 to 0.5 lb per million Btu range

A complex set of formation and destruction reactions takes place that governs the amount of NO_X emitted. An empirical correlation has been developed and is shown in Fig. 16.[7]

The presence of carbon monoxide in the correlation is because of an NO_X destruction reaction in which NO_X is consumed by a reducing species, i.e., carbon or carbon monoxide, to yield nitrogen. While carbon monixide has been chosen for the correlation, there is a strong interrelationship between carbon and carbon monoxide. It is difficult to identify their individual roles in controlling NO_X emissions.

INDUSTRIAL BOILERS

Fig. 17 shows a typical thermal-circulation AFB industrial boiler. Shop-assembled, rail-shippable units can generally be designed for

capacities up to 200,000 lb/hr of steam. Larger size units must be field erected.

The bed area in units of this type is designed for a fluidizing gas velocity of 7 fps at design heat input. An expanded bed height of 3 feet is maintained during operation. The bed contains both steam-generating and superheater heat-transfer surface to extract heat from the bed and maintain a bed temperature of 1550°F.

The size of the active bed area can be changed for start-up and part load operation. The plenum beneath the air distributor is divided into zones. Air dampers control the airflow to each zone, thereby allowing bed fluidization in increments. This enables the operator to choose the appropriate active area for optimum bed temperature and fluidizing velocity for all load conditions.

Firing additional zones to expand the active plan area of the bed increases boiler steam output. As the additional bed material is fluidized, material transfer in the bed redistributes the heat. Because there are no barriers in the bed between zones, lateral mixing brings the material to a uniform temperature. As the active bed area can be changed in small increments, large variations in bed temperature or superficial velocity are avoided, permitting operation within a narrow range of optimum conditions.

Fig. 18 is a schematic flow diagram of the industrial fluidized-bed process. Coal is unloaded, stored, screened, crushed and dried as required, and mixed with limestone before

Fig. 15 **Sulfur removal vs fluidized-bed temperature (test results[7])**

$$\text{Exp}\left[-3.03 + \frac{507}{d_{coal}} + 0.0016T - 0.02\ CO^{.5}\right]$$

Fig. 16 **NO_x measured vs NO_x calculated with recycle**

Fig. 17 General arrangement of industrial atmospheric-pressure fluidized-bed boiler

being fired in the boiler. Trucks pneumatically discharge the limestone directly into the storage silo. Char from the mechanical collector is also mixed with the coal-limestone stream and fed to the fluidized bed. The products of combustion pass from the boiler through a mechanical collector, tubular air heater, and bag filter before entering the induced-draft fan and stack. The ash system handles material from two sources—the boiler and the flue-gas collection points. Bed material drained from the boiler is cooled and transported pneumatically to storage. Flyash is collected from the mechanical collector, tubular air heater, and baghouse. Char collected from the mechanical cyclone

collector can be reinjected or transported to the storage silo.

UTILITY AFBC BOILERS

An advantageous feature of the larger-scale AFBC units for electric-utility use is the greater freeboard volume available to further enhance the combustion and sulfur-removal processes begun in the bed. Proper design of the free-board conditions yields combustion efficiency near 99 percent and a reduction in the required limestone sorbent consumption to Ca/S ratios less than 2:1.

Within the freeboard region, the residence time for the gaseous combustion products and solids elutriated from the bed is on the order of 3 to 5 seconds. A high solids concentration in the gas, more than 10 percent by weight, is maintained by recycling solids captured by the particulate removal equipment downstream of the boiler back to the bed by reinjection with the fuel feed.

Conditions in the freeboard permit three types of reactions to take place. These are shown diagrammatically in Fig. 19. Above the bed, carbon particles and carbon monoxide released from the bed react with oxides of nitrogen (NO_X) liberated from fuel nitrogen in the combustion process. The NO_X is reduced by the carbon to elemental nitrogen, limiting emissions to the range of 0.2 to 0.4 lb $NO_X/10^6$ Btu. In the freeboard region during the first one or two seconds of residence time, the temperature rises from the burnout of carbon and CO from

Fig. 18 Schematic flow diagram of industrial fluidized-bed boiler plant

the bed. A large freeboard with a high proportion of enclosed volume to heat-absorbing surface permits the temperature to reach the range of 1700° to 1800°F. Thus, carbon burnout is favored. Secondary air in this region will complete burning, control temperatures, and provide turbulence for mixing. Throughout the

freeboard, fine sorbent particles react with the residual SO_2 in the combustion products. While all of these processes take place in industrial size AFBC boilers, the larger size of the utility boiler optimizes them.

A side elevation of a 200 MW AFBC unit is shown in Fig. 20. The design exploits the

Fig. 19 Effective freeboard performance with direct reinjection

Fig. 20 **Side elevation of 200-MW Controlled Circulation atmospheric-pressure fluidized-bed steam generator for electric-utility use**

benefits of a large freeboard. Three seconds residence time is provided, with the peak temperature in the freeboard 1700°F.

A single-cell bed is used which is operated in zones for load control. No division walls separate the zones within the bed itself. Rather, plena supplying the air distributor beneath the bed permit selective activation of bed areas. In effect, then, the bed can be incrementally changed in plan area. Such a single-cell zoned bed unit uses the heat of an adjacent active zone to light-off additions to the active bed area.

Both top and bottom structural supports are used in the 200-MW boiler. The loads of the fluidized bed are carried through the air distributor to steel supported on ground-level foundations. The air distributor is formed of water-cooled tubes which traverse the bed and then become a portion of the furnace sidewall structure: Air distribution nozzles ("bubble caps") are installed in fins between the tubes. An expansion loop is formed in the fin-welded walls to allow the thermal growth between the bottom-supported bed and top-supported convective pass.

Bottom support of the large bed weight and plenum structure results in substantial reduction in the size of the upper girders and the supporting columns. With the bed located at a single level near the ground, material-handling equipment for the fuel feed and bed drains, air ducting, and instrumentation are centrally arranged for convenient maintenance and inspection during operation. Fuel pumps and bed-drain cooling and conveying equipment are ground-supported, further reducing steel support requirements.

Heat-absorbing tube bundles are installed in the bed, with the bed area devoted approximately 30 percent to evaporation, 50 percent to low-temperature superheat, and 20 percent to low-temperature reheat duty. The remaining evaporation is done in the boiler walls. Finishing superheat and reheat are provided by the pendant assemblies in the convective pass.

A multi-tube centrifugal cyclone collects solids from the flue-gas stream for recycling. These solids are conveyed pneumatically to

bins for feeding the collected fines into the fuel feed system along with the coal and limestone. The rate of reinjection can be varied, providing flexibility by controlling the bed heat loss to the reinjected solids passing through the fluidized bed. By this means, the bed temperature can be trimmed during reduced-load and transient conditions. The remainder of the flue-gas equipment includes a regenerative air heater for heat recovery and the final particulate-removal device.

This 200-MW boiler is designed structurally to accommodate cyclical and two-shift operation, since this size unit should find wide acceptance for peaking capability.

AFBC offers ideal advantages for two-shift operation. The bed when slumped is self-insulating and stores heat. The average bed temperature when slumped at 1550°F remains above 1000°F for more than 8 hours. After this period, the boiler can be restarted by refluidizing the bed and initiating coal feed.

CIRCULATING FLUIDIZED BED

In the circulating fluidized-bed furnace, the gas velocities are 3 to 4 times as high as in conventional bubbling fluidized beds. As a consequence, a high-density bed cannot form and all of the solid particles are carried up through the furnace. A more uniform lower-density gas/solid mixture exists throughout the entire furnace. The solids move through the furnace at much lower velocity than the gas; solids residence times in the order of minutes are obtained. The long residence times coupled with the small particle size produce high combustion efficiency and high SO_2 removal with much lower limestone feed.

A fluidized-bed steam generating system employing the concept of a circulating fluidized bed (CFB) process is shown in Fig. 21.

Coal and limestone delivered from the storage piles are pulverized, and conveyed to separate storage bins. The coal and limestone are delivered through gravimetric feeders to a solids inductor. Transport air from the FD-fan discharge is used to pick up the solids and pneumatically transport them to the circulating fluid-bed furnace. The solids are injected into the furnace near the bottom. Primary combustion air from the FD fan discharge is preheated in a conventional air heater using flue gas and is discharged into the circulating fluidized-bed furnace through a bottom air-plenum chamber.

The bottom portion of the furnace is refractory lined to eliminate high heat losses in the primary combustion zone. The upper portion of the furnace contains evaporative waterwalls with sufficient heat removal capability to maintain 1550°F gas/solids average temperature with the furnace. Secondary combustion air is injected into the furnace above the refractory bottom-portion of the furnace to complete combustion and improve SO_2 removal and NO_X attenuation for emission control.

The solids carried from the furnace are separated from the gas by a primary cyclone. To further reduce the solids loading before entering the convective pass of the steam generator, a

second high-efficiency cyclone is used.

Solids discharged from the bottom of the primary cyclone pass through a solids diverter system. The major portion of the cyclone solids is diverted to a solids heat-recovery fluid-bed system and the remainder is reinjected into the bottom of the CFB furnace.

Heat extracted from the solids diverted to the solids heat-recovery bed is used for additional evaporation and superheating. This bed, comprised of several sections separated by partial-bed-height division walls, is a conventional bubbling bed. Air for fluidization of these beds comes from a separate secondary air fan. Because no combustion occurs in the bed, this secondary air (without oxygen depletion) is also heated by the solids and discharged to the CFB furnace above the refractory section.

The small particle size and controlled fluidizing velocity produce in-bed tube heat-transfer rates 3 to 4 times greater than in conventional bubbling beds thus minimizing the

Fig. 21 **Circulating fluid bed process flow diagram**

size and cost of the entire solids heat-removal subsystem.

Solids are discharged from one end of the solids heat-recovery bed, after which some solids are diverted to the waste-disposal system to maintain a constant system-solids inventory. Waste solids are first cooled in an ash cooler system for additional heat recovery before being sent to the ash waste system.

Flue-gas from the cyclone discharge enters a conventional boiler convection backpass in which superheating, reheating and economizing occur. The flue gas leaves the furnace backpass and enters a multiple cyclone collector for additional particulate removal, then through the air heater and a bag filter for final particulate emission control. The flue gas is discharged through the plant stack by use of an induced draft fan. To maintain an optimum solids particle size in the circulating fluidized-bed, the fine solids collected in the baghouse are also discharged to the ash waste system.

Improvements in this system over the conventional bubbling bed furnaces include higher combustion efficiency and limestone utilization due to the use of smaller particle sizes and long solids residence time in the CFB furnace; lower NO_x formation due to staged combustion; simpler control system due to the separation of combustion and heat transfer in the solids heat-recovery bed, and a higher turndown ratio resulting from the large ratio between the operating gas velocity and the solids suspension velocity in the CFB furnace.

MAGNETOHYDRODYNAMIC POWER SYSTEMS

In magnetohydrodynamic (MHD) power generation, an electrically conducting fluid is passed through a magnetic field to generate an electric current without the use of rotating machinery. The concept has its origins in the pioneering work of Faraday.

Large enthalpy extraction from the working fluid is required for commercial power-generation applications. This dictates the use of fluids of high electrical conductivity; to date, research has centered on hot ionized gases and liquid metals.

The machine performing this enthalphy extraction is called the MHD channel. It contains electrodes imbedded in its walls for carrying the current. In general, these electrodes must be electrically isolated from each other and resistant to the electro-chemical corrosive and erosive properties of the working fluid. MHD was considered an unlikely source of energy until it was experimentally determined that coal ash actually formed a protective layer on the electrode walls to significantly increase electrode life.

The basic problem in the design of an MHD channel (Fig. 22) is to select a fluid with enough electrical conductivity and place it in a large enough magnetic field, all while constructing it of materials that will last a reasonable amount of time in a commercial application. These constraints lead to the consideration of superconducting magnets, hot conductive gases (plasmas) or liquid metals, and ceramic or water-cooled electrodes.

The leading choice appears to be a plasma generated by the combustion of coal at high temperatures and seeded with an alkali metal salt (preferably potassium) coupled with cold wall (water-cooled) electrodes. This is the open-cycle system, in which the combustion gases are eventually exhausted to atmosphere much like an open-cycle gas turbine.

Systems utilizing inert gas plasmas or liquid metals are restricted by economic considerations to closed-cycle applications. They suffer from requiring an external source of heat at very high temperatures; such sources require significant additional development of heat-recovery and heat-exchange equipment. Therefore, the remainder of the chapter will discuss coal-fired, open-cycle MHD systems.

COAL-FIRED OPEN-CYCLE MHD

In the coal-fired open-cycle MHD system (Fig. 23), coal and preheated oxidant are fired in a low-residence-time pressurized combustor at pressures between 4 and 8 atmospheres and temperatures greater than 4500°F. At the exit of

***Fig. 22* Basic direct-current-combustion MHD generator**

the combustor, potassium salts are added to the gas such that 1 percent of the gas weight is potassium. Referred to as seed material, the potassium salts are added to increase the electrical conductivity of the gas. This plasma is expanded through a nozzle to near sonic velocity and generates electricity when passed through a magnetic field. The MHD channel is constructed in such a manner as to allow this direct current to flow through electrodes in the walls. Electrode consolidation circuits direct the power to an inverter so that AC power is fed to the switchyard.

As long as the gas remains conductive, the MHD channel will produce power. When the gas temperature drops to where it no longer conducts appreciable electricity (about 3600°F), it is exhausted to the steam bottoming plant. The steam bottoming plant contains conventional fossil-plant equipment including radiant surfaces for steam generation and convective surfaces for superheating, reheating, oxidant preheating, and economizer duty.

The balance of plant, also conventional in nature, includes the steam turbine, feedwater system, cooling towers, stack, and other coal-

***Fig. 23* Coal-fired MHD-topped steam power plant**

fired power-plant equipment. In addition, a seed reprocessing plant is required. This plant takes the seed material recovered in various portions of the steam bottoming plant and extracts sulfur from it. The seed can then be recycled to the MHD combustor. In this manner, sulfur oxides can be reduced to very low levels.

The combined output from the MHD generator and the steam plant is expected to give overall energy conversion efficiencies of approximately 50 percent. It is this efficiency improvement that is the driving factor behind MHD development.

SYSTEM OPTIONS

There are three varieties of coal-fired open cycle MHD power plants, characterized by the method of air preheating:

■ high-temperature, directly preheated air

■ high-temperature, separately fired preheated combustion air

■ intermediate-temperature, oxygen-enriched, preheated air (Fig. 24)

Air preheat is an important part of MHD power generation because of the high combustion temperatures required. For the combustion products to become sufficiently electrically conducting, even with the addition of potassium salts, flame temperatures of over 4500°F are required. These temperatures can only be achieved by very high air-preheat temperatures (from 2500 to 3000°F), or by increasing the oxygen content of the air along with some degree of air preheat.

The directly preheated cycle uses the hot MHD exhaust gases to preheat the combustion air. The heat exchanger in this application is in an extremely hostile environment, being subjected to all the seed material and some of the slag. Moreover, all of the high-temperature gas must pass through without substantial damage to the heat exchanger. Ceramic heat exchangers similar to blast-furnace stoves have been considered for this type of service; but maintenance, pluggage, breakage, corrosion, and erosion are anticipated to be severe problems.

In the separately fired preheat cycle, the external heat exchangers are fired with a clean fuel to avoid such problems. The clean fuel can be derived from a low-calorific-value coal-gasification process, a method that entails some additional equipment expense and some loss of cycle efficiency. It is also more complicated than the directly heated cycle.

The oxygen-enriched system is the simplest and potentially the cheapest of the three sys-

(A) High-Temperature Direct Preheat

(B) High-Temperature Separately-Fired Preheat

(C) Intermediate Temperature Preheat, Oxygen-Enriched

Fig. 24 Types of open-cycle coal-fired MHD/steam power plants

tems, although the requirement of an air-separation plant to separate oxygen from nitrogen adversely affects the efficiency. The oxygen is mixed with air and preheated to more moderate temperatures in an environment more closely resembling conventional boiler superheater or reheater conditions, thereby avoiding complex ceramic heat exchangers. The additional power required to operate the air separation plant is the basic contributor to the lower efficiency of this system.

PLANT DESIGN CONSIDERATIONS

MHD power-plant designs depart from conventional practice in many areas. The considerations which are unique to MHD plants are

- pressurized, high-temperature combustion
- use and recovery of seed materials
- very high air-preheat requirements
- elaborate power consolidation equipment

Total electrical output from an MHD/steam-power plant is a combination of direct power generated in the MHD channel and alternating power generated from the steam bottoming plant. Roughly one-half the total electrical power is generated in each section. This is converted to entirely alternating power in a consolidation facility which also serves to control the MHD generator power output.

MHD EQUIPMENT

The following sections include more detailed descriptions of those items which affect overall MHD plant performance.

MHD CHANNEL

Normally rectangular in cross section, the channel is constructed of four separate walls, mechanically jointed to form a duct. The corners are sealed with a castable refractory. A positive-air-pressure channel behind the refractory seal prevents any leakage from the channel and cools the wall joints. The electrodes, separated by insulating ceramics, are mounted along two opposing walls with minimum insulating thickness determined by the method of manufacturing reliable water-cooled segments. The remaining walls are comprised of insulators.

The load may be divided into a number of segments, each connected across a pair of electrodes. This "Faraday generator" provides essentially constant voltage to each load segment and as such is similar to a DC generator (Fig. 25). A second configuration, the "Hall generator," is developed by shorting out the segmented pairs of electrodes and connecting the load across the first and last pairs of electrodes. This configuration yields essentially a constant current and as such is quite dissimilar to large electrical network operation. A third possibility is to connect electrodes of equal electrical potential. This configuration operates basically as a Hall generator. However, it has a considerable loss of performance under fluctuating load.

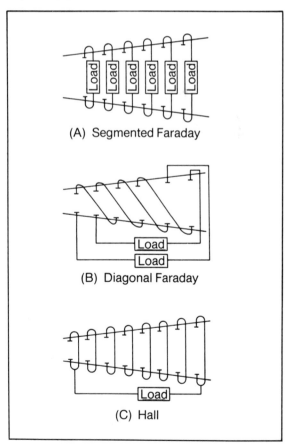

(A) Segmented Faraday

(B) Diagonal Faraday

(C) Hall

Fig. 25 MHD generator electrode configurations

SUPERCONDUCTING MAGNETS

Although much work with small superconducting magnets has been performed, few large ones have been built. For large MHD channels, the magnets are expected to be of the *racetrack* or *saddle* configuration and require 5 to 7 Tesla field strength (50,000–70,000 Gauss). Conductor materials consist of a stabilized cover layer such as copper with a superconducting core of Nb-Ti alloy. Average current densities of 600×10^6 Ampere/m² have been obtained in a field of 4 Tesla.

COAL COMBUSTION AND PROCESSING

Several alternate methods of coal combustion and processing for an MHD plant have been proposed:

■ single-stage direct combustion of all coal

■ multistage combustion; partial oxidation of all the coal in the initial stage or stages, followed by complete combustion in a last stage

■ two-stage with prior coal volatilization

■ combustion of a fuel gas produced from coal by direct chemical regeneration using MHD generator exhaust gases, or by other LCV gasification processes

Experimental work has been successfully carried out on the direct combustion of coal in a single stage. Work on coal gasification by rapid thermal devolatilization and chemical regeneration of the high-temperature MHD generator exhaust gases shows that a large fraction of coal can be volatilized in this way.

For MHD combustion, the coal processing typically consists of drying, pulverizing, and injecting at high pressures through a series of pressurized lockhoppers. Thermal drying is the most commonly proposed method, utilizing hot exhaust gas or preheated nitrogen from an oxygen plant.

SEED INJECTION AND RECOVERY

To date, potassium has been the preferred seed material because of cost considerations.

Fig. 26 **Steam-generator configuration for an open-cycle MHD plant**

The amount of seed material injected ranges up to 1 percent of the gas flow. Injection is in the form of aqueous K_2CO_3, KOH, solid K_2CO_3 powder, or molten potassium formate.

A high degree of recovery of the seed material is required for open-cycle MHD power generation to be economically viable. With a high slag rejection combustor (70 to 90 percent rejection), injecting the seed at the combustor exit minimizes seed loss to slag.

Because the seed-laden combustion products cool as they pass through the steam generator, some of the seed material is deposited on the waterwall and convective surfaces. This material can be removed with sootblowers and collected in hoppers for reprocessing.

Seed from discharge gases can be recovered by electrostatic precipitation with recovery levels of over 99 percent anticipated. The high reaction rate of potassium with sulfur to form K_2SO_4 makes the precipitator an excellent device for recovering seed and particulates from the exhaust gases.

The seed recovered from the precipitators and hoppers of the steam generator is relatively low in flyash concentration. Further, since most of this material has condensed from the gas phase, material interaction or reaction is very small. Thus the seed material recovered as potassium sulfate, which is soluble, can be relatively easily separated from flyash which is essentially insoluble.

The recovered seed has to be regenerated if it is to capture sulfur when it is recycled. Several processes are in development; all use some form of reducing gas to separate sulfur from the seed material. Final products are typically potassium carbonate or potassium formate, and elemental sulfur or calcium sulfate.

STEAM GENERATOR DESIGN CONSIDERATIONS

MHD operation imposes unusual and severe design requirements on all components, including the steam generator. Extremes in temperatures, gas composition, and solids loading lead to the design of a steam generator significantly different from a conventional boiler. To illustrate some of the design problems, a description of a reference conceptual design for oxygen-enriched operation follows. This design evolved from consideration of several MHD-related problem areas and draws heavily from both utility and industrial recovery boiler state of the art. Only the most important design factors are discussed.[9]

NO_x CONTROL

Substoichiometric combustion in the primary MHD combustor reduces the production of thermal NO_x. A factor of 0.90 stoichiometry is expected to satisfy emission requirements. Additional NO_x reduction can be obtained without significantly affecting overall plant efficiency by reducing stoichiometry to as low as 0.85. Substoichiometric combustion requires the addition of air in downstream components of the system to complete combustion. Combustion will be completed in the second boiler chamber (seed-recovery furnace) at temperatures low enough to preclude formation of significant quantities of NO_x.

SEED RECOVERY

Seed material is expected to be predominantly potassium sulfate (K_2SO_4) due to the capture of sulfur from the coal. Condensation and solidification temperatures for K_2SO_4 are 2250°F and 1970°F, respectively. Maintaining the temperature leaving the slag furnace chamber at roughly 2900°F will minimize the amount of seed lost in that chamber from condensation. The remaining boiler chambers are designed to cool the gas from 2900°F to approximately 700°F, during which time the seed will pass through the liquid phase to the solid phase. Some of the seed, together with some of the remaining slag, will deposit on the various walls and pendant surfaces throughout the convective and rear-pass sections. Numerous retractable sootblowers provide for the recovery of this material.

The seed material which is removed from the steam-generator surfaces will be collected in dry-bottom hoppers. It is expected that roughly one-quarter to one-third of the total solids entering the steam generator will be removed in this manner. Essentially all of the remaining solids will be removed in the gas-cleaning precipitator before the gas is sent to the stack. This material, together with that collected in the hoppers, will undergo seed reprocessing.

MATERIALS PROBLEMS

High metal temperatures are expected in some sections of the reheater, the superheater, and the oxidant heater. Therefore, high-temperature alloy steels are used. Operation in a reducing (substoichiometric) environment with vaporous or liquid potassium-sulfate seed material presents a potentially severe corrosion problem. The refractory for the slag furnace chamber is a high-alumina ram material offering both high-temperature protection and resistance to degradation from seed attack in a reducing atmosphere. To protect against corrosion in the seed-recovery furnace, and to provide added corrosion protection in the event of refractory cracking in the slag furnace, the carbon-steel waterwall tubes are aluminized.

STEAM-GENERATOR DESIGN

The high-subcritical-pressure steam generator (Fig. 26) consists of a multisection unit with conventional water-cooled walls. The slag furnace chamber is designed to cool the MHD gas from the diffuser outlet condition (typically 3700°F) to 2900°F for NO_x control. The average uniform gas-cooling rate will be less than 400°F/sec, which will provide the required gas residence time.

SEED RECOVERY SECTION

At the exit of the transition duct from the slag furnace, the 2900°F substoichiometric MHD gas is mixed with preheated burnout air (600°F) for the completion of combustion. The air is introduced through nozzles located in the side walls of the duct. It is expected that burnout will be nearly instantaneous at these temperatures. The final flue-gas composition contains 5 percent excess air.

CONVECTIVE AND ECONOMIZER SECTIONS

The convective section and rear pass contain most of the various pendant surfaces. As the gas passes through the convective section, it passes over the finishing reheat, finishing superheat, oxidant preheat, and rear superheat surfaces before entering the rear pass. The roof and walls are steam-cooled.

The economizer section cools the 700°F gas to the cleanup section inlet temperature of 275°F. Depending upon the specific design and the availability of other sources of 700°F gas, the low-temperature air heaters may also be located in this section rather than external to the steam generator.

FUTURE WORK

A considerable amount of work is still required to analyze such critical functions as startup and shutdown, partial-load operation, load following, control coordination, emergency trips, and hot restart. Designing a practical, highly efficient, low-emissions, coal-fired MHD system could substantially increase the use of coal for power generation.

REFERENCES

[1] Kalfadelis, C.D., Shaw, H., Folsom, B.A., and Corley, T.L., "Environmental Assessment of Gas Turbine/Steam Turbine Combined Cycles," *ASME Gas Turbine Conference,* March 10–13, 1980. ASME Paper No. 80-GT-11

[2] R. L. Vogt, "Low Btu Coal Gas Combustion in High Temperature Turbines," ASME Gas Turbine Conference, March 10–13, 1980. ASME Paper No. 80-GT-170.

[3] Patterson, R.C. and Darling, S.L., "A Low-Btu Coal Gasification System," paper presented at the *72nd An-* nual Meeting of the American Institute of Chemical Engineers, San Francisco, California, November 25–29, 1979; Combustion Engineering publication TIS-6299.

[4] Patterson, R. C. and Yerushalmi, J., "Coal Gasification Process for Clean Fuel Gas," paper presented at Seventh Energy Technology Conference, Washington, DC., March 24–26, 1980; Combustion Engineering publ. TIS-6575.

[5] Bechtel National, Inc., "Economics of Retrofitting Power Plants for Coal Derived Medium-Btu Gas," prepared for

Electric Power Research Institute, Palo Alto, California, October 1979; EPRI Publication AF-1182.

[6] McIver, A.E., "SASOL: Process Coal Into Fuels and Chemicals for the South African Coal, Oil, and Gas Corporation" presented at the *Second Annual Symposium on Coal Gasification and Liquefaction,* August 5–7, 1975.

[7] "The Combustion Engineering Fluidized Bed Sub-Scale Unit: Operating Experience and Test Results," Stephen L. Goodstine, Joseph R. Comparato, Francis T. Matthews, Combustion Engineering, Inc., Windsor, Connecticut; United States Department of Energy, Contract No. EX-76-C-01-2473. Presented at *Coal Technology '79, 2nd International Coal Utilization Conference,* November 6–8, 1979, Houston, Texas.

[8] Anderson, J. B. and Norcross, W. R., "Fluidized Bed Industrial Boiler," Proceedings of the Amer. Power Conf., Vol. 40, pp. 760–769.

[9] Carl R. Bozzuto and James P. Clark, "Magnetohydrodynamic Commercial Plant Study", Proceedings of the American Power Conference, 1980, Vol. 40.

BIBLIOGRAPHY

COAL GASIFICATION

Combustion Engineering, Inc., "Assessment of the Capability of Firing Clean Low-Btu Gases in Existing Coal, Oil and Gas-Fired Steam Generators," prepared for *Electric Power Research Institute,* Palo Alto, California, December 1975; EPRI Publication 265-1.

Kalfadelis, C.D. and Magee, E.M., "Evaluation of Pollution Control in Fossil Fuel Conversion Processes, Gasification: Section 1: Synthane Process, EPA-650/2-74-009b," June 1974 (PB 237 113, NTIS, Springfield, Virginia, 22151).

Shaw, H. and Magee, E.M., "Evaluation of Pollution Control in Fossil Fuel Conversion Processes, Gasification: Section 1, Lurgi Process, EPA-650/2-74-009c," July, 1974.

Hargrove, M. J., et al, "Study of Electric Plant Applications for Low-Btu Gasification of Coal for Electric Power Generation," NTIS Distribution Category un-90c, Report No. FE-1545-44, National Technical Information Service, U.S. Dept. of Commerce, Springfield, VA 22161.

Hargrove, M. J., Jacks, S. T. Liljedahl, B. N., and Moffat, B. K., "Study of Electric Plant Applications for Low Btu Gasification of Coal for Electric Power Generation," August 1978 (FE-1545-59 for DOE).

Beecher, D. T., et al., Energy Conversion Study Alternatives Study (ECAS), Westinghouse Phase I Final Report, Vol. I—Introduction and Summary, NASA CR-134941, Vol. I, February 12, 1976.

Beecher, D. T., et al., Energy Conversion Study Alternatives Study (ECAS) Westinghouse Phase II Final Report, Vol. I, Combined Gas Steam Turbine Plant With an Integrated Low-BTU Gasifier, NASA CR-134942, Vol. I, October 15, 1976.

Beecher, D. T., et al., Energy Conversion Study (ECAS), Westinghouse Phase II Final Report, Vol. II, Summary and Combined Gas-Steam Turbine Plant Using Coal-Derived Liquid Fuel, NASA CR-134942, Vol. II, October 15, 1976.

Sims, C. T., Doering H. von E., and Smith D. P., "Effects of the Combustion Products of Coal Derived Fuels on Gas Turbine Hot Stage Hardware", ASME paper 79-GT-160, March, 1979.

Battista, R. A., and Farrell, R. A., "Development of an Industrial Gas Turbine Combustor Burning a Variety of Coal-Derived Low Btu Fuels and Distillate", ASME Paper 79-GT-172, March, 1979.

Pillsbury, P. W. and Lin, S. S., "Advanced Coal Gasification System for Electric Power Generation. Development of Full-Size Gas Turbine Combustors Using Synthetic Low-Btu Fuel Gas at 350°F", FE-1514-52, July, 1976, Energy Research and Development Administration, Washington, D.C.

Sood, V. M., and Shekleton, J. R., "Ongoing Development of a Low Emission Industrial Gas Turbine Combustion Chamber", ASME Paper 79-GT-203, March, 1979.

Waibel, R. T., Fleming, E. S., and Larson, D. H., "Pollutant Emissions from Dirty Low and Medium Btu Gases", Third Stationary Combustion Symposium, February, 1979.

Folsom, B. A., Courtney, C. W., and Heap, M. P., "The Effects of LBG Composition and Combustor Characteristics on Fuel NO_X Formation", ASME Paper 79-GT-185, March, 1979.

Covell, R.B. and Hargrove, M.J., "Power Cycle Evaluations of the C-E Coal Gasification Process" *Proceedings of the American Power Conference,* Vol. 41, pp. 355–363, 1979, Chicago; Illinois Institute of Technology, Chicago, Illinois.

Fluor Engineers and Constructors, Inc., "Economic Studies of Coal Gasification Combined Cycle Systems for Electric Power Generation," prepared for Electric Power Research Institute, Palo Alto, California, January 1978; EPRI Publication AF-642.

LIQUEFACTION OF COAL

Epperly, W. R., "Status of Coal Liquefaction Technology," Intersociety Energy Conversion Engineering Conference, 9th Process, San Francisco, California, August 26–30, 1974.

McNeese, L. E., R. Salmon, and H. D. Cockran, Jr., "Recent Developments in Coal Liquefaction in the U.S.," Report CONF-790213, Oak Ridge, TN, ORNL, February, 1979.

Schmid, B. K., "The Solvent Refined Coal Process," presented at the Symposium on Coal Gasification and Liquefaction: Best Prospects for Commercialization. University of Pittsburgh, Pittsburgh, PA, August 6–8, 1974.

Johnson, F. A., "H-Coal: How Near to Commercialization," presented at the Symposium on Coal Gasification and Liquefaction: Best Prospects for Commercialization. University of Pittsburgh, Pittsburgh, PA, August 6–8, 1974.

FLUIDIZED-BED COMBUSTION

"Fluidized Bed Combustion Development Facility and Commercial Utility AFBC Design Assessment," Quarterly Progress Report, July through September 1978, prepared for EPRI under Contract R12718-2 by Babcock & Wilcox, Alliance, Ohio.

Keairns, D. L., et al, "Fluidized Bed Combustion Process Evaluation Phase II Pressurized Fluidized Bed Coal Combustion Development," Westinghouse Research Laboratory, Pittsburgh, Pennsylvania, EPA-650/2-75-027-C.

Norcross, W. R. and Comparato, J. R., "Industrial Coal-Fired Fluidized Bed Demonstration Plant," paper presented at Coal and Illinois Industry Conference, May 9–10, 1979, Chicago, Illinois; Combustion Engineering publication TIS-6302. U.S. Dept. of Energy Contract No. EX-76-C-01-2473

MHD POWER GENERATION

F. Becker, F. Hals, R. Kessler, L. Westra, W. Morgan, and C. Bozzuto, "Conceptual Design of a Pilot Scale MHD/Steam Power Plant (ETF) and Preliminary Analyses of Early Commercial MHD Power Plants," paper presented at the 18th Symposium on Engineering Aspects of MHD, Butte, Montana, June 18–20, 1979. Combustion Engineering publication TIS-6265.

Harris, L. P. and Shah, R. P., Energy Conversion Alternatives Study (ECAS), General Electric Phase II Final Report, Vol. II, Advanced Energy Conversion Systems—Conceptual Designs, Part 3, Open Cycle Gas Turbines and Open Cycle MHD, NASA CR-134949, Vol. II, Part 3, December 1976.

Avco Everett Research Laboratory, Inc., "Engineering Test Facility Conceptual Design," Final Report FE-2614-2, June, 1978.

Enos, G., et al, "Design Description and Performance Predictions for the First CDIF Power Train," 18th Symposium on Engineering Aspects of MHD, Butte, MT, June, 1979.

Demirjian, A., et al, "Electrode Development for Coal-Fired MHD Generators," 17th Symposium on Engineering Aspects of MHD, Stanford, CA, March, 1978.

Zar, J., "A Modular Design for a Superconducting Magnet for the ETF and Larger MHD Generators," 18th Symposium on Engineering Aspects of MHD, Butte, MT, June, 1979.

Vasil'eva, I., et al, "Joint US-USSR Experimental Studies of Plasma Electrical Conductivity," 15th Symposium on Engineering Aspects of MHD, Philadelphia, PA, May, 1976.

Hals, F. A., et al, "Development of High Temperature Air Preheaters for Open Cycle MHD Energy Conversion Systems," 15th Symposium on Engineering Aspects of MHD, Philadelphia, PA, May, 1976.

Appendix A. Coals of the World

This appendix is comprised of two sections. The first has reference data on all the coals of all producing countries of the world; approximate reserves are given, along with some historical and geographical information. Analyses of the coals and their ashes, along with fusibility data, are included to be used in preliminary design of boilers to burn coals from these countries. The data are not intended and are not adequate for the actual design of a steam generator to burn a specific local fuel. Mine or core samples, or detailed fuel analyses, are needed for that purpose.

The International Systems of coal classification are described in the second section. These systems result from a significant effort to categorize in a consistent, rational manner all the different coals (excluding peat) found worldwide. This is vitally important where engineers from one country are involved in the design of fuel-preparation-and-burning equipment, steam-generating equipment, or ash-handling systems for another country where coals may be designated by local custom rather than on a useful engineering basis.

Sources of information for the statistical and analytical data in this chapter have been fuel investigations by the C-E Kreisinger Development Laboratory; publications of the U.S. Bureau of Mines and the Canadian Department of Energy, Mines and Resources; the National Coal Association, Washington, DC; the World Energy Conference Surveys of Energy Resources; the Report of the Commission of Inquiry into the Coal Resources of the Republic of South Africa (1975); and COAL—Bridge to the Future, summary report of World Coal Study.

* * * *

In this Appendix, high heat values are given in both Btu per pound and Megajoules per kilogram. Tonnages of coal resources or production are in metric tonnes (2,204.6 pounds). Where a tonne of coal equivalent is shown, it is a metric tonne of coal with a heating value of 12,600 Btu/lb, 7,000 kcal/kg, or 29.31 MJ/kg. Because coals vary significantly in calorific value, much more than 1 tonne of subbituminous, lignitic, and brown coals is required to produce the energy of 1 tonne of coal equivalent (1 tce).

The estimates of economically recoverable coal are at best approximate, and depend just as much on economic and political considerations as they do on exploratory techniques. There are no universally agreed upon definitions of reserves and resources, many of them being a function of quantity of overburden or depth of mining. And, depending upon the source of data and the purpose for which it was gathered, the values may represent undue optimism or conservativeness. In any case, they should be read in the context of this statement by Carroll Wilson (Future Coal Prospects: Country and Regional Assessments—the World Coal Study, 1980): ". . . the use of different fuels is heavily constrained by decisions made in the past and by the fact that new energy facilities being planned now cannot be brought to completion in less than 5 to 10 years. The substantial shift to coal will therefore begin in the mid to late 1980's based on decisions made in the early 1980's. Major effects of this expansion will be felt in the 1985–2000 period . . . The full effects of the switch to coal will, however, not be seen until the early decades of the next century."

ANALYSES BY CONTINENT AND COUNTRY

Coal is found on all continents and in most countries throughout the world. However, some countries, such as Italy and Sweden, have resources so meager in proportion to their energy demands as to be inconsequential. By far, the largest world coal deposits are located in the Northern hemisphere.

Economically recoverable reserves are those that can be successfully exploited and used within the foreseeable future; they represent about 1/15th of the total world geological resources of solid fuel. The estimated total of such resources for the entire world is in excess of 600,000 million tce; over 95 percent is found in just 13 countries, approximately as follows:

United States	28%
U.S.S.R.	17%
People's Republic of China	16%
United Kingdom	7%
Federal Republic of Germany	5%
India	5%
Australia	4%
Republic of South Africa	4%
Poland	3%
Canada	2%
Brazil	1%
Yugoslavia	1%
German Democratic Republic	1%

The preceding tabulation may very well overstate the resources of such countries as the United States and West Germany in comparison to the others, because exploration has reached a higher level. The eventual resources, which disregard climate and other factors making recovery difficult, of both Russia and China may be greater than shown. Also, there can be considerable loss in recovering coal, particularly in deep mining—and there can be great differences between run-of-mine coal and a marketable, ash-reduced product.

Further general information on the reserves of all coal-producing countries of the world is found under the individual country headings.

BASIS FOR ANALYTICAL DATA

A most important consideration in the use of coal analyses is the determination of coal type or rank from the data presented. The selection of pulverizing equipment, for instance, depends upon characteristics related to coal rank, as does establishing the heat transfer requirement and size of an air heater.

For the best use of world coal data, the tabulations in this Appendix make it easy to ascertain coal rank. Volatile contents and high heating values are normalized to a moisture- and ash-free basis; ash and moisture contents are given on an as-analyzed basis.

Ash analyses, some of them available from U.S. Bureau of Mines and Canadian Department of Energy, Mines and Resources publications, but mostly done in C-E's laboratory, are given for use in furnace sizing, determining convection-pass fouling potential, and designing ash-transport and storage equipment. All ash fusibility figures are for ASTM reducing atmosphere, as described in Chapter 3.

Regarding the moisture contents shown, realize that there can be no assurance that samples received for analysis have their moisture-sealing intact, so there can be some air-drying before tests occur. In using the moisture contents for pulverizing-system, boiler, and air

Table I. Correlation of Coal Properties (Based on Typical Analyses)

	Bituminous		High-Volatile Bit.			Subbituminous			Lignite and
	Low VM.	Med. VM.	A	B	C	A	B	C	Brown Coal
Volatile Matter (VM) MAF	15 to 24	25 to 36	34 to 46	38 to 49	42 to 54	41 to 46	42 to 48	43 to 50	45 and higher
$\dfrac{C + H}{O_2}$ (Typical)	19.5	11.8	11.2	7.0	5.4	4.3	3.2	2.8	2.7 and lower
Btu/lb, MAF	15,100 to 16,000	15,000 to 15,700	14,600 to 15,400	14,000 to 14,800	13,400 to 14,200	12,900 to 13,800	11,900 to 13,300	11,200 to 12,900	10,200 to 12,700
MJ/kg, MAF	35 to 37	35 to 36.5	34 to 36	32.5 to 34.5	31 to 33	30 to 32	27.5 to 31	26 to 30	23.5 to 29.5

MAF = moisture- and ash-free

heater design, values must be corrected to probable "as-received at the power-plant" moisture. This is particularly important with coals that are transported long distances before analyses, as is frequently the case.

CORRELATION OF COAL PROPERTIES

In addition to the *ASTM Standards* D388, Classification of Coals by Rank (Table II, Chapter 2), a review of the actual coal analyses presented in this Appendix will produce a correlation that is useful in preliminary ranking of coals based on proximate and ultimate analyses. Table I is such a correlation, based on a study of analyses of many typical coals. For such preliminary ranking, refer also to Fig. 1, Chapter 2, which is a graphical presentation of ranking parameters.

COAL DEPOSITS OF NORTH AMERICA

This section describes the coalfields of Canada, the United States, and Mexico, with Alaska being given separate treatment.

CANADA

Canada (Fig. 1) has over 9,000 million tonnes of economically recoverable coal reserves, ranging from anthracite to lignite. Table II shows measured resources (for which tonnages have been computed) of immediate interest for exploration or exploitation activities; generally, for most regions, coal seams have to be at least 5-ft thick to be included in this category. The resources in the table exclude coal that may be present north of 60° North latitude and small occurrences known in Newfoundland and Manitoba.

Ninety-five percent of the recoverable reserves are in western Canada (British Columbia, Alberta, and Saskatchewan), of which about 80 percent can be open-pit mined. As in the United States, coals in western Canada are low in sulfur content, rarely exceeding 0.6 percent on a mass basis, but are high in ash. Eastern Canadian coals generally have high sulfur, particularly those from Nova Scotia.

Approximately 14 percent of the Canadian

ARCTIC CIRCLE

60° N

High-Volatile Bituminous
Subbituminous
Lignite and Brown Coal
Bituminous and Semianthracite

Fig. 1 Coal Map of Canada

coal produced is bituminous coal from underground mines; the balance is bituminous, subbituminous and lignitic coals taken by strip-mining. Over 70 percent of the domestic consumption is for power generation; most of the balance for metallurgical uses.

Production of coal in the year 2000 is estimated to be between 75 and 115 million tonnes coal equivalent per year. A steadily growing portion of the production will be used at mine-mouth plants in the West. In Alberta, for instance, coal is planned to supply about 95 percent of the province's electrical needs at the turn of the century. Canada's coal deposits are located in four definable regions.

1. The Mountain Region:
Most of the bituminous coal resources are in the provinces of Alberta and British Columbia (BC), extending in a belt up to 50 km wide from the U.S. border, northwest into the East Kootenay region of southeastern BC, north into Alberta (in the Crowsnest Pass area) and into northeastern BC (Fig. 1). The main center of deposition is located in southeastern BC. Large resources are also being found in the Peace River area to the north.

2. The Foothills Region of Alberta:
Coals from this area are mainly of high-volatile bituminous B and C rank. Mining conditions are not as severe as in the mountain region, but eventually most of the resources will have to be extracted by underground methods.

3. The Plains Regions of Saskatchewan and Alberta:
The four lignite deposits of Saskatchewan are located along the U.S. border and form the northern fringes of the main lignite zone centered in North Dakota. The subbituminous seams of Alberta underlie the southern part of that province from the Rocky Mountains in the west to their outcrops about 250 km farther east, and form an immense arc from the U.S. border up to about 56°N latitude, passing east of the cities of Calgary and Edmonton.

4. The Atlantic Region:
The Cape Breton Island coalfield in Nova Scotia is the most important of the region, although a small quantity of high-sulfur bituminous coal is produced by surface mining in the province of New Brunswick. The Cape Breton field is located on the north shore of the island, facing the Cabot Strait and the Atlantic Ocean. The coal is mostly of high-volatile bituminous A rank, varying from medium to high in sulfur content.

Canadian reserves of peat, which have not been surveyed, are thought to be approximately equal to those of the United States.

Table III gives the analyses of typical Canadian coals. For the ultimate analyses and ash constituents, see Analysis Directories of Cana-

Table II. Measured Canadian Coal Resources of Immediate Interest (1978)

Province and Area	Coal Rank	Millions of tonnes
Nova Scotia		
Sydney	hvb	175
Other	hvb	48
Subtotal	hvb	223
New Brunswick		
Minto	hvb	18
Other	hvb	14
Subtotal		32
Ontario	lig	218
Saskatchewan		
Estevan	lig	310
Willow Bunch	lig	748
Wood Mountain	lig	278
Cypress	lig	162
Subtotal		1,498
Alberta		
Plains	sub	30,000
Foothills	hvb	1,300
Mountains	lvb-mvb	8,000
British Columbia		
Southeastern	lvb-mvb	6,286
Northeastern	lvb-mvb	996
Other	mainly lig some sub-hvb	1,845
Canada total	lig	3,561
	sub	30,000
	hvb	1,555
	lvb-mvb	15,282

lig = lignitic; sub = subbituminous; hvb = high-volatile bituminous; mvb = medium-volatile bituminous; lvb = low-volatile bituminous.

Table III. Analyses of Typical Canadian Coals

Province and Area or seam	Rank	As received		Moisture- and ash-free		HHV		Ash ST, Red., °F	Hardgrove Grind.
		% Ash	% H$_2$O	% VM	% S	Btu/lb	MJ/kg		
Nova Scotia									
Thorburn	Hvab	14.4	3.0	33.4	0.5	15,180	35.3	2440	60
Broughton	Hvab	14.4	5.2	40.4	7.6	14,560	33.9	2100	59
River Hebert	Hvab	19.3	1.5	41.0	6.8	14,530	33.8	2070	61
Phalen	Hvab	14.4	1.7	34.9	6.6	15,200	35.3	2180	84
Harbour	Hvab	9.3	1.2	40.6	2.7	15,420	35.9	2480	70
Westville	Hvab	15.4	2.8	32.9	0.9	15,020	34.9	2240	64
Sydney	Hvab	10.2	3.8	42.7	6.4	14,660	34.1	2130	63
Joggins	Hvab	15.8	3.7	42.4	6.3	14,460	33.6	2140	60
Inverness	Hvcb	14.2	9.3	44.1	8.0	13,530	31.5	2070	60
New Brunswick									
Minto	Hvab	14.0	3.4	39.0	8.4	15,150	35.2	1980	66
Chipman	Hvab	17.6	2.1	42.2	9.3	14,970	34.8	1920	63
Coal Creek	Hvab	18.3	1.8	41.7	10.3	14,780	34.4	1960	57
Saskatchewan									
Bienfait	Lig A	6.0	34.1	49.9	0.8	12,390	28.8	2300	63
Roche Percée	Lig A	6.3	30.8	46.6	1.0	12,450	28.9	2250	52
Alberta									
Cascade	Sa	8.5	3.1	13.9	0.8	15,580	36.2	2750+	88
Crowsnest	Mvb	10.4	4.6	27.5	0.6	15,200	35.3	2750+	77
Coalspur	Hvcb	10.5	6.3	41.5	0.1	13,680	31.8	2170	52
Lethbridge	Hvcb	10.5	10.2	45.4	0.8	13,590	31.6	2330	40
Pembina	Subc	8.8	19.6	41.3	0.3	12,440	28.9	2450	49
Drumheller	Subb	9.1	17.2	42.2	0.7	13,150	30.6	2270	33
Castor	Subb	5.5	24.8	43.6	0.6	12,470	29.0	2140	45
Edmonton	Subc	13.7	23.5	44.3	0.3	12,870	29.9	2370	38
Taber	Suba	9.9	14.2	44.3	1.8	13,350	31.0	2350	47
Camrose	Subc	5.8	21.4	44.5	0.4	12,710	29.5	2160	31
British Columbia									
East Kootenay	Mvb	9.5	2.4	25.5	0.5	15,350	35.7	2740	88
Vancouver Island	Hvab	12.9	1.4	38.6	1.6	14,910	34.7	2320	57

dian Coals published by the Canadian Department of Mines and Technical Surveys, Mines Branch, Fuels Division.

UNITED STATES

Coal is found in 36 of the states and is currently mined in about 26. Six states contain more than 75 percent of the estimated 245,000 million tonnes of economically recoverable reserves: Montana (28%), Illinois (16%), Wyoming (13%), West Virginia (9%), Pennsylvania (7%) and Kentucky (6%), Fig. 2.

The reserves of peat, not detailed in this text, are estimated to be equal in heating value to about 30 percent of the currently recoverable coal reserves. Peat is located in low-lying coastal areas, in the flatlands of the Great Lakes, and in Alaska.

The electric utilities of the U.S. consume 78 percent of all the coal produced in the states.

The U.S. Geological Survey has divided the coal-bearing areas of the contiguous U.S. into six main provinces designated as (1) Eastern, (2) Interior, (3) Gulf, (4) Northern Great Plains, (5) Rocky Mountain, and (6) Pacific Coast. The provinces are subdivided into coal regions, coal fields, and coal districts. (Alaska is treated as a separate province.)

The Eastern Province

This includes the anthracite regions of Pennsylvania and Rhode Island; the Atlantic Coast region, including the Triassic fields of Virginia and North Carolina; and the Appalachian region extending from Pennsylvania through eastern Ohio, Kentucky, West Virginia, western Virginia, and Tennessee into Alabama. The Appalachian basin contains the largest deposit of the high-grade bituminous and semibituminous coals. The Triassic deposits of central Virginia and North Carolina occur in irregular pockets rather than in seams and are at present of little commercial value, because of expensive mining and rather low-grade quality of coal.

The Interior Province

This province includes all the bituminous coal area of the Mississippi Valley region and the coal fields of Texas and Michigan. This province is subdivided into the Northern re-gion consisting of the coal field of Michigan; the Eastern region, or Illinois basin, comprising the fields of Illinois, Indiana and western Kentucky; and also the Western region embracing the coal fields of Iowa, Missouri, Nebraska, Kansas, Arkansas, Oklahoma, and the southwestern region of Texas. With some exceptions, the bituminous coals of this province are of lower rank and higher sulfur content than those of the Eastern province. Much of the surface-minable coal in the Illinois basin having low chlorine and sodium content has been mined or committed to be mined. Much of the remaining coal, with high chlorine content (above 0.15 percent as fired), will have to be deep-mined and will comprise a large proportion of the future production.

The Gulf Province

This consists of the Mississippi region in the east and the Texas region in the west. The Mississippi region includes the lignite fields of

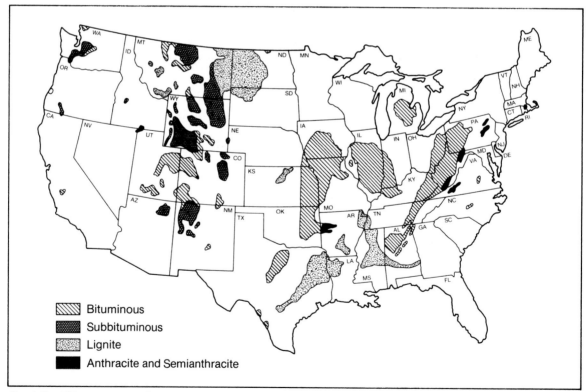

Fig. 2 **Coal Map of United States**

Table IV. Source, Analysis and Classification of U.S. Bituminous Coals

State, County, and Bed	As received % Ash	As received % H₂O	Moisture- and ash-free % VM	% C	% H	% O	% N	% S	HHV Btu/lb	HHV MJ/kg	FSI[A]	A-AD[B]	Classification ASTM[C]	Classification IC No.[D]
Alabama														
Blount, Bynum	7.2	4.6	35.0	85.4	5.4	5.5	2.0	1.7	15,220	35.4	7	120	Hvab	634
Jefferson, Blue Creek	7.1	2.3	29.1	87.2	5.2	4.8	1.8	1.0	15,500	36.0	8½	250	Mvb	535
Jefferson, Mary Lee	10.0	1.9	29.6	87.5	4.9	4.8	1.9	0.9	15,420	35.9	7½	200	Mvb	535
Jefferson, Pratt	6.2	1.6	31.9	87.3	5.4	3.8	1.8	1.7	15,590	36.3	7½	280	Hvab	535
Marion, Black Creek	5.5	4.9	41.5	82.5	5.5	8.6	1.8	1.6	14,750	34.3	3	−27	Hvab	622
Tuscaloosa, Milldale	7.1	5.8	37.6	83.5	5.5	7.4	1.6	2.0	14,900	34.7	5½	30	Hvab	633
Arkansas														
Sebastian, Upp. Hartshorne	7.4	2.4	19.0	90.0	4.5	2.6	1.9	1.0	15,550	36.2	8½	50	Lvb	333
Colorado														
Gunnison, C	3.1	5.8	42.0	81.8	5.7	9.9	1.9	0.7	14,570	33.9	3	−43	Hvbb	721
LaPlata, No. 1	5.8	2.7	41.8	83.7	5.9	7.8	1.6	1.0	15,150	35.2	7	52	Hvab	634
Illinois														
Gallatin, Willis	11.3	3.1	36.3	84.5	5.4	5.1	1.5	3.5	15,170	35.3	5	10	Hvab	633
Knox, No. 6	6.2	18.3	47.9	78.7	5.5	10.9	1.4	3.5	14,130	32.9	3½	−39	Hvcb	821
Vermillion, No. 7	9.0	12.2	49.3	79.2	5.7	9.5	1.5	4.1	14,400	33.5	3½	35	Hvcb	823
Williamson, No. 6	11.7	5.8	43.8	80.5	5.5	9.1	1.6	3.3	14,430	33.6	5	60	Hvbb	734
Indiana														
Knox, No. 5	7.5	9.7	47.0	80.1	5.6	8.5	1.6	4.2	14,530	33.8	4½	70	Hvbb	734
Kentucky														
Bell, Sterling	6.6	4.8	39.5	83.1	5.5	8.4	1.9	1.1	14,870	34.6	4	−5	Hvab	622
Harlan, D	7.0	2.5	39.8	84.0	5.5	7.8	1.7	1.0	15,040	35.0	6	30	Hvab	633
Hopkins, No. 9	11.2	6.1	45.1	80.1	5.5	8.0	1.7	4.7	14,590	33.9	4½	52	Hvbb	734
Hopkins, No. 12	11.2	8.3	46.5	79.0	5.6	10.1	1.7	3.6	14,420	33.5	4	40	Hvbb	723
Muhlenberg, No. 11	8.6	9.0	44.2	79.5	5.6	9.4	1.6	3.9	14,340	33.3	4	25	Hvbb	823
Pike, Alma	3.3	2.5	39.0	85.5	5.5	6.7	1.6	0.7	15,370	35.7	6	100	Hvab	634
Maryland														
Allegany, Pittsburgh	10.2	3.1	20.4	88.5	5.0	3.5	2.0	1.0	15,510	36.1	7½	10	Lvb	433

Table IV. Source, Analysis and Classification of U.S. Bituminous Coals — *Continued*

State, County, and Bed	As received % Ash	As received % H₂O	Moisture- and ash-free % VM	% C	% H	% O	% N	% S	HHV Btu/lb	HHV MJ/kg	FSI[A]	A-AD[B]	Classification ASTM[C]	IC No.[D]
Maryland (Continued)														
Allegany, Tyson	9.1	2.8	21.4	89.0	4.9	2.8	1.9	1.4	15,650	36.4	8½	110	Lvb	434
Ohio														
Belmont, Pittsburgh No. 8	9.1	3.6	45.8	80.9	5.7	7.4	1.4	4.6	14,730	34.3	6	200	Hvab	635
Morgan, Middle Kittaning No. 6	8.5	8.7	45.8	79.4	5.7	10.9	1.5	2.5	14,340	33.3	4½	2	Hvbb	733
Pennsylvania														
Allegheny, Pittsburgh	7.6	2.6	39.5	84.3	5.6	6.7	1.7	1.7	14,870	34.6	8½	180	Hvab	635
Butler, Lower Freeport	8.0	3.7	42.0	82.2	5.6	7.3	1.6	3.3	14,970	34.8	5½	75	Hvab	634
Cambria, Upper Freeport	7.5	1.1	20.0	89.5	4.8	2.9	1.5	1.3	15,660	36.4	9	75	Lvb	334
Clearfield, Lower Freeport	7.9	2.1	35.4	85.3	5.4	3.8	1.6	3.9	15,360	35.7	7	300	Hvab	635
Fayette, Lower Kittanning	8.8	1.7	29.4	87.8	5.2	3.2	1.5	2.3	15,500	36.0	9	310	Mvb	535
Greene, Pittsburgh	8.2	1.8	40.6	84.1	5.6	6.4	1.7	2.2	15,160	35.3	9	250	Hvab	635
Indiana, Lower Freeport	9.7	2.3	24.6	88.5	5.1	3.7	1.5	1.2	15,680	36.5	9	150	Mvb	435
Lawrence, Brookville	10.1	5.2	42.9	81.5	5.7	7.3	1.7	3.8	14,830	34.5	4½	75	Hvab	634
Washington, Pittsburgh	5.1	1.6	40.5	84.2	5.6	7.2	1.6	1.4	15,070	35.0	7½	180	Hvab	635
Tennessee														
Campbell, Jordon	3.8	4.7	38.1	83.2	5.4	8.6	2.0	0.8	14,820	34.5	3	−21	Hvab	622
Utah														
Carbon, D	7.3	3.3	47.2	80.7	5.8	11.7	1.4	0.4	14,330	33.3	2	−45	Hvbb	711
Carbon, Lower Sunnyside	5.6	4.1	42.9	82.1	5.6	9.3	1.8	1.2	14,770	34.3	5	5	Hvab	633
Emery, Lower Sunnyside	6.4	5.2	43.2	79.8	5.6	11.8	1.7	1.1	14,260	33.2	3	−35	Hvbb	721
Washington														
Kittitas, No. 1 (Big)	8.8	3.7	42.4	81.8	6.0	9.7	1.9	0.6	14,710	34.2	4	5	Hvab	623
Kittitas, No. 5 (Roslyn)	9.9	2.9	45.1	82.7	6.2	8.6	2.0	0.5	14,920	34.7	4	35	Hvab	623

Table IV. **Source, Analysis and Classification of U.S. Bituminous Coals — *Continued***

State, County, and Bed	As received		Moisture- and ash-free						HHV				Classification	
	% Ash	% H₂O	% VM	% C	% H	% O	% N	% S	Btu/lb	MJ/kg	FSI[A]	A-AD[B]	ASTM[C]	IC No.[D]
West Virginia														
Boone, Alma	9.8	2.3	42.5	83.5	5.7	6.3	1.5	3.0	15,110	35.1	6	120	Hvab	634
Boone, Chilton	7.8	4.2	40.2	83.8	5.5	7.5	1.7	1.5	14,930	34.7	6	10	Hvab	633
Boone, Hernshaw	7.2	2.0	38.0	86.0	5.5	6.0	1.6	0.9	15,320	35.6	6½	140	Hvab	634
Fayette, Fire Creek	6.2	3.0	20.2	90.0	4.7	2.9	1.3	1.1	15,540	36.1	7	10	Lvb	433
Fayette, Lower Eagle	4.8	1.8	33.4	87.7	5.5	4.4	1.7	0.7	15,610	36.3	8½	310	Hvab	635
Greenbrier, Fire Creek	10.2	3.6	24.2	88.5	5.0	3.6	1.6	1.3	15,540	36.1	8½	150	Mvb	435
Greenbrier, Sewell	3.2	3.2	29.1	88.0	5.3	4.3	1.8	0.6	15,540	36.1	9	220	Mvb	535
Kanawha, Winifrede	9.5	4.8	41.5	83.3	5.6	8.6	1.7	0.8	14,880	34.6	4	−5	Hvab	622
Logan, Cedar Grove	9.3	2.4	39.2	84.2	5.5	7.1	1.6	1.6	15,180	35.3	7	150	Hvab	635
McDowell, Beckley	10.3	2.7	18.4	89.8	4.7	3.2	1.6	0.7	15,630	36.3	7½	25	Lvb	333
McDowell, Bradshaw	6.7	1.9	26.5	88.9	5.1	3.4	1.7	0.9	15,690	36.5	8½	240	Mvb	435
McDowell, Pocahontas No. 3	6.2	3.3	18.7	89.4	4.6	4.1	1.3	0.6	15,690	36.5	8½	10	Lvb	333
McDowell, Pocahontas No. 4	7.3	2.8	26.1	89.4	5.0	3.7	1.3	0.6	15,610	36.3	9	170	Mvb	435
McDowell, Douglas	4.0	2.5	25.6	89.3	5.0	3.1	1.7	0.9	15,680	36.5	9	230	Mvb	435
Marshall, Pittsburgh	10.5	4.1	45.6	81.2	5.6	6.8	1.4	5.0	14,790	34.4	7	230	Hvab	635
Mercer, Pocahontas No. 3	7.1	4.4	17.4	90.7	4.6	2.7	1.2	0.8	15,730	36.6	6	5	Lvb	333
Mercer, Pocahontas No. 6	7.9	5.1	20.8	90.3	4.8	3.0	1.3	0.6	15,710	36.5	7	65	Lvb	434
Mingo, Lower Cedar Grove	5.0	1.7	37.5	85.6	5.5	6.4	1.6	0.9	15,390	35.8	8	160	Hvab	635
Mingo, Upper Cedar Grove	9.1	5.1	36.3	85.5	5.5	6.6	1.6	0.8	15,090	35.1	6½	30	Hvab	633
Monongalia, Pittsburgh	6.6	2.3	37.5	85.5	5.5	5.8	1.8	1.4	15,310	35.6	9	250	Hvab	635
Monongalia, Redstone	12.4	2.6	36.6	84.5	5.5	6.3	1.7	2.0	15,090	35.1	7½	180	Hvab	635

Table IV. **Source, Analysis and Classification of U.S. Bituminous Coals — *Continued***

State, County, and Bed	As received % Ash	As received % H₂O	Moisture- and ash-free % VM	% C	% H	% O	% N	% S	HHV Btu/lb	HHV MJ/kg	FSI[A]	A-AD[B]	Classification ASTM[C]	IC No.[D]
West Virginia (Continued)														
Nicholas, Eagle	6.8	4.0	36.2	85.6	5.5	6.4	1.7	0.8	15,270	35.5	7½	140	Hvab	634
Raleigh, Beckley	5.3	1.5	20.0	89.4	4.8	3.5	1.5	0.8	15,660	36.4	8½	60	Lvb	334
Randolph, Sewell	5.4	1.5	31.2	87.4	5.3	5.2	1.4	0.7	15,420	35.9	8	180	Mvb	535
Wyoming, Campbell Creek	2.0	2.2	31.7	86.8	5.4	5.5	1.5	0.8	15,570	36.2	8½	280	Hvab	535
Wyoming, Eagle	3.6	1.9	29.9	88.5	5.3	4.0	1.5	0.7	15,530	36.1	8½	230	Mvb	535
Wyoming, Sewell	2.4	1.5	23.8	89.8	5.0	3.1	1.6	0.5	15,700	36.5	9	170	Mvb	435
Wyoming														
Sweetwater, Nos. 7, 7½, 9, 15	4.1	10.3	47.0	79.3	5.6	12.2	1.8	1.1	13,900	32.3	1½	−22	Hvcb	811

[A]—FSI = Free Swelling Index
[B]—A-AD = Audibert-Arnu dilatation index
[C]—Abbreviations are listed in Table II; Hvab = high-volatile A bituminous, etc.
[D]—IC = International Classifications

Alabama, Mississippi, and Louisiana. The Texas region comprises the lignite fields of Arkansas and Texas. The lowest rank coals in the U.S. are found in this province, with equilibrium moisture contents as high as 55 percent. Lignites from Texas can have moisture contents to 40 percent, low grindabilities, and heating values, as received, below 4000 Btu/lb. Some of the Louisiana lignites are very similar to those of North Dakota, having moisture to 36 percent and sodium levels of 5 to 8 percent.

The Northern Great Plains Province

This includes all the coal fields of the great plains east of the eastern front range of the Rocky Mountains. In this province are immense lignite areas of the two Dakotas, and the bituminous and subbituminous fields of northern Wyoming and northern and eastern Montana. Lignites from this province can be of very low rank, having moisture content to 45 percent and sodium oxide as high as 15 percent of the ash.

The Rocky Mountain Province

This comprises the coal fields of the mountainous districts of Montana, Wyoming, Utah, Colorado, and New Mexico. It possesses a great variety of coals, ranging from lignite through subbituminous and high grade bituminous coals to anthracite. The subbituminous coals range in moisture from 10 to 30 percent, with calorific-values (HHV) from 6500 to 10,000 Btu/lb. Several sources in this province have high sodium-oxide in ash, ranging to 15 percent.

The Pacific Coast Province

This area is largely confined to the State of Washington, which contains the largest coal fields on the Pacific Coast. It also embraces the small fields of Oregon and California. The coals in this province range from subbituminous through bituminous to anthracite.

The coals of Oregon and California rank somewhat lower than those of Washington.

Those of California consist mainly of noncoking bituminous coals in the southern part of the State, lignite in the northern, and subbituminous in the center. The fields are scattered and limited in area.

Estimates of U.S. coal production in the year 2000 vary from 1200 to 2000 million tonnes per year, depending upon the amount of nuclear-power generation and the extent of coal exports. Appalachia, which now produces about half of the nation's coal, will decrease to 30 percent; the Midwest will produce 11 percent and the West, 50 percent; the balance will be surface-mined Gulf lignite. Surface mining will predominate at that time and is expected to be over 60 percent of the total output.

Table V of Chapter 2 gives analyses of some U.S. coals. Ash analyses of representative U.S. coals are included in Tables IV, V, and VI of Chapter 3.

Table IV gives more detailed analyses of U.S. bituminous coals including free-swelling indices, the Audibert-Arnu dilatation, and the ASTM and International classifications.

ALASKA

Coal is distributed widely throughout Alaska in fields differing greatly in size and in geologic environment; much of it is lignitic or sub-bituminous in rank. Its total reserves are estimated to be 15 percent bituminous coal and 85 percent subbituminous coal and lignite. Only fields close to main lines of transportation have been developed; major reserves occur in more remote parts of the State. The most important fields, in terms of production and known reserves, are the lower Matanuska Valley, northeast of Anchorage, and the Nenana, southwest of Fairbanks. In addition to coal, Alaska has a greater area of peat than all the contiguous states combined.

Alaskan coal deposits are in several regions (Fig. 3). The Northern Alaska and Seward Peninsula regions contain mostly subbituminous and bituminous coal. The biggest Alaskan

Fig. 3 **Coal Map of Alaska**

Table V. Analyses of Typical Alaskan Coals

Region, District And Mine	As received		Moisture- and ash-free				Ash ST, Red., °F
	% Ash	% H$_2$O	% VM	% S	HHV Btu/lb	MJ/kg	
Northern Region							
Wainwright	3.2	20.7	41.8	0.4	12,830	29.8	. . .
Yukon Region							
Broad Pass Field							
Costello Creek	13.3	14.3	49.0	0.7	13,080	30.4	. . .
Eagle	24.4	19.8	59.3	0.4	11,240	26.1	. . .
Nenana Field							
Suntrana	6.5	22.3	52.2	0.1	12,130	28.2	2140
Kuskokwin Region							
Nelson Island	18.2	3.9	30.6	0.5	14,690	34.2	2710
Southwestern Region							
Chignik Bay	21.8	7.1	44.3	1.8	13,850	32.2	. . .
Cook Inlet Region							
Matanuska Field							
Chickaloon	10.4	1.9	23.7	0.8	15,120	35.2	2060
Coal Creek	5.8	1.6	24.7	0.7	15,530	36.1	2450
	11.6	4.1	16.4	0.7	14,950	34.8	2240
Eska	10.9	3.7	48.0	0.6	14,530	33.8	2570
Jonesville	21.3	3.5	48.9	0.3	13,900	32.3	2370
Moose Creek	6.4	3.9	44.6	0.2	14,400	33.5	2660
Gulf Region							
Bering River Field							
Katalla	3.8	5.0	15.0	1.0	15,560	36.2	2240
Southeastern Region							
Admiralty Island							
Harkrader	21.4	3.8	47.1	1.7	14,210	33.0	2250

deposits are in the Arctic slope region, in an area 300 miles long (east and west), and 75 miles wide; the coal is low-volatile bituminous to lignite. The Yukon basin coal, lignite and bituminous, occurs in small, scattered areas that have been inadequately explored.

The Nenana deposits are subbituminous high-rank lignite, primarily strip-mined. The Cook Inlet-Susitna region contains some of the most important fields of lignitic and sub-bituminous rank, in thicknesses up to 40 ft. The Matanuska Valley is divided into the lower field, containing the Moose Creek and Eska fields, and the upper field, comprising the Chickaloon and Anthracite Ridge. The Matanuska fields produce high-volatile B bituminous coal from beds 18 to 20 ft. in thickness. Technical Paper 682 of the U.S. Bureau of Mines (1946), Analyses of Alaska Coals, presents proximate and ultimate analyses, and fusibility data, for coals from all the major Alaskan coal deposits. Table V gives analyses of some typical Alaskan coals.

MEXICO

Mexico has coal deposits in 16 of the 38 Federal States (Fig. 4). Estimated production by the year 2000 is 55 million tonnes. Only three deposits presently have economically recoverable coal reserves: Barrancas basin (Central Sonora), Oaxaca basin and Coahuila basin. In the Coahuila basin, the most significant coal deposits are located within the two largest districts of Sabinas and Rio Escondido.

Brown coals and hard coals are deposited in the Sabinas basin, which is about 35 miles long and 15 miles wide. The hard coals are of medium rank and have ash contents from 14 to 35 percent. These coals are cokable. High-volatile brown coals are deposited in the Rio Escondido basin. Most of the coals in the Barrancas basin are of high rank, some of these coals are anthracitic.

Table VI gives coal and ash analyses of Mexican bituminous and subbituminous coals.

CENTRAL AMERICA

The coal resources of Costa Rica, Guatemala, Honduras, Panama and Puerto Rico (Fig. 4) comprise subbituminous and lignitic coals. The extent is generally unknown in most countries, and the deposits are not currently of economic importance.

COAL DEPOSITS OF SOUTH AMERICA

Compared to those of North America, South America's coal deposits are very small (Fig. 5). The only Southern countries where deposits of any economic importance are known to occur are Brazil, Chile, Colombia, Peru, and Venezuela. Argentina has small resources of low-rank coal. Owing to inaccessibility of most of the deposits and lack of transportation, coal mining has not been developed. Lack of capital and skilled labor also limits development.

ARGENTINA

Argentina's only coal deposit is located in the Southwest of the country, in the Rio Turbio Basin, near the Chilean border. The seams are 1 m to 2 m thick. The coal is generally high in ash but, after treatment or blending with imported coal, it is suitable for steam generation. Mixed with high-grade coking coal, Argentinian coal is made available for steelmaking. The Port of Rio Gallegos is used for shipping coal to other parts of the country. Today, the main consumer is the Hydro and Electric Energy Agency. Annual coal production of about 9 million tonnes is anticipated by the

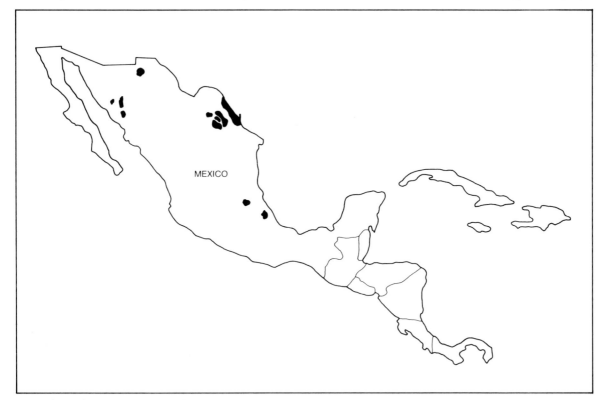

Fig. 4 Coal Map of Mexico and Central America

Fig. 5 **Coal Map of South America**

Table VI. Analyses of Mexican Coals

	Nava District	Rio Escondido	
As received:			
% Ash	30.9	28.3	29.0
% Moisture	4.8	5.2	7.8
Moisture & Ash-Free:			
% Volatile (VM)	50.7	48.3	46.7
% Carbon (C)	76.2	76.5	76.3
% Hydrogen (H)	5.6	5.8	5.7
% Oxygen (O)	14.8	15.0	15.8
% Nitrogen (N)	1.4	1.2	0.9
% Sulfur (S)	2.0	1.5	1.3
HHV, Btu/lb	13,790	13,690	13,260
HHV, MJ/kg	32.1	31.8	30.8
Fusibility Temperature, reducing atmosphere, °F:			
Initial deformation	2700 +	2700 +	2700 +
Ash Composition:			
% SiO_2	60.4	61.7	58.8
% Al_2O_3	25.8	27.7	29.0
% Fe_2O_3	5.0	2.1	2.8
% CaO	3.1	1.4	2.6
% MgO	0.9	0.9	0.6
% Na_2O	0.3	0.5	0.4
% K_2O	0.7	0.8	0.8
% TiO_2	0.8	0.7	1.0
% P_2O_5	0.1	0.1	
% SO_3	1.1	0.8	2.4
Base/acid Ratio	0.11	0.06	0.08
Hardgrove Grindability	58	54	66

year 2000. Analyses of typical Argentinian coals are given in Table VII.

BRAZIL

The principal explored and developed coal deposit of Brazil extends south from southern São Paulo, through the states of Parana, Santa Catarina, and Rio Grande do Sul, to the Uruguay frontier. The seams are thin and lie in flat formations. The coal is classified as bituminous, but is of low-grade because of its high ash content. It is not easily separated from the shale partings and must be crushed to small size to make washing effective. Table VII gives

some proximate analyses of bituminous coals from Brazilian mines.

Large brown coal deposits have been discovered near the border of Peru; also, there are large deposits of lignite in Amazonas, as yet unquantified. Annual production in the year 2000 is expected to be about 19 million tonnes.

CHILE

Chile is the largest producer of coal in South America. The deposits occur in the low lying land along the ocean, and hence are easily accessible. The average thickness of the main coal seam is 150 cm. The Province of Concep-

Table VII. Coals of Argentina — Rio Turbio Area

	Hvcb	Suba
As Received:		
% Ash	10.9	15.4
% Moisture	8.6	10.3
Moist. & Ash-free:		
% Volatile (VM)	47.1	50.1
% Carbon (C)	77.8	73.2
% Hydrogen (H)	6.3	5.9
% Oxygen (O)	14.2	19.4
% Nitrogen (N)	0.7	1.0
% Sulfur (S)	1.0	0.5
HHV, Btu/lb	14,020	13,490
HHV, MJ/kg	32.6	31.4
Fusibility Temps., reducing at., °F:		
Initial deformation	2020	2190
Softening (H = W)	2280	2300
Fluid	2470	2530
Ash Composition:		
% SiO_2	48.1	53.0
% Al_2O_3	25.6	23.7
% Fe_2O_3	7.0	7.6
% CaO	7.6	6.2
% MgO	1.6	1.6
% Na_2O	0.9	0.3
% K_2O	0.3	0.4
% TiO_2	1.7	2.0
% P_2O_5	0.1	. . .
% SO_3	4.6	5.1
Base/acid Ratio	0.23	0.20
Hardgrove Grind.	49	44

ción and the deposits near the Bay of Arauco have thus far yielded the best coal in Chile. Table IX gives the proximate analyses of the representative coals of these regions. In addition, considerable low-sulfur brown coal deposits exist in the south of the country, in the province of Magallanes.

In 1971 the private Lota-Sweiger Coal Company was nationalized. The Empresa National del Carbon S.A. (ENACAR) was founded to operate the state-owned coal mines. Annual production in 2000 is planned to approach 6 million tonnes.

COLOMBIA

Colombia has the largest coal resources in Latin America, but as yet no comprehensive survey has been made of their extent and quality. Estimates of the total geological resources range from 40 to 80 billion tonnes. The coalfields are situated mainly in the Eastern Cordillera; some coal deposits are located in the Western and Central Cordillera region. All coal ranks are available, from brown coal to anthracite. A considerable portion of the coal has good coking properties. Most of the coking coals have ash contents of less than 10 percent and low sulfur contents of 0.3 to 1 percent, making them suitable for export.

In the deposits of El Cerrejon, open-cast mining produces coal low in ash and sulfur content, and high in calorific value. This coal is well suited for power stations, but can also be used for coking. The deposits producing the largest coal output are situated in the district of Paz del Rio. Further deposits occur in Cundinamarca, Boyaca, the Cauca River basin, and Samaca. Colombia plans to increase its present coal production, ensuring the energy supply in the country, and anticipating future exports up to 30 million tonnes. Table X gives analyses of typical Colombian coals.

ECUADOR

Considerable coal deposits occur in various sections of Ecuador; estimated coal deposits are 13 million tonnes. The bulk of the deposits contain subbituminous coal and low-grade lignite, high in ash. In some localities, coals of better quality, approaching anthracite, have been found. However, the general low quality, high cost of mining, and lack of transportation deter exploitation of Ecuadorian resources.

PERU

Coal deposits have been detected in a number of places along the Andean ranges, mainly in the Oyon area. The coals are both anthracite and bituminous. Two coal deposits in Peru

Table VIII. Analysis of Typical Brazilian Coals

District or Mine	As received		Moisture- and ash-free			
					HHV	
	% Ash	% H$_2$O	% VM	% S	Btu/lb	MJ/kg
Butia	13.6	11.5	42.7	1.7	. . .	. . .
Jacuhy	21.2	9.6	28.0	1.3	. . .	. . .
Tubarão	28.2	1.9	41.6	1.6	. . .	. . .
Santa Catalina	27.0	1.3	43.1	5.3	15,060	35.0
Lauro Müller	18.0	2.0	38.8	2.5	14,500	33.7
Rio Deserto	13.8	2.0	35.6	1.2	15,320	35.6
Rio Negro	39.5	7.0	36.1	2.6	12,600	29.3
Cambiu	18.4	2.5	40.6	. . .	14,600	34.0
Rio De Peixe	15.5	6.3	35.7	. . .	14,710	34.2
São Jeronimo	29.0	7.3	36.3	. . .	13,500	31.4

Table IX. Analyses of Typical Chilean Coals

City or Mine	As received		Moisture- and ash-free			
					HHV	
	% Ash	% H$_2$O	% VM	% S	Btu/lb	MJ/kg
Lota*	15.2	2.6	44.6	1.5	14,650	34.1
Schwager	3.6	2.9	44.2	1.0	15,290	35.6
Lebu	7.8	2.2	48.9	4.4	14,700	34.2
Rios	18.0	2.0	52.6	5.0	14,250	33.1
Arauco	14.3	3.4	50.2	6.6	14,500	33.7
Buen Retiro	7.7	1.7	51.5	6.4	15,080	35.1
Mafil	11.8	12.7	47.1	0.8	13,380	31.1
Quila Coya	13.3	1.7	7.2	1.0	14,820	34.5

* Chemical Composition of Ash From Lota Mine

SiO$_2$	42.9%		MgO	1.4%
Al$_2$O$_3$	26.3%		P$_2$O$_5$	0.2%
Fe$_2$O$_3$	14.6%		SO$_3$	4.8%
CaO	7.2%			

Ash Softening Temperature—2280°F

have been developed. Those of Rio Santa mainly consist of anthracite; production ceased in 1962. At present, cokable coals are worked in the district of Cerro de Pasco. Peru plans to bring annual production to about 6 million tonnes by 2000, to meet its future demand for both coking and non-coking coals with no importing required.

The mines at Goyllarisquisga and Quishuarcancha account for the bulk of the Peruvian production. The seams are generally thick, but the quality of coal is low. The analyses of Table XI are of typical Peruvian coals.

VENEZUELA

The main Venezuelan coalfields are in the Eastern Cordillera and in the region of Naricual, in the State of Anzoategui. The coal industry is government-owned. The deposits are in detached basins, some of which cover hundreds of miles. Although most of the coal is of bituminous and lignite rank, some deposits

Table X. Analyses of Typical Colombian Coals

	Hvbb	Subb
As Received:		
% Ash	8.8	7.4
% Moisture	9.0	13.8
Moist. & Ash-free:		
% Volatile (VM)	41.4	47.3
% Carbon (C)	81.0	63.9
% Hydrogen (H)	5.5	6.4
% Oxygen (O)	11.1	27.3
% Nitrogen (N)	1.7	1.4
% Sulfur (S)	0.7	1.0
HHV, Btu/lb	14,360	13,130
HHV, MJ/kg	33.4	30.5
Fusibility Temps., reducing at., °F:		
Initial deformation	2280	2240
Softening (H=W)	2380	2390
Fluid	2575	2500
Ash Composition:		
% SiO_2	61.8	37.2
% Al_2O_3	21.1	31.5
% Fe_2O_3	6.6	7.4
% CaO	2.2	7.8
% MgO	2.1	3.8
% Na_2O	1.1	1.6
% K_2O	2.4	1.2
% TiO_2	0.9	...
% P_2O_5	0.2	...
% SO_3	1.6	9.5
Base/acid Ratio	0.17	0.32
Hardgrove Grind.	48	40

of semianthracite occur in the Coro district of the State of Falcon.

Of the six coal districts of economic importance, Zulia has the largest coal resources; 1,500 million tonnes. The districts of Labotera, with 100 million tonnes, and of Naricual, with about 50 million tonnes, as well as Unare, Taguay and Tachira, are also of economic importance. By 2000, Venezuela's total coal production will be about 16 million tonnes, which may satisfy domestic needs. Table XII gives analyses of some Venezuelen coals.

COAL DEPOSITS OF EUROPE

Most of the European countries, excluding Scandanavia, possess coal resources. Scandanavia (including Iceland) has substantial quantities of peat, which increases in value as oil prices rise and as there is more uncertainty with regard to other fossil fuels.

In continental Europe, the bulk of coal is found in West Germany (the Federal Republic of Germany), Czechoslovakia, Poland, and Yugoslavia (Fig. 6). Many other countries with reasonable reserves have allowed their mines to become idle. French, Belgian, and Spanish coal is expensive to mine. Austria, Denmark, Italy, Luxembourg, the Netherlands, and Switzerland produce little or no coal.

The resources of European Russia are included in the section on the U.S.S.R. and Asia.

AUSTRIA

Coal production from small bituminous coal deposits has been abandoned. Some brown coal deposits, however, have economic impor-

Table XI. Proximate Analyses of Peruvian Coals

Kind of Coal	As received % Ash	As received % H_2O	Moisture- and ash-free % VM	HHV BTU/lb	HHV MJ/kg
Goyllarisquisga, Raw	31.5	3.1	54.5	14,710	34.2
Goyllarisquisga Steam, Washed	17.3	4.0	54.8	15,150	35.2
Goyllarisquisga Coking	17.9	4.0	49.9	15,110	35.1
Quishuarcancha, Raw	26.9	2.5	50.7	13,780	32.1
Santa River Valley	7.1	3.9	7.9	15,560	36.2
Paracas Peninsula	9.0	3.1	39.9	15,530	36.1

Table XII. Analyses of Typical Venezuelan Coals

Region	Rank	As received % Ash	As received % H$_2$O	Moisture- and ash-free % Vol.	HHV Btu/lb	HHV MJ/kg
Naricual	Hvbb	2.3	2.5	46.5	14,460	33.6
Santa Rosa	Hvab	2.4	1.5	40.1	14,520	33.8
Barcelona	Hvab	3.4	3.0	38.6	14,620	34.0
Simplicio	Mvb	4.3	3.8	27.9	. . .	. . .

Fig. 6 Coal Map of Europe

tance. There are deposits of glance brown coal as well as of lignite. The most important lignite district is situated near Köflach-Voitsberg, where two 10 to 15 m thick seams are being extracted, partly by open-cast mining, partly by deep mining. There are further brown coal deposits near Wolfsegg-Traunthal and in the Salzach district near Trimmelkam. Apart from local needs, lignite produced in the country is nearly exclusively used in power plants.

BELGIUM

In Belgium, two main bituminous-coal deposits occur, forming part of the northwest European coal belt. The southern coal deposits comprise the districts of Liège and Namur (Bassin de Liège) and Charleroi (Bassin du Hainant). The northern coal deposits include the district of the Campine. There are no brown coal deposits in Belgium.

The South basin extends through the valley of the Sambre and Meuse rivers, running east to the German frontier and west to the French border. The Campine basin, with large reserves, stretches in a westerly direction from the German border, through the Provinces of Limburg and Antwerp. The Belgian coals range from high-volatile bituminous to anthracite.

Belgium produces about half of the coal necessary for domestic consumption; the balance is imported. Only one-fourth of the coal consumed is used for thermal power plants.

BULGARIA

The country has only small bituminous coal deposits. There is a deposit of anthracite coal north of Sofia. Cokable types of coal (cretaceous coal) exist in the small district of Ojabrovo and in the Dobrudsha. The brown coal deposits of Bulgaria are economically more important than the hard coal deposits, being estimated at greater than 2,000 million t.c.e. Deposits of glance coal and of dull brown coal (cannel coal), most of which are extracted by deep mining, occur near Pernik, in the Pirin Mountains, and in Tscherno. Larger lignite deposits in the district of Maritsa can be extracted by open-cast mining. The brown coal mines mainly serve the domestic market, while the lignite mines supply coal mostly to power plants.

CZECHOSLOVAKIA

There are economically important bituminous and brown coal deposits in Czechoslovakia. Technically and economically recoverable reserves exceed 4,000 million t.c.e. The wide Upper Silesian hard-coal deposits in the district Ostrava/Karvina and the Lower Silesian deposit of Walbrzych, near Zaclér, are being mined. In addition to these two large hard-coal deposits, there are the two districts of Plzeň and Kladno/Rakovnik and a small hard-coal deposit near Rosice. In North Bohemia, there are large and economically very important brown coal deposits. The largest district is situated near Teplice and Chomutov on the border of the Krusnéhory, with a further deposit of economic importance in the district of Sokolov. Smaller brown-coal deposits exist in West Bohemia near Cheb, in the south of Moravia, and in Slovakia near Handlova.

The coals from the districts of Plzeň and Kladno are mostly low-rank types. All types of brown coal, from glance brown coal to lignite, are produced in the country; most of them are used for electricity generation.

FINLAND

Finland has no coal reserves and thus no indigenous coal production. But there are large reserves of peat with about one-third of the country considered peatland. Peat, used mainly for industrial steam production and cogenerating district heat and electricity, currently supplies about 3 percent of the fuel for energy consumption in Finland. Production is expected to exceed 2 million tonnes coal equivalent by 2000, corresponding to about 20 percent of the total energy consumption.

FRANCE

French coal deposits consist of a large number of small fields distributed over the northern, central, and southern parts of France. The deposits are generally deep, jagged, and difficult to mine. Usable deposits are between 700 and 1250 meters deep. The most important are the district of Lorraine adjoining the Saar in

Table XIII. Analyses of Typical French Coals

Area	Mining District or Seam	As received % Ash	As received % H₂O	Moisture- and ash-free % VM	Moisture- and ash-free HHV Btu/lb	Moisture- and ash-free HHV MJ/kg	Ash ST, Red., °F	Hardgrove Grind.
Nord and Pas-De-Calais Basin								
Auchel	Marles	26.5	1.2	35.0	15,570	36.2	2100	86
Bethune	Bethune	47.3	1.0	33.1	14,300	33.3	1920	75
	Noeuds-Les-Mines	32.7	1.5	38.1	14,930	34.7	2120	87
Bruay	Bruay	27.9	1.8	39.0	14,700	34.2	1940	83
Douai	Douai	26.0	1.1	24.6	15,250	35.5	2280	95
	Somain	25.3	0.9	18.6	15,340	35.7	2150	106
Hénin-Liétard	Hénin-Liétard	23.5	1.0	12.8	15,300	35.6	2280	79
Lens	Lens IV	17.6	1.0	21.0	15,420	35.9	2010	89
	Lens VII	36.0	0.9	36.0	14,930	34.7	2010	. . .
Oignies	Oignies	24.0	0.9	12.1	15,190	35.3	2280	78
Valenciennes	Anzin	44.9	1.6	17.2	14,360	33.4	2190	71
	Agache	27.6	0.9	11.7	15,310	35.6	. . .	81
Lorraine Basin								
Petite Rosselle	Simon	5.9	3.3	44.2	13,880	32.3	1970	. . .
	St. Charles	34.8	1.8	40.5	13,450	31.3	1970	76
	Wendel	29.5	3.2	40.0	13,710	31.9	2060	57
Saare & Moselle	Merlebach	6.1	2.8	43.0	14,110	32.8	1920	. . .
	La Houve	35.0	3.2	40.6	13,330	31.0	2060	. . .
Faulquemont	Faulquemont	8.6	4.0	41.9	14,750	34.3	2010	. . .

West Germany, the district of Nord and Pas-de-Calais and some scattered deposits in the district Centre-Midi. In the long term, only coal production in the Lorraine district will be maintained. The smaller brown coal deposits, most of which are in the southwest of the country in Provence and near Arjuzanx, have only local importance for electricity generation.

Most of the French hard coals represented are not cokable. While the mines in the Pas-de-Calais still produce mostly high-rank types of coal and coking coal, the coals from the Lorraine and the Centre-Midi are usually low-rank and only part of them can be used for coking. The low brown coal production is exclusively used in power plants. Table XIII gives analyses of typical French coals.

Economically recoverable reserves of deep-mined hard coal are expected to go from 320 million tonnes in 1985 to 120 million tonnes in 2000; brown coal, from 50 million in 1985 to 20 million in 2000.

GERMAN DEMOCRATIC REPUBLIC (EAST GERMANY)

The coal output from the hard coal districts of Zwickau and Lugan-Ölsnitz in Saxony has been stopped because of the properties of the coal deposits. East Germany, however, has large lignite deposits in the two principal districts in Lasatia near Cottbus-Senftenberg and near Halle-Merseburg. A third smaller lignite district is situated between Magdeburg and Helmstedt (West Germany), which is extracted by both the German Democratic Republic (DDR) and the Federal Republic of Germany. At present, the DDR is the largest lignite producing country in Europe.

Most of the hard coal from the Saxonian districts have unfavorable coking properties and can be used only as a blending coal to the im-

Table XIV. Typical East German Coals

District	As received % Ash	As received % H$_2$O	Moisture- and ash-free % VM	% C	% H	% O	% N	% S	HHV Btu/lb	HHV MJ/kg
Sachsen	5–12	2–6	38.0	81.4	5.5	10.4	1.8	1.0	14,690	34.2
Ostelbe	2–5	58–60	56.5	68.2	5.5	24.9	1.1	0.3	11,390	26.5
Westelbe	5–8	52–56	61.0	70.8	6.1	21.3	0.9	0.9	12,110	28.2
Halle-Bitterfeld	5–7	52–56	57.5	72.0	5.5	18.3	0.8	3.4	12,820	29.8

ported coking coal, or as industrial and power-plant coal. The lignites of the DDR are suitable as power-plant coal, for briquetting and, by employing special methods of coking, they can be used as input coal for coke ovens.

GERMANY, FEDERAL REPUBLIC OF

West Germany has large deposits of bituminous (stein) coal and brown (braun) coal, the latter being unconsolidated lignite. About 60 percent of the currently economical recoverable deposits have sulfur below 1 percent, as received at the power plant.

The principal districts where bituminous coal occurs in greatest abundance are: the Lower Rhine and Westphalia, Silesia, the Rhenish district and the Saar district. In central north Germany, brown coal occurs in the Rhine Province between Cologne and Aachen (Aix-la-Chapelle). Further economically important brown-coal deposits are in Lower Saxony (Helmstedt) and Lower Bavaria (Schwandorf).

The Westphalian and Rhine district fields include the Ruhr Basin, the most important coal field in Germany. These coal districts are connected with those of southern Holland, Belgium, and northern France. The coal ranges from medium to high volatile, and the ash varies considerably from mine to mine. The bulk of the entire German output comes from the Lower Rhenish Westphalian fields.

The Silesian district extends through the province of Silesia, which, geographically, is divided between Germany, Poland and Czechoslovakia. The bulk of the coal in this district is of first-class coking quality, and is widely used in steel industries. The Saar district stretches through parts of Alsace-Lorraine. The coals contain considerable ash, particularly in small sizes, which are usually washed.

The recoverable hard-coal resources of West Germany amount to about 24,000 million tonnes, with about 85 percent of that concentrated in the Ruhr. The balance comes from the Saar, Aachen, and Ibbenbüren districts. All hard coal is deep mined. Production in excess of 100 million tonnes annually is expected by 2000.

Economically recoverable brown coal totals some 35,000 million tonnes, all from open-pit mining. An annual production of 150 million tonnes is anticipated by the end of the century, practically all of which will be consumed in the country, mainly for power generation. Table XV lists typical analyses of West German coals.

GREECE

Greece does not have any bituminous coal deposits of economic importance. However, there are important lignite deposits in the districts of Ptolemais and Megalopolis. The production of brown coal was about 18 million tonnes in 1975, and increases steadily to form an important basis for the production of electric energy. The Greek brown-coal mining industry provides 50 percent of the country's energy demand. Analyses of Greek lignites are given in Table XVI.

HUNGARY

Hungary has some bituminous-coal deposits in the districts of Pécs and of Komlo, and several brown-coal deposits of national importance, both totalling about 1,000 million t.c.e.

A large brown-coal deposit is situated in the Budapest district. Glance brown coal is exploited by deep mining in the districts of Tatabánja and Oroszlány. Large lignite deposits, extracted by open-cast mining, exist in the district of Gyöngyös; in the Combinate Borsod, brown coal is extracted by deep mining. A new brown coal district near Bükkabrány projects an annual output of about 20 million tonnes.

Most of the coal produced is used for electricity generation. The use of Hungarian hard coal for coke production is very limited. Table XVII gives analyses of Hungarian brown coal.

IRELAND

There are 8 coalfield areas in Ireland (the Republic of Ireland and Northern Ireland), all of limited size. Only two are currently being

Table XV. Analyses of Typical West German Coals

District	As received		Moisture- and ash-free						HHV	
	% Ash	% H₂O	% VM	% C	% H	% O	% N	% S	Btu/lb	MJ/kg
Ruhr (Anthracite)	4–7	3–5	7.7	91.8	3.6	2.6	1.4	0.7	15,440	35.9
Ruhr (Low-Vol. Bit.)	6–9	7–10	10.5	90.8	3.8	2.7	1.7	0.8	15,500	36.0
Aachen (Low-Vol. Bit.)	6–9	8–10	13.8	89.8	4.8	2.8	1.5	0.5	15,410	35.8
Ruhr (Med-Vol. Bit.)	6–9	7–10	24.4	88.7	5.0	4.1	1.6	6.7	15,550	36.2
Saar (Med-Vol. Bit.)	7–9	8–10	32.5	86.9	5.2	5.4	1.3	1.1	15,320	35.6
Ruhr (High Vol. Bit.)	6–7	8–10	33.7	85.9	5.5	6.2	1.6	0.8	15,160	35.2
Saar (High Vol. Bit.)	5–8	3–5	38.2	82.7	5.2	9.4	1.2	1.5	14,220	33.0
Peissenberg (Lignite)	12–20	8–12	52.0	74.0	5.5	14.5	1.4	4.6	12,780	29.7
Helmstedt (Brown Coal)	12–22	42–46	59.4	72.6	5.8	16.7	0.4	4.4	12,790	29.7
Rheinland (Brown Coal)	5–20	50–62	55.0	68.3	5.0	27.5	0.5	0.5	11,340	26.4
Schwandorf (Brown Coal)	6–20	50–58	55.0	63.6	5.0	26.1	1.3	4.0	10,890	25.3

Table XVI. Analyses of Greek Lignites

Region	As received		Moisture- and ash-free						HHV	
	% Ash	% H₂O	% VM	% C	% H	% O	% N	% S	Btu/lb	MJ/kg
Kimi	5.9	23.0	55.6	...	...	...	...	2.3	11,560	26.9
Aliveri	8.6	33.5	57.7	...	...	...	...	1.4	11,330	26.3
Aegean	18.6	34.9	57.6	...	...	...	...	6.4	10,650	24.8
Attica	15.0	42.0	59.1	...	...	...	...	6.7	11,740	27.3
Ptolemais	6–22	52–60	57.0	65.3	5.3	26.5	1.6	0.5	10,850	25.2
Megalopolis	13–17	60–64	62.0	60.5	6.2	30.6	1.3	1.4	10,510	24.4

Table XVII. Analyses of Typical Hungarian Coals

Region	As received		Moisture- and ash-free						HHV	
	% Ash	% H₂O	% VM	% C	% H	% O	% N	% S	Btu/lb	MJ/kg
Gyöngyös/Visonta	15–30	46–54	63.0	63.8	4.8	26.8	1.1	3.5	10,670	24.8
Tatabánya	6–12	12–14	52.0	73.0	5.8	17.7	0.9	2.6	13,500	31.4

worked; the Connaught (Arigna) field, which contains semi-bituminous coal with high ash content, provides fuel to an adjacent generating station; the Leinster (Castlecomer) field produces high-grade anthracite for domestic heating purposes. Brown coal occurs in two localities in northeast Ireland, with large reserves in the Thistleborough area.

Peat bogs cover 15 percent of the country; over 3 million tonnes of peat are used yearly for generating electricity and domestic heating. Milled peat powers 8 stations that generate 23 percent of the national electrical demand.

Irish peat in its natural state contains about 95 percent moisture; by long-term air drying, this can be reduced to 20 to 40 percent to produce a commercial fuel. Dried peat has a volatile content between 55 and 70 percent, and ash from 2 to 10 percent. Lower heating value at 30-percent moisture is 6000 Btu/lb (14 KJ/kg); ash softening temperature is about 2100°F.

Current State-owned reserves of peat are equivalent to 40 million tonnes of coal.

ITALY

Italy has no economically important hard coal deposits. The once-mined deposits in Sardinia are to be used again in future. Larger deposits of brown coal and partly also of glance brown coal exist in Toscana, in Calabria, and in the south-west of Sardinia. Outputs are low, about 2 million tonnes annually. The largest open-cast mine is situated in the Valdarno Basin of the district Arezzo. Table XVIII shows analyses of Sardinian coals.

Table XVIII. Range of Analyses of Italian (Sardinian) Coal (As received basis)

Ash, %	15 to 20
Moisture (H_2O) %	12 to 15
Volatile matter (VM) %	32 to 45
Sulfur (S) %	2 to 7
HHV, Btu/lb	9960 to 11,500
HHV, MJ/kg	23.2 to 26.7
Ash softening temp., approx., °F	2000

NETHERLANDS

The most important of the Netherlands coal areas lies in the province of Limburg, where it links up with the Campine basin of Belgium, and extends in a northwest direction into the province of North Brabant. The Netherlands have ample geological resources that are not economically recoverable because of the large Dutch resources of natural gas.

There is an estimated resource base of 100 billion tonnes of hard coal, related to coal seams more than 0.8 m thick and 1500 m deep.

Until 1950 indigenous coal provided more than 70 percent of national coal consumption and about 50 percent of total energy demand, at a production level of some 12 million tonnes per year. Production reached a maximum of 13 million tonnes in 1961 but declined sharply after 1965 as a consequence of the development of world energy prices and low-cost domestic natural gas supply. Coal mining was stopped in 1974, while coal consumption dropped to less than 5 percent of total energy demand.

NORWAY

Economically important hard-coal deposits occur on the arctic island of Spitsbergen; these deposits are currently being worked. The coal produced is used mostly in the north of Norway, for district heating.

POLAND, PEOPLE'S REPUBLIC OF

In Poland, there are several rich and easily accessed hard-coal and brown-coal regions. Hard coals, which are all deep-mined, occur in three basins: the Upper Silesian basin has about 93 percent of the economically recoverable reserves; the Lower Silesian has about 1 percent, found in thin seams (0.4 to 1 m thick) near the towns of Walbrzych and Nowa Ruda. The Lublin basin, with about 6 percent of the reserves, is under development; there, the thickness of the seams ranges from 0.7 to 3.6 m. Most of these coals are high-volatile bituminous in rank, high in calorific value and with sulfur contents about 1 percent.

Brown coal deposits, mined by open-pit methods, occur in the Konin and Adamów districts, and near Turów, Legnica, and Belchatów. Brown coal production is solely for consumption inside Poland, primarily for the generation of electric energy.

Economically mineable reserves of hard coal are said to be 74,000 million tonnes, to a depth of 1,000 m; of brown coal, 9,000 million tonnes, all to be won by open-cast mining. Production of hard coal is expected to be between 250 and 300 million tonnes by 2000, with an additional 200 to 250 million tonnes of brown coal.

Table XIX. Analyses of Typical Polish Coals

	High-Volatile B Bituminous	Subbituminous A
As Received:		
% Ash	11.5	24.4
% Moisture	8.8	17.4
Moist. & Ash-free:		
% Volatile (VM)	37.1	41.9
% Carbon (C)	82.9	74.2
% Hydrogen (H)	5.2	6.0
% Oxygen (O)	9.9	16.7
% Nitrogen (N)	1.0	0.9
% Sulfur (S)	1.0	2.2
HHV, Btu/lb	14,550	13,020
HHV, MJ/kg	33.8	30.3
Fusibility Temps., reducing at., °F:		
Initial deformation	2160	2280
Softening (H=W)	2210	2460
Fluid	2460	2690
Ash Composition:		
% SiO_2	46.8	55.0
% Al_2O_3	21.8	24.1
% Fe_2O_3	9.6	9.3
% CaO	5.8	3.4
% MgO	3.5	1.5
% Na_2O	0.8	1.1
% K_2O	3.1	1.7
% TiO_2	0.7	1.1
% P_2O_5	0.3	. . .
% SO_3	6.6	2.8
Base/acid Ratio	0.33	0.21
Hardgrove Grind.	49	44

ROMANIA

Romania has numerous small coal deposits, especially along the outskirts of the Carpathian Mountains. Hard coal deposits are mined near Schela, Anina and Cozla. The most important district is situated near Petrosani in the Southern Carpathian Mountains. Here, the subbituminous coal seams reach thicknesses of 6 m to more than 10 m deposited in depths from 150 m to 1000 m. Further deposits of brown coal and lignite are situated near Bacau and in the basins of Oltenio, Rovinari Motru and Iilt, most of which are extractable by open-cast mining. Most of the brown coal mined in the country is used in power plants.

SPAIN

Spain has considerable bituminous coal and lignite deposits although, in several deposits, geological conditions render exploitation difficult. The economically important hard coal deposits are concentrated in the province of Asturia in the northwest—the districts of Oviedo and León account for nearly 90 percent of the total Spanish production of hard coal. A second large hard coal deposit is situated in the district of Mariannica, with individual mines in the provinces of Cordoba and Sevilla. The lignite deposits are situated in the northeast of the country between Teruel and the Pyrenees. With its present production, Spain is able to supply more than 75 percent of its demand.

SWEDEN

Swedish coal deposits are small and of low quality; technically recoverable reserves have been estimated to be 30 million tonnes. At present, there is no coal being produced except small amounts obtained from clay produced for the ceramics industry. This coal is consumed locally, and production is expected to increase slightly. Sweden has large resources of peat—estimated at about 15 percent of the country's total area—which are yet to be developed.

UNITED KINGDOM

The coal fields of the UK may be grouped into three principal areas designated as the southern, the central, and the northern coal fields.

Table XX. Analyses of Typical Spanish Coals

	Anthra-cite	Low-Vol. Bitum.	High-Vol. Bitum.	Sub-bituminous	Sub-bituminous	Brown Coal
As Received:						
% Ash	31.9	13.2	49.0	12.4	30.9	18.8
% Moisture	3.1	8.7	6.2	25.0	21.5	47.7
Moist. & Ash-free:						
% Volatile (VM)	10.9	20.9	36.8	48.7	48.1	53.1
% Carbon (C)	87.2	. . .	77.8	70.1	67.2	62.4
% Hydrogen (H)	2.5	. . .	4.9	5.0	4.8	5.6
% Oxygen (O)	8.0	. . .	15.6	15.3	16.2	28.4
% Nitrogen (N)	0.9	. . .	0.8	0.7	0.7	1.5
% Sulfur (S)	1.4	2.0	0.9	8.9	11.1	2.1
HHV, Btu/lb	14,090	14,990	13,190	12,640	11,860	9130
HHV, MJ/kg	32.8	34.9	30.7	29.4	27.6	21.2
Fusibility Temps., reducing at., °F:						
Initial deformation	2160	2280	2700 +	2070	2040	2120
Softening (H=W)	2420	2370	2700 +	2230	2290	2470
Fluid	2640	2510	2700 +	2310	2540	2660
Ash Composition:						
% SiO_2	59.0	40.5	53.6	32.3	54.2	54.7
% Al_2O_3	20.5	22.5	29.2	22.4	21.1	21.8
% Fe_2O_3	7.5	14.8	6.1	16.8	15.7	7.3
% CaO	3.5	6.3	1.2	11.0	3.5	5.2
% MgO	1.9	1.1	1.1	1.9	0.8	1.0
% Na_2O	0.9	0.5	0.4	0.3	0.1	0.2
% K_2O	4.0	3.2	4.6	1.2	1.3	0.5
% TiO_2	1.3	. . .	0.7	0.3	0.8	1.1
% P_2O_5	. . .	. . .	1.4	0.2	. . .	. . .
% SO_3	2.0	8.2	1.2	13.2	3.2	5.3
Base/acid Ratio:	0.22	0.41	0.16	0.57	0.28	0.18
Hardgrove Grind.:	54	81	. . .	83	. . .	. . .

The southern area embraces the fields known as South Wales, Forest of Dean, Bristol and Kent. The central area includes the fields of Lancashire, North Wales, Yorkshire, Derbyshire, Nottinghamshire, Staffordshire and Warwickshire. The northern area comprises the fields of Northumberland, Durham, Cumberland, and the fields of Scotland.

Intensive exploration in recent years has revealed large new areas for development, particularly in the Selby district (a major eastward extension of the Yorkshire field) and North-East Leicestershire, with coal of geological disturbance and at relatively shallow depths. Also, over 200 million tonnes of workable coal have been discovered in an area of Coventry and north of Kenilworth, at depths between 1000 and 2500 ft.

The coal of the southern area varies, from bituminous coal through the well-known Welsh steam coal to anthracite of notable purity. The bulk of the central-area coal fields lies in the south of Lancashire. Coals in this field contain 30 to 35 percent volatile matter. Some

Table XXI. Analyses of Typical British Coals

District	As received % Ash	% H₂O	Moisture- and ash-free % VM	% C	% H	% O	% N	% S	HHV Btu/lb	MJ/kg
Durham (Mvb)	6.9	2.6	29.4	87.8	5.3	4.6	1.4	0.9	15,660	36.4
Yorkshire (Hvab)	6.8	2.0	34.4	84.3	5.2	8.0	1.7	0.8	14,980	34.8
West Midlands (Hvbb)	4.9	9.8	39.6	80.5	5.5	11.9	1.4	0.7	14,180	33.0
Scotland (Hvbb)	4.6	13.8	41.5	81.4	5.4	10.3	2.1	0.8	14,580	33.9

Table XXII. Proximate Analyses of Welsh Coals

District	As received % Ash	% H₂O	Moisture- and ash-free % VM	% S	HHV Btu/lb	MJ/kg
Aberpergwm	4.0	1.3	7.4	0.9	15,820	36.8
Ynisarwed	4.2	1.5	11.3	2.5	15,370	35.7
Bwllfa	4.8	1.1	12.0	0.7	15,560	36.2
Cyfarthfa	4.9	0.8	14.0	0.9	15,430	35.9
Blaenclydach	4.2	0.9	21.3	0.6	15,230	35.4
Meiros	4.4	1.8	36.9	1.2	15,600	36.3

of them yield good coke. In the northern area, the Durham and Northumberland fields are among the most important in Great Britain. The character of the coal varies considerably. It is of exceptionally fine quality for steam, coking, household, manufacturing, and gas-producing purposes. Tables XXI and XXII provide analyses of typical British and Welsh coals.

Coal production in the UK is nearly equal to its domestic consumption, with nearly two-thirds being burned in power-generating stations. Total recoverable reserves are on the order of 45,000 million tonnes; production may be as high as 200 million tonnes annually by the turn of the century, 95 percent deep mined.

YUGOSLAVIA

There is only one hard coal deposit in Yugoslavia, with limited economical importance—on the Istria peninsula in the district of Rasa. Of higher economical importance to Yugoslavia are the brown coal deposits in the districts of Zagorje, Trbovlje, Hrastnik, Kakanj, Jenica, and Nis, with glance brown coals as well as several lignite deposits in Slovenia, such as near Vel-

enje, as well as in Bosnia and Serbia. The economically recoverable deposits, with more than 6.8×10^9 tonnes coal equivalent, are most important to Yugoslavia. Only part of the hard coals of the country are suitable for coking. The vast majority of the coal output is used for electricity generation. Table XXIII gives complete analyses of several Yugoslavian brown coals.

COAL DEPOSITS OF THE U.S.S.R. AND ASIA

The largest countries of this continent in terms of territory, size and population—the U.S.S.R. (Union of Soviet Socialist Republics, also called the Soviet Union or Russia), including the European part, the People's Republic of China, and the Republic of India—are also the countries with the biggest coal deposits. The total technically and economically recoverable reserves are estimated at greater than 200,000 million tonnes coal equivalent; over 10 percent of this is lignite or subbituminous coal, nearly all of which is found in the U.S.S.R. The balance, as described under the individual countries, is mostly bituminous coal.

Table XXIII. Analyses of a Range of Yugoslavian Brown Coals

As Received:				
% Ash	17.8	9.0	19.0	18.7
% Moisture	49.7	49.5	47.8	48.5
Moist. & Ash-free:				
% Volatile (VM)	52.0	51.1	61.0	65.2
% Carbon (C)	61.9	66.0	62.9	62.2
% Hydrogen (H)	4.3	5.1	6.2	4.3
% Oxygen (O)	29.8	25.8	28.3	30.2
% Nitrogen (N)	0.9	1.7	2.0	1.2
% Sulfur (S)	3.1	1.4	0.6	2.1
HHV, Btu/lb	9450	11,110	10,650	10,400
HHV, MJ/kg	22.0	25.8	24.8	24.2
Fusibility Temps., reducing at., °F:				
Initial deformation	2700+	2360	2100	2030
Softening (H=W)	2700+	2390	2420	2090
Fluid	2700+	2400	2450	2150
Ash Composition:				
% SiO_2	21.6	25.3	72.5	36.6
% Al_2O_3	3.1	9.5	12.5	12.9
% Fe_2O_3	6.0	5.7	2.2	7.5
% CaO	45.6	32.5	5.9	25.4
% MgO	2.5	6.6	1.4	3.1
% Na_2O	0.4	2.2	0.6	0.6
% K_2O	0.2	0.6	1.1	1.1
% TiO_2	0.1	0.4	0.5	0.3
% P_2O_5	0.4	0.3	0.1	0.2
% SO_3	15.1	12.8	3.2	11.0
Base/acid Ratio:	1.04	1.35	0.13	0.76
Hardgrove Grindability	A	B		

A: 84 at 35% H_2O; 75 at 30% H_2O; 68 at 22% H_2O; 55 at 16% H_2O; 90 at 7.5% H_2O
B: 58 at 36% H_2O; 47 at 31% H_2O; 48 at 27% H_2O; 45 at 15% H_2O; 53 at 10% H_2O

Fig. 7 is a map of European Russia (that portion of the U.S.S.R. west of the Ural mountains) and Asia, showing the coal-bearing areas.

U.S.S.R.

The Union of Soviet Socialist Republics is divided by the Ural Mountains into European Russia and Asiatic Russia, the latter comprised principally of Siberia. The accessible coal reserves of western and central U.S.S.R. have been largely depleted, while the Siberian and eastern fields are difficult and expensive to develop, and have high transportation costs to the using areas.

Total economically recoverable reserves are estimated at 110,000 million tonnes coal equivalent, of which 75 percent is bituminous coal and the balance lignite and brown coal. Eighty-percent of the presently recoverable resources are located east of the Urals, mostly in northern Siberia.

Fig. **7 Coal Map of U.S.S.R. and Asia**

European U.S.S.R.

There are three main coal fields in European Russia: the Donetz basin, the Pechora basin, and the Moscow coal fields. All are of limited life. The Donetz basin, which lies directly north of the Sea of Azov, in the Ukraine, has both anthracite and high-grade bituminous coal. The anthracite deposit is extensive, with estimated reserves of about two and a half times

those of the bituminous. The quantity of good coking coal is comparatively small, hence the utilization, on a considerable scale, of anthracite for blast furnaces and boilers. The fact that reserves of coal, iron, manganese, and limestone are all within a short distance creates an unusual economic situation in the Donetz territory.

The Vorkuta field, in the basin of the Pechora

Table XXIV. Analyses of Typical Russian Coals

Province or District	Location or Name of Coal	As received		Moisture- and ash-free						HHV	
		% Ash	% H₂O	% VM	% C	% H	% O	% N	% S	Btu/lb	MJ/kg
Ukraine	Aleksandrisk	10.8	55.0	57.0	67.6	6.0	22.0	0.8	3.6	12,150	28.3
	Kirovsk	24.8	45.0	56.0	62.5	5.2	27.6	1.0	3.7	10,062	23.4
Grusine	Tkribulsk	26.4	12.0	40.0	78.4	5.9	13.0	1.5	1.2	13,950	32.4
	Tkvarchelsk	27.9	7.0	35.0	81.5	5.9	9.7	1.7	1.2	14,750	34.3
Ural	Cheliabinsk	21.9	19.0	39.0	72.3	5.1	19.5	1.7	1.4	12,520	29.1
	Bogoslovsk	14.0	30.0	43.0	70.0	4.7	23.3	1.5	0.5	11,710	27.2
	Egroshinsk	22.6	6.0	8.0	90.0	3.7	5.1	0.6	0.6	14,780	34.4
	Poltavsk	18.2	9.0	3.5	95.0	0.8	3.5	0.5	0.2	13,860	32.2
Kazachsky	Karagandinsk	19.5	7.0	25.0	85.5	5.2	6.9	1.4	1.0	15,050	35.0
	Berchogursk	37.6	6.0	47.0	77.8	6.6	9.8	1.4	4.4	14,240	33.1
Kirgiz	Kizil-Kia	11.0	27.0	33.0	76.5	4.2	17.1	1.0	1.2	12,600	29.3
	Syliutka	11.9	21.0	29.0	77.7	4.0	17.0	0.8	0.5	12,660	29.4
Siberia	Minusinsky	10.6	12.0	42.0	79.0	5.8	12.5	2.2	0.5	14,050	32.7
	Kansky	10.2	32.0	44.0	73.1	4.9	20.0	1.3	0.7	12,440	28.9
Trans-Baikal	Chernovsky	7.4	33.0	40.0	75.5	5.0	17.5	1.3	0.7	12,960	30.1
	Bukachachisky	14.6	14.0	39.0	80.0	5.5	12.8	1.1	0.6	14,100	32.8
Far East	Kirdinsky	12.7	33.0	41.0	71.0	4.3	23.2	1.2	0.3	11,530	26.8
	Artemovsky	14.1	26.0	49.0	71.5	5.5	20.9	1.5	0.6	12,510	29.1
	Suchansky	27.3	6.0	32.0	86.0	5.0	7.0	1.4	0.6	14,950	34.8
Kuznetsk	Anzhero-Sudzhesky	11.5	4.0	15.0	91.0	4.3	2.1	1.9	0.7	15,490	36.0
	Leninsky	10.3	6.0	39.0	83.0	5.8	7.8	2.7	0.7	14,880	34.6
	Kamerovsky	12.0	4.0	33.0	85.7	5.4	6.5	2.1	0.3	15,030	35.0
	Prokopiersky	10.3	6.0	20.0	89.0	4.6	3.7	2.2	0.5	15,250	35.5
	Kiselevsky	9.3	7.0	18.0	89.3	4.3	3.6	2.3	0.5	15,210	35.4
	Osinovsky	10.2	7.0	30.0	86.5	5.5	4.8	2.7	0.5	15,410	35.8
Donetz	Anthracite	11.3	2.0	3.5	94.6	1.8	1.8	1.0	0.8	14,590	33.9
	Semi-Anthracite	13.4	4.0	12.0	90.0	4.2	2.1	1.5	2.2	15,380	35.8
	Low-Vol. Bitum.	16.0	3.0	16.0	88.0	4.5	2.9	1.5	3.1	15,400	35.8
	High-Vol. A Bit.	19.0	5.0	32.0	83.0	5.1	5.6	1.5	4.8	15,140	35.2
	High-Vol. B Bit.	14.7	8.0	39.0	82.0	5.5	8.5	1.5	2.5	14,600	34.0
	High Vol. C Bit.	19.8	12.0	44.0	77.0	5.6	12.3	1.6	3.5	13,900	32.3

River, contains one of the biggest fields in the U.S.S.R. It is located beyond the Arctic circle, as far north as the 68th parallel, with the almost unaccessible North Ural mountains to the east. The Vorkuta coal is of high calorific value and is easy to coke.

The Moscow field has a large reserve, but the coal is of low-rank and low-grade. It is lignitic in character, and has high moisture, ash and sulfur content. Coal also occurs in the Konban territory and in the Province of Kontais in the Caucasian region.

In the U.S.S.R. there has been considerable development in the use of local low-grade fuels, such as peat and oil shale, for generation of power. The U.S.S.R. has developed technologies for peat dewatering and harvesting, including the milled-peat harvesting tech-

Table XXV. Proximate Analyses of Chinese Coals

Province	District/Mine	As received		% VM	Moisture- and ash-free HHV	
		% Ash	% H$_2$O		Btu/lb	MJ/kg
Liaoning	Fushun	10.2	6.7	48.0	14,510	33.7
	Sian	1.7	6.8	42.1	15,190	35.3
Jilin	Muling	10.0	3.0	32.2	15,460	36.0
Jehol	Chaoyang	7.0	3.0	35.6	14,350	33.4
	Fusing	7.3	12.3	37.3	14,760	34.3
Heilongjiang	Tangyuan	6.2	2.0	38.2	14,290	33.2
	Lubing	3.7	20.9	48.2	12,660	29.4
Hebei	Lintsing	10.0	1.6	34.1	14,060	32.7
	Wanping	15.0	2.3	9.2	15,360	35.7
Henan	Anyang	11.4	1.1	22.7	15,440	35.9
	Liho	9.9	1.1	9.6	14,790	34.4
	Shen Xien	27.5	4.0	26.9	13,610	31.6
Shandong	Yih Xien	10.0	0.7	30.4	15,500	36.1
	Poshan	8.5	0.3	12.2	15,630	36.3
Shanxi	Dahdong	7.3	3.7	33.7	15,980	37.2
Gansu	Yong Don	3.8	5.6	36.6	15,280	35.5
Hunan	Tzehsin	10.0	2.8	25.7	14,400	33.5
	Siangtan	25.2	3.5	39.8	14,760	34.3
	Ningshian	8.0	6.0	35.6	15,530	36.1
Hubei	Tayei	12.2	1.3	12.0	15,660	36.4
	Tzequai	14.7	4.8	31.9	15,610	36.3
Jiangxi	Po-Loo	10.2	3.1	47.5	13,610	31.7
	Gao Jeng	8.9	1.0	27.1	15,870	36.9
	Jian	6.2	1.5	33.0	12,030	28.0
Anhui	Dahdong	8.9	3.3	41.7	14,600	34.0
	Wheizhou	13.6	0.4	32.1	15,110	35.1
Jiangsu	Xiaohsien	16.2	2.0	26.9	15,550	36.2
Zhejiang	Shangshin	16.6	1.2	44.1	15,530	36.1
Sichuan	Weiyuan	8.2	2.2	33.6	15,610	36.3
	Pahsien	13.2	1.2	21.5	15,940	37.1
Guizhou	Tungtze	12.2	1.0	22.0	15,730	36.6
	Guiyang	15.4	1.8	24.3	14,420	33.5
Yunnan	Shuanwei	12.7	0.9	30.9	15,530	36.1

nique that accounts for 90 percent of the peat won in that country.

Russia consumes 80 million tonnes of peat annually—about 4 percent of the total electrical output is from stations fueled by peat. In the Leningrad district and in White Russia, oil shale and peat are used for generation of power. Oil shale is also used in the Volga Region. The shale contains 50 to 55 percent of ash, which is used as cement for construction purposes. The heating value of the shale is 3200 to 3600 Btu/lb (7.4 to 8.4 MJ/kg) as fired.

Asiatic Russia

The largest coal deposit in Siberia is the Kuznetsk Basin in south central Siberia, which

Table XXVI. Chinese Coals With Ash Analyses

	An-Shan Mine Liaoning Province Hvbb	Guangdong Province Lvb	Shang Shan District South China Lvb
As Received:			
% Ash	1.5	22.5	16.7
% Moisture	2.3	0.5	1.9
Moisture & Ash-free:			
% Volatile (VM)	50.3	13.0	20.1
% Carbon (C)	. . .	. . .	87.0
% Hydrogen (H)	. . .	. . .	4.4
% Oxygen (O)	. . .	. . .	2.9
% Nitrogen (N)	. . .	. . .	0.8
% Sulfur (S)	0.5	1.6	4.9
HHV, Btu/lb	14,290	14,870	15,100
HHV, MJ/kg	33.2	34.6	35.1
Fusibility Temps., reducing atmosphere, °F:			
Initial deformation	. . .	2700+	2470
Softening (H=W)	. . .	2700+	2550
Fluid	. . .	2700+	2700+
Ash Composition:			
% SiO_2	39.7	52.2	51.2
% Al_2O_3	42.7	34.3	29.2
% Fe_2O_3	6.2	6.6	4.6
% CaO	2.7	0.8	4.3
% MgO	1.6	1.1	0.7
% Na_2O	1.3	0.4	0.7
% K_2O	1.6	2.5	0.8
% TiO_2	1.8	1.2	1.8
% P_2O_5	0.3	0.3	. . .
% SO_3	1.4	0.5	6.4
Base/acid Ratio	0.16	0.13	0.14
Hardgrove Grindability	. . .	95	120

produces 20 percent of the U.S.S.R. total. Next in importance are the Tungus, Kansk-Achinsk, Irkutsk and Minusinsk basins, and the Karagandinsk and the Saghalin deposits. To transport coal to European Russia from many of these fields requires journeys averaging over 900 miles, with some up to 1860 miles.

CHINA, PEOPLE'S REPUBLIC OF

Coal deposits of China are extensive, coal being found in almost every province. One very large area is in northern China, extending over most of the southern part of Shanxi, and one in the south extending over southern Hunan, Guizhou, Yunnan and Sichuan. In variety, Chinese coals range from hard anthracite to lignites of pronounced woody structure. The bituminous coals are of medium and high volatile rank, the medium volatile being rather high in ash. Table XXV gives the proximate analyses of many Chinese coals; XXVI includes ash analyses; and XXVII shows coals presently

Table XXVII. Coals in Use in Chinese Power Stations

	Subc	Hvb	Mvb	Lvb
As Received:				
% Ash	32.8	37.0	29.7	27.7
% Moisture	22.6	3.3	10.3	9.6
Moisture & Ash-free:				
% Volatile (VM)	46.8	39.3	22.7	17.0
% Carbon (C)	74.7	79.6	80.8	83.9
% Hydrogen (H)	4.8	5.4	6.0	4.5
% Oxygen (O)	18.6	12.4	10.7	5.1
% Nitrogen (N)	1.3	1.7	1.4	1.4
% Sulfur (S)	0.6	0.9	1.1	5.1
HHV, Btu/lb	10,890	13,090	13,810	14,030
HHV, MJ/kg	25.3	30.4	32.1	32.6
Fusibility Temps., reducing atmosphere, °F:				
Initial deformation	2070	2700+	2280	2280
Softening (H=W)	2120	2700+	2660	2510
Fluid	2280	2700+	2700+	2550+
Hardgrove Grindability	45	44	70	86

in use, categorized by rank.

Most of the coal in China is produced by the longwall retreat method. Hydraulic mining is used in Kailan, with over 3 million tonnes annually being produced by this method, and in Fujian in Shandong province. Most of the coal is found in plains areas rather than in mountain ranges, but have thick overburden. The geological condition of the western part of China is similar to that of the western U.S. Surface production is about 4 percent of the total.

Coal provides two-thirds of China's total energy requirements. Its reserves, estimated to be about 99,000 million tonnes coal equivalent, are exceeded only by those of the U.S. and the U.S.S.R. It ships substantial amounts of steam and coking coal to Japan.

Projects being considered are the design and construction of 20-million tonnes/year surface mines in Shanxi province (the An T'ai Pao mine) and in Heilongjiang province (the Yi Min mine).

By the year 2000, Chinese coal production is projected to be on the order of 2,000 million tonnes annually.

INDIA

India's coalfields are extensive and they contain economically recoverable reserves estimated to be between 10,600 and 33,000 million tonnes of hard coal, and from 500 to 900 million tonnes of lower grades. The coals vary greatly in quality, but are generally low in sulfur—less than 1 percent sulfur, as fired, for most of the production. Ash contents are high, ranging from 15 to 45 percent from most mines.

The main coal deposits are located in a triangle, of which the western edge is in the center of India and the eastern corner is about 150 kilometers west of Calcutta. Most of the active mining areas are in Andhra Pradesh, Maharashtra, Madhya Pradesh, Orissa, Bihar, and West Bengal. The oldest coalfields, those of Raniganj and Jharia in the east, produce both high-quality metallurgical and nonmetallurgical coals. The trend now is toward more development in the western part of the Indian coal-belt triangle.

Brown coals are found mainly in the district of Neyveli and in Tamil Nadu. Sixty percent of the brown coal reserves have sulfur contents

Table XXVIII. Analyses of Typical Indian Coals

Area and Rank →	Jharia Mvb	Hvbb	Uttar P. Hvbb	Renusagar Subb	Singrauli Subc	Neyveli Lig A
As Received:						
% Ash	38.9	31.6	28.0	28.6	31.5	4.5
% Moisture	1.1	6.9	10.0	14.9	7.9	53.1
Moist. & Ash-free:						
% Volatile (VM)	25.3	37.2	41.0	45.1	47.4	57.1
% Carbon (C)	83.6	. . .	. . .	74.1	71.9	70.3
% Hydrogen (H)	4.5	. . .	. . .	4.8	5.0	5.2
% Oxygen (O)	9.9		. . .	18.6	20.3	23.1
% Nitrogen (N)	1.3			1.4	2.0	0.5
% Sulfur (S)	0.7	1.8	0.8	1.1	0.8	0.9
HHV, Btu/lb	14,635	13,500	13,630	12,690	12,230	11,820
HHV, MJ/kg	34.0	31.4	31.7	29.5	28.4	27.5
Fusibility Temps., reducing at., °F:						
Initial deformation	2250	2600	2100	2700 +	2700 +	2170
Softening (H=W)	2670	2700 +	2280	2700 +	2700 +	2200
Fluid	2700 +	2700 +		2700 +	2700 +	2310
Ash Composition:						
% SiO_2	65.9	60.8	66.5	64.3	66.5	41.3
% Al_2O_3	23.7	24.8	26.1	25.2	26.1	12.1
% Fe_2O_3	6.0	6.8	2.8	5.0	2.8	3.3
% CaO	1.1	2.1	0.9	0.8	0.9	12.7
% MgO	0.6	0.5	0.7	0.7	0.7	2.9
% Na_2O	0.1	0.1	0.1	0.1	0.1	0.9
% K_2O	1.4	1.0	0.8	0.9	0.8	0.2
% TiO_2	2.2	. . .	1.5	1.7	1.5	0.4
% P_2O_5			0.2	0.2	0.2	
% SO_3	0.3	1.7	0.4	0.2	0.4	24.3
Base/acid Ratio	0.10	0.12	0.06	0.08	0.06	0.37
Hardgrove Grind.	63	60	50	56	50	*

* Hardgrove Grindability: 98 at 10% H_2O; 134 at 18% H_2O;
                            135 at 29% H_2O; 148 at 38% H_2O

below 1 percent; the rest can be as high as 3-percent sulfur.

Coal mines in India are generally shallow, with depths to within 300 meters of the surface; the deepest mine is about 800 meters. Between 35 and 40 percent of the future production of bituminous and subbituminous coal will be mined by open-cast methods, the balance being by deep mining. Much of the coal is in thick seams—75 percent appears in seams above 4.8 m in thickness. Production is expected to be between 300 and 400 tonnes annually by the year 2000. Analyses of typical coals from several areas are included in Table XXVIII.

JAPAN

Coal is widely distributed throughout all the islands and territories of the Japanese Empire. The islands of Kyusku and Hokkaido are by far the most important for quantity and quality.

Table XXIX. Analyses of Typical Japanese Coals

Area	Mining District or Seam	As received % Ash	% H₂O	Moisture- and ash-free % VM	HHV Btu/lb	MJ/kg	Hardgrove Grind.
Kyushu	Tagawa	35.4	3.9	51.2	13,660	31.8	45
	Iizuka	22.1	2.2	48.3	14,410	33.5	44
	Hiyoshi	24.5	3.0	40.0	14,700	34.2	49
	Kokura	39.1	6.1	53.6	13,160	30.6	37
	Onoura	23.8	2.4	46.2	14,440	33.6	46
	Yamano	51.3	2.2	45.8	13,400	31.2	43
	Meiji-Saga	15.4	2.2	51.7	14,800	34.4	47
	Shinhokusho	23.3	3.6	46.9	14,690	34.2	51
Shikoku	Takamatsu	29.7	4.4	47.6	14,040	32.6	38
Yamaguchi	Sanyo	31.7	2.2	9.5	14,900	34.7	72
Hokkaido	Sunagawa	38.0	1.6	49.7	13,710	31.9	49
	Bihai	15.1	3.6	45.9	14,330	33.3	47
	Yubetsu	21.6	2.4	44.9	14,740	34.3	53
	Akama	30.8	2.6	46.4	14,590	33.9	54
	Hahoro	16.8	12.9	55.8	14,510	33.7	36
	Horonai	8.2	3.4	48.4	14,490	33.7	38

There are two minor deposits on the main island of Honshu. Economically recoverable reserves of coal are about 1,000 million tonnes equivalent, all extractable by deep mining; nearly half of this will come from the Ishikari coalfield on Hokkaido. Production in the year 2000 will be on the order of 20 million t.c.e., which will be less than 10 percent of the national consumption at that time.

The Japanese coals range from anthracite to lignite, but the bituminous outweighs all other in quantity and value. The greater portion of bituminous is of the high-volatile rank containing 6 to 9 percent ash with a high-heat-value range of 12,000 to 13,000 Btu/lb (28 to 30 MJ/kg). Table XXIX gives the proximate analyses of many of the more typical Japanese coals.

KOREA

Although imported bituminous coal is burned in Korea, all of the coal mined in Korea is high-ash-content anthracite. Table XXX gives analyses of several anthracites; as-received sulfur contents range from 0.1 to 0.5 percent.

TURKEY

Considerable deposits of coal and lignite occur in Turkey, the most important so far being those in the northwestern regions of Anatolia. Commercial development, however, has been practically confined to the Erigli Basin. The Erigli coal, when properly cleaned, is suitable for most purposes, and compares favorably wih the bulk of European bituminous. It contains 40 to 45 percent volatile matter, and is utilized by steamships, railways and factories. Table XXXI gives analyses of two coals from Turkey.

VIET NAM

The only known coal deposits in Viet Nam are anthracitic, chiefly from the Nong-Son area. As-received ash content ranges from 15 to 27 percent, with sulfur from 2 to 3.5 percent. Volatile matter (VM) is between 8 and 11 percent, with high heating value (HHV) from 13,800 to 14,600 Btu/lb (32 to 34 MJ/kg), both on a moisture- and ash-free basis. Hardgrove grindability is usually between 32 and 53, with some samples as high as 73.

Table XXX. Analyses of Typical Korean Anthracites

Area or Mine	As received % Ash	As received % H₂O	Moisture- and ash-free % VM	Moisture- and ash-free HHV Btu/lb	Moisture- and ash-free HHV MJ/kg	Ash St, Red., °F	Hardgrove Grind.
Kum-Chun	33.4	6.5	8.7	13,580	31.6	. . .	62
Dan-Gok (Hamback Field)	31.1	7.6	7.5	13,280	30.9	. . .	168
Hung-Jun	31.5	5.3	8.1	13,560	31.5	. . .	66
Bang-Je (Hamback Field)	26.0	6.2	6.9	13,880	32.3	. . .	98
Chengsun	21.1	8.7	5.7	13,980	32.5	. . .	49
Cholam	27.3	5.0	6.1	13,750	32.0	2440	45
Dogye	31.5	3.4	7.4	12,980	30.2	2220	59
Yonawol	49.5	2.6	11.7	12,760	29.7	2200	. . .

A representative ash composition is

% SiO_2 -65.0	% MgO - 1.0
% Al_2O_3 - 20.1	% Na_2O - 0.5
% Fe_2O_3 - 5.3	% K_2O - 5.0
% CaO - 1.0	% TiO_2 - 0.9

Table XXXI. Analyses of Typical Turkish Coals

Area or Mine	As received % Ash	As received % H₂O	Moisture- and ash-free % VM	Moisture- and ash-free % C	Moisture- and ash-free % H	Moisture- and ash-free % O	Moisture- and ash-free % N	Moisture- and ash-free % S	Moisture- and ash-free HHV Btu/lb	Moisture- and ash-free HHV MJ/kg
Tuncbilek Subbituminous	14–22	14–24	44.5	76.4	5.8	13.8	2.5	1.5	13,840	32.2
Elbistan Brown Coal	8–24	48–62	67.0	61.4	5.1	29.6	0.8	5.1	10,190	23.7

AFRICA

Both the geological coal resources and the economically recoverable coal reserves are concentrated in the southern part of the continent. They are preponderantly bituminous coal. Technically and economically recoverable reserves are estimated to be in excess of 30,000 million tonnes coal equivalent; the Republic of South Africa has nearly 80 percent of these; Botswana, 10 percent; Swaziland, about 5 percent; and Rhodesia, 2 percent.

BOTSWANA, REPUBLIC OF

Most of the coal reserves are in the eastern part of the country. Coal qualities are poor and there are no existing coking-coal deposits. The present coal output is low, but increases in production have recently taken place at the Morupule Colliery near Palapye. Consumers of coal production are the Botswana Power Cor-

poration and a local nickel-copper mine. The annual production is projected to reach up to 1 million tonnes in the future.

MOROCCO

The coal, mainly anthracite, is mined by the state-owned Société des Charbonnages Nord-Africains (CNA) at Djerada in the east. There are plans to increase the production to over 2 million tonnes by 2000. Nearly 80 percent of the annual production is burned in the power station at Djerada. In future, limited quantities of anthracite could be for export.

MOZAMBIQUE

Since early 1978 the only existing mining company, Companhia Carbonifera de Mozambique (CCM), has been state owned. The annual output is about 700,000 tonnes and consideration is being given to its expansion. A great part

Fig. 8 **Coal Map of Africa**

of the annual production consists of coking coal. It is possible to increase production up to 7 million tonnes, with a coal export potential of about 5 million tonnes before the end of the century. Today Romania, Japan, Malawi and the German Democratic Republic are importing coal from Mozambique.

NIGERIA

Coal production is now some 300,000 tonnes per year. The coal is produced by the state-owned Nigerian Coal Corporation, with recoverable reserves being on the order of 90 million tonnes. A peak production of 1.5 million tonnes is anticipated by the end of the century. Exports to Ghana are mainly for railways.

SOUTH AFRICA, REPUBLIC OF

The Republic of South Africa (RSA) has about 75 percent of all the coal resources of the

African continent. Most of the coal deposits are situated at shallow depth; more than 10 percent of the RSA coal output is obtained by open-cast mining. In the future, many abandoned "deep" mines will be reworked from the surface with modern heavy equipment.

South African coal production consistently exceeds its domestic requirements; it exports both bituminous and anthracite coals. At this time, the Republic of South Africa (RSA) is one of the 10 largest coal producers and exporters in the world.

The proportion of total coal consumption for the generation of electricity has grown steadily, with approximately 60 percent presently for that purpose. All new thermal stations are located at minemouth, with boilers and pulverizers designed to use run-of-mine coal.

South African coal is deposited in relatively small, isolated basins. The coal seams are thickest and of best quality in the middle of each basin, but pinch out and increase in ash content toward the periphery. The biggest single drawback of the coals of the RSA, particularly for export, is that much of the inert mineral matter present is so intimately associated with the organic matter that its reduction to reasonable levels is generally difficult and costly.

The lowest rank coals in South Africa are found in the Orange Free State; the fields there may be regarded as the southern extension of the Transvaal fields. They have a dry ash-free carbon content of 77 percent; the highest rank coals are the anthracites southeast of Vryheid, with a dry ash-free carbon content of 91.6 percent. The ranks of all the other coals fall between these two limits. Aside from a few minor peat and lignite occurrences, all coals vary in rank from about the lower limit of high-volatile bituminous (or upper limit of subbituminous) coal to anthracite. The higher rank coals are largely confined to Natal, where the fields are essentially an extension of the Transvaal fields.

The coal-bearing areas of the Republic are first subdivided into coal provinces, which in turn are split into coal fields, based either on physical separation of the areas or on conspicuous or slight stratigraphical differences in the coal successions.

The main Witbank field is the center of the coal-mining industry in the RSA; it produces more than half of the coal consumed in the country. Highveld is the biggest of the coal fields in area, but exploitation on a large scale has just begun. Waterberg adjoins the Botswana coal field where the Morupule open-cast is in operation; although it has been intensively prospected and contains 7 seams of workable quality, there are formidable obstacles to economic extraction at this time. Vereeniging-Sasolburg is an important field, with three thick seams. In many of the smaller fields, coal is still being prospected or its mining is yet to be fully developed.

Economically recoverable reserves in the RSA are variously stated to be between one-third and 80 percent of the proven reserves shown in Table XXXII. Estimates of South Africa's coal production in 2000 range from 155 to over 230 million tonnes annually. The quantity of coal to be mined for export is a major variable; an unfavorable political climate toward the RSA will tend to restrict exports below a physically attainable level.

Two bituminous coals from South Africa, together with their ash analyses, are given in Table XXXIII.

SWAZILAND

The Swaziland Collieries Ltd., a subsidiary of Anglo-American Corporation, produces coal for railway, industrial and domestic markets. Only a small quantity is exported. Future prospects are considered to be good as recoverable reserves are in excess of 1500 million tonnes of bituminous coal; production of about 6 million tonnes, nearly 4 million for export, is possible by 2000. Coking coal is exported to Kenya, Japan and Mozambique.

ZAIRE

The coal is produced by Charbonnages de la Luena S.A., Brüssel, a subsidiary of Union Minière. The consumers of the coal are the power stations and the copper industry. A part of the coal is blended with Rhodesian coking coal for producing a coke suitable for copper smelting. Production of over one million tonnes by 2000 is expected.

ZAMBIA

The coal is produced by Maamba Collieries Ltd., Lusaka, in the south of the country. With capital aid from the African Development Bank and the Federal Republic of Germany, the mines at the Maamba region are to be modernized. The main uses of Maamba coal are in copper smelting, cement and fertilizer production, and for steam generation. By the year 2000 production is anticipated at about 3 million tonnes.

ZIMBABWE (RHODESIA)

Coal is mined by Wankie Colliery Company Ltd., Salisbury, a subsidiary of Anglo-American Corporation. Economically recoverable bituminous-coal reserves approximate 800 million tonnes. The export potential depends on political considerations. Production at present is largely geared to satisfy home consumption, but coal is exported also to Zaire and Zambia. The coal has excellent steaming and coking qualities. The average analysis is:

H₂O	VM	FC	Ash	S	Btu/lb	MJ/kg
0.7	21.0	66.8	11.5	2.8	12,750	29.7

Table XXXII. Proven Resources of Mineable Bituminous Coal (In Situ)

	Millions of tonnes
Witbank, including Springs-Vischkuil	14,186
Highveld	7,231
Waterberg	6,386
Vereeniging-Sasolburg	1,232
Carolina-Wakkerstroom (Eastern Transvaal)	805
Newcastle-Dundee (Klip River)	748
South Rand	600
Other fields, below 600 × 10⁶ tonnes each	1,034
Total	32,222

OCEANIA

Oceania is usually considered to include the lands of the central and south Pacific, including Australia, New Zealand, Tasmania, and sometimes, the Malay archipelago. For convenience, we have included coal data from Indonesia and the Phillipine Islands in this section. Fig. 9 shows the coal fields of Australia, New Zealand, and Tasmania.

Table XXXIII. Analyses of Typical South African Coals

	Bituminous Coal and Ash Analyses	
As Received:		
% Ash	13.9	16.6
% Moisture	2.9	6.3
Moist. & Ash-free:		
% Volatile (VM)	33.8	31.8
% Carbon (C)	84.6	82.4
% Hydrogen (H)	4.9	4.4
% Oxygen (O)	7.2	10.6
% Nitrogen (N)	2.2	1.6
% Sulfur (S)	1.1	1.0
HHV, Btu/lb	14,070	14,250
HHV, MJ/kg	32.7	33.1
Fusibility Temps., reducing at., °F:		
Initial deformation	2410	2390
Softening (H=W)	2430	2470
Fluid	2700	2690
Ash Composition:		
% SiO₂	41.5	41.9
% Al₂O₃	30.8	29.4
% Fe₂O₃	4.8	7.2
% CaO	8.7	7.3
% MgO	2.2	1.6
% Na₂O	0.2	0.6
% K₂O	0.3	0.7
% TiO₂	1.0	1.5
% P₂O₅	1.0	
% SO₃	7.6	7.9
Base/acid Ratio	0.22	0.24
Hardgrove Grind.	46	50

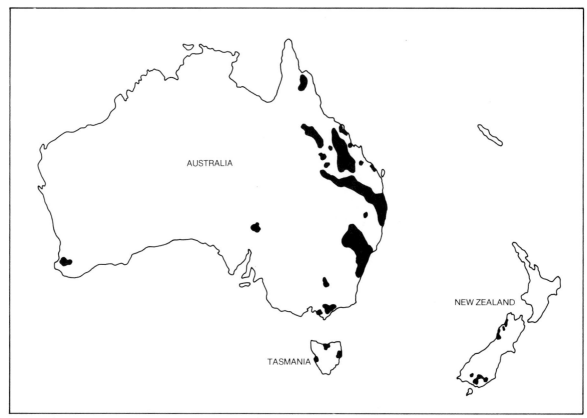

Fig. 9 Coal Map of Oceania

AUSTRALIA

Australia's large coal resources are concentrated in the Eastern States. The largest and economically most significant deposits of bituminous coal are found in the Bowen Basin of Eastern Queensland and the Sydney Basin in New South Wales. Nearly half of the country's production is from underground mines in New South Wales; another 30 percent is from open-cut mines in Queensland. The Galilee Basin in Queensland also contains a large resource and the Surat and Clarence-Moreton Basins are of significance. In Australia, a depth of 1,000 meters is generally taken as the current limit for bituminous coal to be regarded as economically extractable.

Major brown coal deposits are located in Victoria where the Latrobe Valley contains proved recoverable reserves of some 35,000 million tons within the limits of a maximum mining depth of 200 meters and a minimum seam thickness of 15 meters. The coal is used predominantly for power generation. The average moisture content is 62 percent and the lower heating value, as received, ranges from 6.0 to 12.5 MJ/kg (2,580 to 5,370 Btu/lb).

The coal resources in other States are relatively small, in most cases comprising isolated deposits of subbituminous coal or lignite. The major use for these coals in South Australia and Western Australia, such as from the Collie basin, is in power stations.

Australia's economically recoverable reserves are in excess of 25,000 million tonnes, about 60 percent of which is bituminous coal and the balance lower ranked types. About 20 percent of the bituminous coal is capable of being surface-mined. Production of all types of coal is anticipated to be as high as 300 million tonnes coal equivalent in the year 2000.

Table XXXIV. Analyses of Typical Australian Coals

	Farrells C.K.	Bayswater	Liddell Seam	Foxbrook	Puxtrees	Yallourn
As Received:						
% Ash	16.4	25.3	24.7	16.5	26.0	0.8
% Moisture	7.8	6.1	3.3	4.1	7.3	60.2
Moist. & Ash-free:						
% Volatile (VM)	33.5	36.0	39.3	44.7	46.5	60.5
% Carbon (C)	83.4	79.1	80.1	81.2	77.4	. . .
% Hydrogen (H)	4.6	4.8	4.9	6.1	5.5	. . .
% Oxygen (O)	10.6	14.0	12.8	11.0	15.3	. . .
% Nitrogen (N)	1.0	1.7	1.5	1.1	1.2	. . .
% Sulfur (S)	0.4	0.4	0.7	0.6	0.6	0.5
HHV, Btu/lb	14,340	13,650	13,650	14,630	13,490	12,180
HHV, MJ/kg	33.3	31.7	31.7	34.0	31.4	28.3
Fusibility Temps., reducing at., °F:						
Initial deformation	2700+	2700+	2700+	2280	2280	2700+
Softening (H=W)	2700+	2700+	2700+	2500	2480	2700+
Fluid	2700+	2700+	2700+	2700+	2700+	2700+
Ash Composition:						
% SiO_2	55.1	54.9	48.2	56.1	54.5	5.0
% Al_2O_3	31.9	30.6	31.6	25.9	24.0	62.5
% Fe_2O_3	6.6	8.8	7.9	3.8	6.7	2.5
% CaO	0.7	1.1	3.8	5.0	3.7	1.8
% MgO	0.5	0.8	1.5	2.1	2.3	4.1
% Na_2O	0.4	0.5	0.2	0.6	0.3	8.7
% K_2O	1.1	0.8	0.4	0.7	1.0	0.9
% TiO_2	1.3	1.2	1.2	1.1	1.8	2.6
% P_2O_5	0.6		0.5	0.5	0.2	0.3
% SO_3	0.1	0.1	2.9	3.2	3.3	6.6
Base/acid Ratio	0.11	0.14	0.17	0.15	0.17	0.26
Hardgrove Grind.	52	45	50	48	45	

Table XXXIV gives analyses of Australian coals from several mining areas.

NEW ZEALAND

Coal ranging from anthracite to lignite occurs in many sections of New Zealand. The Buller-Mokihinui is the best known bituminous field. The coal is of good quality and makes an excellent steam fuel. It is coking, but the coke produced is not rated high. Table XXXV gives complete coal and ash analyses of two New Zealand coals.

INDONESIA

Since 1972, only two state-owned coal mines are in active production: Ombilin in West Sumatra and Bukit Asam in South Sumatra.

Coal deposits of economic significance are confined to the western part of Indonesia, on the islands of Sumatra and Kalimantan. Estimates of measured reserves of bituminous coal and lignite on these islands are 200 million and 100 million tonnes respectively.

Ombilin coal is a hard bituminous to sub-bituminous coal. It is excellent steam coal with mild coking properties. Detailed explorations carried out in some parts of the Ombilin basin have indicated about 35 million tonnes of mineable coal reserves.

The proximate analysis of a typical Ombilin coal sample is as follows:

Moisture	: 6.0%
Ash	: 1.5%
Sulfur	: less than 0.5%
Volatile Matter	: 46%, m.a.f. basis
Calorific Value	: 14,590 Btu/lb (33.9 MJ/kg)

The coal in the region of Bukit Asam ranges from lignite through bituminous, subbituminous to anthracitic coal and anthracite. The Air Laya opencast mine of Bukit Asam remains the field with the most potential. Recent studies indicate that there is a reserve of close to 100 million tonnes of coal in this field.

The average proximate analyses of the various coals presently produced in Bukit Asam are

Air Laya subbituminous coal

Moisture	: 18.0% to 23.2%
Ash	: 4.4% to 8.9%
Sulfur	: 0.16% to 0.41%
Volatile Matter	: 29.4% to 32.1% as received
Calorific Value	: 10,800 to 11,700 Btu/lb (25.1 to 27.2 MJ/kg), as received

Suban low-volatile bituminous coal

Moisture	: 0.5% to 1.2%
Ash	: 3.6% to 4.4%
Sulfur	: negligible
Volatile Matter	: 15% to 19%
Calorific Value	: 14,400 to 14,760 Btu/lb (33.5 to 34.3 MJ/kg), as received

PHILIPPINE ISLANDS

Coal is mined in eight localities in the Philippine Islands, namely: Bataan, Cebu, Zamboanga, Politti, Masbati, Mindoro, Luzon and Mindanao. The basins are small and discontinuous. The deposits contain lignite, subbituminous and bituminous coals. The bulk of

Table XXXV. Analyses of Typical New Zealand Subbituminous Coals

	Maori Farm	Ohinewai Area
As Received:		
% Ash	5.4	3.0
% Moisture	16.2	22.2
Moist. & Ash-free:		
% Volatile (VM)	48.7	47.6
% Carbon (C)	. . .	73.9
% Hydrogen (H)	. . .	5.5
% Oxygen (O)	. . .	19.4
% Nitrogen (N)	. . .	0.9
% Sulfur (S)	0.4	0.3
HHV, Btu/lb	12,490	12,600
HHV, MJ/kg	29.0	29.3
Fusibility Temps., reducing at., °F:		
Initial deformation	2320	2120
Softening (H=W)	2370	2150
Fluid	2600	2230
Ash Composition:		
% SiO_2	20.1	21.4
% Al_2O_3	7.8	10.8
% Fe_2O_3	9.4	8.7
% CaO	34.9	36.1
% MgO	2.2	4.1
% Na_2O	1.2	2.7
% K_2O	0.2	0.6
% TiO_2	0.3	1.8
% SO_3	18.0	12.8
Base/acid Ratio	1.7	1.5
Hardgrove Grind.	. . .	39

the lignite is black, and seldom displays a woody structure or brown color. The bituminous coals are black, hard and lustrous. They are generally noncoking. Table XXXVI gives the analysis of a typical Philippine coal.

A typical Philippine coal, from Liguan, has an as-received ash content of 11.5%, and moisture of 9.4%. On a moisture- and ash-free basis, volatile matter is 45.3%, sulfur is 0.8%, and HHV is 13,480 Btu/lb (31.3 MJ/kg). Ash softening temperature of such a coal, in a reducing atmosphere, is approximately 2190°F.

Table XXXVI. Typical Philippine Island Coal

| | As received | | Moisture- and ash-free | | | | Ash ST, |
	% Ash	% H₂O	% VM	% S	HHV Btu/lb	MJ/kg	Red., °F
Liguan	11.5	9.4	45.3	0.8	13,480	31.3	2190

INTERNATIONAL COAL CLASSIFICATION

As the international trade in coal increased following World War II, the Coal Committee of the Economic Commission for Europe established a Classification Working Party in 1949 to develop an international system for classifying coal. The system for classifying hard coals was published in 1956 as a document of the United Nations.[1] In 1958, the U.S. Bureau of Mines published the results of its study of how this classification system would apply to American coals. Two years later the classification system was applied to brown coals and lignites.[2,3] Based on European terminology, the expression *hard coal* as used in the international classification system is defined as coal with a gross calorific value of more than 10,260 Btu per lb (5,700 kg-cal per kg or 23.86 MJ/kg) on the moist, ash-free basis. Coals classified by the American Society for Testing Materials as anthracitic, bituminous, and higher rank sub-bituminous are included in the hard-coal category. Brown coals and lignites are those coals having gross calorific values below 10,260 Btu per lb, moist but ash-free.

Excerpts from the two referenced classification systems are included in the following text. These excerpts will assist users of various types of coals world-wide, in relating such coals to the American types referred to frequently in this and other engineering references.

CLASSIFICATION OF HARD COALS BY TYPE

Table XXXVII shows the international system of classifying hard coals according to their volatile-matter content, calculated on a dry,

ash-free basis, resulting in nine classes of coals. As volatile matter (VM) is not an entirely suitable parameter for classifying coals containing more than about 33 percent of this constituent, the calorific value on a moist, ash-free basis is used for such coals. The nine classes of hard coal, based on volatile-matter content and calorific value, are then divided into groups according to their caking properties, as measured by tests when the coal is heated rapidly. The coal groups are further subdivided according to coking properties determined by tests in which the coal is heated slowly.

DIVISION OF HARD COALS INTO CLASSES

Hard coals are first classified in the international system according to their volatile-matter content, calculated on a dry, ash-free basis. These classifications are:

Class No.	VM dry, ash-free %
1 A	3 – 6.5
1 B	> 6.5 –10
2	>10 –14
3	>14 –20
4	>20 –28
5	>28 –33
6–9	>33

As volatile matter is not an entirely suitable parameter for classifying coals containing more than about 33 percent volatile matter, calorific value on a moist, ash-free basis is used for such coals, as follows:

Class No.	Gross calorific value, moist., ash-free basis, Btu/lb	Approximate limits of VM, dry, ash-free %
6	>13,950	33–41
7	>12,960–13,950	33–44
8	>10,980–12,960	35–50
9	>10,260–10,980	42–50

The gross calorific value of coal on the moist, ash-free basis means the calorific value of the

Table XXXVII. International classification of hard coals by type (Ref. 2)

Group Number	Free-swelling index (crucible-swelling number)	Roga Index	c0	c1	c2	c3	c4	c5	c6	c7	c8	c9	Sub-Group Number	Dilatometer	Gray-King
							435	535	635				5	>140	>G$_8$
3	>4	>45				334	434	534	634	734			4	>50–140	G$_5$–G$_8$
						333	433	533	633	733			3	>0–50	G$_1$–G$_4$
						332a 332b	432	532	632	732	832		2	≥0	E-G
						323	423	523	623	723	823		3	>0–50	G$_1$–G$_4$
2	2½-4	>20-45				322	422	522	622	722	822		2	≥0	E-G
						321	421	521	621	721	821		1	Contraction only	B-D
					212	312	412	512	612	712	812		2	≤0	E-G
1	1-2	>5-20			211	311	411	511	611	711	811		1	Contraction only	B-D
0	0-½	0-5		100 (A / B)	200	300	400	500	600	700	800	900	0	Non-softening	A

Code Numbers: The first figure of the code number indicates the class of coal, determined by volatile matter content up to 33% VM and by calorific parameter above 33% VM. The second figure indicates the group of coal, determined by coking properties. The third figure indicates the subgroup, determined by coking properties.

Class Parameters	Class Number	0	1 (A | B)	2	3	4	5	6	7	8	9
	Volatile matter, VM (dry, ash-free)	0-3	>3-10 (>3-6.5 | >6.5-10)	>10-14	>14-20	>20-28	>28-33	>33	>33	>33	>33
	Calorific parameter	—	—	—	—	—	—	13.950	>12.960-13.950	>10.980-12.960	>10.260-10.980

As an indication, the following classes have an approximate VM content of:
Class 6 33-41% VM
7 33-44% VM
8 35-50% VM
9 42-50% VM

CLASSES
(Determined by volatile matter up to 33% VM and by calorific parameter above 33% VM)

Note: (i) Where the ash content of coal is too high to allow classification according to the present systems. it must be reduced by laboratory float-and-sink method (or any other appropriate means). The specific gravity selected for flotation should allow a maximum yield of coal with 5 to 10 percent of ash.
(ii) 332a . . . >14-16% VM
332b . . . >16-20% VM
(iii) Gross calorific value on moist. ash-free basis (30°C., 96% relative humidity). Btu/lb

coal in equilibrium with air at 30°C and 96 percent relative humidity, calculated to an ash-free basis. For practical purposes, the moisture in the equilibrated sample is considered equivalent to the natural bed moisture of the coal, that is, the coal moisture at freshly exposed bed faces free of visible water.

DIVISION OF HARD-COAL CLASSES INTO GROUPS

The nine classes of hard coal, based on volatile-matter content and calorific value, are divided into groups according to their caking properties. Caking properties, as used in the classification system, are a measure of the behavior of coal when heated rapidly. Either of two methods—the free-swelling test (crucible-swelling test) or Roga test—may be used to measure caking properties. The division of classes into groups, according to free-swelling index or Roga index, are:

Group No.	Free-swelling index	Roga index
0	0–½	0–5
1	1–2	>5–20
2	2½–4	>20–45
3	>4	>45

Division of Groups into Subgroups

The hard-coal groups are further subdivided according to coking properties, as measured by tests in which the coal is heated slowly. Coking properties are measured either by maximum dilatation, using the Audibert-Arnu method, or by Gray-King coke type. The division into subgroups follows:

Subgroup No.	Maximum dilatation	Gray-King coke type
0	Nonsoftening	A
1	Contraction only	B-D
2	0 and less	E-G
3	>0 to 50	G_1-G_4
4	>50 to 140	G_5-G_8
5	>140	>G_8

CODE NUMBERS

A three-figure code number is used to express the classification of a hard coal. The first figure indicates its class, the second figure the

group, and the third figure the subgroup. An example of the use of the system follows, based on a coal with the following characteristics:

Volatile matter, dry, ash-free, %	37
Calorific value, moist ash-free Btu/lb	14,510
Caking properties:	
Free swelling index	6
Roga index	85
Coking properties:	
Maximum dilatation	60
Gray-King coke type	G_5

As the volatile-matter content on a dry, ash-free basis is greater than 33 percent, the class number is determined by the gross calorific value on a moist, ash-free basis. As the gross calorific value is more than 13,950 Btu the coal belongs in class 6, which becomes the first figure of the code number. The free-swelling index is 6; alternatively, the Roga index is 85, so the coal belongs in group 3, which becomes the second figure of the code number. As the maximum dilatation is 60, or the Gray-King coke type is G_5, the coal belongs in subgroup 4, which is the third figure of the code number. Therefore the code number of the coal is 634.

CLASSIFICATON OF LOWER-RANK COALS

Table XXXVIII shows the international system of classifying brown coals and lignites, those fuels having gross calorific values below 10,260 Btu/lb (5,700 kcal/kg or 23.86 MJ/kg). The parameters for classifying these coals are their total moisture and yield of low-temperature tar. As a correlation exists between the total moisture and calorific values of the lower rank coals, the moisture parameter indicates the value of the coal as a fuel; the tar indicates the value of the coal for chemical processing.

DIVISION OF LOWER-RANK COALS INTO CLASSES

The coals are first classified according to their total moisture content as ash-free coals. Total moisture is that contained in freshly mined coal. The class numbers and corresponding range of moisture values are:

Class No.	Total moisture, ash free, %
10	20 and less
11	>20–30
12	>30–40
13	>40–50
14	>50–60
15	>60–70

The numbering system starts with 10 to follow consecutively after the classes numbered 0 to 9 in the international classification of hard coals by type.

Division of Classes in Groups

The lower-rank coals divided into classes according to total moisture are subdivided into groups by yield of low-temperature tar, calculated dry and ash-free. Group numbers with corresponding range of tar yields are:

Group No.	Tar, dry, ash free, %
00	10 and less
10	>10–15
20	>15–20
30	>20–25
40	>25

CODE NUMBERS

A four-figure code number indicates the classification of lower-rank coals. The first two figures identify the class; the last two, the group. For example, if total moisture, ash free, is 35 percent, the coal is placed in class 12; if the yield of tar is 11 percent, the coal is assigned to group 10 and the code number of the coal is 1210.

METHODS OF COAL ANALYSIS AND TEST

The international classification system provides that standard methods of the International Organization for Standardization (ISO) shall be used when such methods become available. Much progress has been made in the work of standardization, although the methods have not been approved in final form. Until standard methods are adopted, it is provided that national standards may be used. The following provisional tolerances are to be used for the parameters pending adoption of international methods of analysis and test:

Volatile matter, VM

20% or less	± 1.0 unit
More than 20%	± 5.0% of value
Free-swelling index	± ½ unit
Roga index	± 5 units

Maximum dilatation:

Subgroups 0, 1, 2, 3	± 5 units
Subgroup 4	± 10 units
Subgroup 5	± 15 units
Gray-King coke type	± 1 type
Gross calorific value	± 110 Btu/lb

The appendix to reference 2 includes methods for determining equilibrium moisture content (moisture-holding capacity) and several of the above indices. The methods are summarized in the following text.

EQUILIBRIUM MOISTURE CONTENT

In the international system, coals with more than 33 percent volatile matter on the dry, ash-free basis are classified according to calorific value on the moist, ash-free basis. The term moist refers to coal containing its natural bed moisture but no visible water on the surface. It is assumed that the natural bed moisture of coal in the ground represents the moisture-holding capacity of the coal when in equilibrium with air at approximately 100 percent relative humidity. Because of the difficulty of equilibrating samples in such an atmosphere, the equilibrium moisture content or moisture-holding capacity is determined at 96 to 97 percent relative humidity, which for practical purposes is considered to represent the moisture in the coal bed.

The test is essential for classifying wet samples of coal in order to bring the coals to their natural-bed-moisture condition. The proposed ISO method for moisture-holding capacity is equivalent to the ASTM method for equilibrium moisture of coal. The method also can restore partially air-dried samples of all coals except lignites to virtually bed-moisture state.

To conduct the test, a sample of coal crushed to pass a no. 16 sieve is wetted, drained of

Table XXXVIII. International Classification of Brown Coals and Lignites

Group No.	Group parameter tar yield (dry, ash free), %	Code Numbers					
40	>25	1040	1140	1240	1340	1440	1540
30	>20–25	1030	1130	1230	1330	1430	1530
20	>15–20	1020	1120	1220	1320	1420	1520
10	>10–15	1010	1110	1210	1310	1410	1510
00	10 and less	1000	1100	1200	1300	1400	1500
Class no.		10	11	12	13	14	15
Class parameter total moisture, ash-free, percent		20 and less	>20 −30	>30 −40	>40 −50	>50 −60	>60 −70

Moist, ash-free basis (30°C and 96 percent relative humidity).

Total moisture content refers to freshly mined coal. For internal purposes, coals with a gross calorific value over 5,700 kcal/kg (maf), considered in the country of origin as brown coals but classified as hard coals for international purposes, may be classified under this system, to ascertain, in particular, their suitability for processing. When total moisture content is over 30 percent, gross calorific value is always below 5,700 kcal/kg

excess water, and equilibrated in a reduced-pressure vessel charged with a pulp of potassium sulfate crystals and water. The saturated solution of potassium sulfate at 30°C maintains a relative humidity of 96 to 97 percent in the vessel. After moisture equilibrium is reached, which usually is within 48 hours, the coal sample is covered, removed from the vessel, and weighed. The moisture content of the conditioned sample is then determined.

FREE-SWELLING INDEX TEST (CAKING)

The test for free-swelling index of coal, which is a measure of the coal's caking properties, was originally developed in Great Britain and is called there the crucible-swelling test. It is a standard method used in several countries, including the United States.

The test consists of heating a 1-gram sample of pulverized coal to 820°±5°C in a covered crucible and comparing the size and shape of the coke button obtained with the outlines of a set of standard profiles numbered in half units from 0 to 9. The number of the profile most closely corresponding to the cross section of the coke button is the free-swelling index or, in British terms, crucible-swelling number.

ROGA-INDEX TEST (CAKING)

The alternative method for determining caking properties is the Roga test, developed and used in Poland. The test is conducted by carbonizing a mixture of 1 gram of coal and 5 grams of a standard anthracite at 850°C for 15 minutes. The mechanical strength of the resulting coke button is measured by an abrasion test in a special rotating drum. At the end of the tumbling period, the residue is screened on a sieve with 1-mm round openings and the oversize weighed. This process is repeated twice. The index is calculated from the results of the screening test by the following formula.

$$\text{Roga index} = \frac{100}{3Q}\left(\frac{a + d}{2} + b + c\right)$$

(1)

where:

Q = weight of residue after carbonization,

a = weight of oversize before first screening,

b = weight of oversize after first screening,

c = weight of oversize after second screening, and

d = weight of oversize after third screening.

No information is available on the use of the Roga index for measuring caking properties of American coals in combustion processes. As there is an approximate correlation between the results of the free-swelling-index and Roga-index tests, the Roga index probably is about as significant as the free-swelling index for measuring caking properties.

AUDIBERT-ARNU DILATOMETER TEST (COKING)

Better known in Europe than in the United States, the Audibert-Arnu dilatometer test is used in studies of coking properties of coal.

A briquetted pencil of coal is carbonized in a vertical tube topped by a steel rod that slides in the bore of the tube. The pencil, which is formed in a die, is lightly tapered; its diameter averages 6½ mm, and its length is 60 mm. The maximum displacement of the rod measured on an external scale is reported as a percentage of the original length of the pencil. The dilatation is calculated as follows

$$\text{Dilatation, \%} = \frac{\text{Displacement of piston, mm} \times 100}{60}$$

(2)

GRAY-KING COKE-TYPE TEST

Developed in Great Britain, the Gray-King coke-type test was used at first as a bench-scale, low-temperature carbonization assay for determining yields of coke, gas, tar and liquor. The Coal Survey adopted the test for indicating coking properties. The method was then standardized by the National Coal Board for classifying coals of the United Kingdom.

The test is conducted by carbonizing a 20-gram sample of coal progressively to 600°C in a horizontal tube furnace. The carbonized residue is classified as to volume, coherence, fissuring, and hardness by comparing it with a series of residues. For coals that form powdery to hard coke residues that occupy the same volume as the original coal (standard coke), the type of residue is assigned letters ranging from A to G. For coals that swell to fill the cross section of the tube, electrode carbon is mixed with the coal to obtain a strong, hard coke of the same volume as the original coal-electrode carbon mixture. The coke type is indicated by the letter G with a subscript figure, that is, G_4, G_5, etc. The subscript shows number of parts of electrode carbon needed in the mixture with coal to give a G–type (standard) coke. Reference 2 gives the Gray-King scheme for examining and classifying coke types.

INTERNATIONAL SYSTEM APPLIED TO AMERICAN COALS

The American Society for Testing Materials system of classification of coals by rank was discussed in Chapter 2. The *ASTM Standard Specification of Coals by Rank* D-388 groups coals according to their degree of metamorphism or progressive alteration in the natural coalification series from lignite to anthracite.

The ASTM classification system is based on the parameters of fixed carbon or volatile matter and calorific value calculated on a mineral-matter-free basis. Higher-rank coals are classified according to fixed carbon or volatile matter on the dry basis, and the lower-rank coals according to calorific value on the moist or bed-moisture basis. Agglomerating and weathering indexes are used to differentiate between some adjacent groups.

COMPARISON OF INTERNATIONAL AND ASTM SYSTEMS

The ASTM system provides for classification of all ranks of coal while the international classification is based on two systems: one for the hard coals and the other mainly for brown coals and lignites. The borderline between the two international classifications occurs at 10,260 Btu/lb (5,700 kcal/kg or 23.86 MJ/kg) moist and ash-free and is nearly the midpoint of the subbituminous B group of the ASTM system. Therefore, some subbituminous B coals and all subbituminous A, bituminous, and anthracitic coals of the ASTM system are identified according to the international classification of hard coals by type. The other subbituminous B and all subbituminous C and lignitic coals are covered in the international classification of

Table XXXIX. Source, Analysis and Classification of Exchange Samples of Low-Rank Coal

Source of Sample	As received % Ash	% H₂O	Moisture- and ash-free % VM	% C	% H	% O	% N	% S	HHV Btu/lb	MJ/kg	Equilib. Moisture,[A] %	Classification ASTM[B]	IC No.[C]
Belgium													
Florennes	2.2	63.3	53.8	70.1	5.0	23.5	0.7	0.7	11,910	27.7	39.8	LigB	1510
Canada													
Alberta	7.3	24.2	39.2	76.6	5.5	15.8	1.6	0.5	13,150	30.6	24.4	Subb	1100
Czechoslovakia													
Northern Bohemia	2.7	20.2	49.0	77.6	5.8	14.7	1.0	0.9	13,890	32.3	20.9	Suba	800
	6.4	31.2	50.5	76.0	6.0	15.7	1.1	1.2	13,560	31.5	30.7	Subc	1220
Central Bohemia	5.9	21.1	38.1	79.5	5.0	13.1	1.2	1.2	13,770	32.0	20.4	Subb	900
	15.9	23.2	43.6	77.1	5.2	11.1	1.5	5.1	13,640	31.7	25.9	Subb	1110
Southern Bohemia	7.4	44.6	56.5	70.2	5.4	19.5	0.9	4.0	12,240	28.5	43.5	LigA	1310
Western Bohemia	6.0	39.7	51.7	76.6	6.1	15.2	1.2	0.9	13,680	31.8	37.0	LigA	1330
Slovakia	12.2	36.1	51.3	69.6	4.9	19.5	1.5	4.5	11,870	27.6	39.0	LigA	1300
Federal Republic of Germany													
Rhine Region	3.3	62.2	55.3	69.1	4.9	24.1	0.9	1.0	11,580	26.9	48.4	LigB	1510
Bavaria, Peissenberg	11.9	9.7	52.8	72.8	5.4	12.4	1.6	7.8	13,200	30.7	12.0	Suba	800
Greece													
Athens Area, Peristeri	6.5	22.4	46.9	71.8	4.7	19.8	1.9	1.8	12,140	28.2	27.4	Subc	1100
Island of Euboea, Aliveri	11.3	33.3	56.1	68.0	5.2	23.9	0.9	2.0	11,600	27.0	36.8	LigA	1210
West Macedonia, Ptolemais	12.2	59.0	57.9	65.4	4.3	27.3	1.9	1.1	10,340	24.0	50.0	LigB	1500
Italy													
Lucania, Mercure	10.1	58.8	58.6	65.4	5.2	25.3	1.8	2.3	11,020	25.6	51.7	LigB	1500
Toscana, Pietrafitta	9.9	60.8	57.3	70.5	4.8	19.9	1.9	2.9	11,840	27.5	51.7	LigB	1500
Toscana, Valdarno	5.3	51.9	56.8	66.5	5.2	26.3	1.0	1.0	11,350	26.4	47.2	LigB	1420
Umbria, Spoleto	7.8	31.8	60.4	64.8	5.3	27.3	1.1	1.5	11,140	25.9	34.1	LigA	1210
Federation of Maylaya													
Selangor, Batu Arang	7.5	17.7	48.7	77.1	5.8	15.1	1.6	0.4	13,840	32.2	19.1	Suba	800
Poland	7.3	53.9	60.8	71.4	5.8	20.2	0.6	2.0	12,510	29.1	42.2	LigB	1420
	6.7	17.6	44.0	77.7	5.1	14.3	0.9	2.0	13,540	31.5	21.0	Suba	800
U.S.S.R.													
Chelyabinsk Basin	9.9	17.8	43.6	76.2	5.2	16.2	1.9	0.5	12,910	30.0	18.9	Subb	900
Rhiczechinsk	6.9	37.0	43.7	72.2	4.3	22.1	1.1	0.3	11,910	27.7	34.8	LigA	1200
Borneo-Sarawak													
Upper Rajang Valley	1.3	23.3	48.1	72.4	4.9	21.2	1.4	0.1	12,390	28.8	22.9	Subc	1110
East Germany													
Niederlausitz	2.5	59.8	55.6	68.1	4.7	25.8	0.7	0.7	11,720	27.3	44.7	LigB	1510
Bautzen	3.9	63.4	57.6	70.1	5.3	21.9	0.7	2.0	12,100	28.1	43.3	LigB	1510
Oberlausitz	3.2	58.3	54.4	67.7	5.2	26.0	0.6	0.5	12,020	28.0	47.2	LigB	1510

Table XXXIX. Source, Analysis and Classification
of Exchange Samples of Low-Rank Coal — *Continued*

Source of Sample	As received			Moisture- and ash-free						HHV		Equilib. Moisture,[A]	Classification	
	% Ash	% H₂O	% VM	% C	% H	% O	% N	% S		Btu/lb	MJ/kg	%	ASTM[B]	IC No.[C]
Aschersleben	5.0	44.5	72.2	76.4	7.9	12.0	0.4	3.3		14,680	34.1	37.3	LigA	1340
Bitterfeld	5.8	54.6	55.6	71.3	5.1	18.0	0.6	5.0		12,560	29.2	49.3	LigB	1410
Halle	6.0	54.6	58.9	71.6	5.6	17.2	0.6	5.0		12,770	29.7	50.2	LigB	1420
Geiseltal	4.3	55.0	58.0	71.0	5.7	16.5	0.8	6.0		12,920	30.0	48.5	LigB	1420
Borna	4.5	55.1	60.3	72.5	5.9	18.1	0.7	2.8		13,000	30.2	44.2	LigB	1420
United Kingdom	4.0	17.6	43.6	77.6	5.1	13.8	1.4	2.1		13,610	31.7	17.8	Suba	800
United States														
Colorado, Weld County	4.8	25.2	40.8	78.6	5.1	14.1	1.7	0.5		13,630	31.7	24.8	Subb	1110
Montana, Musselshell Co.	7.0	13.9	39.6	80.9	5.1	12.2	1.3	0.5		14,110	32.8	14.1	Suba	800
North Dakota, Burke Co.	4.2	37.2	43.4	74.1	4.7	19.3	1.2	0.7		12,470	29.0	37.5	LigA	1200
North Dakota, Mercer Co.	4.1	38.1	45.3	72.7	4.9	20.8	0.9	0.7		12,330	28.7	37.7	LigA	1200
Texas, Milam Co.	9.4	36.0	49.9	74.7	5.4	16.4	1.5	2.0		12,980	30.2	37.6	LigA	1210
Washington, Lewis Co.	7.1	28.5	50.7	74.6	5.4	18.0	1.3	0.7		12,800	29.8	29.6	Subc	1210
Wyoming, Campbell Co.	5.0	28.2	49.0	74.0	5.6	18.6	0.9	0.9		12,970	30.2	30.8	Subc	1110
Wyoming, Sheridan Co.	3.6	25.9	42.8	75.9	5.1	17.0	1.6	0.4		13,100	30.5	25.3	Subb	1110
Yugoslavia														
Bosnia, Banovici	10.4	17.9	45.6	75.6	5.4	14.7	2.3	2.0		13,310	31.0	19.2	Subb	900
Bosnia, Breza	8.8	17.2	46.9	75.3	5.2	13.6	1.9	4.0		13,330	31.0	18.3	Subb	900
Bosnia, Kakanj	12.5	6.1	49.0	77.2	5.4	11.4	2.3	3.7		13,720	31.9	7.3	Suba	800
Bosnia, Kreka	3.3	39.8	52.0	69.7	5.2	23.7	0.9	0.5		12,110	28.2	37.2	LigA	1310
Serbia, Senjski	10.0	15.6	54.3	71.7	5.6	19.5	1.4	1.8		13,010	30.3	17.1	Subb	900
Slovenia, Trbovlje	7.3	24.9	48.4	71.0	5.0	18.4	1.3	4.3		12,520	29.1	25.9	Subc	1110

[A]—Equilibrium moisture, %, is on an ash-free basis
[B]—Abbreviations are listed in Table II
[C]—IC No. is the International Code Number

coals with a gross calorific value below 5,700 kcal/kg.

To divide lower rank coals into classes, the international system uses the total moisture parameter while the ASTM uses the calorific value. Fig. 10 shows that a good correlation exists between total moisture and calorific value of low-rank coals. The figure is based on analyses of exchange samples of coal given in Table XXXIX.

Fig. 11 compares the class numbers and group boundaries of the international system for hard coals with those of the ASTM classification. As the figure shows, the group boundaries in the two schemes are quite similar; thus, class numbers in the international system are nearly equivalent to group names in the ASTM classification. For example,

Class number in international system	Group name in ASTM system
0	Meta-anthracite
1	Anthracite
2	Semianthracite
3	Low-volatile bituminous coal

Fig. 10 **Relationship of Total Moisture and Calorific Value**

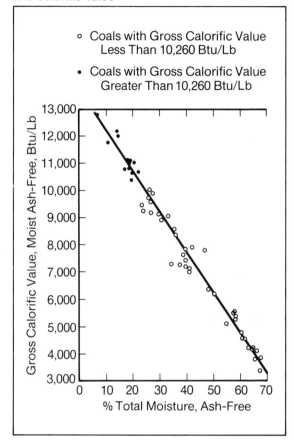

4, 5	Medium-volatile bituminous coal
6	High-volatile A bituminous coal
7	High-volatile B bituminous coal
8	High-volatile C bituminous coal and subbituminous A coal
9	Subbitminous B coal

The international classification system for hard coals differs from the ASTM classification in that parameters of caking and coking properties are introduced to indicate how the coal can be used in combustion and carbonization processes. This concept is followed in several European national systems of classification. While the ASTM classification of coal was being developed, the feasibility of classifying coals according to use was studied. It was decided that this was impractical because many coals can be used for various purposes and the type of equipment in which the coal is used probably is as significant as the kind of coal. On the other hand, the caking and coking tests give general information on the characteristics of coals so they should prove of value in considering a coal for a specific use.

INTERNATIONAL CLASSIFICATION OF AMERICAN BITUMINOUS COALS

As little information is available on the coking properties of American coals by the Gray-

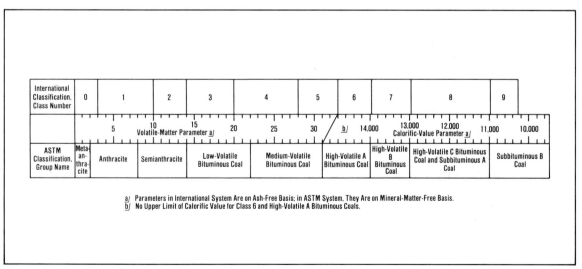

Fig. 11 **Comparison of class numbers and boundary lines of International System for Hard Coals with group names and boundary lines of ASTM System**

King coke-type test or the Audibert-Arnu dilatometer test, tests were made on samples of bituminous coal of varous ranks from nearly every coal-producing state. About 80 coals were tested.[2] They were selected to obtain good geographic representation of seams that contain large reserves, are being mined in quantity, or are entering the export market. The Audibert-Arnu dilatometer test was selected for the coking test. Of the 62 code numbers shown in Table XXXVII, American coals occur in 26.

Table IV in the front of this appendix shows the analytical data and the classification of each coal by the ASTM and international systems. Symbols used in the table for the rank of coal according to the ASTM system are:

Lvb = low-volatile bituminous,
Mvb = medium-volatile bituminous,
Hvab = high-volatile A bituminous,
Hvbb = high-volatile B bituminous,
Hvcb = high-volatile C bituminous.

Based on this data, American bituminous coals are classified in the international system for hard coals as:

Class 0. Although no code number is indicated in the system for coal of this class, coals classified in the U.S. as meta-anthracite would have a code number of 000, as these coals are noncaking and noncoking. The only known deposit of meta-anthracites is in Rhode Island.

Class 1. This class includes most of the anthracites found in the United States, of which Pennsylvania has the most abundant reserves. It includes most of the Sullivan County (PA) coals classified as semianthracites in the ASTM system. The code numbers of the coals are 100A and 100B.

Class 2. The coals included in class 2 are mainly the semianthracites of Arkansas and Virginia. As they are noncaking and noncoking, their code number is 200.

Class 3. This class includes most of the coals classified in the ASTM system as low-volatile bituminous. In general, these coals are strongly coking; if coked alone their coke would be well fused, blocky, and fine-grained, with few fissures. However, they cannot be carbonized alone in commercial slot-type ovens because they expand excessively. In American practice, 10 to 30 percent of low-volatile bituminous coal is usually blended with high-volatile coal to produce blast-furnace coke. The code numbers of most of the low-volatile bituminous coals for which data are available are 333 and 334; coals near the borderline of the medium-volatile group are coded 433 and 434.

Classes 4 and 5. These two classes include all coals classified in the ASTM system as medium-volatile bituminous. If coked alone they form strong, blocky cokes. Their coking properties generally are between those of the low-volatile and the better grades of high-volatile bituminous coals. All coals of these classes that were tested have code numbers of either 435 or 535.

Class 6. This class includes most of the high-volatile A bituminous coals. Many of these coals can be carbonized without blending to produce well-fused, medium- to coarse-grained, though somewhat fingery coke. Usually they are blended with 10 to 30 percent of low-volatile bituminous coal to improve the yield, size, structure, and strength of the coke. Code numbers of coals tested in this class are 635, 634, 633, 623, and 622.

Class 7. This class includes coals classified in the ASTM system as high-volatile B bituminous coals. If carbonized alone they usually produce small, fingery, highly fissured coke with low shatter and tumbler indexes. The relatively poor coke structure is typical of cokes made from high-oxygen coals. If heated rapidly at high oven temperatures, high-oxygen coals yield better coke. In American coking practice, high-volatile B bituminous coals are always blended with more strongly coking coals. The high-volatile B bituminous coals that were tested have code numbers as follows: 734, 733, 723, 721, 711, and 823.

Class 8. This class includes high-volatile C bituminous coals and subbituminous A coals. Coals in this class range from noncoking to fair coking. The noncoking coals include all the subbituminous coals and some of the high-volatile C bituminous coals that are nonslacking on exposure to the weather. Their code number is 800. The other high-volatile C bituminous coals range from virtually noncoking to fair coking. Their cokes range from weak and pebbly to small, fingery, and highly fissured. No American coals in class 8 are coked commercially at present, even in blends with more strongly coking coals. The code numbers of the coals in class 8 that show some caking and coking properties are 823, 821, and 811.

Class 9. This class includes subbituminous B coals with a gross calorific value of more than 10,260 Btu on the moist, ash-free basis. The code number of these noncoking coals is 900.

CLASSIFICATION
OF AMERICAN LOW-RANK COALS

To classify American low-rank coals by the international system would require information on total-moisture content and yield of tar. Although a standard method for determining yield of low-temperature tar has not been adopted internationally, it probably will be based on the Fischer-Schrader method[4] used in many countries. Such a method is used in the Pittsburgh laboratory of the U.S. Bureau of Mines, and a somewhat modified procedure in its Denver and Grand Forks laboratories.[5] Data on yields of tar from typical American coals by the Fischer-Schrader[6] and modified method[7,8] have been published. Although precise information is not available on correlating the results by the two methods, a statistical study of the relation of the chemical analysis of the coals with tar yields indicates that the yields are similar enough to be used in a survey for applying the international classification system to American coals.

Table XL summarizes the total moisture and tar yields for 73 low-rank American coals having calorific values of less than 10,260 Btu/lb moist and ash free. The data were taken from the reports listed in references 6 and 7, unpublished data, and supplemental information obtained from American exchange samples tested in developing the international classification system. Included in the table are the international code numbers of the coals based on the total moisture and the tar yields.

The subbituminous B coals for which data on both moisture and tar are available have a moisture content ranging from 22 to 27 percent. The class number therefore is 11. The tar yield is about 7 to 11 percent, which places the coals in groups 00 or 10. The coals with less than 10-percent tar yield have a code number of 1100; those with 10 percent or more are numbered 1110.

For the subbituminous C coals, data were available on several samples from Wyoming and one from Washington. Coals of this rank also occur in Colorado, Montana, and Oregon. Table XL shows a moisture range of about 27 to 34 percent for the samples tested. The coals are placed in classes 11 or 12 depending on whether the moisture content is less or more than 30 percent.

Tar yield ranges from 6 to 15 percent, which groups the coals into 00 and 10. The table shows that code numbers for the subbituminous coals include 1100, 1110, 1200, and 1210.

American lignites have an ash-free moisture content that ranges from about 35 to 45 percent. Their class number is 12 or 13, depending on whether the moisture is less or more than 40 percent. Lignites of the Fort Union formation in Montana, North Dakota, and South Dakota yield 4 to 9 percent tar, placing them in group 00; code numbers are 1200 and 1300.

Tar yields of the Texas lignites range from 11 to 15 percent; their code numbers would be either 1210 or 1310, depending on total moisture content.

The Arkansas lignites gave a tar yield of about 20 percent; their code numbers are either 1320 or 1330, depending on whether the tar yield is less or more than 20 percent. Because some Arkansas lignites have a total moisture content of less than 40 percent, these coals will have a code number of 1220 or 1230 if their yields of tar are of the same order as for the samples tested. High tar yields from Arkansas lignites probably are due to their relatively large amount of wax and resin.[9]

Table XL. International Code Numbers of American Subbituminous B, C Coals and Lignites

State	Number of samples	Range of total moisture, ash-free %	Range of tar yields, dry, ash-free %	Code No.
		Subbituminous B		
Colorado	2	22.7–25.2	7.4–8.8	1100
"	1	26.5	11.4	1110
Montana	1	23.7	6.6	1100
Utah	1	21.7	11.2	1110
Wyoming	2	23.5–26.3	7.5–7.9	1100
"	2	23.5–26.9	10.2	1110
		Subbituminous C		
Washington	1	30.7	14.8	1210
Wyoming	3	27.4–29.3	6.9–9.0	1100
"	1	29.7	12.2	1110
"	2	30.4–34.2	6.3–7.5	1200
"	1	32.4	12.0	1210
		Lignite		
Arkansas	1	41.0	19.8	1320
"	1	41.2	20.5	1330
Montana	1	39.9	6.6	1200
"	5	40.0–42.3	5.6–7.2	1300
North Dakota	12	36.0–39.9	4.3–8.7	1200
"	25	40.0–47.7	4.0–8.4	1300
South Dakota	1	34.4	3.5	1200
"	1	43.6	4.2	1300
Texas	3	37.6–39.7	11.2–12.2	1210
"	5	40.9–45.7	12.0–14.8	1310
Washington	1	40.6	9.8	1300

WORLD CLASSIFICATION OF LOW-RANK COALS

Early in its study the Classification Working Party found little available information regarding the different types of brown coals and lignites occurring in the various countries. Therefore, an extensive exchange of samples was arranged by the laboratories cooperating in the international classification work. According to the plan of the Classification Working Party, the coals selected were to be freshly mined and representative of the various types of brown coals and lignites in each country. Also, samples of transition coals were requested that would be close to the borderline of the brown coal/lignite class.

Table XXXIX shows the source of the coals, some of the analytical data obtained by the Bureau of Mines, and classificaton of the coals according to the ASTM and International systems. The proximate and ultimate analyses, calorific value, and moisture-holding capacity (equilibrium moisture) were determined by ASTM methods, except that total moisture and the moisture in the air-dried samples were determined by either xylene or toluene distillation as requested by the Working Party.

Total moisture is used rather than moisture-holding capacity (equilibrium moisture) specified in the classification of hard coals. For

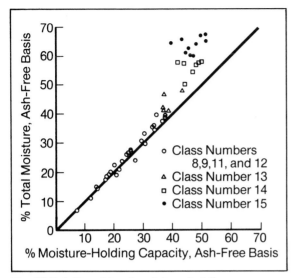

Fig. 12 **Relationship of moisture-holding capacity and total moisture**

practical purposes, moisture-holding capacity is equivalent to natural bed moisture for all ranks of American coals including lignite.[10] However, total moisture and bed moisture are not equivalent for certain European brown coals of higher total moisture content than American lignites. Fig. 12 compares the moisture-holding capacity with total moisture for the exchange samples. The figure shows a linear relationship between moisture-holding capacity and total moisture for coals in the International system with class number 8 to 12 and possibly 13; that is, coals having as much as 40 percent total moisture. For classes 14 and 15, the relationship is poor, with moisture-holding capacity averaging 10 to 15 percentage points lower than total moisture for the coal samples examined.

REFERENCES

[1] United Nations Economic Commission for Europe, *International Classification of Hard Coals by Type.* Document No. E/ECE/247, E/ECE/COAL/110. Publication sales no. 1956 II E.4. New York: Columbia University Press, International Documents Service, 1956.

[2] W.H. Ode and W.H. Frederic, "The International Systems of Hard-Coal Classification and Their Application to American Coals," *U. S. Bureau of Mines Report of Investigations 5435.* Washington: U. S. Government Printing Office, 1958.

[3] W.H. Ode and F.H. Gibson, "International System for Classifying Brown Coals and Lignites and Its Application to American Coals," *U. S. Bureau of Mines Report of Investigations 5695.* Washington: U. S. Government Printing Office, 1960.

[4] Franz Fischer and Hans Schrader, "Crude-Tar Determination with an Aluminum Distillating Apparatus," *Zeitschrift Fuer Angewandte Chemie,* 33 (1): 172–175, 1920.

[5] John B. Goodman, et. al., "Low-Temperature Carbonization Assay of Coal in a Precision Laboratory Apparatus," *U. S. Bureau of Mines Bulletin 530.* Washington: U. S. Government Printing Office, 1953.

[6] W.A. Serlvig and W.H. Ode, "Low-Temperature Carbonization Assays of North American Coals," *U. S. Bureau of Mines Bulletin 571.* Washington: U. S. Government Printing Office, 1957.

[7] Manuel Gomez and J.B. Goodman, "Distillation Assays of Missouri River Basin Coals," *U. S. Bureau of Mines Report of Investigations 5009.* Washington: U. S. Government Printing Office, 1953.

[8] J.J. Hoeppner, et. al., "Carbonication Characteristics of Some North-Central United States Lignites," *U. S. Bureau of Mines Report of Investigations 5260.* Washington: U. S. Government Printing Office, 1956.

[9] W.A. Selvig, et. al., "American Lignites: Geological Occurrence Petrograpic Composition, and Extractable Waxes," *U. S. Bureau of Mines Bulletin 482.* Washington: U. S. Government Printing Office, 1950.

[10] W.A. Selvig and W.H. Ode, "Determination of Moisture-Holding Capacity (Bed Moisture) of Coal for Classification by Rank, *U. S. Bureau of Mines Report of Investigations 4968.* Washington: U. S. Gov. Printing Office, 1953.

BIBLIOGRAPHY

V.F. Parry, "Production, Classification, and Utilization of Western United States Coals," *Economic Geology,* 45: 515–532, 1950.

W.A. Selvig and F.H. Gibson, "Analyses of Ash From United States Coals," *U. S. Bureau of Mines Bulletin 567.* Washington: U. S. Government Printing Office, 1956.

R.F. Abernethy and E.M. Cochrane, "Free-Swelling and Grindability Indexes of United States Coals," *U. S. Bureau of Mines Information Circular 8025.* Washington: U. S. Government Printing Office, 1961.

R.F. Abernethy and E.M. Cochrane, "Fusibility of Ash of United States Coals," *U. S. Bureau of Mines Information Circular 7923.* Washington: U. S. Gov. Printing Office, 1960.

"Analyses of Tipple and Delivered Samples of Coal;" Reports of Investigations of the Bureau of Mines, U. S. Dept of the Interior; comprise analytical data showing composition and quality of coal samples collected by the Bureau for nearly every year since 1948. U. S. Government Printing Office, Washington, D.C.

Appendix B. An Introduction to Furnace Analysis

As indicated in the discussion on combustion processes in laboratory and power-plant furnaces in Chapter 4, a surprising amount of contradiction exists between the university and industrial approach to furnace analysis. In this regard, the Rosin equation, the Semenov thermal-explosion jump, and the Vulis-Essenhigh criteria are little known to industrial furnace designers, largely because these criteria are basically too qualitative for direct design application. But, in terms of establishing an appreciation and understanding of combustion, the discussion which follows is of considerable educational value in this area of steam-generator technology.

THE ROSIN EQUATION

The basis of this section is the R. H. Essenhigh discussion[1] of the Rosin combustion-intensity equation.[2] Fig. 1 gives the classical view of an end-fired combustion chamber. To analyze the system shown in Fig. 1, Rosin assumed that a plug-flow chamber as shown in Fig. 2 could satisfactorily replace the combustion chamber.

The volume flow rate of air supply at temperature T_o is accordingly

$$V_a = \frac{FW_a}{\rho_a}\left(1 + \frac{E\%}{100}\right) ft^3/hr \tag{1}$$

Rosin then assumed that volume of fuel, if coal or oil, could be neglected in contrast with the air volume and that the hot volume of combustion products could be written with sufficient accuracy as

$$V_{af} = \frac{FW_a}{\rho_a}\left(1 + \frac{E\%}{100}\right)\frac{T_f}{T_o} ft^3/hr \tag{2}$$

where T_f is the mean combustion chamber gas temperature. Because there is no reason to restrict the combustion chamber to operation at 1 atmosphere absolute, we further modify the flow-rate equation by writing Eq. 2 as

$$\dot{V}_G = \frac{FW_a}{P\rho_a}\left(1 + \frac{E\%}{100}\right)\frac{T_f}{T_o} ft^3/hr\text{-atm.} \tag{3}$$

Some residence time, τ_r, is required to traverse the combustion chamber volume, V_c. Assuming

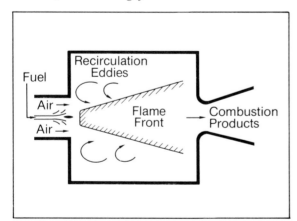

Fig. 1 Classical view of an end-fired combustion chamber

Fig. 2 Rosin's model for end-fired combustion chamber

that the gas volume entering and leaving during time τ_r must equal V_c, we write

$$V_c = \dot{V}_G\,\tau_r \text{ ft}^3/\text{atm.}$$

(4)

Unless the combustion chamber resembles the classic Perfectly Stirred Reactor (PSR), the assumption is rather questionable.

It is obvious that for the flame to be contained within the combustion chamber, the burning time should not exceed the residence time, or, $\tau_b \leq \tau_r$. Rosin now assumed that a combustion chamber would ideally be designed such that $\tau_b = \tau_r$. In which case we can write

$$V_c = \frac{FW_a}{P\rho_a}\left(1 + \frac{E\%}{100}\right)\frac{T_f}{T_o}\,\tau_b$$

(5)

It follows that the average release intensity of combustion is then defined by

---

**Definition of Terms
in the Rosin Equation Discussion**

F = firing rate, lb fuel/hr

B = heat of combustion, Btu/lb

τ_r = mean residence time of fuel, air, and combustion products in combustion chamber, s or hr as appropriate

τ_b = burning time of fuel to consumption, s or hr as appropriate

A_c = combustion chamber cross-sectional area, ft^2

V_c = $L_c A_c$ = combustion chamber volume, ft^3

ρ_a = air density, lb/ft^3 at temperature T_o and at 1 atmosphere (atm.)

$E\%$ = excess air, %

P = furnace pressure, atm. absolute

T_o = ambient air temperature, °R

T_f = mean flame temperature, °R

$\dot{V}_a$ = air volume flow rate, ft^3/hr

L_c = combustion chamber length, ft

$$I = \frac{FB}{V_c P} \text{ Btu/ft}^3\text{-hr}$$

(6)

where, for the definition to be physically meaningful, Eq. 6 has the implied restriction that the flame volume must be approximately equal to the furnace volume. Substituting in Eq. 6 for V_c, we obtain the Rosin Combustion Intensity Equation.

$$I = \frac{B\rho_a T_o}{W_a\left(1 + \dfrac{E\%}{100}\right)T_f\,\tau_b}\quad \frac{\text{Btu}}{\text{ft}^3\text{-hr}}$$

(7)

According to Essenhigh, $B\rho_a/W_a \approx 100$ Btu/ft^3 for all common fuels which gives the modified Rosin form

$$I = \frac{100}{\left(1 + \dfrac{E\%}{100}\right)\dfrac{T_f}{T_o}\,\tau_b}\quad \frac{\text{Btu}}{\text{ft}^3\text{-hr}}$$

(8)

Eqs. 7 and 8 exhibit the undesirable property of decreasing combustion intensity with increasing flame temperature. This implies that τ_b is approximately constant. In practice, however, τ_b is proportional to a negative power of T_f. In line with this, Essenhigh proposes that the burning times be empirically expressed

$$\tau_b = \frac{1}{\alpha\,(T_f/T_o)^n}$$

(9)

where α has dimensions of hr.$^{-1}$

Substituting in Eq. 8 for τ_b gives

$$I = \frac{100\,\alpha\,(T_f/T_o)^{n-1}}{\left(1 + \dfrac{E\%}{100}\right)}\quad \frac{\text{Btu}}{\text{ft}^3\text{-hr}}$$

(10)

Because the intensity is known to increase with flame temperature, it follows that Eq. 10 demands that n ≥ 1. The lower limit value on n is clearly 1. We now rewrite Eq. 9 in the form

$$\frac{T_f}{T_o} = \alpha^{-1/n} \tau_b^{-1/n}$$

(10A)

and substituting into Eq. 8 yields

$$I = \frac{100\,\alpha^{1/n}}{\left(1 + \frac{E\%}{100}\right)\tau_b^{1-1/n}}$$

(11)

For E% small and n ~ 100 or more (which physically does not seem very probable), we get the gross approximation

$$I = 100/\tau_b$$

(11A)

which is an upper limit value. For E% small or stoichiometric and n → 1, we get

$$I \cong 100\,\alpha$$

(11B)

which is a lower-limit value.

For oil, according to M. W. Thring[3], the droplet burning time can be expressed as

$$\tau_b = E_f K\, d_o^2$$

(12)

where:

E_f = a factor related to excess air and believed to be in the range 1 to 2

K = a burning constant, ~ 100 centimeter gram second

d_o = initial oil drop diameter, cm

For realistic furnaces T_f/T_o is ~ 5 and, for n→1, Eq. 9 gives us

$$\alpha \cong \frac{1}{5\tau_b}$$

(12A)

assuming $E_f \cong 2$, we get

$$\alpha \simeq \frac{1}{10\,K\,d_o^2}$$

(12B)

By combining relations 11A through 12B, Essenhigh arrives at the values

$$I_{upper} \simeq 3.6 \times 10^3/d_o^2 \quad Btu/ft^3\text{-}hr$$
$$I_{lower} \simeq 3.6 \times 10^2/d_o^2 \quad Btu/ft^3\text{-}hr$$

Taking $d_o = 10^{-2}$ cm as an upper-limit value for oil-droplet size, we get

$$I_{lower} = 3.6 \times 10^6 \quad Btu/ft^3\text{-}hr$$

This is an impossible condition in reality.

In tangentially fired power-plant furnaces (volume-distributed turbulent diffusion flames), the nominal flame intensity in normal operation is on the order of 10^5 Btu/ft³-hr.

For coal, Essenhigh[4] proposes the burning time relation

$$\tau_b = E_{coal} K_{coal}\, d_o$$
$$d_o \simeq 100\,\mu\ (upper\ limit)$$

K_{coal} = unknown value, but thought to be ~ 100 as an upper limit

E_{coal} = another unknown value, but probably greater than one.

Taking n = 1 and assuming $\tau_b \simeq 2$ s, we obtain from Eq. 9 an alpha value of about 0.1 s⁻¹; such a value implies a release intensity on the order of 10^5 Btu/ft³-hr. Actually, in a C-E furnace, the mean pulverized-coal particle size is about 50 μ and τ_b<1 second. Furthermore, in tangentially fired C-E furnaces, the release intensities for oil, coal, or gas firing are all about on a par; that is to say, we are not talking about multiple orders of magnitude differences. Fig. 3, although nominally for oil, is representative of the operating intensities encountered in tangentially fired utility units in the 500-MW range.

We now have arrived at some expressions for combustion intensity I, which are useful only if we can relate them to some design characteristics such as desired combustor performance. So we define:

NHI = net heat input, Btu/hr

Q_T = heat transferred to furnace walls, Btu/hr

q = average heat transfer rate to furnace walls, Btu/hr-ft²

W_G = lbs combustion products generated in furnace = lbs Fuel × lbs Air/lbs Fuel + lbs Fuel = $F W_a + F = F(1 + W_a)$

C_P = mean specific heat of combustion products, Btu/lb-°F

Q_E = heat leaving through furnace exit, Btu/hr.

It follows that

$$NHI - Q_T = Q_E$$

$$1 - \frac{Q_T}{NHI} = \frac{Q_E}{NHI} = \frac{Q_E/W_G C_P}{NHI/W_G C_P} = \frac{T_E}{T_t}$$

T_E = exit temperature, °F

T_t = theoretical (adiabatic) temperature, °F

A = furnace wall area, ft²

I = combustion intensity, Btu/ft³-hr.

Then

$$T_E = T_t \left[1 - \frac{qA}{IV_c} \right]$$

(13)

Eq. 13 is, of course, strictly subject to the Rosin condition (original assumption) that all or nearly all of the furnace be "flame filled." Writing Eq. 13 as

$$\frac{T_E}{T_t} = \theta = \left(1 - \frac{qA}{IV_c} \right)$$

(13A)

it is clear that

$$0 \leq \frac{qA}{IV_c} \leq 1.0$$

(13B)

Using q, obtained from either experience or calculation and Rosin's combustion intensity I, a furnace may be sized to the required T_E (Fig. 4).

THE SEMENOV JUMP

In the preceding section, the Rosin analysis assumed the vessel-contained chemical species to be a steadily reacting system. This is not always the case, as physical explosions and implosions do occur, even when they are not desired. This can be restated to be an occasional consequence from an inequality in the rate of heat loss versus the rate of heat production. An early researcher in combustion, Semenov[5] proposed a qualitative model for

Fig. 3 Nominal flame release intensity at normal power plant operation (over effective flame volume not furnace volume)

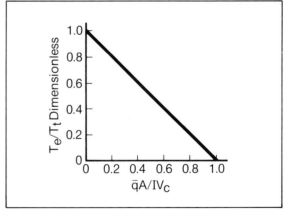

Fig. 4 $T_{furnace\ exit}$ **vs furnace size and loading (IV_c) in accordance with Rosin's analysis**

heat-rate inequality which, has come to be called the Semenov Thermal Jump and, also, the Semenov Temperature Jump. This should not be visualized as necessarily a TNT-like detonation.

In discussing the Semenov jump, preference is given to the treatment by Bradley[6] and, in the main, Bradley's notation is adopted. We assume the vessel walls to be at temperature T_w and the gas (combustion or reaction products) to be at constant temperature T.

The rate of heat loss is then written as

$$\varphi- = \kappa \, S/V \, (T - T_w) \quad \text{Btu/ft}^2\text{-hr} \tag{14A}$$

The rate of heat production is

$$\dot{\varphi} = Q \, F(n) \, Vk_o \, e^{-E/RT} \quad \text{Btu/hr} \tag{15}$$

Dividing by S to match units in Eqs. 14A and 15, we get

$$\varphi+ = Q \, f(n) \frac{Vk_o}{S} e^{-E/RT} \quad \text{Btu/ft}^2\text{-hr}$$

$$= Q \, f(n) \, A \, e^{-E/RT} \quad \text{Btu/ft}^2\text{-hr} \tag{14B}$$

For constant and a specified geometry, Eq. 14A is a single straight line. The term Q f(n) can be thought of, perhaps, as a firing density and Eq. 14B therefore generates a series of curves which may or may not intersect with 14A. Whether it intersects has physical significance, which will be discussed below. Fig. 5 qualitatively illustrates Eqs. 14A and 14B.

Curve 1 clearly indicates an explosive condition, as the heat generation term, φ_+, is always greater than the heat removal term, φ_-. Curve 3 shows two points of intersection. Between the two points, the heat removal term φ_- is always greater than the heat generation term, φ_+, which therefore implies that the intersection, T_{st}, is a point where a stable reaction rate exists.

This "stable point" should not be interpreted to be as necessarily indicating a self-supporting combustion regime. The second intersection point, T_{ign}, indicates an ignition condition which subsequently permits auto-acceleration to explosion or to stable combustion. When we merge the points T_{st} and T_{ign}, we get the critical tangency condition shown in curve 2 where the point, T_c, permits the reaction to proceed without further addition of heat and therefore defines a condition of self-ignition. Increasing the vessel wall temperature, T_w, to a higher value, T_w, has the effect of shifting the φ_+ curves into the thermal-explosion regime; a decrease in T_w has a quenching effect.

Returning to curve 2, we observe that the point T_c also permits us to equate derivatives in addition to equating φ_- and φ_+, or,

---

**Definition of Terms Used
in The Semenov Jump Discussion**

A	= kinetic rate constant = $\dfrac{Vk_o}{S}$ ft/hr
k_o	= kinetic rate constant, hr^{-1}
S	= vessel inside surface area, ft^2
V	= vessel volume, ft^3
κ	= heat transfer coefficient, Btu/hr-ft-°F
T	= gas temperature, °F
T_w	= inside surface temperature, °F or °K as required
$f(n)_c$	= concentration function of reactants, mol/ft^3
$\varphi-$	= heat flux to inside wall area, Btu/ft²-hr
Q	= heat of reaction, Btu Released/mol product
$\varphi+$	= heat generation term, Btu/ft²-hr
T_{st}	= steady-state temperature, °F
T_{ign}	= ignition temperature, °F
$e^{-E/RT}$	= the Arrhenius relation
$\dot{\varphi}$	= total rate of heat production, Btu/hr
T_c	= temperature at critical condition, °F
R	= gas constant, 1.986 kcal/°K-kg mol
n_α	= total mols of component α in volume V

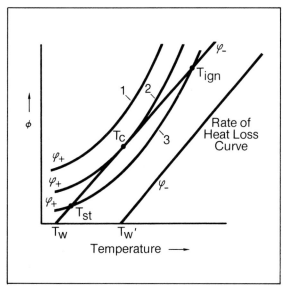

Fig. 5 **Semenov's criterion: rate of heat loss vs rate of heat production**

$$\varphi_-/_{T_c} = \varphi_+/_{T_c}$$
$$\partial\varphi_-/\partial T_c = \frac{\partial\varphi_+}{\partial T_c}$$

(16A)

Imposing conditions Eq. 16A, we write

$$\frac{\kappa S}{V}(T_c - T_w) = Q\, f(n)\, A\, e^{-E/RT_c}$$

(16B)

$$\frac{\kappa S}{V} = Q\, f(n)\, A\, \frac{E}{RT_c^2}\, e^{-E/RT_c}$$

(16C)

Rearranging Eqs. 16B and 16C gives us

$$(T_c - T_w) = \frac{RT_c^2}{E}$$

(17A)

or

$$T_c^2 - \frac{E}{R}T_c + \frac{E}{R}T_w = 0$$

(17B)

which has the solution

$$T_c = \frac{E}{2R} \pm \frac{1}{2}\sqrt{\frac{E}{R}\left(\frac{E}{R} - 4\,T_w\right)}$$

(18)

Because imaginary components are not acceptable, Eq. 18 requires that $E/R \geqslant 4\,T_w$. Taking E to be about 20 kcal/g-mol, this gives an upper limit on T_w of about 2500°K.

In the case where $E/R = 4\,T_w$, we would get $T_c = E/2R \simeq 5000°K$. Imposing the limit condition, $T_w = 0$, we get $T_c = E/2R \pm E/2R$ with the consequence that $T_c = 10{,}000$ °K or 0°K. This tells us that the analysis, per se, is not unreasonable; but in realistic furnace-design terms, the results are preposterous. Neither does it resolve the dilemma whether we should reject the positive or the negative component of Eq. 18. One sidesteps the dilemma of Eq. 17A as follows

$$T_c - T_w = \frac{RT_w^2}{E}\left(\frac{T_c}{T_w}\right)^2 = \frac{RT_w^2}{E}\left[\frac{T_w + T_c - T_w}{T_w}\right]^2$$

which we rewrite as

$$\frac{T_c - T_w}{T_w} = \frac{RT_w}{E}\left[1 + \frac{T_c - T_w}{T_w}\right]^2$$

(19A)

defining $\theta_c = (T_c - T_w)/T_w$, we write

$$\theta_c = \frac{RT_w}{E}(1 + \theta_c)^2$$

(19B)

which is still a quadratic in θ_c. We can, however, consider the case where $\theta_c \ll 1$ and where $\theta_c \gg 1$.

DISCUSSION OF EQUATION 19B

It should be remarked here that neither case, on a practical basis, is physically very realistic. The implication is, of course, that T_w is appreciably less than T_c. In a coal fired furnace this is not necessarily the case, and T_w is at least on the order of 1000°K or more. In a loss-of-flame accident, explosive re-ignition "off-the-wall" is a well-known consequence if the main-fuel-trip is delayed. That is, as the curves approach tangency, T_{ign} and T_c become indistinguishable. It follows that in this particular case $\theta_c \ll 1$. It does not follow that this is in any approximate way applicable to a cold start-up analysis. Thus,

$$\text{if } \theta_c \ll 1, \text{ then } \theta_c \simeq \frac{RT_w}{E} \tag{20}$$

Taking E as 20 kcal/g-mol, T_w as 1000°K and R as $\simeq 2$ kcal/K-kg-mol, we get

$$\theta_c \sim \frac{1}{10}$$

or

$$\frac{T_c - 1000}{1000} = 1/10, \text{ hence } T_c = 1100°K$$

In regions of heavy slagging, it is reasonable to take T_w as $\sim 1500°K$ in which case $\theta_c \sim 0.15$, or

$$\frac{T_c - 1500}{1500} = 0.15, \text{ hence } T_c = 1725°K$$

which illustrates a basic defect in the approximation, if not the analysis, approached from a re-ignition point of view. As T_w increases, the temperature difference $T_c - T_w$ also increases, which is contrary to what one would expect. Bradley, however, considers $T_c - T_w$ to represent the prethermal-explosion heating, the inference being that the lower the T_w value (and therefore T_c), the greater the subsequent thermal-explosion jump. Neither interpretation is particularly significant. To extend the discussion of the Semenov condition somewhat, we consider the consequence if we write the relation Eq. 20 in the form

$$T_c - T_w = \frac{RT_w^2}{E} \tag{21}$$

and substitute this in Eq. 16B

$$\frac{\kappa S}{V}\left(\frac{RT_w^2}{E}\right) = Qf(n)_c Ae^{-E/R}\left(T_w + \frac{RT_w^2}{E}\right) \tag{22}$$

we write the exponent as

$$\frac{E}{R\left(T_w + \frac{RT_w^2}{E}\right)} = \frac{E^2}{ERT_w + R^2T_w^2}$$

Performing the division, we get

$$\frac{E^2}{ERT_w + R^2T_w^2} = \frac{E}{RT_w} - \frac{1}{1 + \frac{RT_w}{E}}$$

where, as a rough approximation, we neglect the RT_w/E term and write Eq. 22 as

$$\frac{\kappa S}{V}\left(\frac{RT_w^2}{E}\right) = Qf(n)_c Ae^{-\frac{E}{RT_w}+1} \tag{23}$$

The concentration limit corresponding to the critical condition is then roughly estimated by

$$f(n)_c = \frac{\kappa S RT_w^2 e^{E/RT_w}}{QAVEe} \tag{24}$$

defining D as

$$D = \frac{\kappa SR}{QAVEe}$$

we write

$$f(n)_c = D T_w^2 e^{E/RT_w} \tag{25A}$$

Actually the e term in the denominator is unnecessarily rough and we can decrease the uncertainty by defining $e^{0.95}$ instead. Thus we define

$$D' = \frac{\kappa SR}{QAVE\, e^{0.95}}$$

or

$$f(n)_c = D'T_w^2\, e^{E/RT_w}$$

(25B)

From which

$$\ln\left[\frac{f(n)_c}{T_w^2}\right] = \frac{E}{RT_w} + \ln D'$$

(25C)

We now consider that, in that branch of chemistry referred to as reaction kinetics, the rate of a chemical reaction is defined as the mols of a particular component, say, component α, converted per unit time and per unit reactor volume.

Or

$$r_\alpha = -\frac{dn_\alpha}{Vd\tau} \qquad \text{mols/ft}^3\text{-hr}$$

A furnace is a dynamic system (flow reactor) where reactants (fuel, air) flow continuously into the vessel, and products (CO_2, H_2O, CO, NO, N_2 and SO_2) are continuously removed. At steady state, the system properties do not change with time at any specified position, but do vary along the path length. In this case, on an overall basis, we write the rate of reaction as

$$r_\alpha = \frac{F_T dm_\alpha'}{dV} \qquad \text{mols/ft}^3\text{-hr}$$

where F_T is the total feed rate (mols/hr) of fuel and air, and m_α' is the mols of reactant α converted to product per mol of total feed.

From the *rate* of reaction to the concept of the *order* of a reaction is a natural extension. In kinetic terms, reactions are classified into first, second, third, and higher orders according to the number of molecules which participate in the reaction. The stoichiometric chemical equation does not necessarily determine the order of reaction. This can be established only by experiment. The rate of reaction has been found (Guldberg-Waage law) to be proportional to the concentrations of the reactants. This is written as

$$r_\alpha = k_\alpha m_\alpha^a m_\beta^b m_\gamma^c \ldots$$

(26)

where k_α = empirically determined reaction rate constant as obtained from an Arrhenius plot

$m_\alpha, m_\beta, m_\gamma$ = concentration of reactants mols/ft^3

a, b, c = empirically determined exponents

The order of the reaction is defined to be the sum of the exponents, $a + b + c + \ldots$. Alternatively, the order may be stated with respect to the components, that is, of order a with respect to α, of order b with respect to reactant β, etc. We now consider that mols and partial pressure are proportional, according to this relationship:

$$P_i = \frac{N_i}{N_{mT}}P_T = \chi_i P_T$$

(26A)

where:

N_i = mols of component i

N_{mT} = total mols of gas present

P_i, P_T = partial and total pressure respectively

In a furnace, the total pressure can usually be taken as one atmosphere, in which case we write

$$P_i = \frac{N_i}{N_{mt}} = \frac{m_i V}{V\Sigma m_i}$$

(26B)

from this it follows that we can write (26) as

$$r_\alpha = (\Sigma m_i) k_\alpha P_\alpha^a m_\beta^b m_\gamma^c \ldots$$

or

$$P_\alpha^a = \frac{r_\alpha (\Sigma m_i)^{-1}}{k_\alpha m_\beta^b m_\gamma^c}$$

which implies that $f(n)_c$ is proportional to P_α^a so we write Eq. 25C as

$$\ln \left[\frac{P_\alpha^a}{T_w^2} \right] = \frac{E}{RT_w} + \ln D'' \tag{27}$$

We have gone through this discussion to rationalize the Bradley assertion that, for a simple j^{th} order reaction in the gas, phase $f(n)_c$ may be replaced by p^j, or, in Bradley's notation

$$\log \left[\frac{P^j}{T_w^2} \right] = \frac{E}{RT_w} + \log B'' \tag{28}$$

Eq. 28 may be considered as a necessary, but not sufficient, condition for a thermal explosion to occur.

As pointed out by Essenhigh[7], the Semenov thermal-explosion system is based on Semenov's concept in which the stable thermal state of a system is determined by the intersection of a heat-gain and a heat-loss curve.

THE VULIS-ESSENHIGH CRITERIA

In the United States, R. H. Essenhigh [7, 8, 9] appears to be the principal researcher and investigator of a considerable body of Soviet combustion research conducted over the last half century. In particular, the Essenhigh approach to combustion analysis is based on the more recent work of Vulis[10]. As pointed out by Essenhigh[7], an important difference between the Semenov and Vulis work is that the

Semenov analysis, and more specifically its later developments, is concerned primarily with the unsteady-state behavior of materially isolated (though not thermally isolated) volumes. Vulis is concerned with the more relevant steady-state flowing systems.

A second point is that the Semenov criterion for ignition depends on the assumption of virtually infinite reactant concentration or else negligible reactant consumption. Vulis, therefore, shows the Semenov ignition criterion to be only an extreme limiting condition of a more general criterion. These essential differences made Vulis a preferred starting point for a PSR type of approach. The Vulis analysis of the zero-dimensional PSR is said to be the most comprehensive available in the literature. The Essenhigh [7, 8, 9] treatment of it is easier to follow than the translation of the Vulis work, and is, therefore, preferred. The following analysis parallels the Essenhigh development very closely, although the formulations are not precisely the same; that is, some corrections were necessary in balancing units across the equal sign. We consider a fuel (reactant)-air mixture to enter a PSR of volume V_c. The mixture is at temperature T_o, reactant concentration C_o, mixture density ρ_o and mass flow rate of mixture $\dot{W}$. Within the PSR, the mixture then instantaneously undergoes reaction to form products at temperature T, at flow rate $\dot{W}$ (no storage, steady-state), residual reactant concentration C, and products density ρ. The entrance flow rate, if we assume gas fuel and the perfect gas law, is

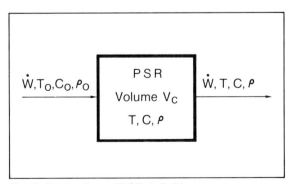

Fig. 6 Illustration of PSR definition

$$V_o = \frac{\dot{W}\,(R/\mu)\,T_o}{P} =$$

$$\frac{kg/hr + (kg\text{-}m/kg\text{-}mol\text{-}{}^oK)\,{}^oK}{kg/m^2 + kg/kg\text{-}mol} = m^3/hr$$

wherefore the nominal PSR transit, residence, or "stay" time is

$$\tau_{so} = \frac{V_c}{V_o} \quad hr$$

The residence time by PSR definition is, of course,

$$\tau_s = \frac{V_c}{V}$$

where V is defined by

$$V = \frac{\dot{W}\,(R/\mu)\,T}{P} \quad m^3/hr$$

hence,

$$\tau_s = \tau_{so}\frac{T_o}{T} \quad hr$$

(29)

τ_{so} and τ_s are, it should be realized, fictitious times. The actual physical-transit (or residence) time is some other value between τ_{so} and τ_s. As a first approximation, however, it is sometimes realistic to assume $\tau_s \simeq \tau$ actual. This depends on the specific case being considered.

Defining h_f to be a heat of formation, that is, heat released per kg of reactant converted to product, we can write a heat generation term for the PSR.

Definition of Terms of the Vulis-Essenhigh Criteria

$\dot{W}$	= total mass flow rate, kg/hr	E	= activation energy, kcal/mol
T_o	= entering mixture temperature, ${}^oK$	Q_G	= rate of heat generation in the PSR, $\frac{kcal}{m^3\text{-}hr}$
ρ_o	= entering mixture density, kg/m³		
C_o	= entering reactant concentration, $kg^{reactant}/kg^{mixture}$	h_f	= heat release, kcal/kg reactant
T	= PSR and exit products temperature, ${}^oK$	η	= combustion efficiency
ρ	= PSR and exit products density, kg/m³	Q_I	= mass rate of heat generation in the PSR, $\frac{kcal}{kg_{prod}\text{-}hr}$
C	= PSR and exit products concentration, $kg^{reactant}/kg^{mixtures}$ i.e., residual (remaining) reactant	K_o	= Arrhenius frequency constant hrs⁻¹
V_o	= entering mixture volume flow rate, m³/hr	Q_{II}	= rate of exit heat flow $\frac{kcal}{kg\text{-}hr}$
V_c	= PSR volume, m³		
R	= universal gas constant, $1.98586 \frac{Btu}{lb\text{-}mol\text{-}{}^oR}$, $1.98586 \frac{kcal}{kg\text{-}mol\text{-}{}^oK}$, 1545.32 ft-lb/lb-mol-${}^oR$	τ_s	= residence time in reactor at temperature T
		τ_{so}	= residence time in reactor at temperature T_o
		$\tau_{s/k}$	= dimensionless time group
μ	= atomic weight, lb/lb-mol, g/g-mol, kg/kg-mol	τ_D	= delay time in reactor from instantaneously diffused fuel/air entry (PSR) until ignition occurs
R_o	= gas constant = R/μ $\frac{kg\text{-}m/kg\text{-}mol\text{-}{}^oK}{kg/kg\text{-}mol} = m/{}^oK$	τ_K	= characteristic chemical reaction time (function of temperature), hrs
		$\psi_{1,2,3}$	= average reaction rate $kg^{reacted}/kg^{mixture} - hr$
θ	= RT/E = dimensionless temperature group	C^*	= localized concentration associated with flame front
		ω	= $\frac{C_o R\,h_f}{E C_p}$ = dimensionless initial concentration group

$$Q_G = \left(C_o - C\right) \frac{\dot{W}}{V_c} h_f = C_o \left(1 - \frac{C}{C_o}\right) \frac{\dot{W}}{V_c} h_f \frac{kcal}{m^3\text{-}hr} \tag{30}$$

The term $(1 - C/C_o)$ is defined by Essenhigh[9] to be the combustion efficiency, η.

$$\eta = \left(1 - \frac{C}{C_o}\right) \tag{31}$$

The Essenhigh term, $\dot{Q}_G$, is related to the Vulis heat-generation term, $\dot{Q}_I$, through the quantity ρ, or

$$\dot{Q}_G = \dot{Q}_I \rho \tag{32}$$

Hence we can write Eqs. 30 and 32 as

$$\dot{Q}_G = C_o \eta \frac{\dot{W}}{V_c} h_f \frac{kcal}{m^3\text{-}hr} \tag{33}$$

$$\dot{Q}_I = C_o \eta \frac{\dot{W}\rho^{-1}}{V_c} h_f \frac{kcal}{kg_{prod}\text{-}hr} \tag{34}$$

By the definition of the PSR, the reactant concentration is always C at any time t. In the classic Arrhenius form we, therefore, write the rate of heat generation term as

$$\dot{Q}_I = h_f C\, K_o e^{-E/RT} \frac{kcal}{kg_{prod}\text{-}hr} \tag{35}$$

The Arrhenius expression must not be written in the apparently plausible form

$$\dot{Q}_I = h_f C_o\, \eta\, K_o e^{-E/RT} \frac{kcal}{kg_{prod}\text{-}hr} \tag{36}$$

Clearly, Eqs. 34, 35, and 36 are not identically the same. Using the same identifying label, $\dot{Q}_I$, on each is, therefore, somewhat misleading. If we plot each as, say, f(Q), against, say, θ or C then we ought to get points of intersection where the expressions do have the same value. This implies that we can equate Eqs. 34 and 35 or 34 and 36, provided we remember they are not identities. That is, we cannot arbitrarily substitute one for the other. This is obvious if we think about the range $0 \le C \le C_o$ for C and η in the above relations.

Suppose that we equate Eqs. 34 and 36. (Some caution in doing this would seem to be indicated as the result may be difficult to justify.) For example,

$$\text{write } V_c \text{ as } V_c = V\tau_s = \frac{W\,RT\,\tau_s}{\mu P}$$

and substitute in Eq. 34

$$\dot{Q}_I = \frac{C_o\,\eta\,\dot{W}\,P\,h_f}{W\rho(R/\mu)T\,\tau_s} = \frac{C_o\,\eta\,\dot{W}\,P\,h_f}{W\,P\,\tau_s} = \frac{C_o\,\eta\,h_f}{\tau_s} \tag{34A}$$

equating Eqs. 34A and 36

$$\frac{C_o\,\eta\,h_f}{\tau_s} = C_o\,\eta\,h_f\,k_o\,e^{-E/RT} \tag{36A}$$

or

$$\frac{1}{\tau_s} = k_o e^{-E/RT}\,hr^{-1} \tag{36B}$$

and

$$1 = \tau_s\,K_o e^{-E/RT} \tag{36C}$$

Rather than being taken as a useful result, this should be interpreted as implying a condition that must be met if the analysis is to be valid. In this sense, relation Eq. 36B is interesting in that for a given fuel at temperature T, the reactor volume V_c is specified. That is, substituting for T_s in Eq. 36B, we get the condition

$$\frac{V}{V_c} = \frac{W \, (R/\mu) \, T}{P \, V_c} = K_o e^{-E/RT}$$

$$(36D)$$

and, since we can write P as $P = \rho \, (R/\mu) \, T$, we can express Eq. 36D as

$$\frac{W}{\rho V_c} = K_o e^{-E/RT}$$

$$(36E)$$

or

$$V_c = \frac{\dot{W}}{\rho K_o} e^{+E/RT}$$

$$(36F)$$

Although V_c in principle is uniquely specified by Eq. 36F, it should be realized that this is still a trial-and-error calculation. That is, for a given fuel, the right-hand side (RHS) is still a function of three variables: independent variable, W, and the W dependent variables ρ and T.

By the definition of the PSR, the temperature leaving the reactor must be the same as the temperature within the reactor. If we make the gross assumption of an adiabatic reactor, then the heat loss is simply written as an exit flow term:

$$Q_{II} = \frac{W \, C_p \, (T - T_o)}{\rho V_c} \qquad \frac{kcal}{kg_{prod}\text{-}hr}$$

$$(37)$$

If we now equate 34A and 35 and multiply both sides by $\tau_s/C_o h_f$ we get,

$$\eta \frac{C_o h_f}{\tau_s} \frac{\tau_s}{C_o h_f} = \frac{\tau_s}{C_o h_f} C \, h_f K_o e^{-1/\theta}$$

$$\eta = \frac{C}{C_o} \tau_s K_o e^{-1/\theta} = \frac{C}{C_o} \tau_{s/k} e^{-1/\theta}$$

$$(38)$$

where we defined $\tau_{s/k} = \tau_s K_o$ which in essence represents a dimensionless time. We now make the substitution $C/C_o = 1 - \eta$ in Eq. 38 and arrive at Essenhigh's result

$$\eta_I = \frac{\tau_{s/k}}{\tau_{s/k} + e^{1/\theta}}$$

$$(39)$$

where the subscript I has been added to remind us that it is derived from a heat-generation condition.

Multiplying top and bottom of Eq. 39 by $e^{-1/\theta}$ we get,

$$\eta_I = \frac{\tau_{s/k} \, e^{-1/\theta}}{\tau_{s/k} \, e^{-1/\theta} + 1} = \frac{1 + \tau_{s/k} \, e^{-1/\theta} - 1}{1 + \tau_{s/k} \, e^{-1/\theta}} = \\ 1 - \frac{1}{1 + \tau_{s/k} \, e^{-1/\theta}}$$

$$(40)$$

which is a modification of the Vulis form and where Essenhigh also redefines $\tau_{s/k}$ as a dimensionless time group referenced to the zero conditions, or

$$\tau_{s/k} = \tau_{s/k}{}^o \, (\theta_o/\theta) \, (P/P_o)$$

$$(41)$$

We now briefly review the Vulis derivation of Eq. 40 which, although less straightforward than the Essenhigh treatment, is of considerable interest as it takes recourse to differentiating between reactor concentration C and a concentration C^* in the flame zone, in Vulis' words, "where C^* is the concentration in the combustion zone, for example, on the coal surface." The Vulis analysis proceeds on the basis of defining various plausible reactor reaction rates. Adopting ψ as denoting the Vulis rate, we write

$$\psi_1 = \frac{C_o - C}{\tau_s} \qquad \frac{kg \text{ reactant consumed}}{kg_{prod}\text{-}hr}$$

$$\psi_2 = \frac{C^*}{\tau_K} e^{-1/\theta}$$

$$\psi_3 = \frac{C - C^*}{\tau_D}$$

Equating the three ψ terms we have

$$\frac{C_o - C}{\tau_s} = \frac{C_o \, \eta}{\tau_s} = \frac{C^*}{\tau_K} e^{-1/\theta} =$$

$$\frac{C - C^*}{\tau_D} = \frac{C_o \, (1 - \eta) - C^*}{\tau_D}$$

Then

$$\frac{\eta}{T^s} = \frac{C^*}{C_o} \frac{e^{-1/\theta}}{\tau_K} = \frac{(1 - \eta) - \dfrac{C^*}{C_o}}{\tau_D} \tag{42}$$

From Eq. 42 we write

$$\frac{C^*}{C_o} = \eta \, e^{+1/\theta} \frac{\tau_K}{\tau_s} = \frac{\eta \, e^{+1/\theta}}{\tau_{s/K}} \tag{43}$$

and

$$1 - \eta - \frac{C^*}{C_o} 1 = \frac{C^*}{C_o} \frac{\tau_D}{\tau_K} e^{-1/\theta} = \frac{C^*}{C_o} \frac{e^{-1/\theta}}{\tau_{K/D}}$$

or

$$1 - \eta = \frac{C^*}{C_o} + \frac{C^*}{C_o} \frac{e^{-1/\theta}}{\tau_{K/D}} \tag{44}$$

equating 43 and 44 by eliminating C^*/C_o

$$\frac{\eta \, e^{1/\theta}}{\tau_{s/K}} = (1 - \eta) \left(1 + \frac{e^{-1/\theta}}{\tau_{K/D}} \right)^{-1}$$

Define

$$\tau_{K/D} = \frac{1}{\tau_{DK}} = \frac{\tau_K}{\tau_D}$$

then

$$\frac{\eta \, e^{1/\theta}}{\tau_{s/K}} = \frac{(1 - \eta)}{1 + \tau_{DK} \, e^{-1/\theta}} = \frac{C^*}{C_o} \tag{45}$$

Solving Eq. 45 for η we get the Vulis equation

$$\eta_I = \frac{1}{1 + \dfrac{1}{\tau_{sD}} + \dfrac{e^{1/\theta}}{\tau_{s/K}}} \tag{46}$$

where

$$\frac{1}{\tau_{sD}} = \frac{\tau_{DK}}{\tau_{s/K}} = \frac{\tau_K}{\tau_s} \frac{\tau_D}{\tau_K} = \frac{\tau_D}{\tau_s} \quad \text{or} \quad \tau_{sD} = \tau_s / \tau_D$$

For instantaneous mixing, the ignition delay time T_D goes to zero, and $T_{sD} \to \infty$ and Eq. 46 becomes

$$\eta_I = \frac{\tau_{s/K}}{\tau_{s/K} + e^{1/\theta}}$$

which is Eq. 39. We now recall Eq. 37

$$Q_{II} = \frac{C_p \, (T - T_o)}{p \, V_c / \dot{W}} = \frac{C_p \, (T - T_o)}{\tau_s}$$

and multiply top and bottom by R/E

$$Q_{II} = C_p \frac{(RT/E - RT_o/E)}{\dfrac{R}{E} \tau_s} = \frac{\theta - \theta_o}{\dfrac{R}{E} \tau_s / C_p} \tag{47}$$

Multiplying both sides of Eq. 47 by $\dfrac{\tau_s}{h_f C_o}$ we get

$$Q_{II} \frac{\tau_s}{h_f C_o} = \eta_{II} = \frac{\theta - \theta_o}{C_o R h_f / E C_p} = \frac{\theta - \theta_o}{\omega} \tag{48}$$

The II subscript on η in this case is a reminder that this efficiency definition has its origin in the exit heat-flow term to distinguish it from the η_I efficiency term, which is based on the heat-generation term. We will subsequently find that η_I and η_{II} share points of intersection and individually define different curves.

At steady state, the heat generated equals the heat lost, or

$$Q_I = Q_{II} \tag{48A}$$

Multiplying both sides by $\dfrac{\tau_s}{h_f C_o}$ we get the dimensionless form

$$\eta_I = \eta_{II} = \frac{\tau_{s/K}}{\tau_{s/K} + e^{1/\theta}} = \frac{\theta - \theta_o}{\omega} \tag{48B}$$

which we can also write in the form

$$1 - \frac{1}{1 + \tau_{s/K}\, e^{-1/\theta}} = \frac{\theta - \theta_o}{\omega} \tag{49}$$

Relation 49 is, of course, a conditional equality not an identity. The left-hand side of Eq. 49 plots as a family of sigmoids and the right-hand side is a family of straight lines. This is illustrated in Fig. 7.

Obviously, an intersection is a solution to Eq. 48B and represents a stable temperature. Excluding the condition of tangency, it is evident that the solution of η with respect to θ can be either single-valued (dashed lines) or triple-valued (line B); that is to say, for given values of the independent variables, there can be three stable temperatures.

In the case of three stable temperatures, however, only two of the intersections represent positively stable values: these are the highest and lowest intersections on line B, and they are positively stable by considering the effects of a slight displacement from the stable point. The subsequent behavior is to return to the original point before displacement. The middle intersection is a metastable point so that, on slight displacement, the system does not return to that point. The metastable point is not, therefore, a significant physical condition. The two positively stable points, however, do represent significant physical conditions: the upper point represents stable operation, with flame and substantial combustion efficiency; the lower point represents passage of reactant through the combustor with theoretically finite, but practically negligible, degree of combustion—the system could operate stably

but has not been ignited. This is in contrast with the single intersection of the left dashed line where there is no combustion and the system cannot be ignited. Conversely, the intersection of the right dashed line represents combustion at a significant temperature level, under conditions such that extinction is (theoretically) impossible. Note that if we rotate line A a small (infinitesimal) displacement leftward (counterclockwise), we get the extinction condition.

In reasonably designed furnaces, the critical conditions are those of ignition and extinction. Graphically, they are represented by the tangency between the heat generation and the heat-loss lines (lines A and C in Fig. 7). Analytically, the condition is

$$d\eta_I/d\theta = d\eta_{II}/d\theta, \tag{50}$$

Differentiation and rearrangement results in this form, according to Essenhigh

$$\eta_{cr} = 1 - |\,\theta^2/(\theta - \theta_o)\,| \tag{51}$$

Eq. 51 applies only to the tangency condition shown by A and C on Fig. 7.

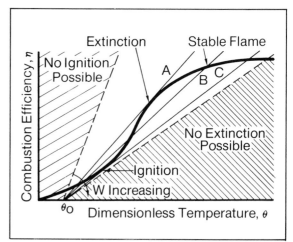

Fig. 7 Graphical solution of Eq. 49 to obtain flame stability

This completes an introduction to an aspect of the Vulis work, that aspect which, because of its potential relation to combustion-chamber design, has been further developed by Essen-high and his co-workers at the Pennsylvania State University. Thus, the discussion also serves as an introduction to Essenhigh's approach to the subject, as referenced.

REFERENCES

[1] Robert H. Essenhigh, "Combustion Phenomena in Industrial Flames," *Industrial and Engineering Chemistry*, 59 (7): 52–59, 1967.

[2] P. O. Rosin, "The Thermodynamic and Economic Basis of Powdered-Coal Firing," *Braunkohle*, 24:241–259, 1925.

[3] Meredith W. Thring, *The Sciences of Flames and Furnaces*, 2nd ed. New York: John Wiley and Sons, 1962.

[4] National Research Council, Committee on Chemistry of Coal, *Chemistry of Coal Utilization, Supplemental Volume*. Prepared by the Committee on Chemistry of Coal, A. R. Powell, Chairman; H. H. Lowry, ed. New York: John Wiley and Sons, 1963.

[5] N. N. Semenov, *Some Problems in Chemical Kinetics and Reactivity*. 2 vols. Translated by M. Boudart. Princeton, New Jersey: Princeton University Press, 1959.

[6] John N. Bradley, *Flame and Combustion Phenomena*, London: Methuen and Co.; and New York: Barnes and Noble, 1969.

[7] Robert H. Essenhigh, *Application of the Perfectly Stirred Reactor (P.S.R.) Theory to Analysis of One-Dimensional Flames*. Report no. AD-805 113 (Pennsylvania State University, Department of Fuel Science Technical Report no. FS66-3 (U) Contract NONR-656 (29). Springfield, VA: National Technical Information Service, October 1966.

[8] Robert H. Essenhigh, *A New Application of the Perfectly Stirred Reactor (P.S.R.) Theory to Design of Combustion Chambers*. Report no. AD-812 114. (Pennsylvania State University, Department of Fuel Science Technical Report no. FS67-1 (U). Contract 656 (29). Springfield, VA: National Technical Information Service, March, 1967.

[9] Robert H. Essenhigh, "An Introduction to Stirred Reactor Theory Applied to Design of Combustion Chambers" in Howard B. Palmer and J. M. Beer, eds., Combustion Technology—*Some Modern Developments*, RP. 374–415. New York and London; Academic Press, 1974.

[10] L. A. Vulis, *Thermal Regimes of Combustion*, Literal translation from the Russian by Morris D. Friedman; Translating editor: Glenn C. Williams. New York: McGraw-Hill, 1961.

Appendix C. Determinations of Coal-Ash Properties

This appendix supplements the data on properties of coal ash included in Chapter 3. Material properties useful in the design of furnaces and ash-handling systems are given. Methods of calculating fusion temperatures and viscosities of coal ash, as well as further descriptions of these properties are outlined, with curves to assist in the determinations.

MATERIAL PROPERTIES OF COAL-ASH SLAG DEPOSITS

There are several properties of slag deposits that are of use in performing such calculations as those of furnace heat-absorption and ash-hopper cooling-water flow.

SURFACE EMISSIVITY

The curves of Figs. 1 and 2 plot surface emissivity of coal-ash slags as a function of temperature. Separate curves are given for fused and particulate states because emissivity differs with the deposit structure. Such emissivities are averaged values of composite data from Australian, Soviet, and U.S. investigations. Heat transfer from the flame to the surrounding surfaces in utility furnaces is predominantly by radiation. It follows that meaningful heat-transfer calculations should include the requirement of a reasonably accurate knowledge of slag-surface emissivities.

THERMAL CONDUCTIVITY

The curves of Fig. 3 show thermal conductivities as a function of temperature. Separate curves are given for fused and particulate states, because thermal conductivity differs with the physical structure of the deposit. The given conductivities are averaged values of composite data obtained from Australian, Soviet, and U.S. investigations.

The particulate deposit referred to is a fine, dry powder that forms an uncompacted layer on the metal surface. The outer deposit layers vary considerably in character from being porous or sintered to being dense, fused, or molten. The conductivity, which will vary with the physical properties of the specific deposit, is expected to increase as the deposit density increases and the deposit becomes more molten.

Heat transfer through a coal-ash deposit to waterwalls is calculated by a conduction model; this requires that the thermal conductivity of the deposits be known.

SPECIFIC HEAT AT CONSTANT PRESSURE

Vargaftik and Oleschuck[1] have measured the specific heat of coal-ash slags at constant pressure with a reference temperature of 60°F. Table I lists these specific heat values.

Fig. 1 Surface emissivity of fused coal-ash deposits

Fig. 2 Surface emissivity of particulate coal-ash deposits

A method for estimating the specific heat of slag from its chemical composition has been developed for blast-furnace slags. Because of the compositional similarity between coal-ash and blast-furnace slags, the method should be applicable to coal-ash slags and is described below. To perform cool-down, ash-hopper evaporation, and transient calculations, knowledge of the slag specific heat is required.

Using a reference temperature of 20°C, Voskoboinikov[2] derived the following empirical equations for estimating the specific heat of blast-furnace slags:

Fig. 3 Thermal conductivity of fused and particulate coal-ash deposits

For the temperature range of 20° to 1350°C

$$c_P = 0.169 + 0.201 \times 10^{-3}t - 0.277 \times 10^{-6}t^2$$
$$+ 0.139 \times 10^{-9}t^3 + 0.17 \times 10^{-4}t\left(1 - \frac{CaO}{\Sigma}\right)$$

where c_P = specific heat (cal/gm °C)
$\quad$ t $\;$ = temperature (°C)
$\quad \Sigma \;$ = $SiO_2 + Al_2O_3 + FeO + MgO + MnO$

(1)

For the temperature range of 1350 to 1600°C

$$c_P = 0.15 \times 10^{-2}t - 0.478 \times 10^{-6}t^2$$
$$- 0.876 + 0.016\left(1 - \frac{CaO}{\Sigma}\right)$$

where c_P = specific heat (cal/gm °C)
$\quad$ t $\;$ = temperature (°C)
$\quad \Sigma \;$ = $SiO_2 + Al_2O_3 + FeO + MgO + MnO$

(2)

Foerster and Weston[3] showed that their experimentally measured values for liquid and solid slags agreed well with the calculated values from Voskoboinikov's equation. Experimental values for liquid and solid slags were slightly higher than the calculated values.

The densities of various forms of coal-ash slag deposits were averaged from several investigations and are as listed in Table II.

SURFACE TENSION

Surface-tension forces are involved in many important stages of the slag-deposition process, such as ash fusion, slag adhesion, and slag flow. The methods of estimating surface tension of oxide systems have been developed in the ceramic and glass industry; they should be applicable to some extent to coal-ash slags because of the similarity in their chemical compositions. Surface tension of liquid slags can be estimated according to the following procedure:

1. Surface tension of liquid slags at 1400°C in air can be approximated from the chemical composition using the following equation developed by Lyon.[4]

$$\gamma = 3.24\,SiO_2 + 5.85\,Al_2O_3 + 4.4\,Fe_2O_3 + 4.92\,CaO$$
$$+ 5.49\,MgO + 1.12\,Na_2O - 0.75\,K_2O$$

where γ = surface tension of slag (dyne/cm)

(3)

2. To estimate surface tension of slags at different temperatures, a temperature coefficient of −0.017 dyne/cm °C is recommended by Parmelee and Harman.[5]

3. To estimate surface tension of slags in different atmospheres, Table III has been derived from data by Parikh.[6]

In general, surface tension of slags does not vary greatly and is within the range of 300 to 400 dyne/cm at 1400°C in air. A lower slag-surface tension will usually lead to more rapid fusion and flow properties, and better wetting characteristics. Good wetting is a necessary, but not sufficient, condition for stronger adhesive properties.

RADIATIVE PROPERTIES OF ASH DEPOSITS

Radiative heat-transfer properties of ash deposits are important in determining heat transfer to lower-furnace waterwall tubes when burning coal. The absorptivity of ash deposits plays an important role in determining the heat absorbed by deposit-laden waterwall tubes, while the emissivity of ash deposits determines how much heat will be reradiated by the tubes. The emissivity and absorptivity of ash deposits are a function of the wavelengths of the absorbed and emitted radiation, the surface temperature of the deposits, the physical state of the deposits, and the properties of the coals from which the deposits originated.

THEORY

In Eq. 4, the rate of radiative heat transfer from a flame to a unit area of deposit-laden wa-

Table I. Specific Heat at Constant Pressure

Temperature (°F)	C_P (Btu/lb °F)
2010	0.243
2190	0.258
2370	0.272
2550	0.285
2730	0.300
2910	0.303
3090	0.310

Table II. Density of Various Coal-Ash Slag Deposits

Deposit Form	Density (lb/ft³)
Liquid Slag	150–180
Dense, Solid Slag	140–170
Solid Ash	120–160
Loose, Powder Ash	15–35
Fine, Ground Slag	60–90

Table III. Surface Tension of Slags at Different Temperatures

Atmosphere	Reduction in Surface Tension (%) (Based on Nitrogen Atmosphere)
Nitrogen	0
Hydrogen	1
Air	3
Carbon Dioxide	7
Sulfur Dioxide	27
Water Vapor	35

terwall tube (q/A) depends upon the overall emissivity (ε) and overall absorptivity (α) of the deposit, the flame temperature (T_f) and the deposit surface temperature (T_s). This heat is conducted through the ash deposit of thickness Δx having a temperature drop ΔT_{ash} and a thermal conductivity, k, and transferred to water flowing through the tubes. This simplified energy balance on a unit area of tube (Fig. 4) can be written as:

$$
\begin{array}{c}
\text{Net thermal} \\
\text{energy trans-} \\
\text{fer to water}
\end{array}
=
\begin{array}{c}
\text{Coal flame} \\
\text{radiation}
\end{array}
-
\begin{array}{c}
\text{Deposit} \\
\text{emission}
\end{array}
=
\begin{array}{c}
\text{Conduction} \\
\text{through} \\
\text{deposit}
\end{array}
$$

or,

$$
q/A = \sigma\,\varepsilon_f\,\alpha\,T_f^4 - \sigma\,\varepsilon\,T_s^4 = k\frac{\Delta T_{ash}}{\Delta x}
$$

(4)

where σ is the Stefan-Boltzmann constant and ε_f is the flame emissivity. It should be noted that the above relationship is simplified and does not consider the view factor from the flame to the wall, nor wall reflection.

As in Eq. 5 the overall deposit emissivity (ε) depends upon the monochromatic emissivity (ε_λ) at surface temperature (T_s) and the monochromatic blackbody emission per unit area (W_{s_λ}) at surface temperature (T_s):

$$
\varepsilon = \frac{\int_0^\infty \varepsilon_\lambda\,W_{s_\lambda}\,d_\lambda}{\int_0^\infty W_{s_\lambda}\,d_\lambda} = \frac{\int_0^\infty \varepsilon_\lambda\,W_{s_\lambda}\,d_\lambda}{\sigma\,T_s^4}
$$

(5)

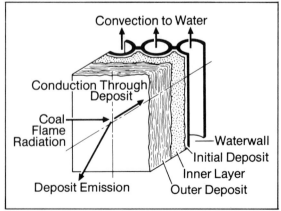

Fig. 4 Section of lower-furnace waterwall depicting heat-transfer mechanism through coal-ash deposit

where $\sigma\,T_s^4$ is introduced using Planck's law.

The overall deposit absorptivity (α) depends upon the monochromatic absorptivity (α_λ) at surface temperature (T_s) and the distribution of monochromatic intensities of incident radiation (I_λ):

$$
\alpha = \frac{\int_0^\infty \alpha_\lambda\,I_\lambda\,d_\lambda}{\int_0^\infty I_\lambda\,d_\lambda}
$$

(6)

where I_λ is dependent of W_{f_λ}, the monochromatic blackbody emission per unit area at flame temperature (T_f) and the monochromatic emissivity (ε_{f_λ}):

$$
I_\lambda = \varepsilon_{f_\lambda}\,W_{f_\lambda}
$$

(7)

Employing Planck's law and the assumption that a coal flame is nearly black at all wavelengths (that is, $\varepsilon_{f_\lambda} \simeq 1$) gives

$$
\alpha = \frac{\int_0^\infty \alpha_\lambda\,W_{f_\lambda}\,d_\lambda}{\sigma\,T_f^4}
$$

(8)

When the radiation from the flame is in steady state with the surface, Kirchoff's law ($\varepsilon_\lambda = \alpha_\lambda$) applies and Eq. 8 can be written as:

$$
\alpha = \frac{\int_0^\infty \varepsilon_\lambda\,W_{f_\lambda}\,d_\lambda}{\sigma\,T_f^4}
$$

(9)

From Eqs. 5 and 9, it is seen that both the overall emissivity and absorptivity depend upon the deposit surface temperature and the monochromatic emissivities; absorptivity is also dependent upon flame temperature. From these equations, it can also be deduced that the overall absorptivity can differ significantly from the overall emissivity, particularly if the monochromatic emissivities vary significantly with wavelength and the flame temperature is significantly different from the deposit surface temperature. Thus, experimental measurement of only the overall emissivity can result in a significant error in prediction of absorptivity.

The experimental determination of the emissivity and absorptivity of coal ash deposits involves a fair amount of procedural and instrumentational complexity. Early investigations in this field by Agababov,[7] Becker[8] and Mulcahy, Boow and Goard[9] assumed that deposits were "gray bodies." This assumption says that the spectral emissivities and absorptivities ε_λ and α_λ did not vary with wavelength, λ, and were equivalent to the overall emissivity and absorptivity (ε and α) respectively. Hence, they measured either overall emissivity or absorptivity. Later investigations by Khrustalev et al.[10] and Smith, Glicksman[11] proved the "gray body" assumption wrong and employed spectral scans to determine ε_λ. Overall emissivities and absorptivities of ash deposits were calculated by integrating their respective spectral emissivities and their absorptivities.

C-E has developed a laboratory technique employing such spectral spans, and a computational procedure, to determine the emissivities and absorptivities of furnace ash deposits.[12]

Table IV summarizes ash-deposit emissivity and absorptivity results. Here deposits are categorized by physical state (initial deposit, inner layer, and outer deposit), as well as by parent coal source (Eastern and Western U.S.).

On the basis of the limited data, it appears that for initial deposits and inner layers, Western coal-ash emissivities and absorptivities tend to be significantly below those of Eastern

coal ashes. This tendency is expected on the basis of chemical composition; that is, materials composed mainly of oxides of iron, magnesium, and silicon tend to be better emitters and absorbers than those containing high sodium or calcium.[8]

As the physical state of the deposit tends toward a molten condition, emissivity and absorptivity approach 1.0, and differences between Eastern and Western coals would be expected to become less significant. The data also indicate that molten deposits have higher emissivities and absorptivities than powdery deposits. It can be generalized that the emissivity of the ash deposit of a given physical state decreases with increasing surface temperature throughout a wide temperature range.

METHODS OF ESTIMATING ASH-FUSIBILITY TEMPERATURES

Many investigators have attempted to calculate characteristic fusion temperatures of coal ash from its chemical composition. Most of the methods require assumptions that tend to over-simplify the composition of the ash. Also, a common inadequacy among many of the relations is that their validity is usually limited to a certain range of coal-ash compositions. The methods described in this section are those that can be applied to a relatively wide range of coal-ash compositions. The references should be consulted for further information on the accuracy and applicability of the correlations.

Table IV. **A Summary of Emissivities and Absorptivities of Ash Deposits**

Physical state	Parent Coal Region	Emissivity	Absorptivity
Initial deposit	Eastern U.S.	0.75–0.76	0.71–0.76
Initial deposit	Western U.S.	0.37–0.56	0.52–0.61
Inner layer	Eastern U.S.	0.79–0.93	0.67–0.84
Inner layer	Western U.S.	0.68	0.62
Outer deposit	Western U.S.	0.66–0.87	0.62–0.82
Molten inner layer	Western U.S.	0.90	0.91

Fig. 5 Hemispherical temperature of coal-ash free of Fe_2O_3, Na_2O, and K_2O

It is very unlikely that calculation of ash-softening temperatures will replace the determination. Nevertheless, using correlations of this type permits conclusions to be drawn as to the relative influence of each component on the ash-softening temperature and the probable effect of addition of reagents.

METHOD OF DUTTA, RAI, AND CHAKRAVORTY[13]

Assuming the British Standard experimental conditions, this method is used to estimate the hemispherical temperature in either a reducing or oxidizing atmosphere. It is based on ash from Indian coals and synthetic ash mixtures. The procedure is as follows:

1. Calculate the $SiO_2/(Al_2O_3 + TiO_2)$ ratio.

2. Obtain the percentage of CaO + MgO based on

$$SiO_2 + Al_2O_3 + TiO_2 + CaO + MgO = 100\% \tag{10}$$

3. From Fig. 5, estimate the hemispherical temperature of the coal ash free of Fe_2O_3, Na_2O, and K_2O.

4. Obtain the percentage of Fe_2O_3 and $Na_2O + K_2O$ based on the following equation

$$SiO_2 + Al_2O_3 + TiO_2 + Fe_2O_3 + CaO + MgO + Na_2O + K_2O = 100\% \tag{11}$$

5. Correct for the presence of Na_2O and K_2O in the ash by reducing the estimated hemispherical temperature by 25°C (45°F) for each percent of $Na_2O + K_2O$ present.

6. Additional corrections for the presence of Fe_2O_3 in the ash are given in the references.

METHOD OF GAUGER

This method, which assumes *ASTM Standards* experimental conditions, is used to estimate the softening temperatures in a reducing atmosphere of ash from Eastern U.S. coals. The procedure is as follows:

1. Calculate S, A, and T, which are defined as:

$$S = SiO_2 + TiO_2 + P_2O_5 \tag{12}$$

$$A = Al_2O_3 \tag{13}$$

$$T = CaO + 0.7 MgO + 2.25 Na_2O + 1.5 K_2O \tag{14}$$

Fig. 6 **Softening temperature of coal ash free of iron oxide**

2. Obtain the percents S, A, and T, which are expressed as:

$$\% \, S = \left(\frac{S}{S + A + T} \right) \times 100$$

(15)

$$\% \, A = \left(\frac{A}{S + A + T} \right) \times 100$$

(16)

$$\% \, T = \left(\frac{T}{S + A + T} \right) \times 100$$

(17)

3. From Fig. 6, estimate the softening temperature of the coal ash free of iron oxide, using the above designated percentages.

4. Define $I = Fe_2O_3$ and calculate the percent I, which is expressed as:

$$\% \, I = \left(\frac{I}{S + A + T + I} \right) \times 100$$

(18)

5. From Fig. 7, estimate the lowering of the softening temperature due to the presence of Fe_2O_3; this will give the softening temperature of the ash.

METHOD OF SCHAEFER[14]

This method, which assumes *ASTM Standards* experimental conditions, is used to estimate the softening temperature in a reducing atmosphere of ash from Eastern U.S. Coals. The procedure is as follows:

1. Calculate R_s, which is expressed as:

$$R_s = \frac{Al_2O_3}{SiO_2} \times \frac{SiO_2 + Al_2O_3}{FeO + 0.6 \, (CaO + MgO + Na_2O + K_2O)}$$

(19)

Fig. 7 **Lowering of the softening temperature** *from* **iron oxide**

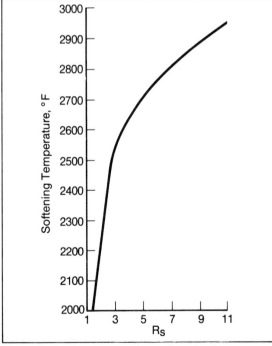

Fig. 8 **Softening temperature of coal ash as a function of** *R_s*

2. Using the value for R_s, estimate the softening temperature of the coal ash from Fig. 8.

METHOD OF ESTEP, SELTZ, BUNKER, AND STRICKLER[15]; AND ESTEP, SELTZ, AND OSBORN[16]

This method, which assumes *ASTM Standards* experimental conditions, is used to estimate the hemispherical temperatures in a reducing atmosphere of ash from Eastern U.S. coals and synthetic ash mixtures. If the coal-ash composition contains mainly SiO_2, Al_2O_3, Fe_2O_3, and CaO, then the hemispherical temperature of the ash can be estimated according to the following procedure:

1. Obtain the percentage of CaO based on:

$$SiO_2 + Al_2 + O_3 + Fe_2O_3 + CaO = 100\%$$

(20)

2. Typical ternary diagrams are given in Figs. 9 and 10, which are to be used for calcium-oxide contents up to 8.5 percent.

Fig. 9 Softening temperature isotherms (°F) at *CaO* = 0−2.5%

Fig. 10 Softening temperature isotherms (°F) at *CaO* = 7.6−8.5%

3. Locate the corresponding composition point inside the SiO_2-Al_2O_3-Fe_2O_3 diagram which is based on the following equation

$$SiO_2 + Al_2O_3 + Fe_2O_3 = 100\%$$

(21)

This gives the estimated hemispherical temperature of the coal ash.

For ashes with CaO content above 8.5 percent, diagrams showing vertical planes through the prism are presented which give plots of CaO versus Fe_2O_3 at constant SiO_2/Al_2O_3 ratios.

For ashes with substantial amounts of MgO or Na_2O, the following corrections apply:

1. The fluxing effect of MgO is identical to that of CaO up to 10 percent MgO; therefore, CaO + MgO can be considered as a single variable.

2. The presence of Na_2O should be corrected by reducing the estimated hemispherical temperature by 50°F for each percentage of Na_2O based on:

$$SiO_2 + Al_2O_3 + Fe_2O_3 + CaO + MgO +$$
$$Na_2O = 100\%$$

(22)

METHOD OF KOVITSKII, KARAGODINA, AND MARTYNOVA[17]

This method, which assumes Soviet Standard experimental conditions, is used to estimate the softening temperature (t_2) and the temperature of the beginning fused state (t_3) in a reducing atmosphere, of ash from Russian coals. The procedure is as follows:

1. Calculate K_{fu} which is expressed as:

$$K_{fu} = \frac{SiO_2 + Al_2O_3}{Fe_2O_3 + CaO + MgO}$$

(23)

2. Estimate the softening temperature and the temperature of the beginning of liquid fused state from the following relations:

$$t_2 = 1094 + 42.5\,K_{fu}$$

(24)

$$t_3 = 1139 + 48.6\,K_{fu}$$

(25)

where

t_2 = softening temperature (°C)

t_3 = temperature of beginning of liquid fused state (°C).

This relation is claimed to be valid for the following range of K_{fu}:

For t_2: $1.8 \leq K_{fu} \leq 9.9$

For t_3: $1.8 \leq K_{fu} \leq 7.5$

METHOD OF MAJUMDAR, BANERJEE, AND LAHIOI

This method, which assumes British Standard experimental conditions, is used to estimate the hemispherical temperature in a reducing atmosphere of ash from Indian coals. The procedure is as follows:

1. Calculate R_m:

$$R_m = 3.3\,SiO_2 + 1.96\,Al_2O_3/2.5\,Fe_2O_3 +$$
$$3.57\,CaO + 5.0\,MgO + 3.22\,Na_2O + 3.22\,K_2O$$

(26)

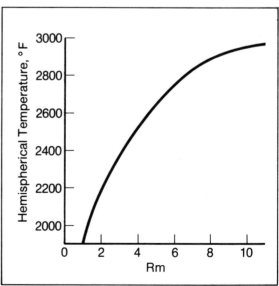

Fig. 11 Hemispherical temperature of coal ash as a function of R_m

2. From Fig. 11, estimate the hemispherical temperature of the coal ash.

This relationship was independently tested on 75 ashes from U.S. coals. The difference between the corresponding estimated and measured values is as follows:

1. In 66.6 percent of the cases the estimated value is within ±100°F of the measured value.

2. The average difference between the two corresponding values is ±84°F.

The original report describing this relation is not available. The curve in Fig. 11 was derived from calculations carried out on ashes from Eastern and Western U.S. coals. The original relation was said to be based on molecular percentages and not on weight percentages. However, the independent tests indicated that the divergence of the estimated values from the corresponding measured values was much smaller when weight percentages were used.

ASH COMPOSITION AND VISCOSITY-TEMPERATURE RELATIONSHIPS

As early as the 1930's, the Bureau of Mines and others conducted studies to measure the flow characteristics of molten ash in wet-bottom furnaces; a method for relating ash composition to viscosity of the molten ash was developed. By placing the ash composition data into such specific arrangements as equivalent ferric oxide, silica equivalent, and calcium oxide percentage, and by developing a series of curves based on relationships of laboratory viscosity to ash composition, viscosity-temperature relationships can be established.

These viscosity-temperature relationships permit the construction of viscosity curves of the ash in both the fluid and plastic states. Although definite predictions are difficult to make from the viscosity curves alone, such plots are particularly useful for predicting the slag characteristics of specific coals by comparing the viscosity-temperature relationships with coals of known performance.

VISCOSITY OF COAL-ASH SLAGS IN THE COMPLETE LIQUID PHASE

The viscosity of coal-ash slag in the complete liquid phase can be measured or estimated at any temperature above its crystallization temperature. Above this temperature range, slag viscosity is mainly a function of temperature and chemical composition. Actual measurement of slag viscosity is usually expensive and difficult; therefore, several methods of estimating slag viscosity from the composition-temperature relationships have been developed. This method should only be used when the slag temperature is above the crystallization temperature, referred to as the temperature of critical viscosity.

METHOD BY REID AND COHEN[18]

The viscosity of coal-ash slags from Eastern U.S. coals in the complete liquid phase can be estimated according to the following procedure:

1. Calculate the silica percentage,

$$SP = \left(\frac{100 \times SiO_2}{SiO_2 + Equiv. \ Fe_2O_3 + CaO + MgO} \right)$$
(27)

2. Read the viscosity at a given temperature, or the temperature at a given viscosity, from the experimentally derived nomogram shown in Fig. 12. Scale C on the nomogram shows a direct relationship between SP and the liquid viscosity at 2600°F. To find viscosity and any other temperature: (a) connect the 2600°F point on scale A with the desired SP or viscosity on scale C; (b) note the pivot point on line B and (c) draw a line through the desired temperature on scale A, through the pivot point, to obtain viscosity on scale C.

METHOD OF HOY, ROBERTS, AND WILKINS[19]

The viscosity of coal-ash slags from British coals in the complete liquid phase can be estimated according to the following procedure:

1. Calculate the silica percentage,

$$SP = \left(\frac{100 \times SiO_2}{SiO_2 + Equiv.\ Fe_2O_3 + CaO + MgO} \right) \tag{28}$$

2. Estimate the slag viscosity from the following equation:

$$\log_{10}\eta = 4.468\,(SP/100)^2 + 1.265\,(10^4/T) - 7.44$$
$$\text{where } \eta = \text{slag viscosity (poise)}$$
$$T = \text{temperature (°K)} \tag{29}$$

The Hoy, Roberts, Wilkins relationship was based on the following range of coal-ash chemical composition:

SiO_2	31–59%
Al_2O_3	19–37%
Equiv. Fe_2O_3	0–38%
CaO	1–37%
MgO	1–12%
$Na_2O + K_2O$	1–6%
SP	45–75%
SiO_2/Al_2O_3	1.2–2.3

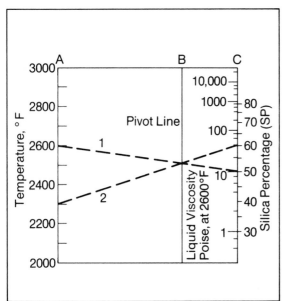

Fig. 12 Nomogram for estimation of coal-ash slag viscosity. See also reference 18.

METHOD OF WATT AND FEREDAY[20]

The viscosity of coal-ash slags from British coals in the complete liquid phase can be estimated according to the following procedure:

1. Normalize the chemical composition of the ash such that:

$$SiO_2 + Al_2O_3 + Equiv.\ Fe_2O_3 + CaO + MgO = 100\% \tag{30}$$

2. Calculate M, defined as:

$$M = 0.00835\,SiO_2 + 0.00601\,Al_2O_3 - 0.109 \tag{31}$$

3. Calculate C, defined as:

$$C = 0.0415\,SiO_2 + 0.0192\,Al_2O_3 + 0.0276\,Equiv.\ Fe_2O_3 + 0.0160\,CaO - 3.92 \tag{32}$$

4. Estimate the slag viscosity from the following equation:

$$\log_{10}\eta = \frac{10^7 M}{(T - 150)^2} + C$$
$$\text{where } \eta = \text{slag viscosity (poise)}$$
$$T = \text{temperature (°C)} \tag{33}$$

The Watt-Fereday relationship was based on the following range of coal-ash chemical composition:

SiO_2	29–56%
Al_2O_3	15–31%
Equiv. Fe_2O_3	2–28%
CaO	2–27%
MgO	1–8%
$Na_2O + K_2O$	1.5–5%
SP	40–81%
SiO_2/Al_2O_3	1.4–2.4

FLOW TEMPERATURE

The flow temperature is defined as the temperature at which slag has sufficient fluidity to allow free flow without difficulty. Normally the flow temperature corresponds to a slag viscosity of approximately 80 poise. For coal-ash slags of known chemical composition, the flow temperature can be calculated by letting $\eta = 80$ poise and obtaining the corresponding T_{80} value. It is used to predict the ease of slag removal in wet-bottom furnaces. It also can be used to estimate the maximum steady-state thickness of furnace-wall deposits, because no accumulation of slag is expected beyond this point.

When estimating slag viscosity in the complete liquid phase, one should consider the existence of the crystallization temperature, which is referred to as the temperature of critical viscosity (T_{cv}). The relation between T_{80} and T_{cv} is as follows:

If $T_{80} > T_{cv}$, then flow temperature = T_{80}
If $T_{80} < T_{cv}$, then flow temperature = T_{cv}

Prior to the development of the viscometer, the flow temperature was determined manually by stirring the liquid slag with a platinum rod. This stirring helped establish a standard "feel" for the flow temperature. An empirical relation was then developed between the flow temperature of coal-ash slags and the ASTM ash-fluid temperature (FT). For a coal-ash slag with a ferric content of about 10 percent, an approximate relation is expressed as:

$$\text{flow temperature (°F)} = 1.2 \, (FT - 470)$$

(34)

SLAG-REMOVAL TEMPERATURE

The slag-removal temperature is the temperature corresponding to the maximum viscosity at which slag can be tapped from a furnace. This upper limit for fluidity of slag is approximately 250 poise. For coal-ash slags of known chemical composition, the slag-removal temperature can be calculated from the relations described above, by letting $\eta = 250$ poise and obtaining the corresponding T_{250} value. T_{250} can also be estimated from the two graphical methods described later.

Generally, for wet-bottom furnaces, T_{250} should not exceed 2600°F. For dry-bottom units, high values of T_{250} are recommended for easier removal (sootblowing) of waterwall deposits.

When estimating slag viscosity in the complete liquid phase, the existence of the crystallization temperature should be considered. T_{cv}, which is referred to as the temperature of critical viscosity, is found as follows:

If $T_{250} > T_{cv}$, then slag-removal temperature = T_{250}
If $T_{250} < T_{cv}$, then slag-removal temperature = T_{cv}

Method of Sage and McIlroy[21]

The T_{250} value for slags from Eastern U.S. coals can be estimated from the curves in Fig. 13. The method is said to be valid for bituminous-type ash and for lignitic ash with acidic content over 60 percent.

Method of Duzy[22]

The T_{250} value for slags from Western coals can be estimated from Fig. 14. The method is said to be valid for lignitic ash having an acidic content under 60 percent.

TEMPERATURE OF NORMAL SLAG REMOVAL

The temperature of normal slag removal, t_{ns}, is defined as the recommended temperature for easy slag-tapping from a furnace. Usually, it corresponds to a slag viscosity of 200 poise. This concept has been widely used in Russia and is identical, in principle, to the U.S. criterion of the slag removal temperature. For coal-ash slags of known chemical composition, the temperature of normal slag removal can be calculated from the relations described above by letting $\eta = 200$ and obtaining the corresponding T_{200} value. Alternatively, it can be estimated by the following method.

When estimating slag viscosity in the complete liquid phase, the existence of the crystallization temperature should be considered. The relationship between T_{200} and T_{cv}, the temperature of critical viscosity, is as follows:

If $T_{200} > T_{cv}$, then $T_{ns} = T_{200}$
If $T_{200} < T_{cv}$, then $T_{ns} = T_{cv}$

Fig. 13 Estimation of T_{250} value according to base/acid ratio

Fig. 14 Estimation of T_{250} value according to dolomite percentage and percent base

According to the method developed by Kovitskii, Karagodina, and Martynova,[17] the T_{200} value for coal-ash slags from Russian coals can be estimated by the following procedure:

1. Calculate K_v which is expressed as

$$K_v = \frac{SiO_2 + P_2O_5}{Al_2O_3 + Fe_2O_3 + CaO + MgO}$$

(35)

2. Estimate the T_{200} value from the following equation

$$T_{200}(°C) = 1085 + 314\,K_v$$

(36)

This relation is claimed to be valid for the following chemical composition range (with K_v between 0.42 and 2.03):

SiO_2	20.9–63.1%
Al_2O_3	14.1–29.0%
Fe_2O_3	3.2–36.3%
CaO	1.2–27.3%
MgO	0.8–7.6%
P_2O_5	0.1–2.9%

EFFECT OF EQUIVALENT Fe$_2$O$_3$ AND FERRIC PERCENTAGE

It has been observed that coal-ash slag viscosity in the complete liquid phase can differ between reducing and oxidizing atmospheric conditions. This difference implies the effect of variation in ferric percentage. However, the difference in viscosity is usually small.

Nicholls and Reid[23] initially observed that the entire slag-viscosity profile was raised as the ferric percentage decreased. Sage and McIlroy[21] indicated the opposite; that is, the viscosity profile was lowered as ferric percentage decreased. In either case, the effect of ferric percentage on slag viscosity in the complete liquid phase seems to be small and can usually be neglected. Accordingly, the original Fe_2O_3 content of the ash can be substituted for the equivalent Fe_2O_3 when estimating slag viscosities according to the methods described above.

To obtain results which reflect actual furnace

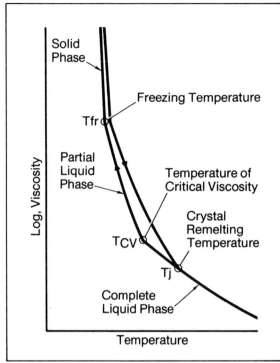

Fig. 15 **Effect of cooling and reheating on the viscosity-temperature relation of coal-ash slag**

conditions more closely, it is suggested that estimations be carried out at a ferric percentage of 20 percent.

VISCOSITY OF COAL-ASH SLAGS IN THE PARTIAL-LIQUID (CRYSTALLIZATION) PHASE

As coal-ash slags in the complete liquid phase are gradually cooled, the logarithm of viscosity will increase nearly linearly with decreasing temperature. But at a certain temperature, the viscosity departs from this approximate straight line and tends to increase rapidly as temperature decreases. The temperature at which this almost discontinuous transition occurs is referred to as the temperature of critical viscosity, T_{cv}, illustrated in Fig. 15. T_{cv} is believed to be the temperature at which solid phases begin to crystallize and separate out from the liquid and, hence, it can be considered as a crystallization temperature. Actual measurement of T_{cv} is expensive and difficult.

Several methods of estimating T_{cv} from the chemical composition have been developed and are described below.

The temperature of critical viscosity, then, provides the limiting temperature below which slag viscosities cannot be calculated using the methods described earlier. It also allows the prediction of the boundary temperature at which molten slag ceases to flow on furnace waterwall deposits.

Typical cooling curves for four different coal-ash slags are shown in Fig. 16. The explanation of the four curves is as follows:

Curve 1. Represents a true glass which does not have a distinct crystallization temperature. Very few coal-ash slags are of this type.

Curve 2. Represents a slag which is close to glass in behavior. Separation of solids begins after a long cooling period. T_{cv} is usually very low. Slags of this type are frequently referred to as "long" slags.

Curve 3. Represents a slag with a long freezing range. Separation of solids begins at high temperatures at low rates and freezes to essentially a solid at much lower temperatures. T_{cv} is usually high.

Curve 4. Represents a slag with rapid crystallization and freezing characteristics. T_{cv} can be either high or low. Slags of this type are frequently referred to as "short" slags.

METHOD OF SAGE AND McILROY[21]

T_{cv} of coal-ash slags from Eastern U.S. coals at a ferric percentage of 20 percent can be estimated from the following equation:

$$T_{cv}(°F) = HT + 200$$

(37)

where HT is the hemispherical temperature of coal ash (°F).

METHOD OF WATT[20]

T_{cv} of coal-ash slags from British coals can be estimated according to the following procedure:

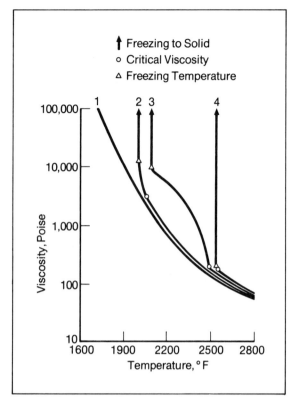

Fig. 16 Typical cooling curves for different types of coal-ash slag

1. Normalize the chemical composition of the ash, such that:

$$SiO_2 + Al_2O_3 + \text{Equiv. } Fe_2O_3 + CaO + MgO = 100\%$$

(38)

2. Estimate T_{cv} from the following equation:

$$T_{cv}(°C) = 2990 - 1470\left(\frac{SiO_2}{Al_2O_3}\right) + 360\left(\frac{SiO_2}{Al_2O_3}\right)^2$$
$$- 14.7\,(\text{Equiv. } Fe_2O_3 + CaO + MgO)$$
$$+ 0.15\,(\text{Equiv. } Fe_2O_3 + CaO + MgO)^2$$

(39)

METHOD OF MARSHAK AND RYZHAKOV FOR SOVIET COALS[24]

The temperature of critical viscosity is referred to as the temperature of the true liquid state, t_o, in the Soviet literature. It has been shown that t_o can be estimated from the following empirical equation:

$$T_o(°C) = 0.75\,t_2 + 480$$

(40)

where t_2 is the softening temperature of coal ash according to the Soviet standard (°C).

VISCOSITY OF COAL-ASH SLAGS IN THE SOLID PHASE

As coal-ash slags are cooled beyond the temperature of critical viscosity, a certain temperature is reached where the movement of the slag is completely terminated. The temperature at which this transition occurs, referred to as the freezing temperature, T_{fr}, is the point of solidification of the slag, as Figs. 15 and 16 illustrate. Only one method of estimation of T_{fr} is available, that by Reid and Cohen[18].

COAL-ASH SLAG DEPOSIT ACCUMULATION AND STRUCTURE

Molten to semimolten coal-ash slag deposits usually will not form on clean waterwall tubes since, upon approaching the relatively cooler tube surface, the slag particles become less adhesive because of rapid cooling in the wall-adjacent area. Accordingly, coal-ash deposition is generally considered to be a two-stage process. A primary layer of deposit first forms on the waterwall tube surface. The resulting rise in the surrounding surface temperatures subsequently allows the adherence of rigid plastic secondary deposits.

MECHANISM OF COAL-ASH SLAG DEPOSITION

The following two types of primary deposits are most commonly observed:

1. Primary deposits that result from the settling of the finer fractions (smaller than 30 microns) of flyash. This type of primary deposit is loose in structure and does not provide strong cohesive or adhesive bonds.

2. Primary deposits that result from the selective deposition of certain reactive components

of the ash (iron, calcium, or alkalies). These components can be present in the deposit in high concentrations as oxides and/or sulfur compounds, leading to the formation of low-melting eutectic mixtures. This type of primary deposit is more dense in structure and has stronger cohesive and adhesive bonds. The properties of the primary layer, which provides the link between the rigid secondary deposits and the tubes, have an appreciable influence on the ease of removal of the deposits by sootblowing.

During the deposition process, there is a transitional stage where the plastic secondary deposits begin to stick on the primary layer. These secondary deposits are strengthened by time and increasing temperatures.

INITIAL SLAGGING TEMPERATURE

The transition from primary to secondary deposits has been shown to be a function of the immediate gas temperature outside the deposit. The temperature at which the secondary deposits begin to form has been referred to as the initial slagging temperature, t_{is}. Methods of estimation of t_{is} are described below.

METHOD BY ALEKHNOVICH, BOGOMOLOV, NOVITSKII, AND IVANOVA[25]

The t_{is} of a coal-ash deposit from Soviet (Kuznetsk) coals can be estimated from the chemical composition of the ash according to the following procedure, using constituents on a weight-fraction (not percentage) basis:

1. Calculate K,

$$K = (Na_2O + K_2O)^2 + 0.048 (CaO + Fe_2O_3)^2 \tag{41}$$

2. Estimate t_{is} from the following equation:

$$t_{is} (°C) = 1025 + 3.57 (18 - K) \tag{42}$$

METHOD BY DIK AND SIKHORA[26]

Experimental investigations on deposits of

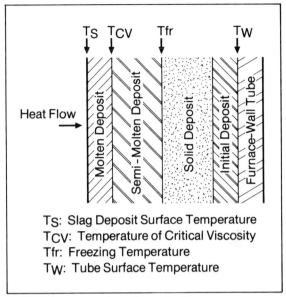

Fig. 17 Cross section of a typical furnace-wall slag deposit

coal-ash from Soviet (Kansk-Achinsk) coals showed the following results:

1. t_{is} corresponds to a temperature of approximately 950°C.

2. t_{is} is not strongly affected by the local gas velocity.

DEPOSIT STRUCTURE AND MAXIMUM THICKNESS

Fig. 17 shows a cross section of a typical waterwall slag deposit that has reached a maximum steady-state thickness. The slag surface temperature, T_s, can vary depending on furnace conditions and deposit characteristics. However, in general, T_s should not exceed the flow temperature. From the flow and depositional characteristics of coal-ash slags described in previous sections, it is possible to estimate an approximate structure profile of slag deposits. By knowing the heat flow into the deposit from the furnace flame and the thermal conductivity of the slag, it is also possible to calculate the maximum thickness of a waterwall deposit. This can give an indication of the degree of slagging of different coal types and the effect on heat transfer.

REFERENCES

[1] N. B. Vargaftik and O. N. Oleschuck, "Thermal Capacity of Slags of Various Fuels," *Teploenergetika*, 2(4): 13–17, 1955.

[2] V. G. Voskoboinikov, "The Heat Capacity of Blast-Furnace Slags at High Temperatures," *Teoriya Prabtiba Metallurgii*, 12 (10): 3–5, 1940.

[3] E. F. Foerster and P. L. Weston, Jr., "Heat Content of Some Blast-Furnace and Synthetic Slags" *U.S. Bureau of Mines Report of Investigation 6886*, Washington: U.S. Bureau of Mines, 1967.

[4] K. C. Lyon, "Calculation of Surface Tension of Glasses," Journal of the American Ceramic Society, 27: 186–189, 1944.

[5] C. W. Parmelee and C. G. Harman, "Effect of Alumina on Surface Tension of Molten Glass," *Journal of the American Ceramic Society*, 20: 224–230, 1937.

[6] N. M. Parikh, "Effect of Atmosphere on Surface Tension of Glass," *Journal of the American Ceramic Society*, 41: 18–22, 1958.

[7] S. G. Agababov, "Emissivity of Boiler Furnace Slag," *Teploenergetika*, 8, 1958, pp. 56–60.

[8] H. Becker, "The Effect of Ash Fouling on Heat Transfer to Boiler Tubes, Part 2: Thermal Properties of Particulate Brown Coal Ash," Report No. 252, State Electricity Commission of Victoria—Scientific Division, Australia, 1972.

[9] M. F. R. Mulcahy, J. Boow, and P. R. C. Goard, "Fireside Deposits and Their Effect on Heat Transfer in a Pulverized-Fuel-Fired Boiler, Part I: The Radiant Emittance and Effective Thermal Conductance of the Deposits," *Institute of Fuel Journal*, 1966, pp. 385–394.

[10] B. A. Khrustalev, "Spectral Radiation Properties of Some Materials at High Temperatures and Their Influence on the Integral Absorption and Radiation Properties," *Heat Transfer-Soviet Research*, 5, (2) Mar-Apr 1973, pp. 60–64.

B. A. Khrustalev and A. M. Rakov, "Methods of Determining the Integral and Spectral Radiative Properties of Materials at High Temperatures," *Heat Transfer-Soviet Research*, 1, (4), Jul 1969, pp. 163–177.

[11] R. A. Smith and L. R. Glicksman, "Radiation Properties of Slag," Report No. DSR-70332-61, Mech Eng Dept., MIT, Feb 1969.

[12] G. J. Goetz, et al., "Development of a Method for Determining Emissivities and Absorptives of Coal—Ash Deposits," *ASME Paper 78-WA/FU-6*. New York: American Society of Mechanical Engineers, 1978; also Combustion Engineering publication TIS-5890.

[13] B. K. Dutta, B. Rai, and K. A. Chabravorty, "Fusion Characterization of Coal Ashes; Softening Temperature of Coal Ashes in Oxidizing Atmosphere," *Journal of Scientific and Industrial Research*, 19B: 206–212, 1960.

B. K. Dutta, et al., "Study of the Fusion Characteristics of Coal Ashes: Softening Temperature of Coal Ashes in Mild Reducing Atmosphere," *Journal of Scientific and Industrial Research*, 21D (2): 44–48, February 1962.

[14] Roger Lewis Schaefer, *The Relation Between the Chemical Constituents and the Fusibility of Coal Ash*, M. S. Thesis. The Ohio State University, 1933.

[15] Thomas G. Estep, Harry Seltz, Henry L. Bunker, Jr., and Herbert S. Strickler, "The Effect of Mixing Coals on the Ash Fusion Temperature of the Mixture," *Mining and Metallurgical Investigations*, Carnegie Institute of Technology, Mining and Metallurgical Advisory Boards, Cooperative Bulletin 62, 1934.

[16] T. G. Estep, H. Seltz, and W. J. Osborn, "Determination of the Effect of Oxides of Sodium, Calcium, and Magnesium on the Ash Fusion Temperature by the Use of Synthetic Coal Ash," *Mining and Metallurgical Investigations*, Carnegie Institute of Technology, Mining and Metallurgical Advisory Boards, Cooperative Bulletin 74, 1937.

[17] N. V. Kovitskii, N. V. Karagodina, and M. I. Martynova, "Investigation of the Influence of the Chemical Composition of the Ash of Power Coals in Its Fusibility and Viscosity," *Solid Fuel Chemistry* (Translation of *Khimiya Tverdogo Topliva*), 9(3): 59–63, 1975.

[18] W. T. Reid and P. Cohen, "The Flow Characteristics of Coal-Ash Slags in the Solidification Range," *Transactions of the ASME*, 66, Furnace Performance Factors: 83–97, 1944.

[19] H. R. Hoy, A. G. Roberts, and D. M. Wilkins, "Behavior of Mineral Matter in Slagging Gasification Processes," *Institution of Gas Engineers, Journal*, 5(6): 444–469, 1965.

[20] J. D. Watt and F. Fereday, "The Flow Properties of Slags Formed from the Ashes of British Coals: Part I. Viscosity of Homogeneous Liquid Slags in Relation to Slag Composition," *Journal of the Institute of Fuel*, 42(338): 99–103, March 1969.

[21] W. L. Sage and J. B. McIlroy, "Relationship of Coal Ash Viscosity to Chemical Composition," *Combustion*, 31(5): 41–48, November 1959.

[22] A. F. Duzy, "Fusibility-Viscosity of Lignite-Type Ash," *ASME Paper no. 65-WA/FU-7*. New York: American Society of Mechanical Engineers, 1965.

[23] P. Nicholls and W. T. Reid, "Viscosity of Coal-Ash Slags," *Transactions of the ASME*, 63: 141–153, 1940.

[24] Y. L. Marshak and A. V. Ryzhakov, "Flow of Slag Film When Affected by Gas Flow," *Thermal Engineering* (Translation of *Teploenergetika*), 16(10): 12–16, 1969.

[25] A. N. Alekhnovich, V. V. Bogomolov, N. V. Novitskii, and N. I. Ivanova, "A Study of the Slagging Properties of Kuznetsk Coal Ash," *Soviet Power Engineering* (Translation of *Elektricheskie Stantsii*), 6: 509–513, September 1977.

[26] E. P. Dik, and R. A. Sikhora, "Study of the Conditions of Formation of Ash Deposits When Burning Nazarova Coal," *Thermal Engineering* (Translation of *Teploenergetika*), 16(10): 23–27, 1969.

Appendix D. Combustion Calculations by Graphical Methods

Besides presenting a unique method of accomplishing detailed calculations of combustion products of many fuels, this appendix supplements information from Chapter 2 on the production, transportation, and physical condition of these fuels as they are received in a steam-generating facility. Many of these factors (particularly temperature and water content) influence the calculation of air and gas weights, as well as the boiler efficiency itself. For the reader's convenience, some of the fuel-analysis data of Chapter 2 appear again in this appendix. The order of presentation parallels that of Chapter 2, "Fossil Fuels": first, solid fuels; then, liquid fuels; finally, gaseous fuels.

THE GENERAL METHOD FOR ALL FUELS

Combustion calculations by the designer are one of the first steps in proportioning a steam boiler. For example, the gas weight that results from fuel combustion is required to determine proper arrangement and extent of heating surface in furnace, boiler, economizer, and air heater. The gas weight is also necessary for proportioning gas ducts, dust-collection equipment, induced-draft fans, and stacks. Air weight is used to proportion air heaters, air ducts, fuel-burning equipment, and forced-draft fans.

This appendix will discuss the following items in detail and will present graphical calculation methods for each.

1. Fuel in products
2. Atmospheric air for combustion
3. Effect of unburned combustible
4. Products of combustion
5. Moisture in the combustion air
6. Moisture from fuel
7. Dry gas content of the combustion products
8. Carbon dioxide in products

In the method outlined here, the first four items are needed for the calculation of gas and air quantities. Items five to seven form the basis of heat-balance calculations in either the design or the testing of a steam-generating unit, when the *ASME Performance Test Codes*, Short Form, is used. The last item, carbon dioxide, and its relationship to excess air, is important in combustion calculations because in test work the CO_2 in the gases is measured and from it the excess air is calculated. The equipment designer works with excess air even though he may appear to have based his estimates on the percentage of CO_2.

The charts make allowance for all the important variables in the analysis. For practical purposes, therefore, they are as accurate as more laborious methods of calculation. On the other hand, even in working with a complete ultimate analysis and calculating the combustion requirements and products of combustion of each constituent, gross errors may result if, say, the heat value used is not correct for the given analysis.

The method employed here is based on the concept that the weight of air required in the combustion of a unit weight of any commercial fuel is more nearly proportional to the unit heat value than to the unit weight of that fuel. Consequently, the weights of air, dry gas, moisture, wet gas, etc., are expressed in pounds per million Btu fired. In the case of solid fuels, it is difficult to burn 100 percent of the combustible, so a correction for solid combustible loss must be made.

Before considering in detail the terms found on the charts and in the sample calculations, a quick review of the combustion process of a fuel is necessary. Take, for example, a fuel with no ash; when this fuel burns completely, the weight of the fuel is simply added to the weight of atmospheric air supplied for its combustion to obtain the wet products of combustion or total wet gas. Thus: fuel (F) + air (A) = products (P). But, if some of the fuel is ash, or, if because of incomplete combustion, some of the fuel does not pass out of the furnace with the gases, then F in the above equation will be less and both A and P will also be reduced. This concept of adding F and A to get P is the basis of the method.

FUEL IN PRODUCTS, F

By definition, fuel in products, F, is that portion of the fuel fired which reappears in gaseous form as separate elements or in chemical combination with other elements, after combustion in the gaseous products of combustion. Since with the present method all quantities are to be those required for or resulting from firing 1,000,000 Btu, F must also be calculated on that basis. If a fuel contains no ash and if, in addition, it deposits no carbon in the furnace or on other heating surfaces, F is simply obtained by dividing 1,000,000 by the "as-fired" heat value of the fuel in Btu per lb. For the other cases where ash and/or solid combustible loss must be considered, Eq. 1 may be used.

$$F = \frac{10^4(100 - \% \text{ ash} - \% \text{ solid combustible loss})}{\text{fuel heat value}}$$

where:

F = lb per million Btu fired

% ash = percent by weight in fuel as fired

% solid combustible loss = percent by weight in fuel as fired

fuel heat value (HHV) = high heat value as fired, Btu/lb

(1)

Fig. 1 is a graphical solution of Eq. 1, and applies to all fuels.

In the United States and many other countries of the world, the high heat value is the accepted standard and is obtained by calorimetric analysis of the fuel in a laboratory. Producers often sell fuel on the basis of its heat value and users generally check it periodically. In any event, manufacturers of steam-generating equipment need to know it; and, if it is not furnished, they must make an independent test or calculate it from constituents. For solid and liquid fuels, empirical formulas must be used, but for gaseous fuels the sum of the heat value of the various combustible constituents may be employed. Considerable difference may exist between the analysis "as received" and "as fired," even though nothing is intentionally done to the fuel between the time it is received and the time it is burned. Contrarily, certain fuels are purposely dried before they are fired and others take on moisture hygroscopically or are purposely "tempered." In the storage system of pulverized-coal firing, the moisture removed from the coal may actually be vented directly to a stack. In the direct-fired system, the moisture, although removed from the coal, is fired with the coal and therefore does not truly alter the combustion quantities.

Similarly, the heat value and analysis of gaseous fuels are generally reported on the volumetric basis; therefore, the temperature and the pressure conditions of the fuel are an essential part of the analysis. Standard conditions are commonly stated as 60°F and 30 in. Hg.

ATMOSPHERIC AIR, A

All combustion requires oxygen which in commercial practice must be supplied from the atmosphere. The theoretical quantity of oxygen may be calculated accurately from the fuel analysis and simple reaction formulas, such as

$$C + O_2 = CO_2$$

(2)

The corresponding weight or volume of dry air required to supply this oxygen may then be calculated, knowing that air contains approximately 23.1-percent oxygen by weight (20.9 percent by volume).

Natural and manufactured fuels, however, contain varying proportions of several different combustible constituents, such as C, H_2, S, and various hydrocarbons. Some also contain inert constituents, such as ash, N_2, H_2O, CO_2, as well as oxygen in varying quantities. Obviously, determination of air for combustion then becomes a time-consuming task with shorter methods desirable if accuracy can, at the same time, be maintained.

Fig. 1 **Weight of fuel in products of combustion**

Throughout this appendix, the curves labeled "A" give the relation of air quantity to percent excess air calculated for the several different fuels. These curves A are based on "atmospheric air," which means that an arbitrary amount of moisture has been added to the air. The American Boiler Manufacturers Association suggests basing all proposals on 60-percent relative humidity at 80°F, which is equivalent to 0.013 lbs of water vapor per lb of dry air. (To neglect this would introduce an error of approximately 1 percent.)

EFFECT OF UNBURNED COMBUSTIBLE

With a well-designed burner and furnace, it is commercially possible to burn liquid and gaseous fuels completely; no allowance is ordinarily made for loss of combustible in gas and air weight calculations. In the combustion of solid fuels, even in pulverized form, it is not commercially feasible to burn all the available combustible material in the fuel.

The method used to determine the solid combustible loss consists of collecting flyash and refuse from various hoppers. From a dry sample burned in a muffle furnace, weight loss due to combustion is measured. This loss can be expressed as percent by weight of fuel as fired.

In the combustion of a fuel having pure carbon as the only combustible constituent, the air required may be accurately obtained by multiplying a Curve A reading by the factor

$$C = 1 - \frac{\% \text{ solid combustible weight loss}}{100}$$

(3)

because, in this case, air for combustion is directly proportional to carbon in the fuel. If, however, all heat in the fuel does not come from carbon alone (so that the air is not strictly proportional to carbon burned), the factor C will not be exact. For high-carbon, low-volatile fuels it will be nearly exact and will result in only a small error even for fuels low in fixed carbon and high in hydrogen. The error involved by using Eq. 3 in all cases is quite within the limits of accuracy of all other combustion calculations.

For a heat balance the combustible weight loss must be converted to percent heat loss. This can be done conveniently by dividing the percent solid combustible weight loss by the heat value of the fuel as fired and multiplying by 14,500, which is the heat value for combustible in the refuse recommended by *ASME Performance Test Codes*, PTC 4.1.

PRODUCTS OF COMBUSTION, P

Having calculated the foregoing quantities F and A, the gaseous products of combustion may readily be determined by the addition of F and A, as previously corrected. Thus:

$$P = F + CA$$

where:

P = total gaseous products of combustion, lb/10⁶ Btu fired
F = fuel fired exclusive of ash or solid carbon loss, lb/10⁶ Btu fired
A = atmospheric air consumed, lb/10⁶ Btu fired
C = combustible loss correction factor

(4)

MOISTURE IN AIR, Wₐ

Since the *ASME Performance Test Codes* requires that heat loss due to moisture in air be reported as a separate item in the test heat balance of a steam-generating unit, engineers customarily include it in a predicted heat balance. In an actual test, the moisture in air can be determined from wet- and dry-bulb temperature readings, but for a predicted heat balance it must be assumed. It may vary from day to day even in the same locality, but the American Boiler Manufacturers Association has sug-

gested an arbitrary value for use in preparing proposals. As mentioned, this is taken as 0.013 lbs of water per lb of dry air and is included in the atmospheric air, A, as read from the air-weight curve. When required as a separate item for heat-balance calculations, an assumed value from the following equation will be sufficiently accurate.

$$W_a = 0.013A$$

(5)

MOISTURE FROM FUEL, Wf

This is another item which is separately reported both in an *ASME Performance Test Codes* heat balance and in a predicted heat balance. In the case of some fuels (such as natural and refinery gases), the heat loss due to this moisture may be the largest single item in the heat balance. W_f includes the combined surface and inherent moisture, W_c, from a fuel plus the moisture formed by the combustion of hydrogen, W_h. W_c will vary from zero or a mere trace in fuel oil to over 115 lb per million Btu fired in the case of green wood; W_h will vary from zero or a trace in lamp-black to 100 lb per million Btu fired in the case of some refinery gases.

Special charts, or groups of curves, are used to calculate W_f for each fuel.

DRY GAS, Pd

The need to calculate the "dry gas" or "dry products," in addition to the total products, is due to the *ASME Performance Test Codes*. Dry gas loss is a separate item of the heat balance.

The dry gas may be determined by subtracting the water vapor from the total products, thus

$$P_d = P - (W_a + W_f)$$

where:

P_d = dry gas, lb/10⁶ Btu fired
P = total products of combustion
W_a = moisture in air
W_f = moisture from fuel

(6)

CARBON DIOXIDE IN PRODUCTS, CO₂

Operators can use the CO_2 in the gases leaving a furnace or boiler as a guide in adjusting the air supplied, so as not to use too much excess air and in this way decrease the boiler efficiency. Conversely, if the CO_2 is maintained too high, so that the excess air is too low, there will be incomplete combustion of volatile fuel and a higher than normal loss in unburned fixed carbon.

The Orsat apparatus and all other chemical, mechanical, or electrical means for analyzing flue gas, measure the constituents of the gases and not the excess air. However, it is desirable that the excess air be known, because in many calculations the direct use of excess air rather than CO_2 greatly simplifies the work.

RELATION BETWEEN CO₂ AND EXCESS AIR

It is, therefore, convenient to know the relationship between CO_2 and excess air. For bituminous coals, the relationship may be quite accurately expressed in graphical form by means of two curves, one for high-volatile and one for low-volatile fuel. Since in other fuels as oil and gas, there is greater variation in the ratio of carbon to hydrogen, a whole family of curves may be required to cover the full range of analyses. As illustrated by these curves, the wide variation in excess air for a given CO_2, proves that it is unwise to think of CO_2 as synonymous with excess air except when dealing with one particular fuel analysis for which the CO_2-versus-excess-air relationship is known.

The relationship between CO_2 and excess air for a fuel of known analysis can be calculated by methods given in Chapter 4. Some engineers prefer to make calculations on a weight basis even for gaseous fuels, while others prefer the volume or mol system for all fuels.

COAL

Chapter 2 and Appendix A give the properties of the many types of coal found throughout the world. Particularly relevant to the calculation of the combustion products of coal are the methods of laboratory analysis described in Chapter 2, and found in the ASTM Standards referenced there.

PROXIMATE ANALYSIS

This quick and simple method is used to determine the moisture, volatile matter, fixed carbon, and ash of a given coal sample, by weight. The moisture content is obtained by noting the loss of weight in the sample when it is heated to a temperature of about 220°F for an hour. The moisture determined includes surface as well as inherent or hygroscopic moisture. The volatile matter is the loss in weight which follows additional heating of the sample to a temperature of about 1750°F for a half-hour, with all air excluded. The fixed carbon is calculated from the further reduction in weight of the sample which takes place when the coal is completely burned in the presence of air, while the ash is the residue at the end of complete combustion.

Since this laboratory method is approximate in nature, it is well to remember that combustion calculations which are based on it may be considerably in error. For example, it is necessary to know the hydrogen in the coal to evaluate the moisture loss in a heat balance. Fig. 2 shows two curves, taken from DeBaufre's original correlation,[1] which relates the percentage of volatile matter in the proximate

Fig. 2 Determination of hydrogen, moisture and ash free (W. L. De Baufre, "Composition in Heating Value of Fuels," *Combustion*, 2(11): 29–35, May 1931)

analysis to the percentage of hydrogen in the fuel. Actual values of hydrogen for certain coals will differ from these average curves by as much as 1.7 percent. This represents a variation of 12 lbs per million Btu in the water formed by combustion of the hydrogen, which means that the moisture loss estimated from a proximate analysis may be 1.5 percent greater or smaller than it should be, if such loss is based on 500°F. This discrepancy alone may, then, be sufficient to absorb the entire manufacturer's margin and unaccounted-for loss of 1.5 percent.

The character of the volatile matter is not the same for all coals, because some contain more carbon dioxide than others. This fact accounts for the two distinct groups of points occurring on Fig. 3, which is a correlation of the percent CO_2 in the dry products of combustion with the volatile matter in the proximate analysis. Thus, lignites and subbituminous coals form, on the average, about 1 percent more CO_2 than bituminous coals of the same volatile content. The kind of hydrocarbon in the volatile also has a direct bearing on the position of points in Fig. 3, since different hydrocarbons generate different amounts of carbon dioxide. Plotting percent CO_2 against the ratio of fixed carbon to volatile matter does not help to line up the points.

ULTIMATE ANALYSIS

From the foregoing discussion, it is obvious that for accurate combustion calculations it is preferable to have an ultimate analysis of the coal as discussed in Chapter 2. Sometimes, instead of being reported as a separate item, the moisture in the ultimate analysis is divided into 8 parts oxygen and 1 part hydrogen and then added to the oxygen and hydrogen of the combustible in the coal. For combustion calculations, this is not a good practice because in computing a heat balance the surface and inherent moisture in the fuel requires a different treatment from the water formed when hydrogen is burned.

Since an ultimate analysis includes the percent hydrogen, the amount of water formed by

Fig. 3 **Variation of theoretical CO_2 with volatile matter (VM)**

Fig. 4 **Variation of theoretical CO_2 with $\left[\dfrac{C}{H_2 - 0.1\,O_2}\right]$**

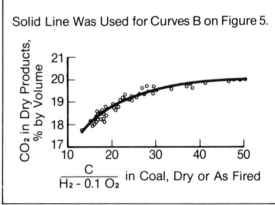

burning it can be accurately calculated. Furthermore, by knowing the ultimate analysis, it is possible to obtain a better correlation between the percent CO_2 in the dry products of combustion and the ratio

$$\left[\frac{C}{H_2 - 0.1\,O_2}\right]$$

for all coals, including lignite and subbituminous. This is shown by Fig. 4 where no CO_2 value plotted deviates from the solid line used in labeling Curves B of Fig. 5 by more than 0.30 percent. These are the principal reasons for preference of the ultimate over the proximate analysis.

Fig. 6 shows the variation of the atmospheric air at zero excess air with volatile matter on a

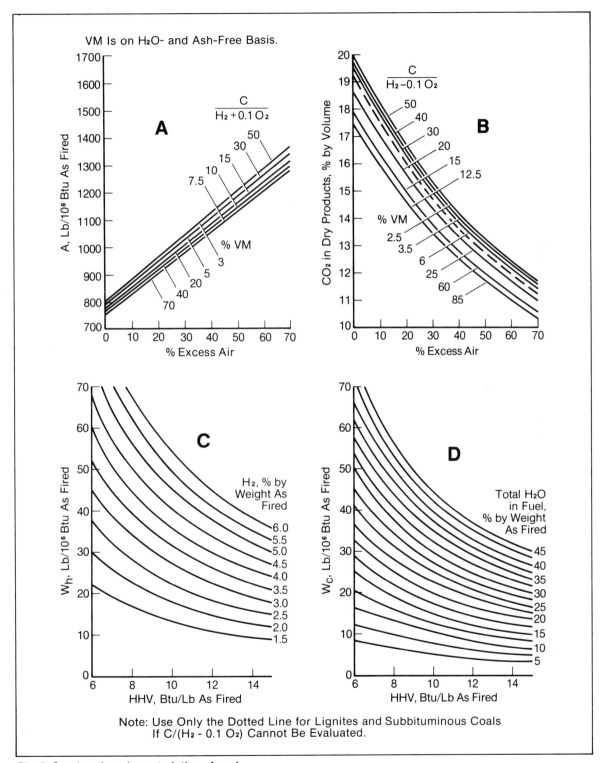

Fig. 5 Combustion characteristics of coal

moisture and ash-free basis, while Fig. 7 indicates the change in atmospheric air with the ratio

$$\left[\frac{C}{H_2 + 0.1O_2}\right]$$

Figs. 6 and 7 reveal that the maximum deviation in the calculated weight of air from the respective average curve is less than ±2.5 percent.

Table I tabulates representative ultimate analyses of various ranks from different states. More extended lists are available in the bulletins issued from time to time by the U.S. Bureau of Mines.

For purposes of reporting or correlation, it is often convenient to express proximate and ultimate analyses on a basis other than as fired.

Fig. 6 **Variation of theoretical air with volatile matter (VM)**

Fig. 7 **Variation of theoretical air with** $\left[\frac{C}{H_2 + 0.1O_2}\right]$

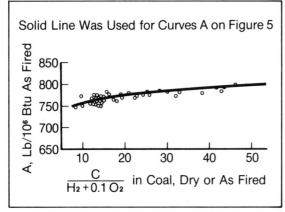

Thus, an analysis on the as-received or as-sampled basis serves to define the condition of the coal at the time it was tested. As dry, the fuel is reported with the moisture item omitted; as ash free, it is without ash, and as moisture and ash free, it has had both moisture and ash eliminated from the analysis.

HEATING VALUE

It is customary to report the high heating value (HHV) of coal, in Btu per pound, along with the analysis, whether proximate or ultimate, and on the same basis as the analysis. Burning a small sample of coal in a bomb calorimeter immersed in water, and measuring the temperature rise of the water, accurately determine the high heating value of constant volume.

Various formulas have been proposed for evaluating the Btu per pound of coal from its proximate or ultimate analysis. All yield only approximate results because they do not take into account the complex thermodynamic changes occurring when coal is burned. If only the coal rank is known, it is best to assume the heating value from some reasonably close analysis in Table I.

COMBUSTIBLE LOSS

Combustible loss in coal-fired furnaces results from incomplete burning of either the solid or the volatile combustible in the fuel. How much loss is determined by the character of the coal itself, the method of firing it, and the furnace design and operation. With proper furnace design and operation, the loss due to unburned volatile, as determined by the presence of CO in the flue gas, is generally negligible. On the other hand, the loss due to solid combustible in the ash, as measured by the reduction in weight which a sample of ash refuse undergoes on being completely burned, may vary from a negligible amount in burning pulverized coal to 20 percent of the coal fired, or more, with certain sizes of anthracite.

If K_1, K_2, etc., are known or assumed constants representing, respectively, the fractions of the total ash in a pound of coal which is deposited in the ash hopper, as flyash, etc., W. S. Patterson has shown[2] that the total combustible loss may be expressed by Eq. 7.

$$\text{\% solid combustible weight loss} = \\ 100 \left[\left(\frac{C_{R1}K_1}{1 - C_{R1}} + \frac{C_{R2}K_2}{1 - C_{R2}} \cdots \right) \right. \\ \left. \times \text{ ash in coal as fired} \right]$$

(7)

where C_{R1}, C_{R2}, etc., are the respective weights of combustible per pound of dry refuse from siftings, ash hopper, flyash, etc. For a given coal burning unit, the sum of all K's is, then, equal to 1.

The results of Eq. 7 may be substituted in Eq. 3 to find the unburned combustible factor, C.

FUEL IN PRODUCTS, F

Knowing the high heating value of the coal, its ash content, and its combustible loss factor C, that portion of the fuel which reappears in the products of combustion, F, is taken directly from Fig. 1.

ATMOSPHERIC AIR, A

For any value of excess air up to 100 percent, the atmospheric air in pounds per million Btu as fired may be taken from Curves A, Fig. 5, after determining either the ratio

$$\left[\frac{C}{H_2 + 0.1 O_2} \right]$$

from an ultimate analysis of the coal or the moisture- and ash-free volatile matter from a proximate analysis.

The empirical relation between A and

$$\left[\frac{C}{H_2 + 0.1 O_2} \right]$$

is shown by Fig. 7, while Fig. 6 indicates the trend of A with a change in the moisture- and ash-free volatile of the coal.

MOISTURE IN FUEL W_f

As already explained, the loss in weight caused by drying the coal at 220°F constitutes the total moisture reported in an analysis. To this moisture, when converted to pounds per million Btu, the symbol W_c has already been assigned. It is the sum of the surface moisture, which produces "wetness" in the coal, and the inherent or hygroscopic moisture, which being intimately held by the coal is not readily sensed. Table I reveals that, in some high-volatile bituminous coals, the total moisture may be as low as 1.4 percent, while it may increase to 34.8 percent in lignite. The portion of W_c that is inherent moisture, likewise, varies from negligible amounts in super-anthracites to high values in lignites. Curves D of Fig. 5 offer a convenient method of obtaining W_c from the percent moisture and high heating value of the coal as fired.

In addition to W_c, coal will yield water from the burning of its hydrogen content. Curves C, Fig. 5, make it possible to determine this water, W_h, in pounds per million Btu, from the percent hydrogen and high heating value of the coal as fired. If only a proximate analysis of the coal is available, its hydrogen content must first be read from Fig. 2. Special attention is called to the fact that Curves C are based on hydrogen as fired, while the hydrogen from Fig. 2 is on a moisture- and ash-free basis, and must be converted to the as fired condition before entering on Curves C of Fig. 5.

W_f is the sum of W_c and W_h.

PERCENT CO₂ IN PRODUCTS

The percent CO_2 by volume in the dry products of combustion may be read from Curves B, Fig. 5, for excess-air values up to 100 percent of theoretical requirements and for ratios from 12.5 to 50. The ratio

$$\left[\frac{H_2 - C}{H_2 - 0.1 O_2} \right]$$

can, of course, be calculated from an ultimate analysis of the coal. Fig. 6 shows the relation between percent CO_2 at zero excess air and

$$\left[\frac{C}{H_2 - 0.1 O_2} \right]$$

which was the CO_2 curves on Fig. 5.

When only a proximate analysis is given, the moisture- and ash-free volatile matter may be

Table I. Analyses of Typical U.S. Coals, as Fired

State	Rank	% Proximate Analysis				% Ultimate Analysis							HHV, Btu/Lb	A at Zero Excess Air, Lb/10⁶Btu
		H_2O	VM	FC	Ash	H_2O	C	H_2	S	O_2	N_2	Ash	Btu/Lb	Lb/10^6Btu
RI	A	13.3	2.5	65.3	18.9	13.3	64.2	0.4	0.3	2.7	0.2	18.9	9,313	808
CO	B	2.5	5.7	83.8	8.0	2.5	83.9	2.9	0.7	0.7	1.3	8.0	13,720	787
NM	"	2.9	5.5	82.7	8.9	2.9	82.3	2.6	0.8	1.3	1.2	8.9	13,340	786
PA														
*	"	5.4	3.8	77.1	13.7	5.4	76.1	1.8	0.6	1.8	0.6	13.7	11,950	791
**	"	2.3	3.1	87.7	6.9	2.3	86.7	1.9	0.5	0.9	0.8	6.9	13,540	794
***	"	4.9	3.7	82.2	9.2	4.9	81.6	1.8	0.5	1.3	0.7	9.2	12,820	788
AR	C	2.1	9.8	78.8	9.3	2.1	80.3	3.4	1.7	1.7	1.5	9.3	13,700	770
PA	"	3.0	8.4	78.9	9.7	3.0	80.2	3.3	0.7	2.0	1.1	9.7	13,450	777
VA	"	3.1	10.6	66.7	19.6	3.1	70.5	3.2	0.6	2.2	0.8	19.6	11,850	782
AR	D	3.4	16.2	71.8	8.6	3.4	79.6	3.9	1.0	1.8	1.7	8.6	13,700	774
MD	"	3.2	18.2	70.4	8.2	3.2	79.0	4.1	1.0	2.9	1.6	8.2	13,870	761
OK	"	2.6	16.5	72.2	8.7	2.6	80.1	4.0	1.0	1.9	1.7	8.7	13,800	775
WV	"	2.7	17.2	76.1	4.0	2.7	84.7	4.3	0.6	2.2	1.5	4.0	14,730	767
PA	E	3.3	20.5	70.0	6.2	3.3	80.7	4.5	1.8	2.4	1.1	6.2	14,310	765
VA	"	3.1	21.8	67.9	7.2	3.1	80.1	4.7	1.0	2.4	1.5	7.2	14,030	778
AL	F	5.5	30.8	60.9	2.8	5.5	80.3	4.9	0.6	4.2	1.7	2.8	14,210	768
CO	"	1.4	32.6	54.3	11.7	1.4	73.4	5.1	0.6	6.5	1.3	11.7	13,210	763
KS	"	7.4	31.8	52.4	8.4	7.4	70.7	4.6	2.6	5.0	1.3	8.4	12,670	769
KY	"	3.1	35.0	58.9	3.0	3.1	79.2	5.4	0.6	7.2	1.5	3.0	14,290	758
MO	"	5.4	32.1	53.5	9.0	5.4	71.6	4.8	3.6	4.2	1.4	9.0	12,990	769
NM	"	2.0	33.5	50.6	13.9	2.0	70.6	4.8	1.3	6.2	1.2	13.9	12,650	766
OH	"	4.9	36.6	51.2	7.3	4.9	71.9	4.9	2.6	7.0	1.4	7.3	12,990	762
OK	"	.2.1	35.0	57.0	5.9	2.1	76.7	4.9	0.5	7.9	2.0	5.9	13,630	757
PA	"	2.6	30.0	58.3	9.1	2.6	76.6	4.9	1.3	3.9	1.6	9.1	13,610	773
TN	"	1.8	35.9	56.1	6.2	1.8	77.7	5.2	1.2	6.0	1.9	6.2	13,890	767
TX	"	4.0	48.9	34.9	12.2	4.0	65.5	5.9	2.0	9.1	1.3	12.2	12,230	767
UT	"	4.3	37.2	51.8	6.7	4.3	72.2	5.1	1.1	9.0	1.6	6.7	12,990	758
VA	"	2.2	36.0	58.0	3.8	2.2	80.6	5.5	0.7	5.9	1.3	3.8	14,510	764
WA	"	4.3	37.7	47.1	10.9	4.3	68.9	5.4	0.5	8.5	1.5	10.9	12,610	758
WV	"	2.4	33.0	60.0	4.6	2.4	80.8	5.1	0.7	4.8	1.6	4.6	14,350	768
IL	G	8.0	33.0	50.6	8.4	8.0	68.7	4.5	1.2	7.6	1.6	8.4	12,130	766
KY	"	7.5	37.7	45.3	9.5	7.5	66.9	4.8	3.5	6.4	1.4	9.5	12,080	774
MO	"	10.5	32.0	44.6	12.9	10.5	63.4	4.2	2.5	5.2	1.3	12.9	11,300	773
OH	"	8.2	36.1	48.7	7.0	8.2	68.4	4.7	1.2	9.1	1.4	7.0	12,160	762
WY	"	5.1	40.5	49.8	4.6	5.1	73.0	5.0	0.5	10.6	1.2	4.6	12,960	757
IL	H	12.1	40.2	39.1	8.6	12.1	62.8	4.6	4.3	6.6	1.0	8.6	11,480	769
IN	"	12.4	36.6	42.3	8.7	12.4	63.4	4.3	2.3	7.6	1.3	8.7	11,420	758

Table I. **Analyses of Typical U.S. Coals, as Fired — *Continued***

State	Rank	% Proximate Analysis				% Ultimate Analysis							HHV, Btu/Lb	A at Zero Excess Air, Lb/10⁶Btu
		H_2O	VM	FC	Ash	H_2O	C	H_2	S	O_2	N_2	Ash		
IA	"	14.1	35.6	39.3	11.0	14.1	58.5	4.0	4.3	7.2	0.9	11.0	10,720	754
MI	"	12.4	35.0	47.0	5.6	12.4	65.8	4.5	2.9	7.4	1.4	5.6	11,860	762
CO	I	19.6	30.5	45.9	4.0	19.6	58.8	3.8	0.3	12.2	1.3	4.0	10,130	756
WY	"	23.2	33.3	39.7	3.8	23.2	54.6	3.8	0.4	13.2	1.0	3.8	9,420	757
ND	J	34.8	28.2	30.8	6.2	34.8	42.4	2.8	0.7	12.4	0.7	6.2	7,210	750
TX	"	33.7	29.3	29.7	7.3	33.7	42.5	3.1	0.5	12.1	0.8	7.3	7,350	752

*Orchard Bed
**Mammoth Bed
***Holmes Bed
A—Meta-anthracite,

B—Anthracite,
C—Semianthracite,
D—Low-volatile bituminous,

E—Medium-volatile bituminous,
F—High-volatile bituminous A,
G—High-volatile bituminous B,

H—High-volatile bituminous C,
I—Subbituminous, and
J—Lignite

used to obtain the CO_2 from Curves B of Fig. 5 for all but subbituminous coals and lignites. Because, as explained before, the volatile in the latter ranks does not possess the characteristics of other coals, the dotted line on Fig. 5 should be used when the ultimate analysis for sub-bituminous and lignitic coals is unavailable.

COKE AND COKE BREEZE

Coke is the fused solid residue left when certain coals, petroleum, or tar pitch are heated in

EXAMPLE

Assume that a bituminous coal, having the typical proximate analysis of line PA, Table I, is burned with 20-percent excess air and that the expected solid combustible loss is 0.8 percent by weight. Then

1. Fuel, F. The sum of the ash plus solid combustible loss is $9.1 + 0.8 = 9.9$ percent by weight. With this sum, and a high heating value from line PA, Table I, of 13,610 Btu per lb, read from Fig. 1, F = 66 lb per million Btu.

2. Atmospheric Air, A. The sum of the ash plus moisture in the coal is $9.1 + 2.6 = 11.7$ percent, and the moisture- and ash-free volatile matter =

$$\left[\frac{30}{1 - \frac{11.7}{100}} \right] = 34 \text{ percent}$$

For this value of volatile matter and 20-percent excess air, read from Curves A Fig. 5 A = 920 lb per million Btu.

3. Unburned Combustible Factor, C. Since the solid combustible loss is 0.8 percent, from Eq. 3 obtain

$$C = \frac{1 - \% \text{ solid combustible weight loss}}{100}$$

$$= \left[1 - \frac{0.8}{100} \right] = 0.992.$$

4. Total Products, P. From Eq. 4, $P = F + CA = 66 + 0.992 \times 920 = 979$ lb per million Btu.

5. Moisture in Air, Wa. From Eq. 5, $W_a = 0.013 \times 920 = 12$ lb per million Btu.

6. Moisture from Fuel, Wf This is the sum of W_c, the moisture in the coal as fired, and W_h, the water formed in combustion. From Curves D, Fig. 5, for 2.6-percent moisture in the fuel and a high heating value of 13,610 Btu per lb, read $W_c = 2$ lb per million Btu.

Next, convert the high heating value as fired to a moisture- and ash-free basis, as follows:

$$\left[\frac{13.610}{1 - \frac{11.7}{100}} \right] = 15,400 \text{ Btu}$$

per lb. and use it, together with the moisture-and ash-free volatile determined for A, to read from Fig. 2, $H_2 = 5.4$-percent moisture and ash free, or reverting to the as-fired basis, 5.4

$$\left(1 - \frac{11.7}{100} \right) = 4.8\text{-percent hydrogen.}$$

From Curves C, Fig. 5, for a high heating value of 13,610 Btu per lb and $H_2 = 4.8$ percent, read $W_h = 32$ lb per million Btu. $W_f = W_c + W_h = 2 + 32 = 34$ lb per million Btu.

7. Dry Gas, Pd. From Eq. 6, $P_d = P - (W_a + W_f) = 979 - (12 + 34) = 933$ lb per million Btu.

8. Percent CO_2 in Products. For a moisture-and-ash-free volatile matter of 34 percent and 20-percent excess air, read from Curves B, Fig. 5, $CO_2 = 15.3$ percent.

(*Note:* Many of the foregoing figures will be somewhat different if the ultimate, instead of the proximate, analysis in line PA, Table I, is used.)

an atmosphere excluding oxygen, so as to expel their volatile content. The process of thus decomposing these fuels into their gaseous and solid fractions is known as destructive distillation or carbonization.

Coke breeze is very small-size coke that is particularly well suited for firing on certain types of stokers. As a rule, it contains a higher percentage of ash than the rest of the coke. Table II presents analysis values of constituents in typical cokes, as fired.

HEATING VALUE

As with coal, the high heating value of coke, in Btu per lb, can be determined by a bomb calorimeter. If not given with the ultimate analysis, it may be calculated approximately from a formula of the Dulong type.

$$HHV = 14,600\,C + 62,000\left(H - \frac{O}{8}\right) + 4050\,S \tag{8}$$

where C, H_2, O_2 and S are weight fractions in the ultimate analysis.

COMBUSTIBLE LOSS

In burning coke or coke breeze in pulverized form or on stokers, a certain amount of the combustible in the fuel is lost as siftings with the flyash, etc., in the manner described in the section on coals. With coke, as with coal, the

$$
\begin{aligned}
\% \text{ solid combustible weight loss} = \\
100\left[\left(\frac{C_{R1}K_1}{1-C_{R1}} + \frac{C_{R2}K_2}{1-C_{R2}}\cdots\right)\right. \\
\left. \times \text{ash in coke as fired}\right]
\end{aligned}
\tag{9}
$$

where C_{R1}, C_{R2}, etc., are the respective weights of combustible per pound of dry refuse from siftings, ash hopper, etc., and K_1, K_2, etc., are constants representing fractions of the ash in a pound of coke found, respectively, in siftings, ash hopper, etc.

FUEL IN PRODUCTS, F

Knowing the high heating value of coke, its ash content, and its combustible loss factor C, that portion of fuel, F, which reappears in the products of combustion, is taken from Fig. 1.

ATMOSPHERIC AIR, A

Analyses of coke are reported on either the proximate or the ultimate basis. The chart, Fig. 8, was prepared so that values of atmospheric

Table II. Analyses of Typical Cokes, as Fired

Kind	% Proximate Analysis				% Ultimate Analysis							HHV, Btu/Lb	A at Zero Excess Air, Lb/10⁶ Btu	CO₂ at Zero Excess Air, %
	H₂O	VM	FC	Ash	H₂O	C	H₂	S	O₂	N₂	Ash			
High-temperature coke	5.0	1.3	83.7	10.0	5.0	82.0	0.5	0.8	0.7	1.0	10.0	12,200	798	20.7
Low-temperature coke	2.8	15.1	72.1	10.0	2.8	74.5	3.2	1.8	6.1	1.6	10.0	12,600	763	19.3
Beehive coke	0.5	1.8	86.0	11.7	0.5	84.4	0.7	1.0	0.5	1.2	11.7	12,527	807	20.5
Byproduct coke	0.8	1.4	87.1	10.7	0.8	85.0	0.7	1.0	0.5	1.3	10.7	12,690	802	20.5
High-temperature coke breeze	12.0	4.2	65.8	18.0	12.0	66.8	1.2	0.6	0.5	0.9	18.0	10,200	805	20.1
Gas Works coke:														
Horizontal retorts	0.8	1.4	88.0	9.8	0.8	86.8	0.6	0.7	0.2	1.1	9.8	12,820	808	20.6
Vertical retorts	1.3	2.5	86.3	9.9	1.3	85.4	1.0	0.7	0.3	1.4	9.9	12,770	809	20.4
Narrow coke ovens	0.7	2.0	85.3	12.0	0.7	84.6	0.5	0.7	0.3	1.2	12.0	12,550	802	20.6

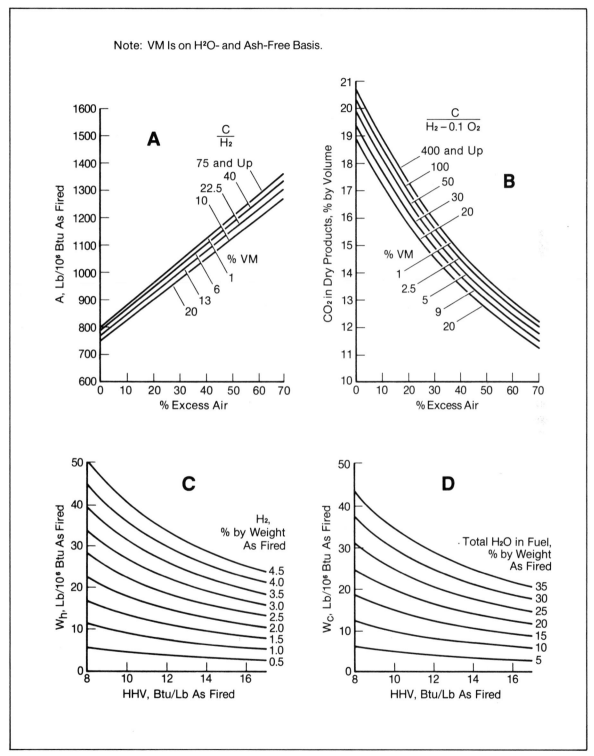

Note: VM Is on H²O- and Ash-Free Basis.

Fig. 8 **Combustion characteristics of coke**

air, A, in pounds per million Btu as fired may be obtained after knowing either the moisture- and ash-free volatile matter in the coke or its C/H_2 ratio.

Fig. 9 shows the empirical relation between A and the volatile matter on a moisture- and ash-free basis and Fig. 10 indicates how A varies with the ratio C/H_2. It will be seen that no calculated point deviates from the solid, average lines on these figures by more than ± 2.0 percent. The solid lines were used in labeling Curves A of Fig. 8.

TOTAL PRODUCTS, P

The unburned combustible factor is obtained from Eq. 3. This factor C is then used in correcting F, the fuel in products, and A, the atmospheric air when determining the total products P from Eq. 4.

MOISTURE IN FUEL, W_f

The moisture reported in a coke analysis, just as for coal, is the loss in its weight when dried at 220°F.

Any moisture present in coke results either from the quenching process or outdoor storage. W_c, which is this moisture in pounds per million Btu, may, therefore, be a small quantity if the quenching is done rapidly, or may amount to 12 lb or more in cases where storage conditions enabled the coke to absorb moisture, readily because of its porous nature.

Knowing the high heating value and the percent moisture in the coke as fired, W_c may be read from Curves D, Fig. 8.

W_h, the pounds of water per million Btu fired formed by combustion of the hydrogen in coke, may be obtained from Curves C of Fig. 8, provided the hydrogen in the ultimate analysis is given. With only a proximate analysis of coke available, W_h is determined from Fig. 11, after converting the volatile matter to a moisture- and ash-free basis. This curve is based on the graphical correlation shown in Fig. 12, and as such, is of limited accuracy. As in previous sections, W_f is the sum of W_c and W_h.

PERCENT CO₂ IN PRODUCTS

Curves B of Fig. 8 offer a convenient way of determining the percent CO_2 by volume in the dry products of combustion of coke, for any value of excess air from zero to 100

EXAMPLE

Assume that a high-temperature coke breeze, having the typical proximate analysis shown in Table II is burned with 35-percent excess air and that the expected combustible loss is 10 percent by weight. Then

1. Fuel, F. The sum of the ash plus solid combustible loss is $18.0 + 10.0 = 28.0$ percent by weight. With this sum, and a high heating value from Table II of 10,200 Btu per lb, read from Fig. 1, F = 70 lb per million Btu.

2. Atmospheric Air, A. The sum of the ash plus moisture in the coal is $18.0 + 12.0 = 30$ percent, and the moisture- and ash-free volatile matter =

$$\left[\frac{4.2}{1 - (30.0/100)} \right]$$

= 6 percent. For this value of volatile matter and 35-percent excess air, read from Curves A, Fig. 8, A = 1065 lb per million Btu.

3. Unburned Combustible Factor, C. Since the solid combustible loss is 10 percent, from Eq. 3 obtain

$$\frac{1 - \% \, solid \, combustible \, weight \, loss}{100}$$

$$= \left[1 - \frac{10}{100} \right] = 0.90.$$

4. Total Products, P. From Eq. 4, $P = F + CA = 70 + 0.90 \times 1065 = 1028$ lb per million Btu.

5. Moisture in Air, W_a. From Eq. 5, $W_a = 0.013A = 0.013 \times 1065 = 14$ lb per million Btu.

6. Moisture from Fuel, W_f. This is the sum of W_c, the moisture in the coke as fired, and W_h, the water formed in combustion. From Curves D, Fig. 8, for 12 percent moisture in the fuel and a high heating value of 10,200 Btu per lb read $W_c = 12$ lb per million Btu.

Next, with 6 percent moisture- and ash-free volatile determined for A, read from Fig. 11 $W_h = 10$ lb per million Btu. Then

$$W_f = W_c + W_h = 12 + 10 = 22 \text{ lb per million Btu.}$$

7. Dry Gas, P_d. From Eq. 6, $P_d = P - ((W_a + W_f)) = 1028 - (14 + 22) = 992$ lb per million Btu.

8. Percent CO₂ in Products. For a moisture- and ash-free volatile matter of 6 percent and 35 percent excess air, read from Curves B, Fig. 8, $CO_2 = 14.7$ percent.

(Note: Many of the quantities calculated in the example will be different if the ultimate, instead of the proximate, analysis of coke breeze is used.)

Fig. 9 Variation of theoretical air with volatile matter (VM)

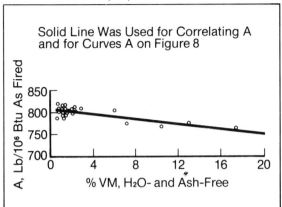

Fig. 10 Variation of theoretical air with C/H₂

Fig. 11 Predicted moisture from combustion of coke

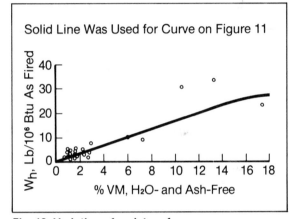

Fig. 12 Variation of moisture from combustion of coke with volatile matter (VM)

percent. As in drawing the lines for A, Curves B are plotted so that CO_2 values may be obtained after calculating the ratio

$$\left[\frac{C}{H_2 - 0.1\,O_2}\right]$$

from the ultimate analysis, or after converting the volatile matter in the proximate analysis as fired to the moisture and ash-free basis.

Comparing Fig. 13, which relates moisture and ash-free volatile matter to the percent CO_2 at zero excess air, with Fig. 14, which shows the variation of CO_2 with the ratio

$$\left[\frac{C}{H_2 - 0.1\,O_2}\right]$$

it is apparent that the latter is a more accurate correlation. Accordingly, in reading Curves B, an ultimate analysis of coke is preferable to a proximate analysis.

WOOD AND BAGASSE

The origin of these two cellulose fuels is described in Chapter 2; typical analyses are shown in Tables III and IV.

Moisture is the most variable single item in the composition of both wood and bagasse, its value ranging from 6 percent in a kiln-dried woods to over 60 percent in green wood or bagasse and up to 80 percent in bark. It is of importance in combustion calculations because it

Fig. 13 Variation of theoretical CO_2 with volatile matter (VM)

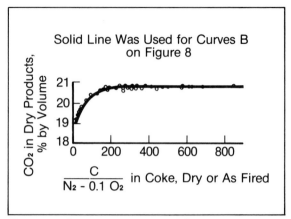

Fig. 14 Variation of theoretical CO_2 with $\left[C/H_2 - 0.1\ O_2 \right]$

directly influences the heating value of the fuel burned by increasing the proportion of inert matter present. Furthermore, it requires some of the heat released by the dry substance to evaporate and superheat it.

DETERMINATION OF MOISTURE CONTENT

An accurate determination of the moisture content in wood or bagasse is, therefore, necessary. To obtain this, a weighed sample is placed in a steam or electric oven and heated to 212°F until no further loss of weight occurs. The difference between the original weight and that of the dried sample divided by the original weight is the moisture fraction as received. In the lumber industry, it is customary to speak of moisture in wood on an oven-dry basis, whereby the loss of weight in the sample tested is divided by the oven-dried weight rather than the original weight. The percent moisture oven-dry must then be converted to the as-received basis before using it in combustion calculations.

The oven-drying method of determining the moisture content is not accurate with woods such as southern yellow pine, which contain oils that are easily volatilized, because these oils will distill with the moisture. It is then necessary to use the more elaborate distillation method, wherein the water and the oil are measured separately.

Other less reliable, but quicker, ways of judging the moisture in wood consist in measuring its electrical resistance or using a wood hygrometer.

As a rule, kiln-dried woods contain from 6 to 10 percent moisture, although softwoods will show a much higher percentage unless properly handled in the kiln. Air-dried woods have had enough moisture evaporated to be in equilibrium with the surrounding atmosphere. The actual percent present depend on both the temperature and relative humidity of the surrounding atmosphere. Fig. 15 shows how the moisture in wood varies with different relative humidities at 70°F. In arid climates, it may be as

Fig. 15 Moisture content of wood at 70°F ambient temperature

low as 5 percent, whereas in humid regions it may go up to 20 percent or more. Green wood, wood waste, and bagasse contain from 40 to over 60 percent moisture.

HEATING VALUE

The high heating value of wood or bagasse is determined by a bomb calorimeter, as in the case of other solid fuels. From the close similarity of the ultimate analyses of different woods, it might be reasonable to assume that equal weights of dry wood will release the same amount of heat, regardless of species. Actually, as Table III indicates, this is not the case, the heating value of wood depending to some extent on the physical structure and form of the

wood tissue, and still more on the presence of resins, gums, tannins, essential oils, or pigments. Resin alone, for instance, may increase the heating value of the same wood as much as 15 percent. Table III shows that the Btu per pound of dry softwoods is a little higher, on the average, than that of hardwoods, due perhaps to the fact that most softwoods are conifers containing resins and oils.

As mentioned, however, the chief factor affecting the heating value of the wood or bagasse as fired into a furnace is its moisture content. In the case of wood refuse, the heating value may also be influenced by the amount of trash and dirt gathered in processing the wood. In harvesting sugar cane, a certain amount of trash,

Table III. Typical Analyses of Dry Wood

	C	H_2	S	O_2	N_2	Ash	HHV, Btu/Lb	A at Zero Excess Air, Lb/10^6 Btu	CO_2 at Zero Excess Air, %
Softwoods†									
Cedar, white	48.80	6.37	...	44.46	...	0.37	8400*	709	20.2
Cypress	54.98	6.54	...	38.08	...	0.40	9870*	711	19.5
Fir, Douglas	52.3	6.3	...	40.5	0.1	0.8	9050	720	19.9
Hemlock, western	50.4	5.8	0.1	41.4	0.1	2.2	8620	706	20.4
Pine, pitch	59.00	7.19	...	32.68	...	1.13	11320*	702	18.7
white	52.55	6.08	...	41.25	...	0.12	8900*	723	20.2
yellow	52.60	7.02	...	40.07	...	0.31	9610*	710	19.3
Redwood	53.5	5.9	...	40.3	0.1	0.2	9040*	722	20.2
Hardwoods†									
Ash, white	49.73	6.93	...	43.04	...	0.30	8920*	709	19.6
Beech	51.64	6.26	...	41.45	...	0.65	8760*	729	20.0
Birch, white	49.77	6.49	...	43.45	...	0.29	8650*	712	20.0
Elm	50.35	6.57	...	42.34	...	0.74	8810*	715	19.8
Hickory	49.67	6.49	...	43.11	...	0.73	8670*	711	20.0
Maple	50.64	6.02	...	41.74	0.25	1.35	8580	719	20.2
Oak, black	48.78	6.09	...	44.98	...	0.15	8180*	714	20.5
red	49.49	6.62	...	43.74	...	0.15	8690*	709	19.9
white	50.44	6.59	...	42.73	...	0.24	8810*	715	19.8
Poplar	51.64	6.26	...	41.45	...	0.65	8920*	716	20.0

* Calculated from reported high heating value of kiln-dried wood assumed to contain 8-percent moisture.

†The terms "hard" and "soft" wood, contrary to popular conception, have no reference to the actual hardness of the wood. According to the *Wood Handbook*, prepared by the Forest Products Laboratory of the U. S. Department of Agriculture, hardwoods belong to the botanical group of trees that are broad-leaved whereas softwoods belong to the group that have needle or scalelike leaves, such as evergreens: cypress, larch, and tamarack are exceptions.

Table IV. Typical Analyses of Bagasse, Dry

	C	H₂	O₂	N₂	Ash	HHV, Btu/Lb	A at Zero Excess Air, Lb/10⁶ Btu	CO₂ at Zero Excess Air, %
	C	H_2	O_2	N_2	Ash			
Cuba	43.15	6.00	47.95	. . .	2.90	7985	629	21.0
Hawaii	46.20	6.40	45.90	. . .	1.50	8160	687	20.3
Java	46.03	6.56	45.55	0.18	1.68	8681	651	20.1
Mexico	47.30	6.08	45.30	. . .	1.32	8740	646	19.4
Peru	49.00	5.89	43.36	. . .	1.75	8380	700	20.5
Puerto Rico	44.21	6.31	47.72	0.41	1.35	8386	627	20.6

leaves, cane tops, and grass may be included which would result in a lower heating value for the bagasse. As a rule, larger quantities of trash and dirt are picked up when the cane is harvested and loaded by mechanical means than when this is done by hand.

Owing to their complex composition, it is not possible to make use of a Dulong-type formula to predict the heating value of either wood or bagasse. The formula appears to give values of available hydrogen in the factor

$$\left(H_2 - \frac{O_2}{8} \right)$$

which are too low and, as a result, the heating values calculated with it are invariably low.

In sugar-mill practice, bagasse analyses are frequently reported in terms of its fiber, sucrose, glucose, moisture, and ash content. If these are given, the high heating value (HHV) of bagasse in Btu per pound may be computed from

$$HHV = 8550(F) + 7119(S) + 6750(G) - 972(M)$$

where
  F = fiber, lb/lb of bagasse
  S = sucrose, lb/lb of bagasse
  G = glucose, lb/lb of bagasse
  M = moisture, lb/lb of bagasse **(10)**

FUEL IN PRODUCTS, F

The combustible loss in burning wood or bagasse is generally assumed to be zero. Therefore, if the high heating value and the ash content of these fuels are known, the portion, F, of the fuel that reappears in the products of combustion may be taken directly from Fig. 1.

ATMOSPHERIC AIR, A

Curves A of Fig. 18 offer a convenient way of obtaining the "atmospheric air," A, in pounds per million Btu fired, for any excess-air value up to 100 percent after calculating the ratio

$$\left[\frac{C}{H_2 + 0.1 O_2} \right]$$

from the ultimate analysis of wood or bagasse. These line are based on the correlation, between this ratio and the theoretical air required, shown by Fig. 16.

PERCENT CO₂ IN PRODUCTS

The percent CO_2 by volume in the dry products of combustion may be determined from Curves B of Fig. 18 for any excess air from zero to 100 percent of theoretical requirements. Curves B are based on the solid line of Fig. 17, which shows the change in the ultimate CO_2 with the ratio.

$$\left[\frac{C}{H_2 - 0.1 O_2} \right]$$

The correlation of Fig. 17 shows that no value deviates from the solid line by more than ±0.2 percent CO_2. This is the accuracy that may be expected in reading Curves B.

MOISTURE IN FUEL, Wf

The total moisture in the products of combustion of either wood or bagasse has been de-

Fig. 16 Moisture of theoretical air
with $\left[C/H_2 + 0.1\,O_2 \right]$

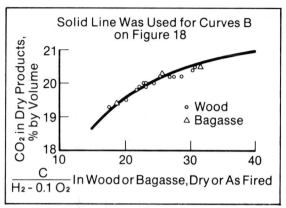

Fig. 17 Variation of theoretical CO₂
with $\left[C/H_2 - 0.1\,O_2 \right]$

noted by the symbol W_f, pounds per million Btu. It is the sum of W_c, the moisture originally in the fuel and W_h, the water formed from the combustion of hydrogen.

When the ultimate analysis of wood or bagasse as fired is known, as well as the high heating value, W_c may be read directly from Curves D and W_h from Curves C of Fig. 18.

EXAMPLE

Assume that saw-mill refuse from Western hemlock, containing 55-percent moisture as fired and having the ultimate analysis shown in Table III, is burned with 45-percent excess air. Then

1. Fuel, F. Convert both the ash and the high heating value of Table III from the dry to the as-fired condition, or, ash

$$= 2.2 \left(\frac{100 - 55}{100} \right) = 1.0$$

percent as fired and

$$HHV = 8620 \left(\frac{100 - 55}{100} \right) = 3880 \text{ Btu per lb}$$

as fired. With these values for ash and HHV, read from Fig. 1, F = 255 lb per million Btu.

2. Atmospheric Air, A. Calculate the ratio

$$\left[\frac{C}{H_2 + 0.1\,O_2} \right] = \left[\frac{50.4}{5.8 + 0.1 \times 41.4} \right] = 5.07$$

and with this ratio read from Curves A, Fig. 18, for 45-percent excess air, A = 1040 lb per million Btu.

3. Unburned Combustible Factor, C. The usual assumption when burning wood in steam boiler furnaces is that the combustible loss of zero, consequently C in Eqs. 3 and 4 may be taken as 1.

4. Total Products, P. From Eq. 4, P = F + CA = 255 + 1 × 1040 = 1295 lb per million Btu.

5. Moisture in Air, Wₐ. From Eq. 5, W_a = 0.013A = 0.013 × 1040 = 14 lb per million Btu.

6. Moisture from Fuel, Wf. The total moisture in the products of combustion of wood, W_f, is the sum of W_c, the moisture in the wood as fired, and W_h, the water formed by its combustion. Since the wood contains 55-percent moisture as fired and its high heating value as determined for F is 3880 Btu per lb, from Curves D of Fig. 18, W_c = 142 lb per million Btu. Next, convert the percent hydrogen in Table III from the dry to the as-fired basis, or

$$H_2 = 5.8 \left(\frac{100 - 55}{100} \right) = 2.6 \text{ percent}$$

as fired, and with a high heating value of 3880 Btu read from Curves C, Fig. 18 W_h = 60 lb per million Btu. Then
$$W_f = W_c + W_h = 142 + 60 = 202 \text{ lb per million Btu}$$

7. Dry Gas, Pd. From Eq. 6, P_d = P − (W_a + W_f) = 1295 − (14 + 202) = 1079 lb per million Btu.

8. Percent CO₂ in Products. Compute the ratio

$$\left[\frac{C}{H_2 - 0.1\,O_2} \right] = \left[\frac{50.4}{5.8 - 0.1 \times 41.4} \right] = 30.4$$

and for 45-percent excess air read on Curves B, Fig. 18, CO_2 = 14.2 percent.

FUEL OILS

The fuel oils ordinarily burned in steam-generating units are derivatives of petroleum comprising the so-called "Bunker" grades, diesel-engine oils, gas oils, kerosene, and gasoline. As they all have a common source, the constituents of their analyses are the same, although the relative quantity of each varies. De Baufre's representative tabulation in his article

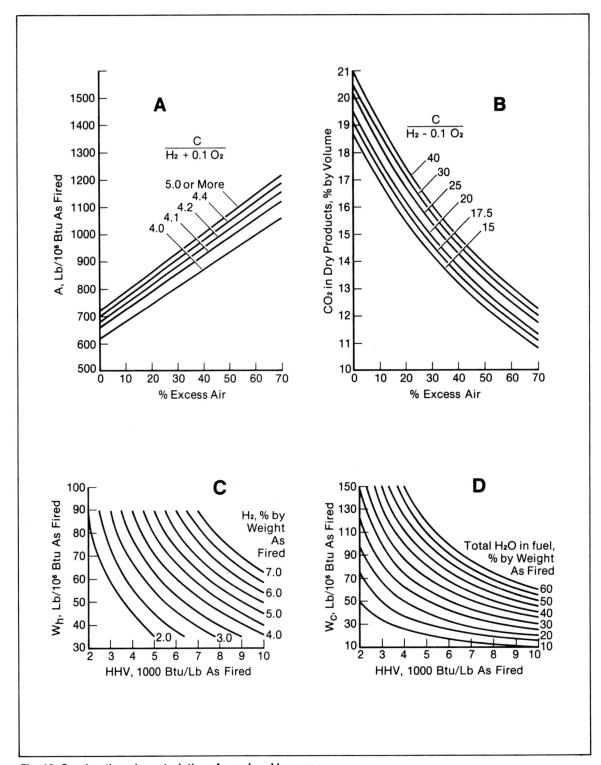

Fig. 18 Combustion characteristics of wood and bagasse

on "Typical Solid and Liquid Fuels"[3] shows that the combustible fraction chiefly consists of carbon and hydrogen with small amounts of sulfur. Negligible percentages of nitrogen and oxygen as well as water and sediment are also frequently found. De Baufre's table is, in part, reproduced as Table V.

The calculated atmospheric air, A, in lbs per million Btu as fired and the percent CO_2 in the products, both for zero excess air, are also tabulated for the different oils.

For commercial furnaces, Bunker C oil is frequently specified. This term has come to be applied to heavier fuel oils having a viscosity from 100 to 300 S.S.F. (Saybolt seconds furol) at 122°F. Bunker C oil roughly corresponds to No. 6 fuel oil in "Commercial Standard for Fuel Oils" by the Bureau of Standards.

FUEL IN PRODUCTS, F

Refer to Fig. 1, or calculate F directly from

$$F = \frac{1,000,000}{HHV}$$

$$(11)$$

ATMOSPHERIC AIR, A

The atmospheric air in pounds per million Btu as fired may be taken from Curve A of Fig. 19 for any value of excess air up to 100 percent. The values obtained are averages for a wide range of fuel oils; no chemical analysis is necessary in using Curve A.

TOTAL PRODUCTS, P

The weight of the products of combustion in pounds per million Btu as fired is given by $P = F + CA = F + A$, where C, the combustible-loss correction, is usually taken as 1.

MOISTURE IN FUEL, W_f

For fuel oil use curve group C of Fig. 19, where W_f is merely the moisture from hydrogen, and W_h is determined from Eq. 12.

$$W_h = 9 \times H_2 \times \left(\frac{10^4}{HHV} \right)$$

where:
W_h = moisture from combustion of H_2, lb/10^6 Btu fired
H_2 = hydrogen in fuel, % by weight
HHV = high (gross) heat value of fuel, Btu/lb

$$(12)$$

PERCENT CO₂ IN PRODUCTS

Curves B of Fig. 19 offer a convenient way of determining the percent CO_2 by volume in the dry products of combustion of fuel oil, for any value of excess air from zero to 100 percent. Curves B are plotted so that CO_2 values may be obtained after calculating the ratio C/H_2 from the ultimate analysis of the fuel.

EXAMPLE

Assume a fuel oil with the typical analysis given in Table V burned with 10-percent excess air. Then,

1. Fuel, F. From Fig. 1 for a high heat value of 18,500 Btu per lb and 0-percent ash read F = 54 lb per million Btu.
2. Atmospheric Air, A. From Curve A, Fig. 19, read A = 825 lb per million Btu.
3. Unburned Combustible. In the combustion of fuel oils in stationary boiler furnaces, it is generally assumed that there is no combustible heat loss. Therefore C in Eq. 3 is equal to 1.
4. Total Products, P. From Eq. 4, P = CA + F = 1 × 825 + 54 = 879 lb per million Btu.
5. Moisture in Air, W_a. From Eq. 5, W_a = 0.013 (A) = 0.013(825) = 11 lb per million Btu.
6. Moisture from Fuel, W_f. Since W_c = 0, from Curves C, Fig. 19, for a high heat value of 18,500 Btu/lb and H_2 of 11.5 percent, read W_f = W_h = 56 lb per million Btu.
7. Dry Gas, P_d. From Eq. 6, P_d = P − (W_a + W_f) = 879 − (11 + 56) = 812 lb per million Btu.
8. Percent CO₂ in Products. From Curves B, Fig. 19, for 10-percent excess air and a C/H_2 ratio of 7.5, read CO_2 = 14.4 percent.

NATURAL GAS

Characteristics of typical natural gases are given in Table VI, with the volumetric heating value on a moisture-free basis.

From the standpoint of combustion calculations, it is important to remember that the terms *dry* or *wet* as commonly applied to natural gas

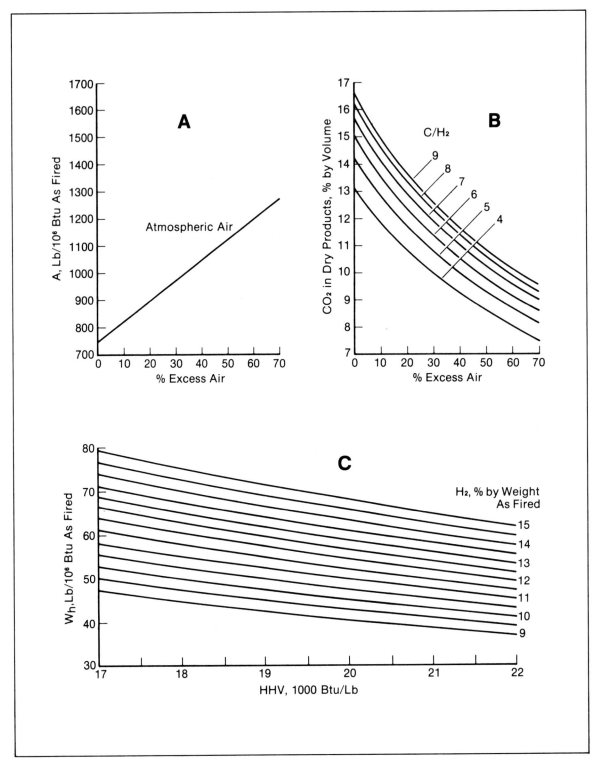

Fig. 19 **Combustion characteristics of fuel oil**

Table V. Characteristics of Typical Liquid Fuels

	° API	% C	% H₂	% S	% N₂	% O₂	HHV, Btu/Lb	A at Zero Excess Air, Lb/10⁶ Btu	CO₂ at Zero Excess Air, %
Gasoline	60	85.0	14.8	...	0.1	0.1	20,200	746	14.87
Kerosene	45	85.0	14.0	...	0.5	0.5	19,900	742	15.12
Gas oil	30	85.0	12.8	0.8	0.7	0.7	19,300	745	15.48
Fuel oil	15	85.5	11.5	1.6	0.7	0.7	18,500	758	15.90

Table VI. Characteristics of Typical Natural Gases at 60°F and 30 In. Hg, Dry

CO₂	N₂	H₂S	CH₄	C₂H₆	C₃H₈	C₄H₁₀	C₅H₁₂	Density, Lb/Cu Ft	HHV Btu/Cu Ft**	HHV Btu/Lb	A at Zero Excess Air, Lb/10⁶ Btu	CO₂ at Zero Excess Air, %
5.50	...	7.00	77.73	5.56	2.40	1.18	0.63*	0.05622	1060	18,880	738	12.1
3.51	32.00	0.50	52.54	3.77	2.22	2.02	3.44*	0.06610	874	13,220	729	12.3
26.2	0.7	...	59.2	13.9	...	...	...	0.06747	849	12,580	732	15.3
0.17	87.69	...	10.50	1.64	...	...	...	0.07120	136	1,907	732	6.9
0.20	0.60	...	99.20	...	...	...	...	0.04491	1006	22,410	732	11.7
...	0.60	...	...	79.40	20.00	...	...	0.08812	1935	21,960	735	13.3
...	0.50	...	...	21.80	77.70	...	...	0.11079	2389	21,560	738	13.7

* All hydrocarbons heavier than C_5H_{12} were assumed to be C_5H_{12} for combustion calculations.

** If gas is saturated with moisture at 60°F and 30. in. Hg, reduce by 1.74%.

refer to its gasoline vapor, and not to its moisture content. In fact, the only time natural gas has any moisture at its point of origin is when it is next to salt water. But this is a relatively unusual occurrence.

TEMPERATURE

The temperature of natural gas as it issues from the ground is dependent on the depth of the well and may vary from 32 to 165°F. The general rule among geologists is to assume an increase in temperature of 1°F for every 50 feet in depth, although this rule will not always check with actual measurements taken in the field.

It is also apparent that gas which has flowed through many miles of pipeline will have whatever ambient temperature that prevails in the locality where it is burned; most probably from 40 to 80°F. In combustion calculations for natural gas, it is deemed sufficiently accurate to assume the standard 60°F, when its actual temperature is not reported.

MOISTURE

As already noted, the only time that natural gas can have any moisture on leaving a well is when it previously has lain in contact with salt water. It may then be considered saturated with moisture at its temperature in the well.

However, gas which is delivered from a pipeline has often been "rehydrated," that is, saturated with water vapor by means of steam jets to lower the cost of maintaining pipe gaskets. Since the steam is ordinarily added to the gas in the high-pressure line, when the pressure is lowered for local distribution, the relative humidity of natural gas will also drop. Still another complication is introduced when a wet displacement meter is employed to measure the gas consumption. In this meter, the gas may be saturated with water.

In view of the variable and uncertain moisture content in natural gas, and in the absence of more definite determinations, it has become practice in industry to assume natural gas to be dry at 60°F and 30 in. Hg.

DENSITY

The density of a gaseous fuel may be obtained by adding the weights of the constituents in the fuel. The following is an example of a density calculation for the natural gas listed first in Table VI.

Density of the individual constituents are taken from Table VII, which lists the "saturated" and "unsaturated" or "illuminant" hydrocarbons that are most frequently found in

	% by Vol.	Vol. cu ft constituent /cu ft fuel	Density of constituent, lb/cu ft	Weight lb/cu ft fuel
CO_2	5.50	0.0550	×0.1170	=0.00644
H_2S	7.00	0.0700	×0.09109	=0.00638
CH_4	77.73	0.7773	×0.04246	=0.03300
C_2H_6	5.56	0.0556	×0.08029	=0.00446
C_3H_8	2.40	0.0240	×0.1196	=0.00287
C_4H_{10}	1.18	0.0118	×0.1582	=0.00187
C_5H_{12}	0.63	0.0063	×0.1904	=0.00120
			Total = Density of Dry Gas	=0.05622

gaseous fuels. Saturated hydrocarbons do not unite directly with hydrogen; i.e., they are stable in the presence of hydrogen, while unsaturated hydrocarbons readily take on more

Table VII. Combustion Constants of Dry Gases at 60°F and 30 In. Hg

Gas	Chemical Formula	Density of Dry Gas, Lb/Cu Ft	HHV of Dry Gas	
			Btu/Cu Ft*	Btu/Lb
Oxygen	O_2	0.08461	. . .	. . .
Nitrogen (atmospheric)	N_2	0.07439	. . .	. . .
Air	. . .	0.07655	. . .	. . .
Carbon dioxide	CO_2	0.1170	. . .	. . .
Water vapor	H_2O	0.04758	. . .	. . .
Hydrogen	H_2	0.005327	325	60,991
Hydrogen sulfide	H_2S	0.09109	647	7,100
Carbon monoxide	CO	0.07404	321	4,323
Saturated Hydrocarbons;				
Methane	CH_4	0.04246	1014	23,896
Ethane	C_2H_6	0.08029	1789	22,282
Propane	C_3H_8	0.1196	2573	21,523
Butane	C_4H_{10}	0.1582	3392	21,441
Pentane	C_5H_{12}	0.1904	4200	22,058
Unsaturated Hydrocarbons or Illuminants;				
Ethylene	C_2H_4	0.07421	1614	21,647
Propylene	C_3H_6	0.1110	2383	21,464
Butylene	C_4H_8	0.1480	3190	21,552
Pentylene	C_5H_{10}	0.1852	4000	21,600
Acetylene	C_2H_2	0.06971	1488	21,344
Benzene	C_6H_6	0.2060	3930	19,068
Toluene	C_7H_8	0.2431	4750	19,537

* If gas is saturated with moisture at 60°F and 30.0 in. Hg, reduce by 1.74%.

hydrogen. The latter are also called illuminants because they burn with a bright luminous flame, as distinguished from the saturated hydrocarbons which have a blue flame.

Extreme accuracy in calculations of density and heating value of gaseous fuels is not warranted; the precise values of the individual constituents continue to change as more accurate experimental procedures are developed, presenting somewhat of a "moving target."

Figs. 20 and 21 and Eq. 13 may be used whenever it is desired to correct for moisture content or for a temperature higher than 60°F.

	% by Volume, Dry	Volume cu ft/ cu ft of Gas		Heating Value, Btu/ cu ft		Heat Evolved by Components Btu/cu ft
H_2S	7.00	0.0700	×	647	=	45
CH_4	77.73	0.7773	×	1014	=	788
C_2H_6	5.56	0.0556	×	1789	=	99
C_3H_8	2.40	0.0240	×	2573	=	62
C_4H_{10}	1.18	0.0118	×	3392	=	40
C_5H_{12}	0.63	0.0063	×	4200	=	26
		Heating Value of Dry Gas			=	1060 Btu/cu ft

$$d_t = \frac{d_{60} + X}{Y} + (D_t + w_c)$$

where:

d_t = density of gas at temperature, t, lb/cu ft
d_{60} = density of dry gas at 60°F, lb/cu ft
X and Y = correction factors read from Fig. 21
D_t = dust content of gas, lb/cu ft at t temperature
w_c = entrained water found only in primary gas, lb/cu ft at t temperature

(13)

Before going to a great deal of refinement, however, remember that the calculated gas density can be no more accurate than the volumetric analysis from which it is derived. A natural-gas analysis which groups all hydrocarbons as CH_4 and C_2H_6, or C_2H_6 and C_3H_8 may indicate a lower density than the actual value.

HEATING VALUE

As with all other gaseous fuels, it is customary to compute the high heating value of natural gas, in Btu per cu ft at 60°F and 30 in. Hg, by adding together the heat evolved by the combustible components reported in the gas analysis. Thus, for a gas such as the first one in Table VI, the procedure indicated below may be employed, using the heating values in Table VII.

The high heating value in Btu per pound is then obtained by dividing the Btu per cubic foot by the density at 60°F and 30 in. Hg. To correct the Btu per pound for the effect of higher

temperature and moisture content, refer to Fig. 22 and Eq. 14.

$$(HHV)_t = M(HHV)_{60} + N$$

(14)

The Btu per cubic foot calculated by the foregoing method will generally be lower than that determined by calorimeter because of the arbitrary grouping of hydrocarbons explained before. For the same reason, the calculated density will also be lower than actual. It follows that the Btu per pound, with which we are primarily concerned, is nearer to its actual value when it is figured from the calculated Btu per cubic foot and calculated density than when it is the ratio of the calorimeter Btu per cubic foot and the calculated density of the gas.

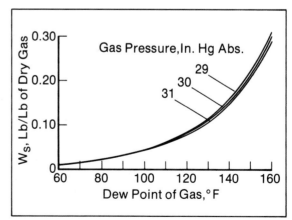

Fig. 20 **Water vapor in gas**

FUEL IN PRODUCTS, F

After determining the Btu per pound (HHV), F, which is that portion of the fuel that reappears in the products of combustion, is easily read from Fig. 1.

ATMOSPHERIC AIR, A

The atmospheric air in pounds per million Btu as fired may be taken from Curve A of Fig. 23 for any value of excess air up to 70 percent. As previously defined, the term *atmospheric air* is used to designate air which contains 0.013 pound of water vapor per pound of dry air, an arbitrary amount equivalent to 60 percent relative humidity at 80°F. The atmospheric air, A, may be corrected for temperatures higher than 60°F using Eq. 15.

$$A_t = \frac{A\,(HHV)_{60}}{(HHV)_t\,(1 + W_s + D_t/d_t)} \tag{15}$$

Note: If $t = 60°F$, the equation reduces to $A_t = A$, regardless of the moisture and dust content.

No chemical analysis of natural gas is necessary to obtain atmospheric air from Curve A.

TOTAL PRODUCTS, P

The weight of the products of combustion in pounds per million Btu as fired is given by $P = F + CA$, where C is a factor to correct A for the combustible loss due to imperfect combustion of the fuel. When burning natural gas, C is assumed to be 1 for any properly designed furnace supplied with the correct amount of excess air.

MOISTURE FROM FUEL, W_f

For the general case of a gaseous fuel, W_f is the sum of W_s, the water vapor required to saturate the fuel; W_c, the entrained moisture; and W_h, the water formed in burning the hydrogen compounds in the fuel.

As explained before, natural gas is usually assumed to be dry, and since it never carries any entrained moisture, the first two terms generally may be taken as zero. If the gas is not

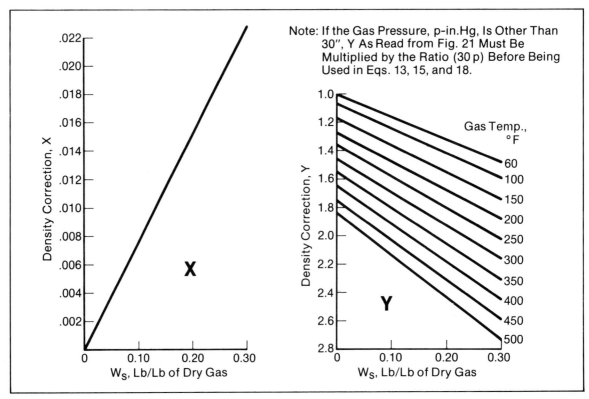

Fig. 21 Density correction for use in Eq. 13

dry, but contains w_s pound of water vapor per pound of dry fuel, the pounds of water vapor per million Btu as fired are given by

$$W_s = \frac{w_s(1 - w_s)10^6}{HHV}$$

(16)

where HHV is the high heating value of the gas in Btu per pound as fired. Fig. 24 is a convenient plot of Eq. 16.

The water produced by the combustion of natural gas is given by equation 17 which follows.

$$W_h = 47,300 \times$$

$$\frac{(H_2S + 2CH_4 + 3C_2H_6 + 4C_3H_8 + 5C_4H_{10} + 6C_5H_{12})}{Btu/cu\ ft\ at\ 60°F\ and\ 30\ in.\ Hg,\ dry}$$

(17)

For dry natural gas at 60°F and 30 in. Hg, W_h may be conveniently read from Curves B of Fig. 23. When it is desired to correct W_h for higher temperature and for moisture content, Eq. 18 may be used.

$$(W_h)_t = \frac{W_h\ (HHV)_{60}}{(HHV)_t\ (1 + W_s + D_t/d_t)}$$

Note: If t = 60°F, the equation reduces to $(W_h)_t = W_h$, regardless of the moisture and dust content.

(18)

PERCENT CO₂ IN PRODUCTS

Curves C, Fig. 23, permit the determination of the percent CO_2 (by volume) in the dry products of combustion for zero excess air. They are a plot of the following approximate equation.

$$\% CO_2\ (at\ zero\ excess\ air) = \frac{100}{6.64 + \dfrac{188 + 0.88(5.5H_2S - 8.5CO_2 - N_2)}{CO_2 + CH_4 + 2C_2H_6 + 3C_3H_8 + 4C_4H_{10} + 5C_5H_{12}}}$$

(19)

Then, by means of guidelines D, the percent CO_2 for any other excess air up to 70 percent may be read. However, it is not advisable to use Curves D for natural gases with a nitrogen percentage of over 40. This is particularly true for high values of excess air.

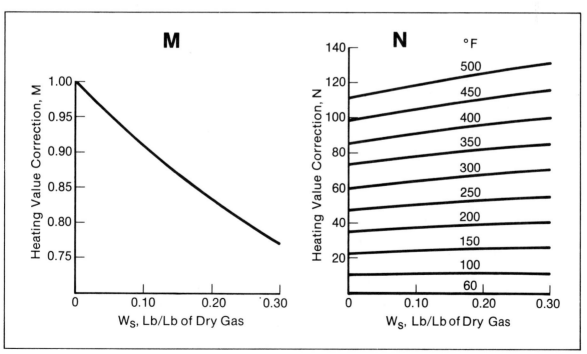

M

Heating Value Correction, M

N °F

Heating Value Correction, N

W_S, Lb/Lb of Dry Gas

Fig. 22 **Heating value corrections for use in Eq. 14**

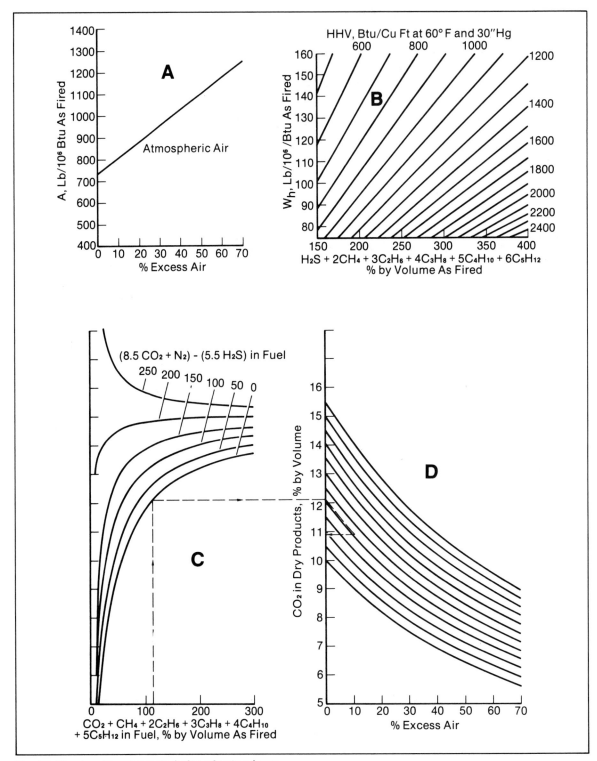

Fig. 23 Combustion characteristics of natural gas

EXAMPLE

Assume a dry natural gas at 60°F and 30 in. Hg to have the typical analysis listed first in Table VI and to be burned with 10-percent excess air. Then

1. Fuel, F. For a high heat value of 18,880 Btu per lb, refer to Fig. 1 and from it read F = 53 lb per million Btu.

2. Atmospheric Air, A. From Curve A, Fig. 23, for 10-percent excess air read A = 807 lb per million Btu.

3. Unburned Combustible. The general assumption when burning natural gas in stationary boiler furnaces is that the combustible loss is zero. Consequently, C in Eqs. 3 and 4 may be taken as 1.

4. Total Products, P. From Eq. 4, P = F + CA = 53 + 1 × 807 = 860 lb per million Btu.

5. Moisture in Air, Wₐ. From Eq. 5, W_a = 0.013A = 0.013 × 807 = 10 lb per million Btu.

6. Moisture from Fuel, Wf. Since W_c, the entrained moisture, is zero and W_s, the saturation moisture, is negligible, from Curves B, Fig. 23, for a high heating value of 1061 Btu per cu ft and $H_2S + 2CH_4 + 3C_2H_6 + 4C_3H_8 + 5C_4H_{10} + 6C_5H_{12}$ = 7.0 + 155.5 + 16.7 + 9.6 + 5.9 + 3.8 = 198.5 percent by volume, read $W_f = W_h$ = 88 lb per million Btu.

7. Dry Gas, Pd. From Eq. 6, P_d = P − ($W_a + W_f$) = 860 − (10 + 88) = 762 lb per million Btu.

8. Percent CO₂ in Products. For $CO_2 + CH_4 + 2C_2H_6 + 3C_3H_8 + 4C_4H_{10} + 5C_5H_{12}$ = 5.5 + 77.7 + 11.1 + 7.2 + 4.7 + 3.2 = 109.4 percent by volume and $8.5 CO_2 + N_2 − 5.5 H_2S$ = 46.7 + 0 − 38.5 = 8.2 percent by volume, from Curves C, Fig. 23, read 12.1 percent CO₂ at zero excess air. Following Curves D as guidelines to 10-percent excess air, read CO₂ = 10.9 percent.

REFINERY AND OIL GAS

The range in composition for refinery gas and oil gas is shown in Table VIII. Refinery gas is predominantly made up of saturated gases of low boiling point, such as, methane (CH_4), ethane (C_2H_6), propane (C_3H_8), butane (C_4H_{10}), and pentane (C_2H_{12}) with small amounts of illuminants. Minor quantities of carbon dioxide (CO_2), carbon monoxide (CO), and hydrogen (H_2) may also be present with oxygen (O_2) and nitrogen (N_2) introduced to lower the hydrocarbon vapor pressure, in some cracking processes. If the original crudes contained sulfur, the ensuing gases include hydrogen sulfide (H_2S) unless the sulfur compounds have been removed by purifying operations. In Table VIII, the last two analyses represent oil gas, whereas the others are representative of refinery gas. Note that the hydrogen content of oil

gas is higher than that of refinery gas, as is also its carbon monoxide content.

DENSITY

In the section on natural gas, a method was outlined for calculating the density of a gaseous fuel, given its analysis by volume. The same method can be used to find the density of refinery gas, or oil gas, either at 60°F or at a higher temperature.

No correction for gas pressure other than the standard 30 in. Hg is required in the calculation of density, because invariably the fuel is burned in a furnace which is at atmospheric pressure. Table VIII indicates that the density of oil gas is considerably lower than that of refinery gas.

HEATING VALUE

The heating value in Btu per cu ft is computed as set forth in the section on natural gas, with appropriate correction factors for temperature and moisture as derived for blast-furnace

Fig. 24 Water vapor in fuel gas

gas. The Btu per pound is the ratio of Btu per cu ft and the density.

Although there is no doubt that some refinery gases contain little or no moisture, others are saturated with it. The values in the table are given on a dry basis.

FUEL IN PRODUCTS, F

With the Btu per pound (HHV) already determined, it is only necessary to refer to Fig. 1 for the value of F which may also be calculated directly from:

$$F = \frac{10^6}{HHV}$$

$$(20)$$

ATMOSPHERIC AIR, A

The air required for combustion may be conveniently read from Curves A of Fig. 26 for amounts of excess air up to 70 percent of the theoretical requirements. Due to the relatively large percentages of carbon monoxide and hydrogen present in some of the oil gases, the magnitude of A in Table VIII varies from 648 to 725 lb per million Btu. The correlation of A at zero excess air with the term $(CO + H_2)$ is brought out by Fig. 25. The average line drawn

through the calculated points on this figure was used as the basis for spacing Curves A of Fig. 26.

The atmospheric air as taken from Fig. 26 can be corrected for temperatures other than 60°F and for moisture content by employing Eq. 15.

TOTAL PRODUCTS, P

Knowing A and F, the total wet products formed by combustion of refinery or oil gas can be easily computed, in pounds per million Btu fired, by the addition $P = F + CA$.

MOISTURE FROM FUEL, W_f

The total amount of moisture in the products of combustion, W_f, which is derived from the fuel itself, is the summation of the entrained moisture W_c, the water vapor held by the gas W_s, and the water produced by burning hydrogen, or hydrogen compounds making up the fuel, W_h.

Unless the refinery gas has undergone a scrubbing or washing operation to remove objectionable elements from the distillate, it contains hardly any entrained moisture. Water vapor, however, may be present in the gas not only because of the purifying treatment, but due to water introduced into the system with

Table VIII. Characteristics of Typical Refinery and Oil Gases at 60°F and 30 In. Hg, Dry

O₂	N₂	CO₂	CO	H₂	H₂S	CH₄	C₂H₆	C₃H₈	C₄H₁₀*	C₅H₁₂†	C₃H₆‡	Density, Lb/Cu Ft	HHV Btu/ Cu Ft**	HHV Btu/Lb	A at Zero Excess Air, Lb/10⁶ Btu	CO₂ at Zero Excess Air, %
. . .	. . .	. . .	. . .	. . .	. . .	2.18	41.62	20.91	19.72	9.05	6.52	. . .	0.08676	1898	21,880	722	13.3
. . .	. . .	. . .	. . .	. . .	. . .	4.30	82.70	13.00	. . .	. . .	. . .	0.08377	1858	22,170	725	13.4
. . .	. . .	. . .	. . .	. . .	. . .	92.10	1.90	4.50	1.30	0.20	. . .	0.04845	1136	23,460	723	12.1
. . .	. . .	. . .	. . .	. . .	. . .	5.0	12.0	30.0	34.0	19.0	. . .	0.13760	2988	21,720	717	13.9
. . .	. . .	3.3	1.5	5.6	. . .	30.9	19.8	38.1	0.6	. . .	0.2	0.08102	1696	20,930	725	13.4
2.3	8.7	. . .	. . .	. . .	. . .	30.3	13.4	19.1	14.7	1.8	9.7	0.09232	1844	19,970	715	13.6
0.9	8.4	2.2	14.3	50.9	. . .	15.9	5.0	. . .	. . .	. . .	2.4	0.03631	519	14,300	648	12.2
0.1	2.7	1.0	6.8	59.2	. . .	25.4	. . .	. . .	. . .	. . .	4.8	0.02756	586	21,270	657	10.6

* Includes both iso-C₄H₁₀ and n-C₄H₁₀.
† Includes all saturated hydrocarbons heavier than C₅H₁₂, also both iso-C₅H₁₂ and n-C₅H₁₂.
‡ Includes all illuminants.
** If gas is saturated with moisture at 60°F and 30 in. Hg, reduce by 1.74%.

the crude oil, or because of steam employed in the distillation process. If the gas contains W_s lb of water vapor per lb of dry fuel, W_s can be determined from Fig. 24.

The water which is formed by combustion, W_h, can be read from Curves B of Fig. 26, which are a plot of the expression

$$W_h = 47,300 \times$$
$$\frac{(H_2 + H_2S + 2CH_4 + 3C_2H_6 + 4C_3H_8 + 5C_4H_{10} + 6C_5H_{12} + 3C_3H_6)}{\text{Btu/cu ft at } 60°F \text{ and } 30 \text{ in. Hg, dry}}$$

$$(21)$$

When, for more accuracy, it is required to correct W_h for the effect of temperature and moisture content, Eq. 18 can be utilized.

PERCENT CO₂ IN PRODUCTS

For zero excess air, the CO_2 in the dry products of combustion is found with the aid of Curves C, Fig. 26. These curves were drawn from the approximate equation.

$$\% \, CO_2 \, \text{(at zero excess air)} =$$
$$\frac{100}{6.64 + \dfrac{188 - 1.88(N_2 + 4CO_2 + 3CO + C_3H_6)}{CO_2 + CO + CH_4 + 2C_2H_6 + 3C_3H_8 + 4C_4H_{10} + 5C_5H_{12} + 3C_3H_6}}$$

$$(22)$$

The guide Curves D of Fig. 26 make it possible to obtain the percent of CO_2 in the products for an excess-air value up to 70 percent.

Fig. 25 Variation of theoretical air with (CO + H₂) in combustion of refinery and oil gas

EXAMPLE

Assume a refinery gas of the typical analysis given on the first line of Table VIII to be fired at a temperature of 60°F with 10-percent excess air. Then

1. **Fuel, F.** With a fuel high heat value of 21,880 Btu per lb, refer to Fig. 1 and obtain F = 46 lb per million Btu.

2. **Atmospheric Air, A.** On Curves A, Fig. 26, for 10-percent excess air and $(CO + H_2) = 0$, read A = 793 lb per million Btu.

3. **Unburned Combustible.** When burning refinery gas in boiler furnaces, it is customary to assume that there is no unburned combustible loss, so that in Eqs. 3 and 4 C = 1.

4. **Total Products, P.** Using Eq. 4, P = F + CA = 46 + 1 × 793 = 839 lb per million Btu.

5. **Moisture, in Air, W_a.** This item is calculated from Eq. 5, W_a = 0.013A = 0.013 × 793 = 10 lb per million Btu.

6. **Moisture from Fuel, W_f.** The moisture content of refinery gas itself is generally negligible. The water formed by its combustion is taken from Curves B, Fig. 26. For a high heat value of 1898 Btu per cu ft and $H_2S + 2CH_4 + 3C_2H_6 + 4C_3H_8 + 5C_4H_{10} + 6C_5H_{12} = 2.18 + 83.24 + 62.73 + 78.88 + 45.25 + 39.12 = 311.40$ percent by volume, $W_f = W_h$ = 78 lb per million Btu.

7. **Dry Gas, P_d.** From Eq. 6, $P_d = P - (W_a + W_f) = 839 - (10 + 78) = 751$ lb per million Btu.

8. **Percent CO₂ in Products.** The CO_2 at zero excess air is determined first. From curves C of Fig. 26, for $CH_4 + 2C_2H_6 + 3C_3H_8 + 4C_4H_{10} + 5C_5H_{12} = 41.62 + 41.82 + 59.16 + 36.20 + 32.60 = 211.40$ percent by volume, and $N_2 + 4CO_2 + 3CO + C_3H_6 = 0.0$ obtain 13.3 percent CO_2. With Curves D as guidelines and 10-percent excess air, then, read CO_2 = 12 percent.

COKE-OVEN GAS

Representative analyses of several byproduct coke-oven gases are given in Table IX. Note that the volumetric heating value is based on the gas being moisture free, and that a correction must be made for moisture of saturation, if the gas has been washed and cooled.

It is important to have the correct calorific value at 60°F and 30 in. Hg for a given analysis, since the method employed here relates all combustion calculations to the heat liberated. Unfortunately, many analyses show the heavier hydrocarbons grouped together as "illuminants." DeBaufre[4] and others have suggested taking the illuminants to be propylene, C_3H_6. While this assumption is valid in calculating the Btu per cu ft, it will not give accurate values of H_2O formed by combustion, and

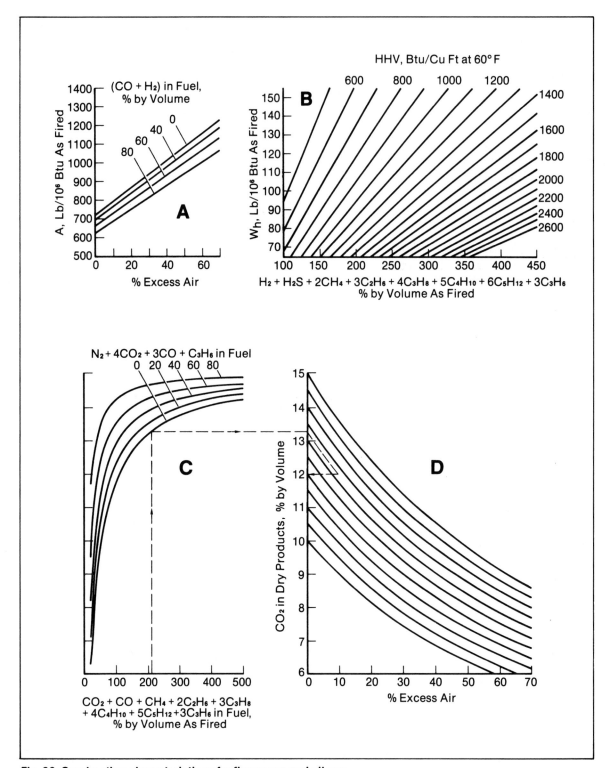

Fig. 26 Combustion characteristics of refinery gas and oil gas

the resulting heat balance will be in error. A complete gas analysis, including all hydrocarbons, is, therefore, essential. To find the high heating value in Btu per lb accurately, divide the Btu per cu ft by the fuel density.

DENSITY

The density of the gaseous fuel, in turn, may be obtained by adding the weights of the constituents in the fuel. The following tabulation is an example of density calculation for the typical coke-oven gas listed first in Table IX the density of the individual constituents being taken from Table VII.

	% by volume	Volume, cu ft constituent/ cu ft fuel		Density of constituent, lb/cu ft		Weight, lb/cu ft fuel
CO_2	1.8	0.018	×	0.1170	=	0.00211
O_2	0.2	0.002	×	0.08461	=	0.00017
N_2	3.4	0.034	×	0.07439	=	0.00253
CO	6.3	0.063	×	0.07404	=	0.00466
H_2	53.0	0.530	×	0.005327	=	0.00282
CH_4	31.6	0.316	×	0.04246	=	0.01342
C_2H_4	2.7	0.027	×	0.07421	=	0.00200
C_6H_6	1.0	0.010	×	0.2060	=	0.00206
		Total = Density of Dry Gas			=	0.02977

The saturation pressure of water vapor at 60°F is 0.52 in. Hg. If the gas is saturated with moisture at 60°F and 30 in. Hg, then the partial pressure of all its dry constituents is $30.0 - 0.52 = 29.48$ in. Hg. A density correction is made as follows.

$$0.02977 \times \frac{29.48}{30.0} = 0.02925$$

add to this the density of the water   0.00083
vapor (from the steam tables)   ———
density of saturated gas   0.03008

It can be seen that the density correction for moisture content will be 1 percent.

FUEL, F

The portion of the fuel which reappears in volatile form in the products of combustion can be read from Fig. 1 when HHV (Btu per lb of fuel) is known. If HHV is not given, it is found by dividing the Btu per cu ft by the fuel density.

No moisture correction is necessary, because F is determined to two significant figures only.

ATMOSPHERIC AIR, A

The atmospheric air required for combustion will vary with the carbon monoxide and hydrogen content of the gas. A correlation of atmospheric air, A, at zero excess air with the term $(CO + H_2)$ is shown in Fig. 27. The atmospheric air in lb per million Btu may be read from the curve family A in Fig. 28. The spacing of these curves is based on the average line drawn in Fig. 27.

TOTAL PRODUCTS, P

The weight of the products of combustion is calculated from $P = F + CA$.

MOISTURE FROM FUEL, W_f

The moisture, W_c, in a fuel gas saturated at 60°F may be neglected as it amounts to less than 2 lb per million Btu as fired. W_h, the water formed by the combustion of hydrogen and the hydrocarbons present in the coke-oven gas, is obtained from Curves B, Fig. 28. Since W_c is neglected, W_f which is the total moisture in the flue gases derived from the fuel is equal to W_h.

In the simple case of hydrogen, the volumetric chemical equation for combustion is

$$H_2 + \tfrac{1}{2}O_2 = H_2O \tag{23}$$

Eq. 23 shows that one volume of hydrogen combines with one-half volume of oxygen to produce one volume of water. Similarly, one volume of CH_4 will form, on burning, two volumes of H_2O, etc. Since a coke-oven gas may contain H_2, CH_4, C_2H_4, and C_6H_6, with the aid of Table VII it is seen that the total volume of H_2O evolved by these constituents is proportional to $(H_2 + 2\ CH_4 + 2\ C_2H_4 + 3\ C_6H_6)$. The following exact relation will convert the volume of H_2O to lb per million Btu.

$$W_h = 47,300 \frac{(H_2 + 2\ CH_4 + 2\ C_2H_4 + 3\ C_6H_6)}{Btu/cu\ ft\ at\ 60°F\ and\ 30\ in.\ Hg,\ dry} \tag{24}$$

which is also plotted as Curves B, Fig. 28.

Fig. 27 **Variation of theoretical air with (CO + H₂) in combustion of coke-oven gas**

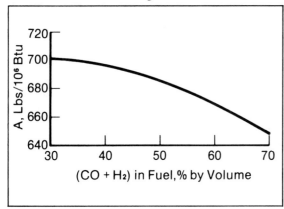

(CO + H₂) in Fuel, % by Volume

PERCENT CO₂ IN PRODUCTS

There are many constituents in coke-oven gas which on burning will evolve CO_2. A simple equation relating exactly the CO_2 in the dry products of combustion to these constituents cannot be written, but the following equation is sufficiently accurate for analyses which do not contain excessive amounts of N_2 or O_2.

$$\% \ CO_2 \ (\text{at zero excess air}) = \frac{100}{1 + \dfrac{0.695 \times \text{Btu/cu ft at 60°F and 30 in. Hg, dry}}{(100 + C_2H_4 + 5C_6H_8) - (H_2 + N_2)}}$$

(25)

Curves C, Fig. 28, are a plot of Eq. 25, while Curves D serve as guidelines for determining the percent CO_2 in the dry products of combustion for any other value of excess air than zero.

EXAMPLE

Assume a coke-oven gas with the typical analysis of the first gas listed in Table IX and saturated with moisture at 60°F and 30 in. Hg to be burned with 10-percent excess air.

1. Heating Value. The high heat value given as 596 Btu per cu ft must first be corrected for moisture content by deducting 1.74 percent; 596 − 10 = 586 Btu per cu ft saturated fuel. This value is divided by the fuel density (neglecting the moisture correction) to obtain the approximate Btu per lb.

$$\text{HHV} = \frac{586}{0.0298} = 19,700 \ \text{Btu/lb}$$

2. Fuel, F. For a high heat value of 19,700 Btu per lb, read from Fig. 1, F = 51 lb per million Btu.

3. Atmospheric Air, A. From Curves A, Fig. 28 for 10-percent excess air and (CO + H₂) = 6.3 + 53.0 = 59.3, read A = 742 lb per million Btu.

4. Unburned Combustible. For stationary boiler furnaces, the general assumption when burning coke-oven gas is that there is no combustible heat loss. Therefore, C in Eqs. 3 and 4 is equal to 1.

5. Total Products, P. From Eq. 4, P = F + CA = 51 + 1 × 742 = 793 lb per million Btu.

6. Moisture in Air, Wₐ. From Eq. 5, W_a = 0.013A = 0.013 × 742 = 10 lb per million Btu.

7. Moisture from Fuel, Wg. Since W_c = 0, from Curves B, Fig. 28, for a high heat value of 596 Btu per cu ft and H₂ = 2CH₄ + 2C₂H₄ + 3C₆H₆ = 53.0 + 63.2 + 5.4 + 3.0 = 124.6 percent by volume, read W_f = W_h = 99 lb per million Btu.

8. Dry Gas, Pd. From Eq. 6, P_d = P − (Wₐ = Wₘ) = 793 − (10 + 99) = 684 lb per million Btu.

9. Percent CO₂ in Products. For a heating value of 596 Btu per cu ft and (100 + C₂H₄ + 5C₆H₆) − (H₂ + N₂) = (100 + 2.7 + 5.0) − (53.0 + 3.4) = 51.3 percent by volume, from Curves C, Fig. 28, read 11.1 percent CO_2 at zero excess air. Following Curves D as guidelines to 10-percent excess air, read CO_2 = 10 percent.

Table IX. **Characteristics of Typical Coke-Oven Gases at 60°F and 30 In. Hg, Dry**

			% by Volume					Density, Lb/Cu Ft	HHV Btu/Cu Ft*	HHV Btu/Lb	A at Zero Excess Air, Lb/10⁶ Btu	CO₂ at Zero Excess Air, %
CO₂	O₂	N₂	CO	H₂	CH₄	C₂H₄	C₆H₆					
1.8	0.2	3.4	6.3	53.0	31.6	2.7	1.0	0.0298	596	20,010	674	11.1
1.4	0.5	4.2	5.1	57.4	28.5	2.9	. . .	0.0263	539	20,490	664	10.0
2.6	0.6	3.7	6.1	47.9	33.9	5.2	. . .	0.0316	603	19,070	676	11.3
3.13	. . .	. . .	11.93	42.16	37.14	4.76	0.88	0.0359	663	18,500	684	12.7
0.1	. . .	2.4	6.8	27.7	50.0	13.0	. . .	0.0393	829	21,100	700	12.3
0.75	. . .	12.1	6.0	53.0	28.15	. . .	. . .	0.0291	477	16,390	668	9.4

* If gas is saturated with moisture at 60°F and 30 in. Hg, reduce by 1.74%.

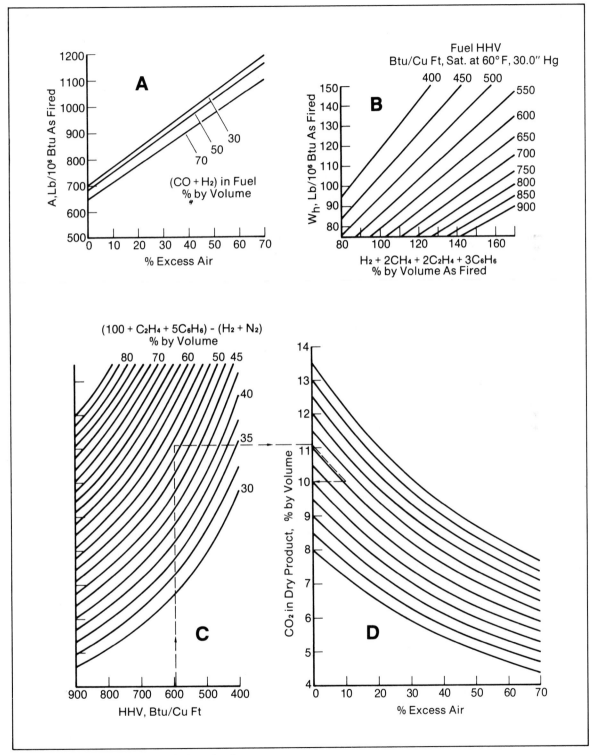

Fig. 28 **Combustion characteristics of coke-oven gas**

BLAST-FURNACE GAS

The range in composition of steel-plant blast-furnace gas is given in Table X. Note that the volumetric heating value is based on the gas being moisture free, and that a connection must be made for moisture of saturation.

MOISTURE FROM CLEANING

In chapter 2, blast-furnace gas was classified into raw gas, gas that had a primary cleaning, and gas that has had a final cleaning. For purposes of combustion calculations, however, it is more convenient to speak of *washed* and *unwashed* gas, and these will be the terms most frequently employed in the discussion which follows.

Washed gas is blast-furnace gas that has gone through either primary or final washers. It may be considered saturated with moisture at whatever temperature it leaves the washer because of the intimate contact between cooling water and hot gas. If the gas has only been given a primary wash, it will contain about 4 grains (0.00057 lb per standard cubic foot) of entrained moisture in addition to the water vapor required to saturate it. This entrained moisture is carried along by the gas in the form of suspended droplets which are effectively removed by a final cleaner.

Unwashed gas, on the other hand, may exist as raw gas or as gas that has had a primary, or even a final, cleaning by means of dry separators. Its temperature is much higher than that of washed gas and because of this it is capable of holding much more moisture, since it will contain all the water vapor that it had on leaving the blast furnace regardless of its degree of cleaning. Using a dew point of 140°F has been recommended for calculating the moisture in unwashed gas, but it is obviously preferable to know the actual dew point of a particular gas than to assume it. Fig. 20, then, offers a convenient curve for determining W_s, the saturation moisture, for any dew-point temperature from 60 to 160°F. There is, of course, no entrained water in unwashed gas.

DENSITY

The density of dry blast-furnace gas at 60°F (d_{60}) is easily computed from its volumetric analysis by the method explained in the section on gas, which assumes that the gas is clean. The true density (d_t) is obtained by correcting d_{60} for the actual temperature (t), moisture content, and dust according to Eq. 13.

As an example, assume that the blast-furnace gas in the first line of Table X is unwashed and goes to a burner with 15 grains of dust, at 500°F with a dew point of 140°F and at a pressure of 30 in. Hg. What is its actual density if there is no entrained moisture?

For a saturation temperature of 140°F and a pressure of 30 in. Hg, read from Fig. 20, $w_s = 0.152$ lb per lb of dry gas, and from Fig. 21

Table X. Characteristics of Typical Blast-Furnace Gases at 60°F and 30 In. Hg, Dry

CO₂	N₂	% by Volume CO	H₂	CH₄	Density, Lb/Cu Ft	HHV Btu/Cu Ft*	Btu/Lb	A at Zero Excess Air, Lb/10⁶ Btu	CO₂ at Zero Excess Air, %
14.5	57.5	25.0	3.0	...	0.0779	90.1	1150	576	26.4
13.0	57.6	26.2	3.2	...	0.0771	94.6	1219	575	25.8
15.59	59.28	23.35	1.7	0.08	0.0792	81.4	1021	577	26.7
8.7	56.5	32.8	1.8	0.2	0.0762	113.3	1478	579	25.3
5.7	59.0	34.0	1.3	...	0.0753	113.6	1498	576	24.0
6.0	60.0	27.0	2.0	5.0	0.0734	144.0	1950	631	20.0

* If gas is saturated with moisture at 60° and 30.0 in. Hg, reduce by 1.74%

	% by Volume, Dry	Volume, cu ft/ cu ft of Gas	Density lb/cu ft at 60°F, Dry[2]		Weight lb/cu ft
CO_2	14.5	0.145	× 0.1170	=	0.01697
N_2	57.5	0.575	× 0.07439	=	0.04277
CO	25.0	0.250	× 0.07404	=	0.01851
H_2	3.0	0.030	× 0.005327	=	0.00016

Density of Clean Dry Gas at 60°F = 0.07841

obtain X = 0.0115 and Y = 2.29. Then the density of clean gas at 500°F and a dew point of 140°F will be expressed as

$$\frac{d_{60} + X}{Y} = \frac{0.0784 + 0.0115}{2.29} = 0.0393 \text{ lb/cu ft}$$

$$\text{Weight of dust in gas} = \frac{15}{7000} \times \frac{0.0393}{0.0784} = 0.0011 \text{ lb/cu ft}$$

$$d_t = 0.0393 + 0.0011 = 0.0404 \text{ lb/cu ft}$$

HEATING VALUE

The Btu per cubic foot of clean and dry blast-furnace gas at 60°F, may be calculated from its analysis and the heating value of its combustible components as obtained from Table X. The Btu per cubic foot thus determined, when divided by the density at 60°F, will give the Btu per pound $(HHV)_{60}$.

However, in calculating the true heating value $(HHV)_t$ of a gas as fired, we must again take into account its dust content, its temperature, and its moisture content.

The dust in blast-furnace gas is made up chiefly of particles of iron ore, limestone, and coke. Since its structure is sandy or granular, there is reason to believe that iron ore is the main component in this mixture, since its structure is sandy or granular, and is, therefore, more easily lifted by the blast than coke or limestone which comes in relatively large lumps. When the dust burns, the coke in it may be thought of as supplying the heat required to reduce both ore and limestone. In the absence of actual tests showing the calorific value of the dust, it may be assumed that the heat evolved by the coke is just equal to that required to reduce the ore and the limestone. If this is true,

the presence of dust will not influence the heating value of blast-furnace gas.

It should also be clear that any increase in the temperature of the gas above 60°F will enhance its heating value by an amount equal to the sensible heat of the gas above 60°F.

Furthermore, assume, as an example, that an unwashed gas is saturated at 140°F. It will then have 0.152 lb of moisture for each pound of dry gas. As an inert vapor, this moisture will reduce the combustible fraction and, therefore, the heating value of blast-furnace gas, at the same time that it augments the heating value by the sensible heat due to its high temperature.

Having obtained the Btu per pound $(HHV)_{60}$, for the dry gas at 60°F, figure the Btu per pound $(HHV)_t$, at its true temperature, t, and moisture content using Eq. 14.

Knowing the actual dew point of this gas, w_s is read from Fig. 20, and M and N from Fig. 22 for use in Eq. 14.

FUEL, F

After determining the true Btu per pound, F, which is that portion of the fuel that shows up in the products of combustion, may be read from Fig. 1. Any dust in unwashed gas may be treated as ash in coal or sediment in oil.

ATMOSPHERIC AIR, A

The air required for the combustion of blast-furnace gas is a function of the ratio $CH_4/(CO + H_2)$ where CH_4, CO, and H_2 represent the percentage fractions by volume of methane, carbon monoxide, and hydrogen in the fuel.

For clean, dry, blast-furnace gas at 60°F, the atmospheric air, A, in pounds per million Btu, may be read from Curves A in Fig. 29 for any value of excess air up to 70 percent.

This value must be corrected for the dust and moisture content and temperature of the actual blast-furnace gas. After finding A from Fig. 29 and the heating value and density as explained before, the true mass of atmospheric air per million Btu as fired is calculated using Eq. 15.

TOTAL PRODUCTS, P

As with other fuels previously discussed, the weight of the products of combustion is given by P = F + CA lb per million Btu as fired. This equation holds true for either washed or unwashed gas, provided F and A are calculated as explained in the foregoing sections.

MOISTURE FROM FUEL, W_f

As defined in the first section, W_f is the total amount of water vapor present in the products of combustion.

In blast-furnace gas, three different moisture sources eventually become part of the products. First, there is the moisture formed in burning the fuel and previously designated by W_h. Equation 26 shows that for clean gas at 60°F

$$W_h = \frac{47,300\,(H_2 + 2CH_4)}{\text{Btu/cu ft at 60°F and 30 in. Hg, dry}}$$

(26)

Curves B of Fig. 29 are plotted from this equation.

If the actual gas is at a temperature higher than 60°F and contains dust and moisture, the readings from Curves B must be multiplied by the same factor used in correcting the atmospheric air, to obtain the true moisture $(W_h)_t$ in pounds per million Btu as fired. This factor is calculated using Eq. 18.

The next moisture source called "entrained moisture" is carried along by the gas in the form of suspended globules. Designated as W_c, it is considered only when the gas has been given a primary wash and averages 7 lb per million Btu.

The last source is in the water vapor required to saturate the blast-furnace gas at any temperature from 60°F up, as the case may be, and is designated as W_s. For blast-furnace gas saturated with moisture at 60°F, 8 lb per million Btu may be assumed for W_s without serious error. This moisture must be considered separately from W_h and W_c in a heat balance since it exists as a vapor requiring no latent heat of vaporization.

Of course, W_s must be subtracted from the total products, along with W_h and W_c, to obtain the dry gas.

EXAMPLE

Assume a blast-furnace gas with the typical analysis of the first gas listed in Table X and saturated with moisture of 60°F and burned with 15-percent excess air after going through a primary washer.

1. Density. The density given as 0.0779 lb per cu ft for the dry gas must first be corrected for moisture content. The saturation moisture for a dew point of 60°F is read from Fig. 20 as $W_s = 0.02$ lb moisture per lb of dry gas. The values of X and Y are read from Fig. 21 for $W_s = 0.02$ and a temperature of 60°F as X = 0.0015 and Y = 1.03. The entrained moisture in a gas given a primary wash is assumed as $w_c = 0.00057$ lb per standard cu ft.

We can now substitute into Eq. 13

$$d_t = \frac{d_{60} + X}{Y} + (D_t + w_c) = \frac{0.0779 + 0.0015}{1.03} +$$
$$(0 + 0.00057) = 0.0771 + (0.00057) = 0.0777 \text{ lb/cu ft.}$$

2. Heating Value. The high heat value given as 90.1 Btu per cu ft is first corrected for moisture content by deducting 1.74 percent; 90.1 − 1.6 = 88.5 Btu per cu ft saturated fuel. This value is divided by the density to obtain the Btu per lb. HHV = 88.5/0.0777 = 1139 Btu per lb.

3. Fuel, F. For a high heat value of 1139 Btu per lb and a negligible amount of dust refer to Fig. 1 and read F = 878 lb per million Btu.

4. Atmospheric Air, A. From Curves A, Fig. 29, for $CH_4/(CO + H_2) = 0$ and for 15-percent excess air, read A = 662 lb per million Btu.

5. Unburned Combustible. The general assumption when burning blast-furnace gas in stationary boiler furnaces is that the combustible loss is zero. Consequently, C in Eqs. 3 and 4 may be taken as 1.

6. Total Products, P. From Eq. 4, P = F + CA = 878 + 1 × 662 = 1540 lb per million Btu.

7. Moisture in Air, W_a. From Eq. 5, W_a = 0.013A = 0.013 × 662 = 9 lb per million Btu.

8. Moisture from Fuel, W_f. As pointed out in the text for a gas that has passed through a primary washer, $W_c = 7$ lb per million Btu. Curves B, Fig. 29, show $W_h = 16$ lb per million Btu for a blast-furnace gas with a high heat value of 90.1 Btu per cu ft and $H_2 + 2\,CH_4 = 3 + 0 = 3$ percent by volume as fired. Therefore, $W_f = W_s + W_c + W_h = 8 + 7 + 16 = 31$ lb per million Btu.

9. Dry Gas, P_d. From Eq. 6, $P_d = P - (W_a + W_f) = 1540 - (9 + 31) = 1500$ lb per million Btu.

10. Percent CO_2 in Products. From the fuel analysis, calculate $CO_2 + CO + CH_4 = 14.5 + 25.0 + 0 = 39.5$ percent by volume and $H_2 + 2\,CO + 8\,CH_4 = 3 + 2 \times 25 + 8 \times 0 = 53$ percent by volume, and from Curves C, Fig. 29 read 26.4 percent CO_2 at zero excess air. Following Curves D as guidelines to 15-percent excess air, read $CO_2 = 24.8$ percent.

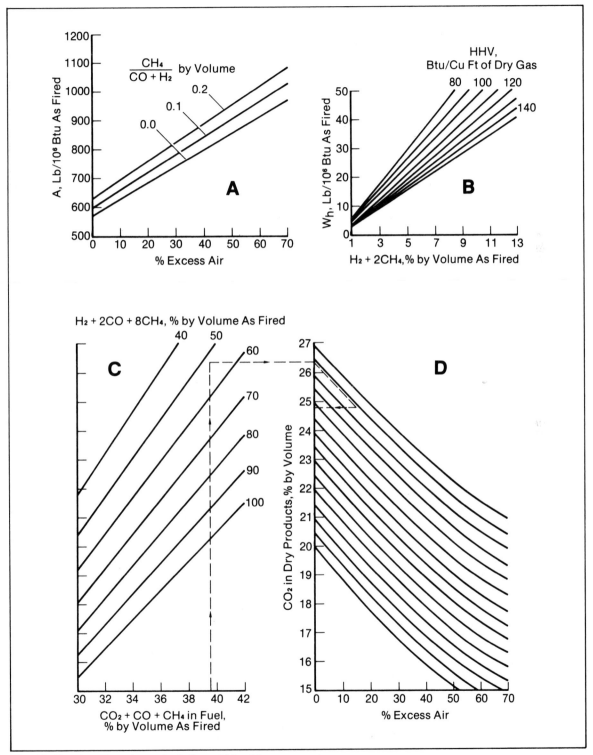

***Fig. 29* Combustion characteristics of blast-furnace gas**

PERCENT CO₂ IN PRODUCTS

Curves C and D of Fig. 29 offer a convenient method to obtain the percent of CO_2 in the dry products of combustion resulting from the combustion of either washed or unwashed blast-furnace gas, provided the dry volumetric analysis of the gas is known. Curves C are plotted from the following equation:

$$\frac{\% \, CO_2}{\text{(at zero excess air)}} = \frac{100(CO_2 + CO + CH_4)}{100 + 0.94(H_2 + 2CO + 8CH_4)} \tag{27}$$

where H_2, CO_2, CO, and CH_4 are the symbols for percent by volume of these constituents in the fuel. This CO_2 must not be confused with the percent carbon dioxide in the dry products of combustion.

REFERENCES

[1] W. L. De Baufre, "Composition in Heating Value of Fuels," *Combustion*, 2(11): 29–35, May 1931.

[2] W. S. Patterson, "Calculations of Air Requirements and Combustion Products of U.S. Coals by Simple Graphical Methods," *Combustion*, 3(8): 9–17, Feb. 1932.

[3] W. L. De Baufre, "Typical Solid and Liquid Fuels," *Combustion*, 3(2): 23–31, Aug. 1931.

[4] W. L. De Baufre, "Typical Gaseous Fuels," *Combustion*, 3(6): 26–33, Dec. 1931.

Appendix E. Velocity Calculations by Graphical Methods

In evaluating any process involving flowing fluids, velocity calculations are important. The following graphical methods have been compiled for quick determination of gas velocities in flues and ducts from pitot-tube and gas-temperature readings.

These graphs are based upon solutions to Eq. 1 with correction factors for both standard and Stauscheibe pitot tubes.

Eq. 1 has been reduced for standard conditions as shown in Table I and plotted in Figs. 1 through 4 for both standard and Stauscheibe pitot tubes. For further background on the theory concerning this equation, the reference list should be consulted.

Pitot-tube measurements should be made on an equal-area basis in the flue or duct. Fig. 5 gives a description of how to determine the lo-

$$V^2 = 64.32 \times \frac{h}{12} \times 1.3253 \times \frac{\dfrac{\varphi \,(\text{at air temp})}{13}}{459.2 + T}$$

where:

V = gas velocity — ft/sec
h = velocity head — "WG
1.3253 = air density correction
B = barometric pressure — in. Hg
$\dfrac{S}{13}$ = static head — in. Hg
T = temperature — °F
φ = density of water at air temperature — lb/ft³

(1)

cation of equal areas for round flues; Fig. 6, for rectangular ducts. Fig. 7 identifies the number

Fig. 1 Velocity vs velocity pressure, standard pitot tube

Table I. Velocity and Mass-Flow Relations for Pitot Tubes

General Derivation

(1) $V = \sqrt{2gH}$

(3) $D = \dfrac{s(T)}{t}$

(2) $H = \dfrac{h(d)}{12(D)}$

(4) $G = V(D)(3600)$

Combining (2) and (3): (5) $H = \dfrac{h(d)(t)}{12(s)(t)}$

Combining (5) and (1): (6) $V = (c)\sqrt{\dfrac{2g(h)(d)(t)}{12(s)(T)}}$

Combining (6) and (4): (7) $G =$

(c) $\sqrt{\dfrac{2g(h)(d)(s)(T)(3600)^2}{12t}}$

Definition of Symbols:

V   gas velocity, ft/sec
G   gas mass flow, lb/hr-sq ft
h   velocity head, "WG
H   velocity head, ft of gas
t   gas temperature, °R
T   standard temperature, 492°R
d   density of gaging liquid, lb/ft³
D   density of measured gas at "t", lb/ft³
s   density of measured gas at 32°F and 29.92 lb/hr-sq ft³
c   coefficient of discharge
g   acceleration of gravity, 32.2 ft/sec²

Special Case (Standard Pitot Tube):

C   coefficient of discharge, 1.00
d   density of water at 32°F, (62.35 lb/ft³)
s   density of dry air, 0.08 lb/ft³
T   standard temperature, 492°R
g   acceleration of gravity, 32.2 ft/sec²

(8) $V = 2.915\sqrt{(h)(t)}$ (9) $G = 412{,}800\sqrt{\dfrac{h}{t}}$

Special Case (Stauscheibe Pitot Tube):

where c = 0.8 (based on calibration)

(10) $V = 2.332\sqrt{(h)(t)}$ (11) $G = 330{,}200\sqrt{\dfrac{h}{t}}$

of sampling points required for good accuracy. For more information on this procedure, refer to *ASME Performance Test Codes* PTC 19.5.

Given a pitot-tube reading and a gas temperature, the velocity can be read directly from the graph. If equal areas are used, the velocities may be averaged to obtain the average velocity in the flue or duct. For example, using a standard pitot tube, the velocity head was measured as 0.19 in. WG at 100°F. The velocity is read directly as 30 ft/sec. In five readings, velocities of 31, 28, 30, 32, and 29 ft/sec were obtained, with an average velocity of 30 ft/sec. The total mass velocity can be read on Fig. 3 as 7,600 lb/hr-sq ft.

If the flue gases contain significant amounts of CO_2 and water vapor, Fig. 8 may be used to correct the velocity. If the gas contains 10 percent H_2O and 10 percent CO_2, the correction factor is 0.9975 and the corrected velocity is 29.9 ft/sec. Fig. 9 contains the SO_2 correction.

Figs. 10 and 11 may be used to obtain velocity correction factors, if the measurements are made in flues with significant differences in static head or barometric pressure. In addition, several of these graphs may be used in correcting gas concentration measurements to standard conditions. Figs. 12 and 13 have been included for temperature correction and saturation vapor pressure of water vapor. Thus, in most circumstances complete gas evaluation can be made. The references describe these procedures in greater detail.   ⬥

REFERENCES

[1] Herman Diederichs and William C. Andrae, *Experimental Mechanical Engineering.* New York: J. Wiley and Sons, Inc. and London: Chapman Hall, Ltd., 1930.

[2] "Application, Part II of Fluid Meters: Interim Supplement on Instrument and Apparatus." *ASME Performance Test Codes,* PTC 19.5, New York: American Society of Mechanical Engineers, latest edition.

[3] See reference 2.

[4] "Dust Separating Apparatus." *ASME Performance Test Codes,* PTC 21, New York: American Society of Mechanical Engineers, latest edition.

[5] "Determining Dust Concentration in a Gas Stream." *ASME Performance Test Codes,* PTC 27, New York: American Society of Mechanical Engineers, latest edition.

[6] See reference 2.

[7] P. G. W. Hawksley, S. Bodzioch, and J. H. Blackett, *Measurement of Solids in Flue Gases.* London: The Institute of Fuel, 1977.

[8] H. J. White, *Industrial Electrostatic Precipitation.* Reading, Mass.: Addison Wesley, 1963.

[9] W. B. Gregory, "The Pitot Tube," *Transactions of the ASME,* 25: 184–211, 1904.

[10] W. C. Rouse, "Pitot Tubes for Gas Measurement," *Transactions of the ASME,* 25: 633–703, 1913.

[11] E. S. Cole, "Pitot Tube Practice," *Transactions of the ASME,* 57:281–282, 1935.

[12] A. S. Folsom, "Review of the Pitot Tube," *Transactions of the ASME,* 78: 1447–1460, Oct. 1956.

[13] C. J. Fechheimer, "Measurement of Static Pressure," *Transactions of the ASME,* 48: 965–977, 1926.

[14] J. M. Zarek, "The Neglected Parameters in Pulsation Flow Measurement," in *Flow Measurement Symposium,* presented at the Fluid Meter Golden Anniversary Flow Measurement Conference, Pittsburgh, Sept. 26–28, 1966, ed. by K. C. Cotton. New York: American Society of Mechanical Engineers, 1966.

Fig. 2 **Velocity vs velocity pressure, Stauscheibe tube**

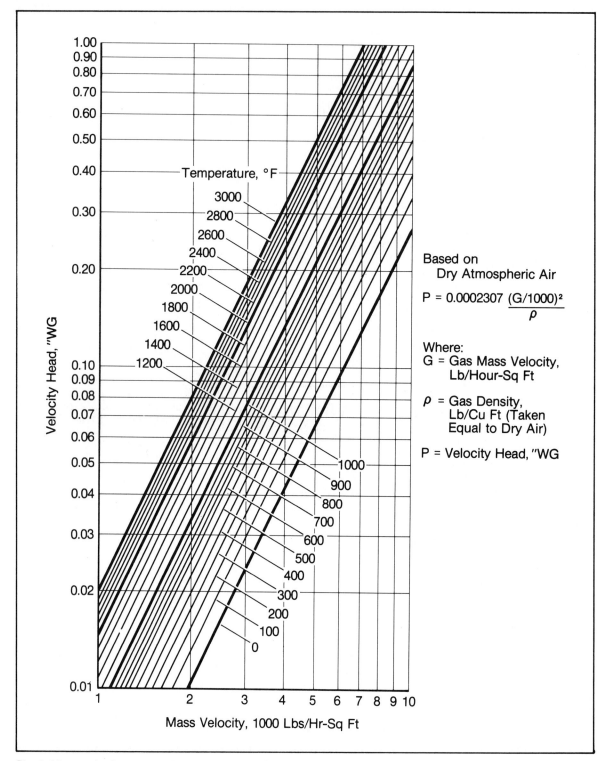

Fig. 3 Mass velocity vs velocity head, standard pitot tube

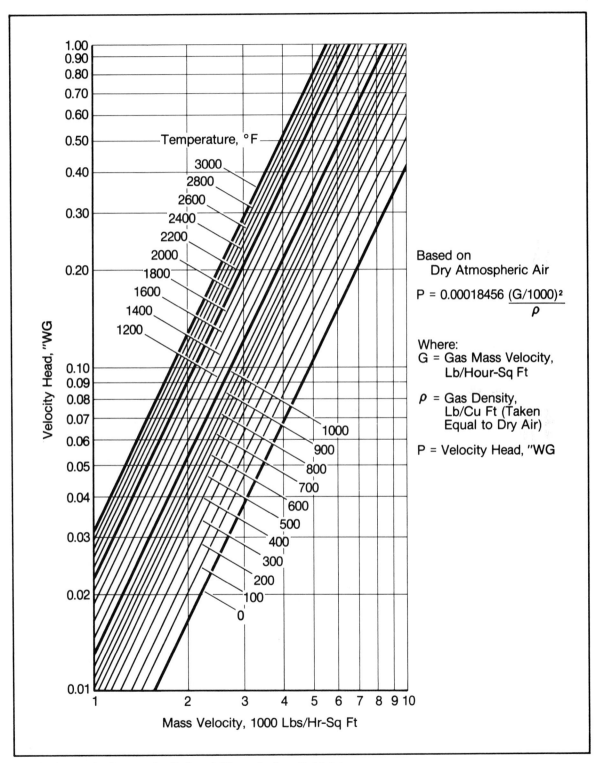

Fig. 4 Mass velocity vs velocity head, Stauscheibe pitot tube

Based on
Dry Atmospheric Air

$$P = 0.00018456 \frac{(G/1000)^2}{\rho}$$

Where:
G = Gas Mass Velocity,
Lb/Hour-Sq Ft

ρ = Gas Density,
Lb/Cu Ft (Taken
Equal to Dry Air)

P = Velocity Head, "WG

Fig. 5. **Velocity traverse for round flues, cross section equal-area sections (read station 1 after reading each other station). R_1, R_2, etc. = distance in inches from center to points where readings should be taken; 2 = area in sq in. of each successive ring**

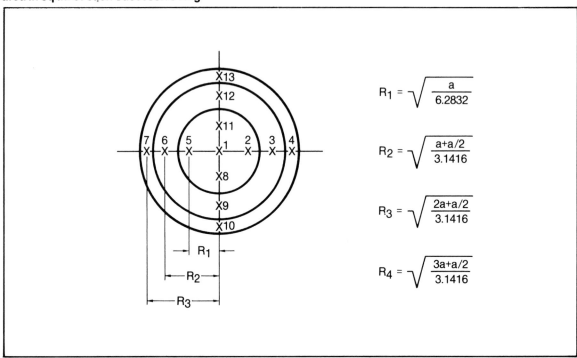

$$R_1 = \sqrt{\frac{a}{6.2832}}$$

$$R_2 = \sqrt{\frac{a+a/2}{3.1416}}$$

$$R_3 = \sqrt{\frac{2a+a/2}{3.1416}}$$

$$R_4 = \sqrt{\frac{3a+a/2}{3.1416}}$$

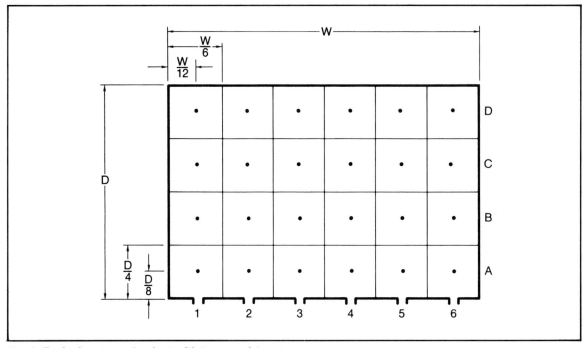

Fig. 6 **Typical rectangular duct with traverse layout**

***Fig. 7.* Accuracy of mass-flow measurement for 95-percent confidence limits—1 sample at each point**

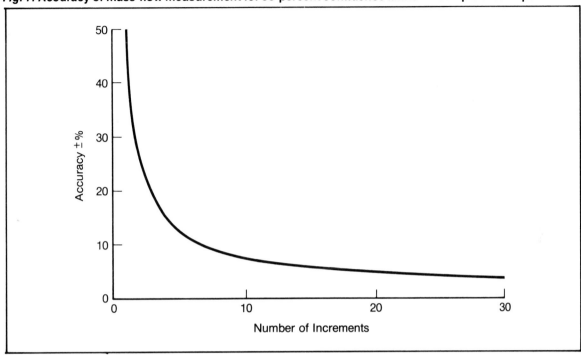

***Fig. 8* Velocity correction factors for flue gases**

Fig. 9 Correction factors for gas measurement due to CO_2, SO_2, and H_2O

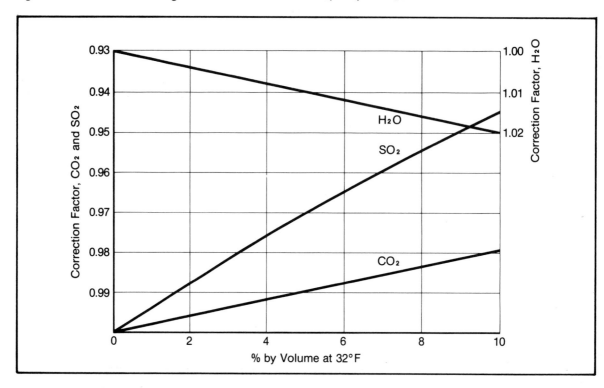

Fig. 10 Static correction curve

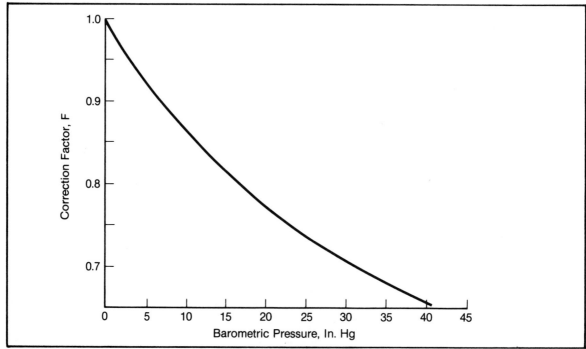

Fig. 11 Correction factors for reducing gas volumes at any pressure to one atmosphere

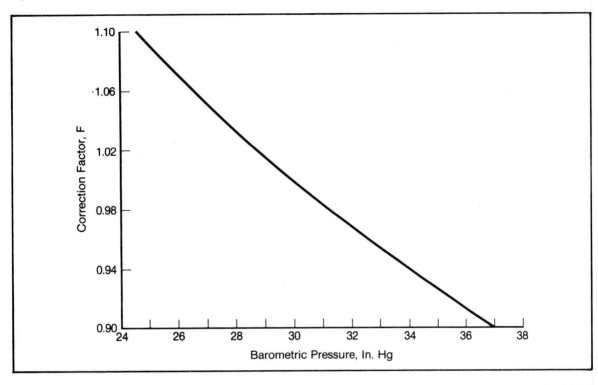

Fig. 12 Correction factors for reducing gas volumes at any temperature to 32°F

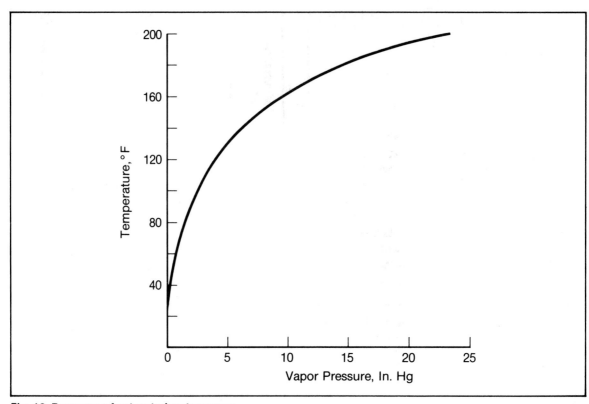

Fig. 13 **Pressure of saturated water vapor**

Appendix F. Steam Tables

The following tables are in accordance with those adopted by The Sixth International Conference on the Properties of Steam and published in the *1967 ASME Steam Tables* by the American Society of Mechanical Engineers. Combustion Engineering, Inc., has permission to reprint the tables in this form. For a copy of *Steam Tables,* with a convenient Mollier diagram included, write to Marketing Communications, C-E Power Systems, Combustion Engineering, Inc., 1000 Prospect Hill Rd., Windsor, CT 06095.

A thorough historical account of the development of formulations of the thermodynamic properties of steam is presented in Appendix D, *Combustion Engineering,* 1967 edition. The article in that appendix describes the early research begun on steam properties in 1741 and fully covers the proceedings of the Sixth International Conference on the Properties of Steam held between 1958 and 1963.

REFERENCE STATE

The liquid phase at the triple point of water substance is the state for which the specific internal energy and the specific entropy are each made exactly zero.

Table I. Saturated Steam: Temperature Table (32 to 705.47°F)

Temp Fahr t	Abs Press. Lb/ Sq In. p	Sat. Liquid v_f	Evap v_{fg}	Sat. Vapor v_g	Sat. Liquid h_f	Evap h_{fg}	Sat. Vapor h_g	Sat. Liquid s_f	Evap s_{fg}	Sat. Vapor s_g	Temp Fahr t
32.0*	0.08859	0.016022	3304.7	3304.7	−0.0179	1075.5	1075.5	0.0000	2.1873	2.1873	32.0*
34.0	0.09600	0.016021	3061.9	3061.9	1.996	1074.4	1076.4	0.0041	2.1762	2.1802	34.0
36.0	0.10395	0.016020	2839.0	2839.0	4.008	1073.2	1077.2	0.0081	2.1651	2.1732	36.0
38.0	0.11249	0.016019	2634.1	2634.2	6.018	1072.1	1078.1	0.0122	2.1541	2.1663	38.0
40.0	0.12163	0.016019	2445.8	2445.8	8.027	1071.0	1079.0	0.0162	2.1432	2.1594	40.0
42.0	0.13143	0.016019	2272.4	2272.4	10.035	1069.8	1079.9	0.0202	2.1325	2.1527	42.0
44.0	0.14192	0.016019	2112.8	2112.8	12.041	1068.7	1080.7	0.0242	2.1217	2.1459	44.0
46.0	0.15314	0.016020	1965.7	1965.7	14.047	1067.6	1081.6	0.0282	2.1111	2.1393	46.0
48.0	0.16514	0.016021	1830.0	1830.0	16.051	1066.4	1082.5	0.0321	2.1006	2.1327	48.0
50.0	0.17796	0.016023	1704.8	1704.8	18.054	1065.3	1083.4	0.0361	2.0901	2.1262	50.0
52.0	0.19165	0.016024	1589.2	1589.2	20.057	1064.2	1084.2	0.0400	2.0798	2.1197	52.0
54.0	0.20625	0.016026	1482.4	1482.4	22.058	1063.1	1085.1	0.0439	2.0695	2.1134	54.0
56.0	0.22183	0.016028	1383.6	1383.6	24.059	1061.9	1086.0	0.0478	2.0593	2.1070	56.0
58.0	0.23843	0.016031	1292.2	1292.2	26.060	1060.8	1086.9	0.0516	2.0491	2.1008	58.0
60.0	0.25611	0.016033	1207.6	1207.6	28.060	1059.7	1087.7	0.0555	2.0391	2.0946	60.0
62.0	0.27494	0.016036	1129.2	1129.2	30.059	1058.5	1088.6	0.0593	2.0291	2.0885	62.0
64.0	0.29497	0.016039	1056.5	1056.5	32.058	1057.4	1089.5	0.0632	2.0192	2.0824	64.0
66.0	0.31626	0.016043	989.0	989.1	34.056	1056.3	1090.4	0.0670	2.0094	2.0764	66.0
68.0	0.33889	0.016046	926.5	926.5	36.054	1055.2	1091.2	0.0708	1.9996	2.0704	68.0
70.0	0.36292	0.016050	868.3	868.4	38.052	1054.0	1092.1	0.0745	1.9900	2.0645	70.0
72.0	0.38844	0.016054	814.3	814.3	40.049	1052.9	1093.0	0.0783	1.9804	2.0587	72.0
74.0	0.41550	0.016058	764.1	764.1	42.046	1051.8	1093.8	0.0821	1.9708	2.0529	74.0
76.0	0.44420	0.016063	717.4	717.4	44.043	1050.7	1094.7	0.0858	1.9614	2.0472	76.0
78.0	0.47461	0.016067	673.8	673.9	46.040	1049.5	1095.6	0.0895	1.9520	2.0415	78.0
80.0	0.50683	0.016072	633.3	633.3	48.037	1048.4	1096.4	0.0932	1.9426	2.0359	80.0
82.0	0.54093	0.016077	595.5	595.5	50.033	1047.3	1097.3	0.0969	1.9334	2.0303	82.0

Table I. Saturated Steam: Temperature Table — *Continued*

Temp Fahr t	Abs Press. Lb/ Sq In. p	Specific Volume Sat. Liquid v_f	Evap v_{fg}	Sat. Vapor v_g	Enthalpy Sat. Liquid h_f	Evap h_{fg}	Sat. Vapor h_g	Entropy Sat. Liquid s_f	Evap s_{fg}	Sat. Vapor s_g	Temp Fahr t
84.0	0.57702	0.016082	560.3	560.3	52.029	1046.1	1098.2	0.1006	1.9242	2.0248	84.0
86.0	0.61518	0.016087	527.5	527.5	54.026	1045.0	1099.0	0.1043	1.9151	2.0193	86.0
88.0	0.65551	0.016093	496.8	496.8	56.022	1043.9	1099.9	0.1079	1.9060	2.0139	88.0
90.0	0.69813	0.016099	468.1	468.1	58.018	1042.7	1100.8	0.1115	1.8970	2.0086	90.0
92.0	0.74313	0.016105	441.3	441.3	60.014	1041.6	1101.6	0.1152	1.8881	2.0033	92.0
94.0	0.79062	0.016111	416.3	416.3	62.010	1040.5	1102.5	0.1188	1.8792	1.9980	94.0
96.0	0.84072	0.016117	392.8	392.9	64.006	1039.3	1103.3	0.1224	1.8704	1.9928	96.0
98.0	0.89356	0.016123	370.9	370.9	66.003	1038.2	1104.2	0.1260	1.8617	1.9876	98.0
100.0	0.94924	0.016130	350.4	350.4	67.999	1037.1	1105.1	0.1295	1.8530	1.9825	100.0
102.0	1.00789	0.016137	331.1	331.1	69.995	1035.9	1105.9	0.1331	1.8444	1.9775	102.0
104.0	1.06965	0.016144	313.1	313.1	71.992	1034.8	1106.8	0.1366	1.8358	1.9725	104.0
106.0	1.1347	0.016151	296.16	296.18	73.99	1033.6	1107.6	0.1402	1.8273	1.9675	106.0
108.0	1.2030	0.016158	280.28	280.30	75.98	1032.5	1108.5	0.1437	1.8188	1.9626	108.0
110.0	1.2750	0.016165	265.37	265.39	77.98	1031.4	1109.3	0.1472	1.8105	1.9577	110.0
112.0	1.3505	0.016173	251.37	251.38	79.98	1030.2	1110.2	0.1507	1.8021	1.9528	112.0
114.0	1.4299	0.016180	238.21	238.22	81.97	1029.1	1111.0	0.1542	1.7938	1.9480	114.0
116.0	1.5133	0.016188	225.84	225.85	83.97	1027.9	1111.9	0.1577	1.7856	1.9433	116.0
118.0	1.6009	0.016196	214.20	214.21	85.97	1026.8	1112.7	0.1611	1.7774	1.9386	118.0
120.0	1.6927	0.016204	203.25	203.26	87.97	1025.6	1113.6	0.1646	1.7693	1.9339	120.0
122.0	1.7891	0.016213	192.94	192.95	89.96	1024.5	1114.4	0.1680	1.7613	1.9293	122.0
124.0	1.8901	0.016221	183.23	183.24	91.96	1023.3	1115.3	0.1715	1.7533	1.9247	124.0
126.0	1.9959	0.016229	174.08	174.09	93.96	1022.2	1116.1	0.1749	1.7453	1.9202	126.0
128.0	2.1068	0.016238	165.45	165.47	95.96	1021.0	1117.0	0.1783	1.7374	1.9157	128.0
130.0	2.2230	0.016247	157.32	157.33	97.96	1019.8	1117.8	0.1817	1.7295	1.9112	130.0
132.0	2.3445	0.016256	149.64	149.66	99.95	1018.7	1118.6	0.1851	1.7217	1.9068	132.0
134.0	2.4717	0.016265	142.40	142.41	101.95	1017.5	1119.5	0.1884	1.7140	1.9024	134.0
136.0	2.6047	0.016274	135.55	135.57	103.95	1016.4	1120.3	0.1918	1.7063	1.8980	136.0
138.0	2.7438	0.016284	129.09	129.11	105.95	1015.2	1121.1	0.1951	1.6986	1.8937	138.0
140.0	2.8892	0.016293	122.98	123.00	107.95	1014.0	1122.0	0.1985	1.6910	1.8895	140.0
142.0	3.0411	0.016303	117.21	117.22	109.95	1012.9	1122.8	0.2018	1.6534	1.8852	142.0
144.0	3.1997	0.016312	111.74	111.76	111.95	1011.7	1123.6	0.2051	1.6759	1.8810	144.0
146.0	3.3653	0.016322	106.58	106.59	113.95	1010.5	1124.5	0.2084	1.6684	1.8769	146.0
148.0	3.5381	0.016332	101.68	101.70	115.95	1009.3	1125.3	0.2117	1.6610	1.8727	148.0
150.0	3.7184	0.016343	97.05	97.07	117.95	1008.2	1126.1	0.2150	1.6536	1.8686	150.0
152.0	3.9065	0.016353	92.66	92.68	119.95	1007.0	1126.9	0.2183	1.6463	1.8646	152.0
154.0	4.1025	0.016363	88.50	88.52	121.95	1005.8	1127.7	0.2216	1.6390	1.8606	154.0
156.0	4.3068	0.016374	84.56	84.57	123.95	1004.6	1128.6	0.2248	1.6318	1.8566	156.0
158.0	4.5197	0.016384	80.82	80.83	125.96	1003.4	1129.4	0.2281	1.6245	1.8526	158.0
160.0	4.7414	0.016395	77.27	77.29	127.96	1002.2	1130.2	0.2313	1.6174	1.8487	160.0
162.0	4.9722	0.016406	73.90	73.92	129.96	1001.0	1131.0	0.2345	1.6103	1.8448	162.0
164.0	5.2124	0.016417	70.70	70.72	131.96	999.8	1131.8	0.2377	1.6032	1.8409	164.0
166.0	5.4623	0.016428	67.67	67.68	133.97	998.6	1132.6	0.2409	1.5961	1.8371	166.0
168.0	5.7223	0.016440	64.78	64.80	135.97	997.4	1133.4	0.2441	1.5892	1.8333	168.0
170.0	5.9926	0.016451	62.04	62.06	137.97	996.2	1134.2	0.2473	1.5822	1.8295	170.0
172.0	6.2736	0.016463	59.43	59.45	139.98	995.0	1135.0	0.2505	1.5753	1.8258	172.0
174.0	6.5656	0.016474	56.95	56.97	141.98	993.8	1135.8	0.2537	1.5684	1.8221	174.0
176.0	6.8690	0.016486	54.59	54.61	143.99	992.6	1136.6	0.2568	1.5616	1.8184	176.0
178.0	7.1840	0.016498	52.35	52.36	145.99	991.4	1137.4	0.2600	1.5548	1.8147	178.0

Table I. Saturated Steam: Temperature Table — *Continued*

Temp Fahr	Abs Press. Lb/ Sq In.	Specific Volume Sat. Liquid	Evap	Sat. Vapor	Enthalpy Sat. Liquid	Evap	Sat. Vapor	Entropy Sat. Liquid	Evap	Sat. Vapor	Temp Fahr
t	p	v_f	v_{fg}	v_g	h_f	h_{fg}	h_g	s_f	s_{fg}	s_g	t
180.0	7.5110	0.016510	50.21	50.22	148.00	990.2	1138.2	0.2631	1.5480	1.8111	180.0
182.0	7.850	0.016522	48.172	48.189	150.01	989.0	1139.0	0.2662	1.5413	1.8075	182.0
184.0	8.203	0.016534	46.232	46.249	152.01	987.8	1139.8	0.2694	1.5346	1.8040	184.0
186.0	8.568	0.016547	44.383	44.400	154.02	986.5	1140.5	0.2725	1.5279	1.8004	186.0
188.0	8.947	0.016559	42.621	42.638	156.03	985.3	1141.3	0.2756	1.5213	1.7969	188.0
190.0	9.340	0.016572	40.941	40.957	158.04	984.1	1142.1	0.2787	1.5148	1.7934	190.0
192.0	9.747	0.016585	39.337	39.354	160.05	982.8	1142.9	0.2818	1.5082	1.7900	192.0
194.0	10.168	0.016598	37.808	37.824	162.05	981.6	1143.7	0.2848	1.5017	1.7865	194.0
196.0	10.605	0.016611	36.348	36.364	164.06	980.4	1144.4	0.2879	1.4952	1.7831	196.0
198.0	11.058	0.016624	34.954	34.970	166.08	979.1	1145.2	0.2910	1.4888	1.7798	198.0
200.0	11.526	0.016637	33.622	33.639	168.09	977.9	1146.0	0.2940	1.4824	1.7764	200.0
204.0	12.512	0.016664	31.135	31.151	172.11	975.4	1147.5	0.3001	1.4697	1.7698	204.0
208.0	13.568	0.016691	28.862	28.878	176.14	972.8	1149.0	0.3061	1.4571	1.7632	208.0
212.0	14.696	0.016719	26.782	26.799	180.17	970.3	1150.5	0.3121	1.4447	1.7568	212.0
216.0	15.901	0.016747	24.878	24.894	184.20	967.8	1152.0	0.3181	1.4323	1.7505	216.0
220.0	17.186	0.016775	23.131	23.148	188.23	965.2	1153.4	0.3241	1.4201	1.7442	220.0
224.0	18.556	0.016805	21.529	21.545	192.27	962.6	1154.9	0.3300	1.4081	1.7380	224.0
228.0	20.015	0.016834	20.056	20.073	196.31	960.0	1156.3	0.3359	1.3961	1.7320	228.0
232.0	21.567	0.016864	18.701	18.718	200.35	957.4	1157.8	0.3417	1.3842	1.7260	232.0
236.0	23.216	0.016895	17.454	17.471	204.40	954.8	1159.2	0.3476	1.3725	1.7201	236.0
240.0	24.968	0.016926	16.304	16.321	208.45	952.1	1160.6	0.3533	1.3609	1.7142	240.0
244.0	26.826	0.016958	15.243	15.260	212.50	949.5	1162.0	0.3591	1.3494	1.7085	244.0
248.0	28.796	0.016990	14.264	14.281	216.56	946.8	1163.4	0.3649	1.3379	1.7028	248.0
252.0	30.883	0.017022	13.358	13.375	220.62	944.1	1164.7	0.3706	1.3266	1.6972	252.0
256.0	33.091	0.017055	12.520	12.538	224.69	941.4	1166.1	0.3763	1.3154	1.6917	256.0
260.0	35.427	0.017089	11.745	11.762	228.76	938.6	1167.4	0.3819	1.3043	1.6862	260.0
264.0	37.894	0.017123	11.025	11.042	232.83	935.9	1168.7	0.3876	1.2933	1.6808	264.0
268.0	40.500	0.017157	10.358	10.375	236.91	933.1	1170.0	0.3932	1.2823	1.6755	268.0
272.0	43.249	0.017193	9.738	9.755	240.99	930.3	1171.3	0.3987	1.2715	1.6702	272.0
276.0	46.147	0.017228	9.162	9.180	245.08	927.5	1172.5	0.4043	1.2607	1.6650	276.0
280.0	49.200	0.017264	8.627	8.644	249.17	924.6	1173.8	0.4098	1.2501	1.6599	280.0
284.0	52.414	0.01730	8.1280	8.1453	253.3	921.7	1175.0	0.4154	1.2395	1.6548	284.0
288.0	55.795	0.01734	7.6634	7.6807	257.4	918.8	1176.2	0.4208	1.2290	1.6498	288.0
292.0	59.350	0.01738	7.2301	7.2475	261.5	915.9	1177.4	0.4263	1.2186	1.6449	292.0
296.0	63.084	0.01741	6.8259	6.8433	265.6	913.0	1178.6	0.4317	1.2082	1.6400	296.0
300.0	67.005	0.01745	6.4483	6.4658	269.7	910.0	1179.7	0.4372	1.1979	1.6351	300.0
304.0	71.119	0.01749	6.0955	6.1130	273.8	907.0	1180.9	0.4426	1.1877	1.6303	304.0
308.0	75.433	0.01753	5.7655	5.7830	278.0	904.0	1182.0	0.4479	1.1776	1.6256	308.0
312.0	79.953	0.01757	5.4566	5.4742	282.1	901.0	1183.1	0.4533	1.1676	1.6209	312.0
316.0	84.688	0.01761	5.1673	5.1849	286.3	897.9	1184.1	0.4586	1.1576	1.6162	316.0
320.0	89.643	0.01766	4.8961	4.9138	290.4	894.8	1185.2	0.4640	1.1477	1.6116	320.0
324.0	94.826	0.01770	4.6418	4.6595	294.6	891.6	1186.2	0.4692	1.1378	1.6071	324.0
328.0	100.245	0.01774	4.4030	4.4208	298.7	888.5	1187.2	0.4745	1.1280	1.6025	328.0
332.0	105.907	0.01779	4.1788	4.1966	302.9	885.3	1188.2	0.4798	1.1183	1.5981	332.0
336.0	111.820	0.01783	3.9681	3.9859	307.1	882.1	1189.1	0.4850	1.1086	1.5936	336.0
340.0	117.992	0.01787	3.7699	3.7878	311.3	878.8	1190.1	0.4902	1.0990	1.5892	340.0
344.0	124.430	0.01792	3.5834	3.6013	315.5	875.5	1191.0	0.4954	1.0894	1.5849	344.0
348.0	131.142	0.01797	3.4078	3.4258	319.7	872.2	1191.1	0.5006	1.0799	1.5806	348.0

Table I. Saturated Steam: Temperature Table — *Continued*

Temp Fahr t	Abs Press. Lb/ Sq In. p	Specific Volume Sat. Liquid v_f	Specific Volume Evap v_{fg}	Specific Volume Sat. Vapor v_g	Enthalpy Sat. Liquid h_f	Enthalpy Evap h_{fg}	Enthalpy Sat. Vapor h_g	Entropy Sat. Liquid s_f	Entropy Evap s_{fg}	Entropy Sat. Vapor s_g	Temp Fahr t
352.0	138.138	0.01801	3.2423	3.2603	323.9	868.9	1192.7	0.5058	1.0705	1.5763	352.0
356.0	145.424	0.01806	3.0863	3.1044	328.1	865.5	1193.6	0.5110	1.0611	1.5721	356.0
360.0	153.010	0.01811	2.9392	2.9573	332.3	862.1	1194.4	0.5161	1.0517	1.5678	360.0
364.0	160.903	0.01816	2.8002	2.8184	336.5	858.6	1195.2	0.5212	1.0424	1.5637	364.0
368.0	169.113	0.01821	2.6691	2.6873	340.8	855.1	1195.9	0.5263	1.0332	1.5595	368.0
372.0	177.648	0.01826	2.5451	2.5633	345.0	851.6	1196.7	0.5314	1.0240	1.5554	372.0
376.0	186.517	0.01831	2.4279	2.4462	349.3	848.1	1197.4	0.5365	1.0148	1.5513	376.0
380.0	195.729	0.01836	2.3170	2.3353	353.6	844.5	1198.0	0.5416	1.0057	1.5473	380.0
384.0	205.294	0.01842	2.2120	2.2304	357.9	840.8	1198.7	0.5466	0.9966	1.5432	384.0
388.0	215.220	0.01847	2.1126	2.1311	362.2	837.2	1199.3	0.5516	0.9876	1.5392	388.0
392.0	225.516	0.01853	2.0184	2.0369	366.5	833.4	1199.9	0.5567	0.9786	1.5352	392.0
396.0	236.193	0.01858	1.9291	1.9477	370.8	829.7	1200.4	0.5617	0.9696	1.5313	396.0
400.0	247.259	0.01864	1.8444	1.8630	375.1	825.9	1201.0	0.5667	0.9607	1.5274	400.0
404.0	258.725	0.01870	1.7640	1.7827	379.4	822.0	1201.5	0.5717	0.9518	1.5234	404.0
408.0	270.600	0.01875	1.6877	1.7064	383.8	818.2	1201.9	0.5766	0.9429	1.5195	408.0
412.0	282.894	0.01881	1.6152	1.6340	388.1	814.2	1202.4	0.5816	0.9341	1.5157	412.0
416.0	295.617	0.01887	1.5463	1.5651	392.5	810.2	1202.8	0.5866	0.9253	1.5118	416.0
420.0	308.780	0.01894	1.4808	1.4997	396.9	806.2	1203.1	0.5915	0.9165	1.5080	420.0
424.0	322.391	0.01900	1.4184	1.4374	401.3	802.2	1203.5	0.5964	0.9077	1.5042	424.0
428.0	336.463	0.01906	1.3591	1.3782	405.7	798.0	1203.7	0.6014	0.8990	1.5004	428.0
432.0	351.00	0.01913	1.30266	1.32179	410.1	793.9	1204.0	0.6063	0.8903	1.4966	432.0
436.0	366.03	0.01919	1.24887	1.26806	414.6	789.7	1204.2	0.6112	0.8816	1.4928	436.0
440.0	381.54	0.01926	1.19761	1.21687	419.0	785.4	1204.4	0.6161	0.8729	1.4890	440.0
444.0	397.56	0.01933	1.14874	1.16806	423.5	781.1	1204.6	0.6210	0.8643	1.4853	444.0
448.0	414.09	0.01940	1.10212	1.12152	428.0	776.7	1204.7	0.6259	0.8557	1.4815	448.0
452.0	431.14	0.01947	1.05764	1.07711	432.5	772.3	1204.8	0.6308	0.8471	1.4778	452.0
456.0	448.73	0.01954	1.01518	1.03472	437.0	767.8	1204.8	0.6356	0.8385	1.4741	456.0
460.0	466.87	0.01961	0.97463	0.99424	441.5	763.2	1204.8	0.6405	0.8299	1.4704	460.0
464.0	485.56	0.01969	0.93588	0.95557	446.1	758.6	1204.7	0.6454	0.8213	1.4667	464.0
468.0	504.83	0.01976	0.89885	0.91862	450.7	754.0	1204.6	0.6502	0.8127	1.4629	468.0
472.0	524.67	0.01984	0.86345	0.88329	455.2	749.3	1204.5	0.6551	0.8042	1.4592	472.0
476.0	545.11	0.01992	0.82958	0.84950	459.9	744.5	1204.3	0.6599	0.7956	1.4555	476.0
480.0	566.15	0.02000	0.79716	0.81717	464.5	739.6	1204.1	0.6648	0.7871	1.4518	480.0
484.0	587.81	0.02009	0.76613	0.78622	469.1	734.7	1203.8	0.6696	0.7785	1.4481	484.0
488.0	610.10	0.02017	0.73641	0.75658	473.8	729.7	1203.5	0.6745	0.7700	1.4444	488.0
492.0	633.03	0.02026	0.70794	0.72820	478.5	724.6	1203.1	0.6793	0.7614	1.4407	492.0
496.0	656.61	0.02034	0.68065	0.70100	483.2	719.5	1202.7	0.6842	0.7528	1.4370	496.0
500.0	680.86	0.02043	0.65448	0.67492	487.9	714.3	1202.2	0.6890	0.7443	1.4333	500.0
504.0	705.78	0.02053	0.62938	0.64991	492.7	709.0	1201.7	0.6939	0.7357	1.4296	504.0
508.0	731.40	0.02062	0.60530	0.62592	497.5	703.7	1201.1	0.6987	0.7271	1.4258	508.0
512.0	757.72	0.02072	0.58218	0.60289	502.3	698.2	1200.5	0.7036	0.7185	1.4221	512.0
516.0	784.76	0.02081	0.55997	0.58079	507.1	692.7	1199.8	0.7085	0.7099	1.4183	516.0
520.0	812.53	0.02091	0.53864	0.55956	512.0	687.0	1199.0	0.7133	0.7013	1.4146	520.0
524.0	841.04	0.02102	0.51814	0.53916	516.9	681.3	1198.2	0.7182	0.6926	1.4108	524.0
528.0	870.31	0.02112	0.49843	0.51955	521.8	675.5	1197.3	0.7231	0.6839	1.4070	528.0
532.0	900.34	0.02123	0.47947	0.50070	526.8	669.6	1196.4	0.7280	0.6752	1.4032	532.0
536.0	931.17	0.02134	0.46123	0.48257	531.7	663.6	1195.4	0.7329	0.6665	1.3993	536.0

Table I. Saturated Steam: Temperature Table — *Continued*

Temp Fahr	Abs Press. Lb/ Sq In.	Specific Volume Sat. Liquid	Evap	Sat. Vapor	Enthalpy Sat. Liquid	Evap	Sat. Vapor	Entropy Sat. Liquid	Evap	Sat. Vapor	Temp Fahr
t	p	v_f	v_{fg}	v_g	h_f	h_{fg}	h_g	s_f	s_{fg}	s_g	t
540.0	962.79	0.02146	0.44367	0.46513	536.8	657.5	1194.3	0.7378	0.6577	1.3954	540.0
544.0	995.22	0.02157	0.42677	0.44834	541.8	651.3	1193.1	0.7427	0.6489	1.3915	544.0
548.0	1028.49	0.02169	0.41048	0.43217	546.9	645.0	1191.9	0.7476	0.6400	1.3876	548.0
552.0	1062.59	0.02182	0.39479	0.41660	552.0	638.5	1190.6	0.7525	0.6311	1.3837	552.0
556.0	1097.55	0.02194	0.37966	0.40160	557.2	632.0	1189.2	0.7575	0.6222	1.3797	556.0
560.0	1133.38	0.02207	0.36507	0.38714	562.4	625.3	1187.7	0.7625	0.6132	1.3757	560.0
564.0	1170.10	0.02221	0.35099	0.37320	567.6	618.5	1186.1	0.7674	0.6041	1.3716	564.0
568.0	1207.72	0.02235	0.33741	0.35975	572.9	611.5	1184.5	0.7725	0.5950	1.3675	568.0
572.0	1246.26	0.02249	0.32429	0.34678	578.3	604.5	1182.7	0.7775	0.5859	1.3634	572.0
576.0	1285.74	0.02264	0.31162	0.33426	583.7	597.2	1180.9	0.7825	0.5766	1.3592	576.0
580.0	1326.17	0.02279	0.29937	0.32216	589.1	589.9	1179.0	0.7876	0.5673	1.3550	580.0
584.0	1367.7	0.02295	0.28753	0.31048	594.6	582.4	1176.9	0.7927	0.5580	1.3507	584.0
588.0	1410.0	0.02311	0.27608	0.29919	600.1	574.7	1174.8	0.7978	0.5485	1.3464	588.0
592.0	1453.3	0.02328	0.26499	0.28827	605.7	566.8	1172.6	0.8030	0.5390	1.3420	592.0
596.0	1497.8	0.02345	0.25425	0.27770	611.4	558.8	1170.2	0.8082	0.5293	1.3375	596.0
600.0	1543.2	0.02364	0.24384	0.26747	617.1	550.6	1167.7	0.8134	0.5196	1.3330	600.0
604.0	1589.7	0.02382	0.23374	0.25757	622.9	542.2	1165.1	0.8187	0.5097	1.3284	604.0
608.0	1637.3	0.02402	0.22394	0.24796	628.8	533.6	1162.4	0.8240	0.4997	1.3238	608.0
612.0	1686.1	0.02422	0.21442	0.23865	634.8	524.7	1159.5	0.8294	0.4896	1.3190	612.0
616.6	1735.9	0.02444	0.20516	0.22960	640.8	515.6	1156.4	0.8348	0.4794	1.3141	616.0
620.0	1786.9	0.02466	0.19615	0.22081	646.9	506.3	1153.2	0.8403	0.4689	1.3092	620.0
624.0	1839.0	0.02489	0.18737	0.21226	653.1	496.6	1149.8	0.8458	0.4583	1.3041	624.0
628.0	1892.4	0.02514	0.17880	0.20394	659.5	486.7	1146.1	0.8514	0.4474	1.2988	628.0
632.0	1947.0	0.02539	0.17044	0.19583	665.9	476.4	1142.2	0.8571	0.4364	1.2934	632.0
636.0	2002.8	0.02566	0.16226	0.18792	672.4	465.7	1138.1	0.8628	0.4251	1.2879	636.0
640.0	2059.9	0.02595	0.15427	0.18021	679.1	454.6	1133.7	0.8686	0.4134	1.2821	640.0
644.0	2118.3	0.02625	0.14644	0.17269	685.9	443.1	1129.0	0.8746	0.4015	1.2761	644.0
648.0	2178.1	0.02657	0.13876	0.16534	692.9	431.1	1124.0	0.8806	0.3893	1.2699	648.0
652.0	2239.2	0.02691	0.13124	0.15816	700.0	418.7	1118.7	0.8868	0.3767	1.2634	652.0
656.0	2301.7	0.02728	0.12387	0.15115	707.4	405.7	1113.1	0.8931	0.3637	1.2567	656.0
660.0	2365.7	0.02768	0.11663	0.14431	714.9	392.1	1107.0	0.8995	0.3502	1.2498	660.0
664.0	2431.1	0.02811	0.10947	0.13757	722.9	377.7	1100.6	0.9064	0.3361	1.2425	664.0
668.0	2498.1	0.02858	0.10229	0.13087	731.5	362.1	1093.5	0.9137	0.3210	1.2347	668.0
672.0	2566.6	0.02911	0.09514	0.12424	740.2	345.7	1085.9	0.9212	0.3054	1.2266	672.0
676.0	2636.8	0.02970	0.08799	0.11769	749.2	328.5	1077.6	0.9287	0.2892	1.2179	676.0
680.0	2708.6	0.03037	0.08080	0.11117	758.5	310.1	1068.5	0.9365	0.2720	1.2086	680.0
684.0	2782.1	0.03114	0.07349	0.10463	768.2	290.2	1058.4	0.9447	0.2537	1.1984	684.0
688.0	2857.4	0.03204	0.06595	0.09799	778.8	268.2	1047.0	0.9535	0.2337	1.1872	688.0
692.0	2934.5	0.03313	0.05797	0.09110	790.5	243.1	1033.6	0.9634	0.2110	1.1744	692.0
696.0	3013.4	0.03455	0.04916	0.08371	804.4	212.8	1017.2	0.9749	0.1841	1.1591	696.0
700.0	3094.3	0.03662	0.03857	0.07519	822.4	172.7	995.2	0.9901	0.1490	1.1390	700.0
702.0	3135.5	0.03824	0.03173	0.06997	835.0	144.7	979.7	1.0006	0.1246	1.1252	702.0
704.0	3177.2	0.04108	0.02192	0.06300	854.2	102.0	956.2	1.0169	0.0876	1.1046	704.0
705.0	3198.3	0.04427	0.01304	0.05730	873.0	61.4	934.4	1.0329	0.0527	1.0856	705.0
705.47*	3208.2	0.05078	0.00000	0.05078	906.0	0.0	906.0	1.0612	0.0000	1.0612	705.47*

*The states shown are meta stable

Table II. Saturated Steam: Pressure Table

Abs Press. Lb/Sq In. p	Temp Fahr t	Specific Volume			Enthalpy			Entropy			Abs Press. Lb/Sq In. p
		Sat. Liquid v_f	Evap v_{fg}	Sat. Vapor v_g	Sat. Liquid h_f	Evap h_{fg}	Sat. Vapor h_g	Sat. Liquid s_f	Evap s_{fg}	Sat. Vapor s_g	
0.08865	32.018	0.016022	3302.4	3302.4	0.0003	1075.5	1075.5	0.0000	2.1872	2.1872	0.08865
0.25	59.323	0.016032	1235.5	1235.5	27.382	1060.1	1087.4	0.0542	2.0425	2.0967	0.25
0.50	79.586	0.016071	641.5	641.5	47.623	1048.6	1096.3	0.0925	1.9446	2.0370	0.50
1.0	101.74	0.016136	333.59	333.60	69.73	1036.1	1105.8	0.1326	1.8455	1.9781	1.0
5.0	162.24	0.016407	73.515	73.532	130.20	1000.9	1131.1	0.2349	1.6094	1.8443	5.0
10.0	193.21	0.016592	38.404	38.420	161.26	982.1	1143.3	0.2836	1.5043	1.7879	10.0
14.696	212.00	0.016719	26.782	26.799	180.17	970.3	1150.5	0.3121	1.4447	1.7568	14.696
15.0	213.03	0.016726	26.274	26.290	181.21	969.7	1150.9	0.3137	1.4415	1.7552	15.0
20.0	227.96	0.016834	20.070	20.087	196.27	960.1	1156.3	0.3358	1.3962	1.7320	20.0
30.0	250.34	0.017009	13.7266	13.7436	218.9	945.2	1164.1	0.3682	1.3313	1.6995	30.0
40.0	267.25	0.017151	10.4794	10.4965	236.1	933.6	1169.8	0.3921	1.2844	1.6765	40.0
50.0	281.02	0.017274	8.4967	8.5140	250.2	923.9	1174.1	0.4112	1.2474	1.6586	50.0
60.0	292.71	0.017383	7.1562	7.1736	262.2	915.4	1177.6	0.4273	1.2167	1.6440	60.0
70.0	302.93	0.017482	6.1875	6.2050	272.7	907.8	1180.6	0.4411	1.1905	1.6316	70.0
80.0	312.04	0.017573	5.4536	5.4711	282.1	900.9	1183.1	0.4534	1.1675	1.6208	80.0
90.0	320.28	0.017659	4.8779	4.8953	290.7	894.6	1185.3	0.4643	1.1470	1.6113	90.0
100.0	327.82	0.017740	4.4133	4.4310	298.5	888.6	1187.2	0.4743	1.1284	1.6027	100.0
110.0	334.79	0.01782	4.0306	4.0484	305.8	883.1	1188.9	0.4834	1.1115	1.5950	110.0
120.0	341.27	0.01789	3.7097	3.7275	312.6	877.8	1190.4	0.4919	1.0960	1.5879	120.0
130.0	347.33	0.01796	3.4364	3.4544	319.0	872.8	1191.7	0.4998	1.0815	1.5813	130.0
140.0	353.04	0.01803	3.2010	3.2190	325.0	868.0	1193.0	0.5071	1.0681	1.5752	140.0
150.0	358.43	0.01809	2.9958	3.0139	330.6	863.4	1194.1	0.5141	1.0554	1.5695	150.0
160.0	363.55	0.01815	2.8155	2.8336	336.1	859.0	1195.1	0.5206	1.0435	1.5641	160.0
170.0	368.42	0.01821	2.6556	2.6738	341.2	854.8	1196.0	0.5269	1.0322	1.5591	170.0
180.0	373.08	0.01827	2.5129	2.5312	346.2	850.7	1196.9	0.5328	1.0215	1.5543	180.0
190.0	377.53	0.01833	2.3847	2.4030	350.9	846.7	1197.6	0.5384	1.0113	1.5498	190.0
200.0	381.80	0.01839	2.2689	2.2873	355.5	842.8	1198.3	0.5438	1.0016	1.5454	200.0
210.0	385.91	0.01844	2.16373	2.18217	359.9	839.1	1199.0	0.5490	0.9923	1.5413	210.0
220.0	389.88	0.01850	2.06779	2.08629	364.2	835.4	1199.6	0.5540	0.9834	1.5374	220.0
230.0	393.70	0.01855	1.97991	1.99846	368.3	831.8	1200.1	0.5588	0.9748	1.5336	230.0
240.0	397.39	0.01860	1.89909	1.91769	372.3	828.4	1200.6	0.5634	0.9665	1.5299	240.0
250.0	400.97	0.01865	1.82452	1.84317	376.1	825.0	1201.1	0.5679	0.9585	1.5264	250.0
260.0	404.44	0.01870	1.75548	1.77418	379.9	821.6	1201.5	0.5722	0.9508	1.5230	260.0
270.0	407.80	0.01875	1.69137	1.71013	383.6	818.3	1201.9	0.5764	0.9433	1.5197	270.0
280.0	411.07	0.01880	1.63169	1.65049	387.1	815.1	1202.3	0.5805	0.9361	1.5166	280.0
290.0	414.25	0.01885	1.57597	1.59482	390.6	812.0	1202.6	0.5844	0.9291	1.5135	290.0
300.0	417.35	0.01889	1.52384	1.54274	394.0	808.9	1202.9	0.5882	0.9223	1.5105	300.0
350.0	431.73	0.01912	1.30642	1.32554	409.8	794.2	1204.0	0.6059	0.8909	1.4968	350.0
400.0	444.60	0.01934	1.14162	1.16095	424.2	780.4	1204.6	0.6217	0.8630	1.4847	400.0
450.0	456.28	0.01954	1.01224	1.03179	437.3	767.5	1204.8	0.6360	0.8378	1.4738	450.0
500.0	467.01	0.01975	0.90787	0.92762	449.5	755.1	1204.7	0.6490	0.8148	1.4639	500.0
550.0	476.94	0.01994	0.82183	0.84177	460.9	743.3	1204.3	0.6611	0.7936	1.4547	550.0
600.0	486.20	0.02013	0.74962	0.76975	471.7	732.0	1203.7	0.6723	0.7738	1.4461	600.0

Table II. Saturated Steam: Pressure Table — *Continued*

Abs Press. Lb/Sq In. p	Temp Fahr t	Specific Volume			Enthalpy			Entropy			Abs Press. Lb/Sq In. p
		Sat. Liquid v_f	Evap v_{fg}	Sat. Vapor v_g	Sat. Liquid h_f	Evap h_{fg}	Sat. Vapor h_g	Sat. Liquid s_f	Evap s_{fg}	Sat. Vapor s_g	
650.0	494.89	0.02032	0.68811	0.70843	481.9	720.9	1202.8	0.6828	0.7552	1.4381	**650.0**
700.0	503.08	0.02050	0.63505	0.65556	491.6	710.2	1201.8	0.6928	0.7377	1.4304	**700.0**
750.0	510.84	0.02069	0.58880	0.60949	500.9	699.8	1200.7	0.7022	0.7210	1.4232	**750.0**
800.0	518.21	0.02087	0.54809	0.56896	509.8	689.6	1199.4	0.7111	0.7051	1.4163	**800.0**
850.0	525.24	0.02105	0.51197	0.53302	518.4	679.5	1198.0	0.7197	0.6899	1.4096	**850.0**
900.0	531.95	0.02123	0.47968	0.50091	526.7	669.7	1196.4	0.7279	0.6753	1.4032	**900.0**
950.0	538.39	0.02141	0.45064	0.47205	534.7	660.0	1194.7	0.7358	0.6612	1.3970	**950.0**
1000.0	544.58	0.02159	0.42436	0.44596	542.6	650.4	1192.9	0.7434	0.6476	1.3910	**1000.0**
1050.0	550.53	0.02177	0.40047	0.42224	550.1	640.9	1191.0	0.7507	0.6344	1.3851	**1050.0**
1100.0	556.28	0.02195	0.37863	0.40058	557.5	631.5	1189.1	0.7578	0.6216	1.3794	**1100.0**
1150.0	561.82	0.02214	0.35859	0.38073	564.8	622.2	1187.0	0.7647	0.6091	1.3738	**1150.0**
1200.0	567.19	0.02232	0.34013	0.36245	571.9	613.0	1184.8	0.7714	0.5969	1.3683	**1200.0**
1250.0	572.38	0.02250	0.32306	0.34556	578.8	603.8	1182.6	0.7780	0.5850	1.3630	**1250.0**
1300.0	577.42	0.02269	0.30722	0.32991	585.6	594.6	1180.2	0.7843	0.5733	1.3577	**1300.0**
1350.0	582.32	0.02288	0.29250	0.31537	592.3	585.4	1177.8	0.7906	0.5620	1.3525	**1350.0**
1400.0	587.07	0.02307	0.27871	0.30178	598.8	576.5	1175.3	0.7966	0.5507	1.3474	**1400.0**
1450.0	591.70	0.02327	0.26584	0.28911	605.3	567.4	1172.8	0.8026	0.5397	1.3423	**1450.0**
1500.0	596.20	0.02346	0.25372	0.27719	611.7	558.4	1170.1	0.8085	0.5288	1.3373	**1500.0**
1550.0	600.59	0.02366	0.24235	0.26601	618.0	549.4	1167.4	0.8142	0.5182	1.3324	**1550.0**
1600.0	604.87	0.02387	0.23159	0.25545	624.2	540.3	1164.5	0.8199	0.5076	1.3274	**1600.0**
1650.0	609.05	0.02407	0.22143	0.24551	630.4	531.3	1161.6	0.8254	0.4971	1.3225	**1650.0**
1700.0	613.13	0.02428	0.21178	0.23607	636.5	522.2	1158.6	0.8309	0.4867	1.3176	**1700.0**
1750.0	617.12	0.02450	0.20263	0.22713	642.5	513.1	1155.6	0.8363	0.4765	1.3128	**1750.0**
1800.0	621.02	0.02472	0.19390	0.21861	648.5	503.8	1152.3	0.8417	0.4662	1.3079	**1800.0**
1850.0	624.83	0.02495	0.18558	0.21052	654.5	494.6	1149.0	0.8470	0.4561	1.3030	**1850.0**
1900.0	628.56	0.02517	0.17761	0.20278	660.4	485.2	1145.6	0.8522	0.4459	1.2981	**1900.0**
1950.0	632.22	0.02541	0.16999	0.19540	666.3	475.8	1142.0	0.8574	0.4358	1.2931	**1950.0**
2000.0	635.80	0.02565	0.16266	0.18831	672.1	466.2	1138.3	0.8625	0.4256	1.2881	**2000.0**
2100.0	642.76	0.02615	0.14885	0.17501	683.8	446.7	1130.5	0.8727	0.4053	1.2780	**2100.0**
2200.0	649.45	0.02669	0.13603	0.16272	695.5	426.7	1122.2	0.8828	0.3848	1.2676	**2200.0**
2300.0	655.89	0.02727	0.12406	0.15133	707.2	406.0	1113.2	0.8929	0.3640	1.2569	**2300.0**
2400.0	662.11	0.02790	0.11287	0.14076	719.0	384.8	1103.7	0.9031	0.3430	1.2460	**2400.0**
2500.0	668.11	0.02859	0.10209	0.13068	731.7	361.6	1093.3	0.9139	0.3206	1.2345	**2500.0**
2600.0	673.91	0.02938	0.09172	0.12110	744.5	337.6	1082.0	0.9247	0.2977	1.2225	**2600.0**
2700.0	679.53	0.03029	0.08165	0.11194	757.3	312.3	1069.7	0.9356	0.2741	1.2097	**2700.0**
2800.0	684.96	0.03134	0.07171	0.10305	770.7	285.1	1055.8	0.9468	0.2491	1.1958	**2800.0**
2900.0	690.22	0.03262	0.06158	0.09420	785.1	254.7	1039.8	0.9588	0.2215	1.1803	**2900.0**
3000.0	695.33	0.03428	0.05073	0.08500	801.8	218.4	1020.3	0.9728	0.1891	1.1619	**3000.0**
3100.0	700.28	0.03681	0.03771	0.07452	824.0	169.3	993.3	0.9914	0.1460	1.1373	**3100.0**
3200.0	705.08	0.04472	0.01191	0.05663	875.5	56.1	931.6	1.0351	0.0482	1.0832	**3200.0**
3208.2*	705.47	0.05078	0.00000	0.05078	906.0	0.0	906.0	1.0612	0.0000	1.0612	**3208.2***

*Critical pressure

Table III. Superheated Steam

Abs Press. Lb/Sq In. (Sat. Temp)		Sat. Water	Sat. Steam	200	250	300	350	400	450	500	600	700	800	900
	Sh			98.26	148.26	198.26	248.26	298.26	348.26	398.26	498.26	598.26	698.26	798.26
1	v	0.01614	333.6	392.5	422.4	452.3	482.1	511.9	541.7	571.5	631.1	690.7	750.3	809.8
(101.74)	h	69.73	1105.8	1150.2	1172.9	1195.7	1218.7	1241.8	1265.1	1288.6	1336.1	1384.5	1433.7	1483.8
	s	0.1326	1.9781	2.0509	2.0841	2.1152	2.1445	2.1722	2.1985	2.2237	2.2708	2.3144	2.3551	2.3934
	Sh			37.76	87.76	137.76	187.76	237.76	287.76	337.76	437.76	537.76	637.76	737.76
5	v	0.01641	73.53	78.14	84.21	90.24	96.25	102.24	108.23	114.21	126.15	138.08	150.01	161.94
(162.24)	h	130.20	1131.1	1148.6	1171.7	1194.8	1218.0	1241.3	1264.7	1288.2	1335.9	1384.3	1433.6	1483.7
	s	0.2349	1.8443	1.8716	1.9054	1.9369	1.9664	1.9943	2.0208	2.0460	2.0932	2.1369	2.1776	2.2159
	Sh			6.79	56.79	106.79	156.79	206.79	256.79	306.79	406.79	506.79	606.79	706.79
10	v	0.01659	38.42	38.84	41.93	44.98	48.02	51.03	54.04	57.04	63.03	69.00	74.98	80.94
(193.21)	h	161.26	1143.3	1146.6	1170.2	1193.7	1217.1	1240.6	1264.1	1287.8	1335.5	1384.0	1433.4	1483.5
	s	0.2836	1.7879	1.7928	1.8273	1.8593	1.8892	1.9173	1.9439	1.9692	2.0166	2.0603	2.1011	2.1394
	Sh				38.00	88.00	138.00	188.00	238.00	288.00	388.00	488.00	588.00	688.00
14.696	v	.0167	26.799		28.42	30.52	32.60	34.67	36.72	38.77	42.86	46.93	51.00	55.06
(212.00)	h	180.17	1150.5		1168.8	1192.6	1216.3	1239.9	1263.6	1287.4	1335.2	1383.8	1433.2	1483.4
	s	.3121	1.7568		1.7833	1.8158	1.8459	1.8743	1.9010	1.9265	1.9739	2.0177	2.0585	2.0969
	Sh				36.97	86.97	136.97	186.97	236.97	286.97	386.97	486.97	586.97	686.97
15	v	0.01673	26.290		27.837	29.899	31.939	33.963	35.977	37.985	41.986	45.978	49.964	53.946
(213.03)	h	181.21	1150.9		1168.7	1192.5	1216.2	1239.9	1263.6	1287.3	1335.2	1383.8	1433.2	1483.4
	s	0.3137	1.7552		1.7809	1.8134	1.8437	1.8720	1.8988	1.9242	1.9717	2.0155	2.0563	2.0946
	Sh				22.04	72.04	122.04	172.04	222.04	272.04	372.04	472.04	572.04	672.04
20	v	0.01683	20.087		20.788	22.356	23.900	25.428	26.946	28.457	31.466	34.465	37.458	40.447
(227.96)	h	196.27	1156.3		1167.1	1191.4	1215.4	1239.2	1263.0	1286.9	1334.9	1383.5	1432.9	1483.2
	s	0.3358	1.7320		1.7475	1.7805	1.8111	1.8397	1.8666	1.8921	1.9397	1.9836	2.0244	2.0628
	Sh				9.93	59.93	109.93	159.93	209.93	259.93	359.93	459.93	559.93	659.93
25	v	0.01693	16.301		16.558	17.829	19.076	20.307	21.527	22.740	25.153	27.557	29.954	32.348
(240.07)	h	208.52	1160.6		1165.6	1190.2	1214.5	1238.5	1262.5	1286.4	1334.6	1383.3	1432.7	1483.0
	s	0.3535	1.7141		1.7212	1.7547	1.7856	1.8145	1.8415	1.8672	1.9149	1.9588	1.9997	2.0381
	Sh					49.66	99.66	149.66	199.66	249.66	349.66	449.66	549.66	649.66
30	v	0.01701	13.744			14.810	15.859	16.892	17.914	18.929	20.945	22.951	24.952	26.949
(250.34)	h	218.93	1164.1			1189.0	1213.6	1237.8	1261.9	1286.0	1334.2	1383.0	1432.5	1482.8
	s	0.3682	1.6995			1.7334	1.7647	1.7937	1.8210	1.8467	1.8946	1.9386	1.9795	2.0179
	Sh					40.71	90.71	140.71	190.71	240.71	340.71	440.71	540.71	640.71
35	v	0.01708	11.896			12.654	13.562	14.453	15.334	16.207	17.939	19.662	21.379	23.092
(259.29)	h	228.03	1167.1			1187.8	1212.7	1237.1	1261.3	1285.5	1333.9	1382.8	1432.3	1482.7
	s	0.3809	1.6872			1.7152	1.7468	1.7761	1.8035	1.8294	1.8774	1.9214	1.9624	2.0009
	Sh					32.75	82.75	132.75	182.75	232.75	332.75	432.75	532.75	632.75
40	v	0.01715	10.497			11.036	11.838	12.624	13.398	14.165	15.685	17.195	18.699	20.199
(267.25)	h	236.14	1169.8			1186.6	1211.7	1236.4	1260.8	1285.0	1333.6	1382.5	1432.1	1482.5
	s	0.3921	1.6765			1.6992	1.7312	1.7608	1.7883	1.8143	1.8624	1.9065	1.9476	1.9860
	Sh					25.56	75.56	125.56	175.56	225.56	325.56	425.56	525.56	625.56
45	v	0.01721	9.399			9.777	10.497	11.201	11.892	12.577	13.932	15.276	16.614	17.950
(274.44)	h	243.49	1172.1			1185.4	1210.4	1235.7	1260.2	1284.6	1333.3	1382.3	1431.9	1482.3
	s	0.4021	1.6671			1.6849	1.7173	1.7471	1.7748	1.8010	1.8492	1.8934	1.9345	1.9730

Sh = superheat, °F
v = specific volume, cu ft/lb
h = enthalpy, Btu/lb
s = entropy, Btu/°F/lb

Table III. Superheated Steam — *Continued*

Abs Press. Lb/Sq In. (Sat. Temp)		Sat. Water	Sat. Steam	200	250	300	350	400	450	500	600	700	800	900
50 (281.02)	Sh					18.98	68.98	118.98	168.98	218.98	318.98	418.98	518.98	618.98
	v	0.01727	8.514			8.769	9.424	10.062	10.688	11.306	12.529	13.741	14.947	16.150
	h	250.21	1174.1			1184.1	1209.9	1234.9	1259.6	1284.1	1332.9	1382.0	1431.7	1482.2
	s	0.4112	1.6586			1.6720	1.7048	1.7349	1.7628	1.7890	1.8374	1.8816	1.9227	1.9613
55 (287.07)	Sh					12.93	62.93	112.93	162.93	212.93	312.93	412.93	512.93	612.93
	v	0.01733	7.787			7.945	8.546	9.130	9.702	10.267	11.381	12.485	13.583	14.677
	h	256.43	1176.0			1182.9	1208.9	1234.2	1259.1	1283.6	1332.6	1381.8	1431.5	1482.0
	s	0.4196	1.6510			1.6601	1.6933	1.7237	1.7518	1.7781	1.8266	1.8710	1.9121	1.9507
60 (292.71)	Sh					7.29	57.29	107.29	157.29	207.29	307.29	407.29	507.29	607.29
	v	0.01738	7.174			7.257	7.815	8.354	8.881	9.400	10.425	11.438	12.446	13.450
	h	262.21	1177.6			1181.6	1208.0	1233.5	1258.5	1283.2	1332.3	1381.5	1431.3	1481.8
	s	0.4273	1.6440			1.6492	1.6934	1.7134	1.7417	1.7681	1.8168	1.8612	1.9024	1.9410
65 (297.98)	Sh					2.02	52.02	102.02	152.02	202.02	302.02	402.02	502.02	602.02
	v	0.01743	6.653			6.675	7.195	7.697	8.186	8.667	9.615	10.552	11.484	12.412
	h	267.63	1179.1			1180.3	1207.0	1232.7	1257.9	1282.7	1331.9	1381.3	1431.1	1481.6
	s	0.4344	1.6375			1.6390	1.6731	1.7040	1.7324	1.7590	1.8077	1.8522	1.8935	1.9321
70 (302.93)	Sh						47.07	97.07	147.07	197.07	297.07	397.07	497.07	597.07
	v	0.01748	6.205				6.664	7.133	7.590	8.039	8.922	9.793	10.659	11.522
	h	272.74	1180.6				1206.0	1232.0	1257.3	1282.2	1331.6	1381.0	1430.9	1481.5
	s	0.4411	1.6316				1.6640	1.6951	1.7237	1.7504	1.7993	1.8439	1.8852	1.9238
75 (307.61)	Sh						42.39	92.39	142.39	192.39	292.39	392.39	492.39	592.39
	v	0.01753	5.814				6.204	6.645	7.074	7.494	8.320	9.135	9.945	10.750
	h	277.56	1181.9				1205.0	1231.2	1256.7	1281.7	1331.3	1380.7	1430.7	1481.3
	s	0.4474	1.6260				1.6554	1.6868	1.7156	1.7424	1.7915	1.8361	1.8774	1.9161

Abs Press. Lb/Sq In. (Sat. Temp)		Sat. Water	Sat. Steam	350	400	450	500	550	600	700	800	900	1000	1100
80 (312.04)	Sh			37.96	87.96	137.96	187.96	237.96	287.96	387.96	487.96	587.96	687.96	787.96
	v	0.01757	5.471	5.801	6.218	6.622	7.018	7.408	7.794	8.560	9.319	10.075	10.829	11.581
	h	282.15	1183.1	1204.0	1230.5	1256.1	1281.3	1306.2	1330.9	1380.5	1430.5	1481.1	1532.6	1584.9
	s	0.4534	1.6208	1.6473	1.6790	1.7080	1.7349	1.7602	1.7842	1.8289	1.8702	1.9089	1.9454	1.9800
85 (316.26)	Sh			33.74	83.74	133.74	183.74	223.74	283.74	383.74	483.74	583.74	683.74	783.74
	v	0.01762	5.167	5.445	5.840	6.223	6.597	6.966	7.330	8.052	8.768	9.480	10.190	10.898
	h	286.52	1184.2	1203.0	1229.7	1255.5	1280.8	1305.8	1330.6	1380.2	1430.3	1481.0	1532.4	1584.7
	s	0.4590	1.6159	1.6396	1.6716	1.7008	1.7279	1.7532	1.7772	1.8220	1.8634	1.9021	1.9386	1.9733
90 (320.28)	Sh			29.72	79.72	129.72	179.72	229.72	279.72	379.72	479.72	579.72	679.72	779.72
	v	0.01766	4.895	5.128	5.505	5.869	6.223	6.572	6.917	7.600	8.277	8.950	9.621	10.290
	h	290.69	1185.3	1202.0	1228.9	1254.9	1280.3	1305.4	1330.2	1380.0	1430.1	1480.8	1532.3	1584.6
	s	0.4643	1.6113	1.6323	1.6646	1.6940	1.7212	1.7467	1.7707	1.8156	1.8570	1.8957	1.9323	1.9669
95 (324.13)	Sh			25.87	75.87	125.87	175.87	225.87	275.87	375.87	475.87	575.87	675.87	775.87
	v	0.01770	4.651	4.845	5.205	5.551	5.889	6.221	6.548	7.196	7.838	8.477	9.113	9.747
	h	294.70	1186.2	1200.9	1228.1	1254.3	1279.8	1305.0	1329.9	1379.7	1429.9	1480.6	1532.1	1584.5
	s	0.4694	1.6069	1.6253	1.6580	1.6876	1.7149	1.7404	1.7645	1.8094	1.8509	1.8897	1.9262	1.9609

Sh = superheat, °F
v = specific volume, cu ft/lb
h = enthalpy, Btu/lb
s = entropy, Btu/°F/lb

Table III. Superheated Steam — *Continued*

Abs Press. Lb/Sq In. (Sat. Temp)		Sat. Water	Sat. Steam	350	400	450	500	550	600	700	800	900	1000	1100
	Sh			22.18	72.18	122.28	172.18	222.18	272.18	372.18	472.18	572.18	672.18	772.18
100	v	0.01774	4.431	4.590	4.935	5.266	5.588	5.904	6.216	6.833	7.443	8.050	8.655	9.258
(327.82)	h	298.54	1187.2	1199.9	1227.4	1253.7	1279.3	1304.6	1329.6	1379.5	1429.7	1480.4	1532.0	1584.4
	s	0.4743	1.6027	1.6187	1.6516	1.6814	1.7088	1.7344	1.7586	1.8036	1.8451	1.8839	1.9205	1.9552
	Sh			18.63	68.63	118.63	168.63	218.63	268.63	386.63	468.63	568.63	668.63	768.63
105	v	0.01778	4.231	4.359	4.690	5.007	5.315	5.617	5.915	6.504	7.086	7.665	8.241	8.816
(331.37)	h	302.24	1188.0	1198.8	1226.6	1253.1	1278.8	1304.2	1329.2	1379.2	1429.4	1480.3	1531.8	1584.2
	s	0.4790	1.5988	1.6122	1.6455	1.6755	1.7031	1.7288	1.7350	1.7981	1.8396	1.8785	1.9151	1.9498
	Sh			15.21	65.21	115.21	165.21	215.21	265.21	365.21	465.21	565.21	665.21	765.21
110	v	0.01782	4.048	4.149	4.468	4.772	5.068	5.357	5.642	6.205	6.761	7.314	7.865	8.413
(334.79)	h	305.80	1188.9	1197.7	1225.8	1252.5	1278.3	1303.8	1328.9	1379.0	1429.2	1480.1	1531.7	1584.1
	s	0.4834	1.5950	1.6061	1.6396	1.6698	1.6975	1.7233	1.7476	1.7928	1.8344	1.8732	1.9099	1.9446
	Sh			11.92	61.92	111.92	161.92	211.92	261.92	361.92	461.92	561.92	661.92	761.92
115	v	0.01785	3.881	3.957	4.265	4.558	4.841	5.119	5.392	5.932	6.465	6.994	7.521	8.046
(338.08)	h	309.25	1179.6	1196.7	1225.0	1251.8	1277.9	1303.3	1328.6	1378.7	1429.0	1479.9	1531.6	1584.0
	s	0.4877	1.5913	1.6001	1.6340	1.6644	1.6922	1.7181	1.7425	1.7877	1.8294	1.8682	1.9049	1.9396
	Sh			8.73	58.73	108.73	158.73	208.73	258.73	358.73	458.73	558.73	658.73	758.73
120	v	0.01789	3.7275	3.7815	4.0786	4.3610	4.6341	4.9009	5.1637	5.6813	6.1928	6.7006	7.2060	7.7096
(341.27)	h	312.58	1190.4	1195.6	1224.1	1251.2	1277.4	1302.9	1328.2	1378.4	1428.8	1479.8	1531.4	1583.9
	s	0.4919	1.5879	1.5943	1.6286	1.6592	1.6872	1.7132	1.7376	1.7829	1.8246	1.8635	1.9001	1.9349
	Sh			2.67	52.67	102.67	152.67	202.67	252.67	352.67	452.67	552.67	652.67	752.67
130	v	0.01796	3.4544	3.4699	3.7489	4.0129	4.2672	4.5151	4.7589	5.2384	5.7118	6.1814	6.6486	7.1140
(347.33)	h	318.95	1191.7	1193.4	1222.5	1249.9	1276.4	1302.1	1327.5	1377.9	1428.4	1479.4	1531.1	1583.6
	s	0.4998	1.5813	1.5833	1.6182	1.6493	1.6775	1.7037	1.7283	1.7737	1.8155	1.8545	1.8911	1.9259
	Sh				46.96	96.96	146.96	196.96	246.96	346.96	446.96	546.96	646.96	746.96
140	v	0.01803	3.2190		3.4661	3.7143	3.9526	4.1844	4.4119	4.8588	5.2995	5.7364	6.1709	6.6036
(353.04)	h	324.96	1193.0		1220.8	1248.7	1275.3	1301.3	1326.8	1377.4	1428.0	1479.1	1530.8	1583.4
	s	0.5071	1.5752		1.6085	1.6400	1.6686	1.6949	1.7196	1.7652	1.8071	1.8461	1.8828	1.9176
	Sh				41.57	91.57	141.57	191.57	241.57	341.57	441.57	541.57	641.57	741.57
150	v	0.01809	3.0139		3.2208	3.4555	3.6799	3.8978	4.1112	4.5298	4.9421	5.3507	5.7568	6.1612
(358.43)	h	330.65	1194.1		1219.1	1247.4	1274.3	1300.5	1326.1	1376.9	1427.6	1478.7	1530.5	1583.1
	s	0.5141	1.5695		1.5993	1.6313	1.6602	1.6867	1.7115	1.7573	1.7992	1.8383	1.8751	1.9099
	Sh				36.45	86.45	136.45	186.45	236.45	336.45	436.45	536.45	636.45	736.45
160	v	0.01815	2.8336		3.0060	3.2288	3.4413	3.6469	3.8480	4.2420	4.6295	5.0132	5.3945	5.7741
(363.55)	h	336.07	1195.1		1217.4	1246.0	1273.3	1299.6	1325.4	1376.4	1427.2	1478.4	1530.3	1582.9
	s	0.5206	1.5641		1.5906	1.6231	1.6522	1.6790	1.7039	1.7499	1.7919	1.8310	1.8678	1.9027
	Sh				31.58	81.58	131.58	181.58	231.58	331.58	431.48	531.58	631.58	731.58
170	v	0.01821	2.6738		2.8162	3.0288	3.2306	3.4255	3.6158	3.9879	4.3536	4.7155	5.0749	5.4325
(368.42)	h	341.24	1196.0		1215.6	1244.7	1272.2	1298.8	1324.7	1375.8	1426.8	1478.0	1530.0	1582.6
	s	0.5269	1.5591		1.5823	1.6152	1.6447	1.6717	1.6968	1.7428	1.7850	1.8241	1.8610	1.8959
	Sh				26.92	76.92	126.92	176.92	226.92	326.92	426.92	526.92	626.92	726.92
180	v	0.01827	2.5312		2.6474	2.8508	3.0433	3.2286	3.4093	3.7621	4.1084	4.4508	4.7907	5.1289
(373.08)	h	346.19	1196.9		1213.8	1243.4	1271.2	1297.9	1324.0	1375.3	1426.3	1477.7	1529.7	1582.4
	s	0.5328	1.5543		1.5743	1.6078	1.6376	1.6647	1.6900	1.7362	1.7784	1.8176	1.8545	1.8894

Sh = superheat, °F   h = enthalpy, Btu/lb
v = specific volume, cu ft/lb   s = entropy, Btu/°F/lb

Table III. Superheated Steam — *Continued*

Abs Press. Lb/Sq In. (Sat. Temp)		Sat. Water	Sat. Steam	350	400	450	500	550	600	700	800	900	1000	1100
				Temperature — Degrees Fahrenheit										
190 (377.53)	Sh				22.47	72.47	122.47	172.47	222.47	322.47	422.47	522.47	622.47	722.47
	v	0.01833	2.4030		2.4961	2.6915	2.8756	3.0525	3.2246	3.5601	3.8889	4.2140	4.5365	4.8572
	h	350.94	1197.6		1212.0	1242.0	1270.1	1297.1	1323.3	1374.8	1425.9	1477.4	1529.4	1582.1
	s	0.5384	1.5498		1.5667	1.6006	1.6307	1.6581	1.6835	1.7299	1.7722	1.8115	1.8484	1.8834
200 (381.80)	Sh				18.20	68.20	118.20	168.20	218.20	318.20	418.20	518.20	618.20	718.20
	v	0.01839	2.2873		2.3598	2.5480	2.7247	2.8939	3.0583	3.3783	3.6915	4.0008	4.3077	4.6128
	h	355.51	1198.3		1210.1	1240.6	1269.0	1296.2	1322.6	1374.3	1425.5	1477.0	1529.1	1581.9
	s	0.5438	1.5454		1.5593	1.5938	1.6242	1.6518	1.6773	1.7239	1.7663	1.8057	1.8426	1.8776

Abs Press. Lb/Sq In. (Sat. Temp)		Sat. Water	Sat. Steam	400	450	500	550	600	700	800	900	1000	1100	1200
				Temperature — Degrees Fahrenheit										
210 (385.91)	Sh			14.09	64.09	114.09	164.09	214.09	314.09	414.09	514.09	614.09	714.09	814.09
	v	0.01844	2.1822	2.2364	2.4181	2.5880	2.7504	2.9078	3.2137	3.5128	3.8080	4.1007	4.3915	4.6811
	h	359.91	1199.0	1208.2	1239.2	1268.0	1295.3	1321.9	1373.7	1425.1	1476.7	1528.8	1581.6	1635.2
	s	0.5490	1.5413	1.5522	1.5872	1.6180	1.6458	1.6715	1.7182	1.7607	1.8001	1.8371	1.8721	1.9054
220 (389.88)	Sh			10.12	60.12	110.12	160.12	210.12	310.12	410.12	510.12	610.12	710.12	810.12
	v	0.01850	2.0863	2.1240	2.2999	2.4638	2.6199	2.7710	3.0642	3.3504	3.6327	3.9125	4.1905	4.4671
	h	364.17	1199.6	1206.3	1237.8	1266.9	1294.5	1321.2	1373.2	1424.7	1476.3	1528.5	1581.4	1635.0
	s	0.5540	1.5374	1.5453	1.5808	1.6120	1.6400	1.6658	1.7128	1.7553	1.7948	1.8318	1.8668	1.9002
230 (393.70)	Sh			6.30	56.30	106.30	156.30	206.30	306.30	406.30	506.30	606.30	706.30	806.30
	v	0.01855	1.9985	2.0212	2.1919	2.3503	2.5008	2.6461	2.9276	3.2020	3.4726	3.7406	4.0068	4.2717
	h	368.28	1200.1	1204.4	1236.3	1265.7	1293.6	1320.4	1372.7	1424.2	1476.0	1528.2	1581.1	1634.8
	s	0.5588	1.5336	1.5385	1.5747	1.6062	1.6344	1.6604	1.7075	1.7502	1.7897	1.8268	1.8618	1.8952
240 (397.39)	Sh			2.61	52.61	102.61	152.61	202.61	302.61	402.61	502.61	602.61	702.61	802.61
	v	0.01860	1.9177	1.9268	2.0928	2.2462	2.3915	2.5316	2.8024	3.0661	3.3259	3.5831	3.8385	4.0926
	h	372.27	1200.6	1202.4	1234.9	1264.6	1292.7	1319.7	1372.1	1423.8	1475.6	1527.9	1580.9	1634.6
	s	0.5634	1.5299	1.5320	1.5687	1.6006	1.6291	1.6552	1.7025	1.7452	1.7848	1.8219	1.8570	1.8904
250 (400.97)	Sh				49.03	99.03	149.03	199.03	299.03	399.03	499.03	599.03	699.03	799.03
	v	0.01865	1.8432		2.0016	2.1504	2.2909	2.4262	2.6872	2.9410	3.1909	3.4382	3.6837	3.9278
	h	376.14	1201.1		1233.4	1263.5	1291.8	1319.0	1371.6	1423.4	1475.3	1527.6	1580.6	1634.4
	s	0.5679	1.5264		1.5629	1.5951	1.6239	1.6502	1.6976	1.7405	1.7801	1.8173	1.8524	1.8858
260 (404.44)	Sh				45.56	95.56	145.56	195.56	295.56	395.56	495.56	595.56	695.56	795.56
	v	0.01870	1.7742		1.9173	2.0619	2.1981	2.3289	2.5808	2.8256	3.0663	3.3044	3.5408	3.7758
	h	379.90	1201.5		1231.9	1262.4	1290.9	1318.2	1371.1	1423.0	1474.9	1527.3	1580.4	1634.2
	s	0.5722	1.5230		1.5573	1.5899	1.6189	1.6453	1.6930	1.7359	1.7756	1.8128	1.8480	1.8814
270 (407.80)	Sh				42.20	92.20	142.20	192.20	292.20	392.20	492.20	592.20	692.20	792.20
	v	0.01875	1.7101		1.8391	1.9799	2.1121	2.2388	2.4824	2.7186	2.9509	3.1806	3.4084	3.6349
	h	383.56	1201.9		1230.4	1261.2	1290.0	1317.5	1370.5	1422.6	1474.6	1527.1	1580.1	1634.0
	s	0.5764	1.5197		1.5518	1.5848	1.6140	1.6406	1.6885	1.7315	1.7713	1.8085	1.8437	1.8771
280 (411.07)	Sh				38.93	88.93	138.93	188.93	288.93	388.93	488.93	588.93	688.93	788.93
	v	0.01880	1.6505		1.7665	1.9037	2.0322	2.1551	2.3909	2.6194	2.8437	3.0655	3.2855	3.5042
	h	387.12	1202.3		1228.8	1260.0	1289.1	1316.8	1370.0	1422.1	1474.2	1526.8	1579.9	1633.8
	s	0.5805	1.5166		1.5464	1.57.98	1.6093	1.6361	1.6841	1.7273	1.7671	1.8043	1.8395	1.8730

Sh = superheat, °F   h = enthalpy, Btu/lb
v = specific volume, cu ft/lb   s = entropy, Btu/°F/lb

Table III. Superheated Steam — *Continued*

Abs Press. Lb/Sq In. (Sat. Temp)		Sat. Water	Sat. Steam	400	450	500	550	600	700	800	900	1000	1100	1200
290 (414.25)	Sh				35.75	85.75	135.75	185.75	285.75	385.75	485.75	585.75	685.75	785.75
	v	0.01885	1.5948		1.6988	1.8327	1.9578	2.0772	2.3058	2.5269	2.7440	2.9585	3.1711	3.3824
	h	390.60	1202.6		1227.3	1258.9	1288.1	1316.0	1369.5	1421.7	1473.9	1526.5	1579.6	1633.5
	s	0.5844	1.5135		1.5412	1.5750	1.6048	1.6317	1.6799	1.7323	1.7630	1.8003	1.8356	1.8690
300 (417.35)	Sh				32.65	82.65	132.65	182.65	282.65	382.65	482.65	582.65	682.65	782.65
	v	0.01889	1.5427		1.6356	1.7665	1.8883	2.0044	2.2263	2.4407	2.6509	2.8585	3.0643	3.2688
	h	393.99	1202.9		1225.7	1257.7	1287.2	1315.2	1368.9	1421.3	1473.6	1526.2	1579.4	1633.3
	s	0.5882	1.5105		1.5361	1.5703	1.6003	1.6274	1.6758	1.7192	1.7591	1.7964	1.8317	1.8652
310 (420.36)	Sh				29.64	79.64	129.64	179.64	279.64	379.64	479.64	579.64	679.64	779.64
	v	0.01894	1.4939		1.5763	1.7044	1.8233	1.9363	2.1520	2.3600	2.5638	2.7650	2.9644	3.1625
	h	397.30	1203.2		1224.1	1256.5	1286.3	1314.5	1368.4	1420.9	1473.2	1525.9	1579.2	1633.1
	s	0.5920	1.5076		1.5311	1.5657	1.5960	1.6233	1.6719	1.7153	1.7553	1.7927	1.8280	1.8615
320 (423.31)	Sh				26.69	76.69	126.69	176.69	276.69	376.69	476.69	576.69	676.69	776.69
	v	0.01899	1.4480		1.5207	1.6462	1.7623	1.8725	2.0823	2.2843	2.4821	2.6774	2.8708	3.0628
	h	400.53	1203.4		1222.5	1255.2	1285.3	1313.7	1367.8	1420.5	1472.9	1525.6	1578.9	1632.9
	s	0.5956	1.5048		1.5261	1.5612	1.5918	1.6192	1.6680	1.7116	1.7516	1.7890	1.8243	1.8579
330 (426.18)	Sh				23.82	73.82	123.82	173.82	273.82	373.82	473.82	573.82	673.82	773.82
	v	0.01903	1.4048		1.4684	1.5915	1.7050	1.8125	2.0168	2.2132	2.4054	2.5950	2.7828	2.9692
	h	403.70	1203.6		1220.9	1254.0	1284.4	1313.0	1367.3	1420.0	1472.5	1525.3	1578.7	1632.7
	s	0.5991	1.5021		1.5213	1.5568	1.5876	1.6153	1.6643	1.7079	1.7480	1.7855	1.8208	1.8544
340 (428.99)	Sh				21.01	71.01	121.01	171.01	271.01	371.01	471.01	571.01	671.01	771.01
	v	0.01908	1.3640		1.4191	1.5399	1.6511	1.7561	1.9552	2.1463	2.3333	2.5175	2.7000	2.8811
	h	406.80	1203.8		1219.2	1252.8	1283.4	1312.2	1366.7	1419.6	1472.2	1525.0	1578.4	1632.5
	s	0.6026	1.4994		1.5165	1.5525	1.5836	1.6114	1.6606	1.7044	1.7445	1.7820	1.8174	1.8510
350 (431.73)	Sh				18.27	68.27	118.27	168.27	268.27	368.27	468.27	568.27	668.27	768.27
	v	0.01912	1.3255		1.3725	1.4913	1.6002	1.7028	1.8970	2.0832	2.2652	2.4445	2.6219	2.7980
	h	409.83	1204.0		1217.5	1251.5	1282.4	1311.4	1366.2	1419.2	1471.8	1524.7	1578.2	1632.3
	s	0.6059	1.4968		1.5119	1.5483	1.5797	1.6077	1.6571	1.7009	1.7411	1.7787	1.8141	1.8477
360 (434.41)	Sh				15.59	65.59	115.59	165.59	265.59	365.59	465.59	565.59	665.59	765.59
	v	0.01917	1.2891		1.3285	1.4454	1.5521	1.6525	1.8421	2.0237	2.2009	2.3755	2.5482	2.7196
	h	412.81	1204.1		1215.8	1250.3	1281.5	1310.6	1365.6	1418.7	1471.5	1524.4	1577.9	1632.1
	s	0.6092	1.4943		1.5073	1.5441	1.5758	1.6040	1.6536	1.6976	1.7379	1.7754	1.8109	1.8445
380 (439.61)	Sh				10.39	60.39	110.39	160.39	260.39	360.39	460.39	560.39	660.39	760.39
	v	0.01925	1.2218		1.2472	1.3606	1.4635	1.5598	1.7410	1.9139	2.0825	2.2484	2.4124	2.5750
	h	418.59	1204.4		1212.4	1247.7	1279.5	1309.0	1364.5	1417.9	1470.8	1523.8	1577.4	1631.6
	s	0.6156	1.4894		1.4982	1.5360	1.5683	1.5969	1.6470	1.6911	1.7315	1.7692	1.8047	1.8384

Abs Press. Lb/Sq In. (Sat. Temp)		Sat. Water	Sat. Steam	450	500	550	600	650	700	800	900	1000	1100	1200
400 (444.60)	Sh			5.40	55.40	105.40	155.40	205.40	255.40	355.40	455.40	555.40	655.40	755.40
	v	0.01934	1.1610	1.1738	1.2841	1.3836	1.4763	1.5646	1.6499	1.8151	1.9759	2.1339	2.2901	2.4450
	h	424.17	1204.6	1208.8	1245.1	1277.5	1307.4	1335.9	1363.4	1417.0	1470.1	1523.3	1576.9	1631.2
	s	0.6217	1.4847	1.4894	1.5282	1.5611	1.5901	1.6163	1.6406	1.6850	1.7255	1.7632	1.7988	1.8325

Sh = superheat, °F   h = enthalpy, Btu/lb
v = specific volume, cu ft/lb   s = entropy, Btu/°F/lb

Table III. Superheated Steam — *Continued*

Abs Press. Lb/Sq In. (Sat. Temp)		Sat. Water	Sat. Steam	450	500	550	600	650	700	800	900	1000	1100	1200
420 (449.40)	Sh			.60	50.60	100.60	150.60	200.60	250.60	350.60	450.60	550.60	650.60	750.60
	v	0.01942	1.1057	1.1071	1.2148	1.3113	1.4007	1.4856	1.5676	1.7258	1.8795	2.0304	2.1795	2.3273
	h	429.56	1204.7	1205.2	1242.4	1275.4	1305.8	1334.5	1362.3	1416.2	1469.4	1522.7	1576.4	1630.8
	s	0.6276	1.4802	1.4808	1.5206	1.5542	1.5835	1.6100	1.6345	1.6791	1.7197	1.7575	1.7932	1.8269
440 (454.03)	Sh				45.97	95.97	145.97	195.97	245.97	345.97	445.97	545.97	645.97	745.97
	v	0.01950	1.0554		1.1517	1.2454	1.3319	1.4138	1.4926	1.6445	1.7918	1.9363	2.0790	2.2203
	h	434.77	1204.8		1239.7	1273.4	1304.2	1333.2	1361.1	1415.3	1468.7	1522.1	1575.9	1630.4
	s	0.6332	1.4759		1.5132	1.5474	1.5772	1.6040	1.6286	1.6734	1.7412	1.7521	1.7878	1.8216
460 (458.50)	Sh				41.50	91.50	141.50	191.50	241.50	341.50	441.50	541.50	641.50	741.50
	v	0.01959	1.0092		1.0939	1.1852	1.2691	1.3482	1.4242	1.5703	1.7117	1.8504	1.9872	2.1226
	h	439.83	1204.8		1236.9	1271.3	1302.5	1331.8	1360.0	1414.4	1468.0	1521.5	1575.4	1629.9
	s	0.6387	1.4718		1.5060	1.5409	1.5711	1.5982	1.6230	1.6680	1.7089	1.7469	1.7826	1.8165
480 (462.82)	Sh				37.18	87.18	137.18	187.18	237.18	337.18	437.18	537.18	637.18	737.18
	v	0.01967	0.9668		1.0409	1.1300	1.2115	1.2881	1.3615	1.5023	1.6384	1.7716	1.9030	2.0330
	h	444.75	1204.8		1234.1	1269.1	1300.8	1330.5	1358.8	1413.6	1467.3	1520.9	1574.9	1629.5
	s	0.6439	1.4677		1.4990	1.5346	1.5652	1.5925	1.6176	1.6628	1.7038	1.7419	1.7777	1.8116
500 (467.01)	Sh				32.99	82.99	132.99	182.99	232.99	332.99	432.99	532.99	632.99	732.99
	v	0.01975	0.9276		0.9919	1.0791	1.1584	1.2327	1.3037	1.4397	1.5708	1.6992	1.8256	1.9507
	h	449.52	1204.7		1231.2	1267.0	1299.1	1329.1	1357.7	1412.7	1466.6	1520.3	1574.4	1629.1
	s	0.6490	1.4639		1.4921	1.5284	1.5595	1.5871	1.6123	1.6578	1.6990	1.7371	1.7730	1.8069
520 (471.07)	Sh				28.93	78.93	128.93	178.93	228.93	328.93	428.93	528.93	628.93	728.93
	v	0.01982	0.8914		0.9466	1.0321	1.1094	1.1816	1.2504	1.3819	1.5085	1.6323	1.7542	1.8746
	h	454.18	1204.5		1228.3	1264.8	1297.4	1327.7	1356.5	1411.8	1465.9	1519.7	1573.9	1628.7
	s	0.6540	1.4601		1.4853	1.5223	1.5539	1.5818	1.6072	1.6530	1.6943	1.7325	1.7684	1.8024
540 (475.01)	Sh				24.99	74.99	124.99	174.99	224.99	324.99	424.99	524.99	624.99	724.99
	v	0.01990	0.8577		0.9045	0.9884	1.0640	1.1342	1.2010	1.3284	1.4508	1.5704	1.6880	1.8042
	h	458.71	1204.4		1225.3	1262.5	1295.7	1326.3	1355.3	1410.9	1465.1	1519.1	1573.4	1628.2
	s	0.6587	1.4565		1.4786	1.5164	1.5485	1.5767	1.6023	1.6483	1.6897	1.7280	1.7640	1.7981
560 (478.84)	Sh				21.16	71.16	121.16	171.16	221.16	321.16	421.16	521.16	621.16	721.16
	v	0.01998	0.8264		0.8653	0.9479	1.0217	1.0902	1.1552	1.2787	1.3972	1.5129	1.6266	1.7388
	h	463.14	1204.2		1222.2	1260.3	1293.9	1324.9	1354.2	1410.0	1464.4	1518.6	1572.9	1627.8
	s	0.6634	1.4529		1.4720	1.5106	1.5431	1.5717	1.5975	1.6438	1.6853	1.7237	1.7598	1.7939
580 (482.57)	Sh				17.43	67.43	117.43	167.43	217.43	317.43	417.43	517.43	617.43	717.43
	v	0.02006	0.7971		0.8287	0.9100	0.9824	1.0492	1.1125	1.2324	1.3473	1.4593	1.5693	1.6780
	h	467.47	1203.9		1219.1	1258.0	1292.1	1323.4	1353.0	1409.2	1463.7	1518.0	1572.4	1627.4
	s	0.6679	1.4495		1.4654	1.5049	1.5380	1.5668	1.5929	1.6394	1.6811	1.7196	1.7556	1.7898
600 (486.20)	Sh				13.80	63.80	113.80	163.80	213.80	313.80	413.80	513.80	613.80	713.80
	v	0.02013	0.7697		0.7944	0.8746	0.9456	1.0109	1.0726	1.1892	1.3008	1.4093	1.5160	1.6211
	h	471.70	1203.7		1215.9	1255.6	1290.3	1322.0	1351.8	1408.3	1463.0	1517.4	1571.9	1627.0
	s	0.6723	1.4461		1.4590	1.4993	1.5329	1.5621	1.5884	1.6351	1.6769	1.7155	1.7517	1.7859
650 (494.89)	Sh				5.11	55.11	105.11	155.11	205.11	305.11	405.11	505.11	605.11	705.11
	v	0.02032	0.7084		0.7173	0.7954	0.8634	0.9254	0.9835	1.0929	1.1969	1.2979	1.3969	1.4944
	h	481.89	1202.8		1207.6	1249.6	1285.7	1318.3	1348.7	1406.0	1461.2	1515.9	1570.7	1625.9
	s	1.6828	1.4381		1.4430	1.4858	1.5207	1.5507	1.5775	1.6249	1.6671	1.7059	1.7422	1.7765

Sh = superheat, °F	h = enthalpy, Btu/lb
v = specific volume, cu ft/lb	s = entropy, Btu/°F/lb

Table III. Superheated Steam — *Continued*

Abs Press. Lb/Sq In. (Sat. Temp)		Sat. Water	Sat. Steam	450	500	550	600	650	700	800	900	1000	1100	1200
	Sh					46.92	96.92	146.92	196.92	296.92	396.92	496.92	596.92	696.92
700	v	0.02050	0.6556			0.7271	0.7928	0.8520	0.9072	1.0102	1.1078	1.2023	1.2948	1.3858
(503.08)	h	491.60	1201.8			1243.4	1281.0	1314.6	1345.6	1403.7	1459.4	1514.4	1569.4	1624.8
	s	0.6928	1.4304			1.4726	1.5090	1.5399	1.5673	1.6154	1.6580	1.6970	1.7335	1.7679
	Sh					39.16	89.16	139.16	189.16	289.16	389.16	489.16	589.16	689.16
750	v	0.02069	0.6095			0.6676	0.7313	0.7882	0.8409	0.9386	1.0306	1.1195	1.2063	1.2916
(510.84)	h	500.89	1200.7			1236.9	1276.1	1310.7	1342.5	1401.5	1457.6	1512.9	1568.2	1623.8
	s	0.7022	1.4232			1.4598	1.4977	1.5296	1.5577	1.6065	1.6494	1.6886	1.7252	1.7598
	Sh					31.79	81.79	131.79	181.79	281.79	381.79	481.79	581.79	681.79
800	v	0.02087	0.5690			0.6151	0.6774	0.7323	0.7828	0.8759	0.9631	1.0470	1.1289	1.2093
(518.21)	h	509.81	1199.4			1230.1	1271.1	1306.8	1339.3	1399.1	1455.8	1511.4	1566.9	1622.7
	s	0.7111	1.4163			1.4472	1.4869	1.5198	1.5484	1.5980	1.6413	1.6807	1.7175	1.7522
	Sh					24.76	74.76	124.76	174.76	274.76	374.76	474.76	574.76	674.76
850	v	0.02105	0.5330			0.5683	0.6296	0.6829	0.7315	0.8205	0.9034	0.9830	1.0606	1.1366
(525.24)	h	518.40	1198.0			1223.0	1265.9	1302.8	1336.0	1396.8	1454.0	1510.0	1565.7	1621.6
	s	0.7197	1.4096			1.4347	1.4763	1.5102	1.5396	1.5899	1.6336	1.6733	1.7102	1.7450
	Sh					18.05	68.05	118.05	168.05	268.05	368.05	468.05	568.05	668.05
900	v	0.02123	0.5009			0.5263	0.5869	0.6388	0.6858	0.7713	0.8504	0.9262	0.9998	1.0720
(531.95)	h	526.70	1196.4			1215.5	1260.6	1298.6	1332.7	1394.4	1452.2	1508.5	1564.4	1620.6
	s	0.7279	1.4032			1.4223	1.4659	1.5010	1.5311	1.5822	1.6263	1.6662	1.7033	1.7382

Abs Press. Lb/Sq In. (Sat. Temp)		Sat. Water	Sat. Steam	550	600	650	700	750	800	850	900	1000	1100	1200
	Sh			11.61	61.61	111.61	161.61	211.61	261.61	311.61	361.61	461.61	561.61	661.61
950	v	0.02141	0.4721	0.4883	0.5485	0.5993	0.6449	0.6871	0.7272	0.7656	0.8030	0.8753	0.9455	1.0142
(538.39)	h	534.74	1194.7	1207.6	1255.1	1294.4	1329.3	1361.5	1392.0	1421.5	1450.3	1507.0	1563.2	1619.5
	s	0.7358	1.3970	1.4098	1.4557	1.4921	1.5228	1.5500	1.5748	1.5977	1.6193	1.6595	1.6967	1.7317
	Sh			5.42	55.42	105.42	155.42	205.42	255.42	305.42	355.42	455.42	555.42	655.42
1000	v	0.02159	0.4460	0.4535	0.5137	0.5636	0.6080	0.6489	0.6875	0.7245	0.7603	0.8295	0.8966	0.9622
(544.58)	h	542.55	1192.9	1199.3	1249.3	1290.1	1325.9	1358.7	1389.6	1419.4	1448.5	1505.4	1561.9	1618.4
	s	0.7434	1.3910	1.3973	1.4457	1.4833	1.5149	1.5426	1.5677	1.5908	1.6126	1.6530	1.6905	1.7256
	Sh				49.47	99.47	149.47	199.47	249.47	299.47	349.47	449.47	549.47	649.47
1050	v	0.02177	0.4222		0.4821	0.5312	0.5745	0.6142	0.6515	0.6872	0.7216	0.7881	0.8524	0.9151
(550.53)	h	550.15	1191.0		1243.4	1285.7	1322.4	1355.8	1387.2	1417.3	1446.6	1503.9	1560.7	1617.4
	s	0.7507	1.3851		1.4358	1.4748	1.5072	1.5354	1.5608	1.5842	1.6062	1.6469	1.6845	1.7197
	Sh				43.72	93.72	143.72	193.72	243.72	293.72	343.72	443.72	543.72	643.72
1100	v	0.02195	0.4006		0.4531	0.5017	0.5440	0.5826	0.6188	0.6533	0.6865	0.7505	0.8121	0.8723
(556.28)	h	557.55	1189.1		1237.3	1281.2	1318.8	1352.9	1384.7	1415.2	1444.7	1502.4	1559.4	1616.3
	s	0.7578	1.3794		1.4259	1.4664	1.4996	1.5284	1.5542	1.5779	1.6000	1.6410	1.6787	1.7141
	Sh				39.18	89.18	139.18	189.18	239.18	289.18	339.18	439.18	539.18	639.18
1150	v	0.02214	0.3807		0.4263	0.4746	0.5162	0.5538	0.5889	0.6223	0.6544	0.7161	0.7754	0.8332
(561.82)	h	564.78	1187.0		1230.9	1276.6	1315.2	1349.9	1382.2	1413.0	1442.8	1500.9	1558.1	1615.2
	s	0.7647	1.3738		1.4160	1.4582	1.4923	1.5216	1.5478	1.5717	1.5941	1.6353	1.6732	1.7087

Sh = superheat, °F   h = enthalpy, Btu/lb
v = specific volume, cu ft/lb   s = entropy, Btu/°F/lb

Table III. Superheated Steam — *Continued*

Abs Press. Lb/Sq In. (Sat. Temp)		Sat. Water	Sat. Steam	550	600	650	700	750	800	850	900	1000	1100	1200
	Sh				32.81	82.81	132.81	182.81	232.81	282.81	332.81	432.81	532.81	632.81
1200	v	0.02232	0.3624		0.4016	0.4497	0.4905	0.5273	0.5615	0.5939	0.6250	0.6845	0.7418	0.7974
(567.19)	h	571.85	1184.8		1224.2	1271.8	1311.5	1346.9	1379.7	1410.8	1440.9	1499.4	1556.9	1614.2
	s	0.7714	1.3683		1.4061	1.4501	1.4851	1.5150	1.5415	1.5658	1.5883	1.6298	1.6679	1.7035
	Sh				22.58	72.58	122.58	172.58	222.58	272.58	322.58	422.58	522.58	622.58
1300	v	0.02269	0.3299		0.3570	0.4052	0.4451	0.4804	0.5129	0.5436	0.5729	0.6287	0.6822	0.7341
(577.42)	h	585.58	1180.2		1209.9	1261.9	1303.9	1340.8	1374.6	1406.4	1437.1	1496.3	1554.3	1612.0
	s	0.7843	1.3577		1.3860	1.4340	1.4711	1.5022	1.5296	1.5544	1.5773	1.6194	1.6578	1.6937
	Sh				12.93	62.93	112.93	162.93	212.93	262.93	312.93	412.93	512.93	612.93
1400	v	0.02307	0.3018		0.3176	0.3667	0.4059	0.4400	0.4712	0.5004	0.5282	0.5809	0.6311	0.6798
(587.07)	h	598.83	1175.3		1194.1	1251.4	1296.1	1334.5	1369.3	1402.0	1433.2	1493.2	1551.8	1609.9
	s	0.7966	1.3474		1.3652	1.4181	1.4575	1.4900	1.5182	1.5436	1.5670	1.6096	1.6484	1.6845
	Sh				3.80	53.80	103.80	153.80	203.80	253.80	303.80	403.80	503.80	603.80
1500	v	0.02346	0.2772		0.2820	0.3328	0.3717	0.4049	0.4350	0.4629	0.4894	0.5394	0.5869	0.6327
(596.20)	h	611.68	1170.1		1176.3	1240.2	1287.9	1328.0	1364.0	1397.4	1429.2	1490.1	1549.2	1607.7
	s	0.8085	1.3373		1.3431	1.4022	1.4443	1.4782	1.5073	1.5333	1.5572	1.6004	1.6395	1.6759
	Sh					45.13	95.13	145.13	195.13	245.13	295.13	395.13	495.13	595.13
1600	v	0.02387	0.2555			0.3026	0.3415	0.3741	0.4032	0.4301	0.4555	0.5031	0.5482	0.5915
(604.87)	h	624.20	1164.5			1228.3	1279.4	1321.4	1358.5	1392.8	1425.2	1486.9	1546.6	1605.6
	s	0.8199	1.3272			1.3861	1.4312	1.4667	1.4968	1.5235	1.5478	1.5916	1.6312	1.6678
	Sh					36.87	86.87	136.87	186.87	236.87	286.87	386.87	486.87	586.87
1700	v	0.02428	0.2361			0.2754	0.3147	0.3468	0.3751	0.4011	0.4255	0.4711	0.5140	0.5552
(613.13)	h	636.45	1158.6			1215.3	1270.5	1314.5	1352.9	1388.1	1421.2	1483.8	1544.0	1603.4
	s	0.8309	1.3176			1.3697	1.4183	1.4555	1.4867	1.5140	1.5388	1.5833	1.6232	1.6601
	Sh					28.98	78.98	128.98	178.98	228.98	278.98	378.98	478.98	578.98
1800	v	0.02472	0.2186			0.2505	0.2906	0.3223	0.3500	0.3752	0.3988	0.4426	0.4836	0.5229
(621.02)	h	648.49	1152.3			1201.2	1261.1	1307.4	1347.2	1383.3	1417.1	1480.6	1541.4	1601.2
	s	0.8417	1.3079			1.3526	1.4054	1.4446	1.4768	1.5049	1.5302	1.5753	1.6156	1.6528
	Sh					21.44	71.44	121.44	171.44	221.44	271.44	371.44	471.44	571.44
1900	v	0.02517	0.2028			0.2274	0.2687	0.3004	0.3275	0.3521	0.3749	0.4171	0.4565	0.4940
(628.56)	h	660.36	1145.6			1185.7	1251.3	1300.2	1341.4	1378.4	1412.9	1477.4	1538.8	1599.1
	s	0.8522	1.2981			1.3346	1.3925	1.4338	1.4672	1.4960	1.5219	1.5677	1.6084	1.6458
	Sh					14.20	64.20	114.20	164.20	214.20	264.20	364.20	464.20	564.20
2000	v	0.02565	0.1883			0.2056	0.2488	0.2805	0.3072	0.3312	0.3534	0.3942	0.4320	0.4680
(635.80)	h	672.11	1138.3			1168.3	1240.9	1292.6	1335.4	1373.5	1408.7	1474.1	1536.2	1596.9
	s	0.8625	1.2881			1.3154	1.3794	1.4231	1.4578	1.4874	1.5138	1.5603	1.6014	1.6391
	Sh					7.24	57.24	107.24	157.24	207.24	257.24	357.24	457.24	557.24
2100	v	0.02615	0.1750			0.1847	0.2304	0.2624	0.2888	0.3123	0.3339	0.3734	0.4099	0.4445
(642.76)	h	683.79	1130.5			1148.5	1229.8	1284.9	1329.3	1368.4	1404.4	1470.9	1533.6	1594.7
	s	0.8727	1.2780			1.2942	1.3661	1.4125	1.4486	1.4790	1.5060	1.5532	1.5948	1.6327
	Sh					.55	50.55	100.55	150.55	200.55	250.55	350.55	450.55	550.55
2200	v	0.02669	0.1627			0.1636	0.2134	0.2458	0.2720	0.2950	0.3161	0.3545	0.3897	0.4231
(649.45)	h	695.46	1122.2			1123.9	1218.0	1276.8	1323.1	1363.3	1400.0	1467.6	1530.9	1592.5
	s	0.8828	1.2676			1.2691	1.3523	1.4020	1.4395	1.4708	1.4984	1.5463	1.5883	1.6266

Sh = superheat, °F
v = specific volume; cu ft/lb
h = enthalpy, Btu/lb
s = entropy, Btu/°F/lb

Table III. Superheated Steam — *Continued*

Abs Press. Lb/Sq In. (Sat. Temp)		Sat. Water	Sat. Steam	550	600	650	700	750	800	850	900	1000	1100	1200
	Sh						44.11	94.11	144.11	194.11	244.11	344.11	444.11	544.11
2300	v	0.02727	0.1513				0.1975	0.2305	0.2566	0.2793	0.2999	0.3372	0.3714	0.4035
(655.89)	h	707.18	1113.2				1205.3	1268.4	1316.7	1358.1	1395.7	1464.2	1528.3	1590.3
	s	0.8929	1.2569				1.3381	1.3914	1.4305	1.4628	1.4910	1.5397	1.5821	1.6207

Abs Press. Lb/Sq In. (Sat. Temp)		Sat. Water	Sat. Steam	700	750	800	850	900	950	1000	1050	1100	1150	1200
	Sh			37.89	87.89	137.89	187.89	237.89	287.89	337.89	387.89	437.89	487.89	537.89
2400	v	0.02790	0.1408	0.1824	0.2164	0.2424	0.2648	0.2850	0.3037	0.3214	0.3382	0.3545	0.3703	0.3856
(662.11)	h	718.95	1103.7	1191.6	1259.7	1310.1	1352.8	1391.2	1426.9	1460.9	1493.7	1525.6	1557.0	1588.1
	s	0.9031	1.2460	1.3232	1.3808	1.4217	1.4549	1.4837	1.5095	1.5332	1.5553	1.5761	1.5959	1.6149
	Sh			31.89	81.89	131.89	181.89	231.89	281.89	331.89	381.89	431.89	481.89	531.89
2500	v	0.02859	0.1307	0.1681	0.2032	0.2293	0.2514	0.2712	0.2896	0.3068	0.3232	0.3390	0.3543	0.3692
(668.11)	h	731.71	1093.3	1176.7	1250.6	1303.4	1347.4	1386.7	1423.1	1457.5	1490.7	1522.9	1554.6	1585.9
	s	0.9139	1.2345	1.3076	1.3701	1.4129	1.4472	1.4766	1.5029	1.5269	1.5492	1.5703	1.5903	1.6094
	Sh			26.09	76.09	126.09	176.09	226.09	276.09	326.09	376.09	426.09	476.09	526.09
2600	v	0.02938	0.1211	0.1544	0.1909	0.2171	0.2390	0.2585	0.2765	0.2933	0.3093	0.3247	0.3395	0.3540
(673.91)	h	744.47	1082.0	1160.2	1241.1	1296.5	1341.9	1382.1	1419.2	1454.1	1487.7	1520.2	1552.2	1583.7
	s	0.9247	1.2225	1.2908	1.3592	1.4042	1.4395	1.4696	1.4964	1.5208	1.5434	1.5646	1.5848	1.6040
	Sh			20.47	70.47	120.47	170.47	220.47	270.47	320.47	370.47	420.47	470.47	520.47
2700	v	0.03029	0.1119	0.1411	0.1794	0.2058	0.2275	0.2468	0.2644	0.2809	0.2965	0.3114	0.3259	0.3399
(679.53)	h	757.34	1069.7	1142.0	1231.1	1289.5	1336.3	1377.5	1415.2	1450.7	1484.6	1517.5	1549.8	1581.5
	s	0.9356	1.2097	1.2727	1.3481	1.3954	1.4319	1.4628	1.4900	1.5148	1.5376	1.5591	1.5794	1.5988
	Sh			15.04	65.04	115.04	165.04	215.04	265.04	315.04	365.04	415.04	465.04	515.04
2800	v	0.03134	0.1030	0.1278	0.1685	0.1952	0.2168	0.2358	0.2531	0.2693	0.2845	0.2991	0.3132	0.3268
(684.96)	h	770.69	1055.8	1121.2	1220.6	1282.2	1330.7	1372.8	1411.2	1447.2	1481.6	1514.8	1547.3	1579.3
	s	0.9468	1.1958	1.2527	1.3368	1.3867	1.4245	1.4561	1.4838	1.5089	1.5321	1.5537	1.5742	1.5938
	Sh			9.78	59.78	109.78	159.78	209.78	259.78	309.78	359.78	409.78	459.78	509.78
2900	v	0.03262	0.0942	0.1138	0.1581	0.1853	0.2068	0.2256	0.2427	0.2585	0.2734	0.2877	0.3014	0.3147
(690.22)	h	785.13	1039.8	1095.3	1209.6	1274.7	1324.9	1368.0	1407.2	1443.7	1478.5	1512.1	1544.9	1577.0
	s	0.9588	1.1803	1.2283	1.3251	1.3780	1.4171	1.4494	1.4777	1.5032	1.5266	1.5485	1.5692	1.5889
	Sh			4.67	54.67	104.67	154.67	204.67	254.67	304.67	354.67	404.67	454.67	504.67
3000	v	0.03428	0.0850	0.0982	0.1483	0.1759	0.1975	0.2161	0.2329	0.2484	0.2630	0.2770	0.2904	0.3033
(695.33)	h	801.84	1020.3	1060.5	1197.9	1267.0	1319.0	1363.2	1403.1	1440.2	1475.4	1509.4	1542.4	1574.8
	s	0.9728	1.1619	1.1966	1.3131	1.3692	1.4097	1.4429	1.4717	1.4976	1.5213	1.5434	1.5642	1.5841
	Sh				49.72	99.72	149.72	199.72	249.72	299.72	349.72	399.72	449.72	499.72
3100	v	0.03681	0.0745		0.1389	0.1671	0.1887	0.2071	0.2237	0.2390	0.2533	0.2670	0.2800	0.2927
(700.28)	h	823.97	993.3		1185.4	1259.1	1313.0	1358.4	1399.0	1436.7	1472.3	1506.6	1539.9	1572.6
	s	0.9914	1.1373		1.3007	1.3604	1.4024	1.4364	1.4658	1.4920	1.5161	1.5384	1.5594	1.5794
	Sh				44.92	94.92	144.92	194.92	244.92	294.92	344.92	394.92	444.92	494.92
3200	v	0.04472	0.0566		0.1300	0.1588	0.1804	0.1987	0.2151	0.2301	0.2442	0.2576	0.2704	0.2827
(705.08)	h	875.54	931.6		1172.3	1250.9	1306.9	1353.4	1394.9	1433.1	1469.2	1503.8	1537.4	1570.3
	s	1.0351	1.0832		1.2877	1.3515	1.3951	1.4300	1.4600	1.4866	1.5110	1.5335	1.5547	1.5749

Sh = superheat, °F   h = enthalpy, Btu/lb
v = specific volume, cu ft/lb   s = entropy, Btu/°F/lb

Table III. Superheated Steam — *Continued*

Abs Press. Lb/Sq In. (Sat. Temp)		Sat. Water	Sat. Steam	Temperature — Degrees Fahrenheit										
				700	750	800	850	900	950	1000	1050	1100	1150	1200
3300	v				0.1213	1.1510	1.1727	0.1908	0.2070	0.2218	0.2357	0.2488	0.2613	0.2734
	h				1158.2	1242.5	1300.7	1348.4	1390.7	1429.5	1466.1	1501.0	1534.9	1568.1
	s				1.2742	1.3425	1.3879	1.4237	1.4542	1.4813	1.5059	1.5287	1.5501	1.5704
3400	v				0.1129	0.1435	0.1653	0.1834	0.1994	0.2140	0.2276	0.2405	0.2528	0.2646
	h				1143.2	1233.7	1294.3	1343.4	1386.4	1425.9	1462.9	1498.3	1532.4	1565.8
	s				1.2600	1.3334	1.3807	1.4174	1.4486	1.4761	1.5010	1.5240	1.5456	1.5660
3500	v				0.1048	0.1364	0.1583	0.1764	0.1922	0.2066	0.2200	0.2326	0.2447	0.2563
	h				1127.1	1224.6	1287.8	1338.2	1382.2	1422.2	1459.7	1495.5	1529.9	1563.6
	s				1.2450	1.3242	1.3734	1.4112	1.4430	1.4709	1.4962	1.5194	1.5412	1.5618
3600	v				0.0966	0.1296	0.1517	0.1697	0.1854	0.1996	0.2128	0.2252	0.2371	0.2485
	h				1108.6	1215.3	1281.2	1333.0	1377.9	1418.6	1456.5	1492.6	1527.1	1561.3
	s				1.2281	1.3148	1.3662	1.4050	1.4374	1.4658	1.4914	1.5149	1.5369	1.5576
3800	v				0.0799	0.1169	0.1395	0.1574	0.1729	0.1868	0.1996	0.2116	0.2231	0.2340
	h				1064.2	1195.5	1267.6	1322.4	1369.1	1411.2	1450.1	1487.0	1522.4	1556.8
	s				1.1888	1.2955	1.3517	1.3928	1.4265	1.4558	1.4821	1.5061	1.5284	1.5495
4000	v				0.0631	0.1052	0.1284	0.1463	0.1616	0.1752	0.1877	0.1994	0.2105	0.2210
	h				1007.4	1174.3	1253.4	1311.6	1360.2	1403.6	1443.6	1481.3	1517.3	1552.2
	s				1.1396	1.2754	1.3371	1.3807	1.4158	1.4461	1.4730	1.4976	1.5203	1.5417
4200	v				0.0498	0.0945	0.1183	0.1362	0.1513	0.1647	0.1769	0.1883	0.1991	0.2093
	h				950.1	1151.6	1238.6	1300.4	1351.2	1396.0	1437.1	1475.5	1512.2	1547.6
	s				1.0905	1.2544	1.3223	1.3686	1.4053	1.4366	1.4642	1.4893	1.5124	1.5341
4400	v				0.0421	0.0846	0.1090	0.1270	0.1420	0.1552	0.1671	0.1782	0.1887	0.1986
	h				909.5	1127.3	1223.3	1289.0	1342.0	1388.3	1430.4	1469.7	1507.1	1543.0
	s				1.0556	1.2325	1.3073	1.3566	1.3949	1.4272	1.4556	1.4812	1.5048	1.5268

Abs Press. Lb/Sq In. (Sat. Temp)		Sat. Water	Sat. Steam	Temperature — Degrees Fahrenheit										
				750	800	850	900	950	1000	1050	1100	1150	1200	1250
4600	v			0.0380	0.0751	0.1005	0.1186	0.1335	0.1465	0.1582	0.1691	0.1792	0.1889	0.1982
	h			883.8	1100.0	1207.3	1277.2	1332.6	1380.5	1423.7	1463.9	1501.9	1538.4	1573.8
	s			1.0331	1.2084	1.2922	1.3446	1.3847	1.4181	1.4472	1.4734	1.4974	1.5197	1.5407
4800	v			0.0355	0.0665	0.0927	0.1109	0.1257	0.1385	0.1500	0.1606	0.1706	0.1800	0.1890
	h			866.9	1071.2	1190.7	1265.2	1323.1	1372.6	1417.0	1458.0	1496.7	1533.8	1569.7
	s			1.0180	1.1835	1.2768	1.3327	1.3745	1.4090	1.4390	1.4657	1.4901	1.5128	1.5341

Sh = superheat, °F   h = enthalpy, Btu/lb
v = specific volume, cu ft/lb   s = entropy, Btu/°F/lb

Table III. Superheated Steam — *Continued*

Abs Press. Lb/Sq In. (Sat. Temp)	Sat. Water	Sat. Steam	Temperature — Degrees Fahrenheit										
			750	800	850	900	950	1000	1050	1100	1150	1200	1250
5000 v			0.0338	0.0591	0.0855	0.1038	0.1185	0.1312	0.1425	0.1529	0.1626	0.1718	0.1806
h			854.9	1042.9	1173.6	1252.9	1313.5	1364.6	1410.2	1452.1	1491.5	1529.1	1565.5
s			1.0070	1.1593	1.2612	1.3207	1.3645	1.4001	1.4309	1.4582	1.4831	1.5061	1.5277
5200 v			0.0326	0.0531	0.0789	0.0973	0.1119	0.1244	0.1356	0.1458	0.1553	0.1642	0.1728
h			845.8	1016.9	1156.0	1240.4	1303.7	1356.6	1403.4	1446.2	1486.3	1524.5	1561.3
s			0.9985	1.1370	1.2455	1.3088	1.3545	1.3914	1.4229	1.4509	1.4762	1.4995	1.5214
5400 v			0.0317	0.0483	0.0728	0.0912	0.1058	0.1182	0.1292	0.1392	0.1485	0.1572	0.1656
h			838.5	994.3	1138.1	1227.7	1293.7	1348.4	1396.5	1440.3	1481.1	1519.8	1557.1
s			0.9915	1.1175	1.2296	1.2969	1.3446	1.3827	1.4151	1.4437	1.4694	1.4931	1.5153
5600 v			0.0309	0.0447	0.0672	0.0856	0.1001	0.1124	0.1232	0.1331	0.1422	0.1508	0.1589
h			832.4	975.0	1119.9	1214.8	1283.7	1340.2	1389.6	1434.3	1475.9	1515.2	1552.9
s			0.9855	1.1008	1.2137	1.2850	1.3348	1.3742	1.4075	1.4366	1.4628	1.4869	1.5093
5800 v			0.0303	0.0419	0.0622	0.0805	0.0949	0.1070	0.1177	0.1274	0.1363	0.1447	0.1527
h			827.3	958.8	1101.8	1201.8	1273.6	1332.0	1382.6	1428.3	1470.6	1510.5	1548.7
s			0.9803	1.0867	1.1981	1.2732	1.3250	1.3658	1.3999	1.4297	1.4564	1.4808	1.5035
6000 v			0.0298	0.0397	0.0579	0.0757	0.0900	0.1020	0.1126	0.1221	0.1309	0.1391	0.1469
h			822.9	945.1	1084.6	1188.8	1263.4	1323.6	1375.7	1422.3	1465.4	1505.9	1544.6
s			0.9758	1.0746	1.1833	1.2615	1.3154	1.3574	1.3925	1.4229	1.4500	1.4748	1.4978
6500 v			0.0287	0.0358	0.0495	0.0655	0.0793	0.0909	0.1012	0.1104	0.1188	0.1266	0.1340
h			813.9	919.5	1046.7	1156.3	1237.8	1302.7	1358.1	1407.3	1452.2	1494.2	1534.1
s			0.9661	1.0515	1.1506	1.2328	1.2917	1.3370	1.3743	1.4064	1.4347	1.4604	1.4841
7000 v			0.0279	0.0334	0.0438	0.0573	0.0704	0.0816	0.0915	0.1004	0.1085	0.1160	0.1231
h			806.9	901.8	1016.5	1124.9	1212.6	1281.7	1340.5	1392.2	1439.1	1482.6	1523.7
s			0.9582	1.0350	1.1243	1.2055	1.2689	1.3171	1.3567	1.3904	1.4200	1.4466	1.4710
7500 v			0.0272	0.0318	0.0399	0.0512	0.0631	0.0737	0.0833	0.0918	0.0996	0.1068	0.1136
h			801.3	889.0	992.9	1097.7	1188.3	1261.0	1322.9	1377.2	1426.0	1471.0	1513.3
s			0.9514	1.0224	1.1033	1.1818	1.2473	1.2980	1.3397	1.3751	1.4059	1.4335	1.4586
8000 v			0.0267	0.0306	0.0371	0.0465	0.0571	0.0671	0.0762	0.0845	0.0920	0.0989	0.1054
h			796.6	879.1	974.4	1074.3	1165.4	1241.0	1305.5	1362.2	1413.0	1459.6	1503.1
s			0.9455	1.0122	1.0864	1.1613	1.2271	1.2798	1.3233	1.3603	1.3924	1.4208	1.4467
8500 v			0.0262	0.0296	0.0350	0.0429	0.0522	0.0615	0.0701	0.0780	0.0853	0.0919	0.0982
h			792.7	871.2	959.8	1054.5	1144.0	1221.9	1288.5	1347.5	1400.2	1448.2	1492.9
s			0.9402	1.0037	1.0727	1.1437	1.2084	1.2627	1.3076	1.3460	1.3793	1.4087	1.4352

Sh = superheat, °F	h = enthalpy, Btu/lb
v = specific volume, cu ft/lb	s = entropy, Btu/°F/lb

Table III. Superheated Steam — *Continued*

Abs Press. Lb/Sq In. (Sat. Temp)	Sat. Water	Sat. Steam	750	800	850	900	950	1000	1050	1100	1150	1200	1250
9000 v			0.0258	0.0288	0.0335	0.0402	0.0483	0.0568	0.0649	0.0724	0.0794	0.0858	0.0918
h			789.3	864.7	948.0	1037.6	1125.4	1204.1	1272.1	1333.0	1387.5	1437.1	1482.9
s			0.9354	0.9964	1.0613	1.1285	1.1918	1.2468	1.2926	1.3323	1.3667	1.3970	1.4243
9500 v			0.0254	0.0282	0.0322	0.0380	0.0451	0.0528	0.0603	0.0675	0.0742	0.0804	0.0862
h			786.4	859.2	938.3	1023.4	1108.9	1187.7	1256.6	1318.9	1375.1	1426.1	1473.1
s			0.9310	0.9900	1.0516	1.1153	1.1771	1.2320	1.2785	1.3191	1.3546	1.3858	1.4137
10000 v			0.0251	0.0276	0.0312	0.0362	0.0425	0.0495	0.0565	0.0633	0.0697	0.0757	0.0812
h			783.8	854.5	930.2	1011.3	1094.2	1172.6	1242.0	1305.3	1362.9	1415.3	1463.4
s			0.9270	0.9842	1.0432	1.1039	1.1638	1.2185	1.2652	1.3065	1.3429	1.3749	1.4035
10500 v			0.0248	0.0271	0.0303	0.0347	0.0404	0.0467	0.0532	0.0595	0.0656	0.0714	0.0768
h			781.5	850.5	923.4	1001.0	1081.3	1158.9	1228.4	1292.4	1351.1	1404.7	1453.9
s			0.9232	0.9790	1.0358	1.0939	1.1519	1.2060	1.2529	1.2946	1.3371	1.3644	1.3937
11000 v			0.0245	0.0267	0.0296	0.0335	0.0386	0.0443	0.0503	0.0562	0.0620	0.0676	0.0727
h			779.5	846.9	917.5	992.1	1069.9	1146.3	1215.9	1280.2	1339.7	1394.4	1444.6
s			0.9196	0.9742	1.0292	1.0851	1.1412	1.1945	1.2414	1.2833	1.3209	1.3544	1.3842
11500 v			0.0243	0.0263	0.0290	0.0325	0.0370	0.0423	0.0478	0.0534	0.0588	0.0641	0.0691
h			777.7	843.8	912.4	984.5	1059.8	1134.9	1204.3	1268.7	1328.8	1384.4	1435.5
s			0.9163	0.9698	1.0232	1.0772	1.1316	1.1840	1.2308	1.2727	1.3107	1.3446	1.3750
12000 v			0.0241	0.0260	0.0284	0.0317	0.0357	0.0405	0.0456	0.0508	0.0560	0.0610	0.0659
h			776.1	841.0	907.9	977.8	1050.9	1124.5	1193.7	1258.0	1318.5	1374.7	1426.6
s			0.9131	0.9657	1.0177	1.0701	1.1229	1.1742	1.2209	1.2627	1.3010	1.3353	1.3662
12500 v			0.0238	0.0256	0.0279	0.0309	0.0346	0.0390	0.0437	0.0486	0.0535	0.0583	0.0629
h			774.7	838.6	903.9	971.9	1043.1	1115.2	1184.1	1247.9	1308.8	1365.4	1418.0
s			0.9101	0.9618	1.0127	1.0637	1.1151	1.1653	1.2117	1.2534	1.2918	1.3264	1.3576
13000 v			0.0236	0.0253	0.0275	0.0302	0.0336	0.0376	0.0420	0.0466	0.0512	0.0558	0.0602
h			773.5	836.3	900.4	966.8	1036.2	1106.7	1174.8	1238.5	1299.6	1356.5	1409.6
s			0.9073	0.9582	1.0080	1.0578	1.1079	1.1571	1.2030	1.2445	1.2831	1.3179	1.3494
13500 v			0.0235	0.0251	0.0271	0.0297	0.0328	0.0364	0.0405	0.0448	0.0492	0.0535	0.0577
h			772.3	834.4	897.2	962.2	1030.0	1099.1	1166.3	1229.7	1291.0	1348.1	1401.5
s			0.9045	0.9548	1.0037	1.0524	1.1014	1.1495	1.1948	1.2361	1.2749	1.3098	1.3415
14000 v			0.0233	0.0248	0.0267	0.0291	0.0320	0.0354	0.0392	0.0432	0.0474	0.0515	0.0555
h			771.3	832.6	894.3	958.0	1024.5	1092.3	1158.5	1221.4	1283.0	1340.2	1393.8
s			0.9019	0.9515	0.9996	1.0473	1.0953	1.1426	1.1872	1.2282	1.2671	1.3021	1.3339

Sh = superheat, °F   h = enthalpy, Btu/lb
v = specific volume, cu ft/lb   s = entropy, Btu/°F/lb

Table III. Superheated Steam — *Continued*

Abs Press. Lb/Sq In. (Sat. Temp)	Sat. Water	Sat. Steam	Temperature — Degrees Fahrenheit										
			750	800	850	900	950	1000	1050	1100	1150	1200	1250
14500 v			0.0231	0.0246	0.0264	0.0287	0.0314	0.0345	0.0380	0.0418	0.0458	0.0496	0.0534
h			770.4	831.0	891.7	954.3	1019.6	1086.2	1151.4	1213.8	1275.4	1332.9	1386.4
s			0.8994	0.9484	0.9957	1.0426	1.0897	1.1362	1.1801	1.2208	1.2597	1.2949	1.3266
15000 v			0.0230	0.0244	0.0261	0.0282	0.0308	0.0337	0.0369	0.0405	0.0443	0.0479	0.0516
h			769.6	829.5	889.3	950.9	1015.1	1080.6	1144.9	1206.8	1268.1	1326.0	1379.4
s			0.8970	0.9455	0.9920	1.0382	1.0846	1.1302	1.1735	1.2139	1.2525	1.2880	1.3197
15500 v			0.0228	0.0242	0.0258	0.0278	0.0302	0.0329	0.0360	0.0393	0.0429	0.0464	0.0499
h			768.9	828.2	887.2	947.8	1011.1	1075.7	1139.0	1200.3	1261.1	1319.6	1372.8
s			0.8946	0.9427	0.9886	1.0340	1.0797	1.1247	1.1674	1.2073	1.2457	1.2815	1.3131

Sh = superheat, °F   h = enthalpy, Btu/lb
v = specific volume, cu ft/lb   s = entropy, Btu/°F/lb

Appendix G. Engineering Conversion Factors

The following table is designed to provide accurate conversion of units between various equivalent representational forms. To convert a unit, locate the unit in the MULTIPLY column of the table, select the desired unit in the TO OBTAIN column, and then multiply the quantity to be converted by the appropriate factor to obtain the desired units.

For example, you have exactly 2.5 acres and you need to know how many square meters. In the table: acre × 4046.86 = square meter. Therefore, 2.50000 acres = [2.50000] × [4046.86] = 10117.2 square meters.

A note should be made regarding scientific notation: 1×10^1, 1×10^2, 1×10^3 are equivalent to 10, 100, 1000. For negative powers, 1×10^{-1}, 1×10^{-2}, 1×10^{-3} represent the numbers 0.1, 0.01, 0.001. Therefore, the number 2.345×10^3 is 2345.0 and 2.345×10^{-3} represents 0.002345.

An effort has been made to indicate to the user those conversions which involve Système International (SI) metric units. Whenever an SI unit is involved, an asterisk (*) will appear either in the MULTIPLY or TO OBTAIN column. The unit *pound* in the table is used as a mass unit; e.g. ampere/pound (mass). The pound is pound avoirdupois.

Accuracy is an important concern with conversion factors. This table presents all conversions with six significant figures; for example, 4046.86 and 0.453592. The actual number of significant figures allowed in a conversion is equal to the number of significant figures in the least accurate of the conversion factors or the unit being converted. For example, in the acre to square meter illustration: if acres was only known to two significant figures, then the conversion square meters would be (2.5) acres × 4046.86 = 10,000 square meters.

Table 1. Engineering Conversion Factors

MULTIPLY	BY	TO OBTAIN
A		
acre	4046.86	*square meter
acre foot	1233.49	*cubic meter
ampere/centimeter	2.54000	ampere/inch
ampere/inch	39.3701	*ampere/meter
*ampere/kilogram	0.453592	ampere/pound (mass)
*ampere/meter	0.025400	ampere/inch
ampere/pound (mass)	2.20462	*ampere/kilogram
ampere/square foot	10.7639	*ampere/square meter
ampere/square inch	1550.00	ampere/square meter
*ampere/square meter	0.000645	ampere/square inch
amper/square meter	0.092903	ampere/square foot
ampere/volt	1.00000	*siemens
ampere/volt inch	39.3701	*siemens/meter
ampere/weber	1.00000	*unit/henry
*ampere turn	1.25664	gilbert
ampere turn/inch	39.3701	*ampere turn/meter
*ampere turn/meter	0.025400	ampere turn/inch

MULTIPLY	BY	TO OBTAIN
ampere turn/meter	0.012566	Oersted
atmosphere (kilogram (force)/cm²)	98.0665	*kilopascal
atmosphere (760 torr)	101.325	kilopascal

B

MULTIPLY	BY	TO OBTAIN
bar	100.000	kilopascal
barrel (42 U.S. gallons)	0.158987	*cubic meter
barrel/ton (U.K.)	0.156476	*cubic meter/metric ton
barrel/ton (U.S.)	0.175254	cubic meter/metric ton
barrel/day	0.001840	cubic decimeter/second
barrel/hour	0.044163	cubic decimeter/second
barrel/million std cubic feet	0.133010	cubic decimeters/kilomol
British thermal unit	0.251996	kilogram calorie (International Table—I.T.)
Btu (mean)	1.05587	*kilojoule
Btu (thermochemical)	1.05435	kilojoule
Btu (39°F)	1.05967	kilojoule
Btu (60°F)	1.05680	kilojoule
Btu (I.T.)	1.05506	kilojoule
Btu (I.T.)/brake horsepower hour	0.000393	kilowatt/kilowatt
Btu (I.T.)/cubic foot	37.2589	*kilojoule/cubic meter
Btu (I.T.)/hour	0.293071	*watt
Btu (I.T.)/hour cubic foot	0.010349	*kilowatt/cubic meter
Btu (I.T.)/hour cubic foot °F	0.018629	*kilowatt/cubic meter kelvin
Btu (I.T.)/hour square foot	3.15459	*watt/square meter
Btu (I.T.)/hour square foot °F	5.67826	*watt/square meter kelvin
Btu (I.T.)/hour square foot °F/foot	1.73074	*watt/meter kelvin
Btu (I.T.)/minute	0.017581	*kilowatt
Btu (I.T.)/pound mol	2.32600	*joule/mol
Btu (I.T.)/pound mol °F	4.18680	*kilojoule/kilomol kelvin
Btu (I.T.)/pound (mass)	0.555555	kilocalorie/kilogram
Btu (I.T.)/pound (mass)	2.32600	*kilojoule/kilogram
Btu (I.T.)/pound (mass) °F	4.18680	kilojoule/kilogram kelvin
Btu (I.T.)/pound (mass) °F	1.00000	kilocalorie/kilogram kelvin
Btu (I.T.)/second	1.05487	*kilowatt
Btu (I.T.)/second cubic foot	37.2590	*kilowatt/cubic meter
Btu (I.T.)/second cubic foot °F	67.0661	*kilowatt/cubic meter kelvin
Btu (I.T.)/second square foot	11.3565	*kilowatt/square meter
Btu (I.T.)/second square foot °F	20.4418	*kilowatt/square meter kelvin
Btu (I.T.)/gallon (U.K.)	232.080	*kilojoules/cubic meter
Btu (I.T.)/gallon (U.S.)	278.716	kilojoules/cubic meter

C

MULTIPLY	BY	TO OBTAIN
calorie (I.T.)	4.18680	*joule
calorie (mean)	4.19002	joule
calorie (thermochemical)	4.18400	joule
calorie (thermochemical)	0.003966	Btu (I.T.)
calorie (15°C)	4.18580	*joule

MULTIPLY	BY	TO OBTAIN
calorie (20°C)	4.18190	joule
calorie (thermochemical)/gram kelvin	4.18400	*kilojoule/kilogram kelvin
calorie (thermochemical)/hour cm^3	1.16222	*kilowatt/cubic meter
calorie (thermochemical)/hour cm^2	0.011622	*kilowatt/square meter
calorie (thermochemical)/milliliter	4.18400	*megajoule/cubic meter
calorie (thermochemical)/pound (mass)	9.22414	*joule/kilogram
calorific heat hour	2.64778	*megajoule
calorific value	0.735500	*kilowatt
calorific heat unit	1.89910	*kilojoules
*candela/square meter	0.291864	foot lambert
candela/square meter	0.000314	lambert
centimeter water (4°C)	0.098064	*kilopascals
centipoise	0.001000	*pascal second
centistoke	1.00000	*square millimeter/second
chain	20.1168	*meter
coulomb/cubic foot	35.3146	*coulomb/cubic meter
*coulomb/cubic meter	0.028317	coulomb/cubic foot
coulomb/foot	3.28084	coulomb/meter
coulomb/inch	39.3701	coulomb/meter
*coulomb/meter	0.304800	coulomb/foot
coulomb meter	0.025400	coulomb/inch
coulomb/square foot	10.7639	*coulomb/square meter
coulomb/square meter	0.092930	coulomb/square foot
*cubic centimeter	0.035195	ounce fluid (U.K.)
cubic centimeter	0.038140	ounce fluid (U.S.)
*cubic centimeter/cubic meter	0.034972	gallon (U.K.)/1000 barrels
cubic centimeter/cubic meter	0.042000	gallon (U.S.)/1000 barrels
cubic centimeter/cubic meter	1.00000	volume parts/million
*cubic decimeter	0.035315	cubic foot
cubic decimeter	0.219969	gallon (U.K.)
cubic decimeter	0.264172	gallon (U.S.)
cubic decimeter	0.879877	quart (U.K.)
cubic decimeter	1.05669	quart (U.S.)
*cubic decimeter/cubic meter	0.006229	gallon (U.K.)/cubic foot
cubic decimeter/cubic meter	0.007481	gallon (U.S.)/cubic foot
*cubic decimeter/kilogram	0.119826	gallon (U.S.)/pound (mass)
cubic decimeter/kilogram	0.016018	cubic foot/pound (mass)
cubic decimeter/kilogram	0.099776	gallon (U.K.)/pound (mass)
*cubic decimeter/kilomol	7.51823	barrel/million std ft^3
cubic decimeter/kilomol	0.315765	gallon (U.S.)/1000 std ft^3
*cubic decimeter/second	22.6433	barrel/hour
cubic decimeter/second	127.133	cubic foot/hour
cubic decimeter/second	543.440	barrel/day
*cubic decimeter/second	3051.19	cubic foot/day
cubic decimeter/second	13.1982	gallon (U.K.)/minute
cubic decimeter/second	15.8503	gallon (U.S.)/minute

MULTIPLY	BY	TO OBTAIN
cubic decimeter/second	2.11888	cubic foot/minute
cubic decimeter/second	0.035315	cubic foot/second
*cubic decimeter/metric ton	0.005706	barrel/ton (U.S.)
cubic decimeter/metric ton	0.006391	barrel/ton (U.K.)
cubic decimeter/metric ton	0.268411	gallon (U.S.)/ton (U.K.)
cubic decimeter/metric ton	0.239653	gallon (U.S.)/ton (U.S.)
cubic foot	0.028317	*cubic meter
cubic foot	28.3169	*cubic decimeter
cubic foot/foot	0.092903	*cubic meter/meter
cubic foot/hour	0.007866	*cubic decimeter/second
cubic foot/minute	0.471947	cubic decimeter/second
cubic foot/minute square foot	0.005080	*cubic meter/second square meter
cubic foot/pound (mass)	62.4280	*cubic decimeter/kilogram
cubic foot/pound (mass)	0.062428	*cubic meter/kilogram
cubic foot/second	28.3169	*cubic decimeter/second
cubic inch	0.016387	*cubic decimeter
*cubic kilometer	0.239913	cubic mile
*cubic meter	6.28976	barrel (42 U.S. gallons)
cubic meter	35.3147	cubic foot
cubic meter	1.30795	cubic yard
cubic meter	219.969	gallon (U.K.)
cubic meter	264.172	gallon (U.S.)
*cubic meter/kilogram	16.0185	cubic foot/pound (mass)
*cubic meter/meter	10.7639	cubic foot/foot
cubic meter/meter	80.5196	gallon (U.S.)/foot
*cubic meter/second meter	289870.	gallon (U.S.)/hour foot
cubic meter/second meter	4022.80	gallon (U.K.)/minute foot
cubic meter/second meter	4831.18	gallon (U.S.)/minute foot
cubic meter/second meter	20114.0	gallon (U.K.)/hour inch
cubic meter/second meter	24155.9	gallon (U.S.)/hour inch
*cubic meter/square meter	88352.6	gallon (U.S.)/hour square foot
cubic meter/square meter	3.28084	cubic foot/second square foot
cubic meter/square meter	196.850	cubic foot/minute square foot
cubic meter/square meter	510.895	gallon (U.K.)/hour square inch
cubic meter/square meter	613.560	gallon (U.S.)/hour square inch
cubic meter/metric ton	5.70602	barrel/ton (U.S.)
cubic meter/metric ton	6.39074	barrel/ton (U.K.)
cubic mile	4.16818	*cubic kilometer
cubic yard	0.764555	*cubic meter

D

MULTIPLY	BY	TO OBTAIN
*degree Celsius (difference)	(9/5)	degree Fahrenheit (difference)
degree Celsius (traditional)	(9/5)°C+32	degree Fahrenheit (traditional
degree Fahrenheit/100 feet	0.018227	*kelvin/meter
degree Fahrenheit (difference)	(5/9)	*degree Celsius (difference)
degree Fahrenheit (traditional)	(5/9)°F−32	degree Celsius (traditional)

MULTIPLY	BY	TO OBTAIN
degree Rankine	(5/9)	*kelvin
degree (angle)	0.017453	radian
dyne	0.000010	*newton
dyne/square centimeter	0.100000	*pascal
dyne second/square centimeter	0.100000	*pascal second

F

MULTIPLY	BY	TO OBTAIN
farad/inch	39.3701	*farad/meter
*farad/meter	0.025400	farad/inch
fathom (U.S.)	1.82880	*meter
foot	304.800	*millimeter
foot lambert	3.42626	candela/square meter
foot/degree F	0.548640	*meter/kelvin
foot/gallon (U.S.)	80.5196	*meter/cubic meter
foot/barrel	1.91713	meter/cubic meter
foot/cubic foot	10.7639	meter/cubic meter
foot/day	0.003528	*millimeter/second
foot/hour	0.084667	millimeter/second
foot/mile	0.189394	*meter/kilometer
foot/minute	0.005080	*meter/second
foot/second	0.304800	meter/second
foot poundal	0.042140	*joule
foot pound (force)	1.35582	joule
foot pound (force)/gallon (U.S.)	0.358169	*kilojoule/cubic meter
foot pound (force)/second	1.35582	*watt
foot pound (force)/square inch	0.210152	*joule/square centimeter
footcandle	10.7639	lux

G

MULTIPLY	BY	TO OBTAIN
gallon (U.K.)	0.004546	*cubic meter
gallon (U.K.)	4.54609	*cubic decimeter
gallon (U.K.)/hour foot	4.14306×10^{-6}	*cubic meter/second meter
gallon (U.K.)/hour square foot	1.35927×10^{-5}	*cubic meter/second square meter
gallon (U.K.)/minute	0.075768	*cubic decimeter/second
gallon (U.K.)/minute foot	0.000249	*cubic meter/second meter
gallon (U.K.)/minute square foot	0.000816	*cubic meter/second square meter
gallon (U.K.)/pound (mass)	10.0224	*cubic decimeter/kilogram
gallon (U.K.)/1000 barrels	28.5940	*cubic centimeter/cubic meter
gallon (U.S.)	0.832674	gallon (U.K.)
gallon (U.S.)	0.003785	*cubic meter
gallon (U.S.)/cubic foot	133.681	*cubic decimeter/cubic meter
gallon (U.S.)/foot	0.012419	*cubic meter/meter
gallon (U.S.)/hour foot	3.44981×10^{-6}	*cubic meter/second meter
gallon (U.S.)/hour square foot	1.13183×10^{-5}	*cubic meter/second square meter
gallon (U.S.)/minute	0.063090	*cubic decimeter/second
gallon (U.S.)/minute foot	0.000207	*cubic meter/second meter
gallon (U.S.)/minute square foot	0.000679	*cubic meter/second square meter

MULTIPLY	BY	TO OBTAIN
gallon (U.S.)/pound (mass)	8.34540	*cubic decimeter/kilogram
gallon (U.S.)/ton (U.K.)	3.72563	*cubic decimeter/metric ton
gallon (U.S.)/1000 barrels	23.8095	*cubic centimeter/cubic meter
gauss	0.000100	*tesla
gauss/Oersted	1.25664×10^{-6}	*henry/meter
gilbert	0.795775	*ampere turn
gilbert/maxwell	7.95775×10^{7}	*unit/henry
grain	64.7989	*milligram
grain/gallon (U.S.)	17.1181	*gram/cubic meter
grain/cubic foot	2.28835	*milligram/cubic decimeter
grain/100 cubic feet	22.8835	*milligram/cubic meter
*gram	0.035274	ounce (avoirdupois)
gram	0.032151	ounce (troy)
*gram mol	0.001000	kilomol
*gram/cubic meter	3.78541	milligram/gallon (U.S.)
gram/cubic meter	0.058418	grains/gallon (U.S.)
gram/cubic meter	0.350507	pound (mass)/1000 barrels
gram/cubic meter	0.008345	pound (mass)/1000 gallons (U.S.)
grams/cubic meter	0.010022	pound (mass)/1000 gallons (U.K.)
grams/gallon (U.K.)	0.219969	*kilogram/cubic meter
grams/gallon (U.S.)	0.264172	kilogram/cubic meter
gray	100.000	rad

H

*henry	7.95775×10^{7}	maxwell/gilbert
henry	1.00000	weber/ampere
henry	1.00000×10^{8}	line/ampere
*henry/meter	795775	gauss/Oersted
henry/meter	2.54000×10^{6}	lines/ampere inch
horsepower (electric)	0.746000	*kilowatt
horsepower (hydraulic)	0.746043	kilowatt
horsepower (U.S.)	0.745702	kilowatt
horsepower (U.S.)	42.4150	Btu/minute
horsepower hour (U.S.)	2.68452	*megajoule
horsepower hour (U.S.)	2544.99	Btu (I.T.)
horsepower/cubic foot	26.3341	*kilowatt/cubic meter
hundred weight (U.K.)	50.8024	*kilogram
hundred weight (U.S.)	45.3592	kilogram

I

inch	25.4000	*millimeter
inch water (39.2°F)	0.249082	*kilopascal
inch water (60°F)	0.248840	kilopascal
inch mercury (32°F)	3.38639	kilopascal
inch mercury (60°F)	3.37685	kilopascal
inches/minute	0.423333	*millimeter/second
inches/second	25.4000	millimeter/second

MULTIPLY	BY	TO OBTAIN
J		
*joule	0.737562	foot pound (force)
joule	23.7304	foot poundal
joule	1.00000	*watt second
joule	0.239126	calorie (20°C)
joule	0.238903	calorie (15°C)
joule	0.238662	calorie (mean)
joule	0.238846	calorie (I.T.)
joule	0.239006	calorie (thermochemical)
*joule/kilogram	0.108411	calorie (thermochemical)/pound (mass)
*joule/mol	0.429923	Btu (I.T.)/pound mol
*joule/square centimeter	4.75846	foot pound (force)/square inch
joule/square centimeter	0.101972	*kilogram meter/cm²
K		
*kelvin (degree)	(9/5)	degree Rankine
*kelvin (degree) (minus)	−273.16	degree centigrade
*kilocalorie (thermochemical)	4.18400	*kilojoule
*kilocalorie (thermochemical)/hour	1.16222	*watt
*kilocalorie (thermochemical)/hour m²°c	1.16222	*watt/square meter °K
*kilocalorie (thermochemical)/kilogram °C	4.18400	*kilojoule/kilogram °K
*kilogram	0.196841	hundred weight (U.K.)
kilogram	0.220462	hundred weight (U.S.)
kilogram	2.20462	pound (avoirdupois)
*kilogram meter/second	7.23301	pound (mass) foot/second
*kilogram meter/square centimeter	9.80665	*joule/square centimeter
*kilogram/cubic decimeter	8.34541	pound (mass)/gallon (U.S.)
kilogram/cubic decimeter	10.0224	pound (mass)/gallon (U.K.)
*kilogram/cubic meter	0.062428	pound (mass)/cubic foot
kilogram/cubic meter	0.350507	pound (mass)/barrel
kilogram/cubic meter	3.78541	grams/gallon (U.S.)
kilogram/cubic meter	4.54609	grams/gallon (U.K.)
*kilogram/meter	0.671969	pound (mass)/foot
*kilogram/mol	2.20462	pound (mass)/mol
*kilogram/second	7936.64	pound (mass)/hour
kilogram/second	2.20462	pound (mass)/second
kilogram/second	0.059052	ton (mass) (U.K.)/minute
kilogram/second	0.066139	ton (mass) (U.S.)/minute
kilogram/second	3.54314	ton (mass) (U.K.)/hour
kilogram/second	3.96832	ton (mass) (U.S.)/hour
kilogram/second	31037.9	ton (mass) (U.K.)/year
kilogram/second	34762.5	ton (mass) (U.S.)/year
*kilogram/second meter	0.671969	pound (mass)/second foot
kilogram/second meter	2419.09	pound (mass)/hour foot
*kilogram/second square meter	0.204816	pound (mass)/second square foot
kilogram/second square meter	737.338	pound (mass)/hour square foot
*kilogram/square meter	0.204816	pound (mass)/square foot

MULTIPLY	BY	TO OBTAIN
*kilojoule	0.947817	Btu (I.T.)
kilojoule	0.943690	Btu (39°F)
kilojoule	0.948155	Btu (60°F)
kilojoule	0.947086	Btu (mean)
kilojoule	0.948452	Btu (thermochemical)
*kilojoule/cubic meter	0.026884	Btu (I.T.)/cubic foot
kilojoule/cubic meter	0.004309	Btu (I.T.)/gallon (U.K.)
kilojoule/cubic meter	0.003588	Btu (I.T.)/gallon (U.S.)
kilojoule/cubic meter	2.79198	footpound (force)/gallon (U.S.)
*kilojoule/kilogram	0.429923	Btu (I.T.)/pound (mass)
*kilojoule/kilogram kelvin	0.238846	Btu (I.T.)/pound (mass) °F
kilojoule/kilogram kelvin	0.238846	Btu (I.T.)/pound mol °F
kilojoule/kilogram kelvin	0.239006	calorie (thermochemical)/gram kelvin
*kilojoule/kilogram kelvin	0.239006	calorie (thermochemical)/gram mol °C
kilojoule/kilogram kelvin	0.239006	kilocalorie (thermochemical)/kilogram °C
kilojoule/kilogram kelvin	0.000278	*kilowatt hour/kilogram °C
*kilojoule/mol	0.239006	kilocalorie (thermochemical)/gram mol
*kilometer	0.621371	mile
kilometer	0.539957	nautical mile
*kilometer/cubic decimeter	2.35215	mile/gallon (U.S.)
*kilometer/hour	0.539957	knot
kilometer/hour	0.621371	miles/hour
*kilomol	1000.00	gram mol
kilomol	2.20462	pound mol
kilomol	836.610	standard cubic foot (60°F, 1 atmosphere)
kilomol	22.4136	standard cubic meter (0°C, 1 atmosphere)
kilomol	23.6445	standard cubic meter (15°C, 1 atmosphere)
*kilomol/cubic meter	0.0624280	pound mol/cubic foot
kilomol/cubic meter	0.010022	pound mol/gallon (U.K.)
kilomol/cubic meter	0.008345	pound mol/gallon (U.S.)
kilomol/cubic meter	133.010	standard ft^3/barrel (60°F, 1 atmosphere)
*kilomol/second	2.20462	pound mol/second
kilomol/second	7936.64	pound mol/hour
*kilonewton	0.224809	kip (1000 foot pound)
kilonewton	0.100361	ton (force) (U.K.)
kilonewton	0.112405	ton (force) (U.S.)
*kilonewton meter	0.368781	ton force (U.S.) foot
*kilopascal	0.010197	atmosphere (kilogram/square centimeter)
kilopascal	0.009869	atmosphere (760 torr)
kilopascal	0.01000	bar
kilopascal	10.1974	centimeter water (4°C)
kilopascal	4.01474	inch water (39.2°F)
kilopascal	0.295300	inch mercury (32°F)
kilopascal	0.296134	inch mercury (60°F)
kilopascal	7.50062	millimeter mercury (0°C)
kilopascal	20.8854	pound (force)/square foot

MULTIPLY	BY	TO OBTAIN
kilopascal	0.145038	pound (force)/square inch
*kilopascal/meter	0.044208	pound (force)/square inch/foot
*kilopascal second	0.145038	pound (force)/square inch
*kilowatt	56.8690	Btu (I.T.)/minute
kilowatt	0.947817	Btu (I.T.)/second
kilowatt	1.35962	calorific value
kilowatt	1.34048	horsepower (electric)
kilowatt	1.34102	horsepower (550 foot pound/second)
kilowatt	1.34045	horsepower (hydraulic)
kilowatt	0.284345	ton of refrigeration
*kilowatt hour	3.60000	*megajoule
*kilowatt hour/kilogram °C	3600.00	*kilojoule/kilogram kelvin
*kilowatt/cubic meter	96.6211	Btu (I.T.)/hour cubic foot
kilowatt/cubic meter	0.026839	Btu (I.T.)/second cubic foot
kilowatt/cubic meter	0.860421	calorie (thermochemical)/hour cm³
kilowatt/cubic meter	0.037974	horsepower/cubic foot
*kilowatt/cubic meter kelvin	53.6784	Btu (I.T.)/hour cubic foot °F
kilowatt/cubic meter kelvin	0.014911	Btu (I.T.)/second cubic foot °F
*kilowatt/kilowatt	2544.43	Btu (I.T.)/brake horsepower hour
*kilowatt/square meter	0.088055	Btu (I.T.)/second square foot
kilowatt/square meter	86.0421	calorie (thermochemical)/hour cm³
*kilowatt/square meter kelvin	0.048919	Btu (I.T.)/second square foot °F
kip (1000 foot pounds)	4.44822	*kilonewton
kip/square inch	6.89476	*megapascal
knot	1.85325	*kilometer/hour

L

lambert	3183.10	*candela/square meter
line	1.00000	maxwell
line	1.00000×10⁻⁸	*weber
lines/ampere	1.00000×10⁻⁸	*henry
lines/ampere inch	3.93701×10⁻⁷	*henry/meter
lines/square inch	1.55000	*tesla
link	0.201168	*meter
lumen/square foot	10.7639	*lux
lumen/square inch	1550.00	lux
*lux	0.092903	footcandle
lux	0.092903	lumen/square foot
lux	0.000645	lumen/square inch
*lux second	0.092903	foot candle second

M

maxwell	1.00000	line
maxwell	1.00000×10⁻⁸	*weber
maxwell/gilbert	1.25664×10⁻⁸	*henry
*megagram	1.00000	ton (mass) (metric)
megagram	0.984206	ton (mass) (U.K.)

MULTIPLY	BY	TO OBTAIN
megagram	1.10231	ton (mass) (U.S.)
*megagram/square meter	0.102408	ton (mass) (U.S.)/square foot
*megajoule	947.817	Btu (I.T.)
megajoule	0.377675	calorific value hour
megajoule	0.372506	horsepower hour
megajoule	0.277778	*kilowatt hour
megajoule	0.009478	therm
megajoule	0.102408	ton (mass) (U.S.) mile
*megajoule/cubic meter	4.30886	Btu (I.T.)/gallon (U.K.)
megajoule/cubic meter	3.58788	Btu (I.T.)/gallon (U.K.)
megajoule/cubic meter	0.239006	calorie (thermochemical)/milliliter
*megajoule/meter	0.021289	ton (force) (U.S.) mile/foot
*megapascal	0.145038	kip/square inch
megapascal	145.038	pound/square inch
megapascal	10.4427	ton (force) (U.S.)/square foot
megapascal	0.072519	ton (force) (U.S.)/square inch
*megawatt	3.41214	million Btu (I.T.)/hour
*meter	0.049710	chain
meter	0.546807	fathom
meter	3.28084	feet
meter	4.97097	link
meter	0.198839	rod
meter	1.09361	yard
*meter/cubic meter	0.521612	foot/barrel
meter/cubic meter	0.092903	foot/cubic foot
meter/cubic meter	0.012419	foot/gallon (U.S.)
*meter/kelvin	1.82269	foot/°F
*meter/kilometer	5.28000	foot/mile
*meter/second	3.28084	foot/second
meter/second	196.850	foot/minute
microbar	0.100000	*pascal
*micrometer	0.039370	mil
micrometer	1.00000	micron
micron	1.00000	*micrometer
microsecond/foot	3.28084	*microsecond/meter
*microsecond/meter	0.304800	microsecond/foot
mil	25.4000	*micrometer
mile	5280.00	foot
mile	1.60934	*kilometer
mile/gallon (U.S.)	0.425144	*kilometer/cubic decimeter
mile/hour	1.60934	*kilometer/hour
*milligram	0.015432	grain
*milligram/cubic decimeter	0.436996	grain/cubic foot
*milligram/cubic meter	0.043700	grain/100 cubic foot
milligram/gallon (U.S.)	0.264172	*gram/cubic meter
*millimeter	0.039370	inch

MULTIPLY	BY	TO OBTAIN
millimeter	0.003281	foot
millimeter mercury (0°C)	133.322	*pascal
millimeter mercury (0°C)	0.133322	*kilopascal
*millimeter/second	283.465	foot/day
millimeter/second	11.8110	foot/hour
millimeter/second	2.36221	inch/minute
millimeter/second	0.039370	inch/second
million Btu (I.T.)/hour	0.293071	*megawatt
million electron volt	0.160219	*picojoule
million pound (mass)/year	0.014383	kilogram/second
minute (angle)	0.000291	*radian
mol/foot	3.28084	*mol/meter
*mol/kilogram	0.453592	mol/pound (mass)
*mol/meter)	0.304800	mol/foot
mol/pound (mass)	2.20462	*mol/kilogram
mol/square foot	10.7639	*mol/square meter
*mol/square meter	0.092903	mol/square foot

N

nautical mile	1.85325	*kilometer
*newton	1.00000×10^5	dyne
newton	0.224809	pound (force)
newton	7.23301	poundal
*newton meter	0.737562	pound (force) foot
newton meter	8.85075	pound (force) inch
newton meter	23.7304	poundal foot
*newton meter/meter	0.018734	pound (force) foot/inch
newton meter/meter	0.224809	pound (force) inch/inch
*newton/meter	0.068522	pound (force)/foot
newton/meter	0.005710	pound (force/inch

O

Oersted	79.5775	*ampere turn/meter
ohm circular mil/foot	1.66243×10^{-9}*	ohm square meter/meter
ohm foot	0.304800	ohm square meter/meter
ohm inch	0.025400	ohm square meter/meter
*ohm square meter/meter	6.01531×10^8	ohm circular mil/foot
ohm square meter/meter	3.28084	ohm foot
ohm square meter/meter	39.3701	ohm inch
ounce (avoirdupois)	28.3495	*gram
ounce (troy)	31.1035	gram
ounce (fluid) (U.K.)	28.4131	cubic centimeter
ounce (fluid) (U.S.)	29.5735	cubic centimeter

P

*pascal	10.0000	dyne/square centimeter
pascal	10.0000	microbar
pascal	0.007501	millimeter mercury (0°C)

MULTIPLY	BY	TO OBTAIN
*pascal second	1000.00	centipoise
pascal second	10.0000	dyne second/square centimeter
pascal second	0.020885	pound (force) second/square foot
pascal second	2419.09	pound (mass)/foot hour
pascal second	0.671969	pound (mass)/foot second
picojoule	6.24145	million electron volt
pint (liquid) (U.K.)	0.568262	*cubic decimeter
pint (liquid) (U.S.)	0.473167	cubic decimeter
pint (U.K.)/1000 barrels	3.57425	*cubic decimeter/cubic meter
pound mol	0.453592	*kilomol
pound mol/cubic foot	16.0185	*kilomol/cubic meter
pound mol/gallon (U.K.)	99.7763	kilomol/cubic meter
pound mol/gallon (U.S.)	119.826	kilomol/cubic meter
pound mol/hour	0.000126	kilomol/second
pound mol/second	0.453592	*kilomol/second
poundal	0.138255	*newton
poundal	0.031083	pound (force)
poundal foot	0.042140	*newton/meter
pound (force)	4.44822	*newton
pound (force) foot	1.35582	*newton/meter
pound (force) foot/inch	53.3787	*newton meter/meter
pound (force) inch	0.112985	*newton/meter
pound (force)/foot	14.5939	newton/meter
pound (force)/inch	175.127	newton/meter
pound (force)/square foot	0.047880	*kilopascal
pound (force)/square inch	6.89476	kilopascal
pound (force)/square inch/foot	22.6206	*kilopascal/meter
pound (force)/square foot	47.8803	*pascal second
pound (force)/square inch	6.89476	*kilopascal second
pound (mass)	32.1740	poundal
pound (mass)	0.453592	*kilogram
pound (mass)	1.21528	pound (troy)
pound (mass)/barrel	2.85301	*kilogram/cubic meter
pound (mass)/Btu	1.80018	kilogram/kilogram calorie
pound (mass)/cubic foot	16.0185	*kilogram/cubic meter
pound (mass)/foot	1.48816	*kilogram/meter
pound (mass)/foot hour	0.000413	*pascal second
pound (mass)/foot second	1.48816	pascal second
pound (mass)/gallon (U.K.)	0.099776	*kilogram/cubic decimeter
pound (mass)/gallon (U.S.)	0.138255	kilogram/cubic decimeter
pound (mass)/1000 gallons (U.K.)	99.7763	*gram/cubic meter
pound (mass)/1000 gallons (U.S.)	119.826	gram/cubic meter
pound (mass)/hour	0.000126	*kilogram/second
pound (mass)/hour foot	0.000413	*kilogram/second meter
pound (mass)/hour square foot	0.001356	*kilogram/second square meter
pound (mass)/minute	0.007560	*kilogram/second

MULTIPLY	BY	TO OBTAIN
pound (mass)/mol	0.453592	kilogram/mol
pound (mass)/second	0.453592	*kilogram/second
pound (mass)/second foot	1.48816	*kilogram/second meter
pound (mass)/second square foot	4.88243	*kilogram/second square meter
pound (mass)/square foot	4.88243	*kilogram/square meter
pound (mass)/second	0.138255	*kilogram meter/second
pound (mass) square foot	0.042140	*kilogram square meter

Q

quart (dry) (U.K.)	1.03200	quart (dry) (U.S.)
quart (dry) (U.S.)	0.969000	quart (dry) (U.K.)
quart (liquid) (U.K.)	1.136523	*cubic decimeter
quart (liquid) (U.K.)	1.136523	liter
quart (liquid (U.K.)	1.20030	quart (liquid) (U.S.)
quart (liquid) (U.S.)	0.946331	*cubic decimeter
quart (liquid) (U.S.)	0.946331	liter
quart (liquid) (U.S.)	0.859370	quart (dry) (U.S.)
quart (liquid) (U.S.)	0.840593	quart (liquid) (U.K.)

R

rad	0.010000	*gray
*radian	2.06265	second (angle)
radian	3437.75	minute (angle)
radian	57.2958	degree (angle)
*radian/second	0.159155	revolutions/second
radian/second	9.54930	revolutions/minute
*radian/second squared	0.159155	revolutions/second squared
radian/second squared	572.958	revolutions/minute squared
revolutions/minute	0.104720	*radian/second
revolutions/minute squared	0.001745	*radian/second squared
revolutions/second	6.28319	*radian/second
revolutions/second squared	6.28319	*radian/second squared
rod	5.02920	*meter

S

second (angle)	4.84814×10^{-6}	*radian
section	2.58999	*square kilometer
siemens	1.00000	ampere/volt
siemens/meter	0.025400	ampere/volt inch
square foot	0.092903	*square meter
square foot/cubic inch	5669.29	*square meter/cubic meter
square foot/hour	25.8064	*square millimeter/second
square foot/pound (mass)	0.204816	*square meter/kilogram
square foot/second	9290.30	*square millimeter/second
square foot pound (mass)/second squared	0.042140	*joule
square inch	645.160	*square millimeter

MULTIPLY	BY	TO OBTAIN
*square kilometer	0.386102	section
square kilometer	0.386102	square mile
*square meter	10.7639	square foot
square meter	0.000247	acre
square meter	1.19599	square yard
*square meter/cubic meter	0.000176	square foot/cubic inch
*square meter/kilogram	4.88243	square foot/pound (mass)
square mile	2.58999	*square kilometer
*square millimeter	0.001550	square inch
*square millimeter/second	1.07639×10^{-5}	square foot/second
square millimeter/second	0.038750	square foot/hour
square millimeter/second	1.00000	centistoke
square yard	0.836137	*square meter
standard cubic foot/barrel (60°F, 1 atmosphere)	0.007518	*kilomol/cubic meter
standard cubic foot (60°F, 1 atmosphere)	0.001195	*kilomol
standard cubic meter (0°C, 1 atmosphere)	0.044616	kilomol
standard cubic meter (15°C, 1 atmosphere)	0.042293	kilomol

T

MULTIPLY	BY	TO OBTAIN
*tesla	10000.0	gauss
tesla	64516.0	lines/square inch
therm	105.506	*megajoule
ton (force) (U.K.)	9.96402	*kilonewton
ton (force) (U.S.)	8.89644	*kilonewton
ton (force) (U.S.) foot	2.71164	*kilonewton meter
ton (force) (U.S.) mile	14.3174	*megajoule
ton (force) (U.S.) mile/foot	46.9732	*megajoule/meter
ton (force) (U.S.)/square foot	0.095761	*megapascal
ton (force) (U.S.)/square inch	13.7895	*megapascal
ton (mass) (U.K.)	1.01605	*megagram
ton (mass) (U.K.)	1.01605	metric ton
ton (mass) (U.K.)	1.12000	ton (mass) (U.S.)
ton (mass) (U.S.)	0.907185	*megagram
ton (mass) (U.S.)	0.907185	metric ton
ton (mass) (U.S.)	0.892857	ton (mass) (U.K.)
ton (metric)	1.00000	*megagram
ton (metric)	0.904206	ton (mass) (U.K.)
ton (metric)	1.10231	ton (mass) (U.S.)
ton (mass) (U.K.)/day	0.011760	*kilogram/second
ton (mass) (U.S.)/day	0.010500	kilogram/second
ton (mass) (U.K.)/hour	0.282235	kilogram/second
ton (mass) (U.S.)/hour	0.251996	kilogram/second
ton (mass) (U.K.)/minute	16.9341	kilogram/second
ton (mass) (U.S.)/minute	15.1197	kilogram/second
ton (mass) (U.S.)/square foot	9.76486	*megagram/square meter
ton refrigeration	3.51685	*kilowatt

MULTIPLY	BY	TO OBTAIN
U		
unit/foot	3.28084	*unit/meter
*unit/henry	1.00000	ampere/weber
unit/henry	1.25664×10^{-8}	gilbert/maxwell
unit/meter	3.28084	*volt/meter
V		
volt/foot	3.28084	*volt/meter
volt/inch	39.3701	volt/meter
*volt/meter	0.304800	volt/foot
volt/meter	0.025400	volt/inch
volume parts per million	1.00000	*cubic centimeter/cubic meter
W		
*watt	3.41280	Btu (I.T.)/hour
watt	44.2537	foot pound (force)/minute
watt	0.737562	foot pound (force)/second
watt	0.860421	kilocalorie (thermochemical)/hour
watt hour	3.60000	*kilojoule
watt/inch	39.3701	*watt/meter
*watt/meter	0.025400	watt/inch
*watt/meter kelvin	0.577789	Btu (I.T.)/hour square foot°F/foot
watt/meter kelvin	6.93347	Btu (I.T.)/hour square foot °F/inch
watt/meter kelvin	8.60421	calorie (thermochemical/hour cm² °C/cm
watt/meter kelvin	0.002390	calorie (thermochemical) second cm² °C/cm
*watt/square meter	0.316998	Btu (I.T.)/hour square foot
*watt/square meter kelvin	0.176110	Btu (I.T.)/hour square foot °F
watt/square meter kelvin	0.860421	kilocalorie (thermochemical)/hour cm² °C
watt second	1.00000	joule
*weber	1.00000×10^8	lines
weber	1.00000×10^8	maxwell
weber/ampere	1.00000	*henry
Y		
yard	0.914402	*meter

SUBJECT INDEX

Page numbers for tables, charts, and illustrations are in italics.

E

G

H

W

Index prepared by K. D. Bagioni